Geigy
Scientific
Tables

Geigy Scientific Tables

Volume 4

Biochemistry
Metabolism of Xenobiotics
Inborn Errors of Metabolism
Pharmacogenetics and Ecogenetics

Edited by C. Lentner

Eighth, revised and enlarged edition
Published by CIBA-GEIGY

ISBN 0-914168-53-3
Library of Congress Catalogue No. 81-70045

Editor: Cornelius Lentner
Associate editors: Charlotte Lentner and
Anthony Wink
Typography: Ernst Rohner
International Medical and Pharmaceutical
Information, Ciba-Geigy Limited, Basle

American edition published by Medical
Education Division, Ciba-Geigy Corporation,
West Caldwell, New Jersey 07006

International edition published by
Ciba-Geigy Limited, Basle, Switzerland

By way of explanation

This completely revised and expanded 8th edition of the *Geigy Scientific Tables* represents the continuation of a work that has stood the test of time. Its aim is to provide scientists and, in particular, doctors with a concise compendium of scientific data backed by literature references and thus to spare them much laborious searching.

The vast increase in the amount of subject matter to be included has meant that the *Geigy Scientific Tables* have had to be steadily extended, with the result that they are becoming too voluminous to be published in a single book. Dividing the book up into several separate volumes has made it possible to incorporate a number of additional chapters and has also helped to ensure that the data on the various branches of knowledge are more up-to-date than they could have been in a single-volume work.

The volumes so far published are: 'Units of Measurement, Body Fluids, Composition of the Body, Nutrition' (Volume 1), 'Introduction to Statistics, Statistical Tables, Mathematical Formulae' (Volume 2), 'Physical Chemistry, Composition of Blood, Hematology, Somatometric Data' (Volume 3). Further volumes are in preparation.

CIBA-GEIGY Limited, Basle

Foreword

The main part of the present volume consists of the chapters on biochemistry. This part begins with a summary review – largely in the form of tables – dealing with the principal representatives from those classes of substances that are of biochemical importance. The catabolic and anabolic pathways of metabolism, as well as their regulatory mechanisms, are then described. At the end of this part are a few chapters concerned with special areas which have become important for doctors during recent years, e.g. chapters on collagen metabolism, on the action of antibiotics, and on the metabolism of xenobiotics, including drugs.

The second part of this volume contains tables on genetic aspects of biochemical reactions; here, however, it should be pointed out that, owing to the rapid progress now being made in recombinant DNA techniques, such synopses are apt to become quickly overtaken by the kaleidoscopic changes in knowledge. The chapter on 'Pharmacogenetics and Ecogenetics' is intended to show how hereditary factors in combination with environmental factors may upset the equilibrium upon which the maintenance of health depends.

We are sure that our readers will join us in expressing gratitude to all those who have offered us their help and advice in compiling this volume of the *Geigy Scientific Tables*. We are especially indebted to Dr. D. E. NICHOLSON in Leeds for all the work he undertook in the preparation of the chapters on biochemistry; this part of the present volume, which made its first appearance in the 6th edition of the *Geigy Scientific Tables*, had originally been written by the late Sir HANS KREBS and members of his staff. We should also like to thank Prof. R. T. WILLIAMS in London for his chapter on 'Metabolism of Xenobiotics', Prof. L. I. WOOLF in Vancouver for his intensive collaboration in connection with the chapter 'Inborn Errors of Metabolism', as well as Prof. H. W. GOEDDE in Hamburg for compiling the information contained in the chapter on 'Pharmacogenetics and Ecogenetics'. We are likewise indebted to all those readers who have sent us proposals for improvements or have drawn our attention to printing errors. We shall continue in the future to take account, wherever possible, of any suggestions our readers care to send us.

Basle, July 1986   *The Editors*

Acknowledgments

The publishers and editors are indebted to the following for their contributions and assistance in compiling this volume of the Geigy Scientific Tables:

Prof. P. BACK
Medizinische Universitätsklinik Freiburg
D–7800 Freiburg i. Br., Federal Republic of Germany

Dr. B. EXER
CIBA-GEIGY AG
CH–4002 Basle, Switzerland

Prof. H. W. GOEDDE
Institut für Humangenetik der Universität Hamburg
D–2000 Hamburg 54, Federal Republic of Germany

Dr. D. E. NICHOLSON
The University of Leeds
Leeds LS2 9JT, UK

Prof. R. T. WILLIAMS
Metabolic Day Ward (Lab.)
St Mary's Hospital
London W2 1PG, UK

Prof. L. I. WOOLF
The University of British Columbia
Vancouver, B. C., V6T 1W5, Canada

Dr. R. P. ZURBRÜGG
Kinderspital Wildermeth
CH–2502 Biel, Switzerland

The publishers and editors wish to thank the following scientific bodies, journals and publishing houses for permission to reproduce data or illustrations:

Academic Press Inc., Orlando, Fla. (pages 72–74)
Annual Review of Biochemistry, Palo Alto, Cal. (pages 177 and 202)
British Medical Association, London (page 292)
Churchill Livingstone, Edinburgh (pages 20 and 192)
Institute of Medical Microbiology, Göteborg (page 202)
International Union of Biochemistry, Miami, Fla. (pages 72–74)
Lea & Febiger, Publishers, Philadelphia, Pa. (page 222, with kind permission of C. A. FINCH)
McGraw-Hill International Book Company, New York, N. Y. (pages 30–31)
Macmillan Journals Ltd, London (page 202)
Massachusetts Medical Society, London (page 192)
Nature, London (page 202)
Salk Institute, San Diego, Cal. (page 177)
W. B. Saunders Company, Philadelphia, Pa. (page 201)
Science, Washington D. C. (page 177)
Dietrich Steinkopff Verlag, Darmstadt (page 194)
John Wiley & Sons, Ltd, Chichester, Sussex (page 22)

Contents

Notes for the guidance of users

As a rule, all symbols, abbreviations, etc. used are defined or explained at the place where they occur. Zero values are indicated
throughout by the figure 0.

The biochemical nomenclature employed conforms to the recommendations of the International Union of Pure and Applied Chemistry (IUPAC) and of the International Union of Biochemistry
(IUB)[1]; the enzyme nomenclature is based on the recommendations
of the Nomenclature Committee of the International Union of Biochemistry on the Nomenclature and Classification of Enzyme-
Catalysed Reactions (EC)[2].

The abbreviations used in the literature references are those
recommended by UNESCO (*World Medical Periodicals*, 1961 and
1963)[3].

Decimal multiples and submultiples of SI units

exa (E) . . . . for 10^{18}	deci (d) . . . . for 10^{-1}
peta (P) . . . . for 10^{15}	centi (c) . . . . for 10^{-2}
tera (T) . . . . for 10^{12}	milli (m) . . . . for 10^{-3}
giga (G) . . . . for 10^{9}	micro (μ) . . . . for 10^{-6}
mega (M) . . . . for 10^{6}	nano (n) . . . . for 10^{-9}
kilo (k) . . . . for 10^{3}	pico (p) . . . . for 10^{-12}
hecto (h) . . . . for 10^{2}	femto (f) . . . . for 10^{-15}
deca (da) . . . . for 10^{1}	atto (a) . . . . for 10^{-18}

Greek alphabet

Greek character				Greek name	Roman equivalent	
Upright		Italics				
A	α	A	α	alpha	A	a
B	β	B	β	beta	B	b
Γ	γ	Γ	γ	gamma	G	g
Δ	δ	Δ	δ	delta	D	d
E	ε, ϵ	E	ε, ϵ	epsilon	Ĕ	ĕ
Z	ζ	Z	ζ	zeta	Z	z
H	η	H	η	eta	Ē	ē
Θ	ϑ, θ	Θ	ϑ, θ	theta	Th	th
I	ι	I	ι	iota	I	i
K	$\varkappa, \kappa$	K	$\varkappa, \kappa$	kappa	K	k
Λ	λ	Λ	λ	lambda	L	l
M	μ	M	μ	mu	M	m
N	ν	N	ν	nu	N	n
Ξ	ξ	Ξ	ξ	xi	X	x
O	o	O	o	omicron	Ŏ	ŏ
Π	$\pi, \tilde{\omega}$	Π	$\pi, \tilde{\omega}$	pi	P	p
P	ϱ	P	ϱ	rho	R	r
Σ	σ, ς	Σ	σ, ς	sigma	S	s
T	τ	T	τ	tau	T	t
Y	υ	Y	υ	upsilon	Y	y
Φ	φ, ϕ	Φ	φ, ϕ	phi	Ph	ph
X	χ	X	χ	chi	Ch	ch
Ψ	ψ	Ψ	ψ	psi	Ps	ps
Ω	ω	Ω	ω	omega	Ō	ō

References

[1] *Collected Tentative Rules and Recommendations of the Commission on Biochemical Nomenclature IUPAC–IUB and Related Documents*, 2nd ed., American
Society of Biological Chemists, Bethesda, Md., 1975, and addenda published in
biochemical papers up to 1985.

[2] International Union of Biochemistry. *Enzyme Nomenclature 1984*, Academic
Press, Orlando, Fla., 1984.

[3] CLEGG, H. A. (Ed.), *World Medical Periodicals*, 3rd ed., World Medical Association, New York, 1961, and WARE, M. (Ed.), supplement to the 3rd edition,
New York, 1968.

Table 1 *Monosaccharides of biological importance*

Name*	Formula, M_r	Structure	Specific rotation	Occurrence
		Trioses		
D-Glyceraldehyde (2,3-dihydroxypropanal)	$C_3H_6O_3$ 90.08	CHO HCOH CH₂OH	$[\alpha]_D^{20} + 13.5°$	As phosphate, intermediate in glycolysis
Dihydroxyacetone (1,3-dihydroxypropan-2-one, glycerone)	$C_3H_6O_3$ 90.08	CH₂OH CO CH₂OH or CH₂OH COH CHOH	Inactive	As phosphate, intermediate in glycolysis
		Tetroses		
D-Erythrose	$C_4H_8O_4$ 120.10	[structure]	$[\alpha]_D^{20} - 14.8°$	As phosphate, intermediate in the pentose phosphate cycle
L-Erythrulose	$C_4H_8O_4$ 120.10	CH₂OH CO HOCH CH₂OH	$[\alpha]_D^{20} + 12°$	As metabolically active phosphate
		Pentoses		
β-D-Arabinose (Ara)	$C_5H_{10}O_5$ 150.13	[structure]	$[\alpha]_D^{20} - 105°$	In glycosides of aloe and tubercle bacilli. As phosphate, intermediate in the F-type pentose phosphate cycle (page 134). The L form occurs in heteropolysaccharides
D-Ribose (Rib) (D-ribofuranose)	$C_5H_{10}O_5$ 150.13	[structure]	$[\alpha]_D^{20} - 23.1° \rightarrow -23.7°$	Constituent of nucleosides. As phosphate, constituent of nucleotides and ribonucleic acids; intermediate in the pentose phosphate cycle
D-Ribulose (D-*erythro*-2-pentulose, D-adonose, D-arabulose)	$C_5H_{10}O_5$ 150.13	CH₂OH CO HCOH HCOH CH₂OH	–	As phosphate, intermediate in the pentose phosphate cycle
D-Xylose (Xyl) (D-xylopyranose)	$C_5H_{10}O_5$ 150.13	[structure]	α form: $[\alpha]_D^{20} + 93.6° \rightarrow + 18.8°$	Binds polysaccharide units to the protein framework of proteoglycans
D-Xylulose (D-*threo*-2-pentulose, D-xyloketose, D-lyxulose, D-lyxoketose)	$C_5H_{10}O_5$ 150.13	CH₂OH CO HOCH HCOH CH₂OH	$[\alpha]_D^{20} - 33°$	As phosphate, intermediate in the pentose phosphate cycle. The L form is present in the urine in pentosuria

*Three-letter symbols according to the recommendations of the IUPAC–IUB Joint Commission on Biochemical Nomenclature, *Europ. J. Biochem.*, **126**, 433 (1982).

Table 1   *Monosaccharides of biological importance (continued)*

Name*	Formula, M_r	Structure	Specific rotation	Occurrence
		Hexoses		
D-Fructose (Fru) (D-*arabino*-2-hexulose, levulose, fruit sugar)	$C_6H_{12}O_6$ 180.16	β-D-Fructopyranose β-D-Fructofuranose	β form: $[\alpha]_D^{20} - 133.5° \rightarrow -92°$	Constituent of many polysaccharides (bound to glucose in sucrose). Pyranose in free form, but furanose in all natural derivatives. Sweetest of all sugars. Free in the secretion of the seminal vesicles. In phosphate form, intermediate in both glycolysis and pentose phosphate cycle
D-Galactose (Gal) (cerebrose)	$C_6H_{12}O_6$ 180.16		α form: $[\alpha]_D^{20} + 144° \rightarrow +80.5°$ β form: $[\alpha]_D^{20} + 54° \rightarrow +80.5°$	Constituent of oligosaccharides (for example lactose, raffinose, stachyose) as well as of cerebrosides, gangliosides and polysaccharides, both as sugar and amino sugar. In mammalian tissues as phosphate intermediate of galactose metabolism
D-Glucose (Glc, G) (dextrose, blood sugar, grape sugar)	$C_6H_{12}O_6$ 180.16		α form: $[\alpha]_D^{20} + 113.4° \rightarrow +52.5°$ β form: $[\alpha]_D^{20} + 19.3° \rightarrow +52.5°$	Most widely distributed of all sugars. Found free in practically all body fluids. As sugar and amino sugar (see Glucosamine, page 14), constituent of polysaccharides. In the form of phosphates, intermediates in glycolysis as well as in the metabolic process between glucose and glycogen
D-Mannose (Man)	$C_6H_{12}O_6$ 180.16		α form: $[\alpha]_D^{20} + 29.9° \rightarrow +14.5°$ β form: $[\alpha]_D^{20} - 16.3° \rightarrow +14.5°$	Widely distributed as constituent of mannans and hemicelluloses. Limited occurrence as constituent of glycoproteins. As phosphate, intermediate in mannose metabolism. Mannosylphosphodolichol (page 32) serves as a mannose donor in the formation of oligosaccharide sequences of glycoproteins and lipopolysaccharides
		Heptose		
D-Sedoheptulose (D-*altro*-2-heptulose)	$C_7H_{14}O_7$ 210.18	CH₂OH CO HOCH HCOH HCOH HCOH CH₂OH	$[\alpha]_D^{20} + 2–3°$ Ba salt: $[\alpha]_{5461}^{20} + 8°$	As phosphate, intermediate in the pentose phosphate cycle

* Three-letter symbols according to the recommendations of the IUPAC–IUB Joint Commission on Biochemical Nomenclature, *Europ. J. Biochem.*, **126**, 433 (1982); where no ambiguity can arise, the single-letter symbol G may be used for glucose.

Table 2 *Polyhydric alcohols of biological importance*

Name	Formula, M_r	Structure	Specific rotation	Occurrence
Glycerol	$C_3H_8O_3$ 92.09	CH₂OH HCOH CH₂OH	−	Widely distributed in lipids of mammalian tissues. Tastes sweet. Constituent of the cell wall of many gram-positive bacteria
Erythritol	$C_4H_{10}O_4$ 122.12	CH₂OH HCOH HCOH CH₂OH	Inactive	Metabolic product of erythrose 4-phosphate
L-Arabitol	$C_5H_{12}O_5$ 152.15	CH₂OH HCOH HOCH HOCH CH₂OH	$[\alpha]_D - 7.2°$	In human urine in pentosuria
Ribitol (adonitol)	$C_5H_{12}O_5$ 152.15	CH₂OH HCOH HCOH HCOH CH₂OH	−	Component of riboflavin (page 67). Also occurs in *Adonis vernalis*. Constituent of the cell wall of many gram-positive bacteria
Xylitol	$C_5H_{12}O_5$ 152.15	CH₂OH HOCH HCOH HOCH CH₂OH	−	Intermediate in the breakdown of D-glucuronic acid (page 91). Of importance as energy source in parenteral feeding and as substitute for sucrose in caries prophylaxis
Sorbitol (D-glucitol)	$C_6H_{14}O_6$ 182.17	CH₂OH HCOH HOCH HCOH HCOH CH₂OH	$[\alpha]_D - 1.8°$	Component of seminal plasma in many species including man. Of importance as energy source in parenteral feeding
myo-Inositol (mesoinositol)	$C_6H_{12}O_6$ 180.16	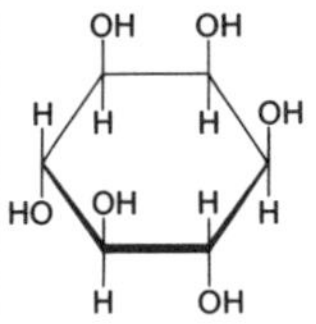	Inactive	Widely distributed in plant and animal kingdoms. Free primarily in the seminal plasma as well as in the male sex organs. As a component of phosphatidylinositols in many tissues. As inositol 1,4,5-tris-phosphate involved in intracellular calcium release (?). As penta-kisphosphate in chicken blood. As hexakisphosphate (phytin), stored reserve substance of green plants
scyllo-Inositol	$C_6H_{12}O_6$ 180.16	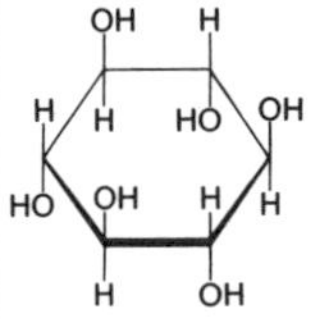	Inactive	Widely distributed in the plant and animal kingdoms. Abundantly present, for example, in ray tissues
Streptidine	$C_8H_{18}N_6O_4$ 262.27	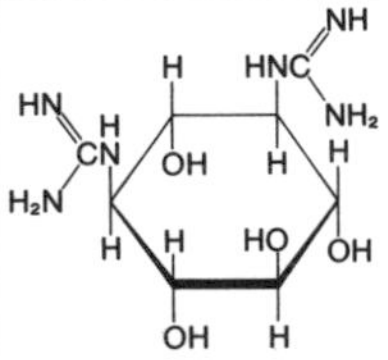	−	Component of streptomycin

Table 3 *Deoxy sugars of biological importance*

Name*	Formula, M_r	Structure	Specific rotation	Occurrence
2-Deoxy-D-ribose (dRib) (2-deoxy-D-*erythro*-pentose, thyminose, deoxyarabinose)	$C_5H_{10}O_4$ 134.13	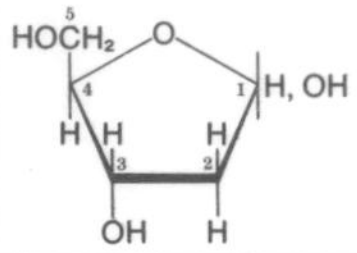	$[\alpha]_D^{25} - 50°$	Component of deoxynucleosides. As phosphate, component of deoxynucleotides and deoxyribonucleic acids
D-Digitoxose (2-deoxy-D-*altro*-methylose)	$C_6H_{12}O_4$ 148.16	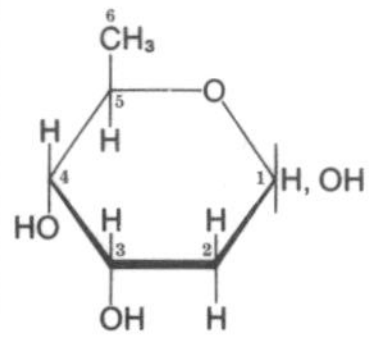	$[\alpha]_D^{20} + 46.5°$	Constituent of digitalis glycosides
L-Fucose (Fuc) (6-deoxy-L-galactose)	$C_6H_{12}O_5$ 164.16	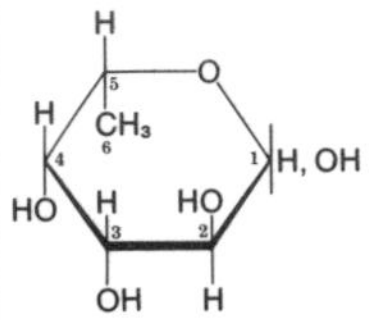	$[\alpha]_D^{20} - 153° \rightarrow + 76°$	Components of oligosaccharides of mother's milk (Table 7, page 15), glycoproteins of the blood-group substances, marine algae and gum tragacanth
L-Rhamnose (Rha) (6-deoxy-L-mannose, isodulcitol)	$C_6H_{12}O_5$ 164.16	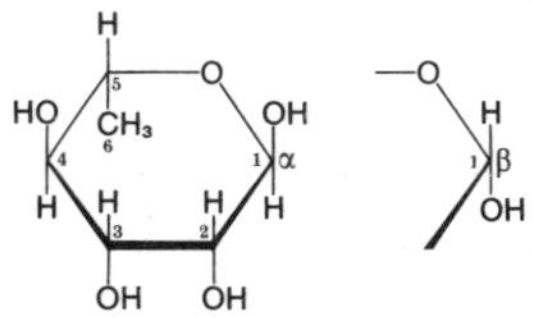	α form, 1 H_2O: $[\alpha]_D^{20} - 9°$ β form: $[\alpha]_D^{20} + 38°$	As glycoside in plant pigments, gums and mucilages. Component of cardiac glycosides

*Symbols according to the recommendations of the IUPAC–IUB Joint Commission on Biochemical Nomenclature, *Europ. J. Biochem.*, **126**, 433 (1982).

Table 4 *Oxidation products of carbohydrates*

Name	Formula, M_r	Structure	Specific rotation	Occurrence
		Aldonic acids		
D-Glyceric acid (D-2,3-dihydroxypropionic acid)	$C_3H_6O_4$ 106.08	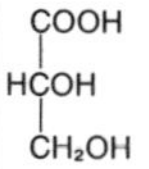	−	As phosphates, intermediates in glycolysis
L-Ascorbic acid (vitamin C)	$C_6H_8O_6$ 176.13	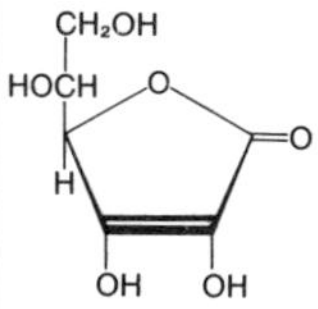	$[\alpha]_D^{20} + 49°$	In all higher plants, especially in cabbage plants, parsley, citrus fruits, rose hips, in small amounts also in animal tissue. Antiscorbutic activity. As ascorbate 2-sulfate in urine
D-Gluconic acid (dextronic acid)	$C_6H_{12}O_7$ 196.16	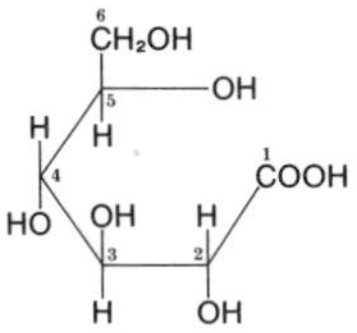	$[\alpha]_D^{20} - 6.7° \rightarrow + 17.5°$	As phosphate, intermediate in pentose phosphate cycle
L-Gulonic acid	$C_6H_{12}O_7$ 196.16	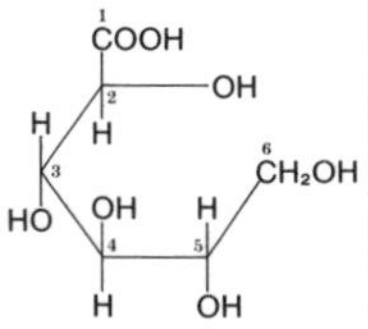	−	Intermediate in formation of L-xylulose from D-glucuronic acid. L-Gulonolactone is oxidized to L-ascorbic acid (L-gulonolactone oxidase is lacking, however, in humans, apes and guinea pigs)

Table 4   *Oxidation products of carbohydrates (continued)*

Name*	Formula, M_r	Structure	Specific rotation	Occurrence
Uronic acids				
α-D-Galacturonic acid (GalA, GalUA)	$C_6H_{10}O_7$ 194.14	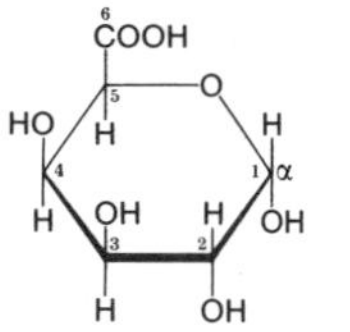	$[\alpha]_D^{21} + 100° \rightarrow + 68°$	Principal component of pectins. Occurs also in plant gums and mucilages as well as in bacterial polysaccharides
β-D-Glucuronic acid (GlcA, GlcUA)	$C_6H_{10}O_7$ 194.14	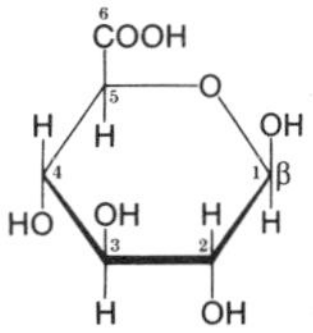	$[\alpha]_D^{20} + 12° \rightarrow + 36°$	Component of glycosaminoglycans (pages 23 and 185–190). Many aliphatic and aromatic hydroxy compounds and acids are excreted as glucuronides (see also page 212). Has pyranose form in natural products
L-Iduronic acid (IdoA, IdoUA)	$C_6H_{10}O_7$ 194.14	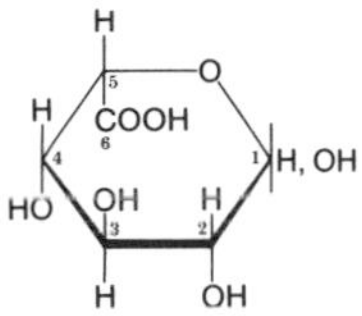	–	Component of dermatan sulfate (page 24), heparan sulfate, heparin (page 24)
Aldaric acid				
D Glucaric acid (D-saccharic acid)	$C_6H_{10}O_8$ 210.14	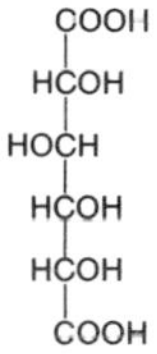	$[\alpha]_D^{19} + 6.9° \rightarrow + 20.6°$	As 1,4-lactone in the urine

*Symbols according to the recommendations of the IUPAC–IUB Joint Commission on Biochemical Nomenclature, *Europ. J. Biochem.*, **126**, 433 (1982).

Table 5   *Amino sugars of biological importance*

Name*	Formula, M_r	Structure	Specific rotation	Occurrence
D-Galactosamine (GalN) (D-chondrosamine, 2-amino-2-deoxy-D-galactose)	$C_6H_{13}NO_5$ 179.17	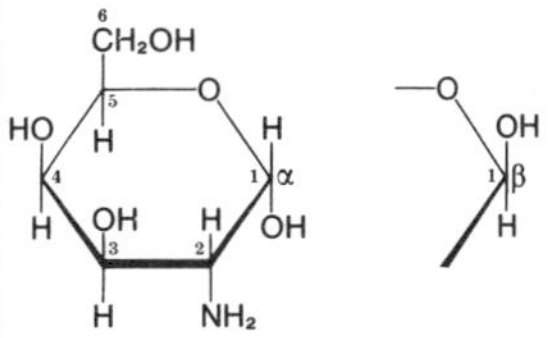	α form, 1 HCl: $[\alpha]_D^{20} + 135° \rightarrow + 93°$ β form, 1 HCl: $[\alpha]_D^{20} + 39° \rightarrow + 93°$	As N-acetylgalactosamine in glycosaminoglycans (chondroitin sulfate, dermatan sulfate) (pages 185–190), as well as in glycoproteins (page 21) and gangliosides (page 32)
N-Acetyl-D-galactosamine (GalNAc)	$C_8H_{15}NO_6$ 221.21	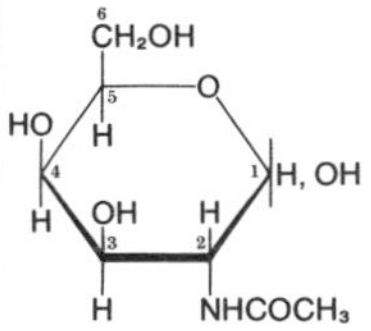	$[\alpha]_D^{20} + 115° \rightarrow + 80°$	See above

*Symbols according to the recommendations of the IUPAC–IUB Joint Commission on Biochemical Nomenclature, *Europ. J. Biochem.*, **126**, 433 (1982).

Table 5   *Amino sugars of biological importance (continued)*

Name*	Formula, M_r	Structure	Specific rotation	Occurrence
D-Glucosamine (GlcN) (chitosamine, 2-amino-2-deoxy-D-glucose)	$C_6H_{13}NO_5$ 179.17	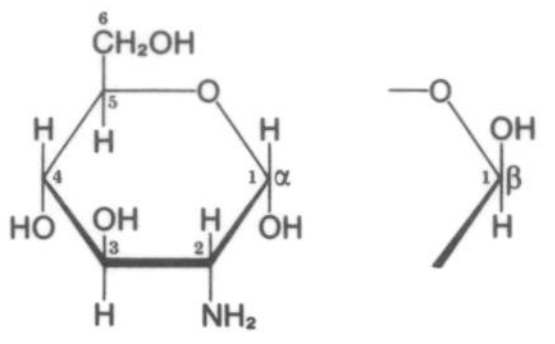 *[structure]*	α form: $[\alpha]_D^{20} + 100° \rightarrow + 47.5°$ β form: $[\alpha]_D^{20} + 14° \rightarrow + 47.5°$	As N-acetylglucosamine, component of hyaluronic acid, chitin, heparin, blood-group substances, glycoproteins of serum, oligosaccharides of mother's milk (Table 7)
N-Acetyl-D-glucosamine (GlcNAc)	$C_8H_{15}NO_6$ 221.21	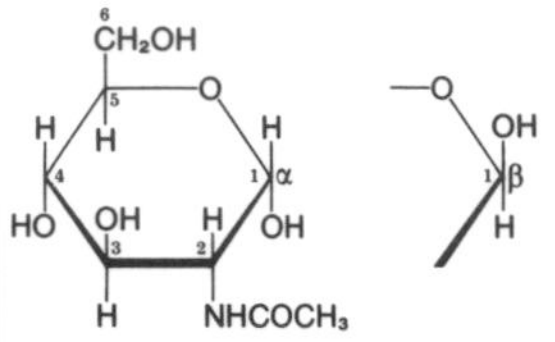 *[structure]*	—	See above. As N-acetylglucosaminyl-diphosphodolichol, precursor in the formation of oligosaccharide sequences (see page 182)
N-Methyl-L-glucosamine (GlcNMe)	$C_7H_{15}NO_5$ 193.20	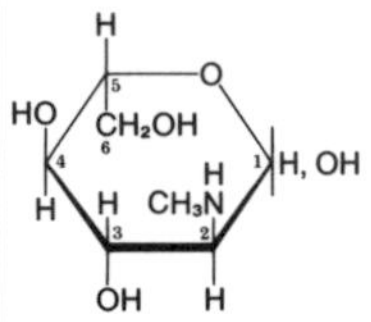 *[structure]*	—	Component of streptomycin
N-Acetyl-D-mannosamine (ManNAc)	$C_8H_{15}NO_6$ 221.21	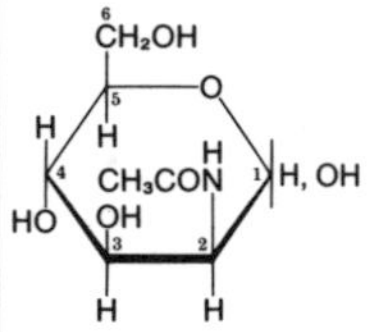 *[structure]*	$[\alpha]_D^{20} - 9.4° \rightarrow + 9.7°$	Intermediate in the biosynthesis of N-acetylneuraminic acid
Muramic acid (Mur) (3-O-carboxyethyl-glucosamine)	$C_9H_{17}NO_7$ 251.24	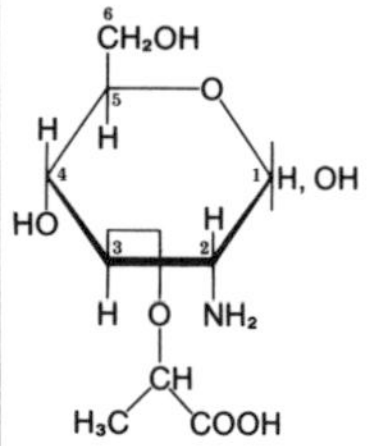 *[structure]*	$[\alpha]_D^{20} + 109°$ (water)	Component of bacterial cell walls in the form of N-acetylmuramic acid
N-Acetylneuraminic acid (AcNeu, NeuAc, Neu5Ac)	$C_{11}H_{19}NO_9$ 309.27	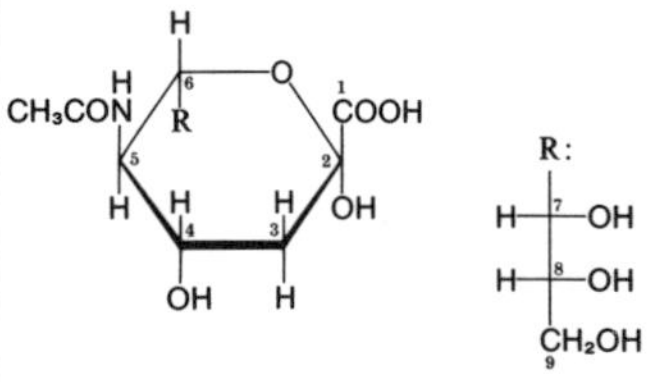 *[structure]*	$[\alpha]_D^{22} - 32°$ No mutarotation	Constituent of mucins of epithelial secretions, of serum glycoproteins, milk oligosaccharides, brain gangliosides, erythrocyte stroma and bacterial cell walls
N-Glycoloylneuraminic acid (NeuGl, Neu5Gl)	$C_{11}H_{19}NO_{10}$ 325.27	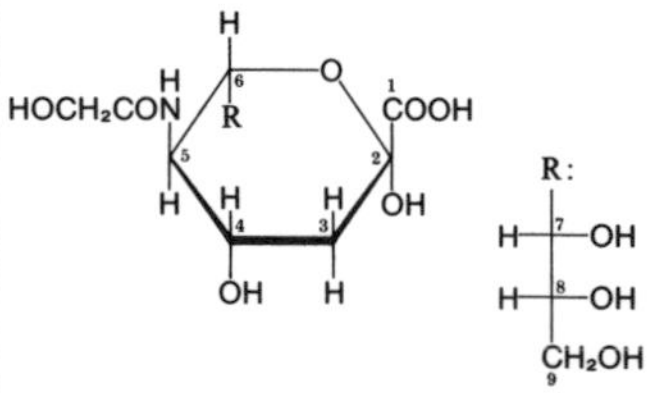 *[structure]*	$[\alpha]_D^{22} - 32°$	Component of mucins of epithelial secretions, serum glycoproteins, erythrocyte stroma. Often in the same molecule as N-acetylneuraminic acid

*Symbols according to the recommendations of the IUPAC–IUB Joint Commission on Biochemical Nomenclature, *Europ. J. Biochem.*, **126**, 433 (1982).

Table 6 *Disaccharides of biological importance*

Name	Structure (Formula: $C_{12}H_{22}O_{11}$; M_r 342.30)	Specific rotation	Remarks
Cellobiose (4-O-β-D-glucopyranosyl-β-D-glucopyranose)	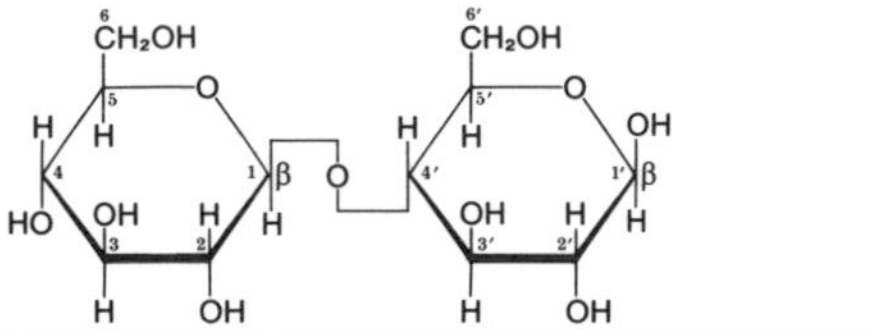	$[\alpha]_D^{20} + 14.2° \rightarrow + 34.6°$	Breakdown product of cellulose arising in herbivores in the course of digestion. Also component of lichenin
Lactose (4-O-β-D-galactopyranosyl-D-glucopyranose)	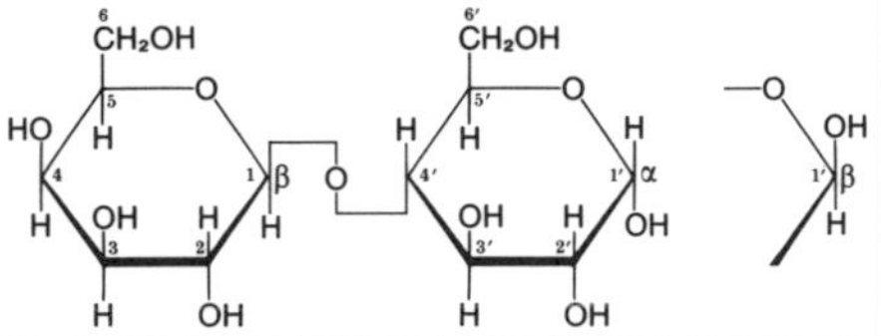	α form, 1 H_2O: $[\alpha]_D^{20} + 85° \rightarrow + 52.6°$ β form: $[\alpha]_D^{20} + 34.9° \rightarrow + 55.4°$	Milk component. Only slightly sweet
Maltose (4-O-α-D-glucopyranosyl-β-D-glucopyranose)	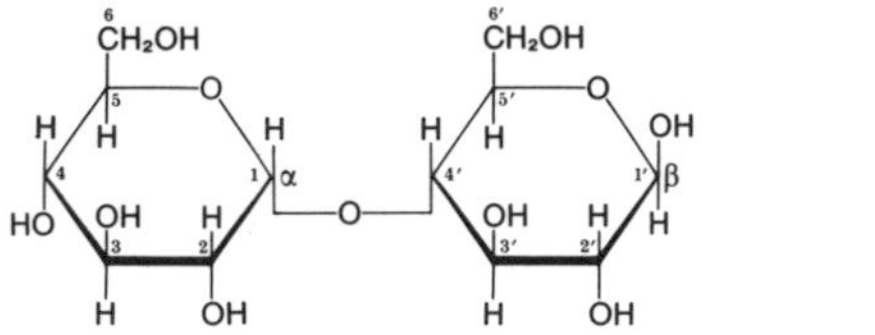	β form, 1 H_2O: $[\alpha]_D^{20} + 111.7° \rightarrow + 130.4°$	Breakdown product of starch and glycogen arising in the course of digestion. Free in some plants and in honey
Sucrose (saccharose, 2-O-β-D-fructofuranosyl α-D-glucopyranoside)	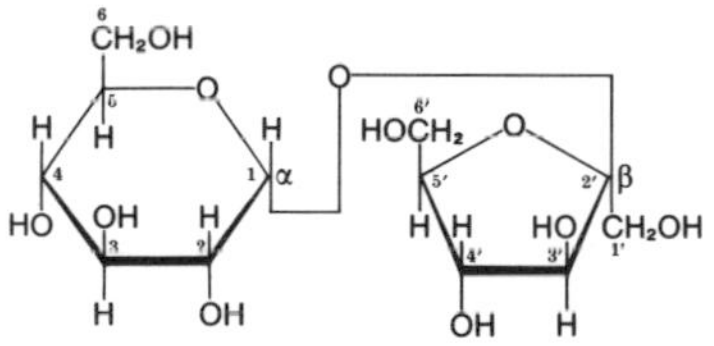	$[\alpha]_D^{20} + 66.53°$	Occurs almost everywhere in the plant kingdom

Table 7 *Examples of trisaccharides and higher oligosaccharides of biological importance*

Fucosyllactose	Fucα1→2Galβ1→4Glc	
Lacto-N-tetraose	Galβ1→3GlcNAcβ1→3Galβ1→4Glc	
Neolacto-N-tetraose	Galβ1→4GlcNAcβ1→3Galβ1→4Glc	

Lacto-N-fucopentaose I	Galβ1→3GlcNAcβ1→3Galβ1→4Glc
	           3
	           ↑
	Fucα1	

Lacto-N-fucopentaose II.............	Galβ1→3GlcNAcβ1→3Galβ1→4Glc
	           4
	           ↑
	Fucα1
		In mother's milk

Lacto-N-hexaose	Galβ1→3GlcNAcβ1↘
	              ₃Galβ1→4Glc
	            ⁶
	Galβ1→4GlcNAcβ1↗	

Neolacto-N-hexaose	Galβ1→4GlcNAcβ1↘
	              ₃Galβ1→4Glc
	            ⁶
	Galβ1→4GlcNAcβ1↗	

Glucose tetrasaccharide	Glcα1→6Glcα1→4Glcα1→4Glc	In normal urine. Increased in glycogen storage diseases II and III

—	Galβ1→4GlcNAcβ1→2Manα1↘
	                 ₃Manβ1→4GlcNAc
	                 ⁶
	Galβ1→4GlcNAcβ1→2Manα1↗
		In the urine in G_{M1} gangliosidosis

—	Galβ1→4GlcNAcβ1→2Manα1→6Manβ1→4GlcNAc	

Carbohydrates are organic compounds that typically contain hydrogen and oxygen in a ratio of 2:1 and thus have the general empirical formula $C_x(H_2O)_y$. The designation 'carbohydrates' is also used for oxidation and reduction products as well as simple derivatives of these compounds, such as amino sugars and phosphorylated sugars.

Carbohydrates are frequently designated as 'sugars' (saccharides) because many of them (especially fructose) taste sweet; the term 'sugar' is, however, often loosely defined. To the chemist it indicates a monosaccharide or oligosaccharide, but never a polysaccharide. Monosaccharides and oligosaccharides receive names with the suffix -ose, such as glucose, fructose and lactose. Polysaccharides, in which a large number of monosaccharide units are linked chainwise, usually bear trivial names, for example 'starch' or 'glycogen', both of which are macromolecular polymers of glucose.

Monosaccharides

Monosaccharides are carbohydrates that cannot be split further by hydrolysis. Chemically they are polyhydroxyaldehydes (aldoses) or polyhydroxyketones (ketoses). Glucose is an example of an aldose; fructose, an example of a ketose:

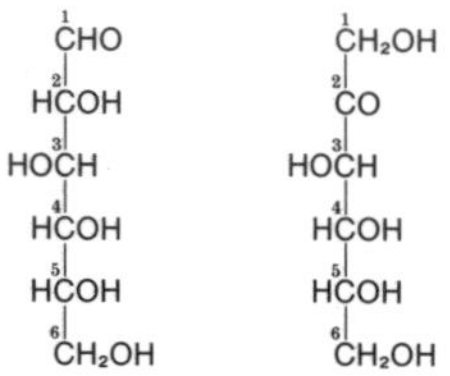

	Glucose	Fructose
1	CHO	CH₂OH
2	HCOH	CO
3	HOCH	HOCH
4	HCOH	HCOH
5	HCOH	HCOH
6	CH₂OH	CH₂OH

In the formulae above the sugars are depicted in the form of an open chain according to convention, with the carbonyl group (alde-

Fig. 1   *Stereoisomerism of glyceraldehyde*

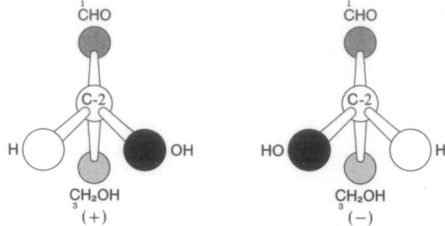

hyde or oxo group) at the upper end. The C atoms are numbered from top to bottom. Sugars with chain lengths of 3, 4, 5, 6, ... C atoms are designated respectively as trioses, tetroses, pentoses, hexoses, etc.

The simplest monosaccharide in theory is glycolaldehyde with the formula OHC—CH₂OH. This is very unstable and hence appears only as an intermediate – though an important one – in metabolism.

The simplest stable carbohydrate is glyceraldehyde, which is an aldose or aldotriose (Fig. 2). Like all other carbohydrates it has an *asymmetric* (chiral) *carbon atom*, i.e. a C atom that is linked to 4 different substituents (—CHO, —H, —OH, —CH₂OH). Since this configuration cannot be superimposed on its mirror image, an isomerism accompanied by optical activity results from this asymmetry.

The 2 sterically possible configurations of the substituents are readily evident if one imagines the carbon atom to be at the center of a regular tetrahedron and the valences oriented towards the corners of the same. The 2 possible configurations of glyceraldehyde in Figure 1 can in no way be superimposed upon one another. They bear the same relationship to each other that an object does to its mirror image and are designated as 'enantiomorphic forms'. No such asymmetry occurs at a carbon atom with at least two identical substituents.

Fig. 2   *Configurational relationships of the D-aldoses*

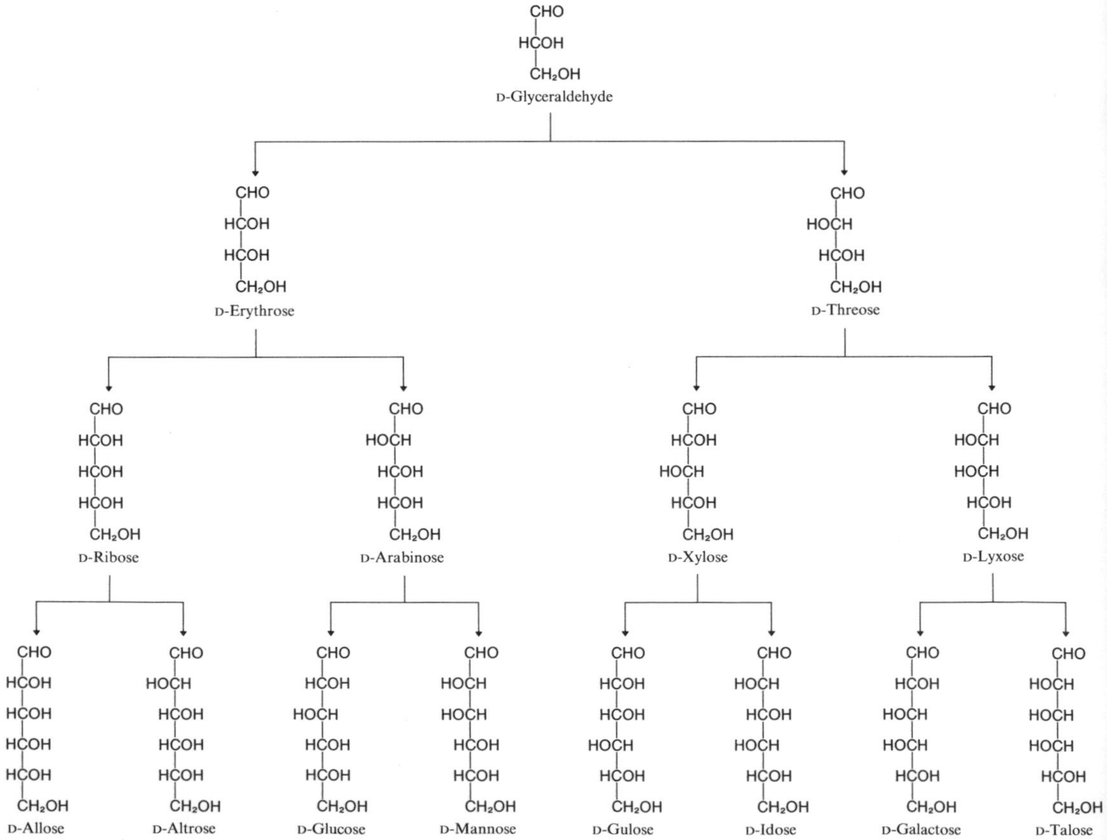

D-Glyceraldehyde
1	CHO
2	HCOH
3	CH₂OH

D-Erythrose
| CHO |
| HCOH |
| HCOH |
| CH₂OH |

D-Threose
| CHO |
| HOCH |
| HCOH |
| CH₂OH |

D-Ribose
| CHO |
| HCOH |
| HCOH |
| HCOH |
| CH₂OH |

D-Arabinose
| CHO |
| HOCH |
| HCOH |
| HCOH |
| CH₂OH |

D-Xylose
| CHO |
| HCOH |
| HOCH |
| HCOH |
| CH₂OH |

D-Lyxose
| CHO |
| HOCH |
| HOCH |
| HCOH |
| CH₂OH |

D-Allose
| CHO |
| HCOH |
| HCOH |
| HCOH |
| HCOH |
| CH₂OH |

D-Altrose
| CHO |
| HOCH |
| HCOH |
| HCOH |
| HCOH |
| CH₂OH |

D-Glucose
| CHO |
| HCOH |
| HOCH |
| HCOH |
| HCOH |
| CH₂OH |

D-Mannose
| CHO |
| HOCH |
| HOCH |
| HCOH |
| HCOH |
| CH₂OH |

D-Gulose
| CHO |
| HCOH |
| HCOH |
| HOCH |
| HCOH |
| CH₂OH |

D-Idose
| CHO |
| HOCH |
| HCOH |
| HOCH |
| HCOH |
| CH₂OH |

D-Galactose
| CHO |
| HCOH |
| HOCH |
| HOCH |
| HCOH |
| CH₂OH |

D-Talose
| CHO |
| HOCH |
| HOCH |
| HOCH |
| HCOH |
| CH₂OH |

Enantiomorphic isomers are optically active; that is, in a solution one of the isomers rotates the plane of polarized light to the right, the other to the same extent to the left. The degree of rotation depends on the length of the polarimeter tube, on the wavelength of the polarized light used, on the type of solvent and on the concentration and temperature of the solution*. The direction of rotation was originally designated by the prefixes *dextro* (*d*) and *levo* (*l*). The equivalent signs (+) and (−) are preferred today.

When 2 enantiomorphic isomers are mixed in equal concentrations the rotations cancel each other out; the optically *inactive* product is called a *racemate* and provided with the symbol (±) or DL.

Racemates only rarely occur in living systems because almost all molecules formed in organisms belong to a specific configurational series, such as L-amino acids or D-monosaccharides.

The classification of carbohydrate molecules is based on their relationship to glyceraldehyde with the following configurations:

---

*The specific rotation [α] is defined as the rotation in degrees produced by 1 g of substance in 1 mL of solution in a polarimeter tube with a length of 10 cm. The D line of sodium is usually used as the light source. Wavelength of the light source, solvent as well as temperature and concentration of the solution are to be given when they deviate from the definition; for example, $[\alpha]_D^{25}$, 20% (H_2O).

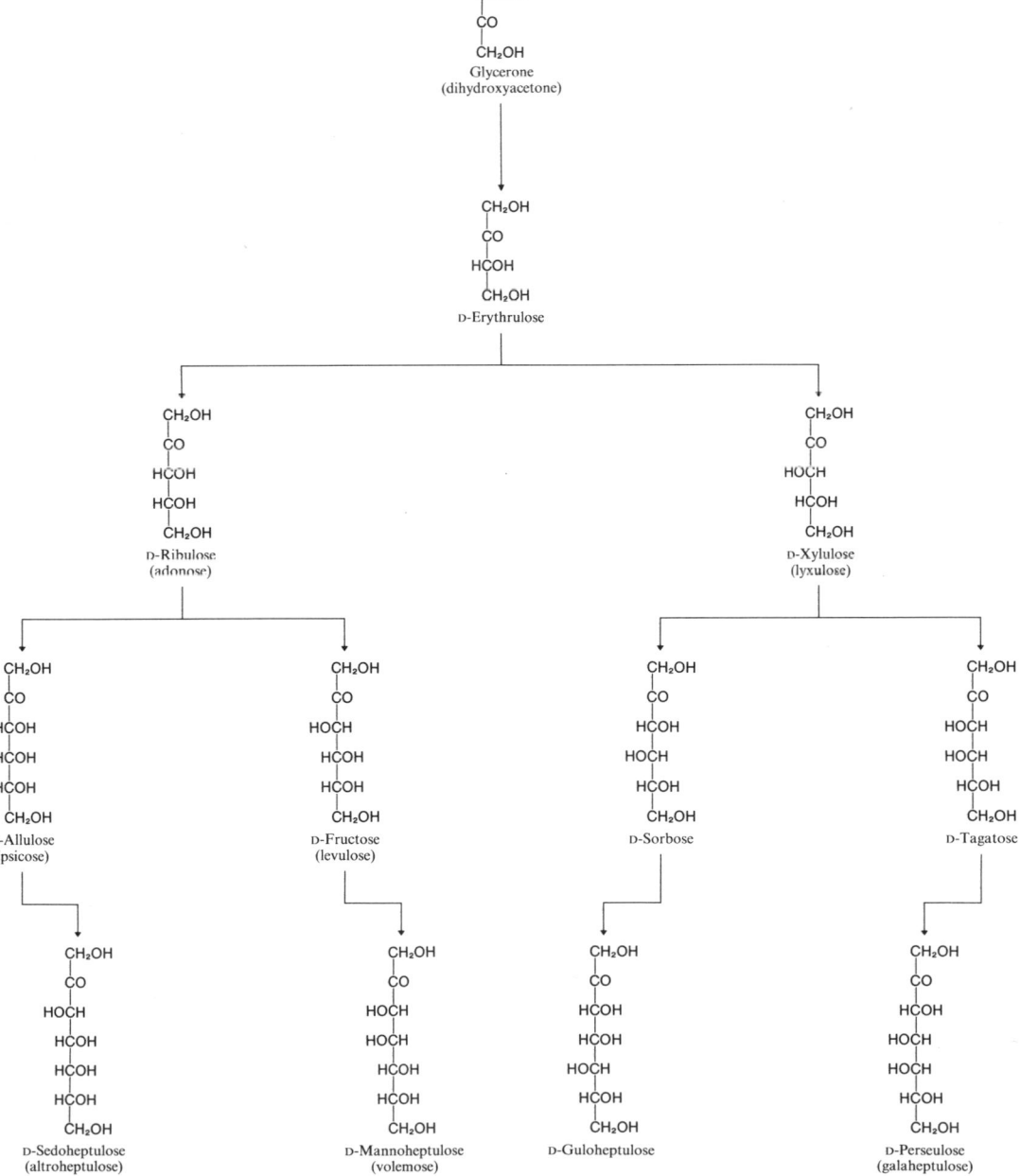

Fig. 3 *Configurational relationships of the D-ketoses*

With the carbonyl group at the upper end, the hydroxy group is to the right of the asymmetric C atom in the dextrorotatory substance, and to the left of it in the levorotatory substance. The 2 structures are designated 'D-glyceraldehyde' or 'L-glyceraldehyde', respectively.

Sugars with longer carbon chains can be considered to be derived from dextro- or levorotatory glyceraldehyde by repeated insertion of secondary alcohol groups ($>$CHOH) at the carbonyl group. With each additional asymmetric center the number of possible isomers increases, whereupon the optical rotation can increase or decrease or even reverse in relation to the preceding compound. The symbols ($+$) or ($-$) for the direction of rotation of a sugar therefore in no way indicate whether the latter is derived from dextro- or levorotatory glyceraldehyde. The latter relationship is given by the symbols D and L introduced by ROSANOFF. All those sugars (and related compounds such as tartaric acid) in which the secondary alcohol group farthest removed from the principal functional group (i.e. aldehyde group, oxo group, carbonyl group, etc.) has the same steric configuration as the dextrorotatory glyceraldehyde are assigned to the D series. If this alcohol group has a configuration corresponding to the levorotatory glyceraldehyde the compound is assigned to the L series. For the case of tartaric acid it could be shown that this arbitrarily assumed configuration agrees with the absolute one.

The sugars occurring naturally belong, with few exceptions, to the D series. The aldoses and ketoses of the D series up to a chain length of 6 or 7 C atoms are listed in Figures 2 and 3. In all these monosaccharides the hydroxy group of the penultimate C atom is on the right-hand side; that of the corresponding L sugar is enantiomorphically on the left-hand side.

Cyclic forms of the carbohydrates

In the case of carbohydrates with more than 4 C atoms in the chain an OH group may react with the carbonyl group to form a so-called *hemiacetal*. A hemiacetal is formed by the addition of an alcohol to a carbonyl group:

| Acet-aldehyde | Ethyl alcohol | | Hemiacetal |

If the reacting hydroxy group is on C-5, a 6-membered ring is formed from 5 C atoms and 1 O atom. By analogy with the heterocyclic substance *pyran*, these cyclic sugars are called *pyranoses*. If the reacting hydroxy group is on C-4, a 5-membered ring, a *furanose*, is formed from 4 C atoms and 1 O atom. Thus D-glucopyranose is formed from D-glucose. Actually 2 different D-glucopyranoses can result, depending on the configuration of the newly formed asymmetric center C-1:

α-D-Glucopyranose   Straight-chain form   β-D-Glucopyranose

The 2 stereoisomers of a cyclic sugar molecule arising in this way are denoted by the symbols α and β, the designation α being given to the isomer in the D series that is more strongly *dextrorotatory*, and β to the isomer in the L series that is more strongly *levorotatory*.

In the FISCHER projection formula the OH group is written at the right of the asymmetric C atom when the isomer rotates more strongly to the right (α-D or β-L configuration); it is written at the left thereof when the isomer rotates more strongly to the left (β-D or α-L configuration):

| Aldose | Ketose | Aldose | Ketose |
| α-D or β-L | | β-D or α-L | |

The α and β isomers yield the corresponding α- and β-glycosides. This is of importance because many glycoside hydrolases are α- or β-specific.

The representation of cyclic sugars in the FISCHER projection formula can best be seen from the example of D-glucose:

| I | II | |
| D-Glucose | α-D-Glucopyranose | α-D-Glucofuranose |

The ring formulae of type II are commonly used because their relationship to the open formula I can be readily seen. Although the steric relationships of the alcohol groups ($>$CHOH) forming the ring are represented correctly, these formulae do not give a true picture of the steric configuration of the groups around the C atom that bears the oxygen bridge (C-5 for glucopyranose and C-4 for glucofuranose) because, according to the convention described above, this group is written with the hydroxy group on the right in chain formulae of the D series.

In the case of the pyranoses, a more correct type of projection formula is that illustrated by III and IV for glucose (derived by imagining the bond between C-4 and C-5 to be rotated through 180° before ring closure):

| III | | IV | |
| D-Glucose | α-D-Glucopyranose | L-Glucose | β-L-Glucopyranose |

In formulae III and IV, however, the D or L configuration at C-5 is no longer easy to recognize. These inadequacies of the FISCHER projection formula induced HAWORTH to work out a ring formula in which the steric relationships of the groups are unambiguously represented. The observer sees the ring at an angle from above, the 3 thickened edges lying closest to him:

Furanose ring   Pyranose ring

The position of the substituents corresponds to that of formulae III and IV:

| α-D-Glucopyranose | β-L-Glucopyranose |
| III | IV |

In the case of the hexofuranoses a side chain is formed by ring closure. If, as for example in the case of glucofuranose, this contains an asymmetric C atom, the configuration at this C atom must be represented in the HAWORTH formula on the basis of an appropriate convention. The derivation from the FISCHER projection formula is best illustrated in the example of α-D-glucofuranose:

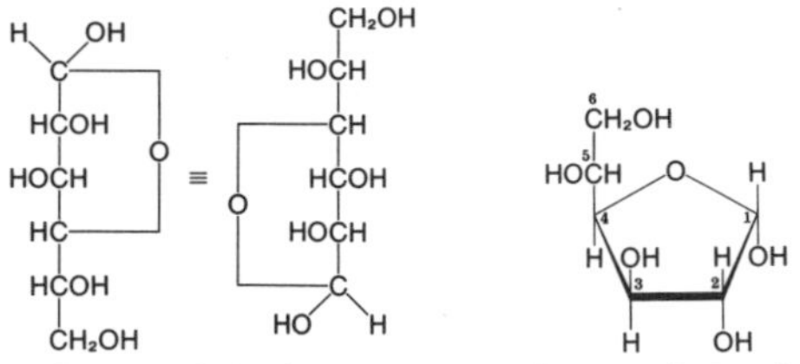

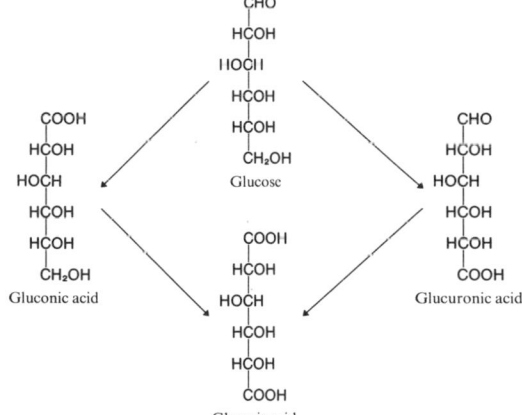

FISCHER projection formula = HAWORTH ring formula

Sometimes, for reasons of convenience, top and bottom or front and back are interchanged in the HAWORTH ring formulae for the representation of polysaccharides and other complex sugar compounds. This takes place by means of a 180° rotation of the ring around two axes lying in the ring plane or around an axis passing vertically through the center of the ring. The alternative representations for α-D-glucopyranose, for example, are the following:

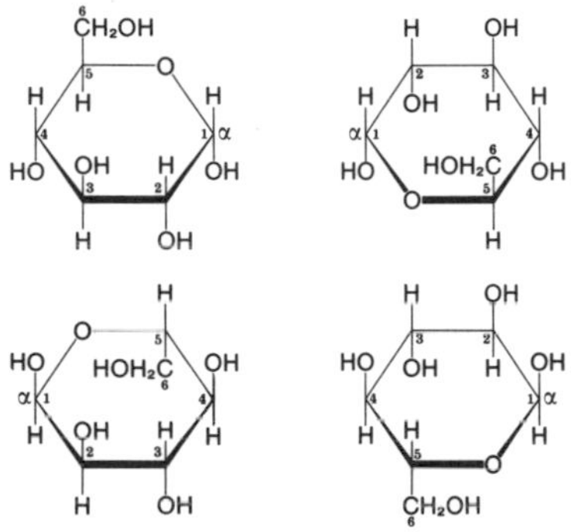

It is known that the pyranose ring, in contrast to the mostly planar furanose ring, is not planar. Most of its properties can be explained by the assumption of a 'chair' form.

Important monosaccharides are listed in Table 1 (pages 9 and 10).

Polyhydric alcohols (reduced sugars)

These substances, formed by reduction of the aldehyde or oxo group of monosaccharides (Table 2, page 11), are widely distributed in the plant kingdom, but occur only to a limited extent in mammalian tissue, except for glycerol, which is a constituent of lipids.

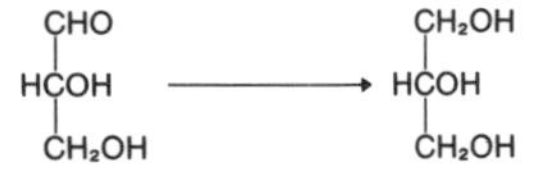

CHO		CH_2OH
HCOH	→	HCOH
CH_2OH		CH_2OH
Glyceraldehyde		Glycerol

Sorbitol is formed by the reduction of glucose or fructose and is an intermediate in the conversion of glucose to fructose in the seminal vesicles. Fructose, the principal energy source of spermatozoa, is formed by oxidation of sorbitol (page 131).

Another important sugar alcohol is inositol[1,2], a completely hydroxylated cyclohexane, for which 2 optically active and 7 *meso* forms are possible. One of the optically inactive *meso* forms is *myo*-inositol (previously referred to as 'mesoinositol'), an almost universal cell constituent which humans obtain primarily in food. *myo*-Inositol is a constituent of phospholipids (phosphatidyl-*myo*-inositol, phosphatidyl-*myo*-inositol 4-phosphate, phosphatidyl-*myo*-inositol 4,5-bisphosphate).

Deoxy sugars

The formation of sugar alcohols proceeds via the addition of hydrogen to the aldehyde or oxo group of the sugar in question. A reduction can, however, also consist in the removal of oxygen; in this case a deoxy sugar is formed (Table 3, page 12). Removal of oxygen from the hydroxy group on C-6 in D-glucose leads, for example, to L-rhamnose:

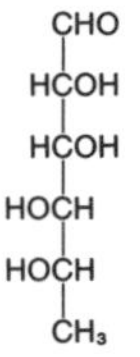

CHO
HCOH
HCOH
HOCH
HOCH
CH_3
L-Rhamnose

An important deoxy sugar is 2-deoxy-D-ribose (a constituent of deoxyribonucleic acid), in which the removal of oxygen in D-ribose takes place at C-2:

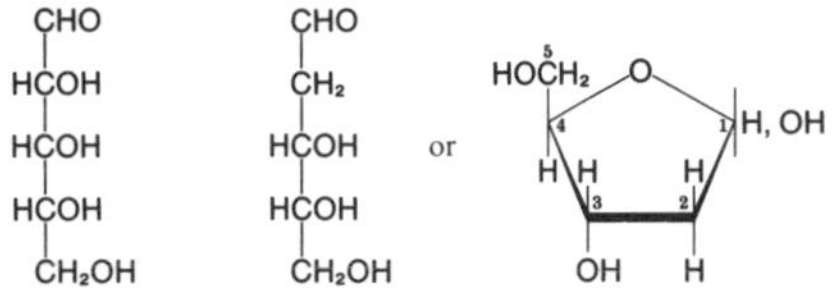

D-Ribose 2-Deoxy-D-ribose

Together with 2- and 6-deoxy sugars, 2,6-, 3,6- and 4,6-dideoxy sugars as well as 2,3,6-trideoxy sugars have also been found in nature.

Products of primary oxidation of carbohydrates

The terminal groups of aldoses are an aldehyde in the position 1 and a primary alcohol in the last position. Oxidation may take place at either of these groups or at both, the results being the formation of aldonic, uronic or aldaric acids (Table 4, pages 12 and 13). Glucose can thus be oxidized to gluconic, glucuronic or saccharic acid:

Gluconic acid Glucose Glucuronic acid

Glucaric acid

Amino sugars

Amino sugars (Table 5, pages 13 and 14) are constituents of many polysaccharides, glycolipids and glycoproteins. More than 60 are known[11], most of which are 2-amino-2-deoxy sugars. D-Glucosamine and D-galactosamine occur most frequently, mainly in the N-acetylated form:

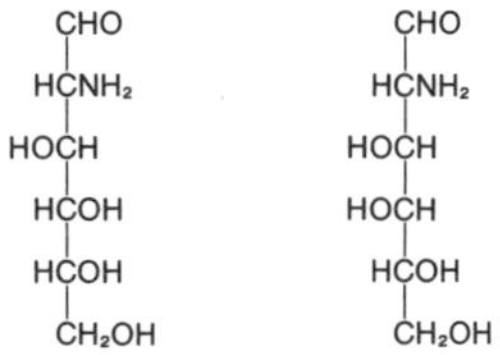

D-Glucosamine D-Galactosamine

The oligosaccharide units are linked by N-acetylglucosamine via an N-glycosidic bond to the asparagine residues of the protein framework of the glycoproteins, and by N-acetylgalactosamine via an O-glycosidic bond to a serine or threonine residue of the protein framework (see Table 11, page 22).

Fig. 4 Positions of substituents on a terminal neuraminic acid molecule from submandibular mucins

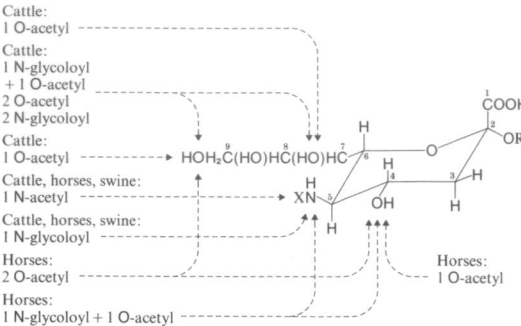

Cattle:
1 O-acetyl

Cattle:
1 N-glycoloyl
+ 1 O-acetyl
2 O-acetyl
2 N-glycoloyl

Cattle:
1 O-acetyl

Cattle, horses, swine:
1 N-acetyl

Cattle, horses, swine:
1 N-glycoloyl

Horses:
2 O-acetyl

Horses:
1 N-glycoloyl + 1 O-acetyl

Horses:
1 O-acetyl

A whole series of unusual amino sugars is found among the antibiotics of the aminoglycoside group, among them diamino sugars[3], compounds with a nitro group[3] or a fluoro group[4], and also a sugar which has an N atom in place of the heterocyclic O atom[5].

Sialic acid is a collective term for N-acetyl- and N-glycoloylneuraminic acids. Only N-acetylneuraminic acid seems to be of importance in humans. Other variants are indicated in Figure 4[6]. The sialic acids occupy a terminal position in the oligosaccharide units of glycoproteins and thus contribute to the acidic character and greater solubility of the glycoproteins. They form an important constituent of mucins, which are secreted, for example, from the mucous membranes of the oral cavity, the stomach, the respiratory tract and the cervix. Sialic-acid-rich glycoproteins are also partly responsible for the negative charge of the cell membrane. A thoroughly studied sialoglycopeptide is glycophorin A of the erythrocyte membrane[7]. Among the glycolipids, for example, hematoside and other gangliosides contain sialic-acid-rich oligosaccharide groups[8].

Oligosaccharides

Oligosaccharides are composed of monosaccharides or their derivatives linked together glycosidically. The bonds can be glycosidic on one or both sides. The designation 'oligosaccharide' is generally employed for compounds consisting of 2 to 10 monosaccharide units. Oligosaccharides can be reducing or nonreducing, depending on whether or not they contain free hemiacetal hydroxy groups. Reducing carbohydrates are called 'glycosyl(glycosyl)$_n$ glycoses'; nonreducing ones are called 'glycosyl(glycosyl)$_n$ glycosides'. In disaccharides the trivial names of the monosaccharide units are named in alphabetical order.

Important disaccharides are listed in Table 6 (page 15). The plant kingdom contains a wide variety of oligosaccharides. The structure of mother's milk oligosaccharides[9] and of oligosaccharides in normal urine[10] or, as an example from pathology, in urine in G_{M1} gangliosidosis may be seen from Table 7 (page 15).

Glycoproteins. The overwhelming majority of the proteins occurring in nature contain covalently bound carbohydrate components (they can consist of more than 10 monosaccharide units). In plasma proteins the carbohydrate content lies in the broad range from 0.4% (in

prealbumin) to 40% (in α_1-acid glycoprotein)[12]. Albumin, retinol-binding protein, lysozyme and amylase, on the other hand, contain no carbohydrates. The carbohydrate content of blood-group substances extends to 85%.

The covalent bonding of the carbohydrate components to the peptide chain can take place in accordance with 3 principal types:

N-Glycosyl linkage between N-acetylglucosamine and asparagine

O-Glycosyl linkage between N-acetylgalactosamine and serine (or threonine)

O-Glycosyl linkage between galactose and hydroxylysine

The first two bond forms often exist in glycoproteins, hence in plasma, cell-membrane and connective-tissue proteins. The binding to serine or threonine is characteristic of the proteins of the mucosal secretions (Table 8), while the binding to hydroxylysine is present in fibrillar collagen as well as in the protein of the glomerular basal membrane. Bonds that occur rarely are, for example, those between galactose or arabinose and hydroxyproline in plant cell-wall proteins.

Examples for the structure of oligosaccharide groups in glycoproteins are found in Table 9.

Polysaccharides

Polysaccharides (glycans), like the oligosaccharides, are built up of monosaccharide units and their derivatives. They differ from the oligosaccharides in that their molecules contain from 10 up to several thousand units. The most frequently occurring building block is D-glucose, though D-mannose, D- and L-galactose, D-xylose, L-arabi-

Table 8 *Properties of mucus and plasma glycoproteins*

Characteristic compounds	Mucus glycoproteins	Plasma glycoproteins
Amino acids	High proportion of serine, threonine and proline. Small proportion of aromatic and sulfur-containing amino acids	Amino-acid composition of a typical protein
Carbohydrate portion	More than 50%	Less than 25%
Linking amino acids	Serine or threonine (O-glycosyl-)	Asparagine (N-glycosyl-)*
Fucose	Present	Present
Galactose	Present	Present
N-Acetylglucosamine	Present	Present
N-Acetylneuraminic acid	Present	Present
Mannose	Small portion or absent	Present
N-Acetylgalactosamine	Present	Small portion or absent

*The plasma protein IgA$_1$ contains O-glycosyl linkages.   **Reference** REID and CLAMP, *Brit. med. Bull.*, **34**, 5 (1978).

Table 9 *Structure of oligosaccharide groups in glycoproteins*

Submandibular saliva (sheep)........	NeuAcα2→6GalNAc→Ser(or Thr)
IgA₁ (human).................... Chorionic gonadotropin (human) .... Epiglycanin in TA-3 cells	Galβ1→3GalNAc→Ser(or Thr)
Epiglycanin in TA-3 cells	NeuAcα2→3Galβ1→3(4)GalNAc→Ser(or Thr)
Fetuin .... Erythrocyte sialoglycoprotein (human)	NeuAcα2→3Galβ1→3GalNAc→Ser(or Thr) $\quad\quad\quad\quad\quad\quad\quad\quad$ 6 $\quad\quad\quad\quad\quad\quad\quad\quad$ ↑ $\quad\quad\quad\quad\quad\quad\quad$ α2NeuAc
Core region of blood-group substances (human, swine)...................	Galβ1→3GlcNAcβ1→3Galβ1→3GalNAc→Ser(or Thr)
Submandibular saliva (swine)........	NeuAc2→6Gal1→3GalNAc→Ser(or Thr) $\quad\quad\quad$ 2 $\quad\quad\quad$ ↑ $\quad\quad\quad$ α1Fuc
Transferrin, fibrinogen, chorionic gonadotropin (human)	NeuAcα2→3(6)Galβ1→4GlcNAcβ1→2Manα1 $\quad\quad\quad\quad\quad\quad\quad\quad\quad\quad\quad\quad\quad\quad\quad\quad\quad$ ₃Manβ1→4GlcNAcβ1→4GlcNAcβ1→Asn $\quad\quad\quad\quad\quad\quad\quad\quad\quad\quad\quad\quad\quad\quad\quad$ ⁶ NeuAcα2→3(6)Galβ1→4GlcNAcβ1→2Manα1
α₁-Acid glycoprotein (human)	NeuAc2α→3(6)Galβ1→4GlcNAcβ1 $\quad\quad\quad\quad\quad\quad\quad\quad\quad\quad\quad$ ↓ $\quad\quad\quad\quad\quad\quad\quad\quad\quad\quad\quad$ 4 NeuAcα2→3(6)Galβ1→4GlcNAcβ1→2Manα1 $\quad\quad\quad\quad\quad\quad\quad\quad\quad\quad\quad\quad\quad\quad\quad\quad$ ₃Manβ1→4GlcNAcβ1→4GlcNAcβ1→Asn NeuAcα2→3(6)Galβ1→4GlcNAcβ1→2Manα1 $\quad$ ⁶ $\quad\quad\quad\quad\quad\quad\quad\quad\quad\quad\quad\quad\quad$ 6 $\quad\quad\quad\quad\quad\quad\quad\quad\quad\quad\quad\quad\quad$ ↑ NeuAcα2→3(6)Galβ1→4GlcNAcβ1
IgE (human).....................	Manα1→3Manβ1→4GlcNAcα1→3Manβ1→4GlcNAcβ1→Asn $\quad\quad\quad$ 6 $\quad\quad\quad\quad\quad\quad$ 6 $\quad\quad\quad$ ↑ $\quad\quad\quad\quad\quad\quad$ ↑ $\quad\quad\quad$ α1Man $\quad$ α1Man2←1αMan
Influenza virus	Man→Man→Manα1 $\quad\quad\quad\quad\quad\quad\quad$ ₃Manβ1→4GlcNAc1→4GlcNAc→Asn $\quad\quad\quad\quad\quad\quad\quad$ ⁶ Man→Man→Manα1 NeuAc→Gal→GlcNAc→Manα1 $\quad\quad\quad\quad\quad\quad\quad\quad\quad\quad$ ₃Manβ1→4GlcNAc1→4GlcNAc→Asn $\quad\quad\quad\quad\quad\quad\quad\quad\quad\quad$ ⁶ NeuAc→Gal→GlcNAc→Manα1

References KORNFELD and KORNFELD, *Ann. Rev. Biochem.*, **45**, 217 (1976); COLLINS and KNIGHT, *J. Virol.*, **26**, 457 (1978); HATTON et al., *Trends biochem. Sci.*, **8**, 287 (1983).

nose, uronic acids (D-glucuronic acid, D-galacturonic acid and L-iduronic acid) and amino sugars (D-glucosamine, D-galactosamine, their N-acetyl derivatives and sulfuric acid esters) also occur. In contrast to the oligosaccharides, many polysaccharides are insoluble in water and are nonreducing.

The polysaccharides can be subdivided according to their structure into homopolysaccharides and heteropolysaccharides[13]. The former consist of a single type of monosaccharide as the building block; the latter consist of 2 or 3 different types of monosaccharides (up to 6 types of monosaccharides in a few cases) as building blocks. Depending on the type of monosaccharide, homopolysaccharides are designated 'glucans', 'fructans', 'mannans', 'xylans', etc. Heteropolysaccharides as a rule are branched-chain molecules linked for the most part by covalent bonds. A grouping by function is likewise possible, although this is not accurately known about all polysaccharides.

Polysaccharides serve primarily as structural substances (such as cellulose in plants, chitin in insects and crustaceans, chondroitin sulfate as a constituent of cartilage tissue) or as energy reserves (such as starch and inulin in plants, and glycogen in the animal kingdom). Special functions may be performed, for example, by hyaluronic acid (as a lubricant) or heparin (as an anticoagulant).

Homopolysaccharides

Starch. The glucan 'starch' is a constituent of some species of algae as well as of all higher plants; in the latter it is primarily present in storage organs. Starch consists of at least 2 components: amylose and amylopectin. The amylose portion extends from less than 2% (in wax corn) to 70%.

Amylose consists chiefly of linear chains of (α1→4)-linked D-glucopyranose units and has a relative molecular mass of 10^4 to 10^6:

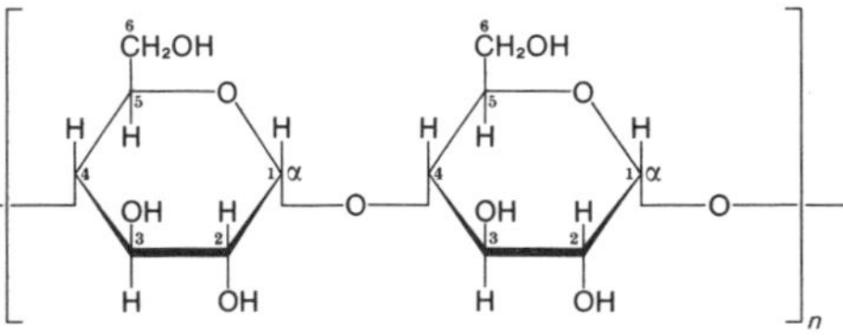

Amylose is water-soluble and assumes in solution a chance-dictated helical conformation. The insoluble amylose–iodine complexes are present in the form of a helix.

Amylopectin, likewise water-soluble, is distinguished as a highly-branched molecule which is substantially bigger than that of amylose, and has a relative molecular mass of 10^6 to 10^7.

Amylopectin consists of linear chains of 20 to 25 (α1→4)-linked D-glucopyranose units; these chains are linked together by (α1→6) bonds:

Roughly the following amylopectin structure results from the arrangement of the branchings[13]:

● Reducing chain end
○ Nonreducing chain end

Glycogen (liver starch) resembles amylopectin in structure, but the degree of branching is greater. The average chain length between the branchings is only 10 to 14 glucose units. Extracted glycogen is very

polydisperse. The relative molecular mass is 10^8 and more. Glycogen in the organs seems to contain small amounts of protein, in which case carbohydrate is linked to amino acids by covalent bonds.

Cellulose is the most frequently occurring organic substance and the most important structural substance of plants; it is, however, also present in some bacteria and algae. The polymer consists of D-glucopyranose units which are linked by ($\beta1 \rightarrow 4$) bonds. The linear chains, in contrast to those of amylose, are very rigid and lie parallel to each other, stabilized by intramolecular and intermolecular hydrogen bridges. In higher plants, cellulose occurs in association with other polysaccharides, with proteins, and also with lignin. Carefully extracted samples of native cellulose have a relative molecular mass of about 10^6.

Dextrans are extracellular polysaccharides which are formed from sucrose by certain species of bacteria. They consist of linear chains of ($\alpha1 \rightarrow 6$)-linked D-glucopyranose units, with branchings via ($\alpha1 \rightarrow 2$), ($\alpha1 \rightarrow 3$) or ($\alpha1 \rightarrow 4$) bonds. Structure and relative molecular mass (up to 5×10^5) are dependent on the species of bacteria under consideration. Dextran-forming bacteria occur primarily in the oral cavity and are the causative agents of plaque due to the presence of food particles containing sucrose between the teeth.

Fructans consist of D-fructofuranose units. They are reserve carbohydrates of certain plants, such as grasses. In inulin, the fructose units are linked by a ($\beta2 \rightarrow 1$) bond. Since inulin is synthesized starting with sucrose, a glucose unit linked by an ($\alpha1 \rightarrow 2$) bond is present at the beginning of the chain. The relative molecular mass of inulin is about 6000.

Table 10   *Structure of some heteropolysaccharides*

Heteropolysaccharide	Basic framework	Side chain	Occurrence
Xyloglucans	D-Glucopyranose linked by ($\beta1 \rightarrow 4$) bonds	D-Xylose or trisaccharide of fucose, galactose and xylose	Seeds, cell walls (in combination with cellulose)
Galactomannans . .	D-Mannopyranose linked by ($\beta1 \rightarrow 4$) bonds	D-Galactose	Seeds (plant mucilage)
Glucuronoxylans . .	D-Xylopyranose linked by ($\beta1 \rightarrow 4$) bonds	4-O-Methyl-α-D-glucuronic acid	Hemicellulose
Arabinoxylans	D-Xylopyranose linked by ($\beta1 \rightarrow 4$) bonds	L-Arabinofuranose	Cereal grains
Arabinogalactans .	(a) D-Galactopyranose linked by ($\beta1 \rightarrow 4$) bonds	L-Arabinofuranose (also as disaccharide)	Pectins in seeds
	(b) D-Galactopyranose linked by ($\beta1 \rightarrow 3$) bonds	L-Arabinofuranose, D-galactose (also as disaccharides)	Cell walls
	(c) Alternating units of β-D-galactopyranose and 3,6-anhydro-α-L-galactopyranose (in certain cases also glucuronic acid), in part with sulfate and methyl groups		Constituent of seaweed (agar) (agarose contains no glucuronic acid)
Pectins	Polymer of galacturonic acid, in between also L-rhamnose	Disaccharides of fucose and xylose or galactose and xylose	Cell walls; also intercellular

Table 11   *Differentiation of glycoproteins and proteoglycans*

Characteristic	Glycoproteins	Proteoglycans
Main occurrence in the body	Membranes; body fluids and secretions (blood, mucus)	Skeleton and connective tissue (bones, cartilage)
Carbohydrate component	Oligosaccharide	Glycosaminoglycan
Size of carbohydrate component	Less than 25 monosaccharide units	More than 50 monosaccharide units
Linking monosaccharide	N-Acetylhexosamine	Xylose*
Repeating structure.	Few or none	Disaccharide units
Shape of carbohydrate component	Branched	Linear; unbranched
Hexuronic acid	Not present	Present*

*Keratan sulfate: glycosaminoglycans are linked with the protein core by N-acetylhexosamine. Contains no hexuronic acid.

Reference
REID and CLAMP, *Brit. med. Bull.*, **34**, 5 (1978).

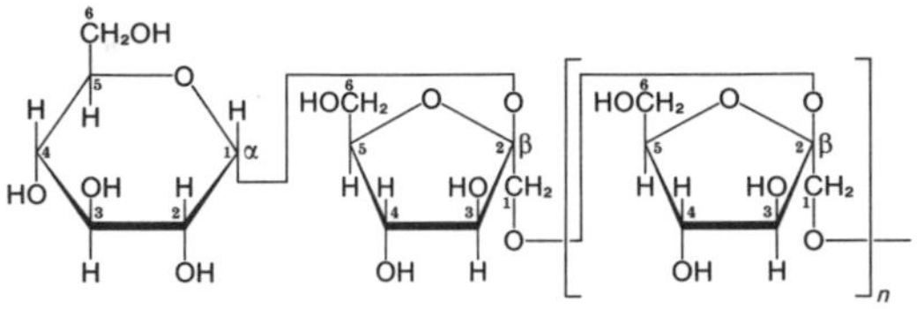

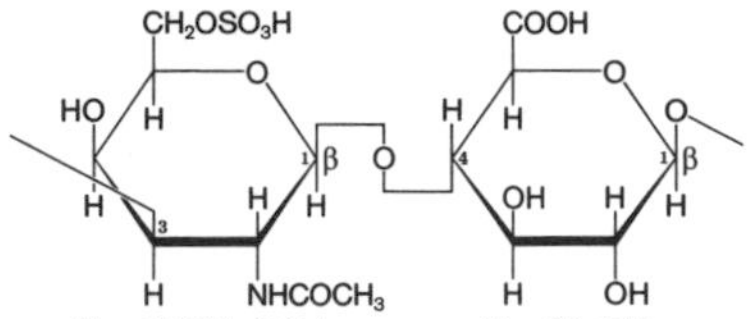

(β-D-GalNAc6SO₄)   (β-D-GlcUA)
Chondroitin 6-sulfate

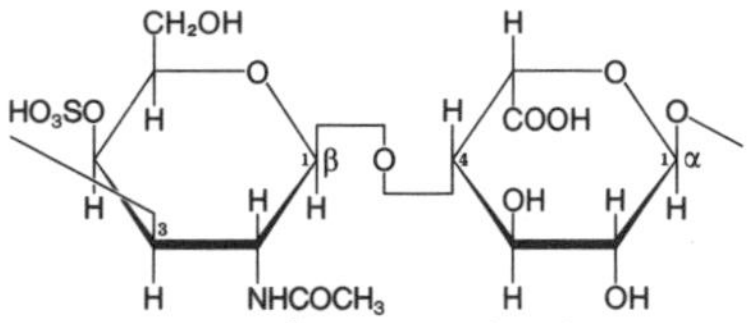

Other fructans, the levans from grasses, contain linear chains of (β2→6)-linked fructose units. Levans from bacteria have additional branchings via (β2→1) bonds.

Galacturonans consist of α-D-galacturonic-acid units which are linked by (α1→4) bonds. Pectinic acid, a constituent of plant cell walls and intercellular substance, belongs in this category. Galacturonic acid is often present as the methyl ester. Pectinic acid is classed with the pectins, which consist mainly of heteropolysaccharides (galacturonic acid combined with other types of monosaccharides).

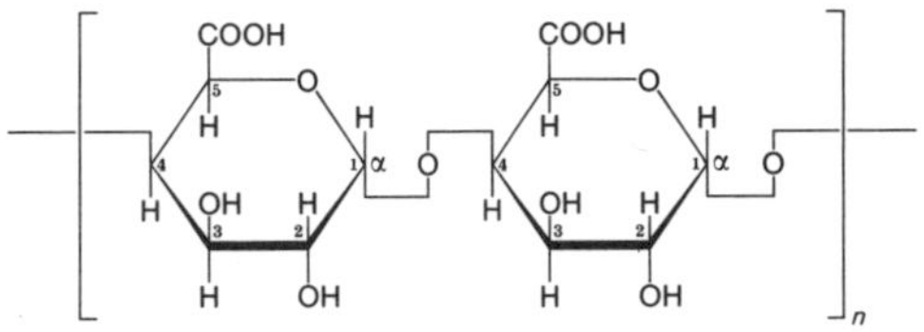

(β-D-GalNAc4SO₄)   (α-L-IdoUA)
Dermatan sulfate

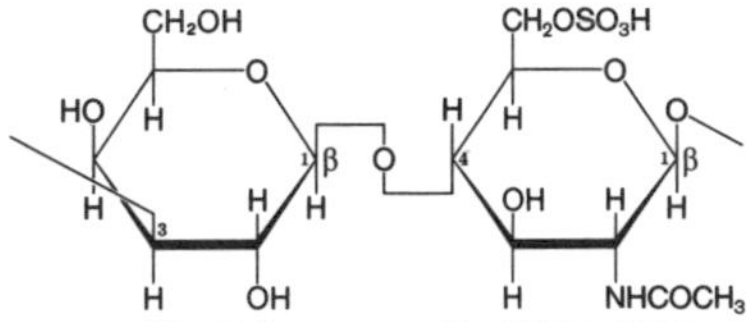

Chitin is the skeletal substance of arthropods and mollusks; however, chitin also occurs in lower plants, fungi and some species of algae. It is a polymer of (β1→4)-linked N-acetyl-D-glucosamine units and thus is similar in structure to cellulose, and also the relative molecular mass is probably in the neighborhood of that of cellulose.

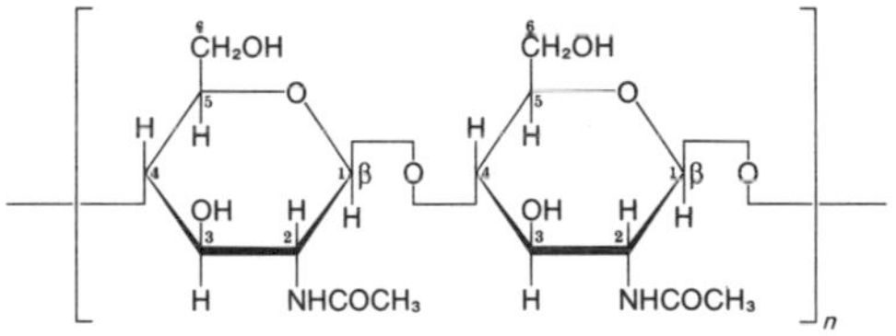

(β-D-Gal)   (β-D-GlcNAc6SO₄)
Keratan sulfate

The occurrence, properties and metabolism of the glycosaminoglycans (Table 12) are described in greater detail on pages 185–190.

Polysaccharides occurring in bacteria are complex and abounding in variants.

Polysaccharides of bacterial capsules differ in composition depending on the species of bacteria. Thus, for example, the polysaccharides of the type-II pneumococcus consist of glucose, glucuronic acid and rhamnose; those of the type-III pneumococcus, of glucose and glucuronic acid; those of the type-XIV pneumococcus, of glucose, galactose and N-acetylglucosamine; those of streptococci of groups A and C, of glucuronic acid and N-acetylglucosamine; and those of *Haemophilus influenzae*, of ribose phosphate. The polymers can be linear or branched in structure. Specific oligosaccharide units of the capsule polysaccharides are responsible for the specific antigenic properties of these types of bacteria.

Gram-negative bacteria bear lipopolysaccharides on their surface. The polysaccharide consists of an outer chain of repeating tetra- or pentasaccharide units which are linked via an inner chain of about 5 or 6 monosaccharide units to lipid by covalent bonds. The outer chain determines the antigenic properties.

Peptidoglycans (mureins) are very large molecules which are responsible for preserving the shape of the bacteria. The linear polysaccharide chain consists of alternating units of N-acetylglucosamine and N-acetylmuramic acid, which are linked by a (β1→4) bond. These chains, 10 to 50 units long, form the substrate for the enzyme lysozyme. The two-dimensional or three-dimensional cross-linkages are formed by peptide chains which are joined via an amide bond to the carboxy group of the N-acetylmuramic acid units of the polysaccharide chain. They occur particularly in gram-positive bacteria, but also to a lesser extent in gram-negative bacteria. In gram-positive bacteria the peptidoglycan is linked via a phosphate group to teichoic acids.

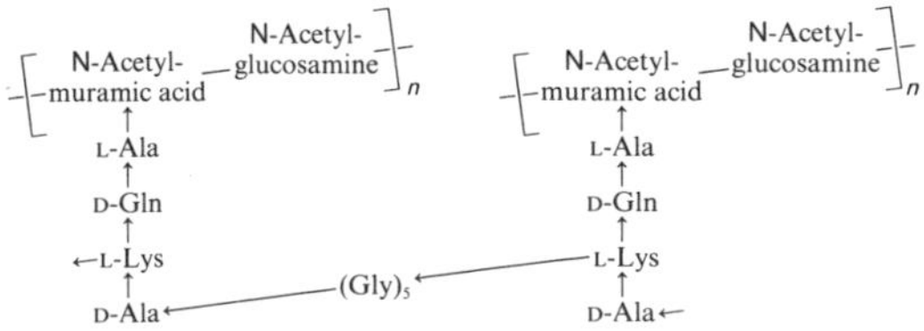

Heteropolysaccharides

The many *plant heteropolysaccharides* can be best classified according to the structure of the principal chain, to which side chains with 1 or more carbohydrate units are attached (Table 10).

Glycosaminoglycans are linear polymers that contain amino sugars. They occur primarily in the animal organism, but also in bacteria. They are mostly linked to protein by covalent bonds. Therefore these complexes (proteoglycans) resemble the glycoproteins (Table 11). The structure of the most frequent disaccharide units of the individual glycosaminoglycans is the following:

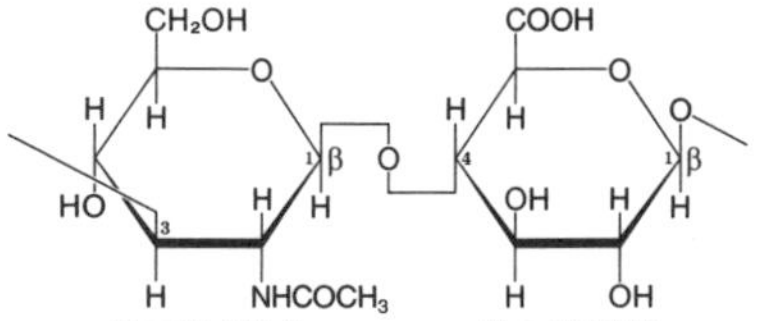

(β-D-GlcNAc)   (β-D-GlcUA)
Hyaluronic acid

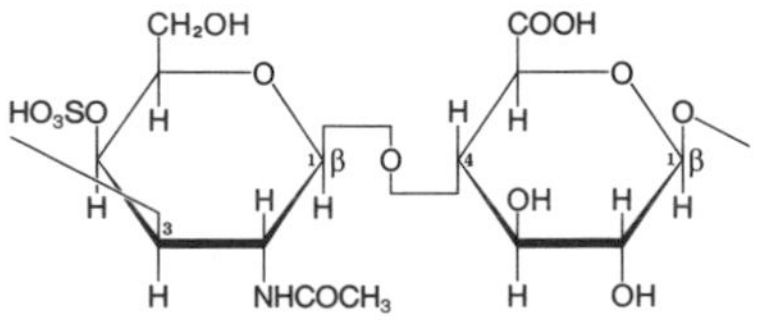

(β-D-GalNAc4SO₄)   (β-D-GlcUA)
Chondroitin 4-sulfate

Structure of a peptidoglycan (↑ peptide bond)

Teichoic acids are essential constituents of the cell walls and membranes of gram-positive bacteria. They are mostly polymers of glycerol phosphate or ribitol phosphate with the typical structures shown on the next page.

Table 12　*Structure and occurrence of glycosaminoglycans*

Polysaccharide	Most frequent disaccharide components		Position of the sulfate group		Occurrence
	Sugar unit 1	Sugar unit 2	Sugar unit 1	Sugar unit 2	
Hyaluronic acid	→3)GlcNAc(β1→4)GlcUA(β1→		0	0	Connective tissue, skin, synovial fluid, vitreous humor, cardiac valve, cartilage, umbilical cord
Chondroitin 4-sulfate . . .	→3)GalNAc4SO₄(β1→4)GlcUA(β1→		(a) 4 (b) 4 + 6	0 0	Cartilage, bones, cornea, skin
Chondroitin 6-sulfate . . .	→3)GalNAc6SO₄(β1→4)GlcUA(β1→		(a) 6 (b) 4 + 6	0 0	Cartilage, bones, intervertebral disc, cardiac valve, umbilical cord
Dermatan sulfate	→3)GalNAc4SO₄(β1→4)IdoUA(α1→		(a) 4 (b) 4 (c) 4 + 6	0 2 or 3 0	Skin, cardiac valve, cartilage, intervertebral disc, bones
Also contains:	→3)GalNAc4SO₄(β1→4)GlcUA(β1→		(d) 4 + 6 (e) 0	2 or 3 2 or 3	
Keratan sulfate	→3)Gal(β1→4)GlcNAc6SO₄(β1→		(a) 0 (b) 0 (c) 6	6 0 6	Cornea, cartilage, intervertebral disc, bones
Heparin group	→4)IdoUA(α1→4)GlcNAc(α1→		(a) 2 (b) 0 (c) 2	0 6 6 (?)	Heparan sulfate: lungs, liver (all body cells?); heparin: lungs, liver, skin, intestinal mucosa
	→4)GlcUA(β1→4)GlcNSO₃(α1→		(a) 0 (b) 0	6 6 + 3	
	→4)GlcUA(β1→4)GlcNAc(α1→		0	6	
	→4)IdoUA(α1→4)GlcNSO₃(α1→		(a) 0 (b) 0 (c) 2	6 6 + 3 6	

Gal: D-galactose
GlcUA: D-glucuronic acid
IdoUA: L-iduronic acid

GalNAc: N-acetyl-D-galactosamine
GlcNAc: N-acetyl-D-glucosamine
SO₄: sulfate ester
NSO₃: N-sulfamino group

Reference
COMPER and LAURENT, *Physiol. Rev.*, **58**, 255 (1978).

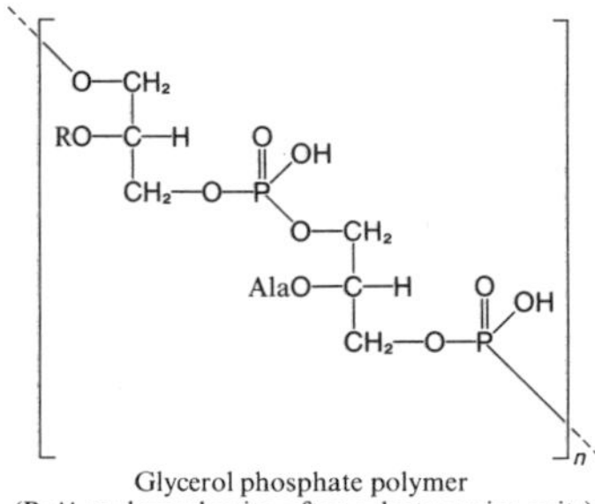

Glycerol phosphate polymer
(R: H or glycosyl units, often galactosamine units)

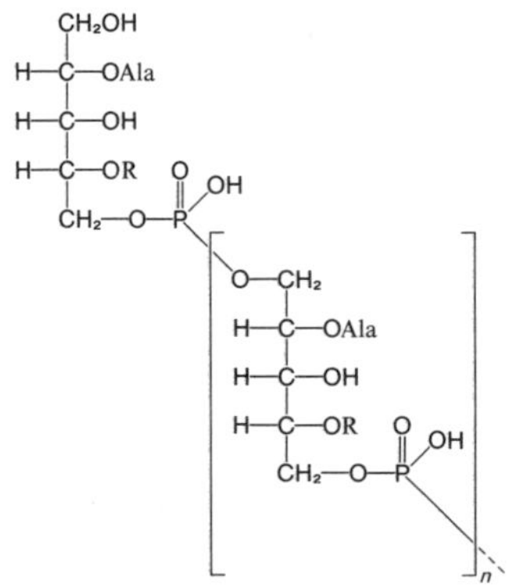

Ribitol phosphate polymer
(R: glucosyl units, often N-acetylglucosamine units)

Ribitol teichoic acid occurs only in cell walls, glycerol teichoic acid in cell walls and membranes.

The function of the teichoic acids evidently consists in the mobilization of mainly divalent cations, which serve as cofactors in numerous enzymatic reactions in the cell membranes of bacteria. In addition, the teichoic acids transfer a negative charge to bacteria and are furthermore involved in the regulation of extracellular lytic enzymes as well as in the formation of receptor sites for bacteriophages.

Teichuronic acids occur in both gram-positive and gram-negative bacteria. They consist of glucose, N-acetylglucosamine and hexuronic acids (glucuronic acid, mannosaminuronic acid, glucosaminuronic acid), but contain no phosphate groups.

References
[1] HAWTHORNE and WHITE, *Vitam. and Horm.*, **33**, 529 (1975).
[2] WELLS and EISENBERG (Eds.), *Cyclitols and Phosphoinositides*, Academic Press, New York, 1978.
[3] WAGMAN and WEINSTEIN, *Ann. Rev. Microbiol.*, **34**, 537 (1980).
[4] KENT, P. W., *Ciba Found. Symp.*, NS 2, 169 (1972).
[5] BENTLEY, R., *Ann. Rev. Biochem.*, **41**, 953 (1972).
[6] PHELPS and STEVENS, *Ciba Found. Symp.*, NS 54, 91 (1978).
[7] MARCHESI and FURTHMAYR, *Ann. Rev. Biochem.*, **45**, 667 (1976).
[8] BAUMANN and ZALC, *Expos. ann. Biochim. méd.*, **34**, 152 (1980).
[9] GROLLMAN and GINSBURG, *Biochem. biophys. Res. Commun.*, **28**, 50 (1967); YAMASHITA et al., *Arch. Biochem.*, **182**, 546 (1977).
[10] SEWELL, A. C., *Europ. J. Pediat.*, **134**, 183 (1980).
[11] SHARON, N., *Sci. Amer.*, **243**, No. 5 (1980).
[12] *Geigy Scientific Tables*, 8th ed., Volume 3, CIBA-GEIGY Ltd., Basle, 1984, page 135.
[13] MACGREGOR and GREENWOOD, *Polymers in Nature*, Wiley, Chichester, 1980.

Table 1 *Classification of the lipids*

Fatty acids
Saturated fatty acids
Unsaturated fatty acids
Branched-chain fatty acids
Hydroxy fatty acids, including prostaglandins
Lipids containing glycerol
Mono-, di- and triacylglycerols
Glyceryl ethers (alkoxydiglycerides)
Glycosylmono- and glycosyldiacylglycerols
Phospholipids (phosphatides)
Plasmalogens (acetal phosphatides)
Lipids containing sphingosine
Sphingomyelins
Ceramides
Neutral glycosphingolipids (cerebrosides)
Sialoglycosphingolipids (gangliosides)
Sulfoglycosphingolipids (sulfatides)
Long-chain aliphatic alcohols and waxes
Complex lipids
Lipoproteins and proteolipids
Lipopolysaccharides
Hydrocarbons such as squalene and carotene
Steroids and related compounds such as vitamin D

'Lipids' is the general term for a group of natural products which are insoluble in water but soluble in relatively nonpolar solvents such as mixtures of methanol and chloroform. Even this definition cannot be applied strictly because lysophosphatidylcholine (lysolecithin), for example, is soluble in water owing to its polar groups. The majority of the lipids are esters or amides of long-chain fatty acids and yield soaps upon alkaline hydrolysis. Any classification of the lipids is to some extent arbitrary, according to whether it is based on physical properties, chemical structure and reactions, or biological function and occurrence.

Fatty acids

Fatty acids are aliphatic monocarboxylic acids, RCOOH, in which the radical R can be saturated or unsaturated, straight-chain or branched, and may contain hydroxy groups or, in rare cases, oxo or fluoro groups, cyclic or acetylenic linkings (Table 2). Straight-chain fatty acids are much more abundant than branched-chain ones, which occur in traces in many fats but are present in larger amounts in wool wax and in the lipids of mycobacteria. The fact that fatty acids with an even number of carbon atoms are much more frequent than those with an odd number agrees with the circumstance that the biosynthesis of fatty acids takes place by condensation of 2-carbon units (acetate) with other 2-carbon units or with larger units, which in turn are built up from 2-carbon units (pages 137 and 138).

Fatty acids branched at the end of the chain are also referred to as *iso* acids, those branched in the next position, as *anteiso* acids.

The naturally occurring unsaturated fatty acids have *cis*-isomer configuration, although *trans* isomers have been detected in traces, thus, for example, elaidic acid (*trans* isomer of oleic acid) and vaccenic acid (*trans*-11-octadecenoic acid). The *cis-trans* isomerism is represented below by the example of oleic acid and elaidic acid:

$$CH(CH_2)_7COOH \qquad CH(CH_2)_7COOH$$
$$CH(CH_2)_7CH_3 \qquad CH_3(CH_2)_7CH$$
Oleic acid (*cis*)   Elaidic acid (*trans*)

Unsaturated fatty acids in mammals are divided into 4 families, depending on the number of C atoms up to the first double bond, the count beginning with the terminal CH_3 group:

ω-3	Linolenic-acid family	$CH_3-CH_2-CH=CH-R$
ω-6	Linoleic-acid family	$CH_3-(CH_2)_4-CH=CH-R$
ω-7	Palmitoleic-acid family	$CH_3-(CH_2)_5-CH=CH-R$
ω-9	Oleic-acid family	$CH_3-(CH_2)_7-CH=CH-R$

Polyunsaturated fatty acids with double bonds beyond the double bond in the C-9 position (counted from the carboxy end) (linoleic acid, linolenic acid) cannot be synthesized by humans and therefore must be supplied with the food. These are the so-called 'essential' fatty acids.

Fatty acids as a constituent of phospholipids are of great importance for the fluidity of membranes. In the ordered, rigid state, saturated fatty acids assume the 'synclinical' conformation; in the random, 'fluid' state they assume the 'antiperiplanar' conformation. The transition from the ordered to the random state is brought about by increasing the temperature. Unsaturated fatty acids with a *cis* configuration are considerably bent and interfere with the ordered state; the transition temperature is thereby lowered.

Prostaglandins. Prostaglandins can be regarded as derivatives of the hypothetical prostanoic acid[1].

Structure of 'prostanoic acid'

All naturally occurring prostaglandins have a double bond in the *trans* configuration between C-13 and C-14; additional double bonds in the *cis* configuration can occur between C-5 and C-6 as well as between C-17 and C-18. Depending on the substituents in the ring they are assigned to series E, F, D, etc. and, depending on the number of double bonds in the side chain, to subgroup E_1, E_2, E_3, F_1, F_2, F_3, etc. (Table 3).

The thromboxanes and prostacyclins are related to the prostaglandins.

Thromboxane A_2

Thromboxane B_2

Prostacyclin

6-Oxo-PGF$_{1\alpha}$

Prostaglandins occur in practically all tissues; they are not, however, stored but synthesized from the corresponding polyunsaturated C_{20} fatty acids only when needed (Table 3). Depending on the organ they show a series of effects: PGE$_2$ is a vasodilator and bron-

Table 2 *Fatty acids of importance for lipid composition*

Trivial name	Formula, M_r	Structure	Melting point (°C)	Systematic name	Numerical symbol
Butyric acid	$C_4H_8O_2$ 88.11	$CH_3(CH_2)_2COOH$	−7.9	Butanoic acid	4:0
Caproic acid..........	$C_6H_{12}O_2$ 116.16	$CH_3(CH_2)_4COOH$	−4	Hexanoic acid	6:0
Caprylic acid	$C_8H_{16}O_2$ 144.22	$CH_3(CH_2)_6COOH$	16	Octanoic acid	8:0
Capric acid..........	$C_{10}H_{20}O_2$ 172.27	$CH_3(CH_2)_8COOH$	31.3	Decanoic acid	10:0
Lauric acid...........	$C_{12}H_{24}O_2$ 200.32	$CH_3(CH_2)_{10}COOH$	43.5	Dodecanoic acid	12:0
Myristic acid	$C_{14}H_{28}O_2$ 228.37	$CH_3(CH_2)_{12}COOH$	54.4	Tetradecanoic acid	14:0
Palmitic acid	$C_{16}H_{32}O_2$ 256.43	$CH_3(CH_2)_{14}COOH$	62.85	Hexadecanoic acid	16:0
Stearic acid...........	$C_{18}H_{36}O_2$ 284.48	$CH_3(CH_2)_{16}COOH$	69.6	Octadecanoic acid	18:0
Arachidic acid	$C_{20}H_{40}O_2$ 312.54	$CH_3(CH_2)_{18}COOH$	68–69	Icosanoic acid	20:0
Behenic acid..........	$C_{22}H_{44}O_2$ 340.59	$CH_3(CH_2)_{20}COOH$	80	Docosanoic acid	22:0
Lignoceric acid	$C_{24}H_{48}O_2$ 368.65	$CH_3(CH_2)_{22}COOH$	84.2	Tetracosanoic acid	24:0
Palmitoleic acid.......	$C_{16}H_{30}O_2$ 254.41	$CH_3(CH_2)_5CH=CH(CH_2)_7COOH$	1	9-Hexadecenoic acid	16:1
Oleic acid	$C_{18}H_{34}O_2$ 282.47	$CH_3(CH_2)_7CH=CH(CH_2)_7COOH$	13	*cis*-9-Octadecenoic acid	18:1(9)
Linoleic acid	$C_{18}H_{32}O_2$ 280.45	$CH_3(CH_2)_3(CH_2CH=CH)_2(CH_2)_7COOH$	−11	*cis,cis*-9,12-Octadecadienoic acid	18:2(9,12)
(9,12,15)-Linolenic acid . (α-linolenic acid)	$C_{18}H_{30}O_2$ 278.44	$CH_3(CH_2CH=CH)_3(CH_2)_7COOH$	−11.2 to −11	9,12,15-Octadecatrienoic acid	18:3(9,12,15)
(6,9,12)-Linolenic acid .. (γ-linolenic acid)	$C_{18}H_{30}O_2$ 278.44	$CH_3(CH_2)_3(CH_2CH=CH)_3(CH_2)_4COOH$	–	6,9,12-Octadecatrienoic acid	18:3(6,9,12)
Arachidonic acid.......	$C_{20}H_{32}O_2$ 304.48	$CH_3(CH_2)_3(CH_2CH=CH)_4(CH_2)_3COOH$	−49.5	5,8,11,14-Icosatetraenoic acid	20:4(5,8,11,14)
Nervonic acid	$C_{24}H_{46}O_2$ 366.63	$CH_3(CH_2)_7CH=CH(CH_2)_{13}COOH$	40.5–41	*cis*-15-Tetracosenoic acid	24:1
Tuberculostearic acid ...	$C_{19}H_{38}O_2$ 298.51	$CH_3(CH_2)_7\underset{\underset{CH_3}{\mid}}{CH}(CH_2)_8COOH$	12.5–12.9	D-(−)-10-Methyloctadecanoic acid	19:br
Phytanic acid..........	$C_{20}H_{40}O_2$ 312.54	$CH_3CH(CH_2)_3CH(CH_2)_3CH(CH_2)_3CHCH_2COOH$ (CH₃ CH₃ CH₃ CH₃)	−7 to −6	3,7,11,15-Tetramethylhexadecanoic acid	20:br
Mycoceranic acid	$C_{31}H_{62}O_2$ 466.83	$CH_3(CH_2)_{21}CHCH_2CHCH_2CHCOOH$ (CH₃ CH₃ CH₃)	27–28	2,4,6-Trimethyloctacosanoic acid	31:br
3-Hydroxymyristic acid .	$C_{14}H_{28}O_3$ 244.37	$CH_3(CH_2)_{10}CH(OH)CH_2COOH$	–	3-Hydroxytetradecanoic acid	–

◊ In the numerical symbol $z:y$, z is the total number of C atoms and y the number of double bonds. Numbers in parentheses give the positions of the double bonds, and br stands for a branched chain.

chodilator, $PGF_{2\alpha}$ is a venoconstrictor and bronchoconstrictor. Thromboxane B_2 is the metabolic product of the unstable thromboxane A_2, which induces platelet aggregation. The prostacyclin formed in the blood vessel wall, on the other hand, prevents aggregation; the unstable compound is converted to 6-oxo-$PGF_{1\alpha}$.

Not only the prostaglandins, but also the monohydroxy-(e)icosatetraenoic acids (HETE) and the leukotrienes are derived from arachidonic acid. 5-HETE and leukotriene B_4 (LTB₄) play a part in the regulation of neutrophil and eosinophil function[2], while the sulfidopeptide leukotrienes (LTC₄, LTD₄, LTE₄, LTF₄) are primarily smooth muscle spasmogens and form the so-called 'slow-reacting substances of anaphylaxis' (SRS-A)[3]. Structure and main functions of the leukotrienes are shown in Table 4.

5-Hydroxy-6,8,11,14-icosatetraenoic acid (5-HETE)

Acylglycerols

Acylglycerols are formed by esterification of glycerol with 1, 2 or 3 fatty acids, yielding respectively a mono-, di- or triacylglycerol.

CH_2OCOR	CH_2OH	CH_2OCOR^1	CH_2OCOR^1	CH_2OCOR^1
$CHOH$	$CHOCOR$	$CHOCOR^2$	$CHOH$	$CHOCOR^2$
CH_2OH	CH_2OH	CH_2OH	CH_2OCOR^2	CH_2OCOR^3
1-Acyl-glycerol (α-monoglyceride)	2-Acyl-glycerol (β-monoglyceride)	1,2-Diacyl-glycerol (α,β-diglyceride)	1,3-Diacyl-glycerol (α,α′-diglyceride)	1,2,3-Triacyl-glycerol (triglyceride)

The fats occurring in nature consist almost exclusively of triacylglycerols (neutral fat), along with traces of mono- and diacylglycerols. The two latter esters, however, are formed in the intestine during digestion and absorption of triacylglycerols and therefore may also be found among circulating lipids of the plasma.

Natural fats may be solid or liquid at room temperature. At least 5 and up to 12 or more different fatty acids occur in fats, which – due to

Table 3 *Structure of prostaglandins of the E and F series as well as of fatty-acid precursors*

Precursor		
Dihomo-γ-linolenic acid [$C_{20:3(8,11,14)}$]	Arachidonic acid [$C_{20:4(5,8,11,14)}$]	Icosapentaenoic acid [$C_{20:5(5,8,11,14,17)}$]
E series		
E_1	E_2	E_3
F series		
$F_{1\alpha}$	$F_{2\alpha}$	$F_{3\alpha}$

Table 4 *Structure and biological function of leukotrienes*

Leukotriene	Structure	Function
LTA₄....................		Intermediate in the biosynthesis of LTB₄ and LTC₄. Action on venules and airways?
LTB₄....................		Chemotactic and chemokinetic factor of granulocytes. Increases vascular permeability. Action on smooth muscle (enhancement of bronchoconstriction during asthmatic attack). Ca²⁺ translocation. Enzyme release and superoxide generation
LTC₄....................		
LTD₄		'Slow-reacting substances of anaphylaxis' (SRS-A). Contraction of smooth muscle. Constriction of small airways. Secretion of mucus. Leakage from post-capillary venules. Formation of edema. Vasoconstriction. Coronary arterial constriction
LTE₄....................		
LTF₄....................		

the tendency to the greatest possible heterogeneity in their composition – are a mixture of extremely diverse triacylglycerols.

The fatty acids of most natural fats consist of mixtures of saturated and unsaturated acids. In general, the melting point of fat increases with the proportion of saturated fatty acids.

Vegetable oils are often rich in the unsaturated C_{18} acids oleic ($C_{18:1}$), linoleic ($C_{18:2}$) and linolenic ($C_{18:3}$). Palm-seed oils are rich in shorter-chain saturated fatty acids (coconut oil: 37–51% C_{12}, some C_{10} and C_8). Myristic acid is obtained from the *Myristicaceae* (nutmeg oil: 60–77% C_{14}).

The fatty-acid composition of the depot fats of land mammals is characterized by a predominance of oleic acid and palmitic acid, and in some species (for example cattle and sheep) also stearic acid. The composition of human depot fat (as mass fraction of the total fatty acids in %) is: oleic acid 45, palmitic acid 25, linoleic acid 8, palmitoleic acid 7, stearic acid 6. There is a shift in favor of shorter-chain saturated fatty acids (C_{12} to C_4 [butyric acid]) in the milk fat of land mammals. The fats of aquatic animals contain chiefly higher unsaturated fatty acids (C_{16} to C_{22}), usually together with 10–18% palmitic acid.

Due to resynthesis of the triacylglycerols after digestion and absorption (page 99) the fat of any particular tissue in the same species as a rule has a typical composition. Drastic changes in dietary fat, however, can exceed the body's metabolic capacity and lead to changes in the composition of depot fat.

Diacylglyceryl ethers (alkoxydiglycerides)

In the liver oils of elasmobranchids there are considerable amounts of various compounds that differ from the triacylglycerols in that they contain an ether linkage. These are diacylglycerols in which the 3rd hydroxy group forms an ether with a higher aliphatic alcohol (ROH).

$$CH_2OR^1$$
$$\mid$$
$$CHOCOR^2$$
$$\mid$$
$$CH_2OCOR^3$$
Diacylglyceryl ether

The liver oil of rays consists almost exclusively of such compounds and contains practically no triacylglycerols. Diacylglyceryl ethers of 1,2-unsaturated higher aliphatic alcohols occur in the plasmalogen fraction (page 29).

Glycosylacylglycerols (glycosylglycerides)

These compounds are widely distributed in the plant kingdom. They consist of diacylglycerol in which the remaining primary alcohol group is condensed with a sugar to form a glycoside, frequently a D-galactopyranoside. A galactosyldiacylglycerol occurs in the myelin of the human brain where it accompanies the glycosphingolipid fraction, and in the testes there is a sulfated monogalactosyl compound (seminolipid) in which glycerol bears an O-alkyl group instead of an acyl group[4].

3-Sulfogalactoglycerolipid
(seminolipid)

Phospholipids

Phospholipids (the earlier term 'phosphatides' is not recommended[5]) are lipids that contain phosphoric acid as a mono- or diester. In the glycerophospholipids, glycerol phosphoric acid is linked with at least 1 O-acyl, O-alkyl or O-(1-alkenyl) group. Analogous definitions hold true for the inositol phospholipids, in which glycerol phosphoric acid is substituted by inositol phosphoric acid, and for the sphingophospholipids, in which glycerol phosphoric acid is replaced by 4-sphingenin phosphoric acid or a related compound.

Phospholipids occur in all organs – especially in brain and nerves – but are notably absent from depot fats. They take part in very many metabolic processes and can be regarded as a form of fat which undergoes metabolic change and is transported through the body. It is established that they are involved in intestinal fat resorption, in

fatty-acid transport and oxidation, and in fatty infiltration of the liver. Moreover, they play a part as structural components of organs and in blood coagulation as well as in prostaglandin synthesis (page 142).

Phospholipid degradation, particularly phosphatidylinositol turnover provoked by various extracellular messengers, appears to be a sign for the transmembrane control of cellular functions[6].

Glycerophospholipids. The basic structure is the compound with the following steric configuration, formerly designated 'α-glycerophosphoric acid':

sn-Glycerol 3-phosphoric acid
L-(glycerol 3-phosphoric acid) ≡ D-(glycerol 1-phosphoric acid)

Glycerol 2-phosphoric acid, formerly designated 'β-glycerophosphoric acid', is probably formed by spontaneous migration of the phosphate group.

Phosphatidic acids. This is the name given to derivatives of glycerol phosphoric acid whose remaining 2 hydroxy groups are esterified with fatty acids. They can assume the following two structures (—COR¹ and —COR² are fatty-acid residues):

3-sn-Phosphatidic acid   2-Phosphatidic acid

Phosphatidic acids have been isolated from a large number of plants and also occur in animal tissues.

Plasmenic acids. In these compounds the fatty-acid residue in position C-1 of the 3-phosphatidic acid is replaced by the O-(1-alkenyl) group. They form the basic substance of the plasmalogens.

Plasmanic acids. The fatty-acid residue in position C-1 of the 3-phosphatidic acid is replaced by an O-alkyl group.

Derivatives of phosphatidic acids

Phosphatidic acids esterified with glycerol. These compounds are widely distributed in nature, primarily in plants and microorganisms. The free hydroxy groups of the glycerol can be esterified with fatty-acid residues.

1-(3-sn-Phosphatidyl)-sn-glycerol

Cardiolipin (originally isolated from the heart muscle) consists of glycerol esterified in the C-1 and C-3 positions with phosphatidic acids; the fatty acids are almost exclusively oleic acid and linoleic acid in a ratio of 1:5. Cardiolipin plays a part in the Wassermann reaction.

1,3-Bis(3-sn-phosphatidyl)glycerol
(cardiolipin)

Phosphatidic acids esterified with amino alcohols. Esterification with ethanolamine, choline or serine yields the following 3 types of phosphatidyl esters:

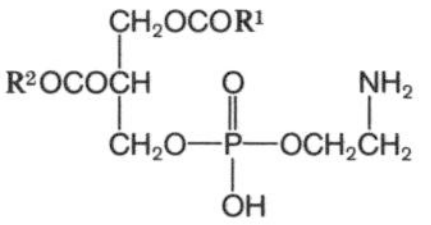

CH₂OCOR¹ structures (top row):

$$\begin{array}{l}
\text{CH}_2\text{OCOR}^1\\
\text{R}^2\text{OCOCH} \quad \text{O} \quad \text{NH}_2\\
\text{CH}_2\text{O}-\text{P}-\text{OCH}_2\text{CH}_2\\
\text{OH}
\end{array}$$

Phosphatidylethanolamine
(cephalin)

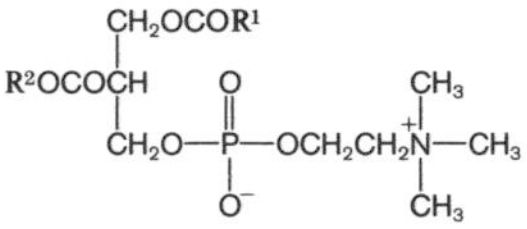

$$\begin{array}{l}
\text{CH}_2\text{OCOR}^1\\
\text{R}^2\text{OCOCH} \quad \text{O} \quad \text{CH}_3\\
\text{CH}_2\text{O}-\text{P}-\text{OCH}_2\text{CH}_2\overset{+}{\text{N}}-\text{CH}_3\\
\text{O}^- \qquad\qquad \text{CH}_3
\end{array}$$

Phosphatidylcholine
(lecithin)

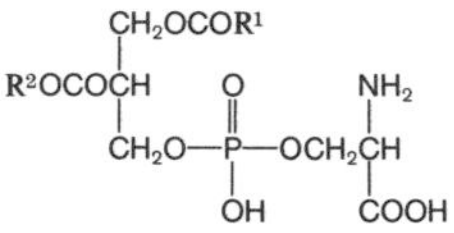

$$\begin{array}{l}
\text{CH}_2\text{OH}\\
\text{HOCH} \quad \text{O} \quad \text{NH}_2\\
\text{CH}_2\text{O}-\text{P}-\text{OCH}_2\text{CH}_2\\
\text{OH}
\end{array}$$

sn-Glycero(3)phosphoethanolamine

$$\begin{array}{l}
\text{CH}_2\text{OH}\\
\text{HOCH} \quad \text{O} \quad \text{CH}_3\\
\text{CH}_2\text{O}-\text{P}-\text{OCH}_2\text{CH}_2\overset{+}{\text{N}}-\text{CH}_3\\
\text{O}^- \qquad\qquad \text{CH}_3
\end{array}$$

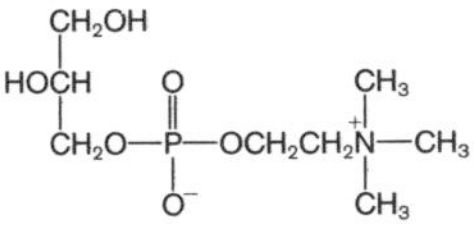

sn-Glycero(3)phosphocholine

$$\begin{array}{l}
\text{CH}_2\text{OCOR}^1\\
\text{R}^2\text{OCOCH} \quad \text{O} \quad \text{NH}_2\\
\text{CH}_2\text{O}-\text{P}-\text{OCH}_2\text{CH}\\
\text{OH} \qquad\quad \text{COOH}
\end{array}$$

Phosphatidylserine

Phosphatidylethanolamines are widely distributed – in animals, plants and microorganisms; the fatty acids are predominantly oleic acid and stearic acid. Small amounts of N-acetylated phosphatidylethanolamine are found in the brain.

Phosphatidylcholines are the most frequently encountered phospholipids in animals; they occur rather seldom in microorganisms. The fatty acids are predominantly oleic acid, palmitic acid and stearic acid. The arachidonic-acid content is of importance for prostaglandin synthesis (page 142). The phosphatidylcholine in the brain differs from that in other organs by a higher content of polyunsaturated fatty acids with a chain length of over C₂₀. The fatty-acid component affects the solubility in nonpolar solvents.

Phosphatidylserines have – although only in small amounts – a wide distribution in animals, plants and microorganisms. The carboxy group is ionized, the associated cations being K⁺, Na⁺ and Ca²⁺.

Lysophospholipids. The lysophospholipids consist of partly hydrolyzed glycerophospholipids. Snake venoms and some bacterial toxins (page 201) contain an enzyme that selectively splits off only 1 of the 2 fatty-acid residues of phosphatidylcholine, whereupon a lysophosphatidylcholine (lysolecithin) is formed:

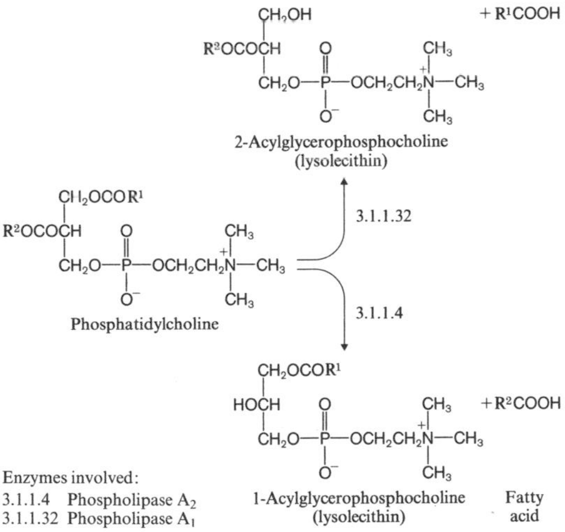

$$\begin{array}{l}
\text{CH}_2\text{OH} \qquad\qquad\qquad\qquad + \text{R}^1\text{COOH}\\
\text{R}^2\text{OCOCH} \quad \text{O} \quad \text{CH}_3\\
\text{CH}_2\text{O}-\text{P}-\text{OCH}_2\text{CH}_2\overset{+}{\text{N}}-\text{CH}_3\\
\text{O}^- \qquad\qquad \text{CH}_3
\end{array}$$

2-Acylglycerophosphocholine
(lysolecithin)

$$\begin{array}{l}
\text{CH}_2\text{OCOR}^1\\
\text{R}^2\text{OCOCH} \quad \text{O} \quad \text{CH}_3\\
\text{CH}_2\text{O}-\text{P}-\text{OCH}_2\text{CH}_2\overset{+}{\text{N}}-\text{CH}_3\\
\text{O}^- \qquad\qquad \text{CH}_3
\end{array}$$

Phosphatidylcholine

3.1.1.32

3.1.1.4

$$\begin{array}{l}
\text{CH}_2\text{OCOR}^1\\
\text{HOCH} \quad \text{O} \quad \text{CH}_3 \qquad + \text{R}^2\text{COOH}\\
\text{CH}_2\text{O}-\text{P}-\text{OCH}_2\text{CH}_2\overset{+}{\text{N}}-\text{CH}_3\\
\text{O}^- \qquad\qquad \text{CH}_3
\end{array}$$

1-Acylglycerophosphocholine   Fatty
(lysolecithin)   acid

Enzymes involved:
3.1.1.4   Phospholipase A₂
3.1.1.32 Phospholipase A₁

Lysobisphosphatidic acid [bis(monoacylglyceryl)phosphate] accumulates in the liver and spleen in Niemann-Pick disease[7].

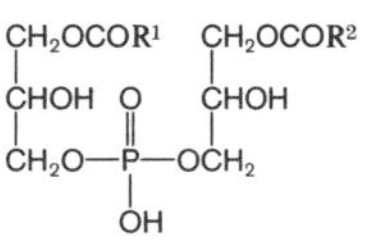

$$\begin{array}{ll}
\text{CH}_2\text{OCOR}^1 & \text{CH}_2\text{OCOR}^2\\
\text{CHOH} \quad \text{O} & \text{CHOH}\\
\text{CH}_2\text{O}-\text{P}-\text{OCH}_2\\
\qquad \text{OH}
\end{array}$$

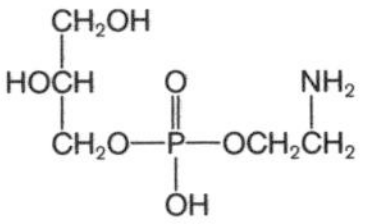

Lysobisphosphatidic acid
[Bis(monoacylglyceryl)phosphate]

Glycero(3)phospho compounds without the 2 fatty acids present in the phosphatidyl esters occur in the tissues and body fluids of mammals. These are glycero(3)phosphoethanolamine and glycero(3)phosphocholine:

Phosphatidic acids esterified with inositol (inositol phospholipids, phosphatidylinositols). These compounds can be regarded either as a derivative of phosphatidic acid, analogous to the phosphatidyl compounds, or as a derivative of inositol phosphates. They occur in liver, heart, wheat germs and soybeans. In addition, one or two hydroxy groups of the inositol can be esterified with phosphoric acid (Table 5).

Inositol phospholipids are important metabolically active components of the myelin sheath with a high turnover rate; they are bound to proteins and peptides (phosphatidopeptides).

Derivatives of plasmenic and plasmanic acids

Plasmalogens. In these compounds the phosphatidyl group of the phosphatidyl ester is replaced by the plasmenyl group. They can also be regarded as vinyl ethers of lysophospholipids. Plasmalogens containing ethanolamine (plasmenylethanolamines) are predominant in nature. Among the myelin lipids containing ethanolamine the major one is plasmenylethanolamine (for structure see below). Plasmenylcholine and plasmenylserine are also found in many tissues.

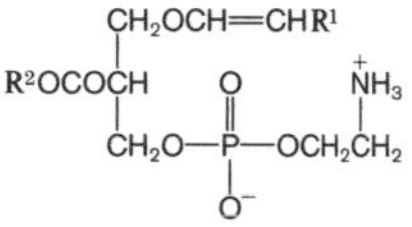

$$\begin{array}{l}
\text{CH}_2\text{OCH}=\text{CHR}^1\\
\text{R}^2\text{OCOCH} \quad \text{O} \quad \overset{+}{\text{NH}}_3\\
\text{CH}_2\text{O}-\text{P}-\text{OCH}_2\text{CH}_2\\
\qquad \text{O}^-
\end{array}$$

Plasmenylethanolamine
[2-acyl-1-(1-alkenyl)-sn-glycero(3)phosphoethanolamine]

Plasmalogens give a positive aldehyde reaction, and the aldehydes of stearic and palmitic acid may be isolated from the crystallized plasmalogens of the brain. About 20 different long-chain aldehydes, many of which are branched, occur in the plasmalogens.

Table 5 *Nomenclature and structure of phosphatidylinositols*

Recommended name [abbreviation]	Structure
1-(3-sn-Phosphatidyl)-1D-myo-inositol [PtdIns]	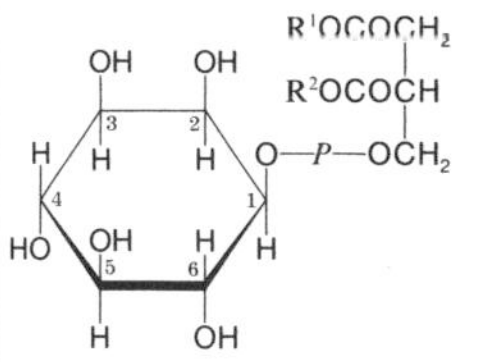 inositol ring structure with R¹OCOCH₂, R²OCOCH, O—P—OCH₂
1-(3-sn-Phosphatidyl)-1D-myo-inositol 4-phosphate [PtdIns4P; PtdIns-4-P]	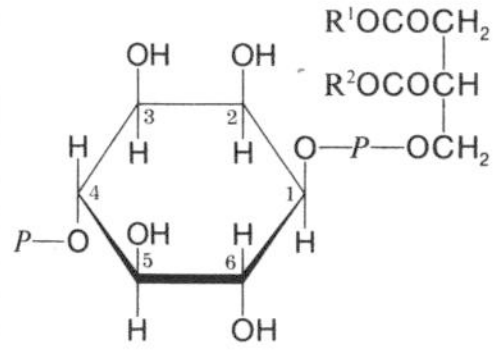 inositol ring structure with R¹OCOCH₂, R²OCOCH, O—P—OCH₂
1-(3-sn-Phosphatidyl)-1D-myo-inositol 4,5-bisphosphate [PtdIns(4,5)P₂; PtdIns-4,5-P₂]	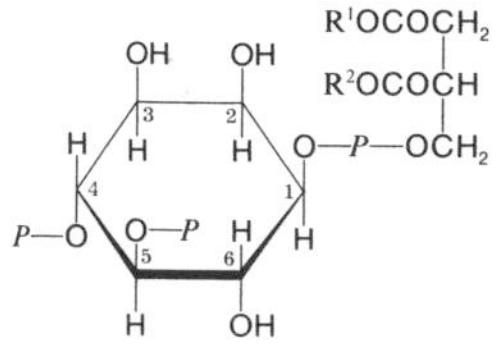 inositol ring structure with R¹OCOCH₂, R²OCOCH, O—P—OCH₂

Reference Nomenclature Committee of IUB (NC-IUB) and IUPAC–IUB Joint Commission on Biochemical Nomenclature (JCNB), *Biol. Chem. Hoppe-Seyler*, **366**, 3 (1985).

Table 6   *Structure and nomenclature of neutral glycosphingolipids[1]*

Family	Structure	Trivial name
Globo ..	Glcβ1→1Cer	Glucocerebroside ....
	Galβ1→4Glcβ1→1Cer	Lactosylceramide ....
	Galα1→4Galβ1→4Glcβ1→1Cer	Ceramide trihexoside, trihexosylceramide
	GalNAcβ1→3Galα1→4Galβ1→4Glcβ1→1Cer	Globoside, cytolipin K...........
	GalNAcα1→3GalNAcβ1→3Galα1→4Galβ1→4Glcβ1→1Cer	Forssman glycolipid hapten[2]........
Gala ...	Galβ1→1Cer	Galactocerebroside........
	Galα1→4Galβ1→1Cer	Digalactosylceramide.............
Ganglio.	GalNAcβ1→4Galβ1→4Glcβ1→1Cer	Asialo-G_{M2}, G_{A2} ....
	Galβ1→3GalNAcβ1→4Galβ1→4Glcβ1→1Cer	Asialo-G_{M1}, G_{A1} ......
Lacto...	Galβ1→3GlcNAc(4←1αFuc)β1→3Galβ1→4Glcβ1→1Cer	Lewis A glycolipid ......
	Galα1→3Gal(2←1αFuc)β1→3GlcNAcβ1→3Galβ1→4Glcβ1→1Cer	Blood-group B glycolipid..........
Neolacto	Galβ1→4GlcNAcβ1→3Galβ1→4Glcβ1→1Cer	Paragloboside ....
	Galβ1→3Galβ1→4GlcNAcβ1→3Galβ1→4Glcβ1→1Cer	....
	Galβ1→4GlcNAc(3←1αFuc)β1→3Galβ1→4Glcβ1→1Cer	X hapten ....
	Fucα1→2Galβ1→4GlcNAcβ1→3Galβ1→4Glcβ1→1Cer	Blood-group H1 glycolipid ....
	Galα1→3Gal(2←1αFuc)β1→4GlcNAcβ1→3Galβ1→4Glcβ1→1Cer	Blood-group B1 glycolipid..........
	GalNAcα1→3Gal(2←1αFuc)β1→4GlcNAcβ1→3Galβ1→4Glcβ1→1Cer	Blood-group A[a] glycolipid.........
	Fucα1→2Galβ1→4GlcNAcβ1→3Galβ1→4GlcNAcβ1→3Galβ1→4Glcβ1→1Cer 6 ↑ Fucα1→2Galβ1→4GlcNAcβ1	Blood-group I glycolipid ....

References   [1] DESNICK and SWEELEY, in STANBURY et al. (Eds.), *The Metabolic Basis of Inherited Disease*, 5th ed., McGraw-Hill, New York, 1983, page 906.

Closely related to the plasmalogens are the *plasmanyl compounds*, which have an O-alkyl group in place of the O-(1-alkenyl) group and can also be regarded as alkyl ethers of the lysophospholipids. Consequently they form no aldehydes. They are constituents of myelin and other tissue. One plasmanylcholine compound – which is linked with a hexadecyl or octadecyl group at position C-1 of the glycerol via an ether bridge and has an acetyl group at position C-2 – is the platelet-activating factor (PAF)[8].

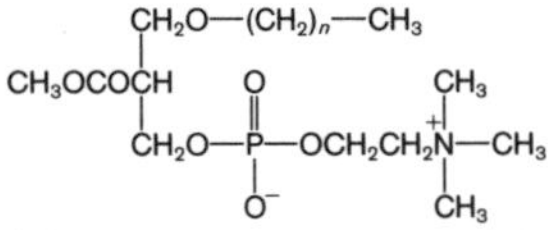

$$CH_2O-(CH_2)_n-CH_3 \qquad n = 15, 17$$
$$CH_3OCOCH$$
$$CH_2O-\overset{O}{\underset{O^-}{P}}-OCH_2CH_2\overset{+}{N}\overset{CH_3}{\underset{CH_3}{-}}CH_3$$

1-Alkyl-2-acetyl-*sn*-glycero(3)phosphocholine (PAF)

Sphingolipids

In sphingolipids the base 4-sphingenin or a related compound replaces glycerol, and the amino group of the base forms an amide with a fatty acid. The resulting compounds are called 'ceramides'.

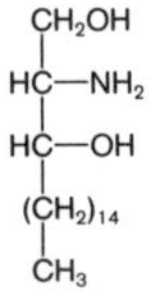

| Sphinganin (dihydro-sphingosine) | *trans*-4-Sphingenin (sphingosine) | 4-Icosa-sphingenin | 4D-Hydroxy-sphinganin |

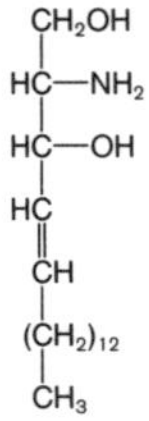

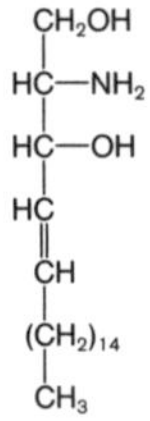

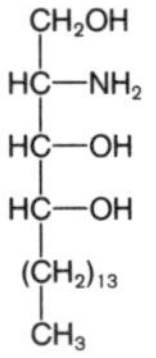

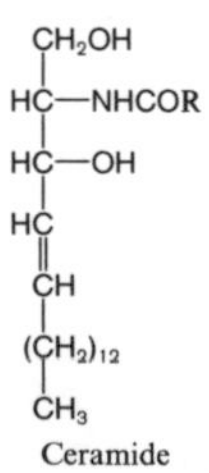

Ceramide

Some sphingolipids are phospholipids, others contain no phosphorus.

Sphinganin, 4-sphingenin, 4-icosasphingenin and 4D-hydroxy-sphinganin occur in the sphingolipids of the human brain. Similar compounds (sphingoids), such as phytosphingosine (1,3,4-trihydroxy-2-aminooctadecane) or branched-chain compounds, occur in other species[9].

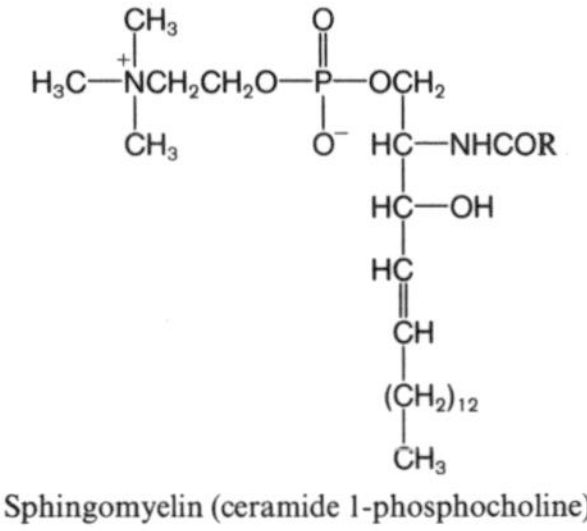

Sphingomyelin (ceramide 1-phosphocholine)

Sphingomyelins. The only sphingolipids closely related to the glycerophospholipids are the sphingomyelins, which are important constituents of the myelin sheath. The sphingomyelin of the gray matter contains chiefly stearic acid, that of the white matter mainly $C_{24:1}$ acid, with smaller amounts of $C_{25:1}$, $C_{26:1}$, C_{24}, C_{25} and C_{16} acids.

A phospholipid occurring in malignant tumors has been described which shows a marked affinity to protoporphyrin IX and is synthesized from choline, spermine, phosphoric acid and fatty acid. The following structure has been assumed to this phospholipid[10]:

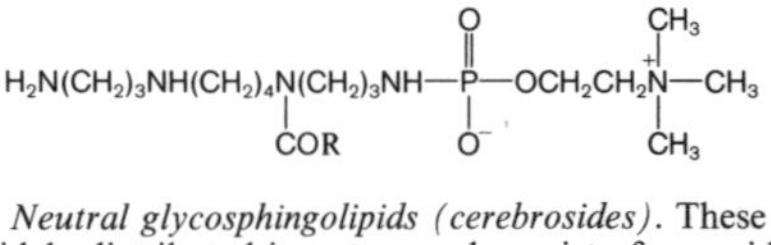

$$H_2N(CH_2)_3NH(CH_2)_4N(CH_2)_3NH-\overset{O}{\underset{COR}{P}}-OCH_2CH_2\overset{+}{N}\overset{CH_3}{\underset{CH_3}{-}}CH_3$$

Neutral glycosphingolipids (cerebrosides). These compounds are widely distributed in nature and consist of ceramide, which is connected by a β-glycosidic linkage to a sugar – in most cases galactose or glucose, but sometimes also di-, tri- or tetrahexosides. Blood-group substances in addition contain fucose. Human neutral glycosphingolipids can be divided into 5 families (Table 6); other species are provided with glycosphingolipids of different compositions.

Myelin contains large amounts of galactosylceramides (galactocerebrosides), which are divided into 4 classes according to the fatty-acid residue in each case: kerasin, phrenosin, nervone, hydro-

(to Table 6)

Approved nomenclature	Suggested abbreviations	Formerly used abbreviations	Family
Glucosylceramide	GlcCer	GL-1, Gl-1a	Globo
Lactosylceramide	LacCer	GL-2, Gl-2a	
Globotriaosylceramide	GbOse$_3$Cer	GL-3, Gl-3a	
Globotetraosylceramide	GbOse$_4$Cer	GL-4, Gl-4a	
Globopentaosylceramide	GbOse$_5$Cer		
Galactosylceramide	GalCer	GL-1b	Gala
Galabiosylceramide	GaOse$_2$Cer		
Gangliotriaosylceramide	GgOse$_3$Cer		Ganglio
Gangliotetraosylceramide	GgOse$_4$Cer		
III^4-α-Fucosyllactotetraosylceramide	III^4-α-Fuc-LcOse$_4$Cer		Lacto
IV^2-α-Fucosyl-IV^3-α-galactosyllactotetraosylceramide	IV^2-α-Fuc-IV^3-α-Gal-LcOse$_4$Cer		
Neolactotetraosylceramide	nLcOse$_4$Cer		Neolacto
IV^3-β-Galactosylneolactotetraosylceramide	IV^3-β-Gal-nLcOse$_4$Cer		
III^3-α-Fucosylneolactotetraosylceramide	III^3-α-Fuc-nLcOse$_4$Cer		
IV^2-α-Fucosylneolactotetraosylceramide	IV^2-α-Fuc-nLcOse$_4$Cer		
IV^2-α-Fucosyl-IV^3-α-galactosylneolactotetraosylceramide	IV^2-α-Fuc-IV^3-α-Gal-nLcOse$_4$Cer		
IV^2-α-Fucosyl-IV^3-α-N-acetylgalactosaminylneolactotetraosylceramide	IV^2-α-Fuc-IV^3-α-GalNAc-nLcOse$_4$Cer		
IV^6-β-Fucosyl-α1, 2galactosyl-β1, 4-N-acetylglucosaminylneolactohexaosylceramide	IV^6-β-Fuc-α1, 2Galβ1, 4GlcNAcnLcOse$_6$Cer		

[2] SVANBORG EDÉN et al., *Ciba Found. Symp.*, NS **80**, 161 (1981).

Table 7 *Structure of gangliosides of the human brain*

Designation	Structure	Designation	Structure
G$_{M3}$ (hematoside)	Galβ1→4Glcβ1→1Cer 3 ↑ 2NeuAc	G$_{T1a}$	GalNAcβ1→4Galβ1→4Glcβ1→1Cer 3 3 ↑ ↑ Galβ1 2NeuAc 3 ↑ 2NeuAc8←2NeuAc
G$_{M2}$ (Tay-Sachs ganglioside)	GalNAcβ1→4Galβ1→4Glcβ1→1Cer 3 ↑ 2NeuAc	G$_{T1b}$	GalNAcβ1→4Galβ1→4Glcβ1→1Cer 3 3 ↑ ↑ Galβ1 2NeuAc8←2NeuAc 3 ↑ 2NeuAc
G$_{M1}$ (monosialoganglioside)	GalNAcβ1→4Galβ1→4Glcβ1→1Cer 3 3 ↑ ↑ Galβ1 2NeuAc	G$_{Ter}$ (G$_O$, G$_{Q1}$)	GalNAcβ1→4Galβ1→4Glcβ1→1Cer 3 3 ↑ ↑ Galβ1 2NeuAc8←2NeuAc 3 ↑ 2NeuAc8←2NeuAc
G$_{D1a}$	GalNAcβ1→4Galβ1→4Glcβ1→1Cer 3 3 ↑ ↑ Galβ1 2NeuAc 3 ↑ 2NeuAc		
G$_{D1b}$	GalNAcβ1→4Galβ1→4Glcβ1→1Cer 3 3 ↑ ↑ Galβ1 2NeuAc8←2NeuAc		

xynervone. A portion of each galactosylceramide contains sphinganin instead of 4-sphingenin.

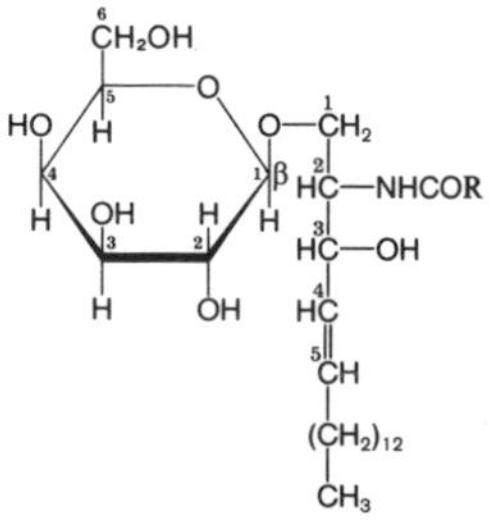

1-β-Galactosylceramide

The fatty acids are C_{13} to C_{25} acids which may be saturated or unsaturated or exist as 2-hydroxy derivatives, in which case they may constitute 50–60 % of the total fatty acids.

Psychosine (galactosylsphingosine) is a galactosylceramide without an acyl group, which accumulates in the brain in Krabbe's disease[11].

In Gaucher's disease a glucosylceramide (glucocerebroside) in which 4-sphingenin has the normal *erythro-trans* configuration is deposited in various tissues. The fatty acids of the glucosylceramide in the spleen (the principal storage organ), the liver and other peripheral tissues have long chains and are mainly saturated (for example $C_{22:0}$) and may be mixtures of hydroxylated and nonhydroxylated acids. The glucosylceramide that accumulates in the central nervous system, on the other hand, contains nonhydroxylated stearic acid ($C_{18:0}$) almost exclusively as the fatty-acid component. Glucosylsphingosine – a glucocerebroside without an acyl group – accumulates in the spleen in Gaucher's disease[12].

Lactosylceramide occurs in many tissues as a constituent of membranes. It was isolated from tumor tissue.

Galabiosylceramide (digalactosylceramide) (for structure see Table 6) is found in human kidneys and urine[13].

Globotriaosylceramide (trihexosylceramide) (for structure see Table 6) accumulates in Fabry's disease.

Gangliotetraosylceramide (asialo-G_{M1}) (for structure see Table 6) occurs in the human brain. Stearic acid constitutes 85–95% of the acyl residues of the ceramide. The compound accumulates in the neurons in Tay-Sachs disease and Sandhoff's disease; however, gangliotetraosylceramide is not the most-stored lipid.

Globotetraosylceramide (globoside) (for structure see Table 6) is the major glycolipid of the human erythrocyte stroma. It accumulates in many tissues in Sandhoff's disease.

Sialoglycosphingolipids (gangliosides). These compounds are acid glycosphingolipids whose acidic nature is due to the content of acylated neuraminic acid (sialic acid). They correspond in structure to the neutral glycosphingolipids. Although their monomeric molecules have a relative molecular mass of about 1500, they form micelles in water.

Gangliosides of varying structure occur in the brain, liver, spleen and erythrocyte stroma. The gangliosides isolated from the human or bovine brain have a common basic structure, namely

Gal—GalNAc—Gal—Glc—Cer

linked to 1 to 4 sialic-acid residues. The monosialoganglioside (G_{M1}) is formed from gangliosides with more than one sialic-acid residue by the action of sialidase (for the structure of gangliosides of the human brain see Table 7).

An outstanding characteristic of the brain gangliosides is the large amount of stearic acid they contain (86–95% of the fatty acids); other fatty acids present are palmitic acid (1–3%) and arachidic acid (2–12%).

The gangliosides of the erythrocyte stroma of horses, cats and dogs contain G_{M3} (hematoside), but no hexosamine; the fatty acids are chiefly $C_{24:1}$, $C_{24:0}$ and $C_{22:0}$. Human, sheep and guinea-pig erythrocytes contain neutral glycosphingolipids but no gangliosides.

While the gangliosides of the bovine brain also contain N-glycoloylneuraminic acid, only N-acetylneuraminic acid is present in those of the human brain.

In Tay-Sachs disease the monosialoganglioside content of both the gray and white matter of the brain is increased about 20-fold; an increased content of neutral glycosphingolipids is likewise found.

Sulfoglycosphingolipids (sulfatides). These compounds are sulfuric-acid esters of glycosphingolipids in which the sulfate group is linked to galactose at position 3. They are strong acids that can form neutral salts with cations and organic amines.

Galactosylsulfatide and lactosylsulfatide occur in the white and gray matter of the brain, but also in the liver, kidneys and other organs. They are important components of myelin; they continue to be formed as long as myelination continues, but once formed they normally undergo changes very slowly.

3-Sulfogalactosylceramide

A sulfated digalactosylceramide is found in the kidneys.

In metachromatic leukodystrophy the content of sulfatides (of normal structure) increases 2- to 5-fold in the white matter of the brain, while the proportion of the other lipids is markedly reduced.

A sulfatide containing sialic acid – 'ungulic acid' – occurs in epidermis, hair, nails and kidneys[14].

Long-chain aliphatic alcohols · Waxes

Dolichols. These long-chain alcohols are polyisoprenyl alcohols with a chain length of 80 to 110 C atoms[15]. They are formed from farnesyl diphosphate by condensation with up to 16 isopentenyl

units in such a way that double bonds in the *cis* configuration result. Thus the first 3 double bonds corresponding to farnesyl diphosphate have *trans* configuration, but the remainder have *cis* configuration (see page 144). The α-isoprene unit is saturated in the dolichols of plants, yeasts, insects and mammals, in contrast to bacterial polyisoprenyl alcohols.

Dolichol

Mannosylphosphodolichol

The dolichols occur, for example, in the liver as phosphates and diphosphates which can form esters with sugars – glycosylphosphodolichols – participating in the formation of oligosaccharide chains of glycoproteins.

Sulfono alcohols. Long-chain diols, both of whose OH groups are esterified with sulfuric acid, are found in the phytoflagellate species *Ochromonas*[16]; these sulfono alcohols can also bear 1 to 6 Cl atoms.

1-(S)-14-Docosane disulfate

threo-(R)-13-Chloro-1-(R)-14-docosane disulfate

Waxes. Waxes, strictly speaking (as distinguished from hydrocarbons and sterol esters), are esters of fatty acids with aliphatic straight-chain monohydric alcohols, usually cetyl alcohol (hexadecanol: $CH_3[CH_2]_{14}CH_2OH$) and octadecyl alcohol (octadecanol: $CH_3[CH_2]_{16}CH_2OH$), but frequently also with higher alcohols up to C_{36}. Among the mostly saturated fatty acids cerotinic acid (hexacosanoic acid: $CH_3[CH_2]_{24}COOH$) occurs most frequently; occasionally hydroxy acids are also found. In many natural waxes the fatty-acid and alcohol components have the same chain length.

In general, waxes are products excreted by animal or plant epidermis which serve as a protective film against water loss or wetting. The surface waxes of plants in arid climates, for example, serve the first purpose, whereas the lanolin occurring on the skin and in the hair of almost all fur-bearing animals and the surface wax of fruits, such as apples, in humid climates serve the second. Waxes are the energy reserve material in many organisms of the zooplankton (copepods), and in some species of marine animals, waxes almost entirely replace the triacylglycerols as the energy reserve material.

Retinols. Retinol and dehydroretinol are long-chain polyunsaturated alcohols with vitamin A activity (for formulae see pages 61 to 62). They are formed from plant carotenoids by cleavage in the intestinal mucosa and are present in the animal organism chiefly stored as esters (in man as retinyl palmitate in the hepatocytes).

Alkylcatechols (urushiols). These 3-n-alk(en)ylcatechols whose side chain contains 15 or 17 C atoms, saturated or unsaturated with 1 to 3 double bonds, are found in the oil of poison ivy and poison oak[17]. These compounds produce contact dermatitis.

3-n-Heptadecylcatechol

cis-3-n-(Heptadec-8-enyl)catechol

Lipopolysaccharides

The most important difference between gram-positive and gram-negative bacteria consists in the fact that the latter possess an additional membrane lying outside the cell wall. This outer membrane is an asymmetric bimolecular coating whose outer layer consists to a large extent of lipopolysaccharides (LPS). Lipopolysaccharides are complex heteropolysaccharides whose structure has been determined for a series of bacteria[18].

Fig. 1 *Molecular structure of lipoglycan from* Thermoplasma acidophilum[19]

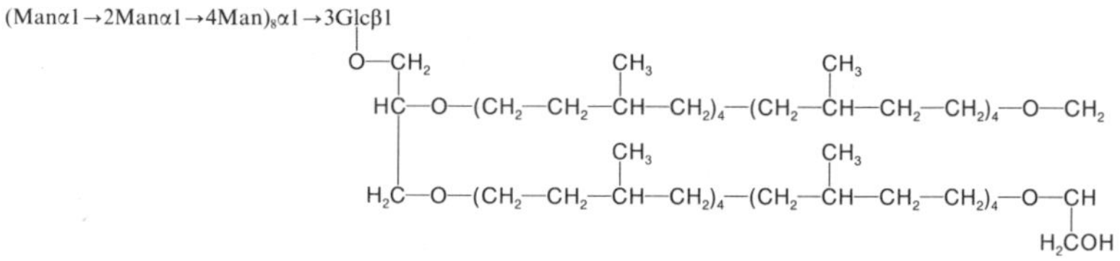

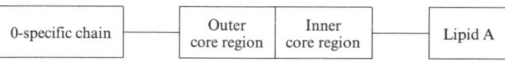

$(\mathrm{Man}\alpha 1 \rightarrow 2\mathrm{Man}\alpha 1 \rightarrow 4\mathrm{Man})_8\alpha 1 \rightarrow 3\mathrm{Glc}\beta 1$

The general structure is as follows:

0-specific chain	Outer core region	Inner core region	Lipid A

The 0-specific chain and the core region are of different compositions in the individual species of bacteria and consist of an extremely wide variety of sugars, many of which are unusual and often methylated. Lipid A, which is reponsible for the endotoxic properties of organisms such as salmonella and shigella, has the basic structure shown in the formula below. This structural principle of lipid A is found in different species of bacteria. In *Salmonella typhimurium* the amino groups of the bisphosphorylated $\beta 1 \rightarrow 6$-linked glucosamine disaccharide carry D-3-hydroxymyristoyl residues, and the available OH groups are esterified with lauric, palmitic and D-3-myristoxy-myristic acid. Lipid A is linked to the inner core region by 3-deoxy-D-*manno*-octulosonic acid (previously referred to as '2-keto-3-deoxy-octonic acid' [KDO]).

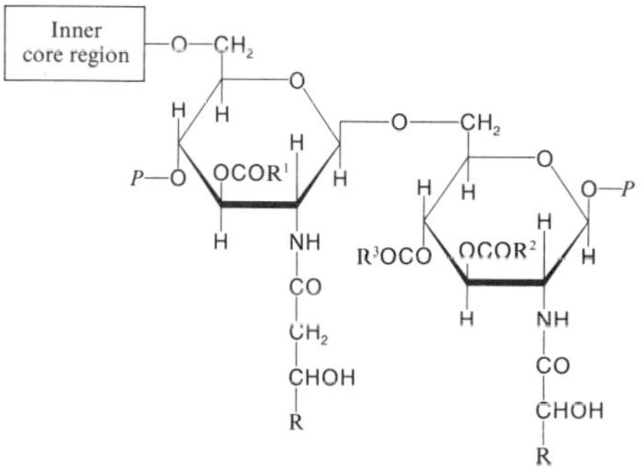

Lipoglycans

These compounds occur as surface structures on wall-less microorganisms, for example mycoplasmas[19]. They differ from the lipo-polysaccharides by their molecular structure and their effect on mammalian cells.

Many lipoglycans consist of a long oligosaccharide chain bound to a diacylglycerol or a related structure (an example is given in Fig. 1), while in others the lipid portion consists of fatty acids distributed along the linear oligosaccharide chain.

Proteolipids

Proteolipids are proteins containing a lipid residue as part of its primary structure[20]. These compounds cannot be called 'lipoproteins', since this term has for a long time been used to identify a water-soluble complex of specific proteins and lipids. The proteolipid 'lipophilin' is a major membrane protein of brain myelin. Proteolipids also occur in bacteria and viruses.

References

[1] MARCUS, A. J., *Progr. Hemat.*, **11**, 147 (1979); WOLFE, L. S., *J. Neurochem.*, **38**, 1 (1982).

[2] GOETZL, E. J., *New Engl. J. Med.*, **303**, 822 (1980); BRAY, M. A., *Brit. med. Bull.*, **39**, 249 (1983).

[3] HAMMARSTRÖM, S., *Ann. Rev. Biochem.*, **52**, 355 (1983); PIPER, P. J., *Brit. med. Bull.*, **39**, 255 (1983); LEWIS and AUSTEN, *J. clin. Invest.*, **73**, 889 (1984).

[4] KOLODNY and MOSER, in STANBURY et al. (Eds.), *The Metabolic Basis of Inherited Disease*, 5th ed., McGraw-Hill, New York, 1983, page 881.

[5] IUPAC–IUB Commission on Biochemical Nomenclature (CBN), *Europ. J. Biochem.*, **79**, 11 (1977).

[6] NISHIZUKA, Y., *Trends biochem. Sci.*, **8**, 13 (1983).

[7] HOSTETLER and POORTHUIS, in WELLS and EISENBERG (Eds.), *Cyclitols and Phosphoinositides*, Academic Press, New York, 1978, page 585.

[8] HANAHAN et al., *J. biol. Chem.*, **255**, 5514 (1980).

[9] CARTER and HIRSCHBERG, *Biochemistry*, **7**, 2296 (1968).

[10] KOSAKI et al., *Science*, **127**, 1176 (1958).

[11] SVENNERHOLM et al., *J. Lipid Res.*, **21**, 53 (1980).

[12] RAGHAVAN et al., *J. Lipid Res.*, **15**, 484 (1974).

[13] MÅRTENSSON, E., *Biochim. biophys. Acta*, **116**, 296 (1966).

[14] LEIKOLA et al., *J. Lipid Res.*, **10**, 440 (1969).

[15] BEHRENS and TÁBORA, in COLOWICK and KAPLAN (Eds.), *Methods in Enzymology*, Volume 50, Part C, Academic Press, New York, 1978, page 402.

[16] HAINES, T. H., *Ann. Rev. Microbiol.*, **27**, 403 (1973).

[17] RYERS et al., *J. clin. Invest.*, **64**, 1437 (1979).

[18] RIETSCHEL et al., *Rev. infect. Dis.*, **6**, 432 (1984).

[19] SMITH, P. F., *CRC Crit. Rev. Microbiol.*, **11**, 157 (1984).

[20] SCHLESINGER, M. J., *Ann. Rev. Biochem.*, **50**, 193 (1981).

Nomenclature and structure of the most important steroid hormones

Trivial name and systematic name	Formula, M_r	Structure	Trivial name and systematic name	Formula, M_r	Structure
Aldosterone 11β,21-Dihydroxy-3,20-dioxo-4-pregnen-18-al	$C_{21}H_{28}O_5$ 360.45	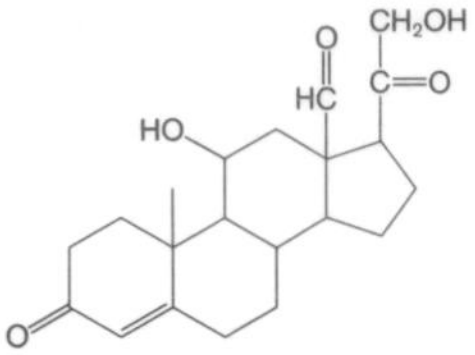	Deoxycorticosterone (DOC, cortexone) 21-Hydroxy-4-pregnene-3,20-dione	$C_{21}H_{30}O_3$ 330.47	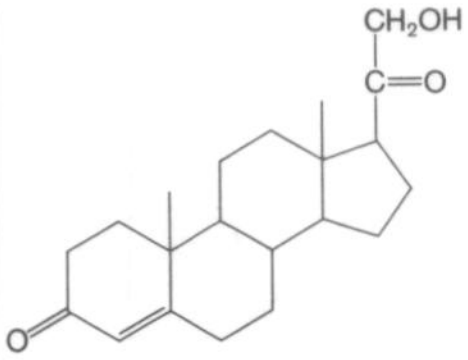
Androstenediol 5-Androstene-3,17-diol	$C_{19}H_{30}O_2$ 290.44	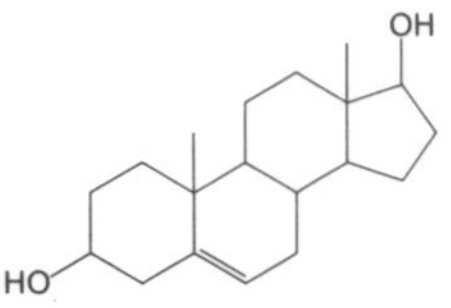	11-Deoxycortisol (cortexolone, substance S) 17,21-Dihydroxy-4-pregnene-3,20-dione	$C_{21}H_{30}O_4$ 346.47	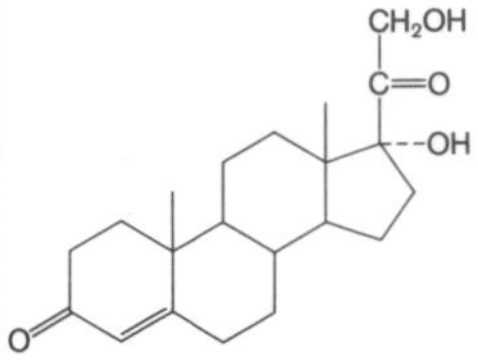
Androstenedione 4-Androstene-3,17-dione	$C_{19}H_{26}O_2$ 286.41	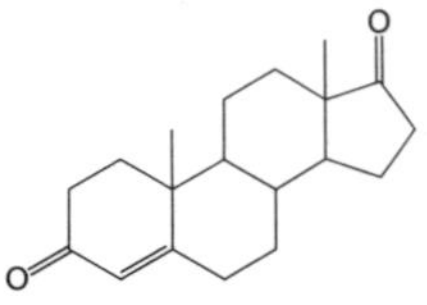	5α-Dihydrotestosterone 17β-Hydroxy-5α-androstan-3-one	$C_{19}H_{30}O_2$ 290.44	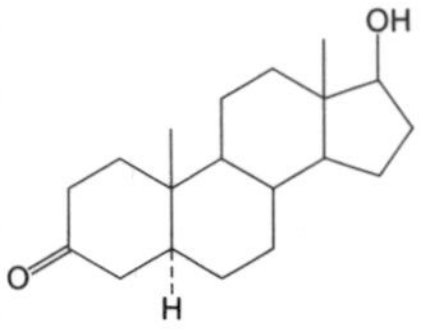
Corticosterone (compound B) 11β,21-Dihydroxy-4-pregnene-3,20-dione	$C_{21}H_{30}O_4$ 346.47	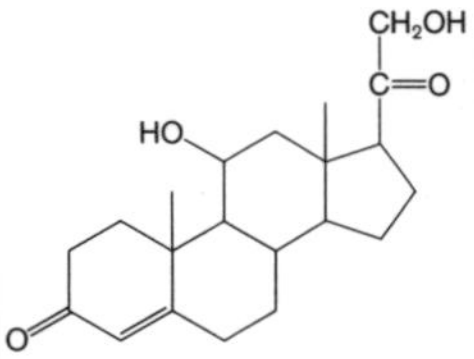	16α,19-Dihydroxy-androstenedione 16α,19-Dihydroxy-4-androstene-3,17-dione	$C_{19}H_{26}O_4$ 318.41	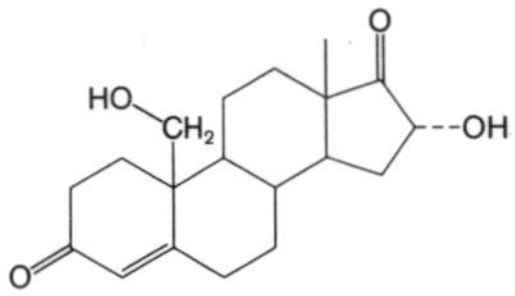
Cortisol (hydrocortisone, compound F) 11β,17,21-Trihydroxy-4-pregnene-3,20-dione	$C_{21}H_{30}O_5$ 362.47	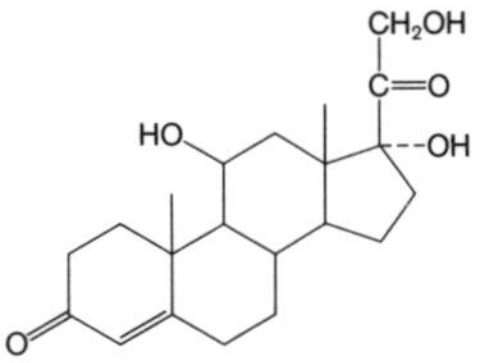	16α-Hydroxyandro-stenedione 16α-Hydroxy-4-androstene-3,17-dione	$C_{19}H_{26}O_3$ 302.41	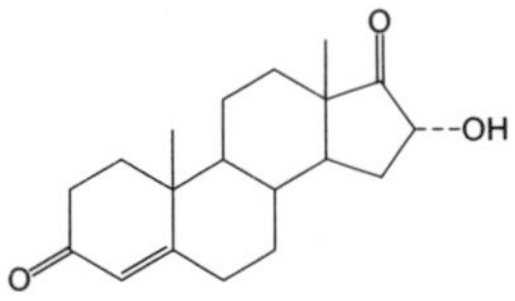
Cortisone (compound E) 17,21-Dihydroxy-4-pregnene-3,11,20-trione	$C_{21}H_{28}O_4$ 360.45	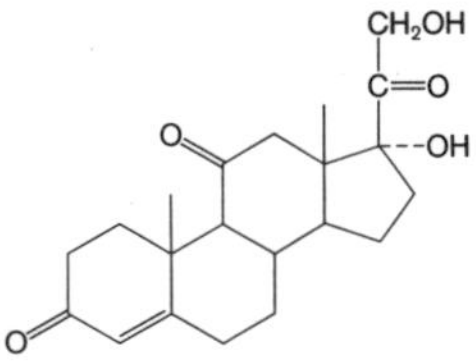	19-Hydroxyandrostene-dione 19-Hydroxy-4-androstene-3,17-dione	$C_{19}H_{26}O_3$ 302.41	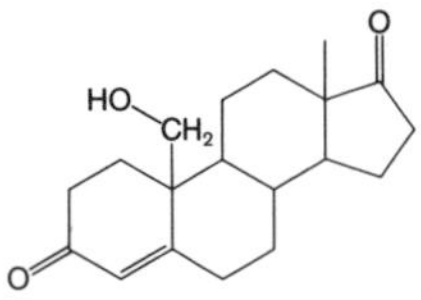
Dehydroepiandrosterone (androstenolone) 3β-Hydroxy-5-androsten-17-one	$C_{19}H_{28}O_2$ 289.44	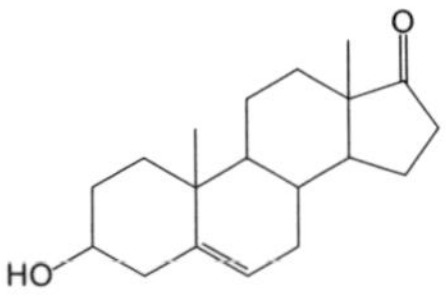	16α-Hydroxydehydro-epiandrosterone 3β,16α-Dihydroxy-5-androsten-17-one	$C_{19}H_{28}O_3$ 305.44	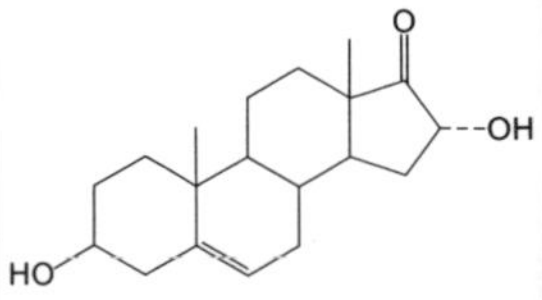

Nomenclature and structure of the most important steroid hormones (continued)

Trivial name and systematic name	Formula, M_r	Structure	Trivial name and systematic name	Formula, M_r	Structure
16α-Hydroxyestrone 3,16α-Dihydroxy-1,3,5(10)-estratrien-17-one	$C_{18}H_{22}O_3$ 286.37	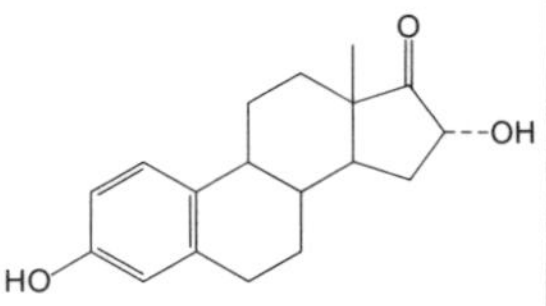	Estriol 1,3,5(10)-Estratriene-3,16α,17β-triol	$C_{18}H_{24}O_3$ 288.39	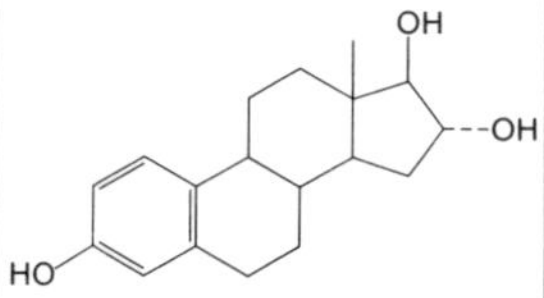
17-Hydroxypregnenolone 3β,17-Dihydroxy-5-pregnen-20-one	$C_{21}H_{32}O_3$ 332.49	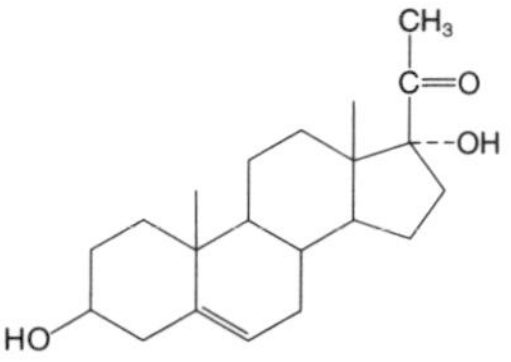	Estrone 3-Hydroxy-1,3,5(10)-estratrien-17-one	$C_{18}H_{22}O_2$ 270.37	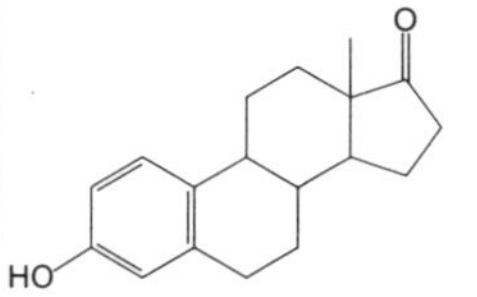
17-Hydroxyprogesterone 17-Hydroxy-4-pregnene-3,20-dione	$C_{21}H_{30}O_3$ 330.47	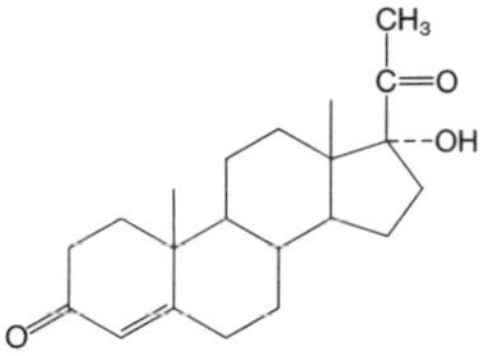	Pregnenolone 3β-Hydroxy-5-pregnen-20-one	$C_{21}H_{32}O_2$ 316.49	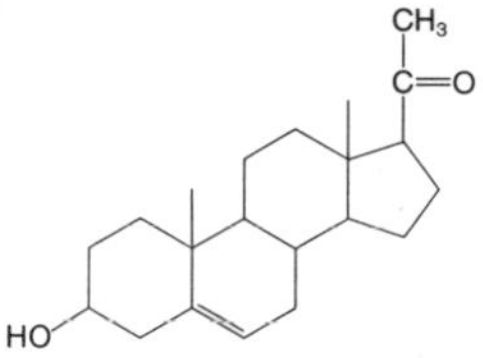
19-Hydroxytestosterone 17β,19-Dihydroxy-4-androsten-3-one	$C_{19}H_{28}O_3$ 304.43	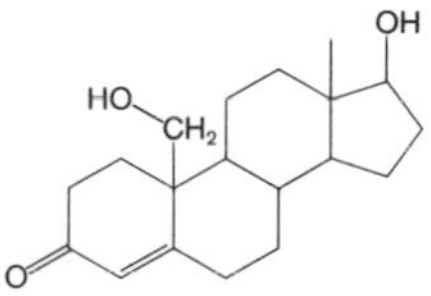	Progesterone 4-Pregnene-3,20-dione	$C_{21}H_{30}O_2$ 314.47	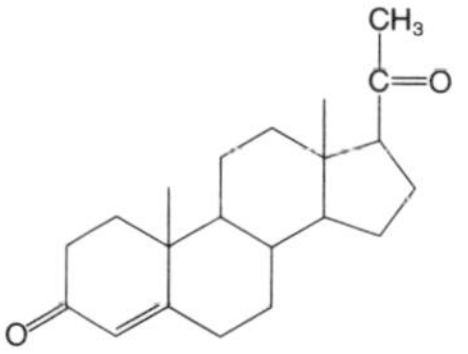
Estradiol 1,3,5(10)-Estratriene-3,17(α)β-diol	$C_{18}H_{24}O_2$ 272.39	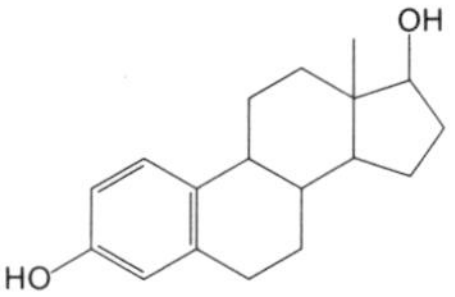	Testosterone 17β-Hydroxy-4-androsten-3-one	$C_{19}H_{28}O_2$ 288.43	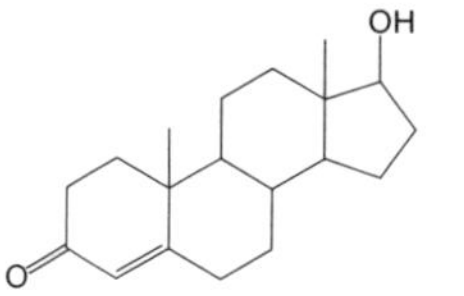

Nomenclature and Stereochemistry

The naturally occurring steroids include the sex hormones, the adrenocortical hormones, cholesterol, bile acids and vitamin D. Common to all steroids is the cyclopentanoperhydrophenanthrene ring system, which can be represented in an approximation as planar on account of its relatively flat structure.

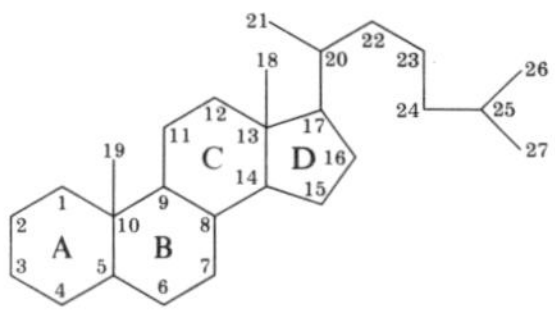

Numbering of the C atoms and nomenclature of the rings in the cyclopentanoperhydrophenanthrene ring system

The skeleton (i.e. the nucleus) of the steroid molecule consists of the 3 six-membered rings A, B and C and a five-membered ring D;

the cyclohexane rings for the most part are in the 'chair' conformation.

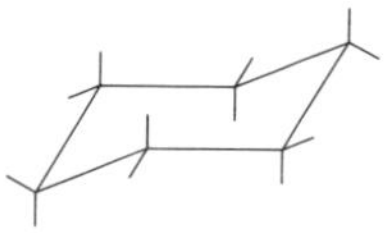

'Chair' conformation

A methyl group or other group may be present on C-10 and C-13, and a side chain with up to 8 C atoms on C-17. Ring A is aromatic in the estrogens. The numbering of the C atoms in the ring system can be seen from the structural formula above.

In this ring system all C atoms that are shared by 2 rings are asymmetric; an additional asymmetry is introduced when the H atoms on the other C atoms are replaced by another monovalent group. Since the biological activity of the steroid hormones is determined by the stereochemical configuration, it is essential to give precise designations. In the ring skeleton represented as a plane (see structural formula above) the side turned toward the observer is designated as the β position, the side turned away from him as the α position. Thus, for example, in cholesterol the hydroxy group stands 'above' the ring plane in this projection, and therefore is in the β position, so that the correct designation for cholesterol is 5-cholesten-3β-ol. In the formulae the β position of substituents is shown as a thick solid line, the α position of substituents as a thick broken line. If the configuration of the substituent is unknown it is denoted by a wavy line in the formula or by the Greek letter ξ in compound names.

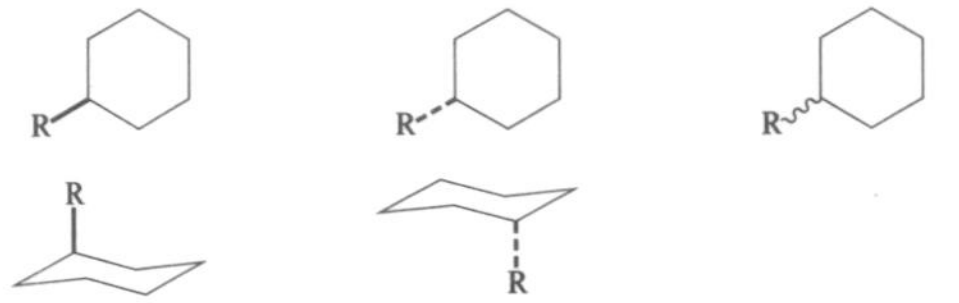

| β configuration (R *above* the ring plane) | α configuration (R *below* the ring plane) | ξ configuration (configuration unknown) |

The prefix 'epi-' in trivial names of steroids denotes inversion at one center. Thus, for example, the more abundant natural form of estradiol is 17β-estradiol; the less common 17α form is often designated as 17-epiestradiol or epiestradiol.

The natural steroids saturated at C-5 occur in 2 stereochemically different series which deviate from each other in the junction of rings A and B. The series with the junction of rings A and B in the *trans* position is designated 5α because the H atom on C-5 is in the α position and is in *trans* position relative to the methyl group on C-10. The series with the junction of rings A and B in the *cis* position is designated 5β because the H atom on C-5 is in the β position and is in *cis* position relative to the methyl group on C-5.

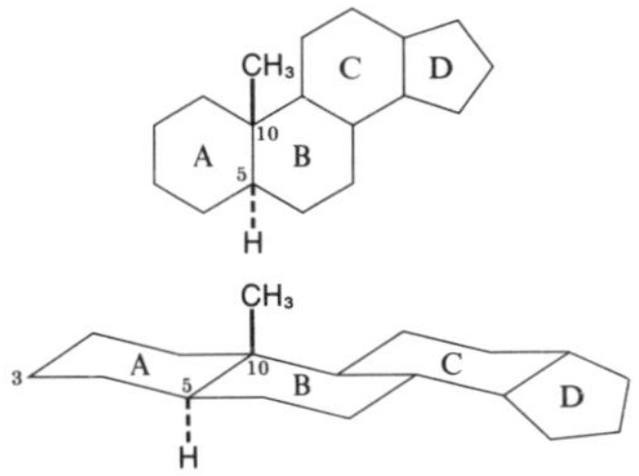

5α series of steroids saturated at C-5

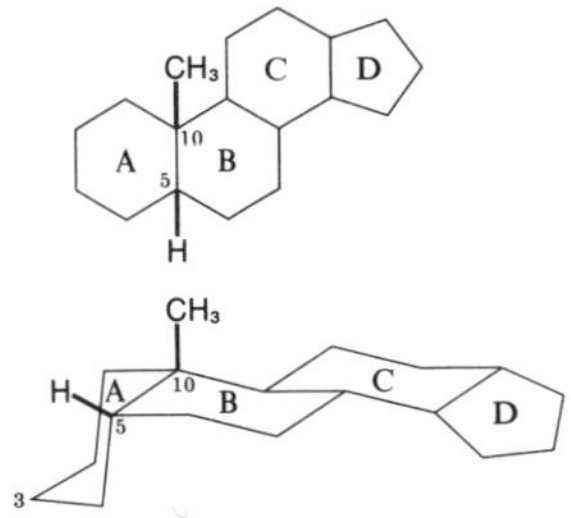

5β series of steroids saturated at C-5

In steroids unsaturated at C-5, i.e. with a double bond between C-4 and C-5 or between C-5 and C-6, there is no H atom at C-5 and hence no stereoisomerism at the ring junction A–B.

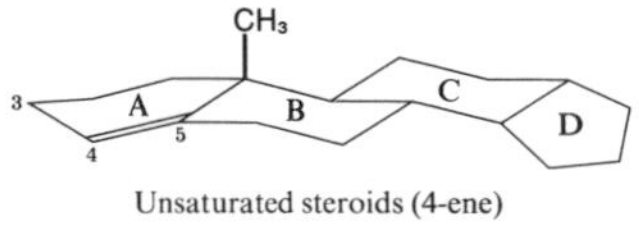

Unsaturated steroids (4-ene)

Side chains in the C-17 position are β-oriented, unless otherwise stated. The C-20 atom in the steroid side chain becomes asymmetric by substitution of one of its H atoms. To identify the configuration of pregnane derivatives at this C atom, the substituents lying to the right in the Fischer projection formula are termed α, those lying to the left, β.

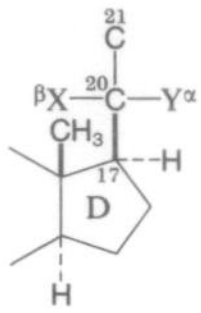

If the side chain is longer than ethyl, the stereochemistry at C-20 and other positions in the steroid side chain is described by the sequence-rule procedure.

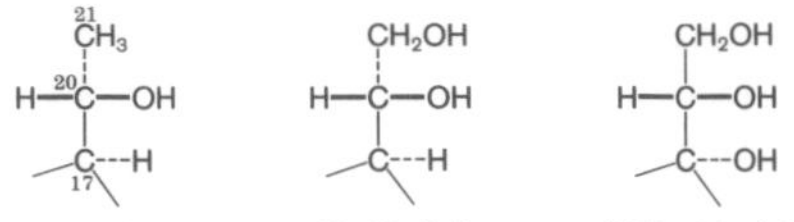

| 20α-ol (20S) | 20α,21-diol (20R) | 17,20α,21-triol (20S) |

Classification

The steroids are classified according to the total number of C atoms in the molecule and according to their function:

C_{17} steroids: parent compound *gonane*; no substituent at C-10, C-13 or C-17.

C_{18} steroids: parent compound *estrane*; methyl group at C-13, without a side chain at C-17. All naturally occurring estrogens belong in this class.

C_{19} steroids: parent compound *androstane*; methyl groups at C-10 and C-13, no side chain at C-17. All naturally occurring androgens belong in this class.

C_{21} steroids: parent compound *pregnane*; methyl groups at C-10 and C-13, a side chain with 2 C atoms at C-17. The naturally occurring corticosteroids belong in this class.

C_{24} steroids: parent compound *cholane*; methyl groups at C-10 and C-13, a branched side chain with 5 C atoms at C-17. Many naturally occurring bile acids belong in this class.

C_{27} steroids: parent compound *cholestane*; methyl groups at C-10 and C-13, a branched side chain with 8 C atoms at C-17. Cholesterol, for example, belongs in this class.

The parent compounds in other naturally occurring steroids are ergostane (24-methyl-5α-cholestane), stigmastane (24-ethyl-5α-cholestane), and lanostane (4,4,14α-trimethyl-5α-cholestane).

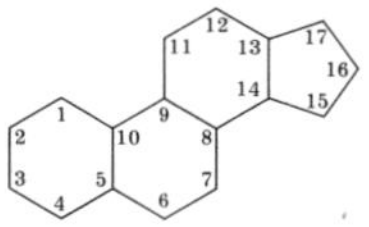

Gonane

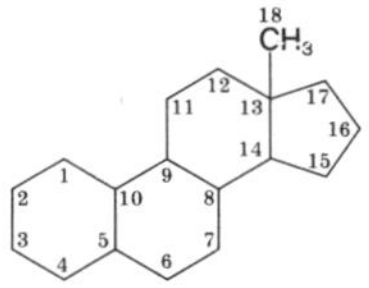

Estrane

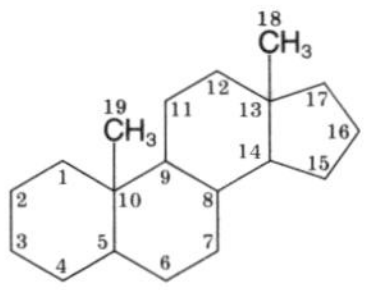

Androstane

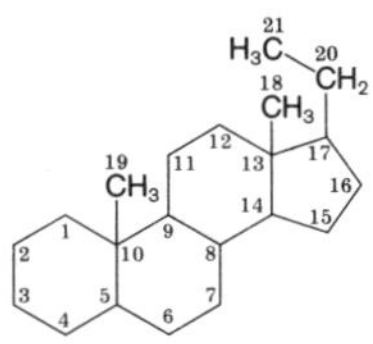

Pregnane

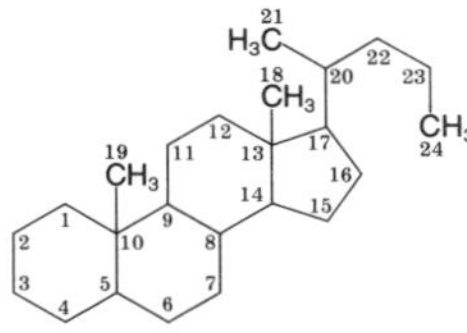

Cholane

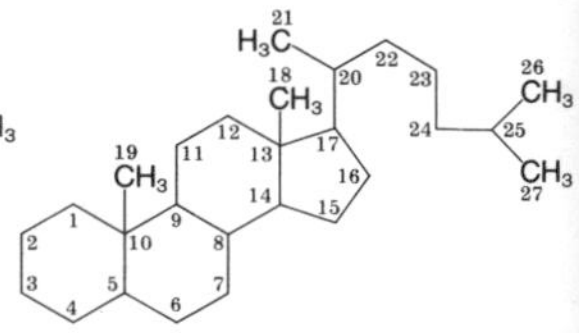

Cholestane

Systematic nomenclature

With respect to substituents of steroids, the IUPAC[20] recommends the addition of several prefixes, but only one suffix, to the name of the parent compound. The double bond between 2 C atoms was formerly indicated by a Δ: pregnenolone, for example, is 3β-hydroxy-5-pregnen-20-one; in the old nomenclature it was Δ⁵-pregnen-3β-ol-20-one. If the double bond is between C atoms with successive position numbers, only the lower one is indicated. If the double bond is between C atoms with nonsuccessive position numbers, the higher one is added in brackets (example: 5[10]-cholestene).

Special prefixes in steroid nomenclature

allo- (in trivial names): formerly used for the 5α series of saturated steroids.

anhydro- (in trivial names): splitting off of H and OH from adjacent C atoms, resulting in a double bond.

dehydro- (in trivial names): splitting off of 2 H from adjacent C atoms, resulting in a double bond.

deoxy- (in trivial names): replacement of OH by H.

de-: absence of an entire ring, for example de-D.

dihydro- (in trivial names): addition of 2 H to a double bond.

epi- (in trivial names): inversion of a substituent from the α-steric configuration to the β-steric one or vice versa.

homo-: ring enlargement; for example, D-homo means a six-membered D ring.

nor- (preceded by number of C atom or ring letter): loss of 1 C atom.

seco- (preceded by position numbers of both C atoms of the split double bond): ring fission with addition of 1 H atom at each of the 2 terminal groups.

Sterols

All steroids that contain a hydroxy group and can thereby form esters are included under the concept 'sterols'. The most important sterol in animals is cholesterol, the most important one in plants is β-sitosterol. Contrary to previous opinion, bacteria also contain sterols which, however, are bound very strongly and thus easily escape detection.

Cholesterol occurs in most mammalian tissues; of course, there are considerable differences in the ratio of free to esterified cholesterol. In serum, for example, 70–80% of the cholesterol is esterified with fatty acids; small amounts are present as cholesteryl sulfate. In the adrenal cortex, more than 80% of the cholesterol is esterified. In the brain and other nerve tissues there is practically nothing but free cholesterol, which constitutes an essential component of myelin. Among the fatty acids of the cholesterol esters in serum, the linoleic-acid portion is almost half; in addition, oleic acid and palmitic acid are quantitatively of importance. Cholesterol is a constituent of eukaryotic cell membranes and influences the membrane fluidity.

Steroid hormones

Steroid hormones are found in all classes of vertebrates and in insects. In vertebrates the hormone-producing organs are the adrenal cortex, the ovaries, the testes and the placenta. Each gland produces a large number of steroids, but not all of them are hormonally active. Since the steps in the metabolic pathway leading to the various classes of hormones are qualitatively the same in each organ, it is not surprising to find differing amounts of the same metabolites in different organs. Each organ has characteristic steroid hormones, but also produces others that may or may not be physiologically significant. Thus cortisol and aldosterone are the characteristic hormones of the adrenal cortex, but this organ also produces dehydroepiandrosterone sulfate, an androgen. 17β-Estradiol is the characteristic estrogen of the ovaries, which also produce physiologically significant amounts of progesterone. Progesterone is the characteristic hormone of the placenta, which also produces estrogens. The characteristic hormone of the testes is testosterone. (For nomenclature and structure of the most important steroid hormones see pages 34 and 35.)

The steroid hormones are also classified according to function into *estrogens* (female sex hormones; C_{18}-steroids with an aromatic A ring), *androgens* (male sex hormones; C_{19}-steroids), and *corticosteroids* (hormones of the adrenal cortex; C_{21}-steroids). Among the last-named a distinction is often made between *mineralocorticoids* (e.g. aldosterone) and *glucocorticoids* (e.g. cortisol). However, the effects of the various hormones overlap considerably and differ from species to species; they differ also from individual to individual depending on the previous dietary and hormonal history.

Reference

[1] IUPAC Commission on the Nomenclature of Organic Chemistry and IUPAC IUB Commission on Biochemical Nomenclature, *Pure appl. Chem.*, **31**, 285 (1972).

Table 1   *Structure and properties of amino acids occurring as protein building blocks*

Name	Symbol*	Formula, M_r	Structure	Solubility (g in 1 kg water at 25 °C)	Occurrence and function
Glycine (aminoethanoic acid)	Gly, G	$C_2H_5NO_2$ 75.07	H_2NCH_2COOH	249.9	Optically inactive. Many animals excrete benzoic acid as benzoylglycine (hippuric acid). Constituent of glutathione. Intermediate in synthesis of creatine, porphyrins, purines
Amino acids with alkyl groups as side chains					
Alanine (2-aminopropanoic acid)	Ala, A	$C_3H_7NO_2$ 89.09	$CH_3CH(NH_2)COOH$	167.2	Nonpolar, hence important in hydrophobic bonding
Valine (2-amino-3-methylbutanoic acid)	Val, V	$C_5H_{11}NO_2$ 117.15	$(CH_3)_2CHCH(NH_2)COOH$	88.5	Like alanine
Leucine (2-amino-4-methylpentanoic acid)	Leu, L	$C_6H_{13}NO_2$ 131.17	$(CH_3)_2CHCH_2CH(NH_2)COOH$	21.9	Like alanine
Isoleucine (2-amino-3-methylpentanoic acid	Ile, I	$C_6H_{13}NO_2$ 131.17	$CH_3CH_2CH(CH_3)CH(NH_2)COOH$	29.3 at 20 °C	Like alanine
Amino acids with secondary amino groups					
Proline (pyrrolidine-2-carboxylic acid)	Pro, P	$C_5H_9NO_2$ 115.13	H₂C–CH₂ H₂C CH N COOH H	1623	Involved in the folding of polypeptide chains
Acidic amino acids and their amides					
Aspartic acid (2-aminobutanedioic acid)	Asp, D	$C_4H_7NO_4$ 133.10	$HOOCCH_2CH(NH_2)COOH$	5.0	In protein the carboxy group of the side chain dissociates at neutral pH, so that active sites of enzymes are formed. Involved in conversion of citrulline to arginine, and in biosynthesis of purines and pyrimidines
Glutamic acid (2-aminopentanedioic acid)	Glu, E	$C_5H_9NO_4$ 147.13	$HOOC(CH_2)_2CH(NH_2)COOH$	8.43	Anionic at neutral pH. Constituent of glutathione and of folic acid vitamins. Found in high concentration in tissues. More readily dehydrogenated in animal tissue and more reactive in enzymatic transamination than any other amino acid. Phosphoglutamic acid is found in collagen
Asparagine (2-amino-3-carbamoylpropanoic acid)	Asn, N Asp(NH₂) Asp | NH₂	$C_4H_8N_2O_3$ 132.12	$H_2NOCCH_2CH(NH_2)COOH$	24.6	Neutral hydrophilic. The amido group is polar, but not acidic. Takes part in the formation of hydrogen bonds. Occurs free in many plant tissues, particularly in etiolated seedlings
Glutamine (2-amino-4-carbamoylbutanoic acid)	Gln, Q Glu(NH₂) Glu | NH₂	$C_5H_{10}N_2O_3$ 146.15	$H_2NOC(CH_2)_2CH(NH_2)COOH$	36 at 18 °C	Like asparagine. Intermediate carrier of amino groups. Phenylacetic acid is excreted by man as phenylacetylglutamine
Basic amino acids					
Arginine (2-amino-5-guanidinopentanoic acid)	Arg, R	$C_6H_{14}N_4O_2$ 174.20	HN CNH(CH₂)₃CH(NH₂)COOH H₂N	150	Has a high pK_a value. Usually basic. Frequently binds phosphate groups. Intermediate in urea cycle and in biosynthesis of creatinine
Histidine (2-amino-3-[1H-imidazol-4-yl]propanoic acid)	His, H	$C_6H_9N_3O_2$ 155.16	HC=CCH₂CH(NH₂)COOH HN N C H	42.9	Important in active sites of many enzymes. May bind metal ions. Decarboxylation yields histamine. Constituent of the dipeptides carnosine and homocarnosine

* Three-letter and one-letter symbols according to IUPAC–IUB Joint Commission on Biochemical Nomenclature, *Europ. J. Biochem.*, **138**, 9 (1984).

Table 1 *Structure and properties of amino acids occurring as protein building blocks (continued)*

Name	Symbol*	Formula, M_r	Structure	Solubility (g in 1 kg water at 25 °C)	Occurrence and function
Lysine (2,6-diaminohexanoic acid)	Lys, K	$C_6H_{14}N_2O_2$ 146.19	$H_2N(CH_2)_4CH(NH_2)COOH$	Very readily soluble	Usually cationic at pH 7. May bind co-factors at active sites of enzymes
Amino acids with alcoholic hydroxy groups					
Serine (2-amino-3-hydroxy-propanoic acid)	Ser, S	$C_3H_7NO_3$ 105.09	$HOCH_2CH(NH_2)COOH$	50.2	Slightly acidic. Important constituent of the active sites of some enzymes. Binding site of oligosaccharides in glycoproteins. Phosphoserine is a constituent of phos-phoproteins (phosvitin, vitellin, casein, myosin), phosphorylated enzymes (for example phosphorylase *a*) as well as phosphatidylserine
Threonine (2-amino-3-hydroxy-butanoic acid)	Thr, T	$C_4H_9NO_3$ 119.12	$CH_3CH(OH)CH(NH_2)COOH$	16.3	Slightly acidic. Important constituent of the active sites of some enzymes. Binding site of oligosaccharides in glycoproteins. Phosphothreonine is a constituent of phosphoproteins (casein, tropomyosin)
Sulfur-containing amino acids					
Cysteine (2-amino-3-mercapto-propanoic acid)	Cys, C	$C_3H_7NO_2S$ 121.15	$HSCH_2CH(NH_2)COOH$	Very readily soluble	The SH group has a slightly acidic reac-tion. Readily converted by oxidoreduc-tion to cystine. Forms disulfide bridges between peptide chains. Constituent of glutathione. Abundantly present in the metallothioneines. Some aromatic sub-stances are excreted in urine as deriva-tives of N-acetylcysteine (mercapturic acids)
Methionine (2-amino-4-[methyl-thio]butanoic acid)	Met, M	$C_5H_{11}NO_2S$ 149.21	$CH_3SCH_2CH_2CH(NH_2)COOH$	33.5	Nonpolar. Furnishes the S atom for cysteine biosynthesis. α-Crystallin of the lens contains N-acetylmethionine as ter-minal amino acid
Aromatic amino acids					
Phenylalanine (2-amino-3-phenyl-propanoic acid)	Phe, F	$C_9H_{11}NO_2$ 165.19	⬡—$CH_2CH(NH_2)COOH$	29,6	Nonpolar. Precursor of tyrosine
Tyrosine (2-amino-3-[4-hydroxyphenyl]-propanoic acid)	Tyr, Y	$C_9H_{11}NO_2$ 181.19	HO—⬡—$CH_2CH(NH_2)COOH$	0.45	The phenolic OH group has slightly acidic properties. Active in enzyme-bonding to substrates. Precursor of thy-roxine, catecholamines and melanins
Tryptophan (2-amino-3-[1H-indol-3-yl]propanoic acid)	Trp, W	$C_{11}H_{12}N_2O_2$ 204.23	$CH_2CH(NH_2)COOH$ (indole)	11.4	Does not dissociate and hence forms hy-drophobic bonds. Precursor of sero-tonin. βs-Crystallin of the lens contains N-acetyltryptophan as terminal amino acid
Examples of posttranslationally modified amino acids					
Cystine (3,3'-dithiobis-[2-aminopropanoic acid])	Cys Cys	$C_6H_{12}N_2O_4S_2$ 240.29	$SCH_2CH(NH_2)COOH$ | $SCH_2CH(NH_2)COOH$	0.11	Readily reduced to cysteine. Abundantly present in hair and keratin. Constituent of insulin
Cysteic acid	Cya	$C_3H_7NO_5S$ 169.15	$HO_3SCH_2CH(NH_2)COOH$	–	Intermediate in formation of taurine from cysteine (page 113)
4-Carboxyglutamic acid	Gla COOH |4 Glu	$C_6H_9NO_6$ 191.14	$HOOCCH(COOH)CH_2CH(NH_2)COOH$	–	Forms Ca^{2+} complexes. Constituent of some coagulation factors and of the poly-peptide osteocalcin in bones

*Three-letter and one-letter symbols according to IUPAC–IUB Joint Commission on Biochemical Nomenclature, *Europ. J. Biochem.*, **138**, 9 (1984).

Table 1 *Structure and properties of amino acids occurring as protein building blocks (continued)*

Name	Symbol*	Formula, M_r	Structure	Solubility (g in 1 kg water at 25 °C)	Occurrence and function
5-Hydroxylysine (2,6-diamino-5-hydroxyhexanoic acid)	5Hyl Lys 5 OH	$C_6H_{14}N_2O_3$ 162.19	$NH_2CH_2CH(OH)(CH_2)_2CH(NH_2)COOH$	–	Constituent of collagen. Bonding site for oligosaccharides
4-Hydroxyproline (4-hydroxypyrrolidine-2-carboxylic acid)	4Hyp Pro 4 OH	$C_5H_9NO_3$ 131.13	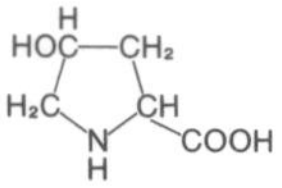	361.1	Constituent of collagen, elastin, acetylcholinesterase and urinary peptides. Free in plants
3-Hydroxyproline (3-hydroxypyrrolidine-2-carboxylic acid)	3Hyp Pro 3 OH	$C_5H_9NO_3$ 131.13	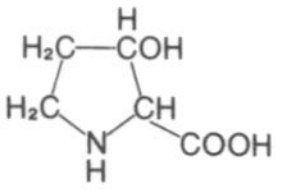	–	Constituent of collagen
N$^\omega$-Methylarginine	–	$C_7H_{16}N_4O_2$ 188.23	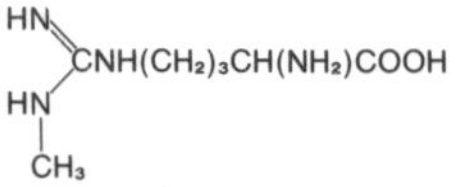	–	Constituent of nucleoproteins as well as of the basic protein of myelin
N$^\omega$-Dimethylarginine	–	$C_8H_{18}N_4O_2$ 202.26	Symmetric: 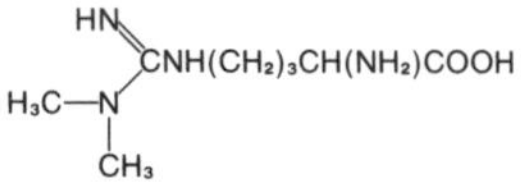	–	Symmetric: constituent of the basic protein of myelin Asymmetric: constituent of nucleoproteins
N$^\tau$-Methylhistidine (3-methylhistidine)	His(τ-Me) His τ Me	$C_7H_{11}N_3O_2$ 169.18	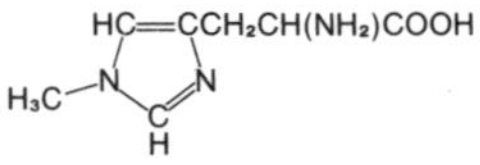	–	Constituent of muscle proteins
N^6-Trimethyllysine	Lys(6-Me$_3$)	$C_9H_{20}N_2O_2$ 188.27	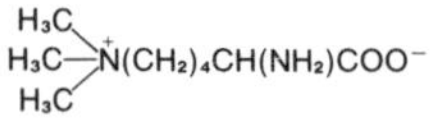	–	Constituent of the Ca^{2+}-binding protein calmodulin
3-Monoiodotyrosine	Tyr(3-I)	$C_9H_{10}NO_3I$ 307.09	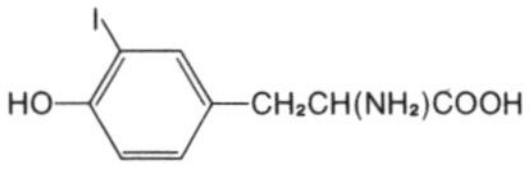	–	Exclusively in thyroid proteins (thyroid hormones)
3,5-Diiodotyrosine	Tyr(I$_2$)	$C_9H_9NO_3I_2$ 432.98	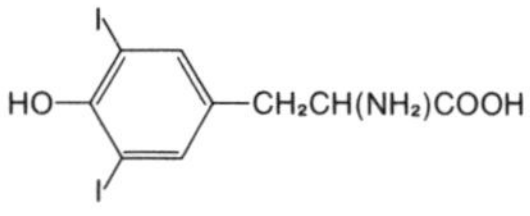	0.62	Like 3-monoiodotyrosine
3,5,3′-Triiodothyronine	–	$C_{15}H_{12}NO_4I_3$ 650.98	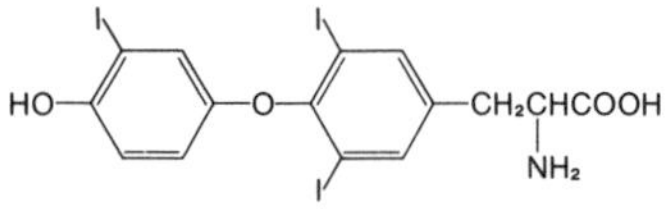	–	Like 3-monoiodotyrosine
3,3′,5′-Triiodothyronine ('reverse' triiodothyronine)	–	$C_{15}H_{12}NO_4I_3$ 650.98	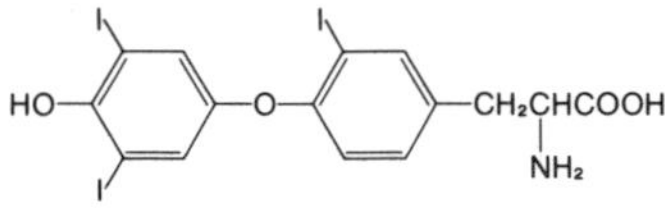	–	Like 3-monoiodotyrosine
Thyroxine (3,5,3′,5′-tetraiodothyronine)	–	$C_{15}H_{11}NO_4I_4$ 776.87	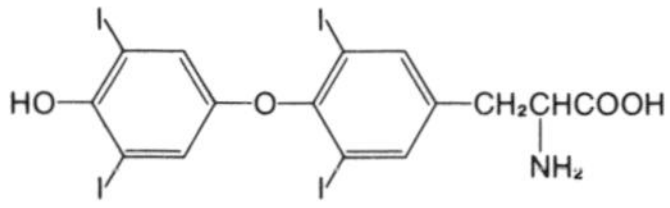	0.01	Like 3-monoiodotyrosine

*Symbols according to IUPAC–IUB Joint Commission on Biochemical Nomenclature, *Europ. J. Biochem.*, **138**, 9 (1984).

Table 2 *Structure and properties of some amino acids not occurring in proteins, but found in free form*

Name*	Formula, M_r	Structure	Solubility (g in 1 kg water at 25 °C)	Occurrence and function
β-Alanine (βAla) (3-aminopropanoic acid)	$C_3H_7NO_2$ 89.09	$H_2NCH_2CH_2COOH$	Very readily soluble	Breakdown product of pyrimidines (page 129). Occurs as constituent of pantothenic acid or coenzyme A, carnosine and anserine
α-Aminoadipic acid (Aad) (2-aminohexanedioic acid)	$C_6H_{11}NO_4$ 161.16	$HOOC(CH_2)_3CH(NH_2)COOH$	2.2 at 20 °C	Intermediate in breakdown of lysine (page 116)
α-Aminobutyric acid (Abu) (2-aminobutanoic acid)	$C_4H_9NO_2$ 103.12	$CH_3CH_2CH(NH_2)COOH$	280 (for the DL acid)	Found in the brain. Constituent of the tripeptide 'ophthalmic acid' in the lens
γ-Aminobutyric acid (4-aminobutanoic acid)	$C_4H_9NO_2$ 103.12	$H_2N(CH_2)_3COOH$	–	In brain, lungs and heart. In macromolecular form in keratinocytes. Neurotransmitter
β-Aminoisobutyric acid (3-aminoisobutanoic acid)	$C_4H_9NO_2$ 103.12	$H_2NCH_2CH(CH_3)COOH$	–	Breakdown product of thymine (page 129). Excretion in the urine genetically influenced
δ-Aminolevulinic acid (5-aminolevulinic acid, 4-oxo-5-aminopentanoic acid)	$C_5H_9NO_3$ 131.13	$H_2NCH_2COCH_2CH_2COOH$	–	Precursor in porphyrin biosynthesis (page 166)
Argininosuccinic acid	$C_{10}H_{18}N_4O_6$ 290.28	$HOOCCH(NH_2)(CH_2)_3NHCNHCH(COOH)CH_2COOH$ $\quad\quad\quad\quad\quad\quad\quad\quad\quad\quad\;\;\parallel$ $\quad\quad\quad\quad\quad\quad\quad\quad\quad\quad\;\;NH$	–	Intermediate in urea cycle (page 111)
Carbamoylaspartic acid (ureidobutanedioic acid)	$C_5H_8N_2O_5$ 176.13	$HOOCCH_2CH(COOH)NHCONH_2$	4.0 at 20 °C	Intermediate in formation of pyrimidines from aspartic acid in mammals and bacteria (page 172)
Citrulline (2-amino-5-urcidopenta-noic acid)	$C_6H_{13}N_3O_3$ 175.19	$H_2NCONH(CH_2)_3CH(NH_2)COOH$	–	Intermediate in urea cycle (page 111)
Creatine (3-methylguanidinoetha-noic acid)	$C_4H_9N_3O_2$ 131.13	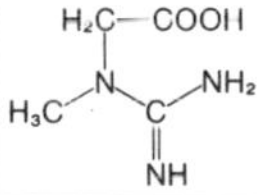 $H_2C-COOH$ structure	13.5 at 18 °C	Cell constituent. Creatine phosphate serves as store of high 'phosphate-bonding energy' in vertebrate muscle (page 158)
Creatinine (3-methylguanidinoetha-noic anhydride)	$C_4H_7N_3O$ 113.12	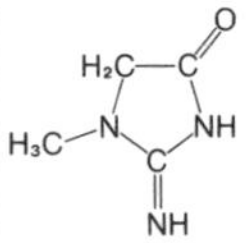 H_2C-C structure	87 at 16 °C	Spontaneous formation from creatine
Cystathionine	$C_7H_{14}N_2O_4S$ 222.26	$HOOCCH(NH_2)CH_2SCH_2CH_2CH(NH_2)COOH$	–	Intermediate in formation of cysteine from methionine (page 122)
Ergothioneine (2-mercaptohistidino-betaine)	$C_9H_{15}N_3O_2S$ 229.30	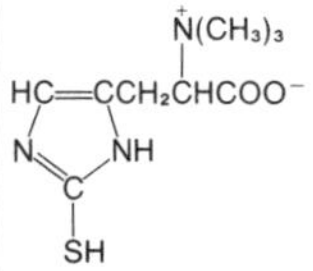 $\overset{+}{N}(CH_3)_3$ structure $HC=CCH_2CHCOO^-$	–	Occurs in erythrocytes, liver, kidney and other tissues, as well as semen. Constituent of ergot
Guanidinosuccinic acid	$C_5H_9N_3O_4$ 175.14	$HN=C(NH_2)NHCH(COOH)CH_2COOH$	–	In urine. Is formed from arginine and aspartic acid (?)
Guanidinoacetic acid (glycocyamine)	$C_3H_7N_3O_2$ 117.11	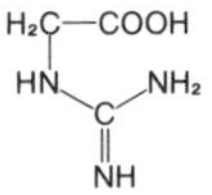 $H_2C-COOH$ structure	Slightly soluble	Formed in liver, kidney, brain, pancreas and spleen from arginine and glycine. Precursor of creatine and creatinine (page 158)
Homoserine (Hse) (2-amino-4-hydroxybuta-noic acid)	$C_4H_9NO_3$ 119.12	$HOCH_2CH_2CH(NH_2)COOH$	–	Precursor in formation of threonine and methionine in microorganisms and plants

*Symbols according to IUPAC–IUB Joint Commission on Biochemical Nomenclature, *Europ. J. Biochem.*, **138**, 9 (1984).

Table 2   *Structure and properties of some amino acids not occurring in proteins, but found in free form (continued)*

Name*	Formula, M_r	Structure	Solubility (g in 1 kg water at 25 °C)	Occurrence and function
N$^\pi$-Methylhistidine [His(π-Me)] (1-methylhistidine)	$C_7H_{11}N_3O_2$ 169.18	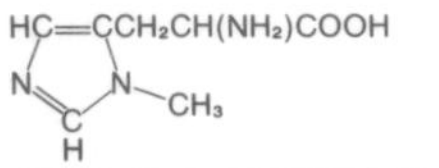 HC=CCH$_2$CH(NH$_2$)COOH	200	With β-alanine forms the dipeptide anserine
Ornithine (Orn) (2,5-diaminopentanoic acid)	$C_5H_{12}N_2O_2$ 132.16	H$_2$N(CH$_2$)$_3$CH(NH$_2$)COOH	Very readily soluble	Intermediate in urea cycle (page 111). Benzoic acid is excreted as N,N'-dibenzoylornithine by poultry
Sarcosine (Sar) (N-methylglycine)	$C_3H_7NO_2$ 89.09	CH$_3$NHCH$_2$COOH	–	Intermediate in transfer of one-carbon units (see page 159)

*Symbols according to IUPAC–IUB Joint Commission on Biochemical Nomenclature, *Europ. J. Biochem.*, **138**, 9 (1984).

Table 3   *Amines as decarboxylation products of amino acids*

Amine	Formula, M_r	Structure	Occurrence and function	Parent amino acid
Adenosylmethylthio-propylamine	$C_{14}H_{23}N_6O_3S$ 355.43	Ado-$\overset{+}{S}$—CH$_2$CH$_2$CH$_2$NH$_2$ $\mid$ CH$_3$	Involved in formation of polyamines (page 160)	S-Adenosyl-methionine
Agmatine	$C_5H_{14}N_4$ 130.19	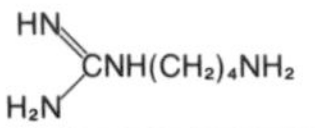 HN CNH(CH$_2$)$_4$NH$_2$ H$_2$N	Bacterial decomposition product	Arginine
β-Alanine	$C_3H_7NO_2$ 89.09	H$_2$NCH$_2$CH$_2$COOH	Constituent of pantothenic acid and coenzyme A	Aspartic acid
γ-Aminobutyric acid	$C_4H_9NO_2$ 103.12	H$_2$N(CH$_2$)$_3$COOH	In the CNS, especially in the hypothalamus. Neurotransmitter with inhibiting action	Glutamic acid
Cadaverine	$C_5H_{14}N_2$ 102.18	H$_2$N(CH$_2$)$_5$NH$_2$	Bacterial decomposition product	Lysine
Cysteamine	C_2H_7NS 77.14	H$_2$NCH$_2$CH$_2$SH	Constituent of coenzyme A	(Cysteine)
Dopamine (3,4-dihydroxy-phenylethylamine)	$C_8H_{11}NO_2$ 153.18	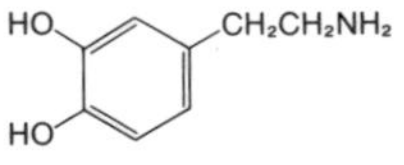 HO CH$_2$CH$_2$NH$_2$ HO	In plants and animal tissues; in man primarily in the dopaminergic sympathetic nervous system. Neurotransmitter. Precursor of norepinephrine and epinephrine	Dopa (3,4-dihydroxy-phenylalanine)
Histamine	$C_5H_9N_3$ 111.15	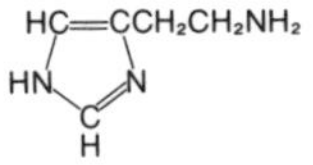 HC=CCH$_2$CH$_2$NH$_2$ HN N	In plants, bacteria and animal tissues (especially skin, lungs, gastrointestinal tract); stored in inactive form in mast cells and basophils. Causes contraction of the smooth musculature and relaxation of the vascular musculature. Stimulates secretion of gastric acid. Neurotransmitter?	Histidine
Hypotaurine	$C_2H_7NO_2S$ 109.14	H$_2$NCH$_2$CH$_2$SO$_2$H	Intermediate of cysteine breakdown (page 113)	3-Sulfino-alanine
Isobutylamine	$C_4H_{11}N$ 73.14	(CH$_3$)$_2$CHCH$_2$NH$_2$	In ergot. Peripherally adrenomimetic	Valine
Lysine	$C_6H_{14}N_2O_2$ 146.19	H$_2$N(CH$_2$)$_4$CH(NH$_2$)COOH	See page 39	*meso*-2,6-Di-aminopimelic acid
3-Methylbutylamine (isoamylamine)	$C_5H_{13}N$ 87.16	(CH$_3$)$_2$CHCH$_2$CH$_2$NH$_2$	In ergot, pepper, horse meat, placenta. Increases blood pressure; paralyzes CNS	Leucine
2-Phenylethylamine	$C_8H_{11}N$ 121.18	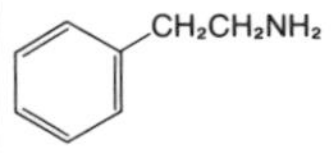 CH$_2$CH$_2$NH$_2$	Bacterial decomposition product	Phenylalanine
Phosphatidyletha-nolamine	–	See page 29	See page 29	Phosphatidyl-serine
Putrescine (diaminobutane)	$C_4H_{12}N_2$ 88.16	H$_2$N(CH$_2$)$_4$NH$_2$	Bacterial decomposition product. In leukocytes and in semen. Primarily N-acetylated in urine	Ornithine

Table 3   *Amines as decarboxylation products of amino acids (continued)*

Amine	Formula, M_r	Structure	Occurrence and function	Parent amino acid
Serotonin (5-hydroxy-tryptamine)	$C_{10}H_{12}N_2O$ 176.22	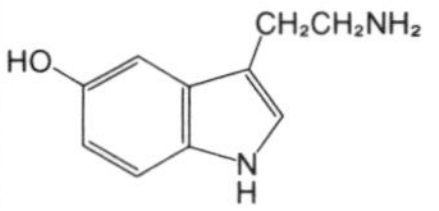 $CH_2CH_2NH_2$	In plants and animal tissues; in man especially in the hypothalamus and other sections of the brain as well as in the gastrointestinal tract. Tissue hormone. Neurotransmitter	5-Hydroxytryptophan
Taurine	$C_2H_7NO_3S$ 125.14	$H_2NCH_2CH_2SO_3H$	In many tissues, especially in the brain of newborns. Formed in the liver of mammals from cysteine (page 113). Constituent of taurocholic acid. Neurotransmitter?	Cysteic acid
Tryptamine	$C_{10}H_{12}N_2$ 160.22	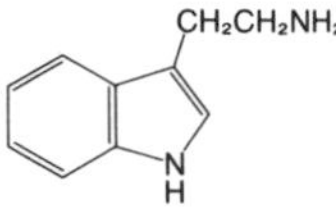 $CH_2CH_2NH_2$	In plants and animal tissues. Stimulates smooth muscles and CNS	Tryptophan
Tyramine	$C_8H_{11}NO$ 137.18	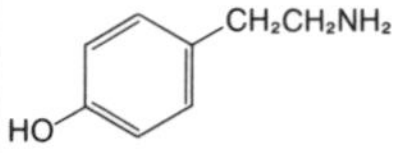 $CH_2CH_2NH_2$	In plants and animal tissues. Increases blood pressure, contracts uterus	Tyrosine

Table 4   *Other products of the amino acid metabolism*

	Formula, M_r	Structure	Occurrence and function
Acetylcholine	$C_7H_{17}NO_3$ 163.22	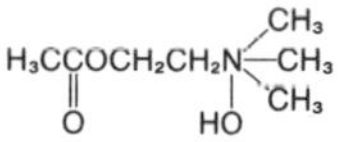 $H_3CCOOCH_2CH_2N{-}CH_3$ (CH_3, CH_3, HO)	In animal tissues. Neurotransmitter. Dilates blood vessels, lowers blood pressure, promotes peristalsis
Choline (2-hydroxyethyltri-methylammonium hydroxide)	$C_5H_{15}NO_2$ 121.18	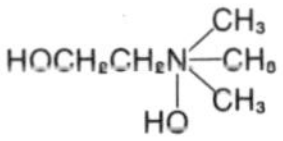 $HOCH_2CH_2N{-}CH_6$ (CH_3, CH_3, HO)	In plants and animal tissues. Constituent of acetylcholine, phosphorylcholine, glycerophosphorylcholine, phosphatidylcholine (lecithin), plasmalogen and sphingomyelin. Methyl donor. Involved in the transport of fatty acids from the liver to the peripheral fat depots
Carnitine (4-trimethylamino-3-hydroxybutanoic acid)	$C_7H_{15}NO_3$ 161.20	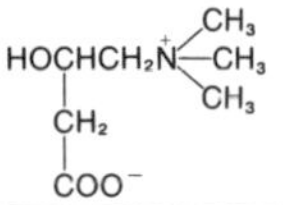 $HOCHCH_2N{-}CH_3$ (CH_3, CH_3); CH_2; COO^-	In all animal tissues. Involved in intracellular fat metabolism in the form of acylcarnitine (page 100)
Ethanolamine (colamine)	C_2H_7NO 61.08	$H_2NCH_2CH_2OH$	Constituent of phosphatidylethanolamine (cephalin), plasmalogen. In the urine as phosphoethanolamine in hypophosphatasia
Spermidine	$C_7H_{19}N_3$ 145.25	$H_2N(CH_2)_4NH(CH_2)_3NH_2$	In yeast, animal tissues, semen. Mainly N-acetylated in the urine
Spermine	$C_{10}H_{26}N_4$ 202.34	$H_2N(CH_2)_3NH(CH_2)_4NH(CH_2)_3NH_2$	In yeast, almost all animal tissues, semen. Mainly N-acetylated in the urine
Norepinephrine (noradrenaline)	$C_8H_{11}NO_3$ 169.18	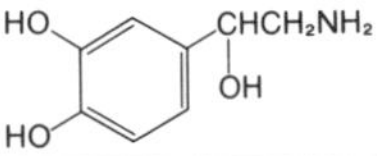 $CHCH_2NH_2$, OH (HO, HO)	In plants and animal tissues; in humans, especially in the adrenal medulla and in the sympathetic nervous system. Neurotransmitter
Epinephrine (adrenaline)	$C_9H_{13}NO_3$ 183.21	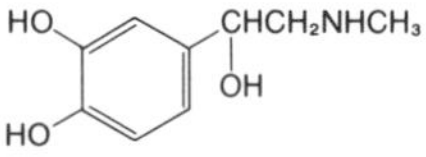 $CHCH_2NHCH_3$, OH (HO, HO)	In plants and animal tissues; in humans, especially in the adrenal medulla and in the sympathetic nervous system. Mediator substance whose action depends on the type of receptors (stimulation of glycogen phosphorylase and lipase)
Octopamine (4-hydroxyphenyl-ethanolamine)	$C_8H_{10}NO_2$ 152.17	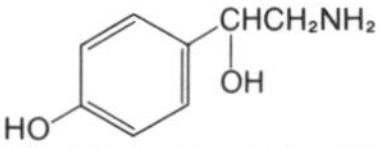 $CHCH_2NH_2$, OH (HO)	In octopod salivary glands. Breakdown product of tyramine (page 120). 'False' neurotransmitter
Melatonin (N-acetyl-5-methoxy-tryptamine)	$C_{13}H_{16}N_2O_2$ 232.28	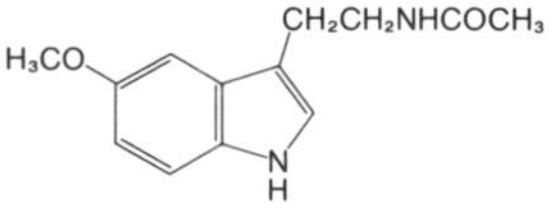 $CH_2CH_2NHCOCH_3$ (H_3CO)	Pineal hormone. Inhibiting effect on gonadal activity in mammals
Urea	CH_4N_2O 60.06	H_2NCONH_2	Breakdown product of amino acids (pages 110–123)

Table 5 *Putative neurotransmitters in mammalian CNS*

Name	Receptor types
γ-Aminobutyric acid	A, B
Glycine	Strychnine-sensitive
Glutamic acid.	Not characterized (possibly 3)
Aspartic acid	Not characterized
Acetylcholine	Muscarinic and nicotinic
Dopamine.	D_1, D_2
Norepinephrine	α_1, α_2, β_1, β_2
Epinephrine	α_1, α_2, β_1, β_2
Serotonin (5-hydroxytrypt- amine).	5-HT_1, 5-HT_2
Histamine	H_1, H_2

Any compound containing at least 1 amino group and 1 or more carboxy groups is an amino acid. In general, the biologically important amino acids contain an amino group in the α position relative to a carboxy group and therefore have the following general formula:

$$\begin{array}{c} NH_2 \\ | \\ R—C—COOH \\ | \\ H \end{array}$$

Due to asymmetry at the α-carbon atom (C-2), the amino acids are optically active except when R = H, as in glycine. Their nomenclature is related to that adopted for the carbohydrates, in which the letters D and L are also used for the configuration at the α-carbon atom and, if desired, the signs for the optical rotation are included in parentheses, for example (+)-L-alanine. In the case of amino acids with 2 centers of asymmetry, 4 stereoisomers are possible; for simplicity's sake the isomer occurring in proteins is assigned to the L series, which, of course, does not present a complete configurational description of this particular amino acid. The value of the specific rotation for a given amino acid varies with concentration, temperature and hydrogen ion concentration. In order to give the identity and purity of an amino acid by means of the specific rotation values, the experimental conditions must be adhered to exactly.

Most amino acids are stable compounds which melt with decomposition at a temperature of more than 200 °C; they are insoluble in the common neutral solvents except water, and they can usually be recrystallized from aqueous ethanol. Their salt-like behavior can be ascribed to their existence as internal salts, or 'zwitterions':

$$\begin{array}{c} \overset{+}{N}H_3 \\ | \\ R—C—COO^- \\ | \\ H \end{array}$$

The amino acids behave as amphoteric compounds and have characteristic isoelectric points at which many of their physical properties show maxima or minima.

Important amino acids occurring in proteins are listed in Table 1 (pages 38–40); the amino acids listed in Table 2 (pages 41–42), on the other hand, have not as yet been detected in proteins. If all the known derivatives of the 20 amino acids specified by the genetic code are taken into account, over 100 different building blocks occur in proteins. The modification of an amino-acid residue after completion of peptide synthesis can take place in various ways[1]: hydroxylation (proline and lysine), carboxylation (glutamic acid), phosphorylation (serine, threonine and tyrosine), galactosylation (serine and threonine), acetylation of a second amino group (lysine), methylation of a second amino group (lysine and arginine) or of the ring nitrogen (histidine) and iodination of the aromatic ring (tyrosine). Posttranslationally modified amino acids of importance are included in Table 1 (pages 38–40).

With rare exceptions, the naturally occurring amino acids are all of the L configuration. D-Amino acids were isolated from plants and certainly occur in bacterial cell walls as well as in the capsule of *Bacillus anthracis*, which is a polymer of D-glutamic acid. Furthermore, they are constituents of various antibiotics (for example D-leucine in colistin, D-phenylalanine in gramicidin S and polymyxin B [page 206]).

D-Aspartic acid formed by racemization of L-aspartic acid may occur in ageing proteins such as lens[2] and erythrocyte membrane[3].

Related to the amino acids are compounds that bear another acid group instead of the carboxy group. Compounds analogous to β-alanine are listed below:

$H_2NCH_2CH_2—COOH$	β-Alanine
$H_2NCH_2CH_2—SO_3H$	Taurine
$H_2NCH_2CH_2—O—PO_3H_2$	Phosphoethanolamine
$NH_2CH_2CH_2—PO_3H_2$	Ciliatin ([2-aminoethyl]phosphonic acid)

Peptides

A peptide is any compound produced by amide formation between a carboxy group of one amino acid and an amino group of another. The amide bonds in peptides may be called 'peptide bonds'. The word 'peptide' usually applies to compounds whose amide bonds are formed between C-1 of one amino acid and N-2 of another (sometimes called 'eupeptide bonds'), but it includes compounds with residues linked by other amide bonds (sometimes called 'isopeptide bonds'). Peptides with fewer than about 10–20 residues may also be called 'oligopeptides'; those with more, 'polypeptides'. Polypeptides of specific sequence of more than about 50 residues are usually known as proteins, but authors differ greatly on where they start using this term[4]. At 100 amino-acid residues the relative molecular mass of the compound is about 12 000. A natural protein subunit consists of about 350 amino acids on the average[5].

Depsipeptides are oligomers formed from amino acids and other bifunctional acids, usually hydroxy acids, linked alternatively via ester and amide bonds. They are often cyclic and occur as metabolites of microorganisms with strong antibiotic action for the most part (enniatine, sporidesmolide, valinomycin).

Amines

Amines are widely distributed in living matter. They are usually formed by decarboxylation of L-amino acids. The carboxylyases which catalyze this reaction are frequently found in bacteria, but also in human tissues such as liver and spleen. The amines and the corresponding amino acids from which they are formed may be seen from Tables 3 and 4.

Some amino acids and amines act as chemical messengers in mammalian neurons (neurotransmitters)[6].

Polyamines such as putrescine and cadaverine (Table 3, page 42), as well as spermidine and spermine (Table 4, page 43), are found in almost all types of cells, although spermine formation takes place chiefly in eukaryotic cells. Polyamines can interact with a series of cell constituents, especially polynucleotides, and thereby affect various enzyme reactions and protein synthesis. These interactions are on the one hand based on the fact that, due to positively charged amino groups, polyamines are polycations which can react with phosphate groups of the nucleotides, for example, and on the other hand to the fact that due to rotation about the C—C or C—N axes different conformations are possible, whereby the steric prerequisite for reactions with other molecules results[7]. Thus they stabilize double-stranded DNA and loops in single-stranded RNA and facilitate the condensation of nucleic acids[8]. The compaction of DNA by spermidine is essential in the concatenation of DNA rings by topoisomerases[9].

References

[1] WOLD, F., *Ann. Rev. Biochem.*, **50**, 783 (1981).
[2] ZIGLER and GOOSEY, *Trends biochem. Sci.*, **6**, 133 (1981).
[3] McFADDEN and CLARKE, *Proc. nat. Acad. Sci. (Wash.)*, **79**, 2460 (1982).
[4] IUPAC–IUB Joint Commission on Biochemical Nomenclature, *Europ. J. Biochem.*, **138**, 9 (1984).
[5] DOOLITTLE, R. F., *Science*, **214**, 149 (1981).
[6] IVERSEN, L. L., *Lancet*, **2**, 914 (1982).
[7] WILLIAMS-ASHMAN and CANELLAKIS, *Perspect. Biol. Med.*, **22**, 421 (1979).
[8] COHEN, S. S., *Fed. Proc.*, **41**, 3061 (1982).
[9] KRASNOW and COZZARELLI, *J. biol. Chem.*, **257**, 2687 (1982).

Porphyrins are the pigments occurring most frequently in nature[1]. The fundamental macrocyclic tetrapyrrolic system of the porphyrins, in which 4 pyrrole-type rings are linked by methene bridges (—CH═), is shown below. The cyclic structure consists of C and N atoms lying in a plane, with a central 16-membered ring of 12 C atoms and 4 N atoms.

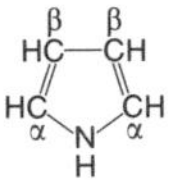

Pyrrole	Porphyrin (former name: 'porphin')	
	(FISCHER numeration)	(1–24 numbering scheme)

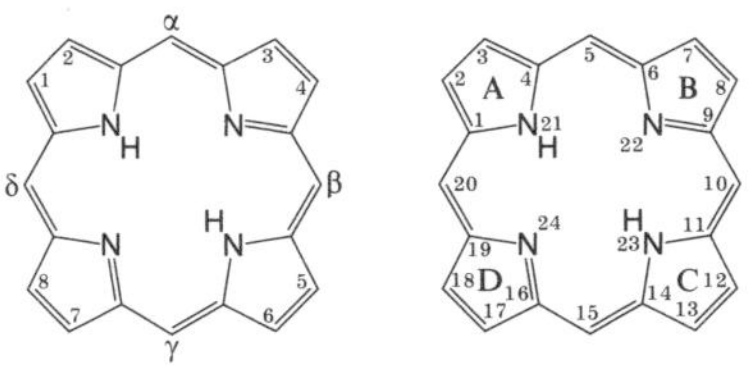

In the substituted porphyrins, some or all of the peripheral C atoms have side chains, for example methyl, ethyl or other groups (Table 1). With 2 different substituents, 4 isomers are possible. These are designated by the Roman numerals I–IV. With 3 different substituents, 15 isomers are possible. The naturally occurring protoporphyrin is isomer IX and belongs to the III series.

17,18-Dihydroporphyrins are called 'chlorins' and are the parent compound of the chlorophylls. 7,8,17,18-Tetrahydroporphyrin is the parent compound of bacteriochlorophyll a. The colorless porphyrinogens, precursors in the biosynthesis of protoheme (page 166), on the other hand, are 5,10,15,20,22,24-hexahydroporphyrins.

The porphyrins mostly occur bound as complexes with divalent metals (Table 2, page 47). Metal coordination complexes consist of a metal ion, coordinated to a roughly planar tetrapyrrole – acting as a tetradentate dianionic ligand – and, possibly, to 1 or 2 axial ligands. Protoheme, the iron(II) complex of protoporphyrin IX, is the prosthetic group of hemoglobin and myoglobin. Protoheme or related compounds are also the prosthetic groups of peroxidases, catalase and cytochromes. The copper complex of uroporphyrin III occurs in quite high concentration in the wing feathers of the Indian plantain eater (*Turacus indicus*)[1]. A copper coproporphyrin is excreted in the urine in familial coproporphyria[2], and protoporphyrin IX may be present in lead poisoning partly as a zinc complex in the erythrocytes[3]. The large group of chlorophylls from plants and bacteria contains complex-bound magnesium. The cobalamins – the parent compound of vitamin B_{12} – contain cobalt (page 83).

Protoporphyrin IX and the coproporphyrins and uroporphyrins of series I and III are practically the only porphyrins occurring free in nature. These compounds, which contain 2, 4 or 8 carboxy groups (Table 1), are found in various body fluids and in urine. In addition,

(*Continued on page 50*)

Table 1 *Porphyrinogens and porphyrins of biological importance*

Porphyrinogens	Porphyrins
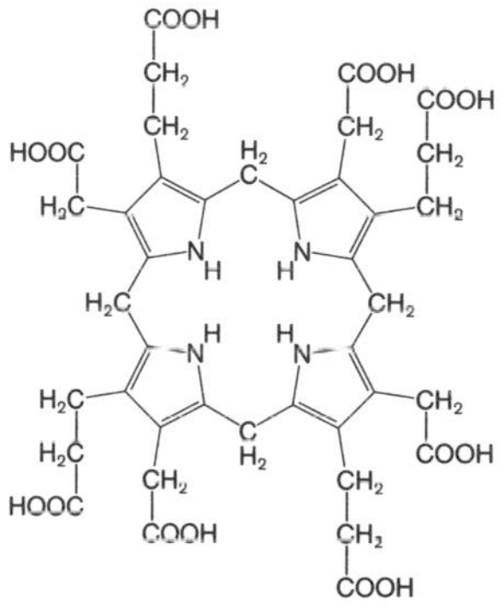 Uroporphyrinogen I $C_{40}H_{44}N_4O_{16}$ (M_r 836.81)	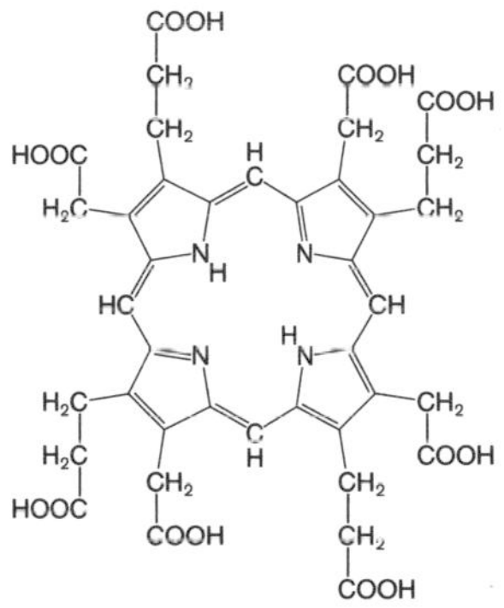 Uroporphyrin I $C_{40}H_{36}N_4O_{16}$ (M_r 830.76)
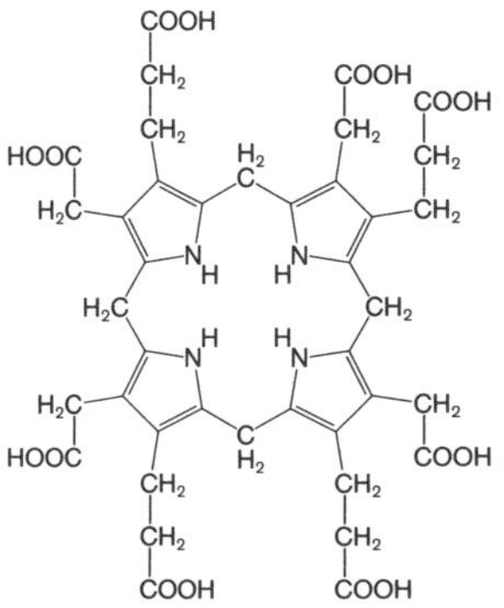 Uroporphyrinogen III $C_{40}H_{44}N_4O_{16}$ (M_r 836.81)	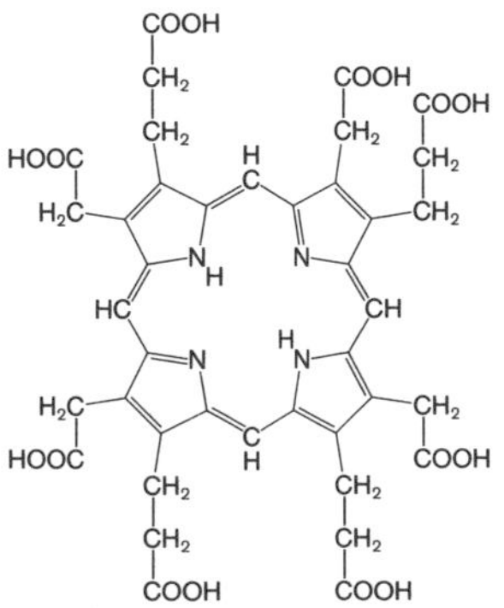 Uroporphyrin III $C_{40}H_{38}N_4O_{16}$ (M_r 830.76)

Table 1 *Porphyrinogens and porphyrins of biological importance (continued)*

Porphyrinogens	Porphyrins
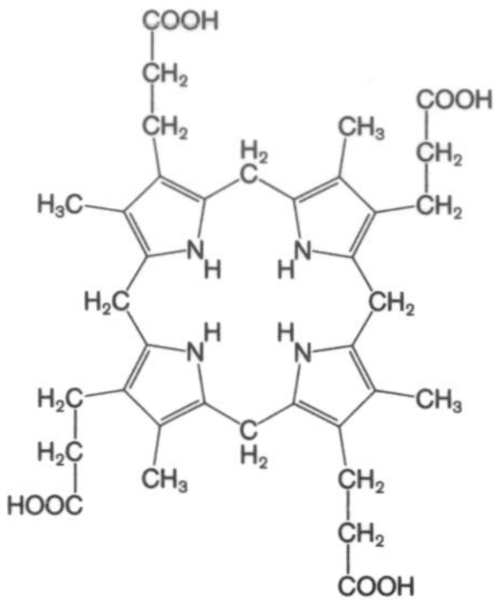 Coproporphyrinogen I $C_{36}H_{44}N_4O_8$ (M_r 660.77)	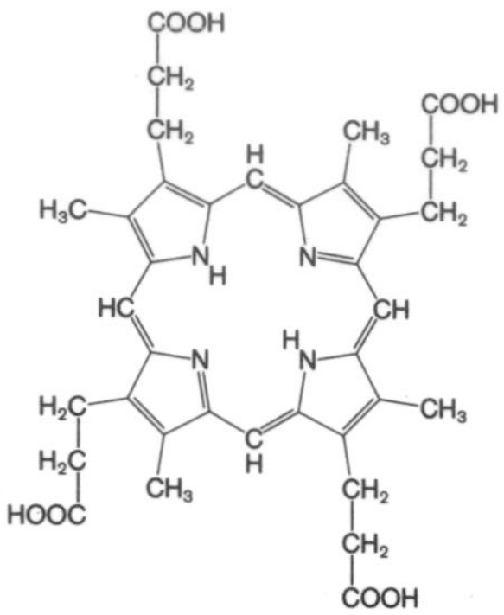 Coproporphyrin I $C_{36}H_{38}N_4O_8$ (M_r 654.72)
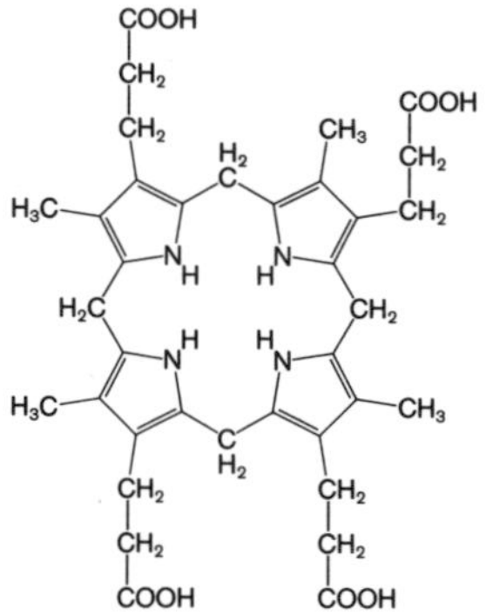 Coproporphyrinogen III $C_{36}H_{44}N_4O_8$ (M_r 660.77)	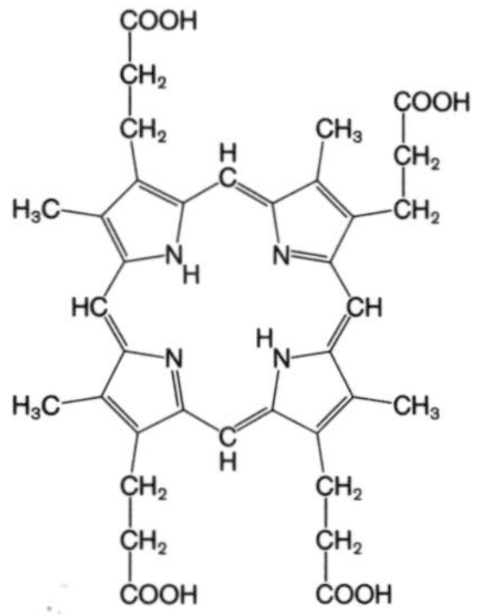 Coproporphyrin III $C_{36}H_{38}N_4O_8$ (M_r 654.72)
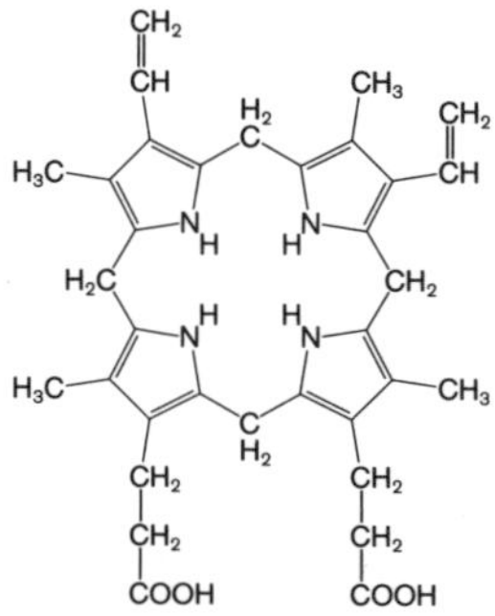 Protoporphyrinogen III $C_{34}H_{40}N_4O_4$ (M_r 568.72)	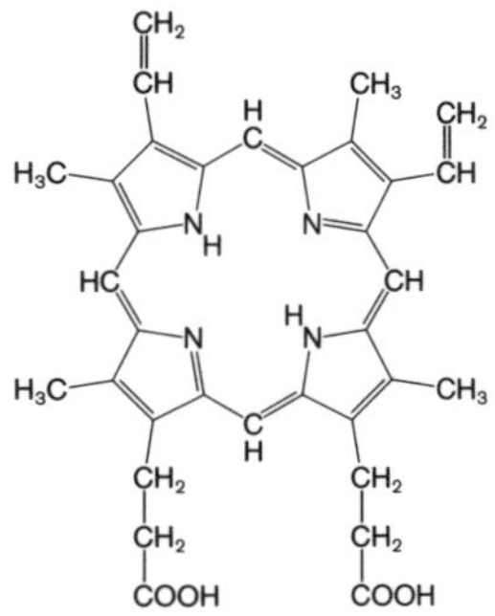 Protoporphyrin IX (protoporphyrin III) $C_{34}H_{34}N_4O_4$ (M_r 562.67)

Table 1   *Porphyrinogens and porphyrins of biological importance (continued)*

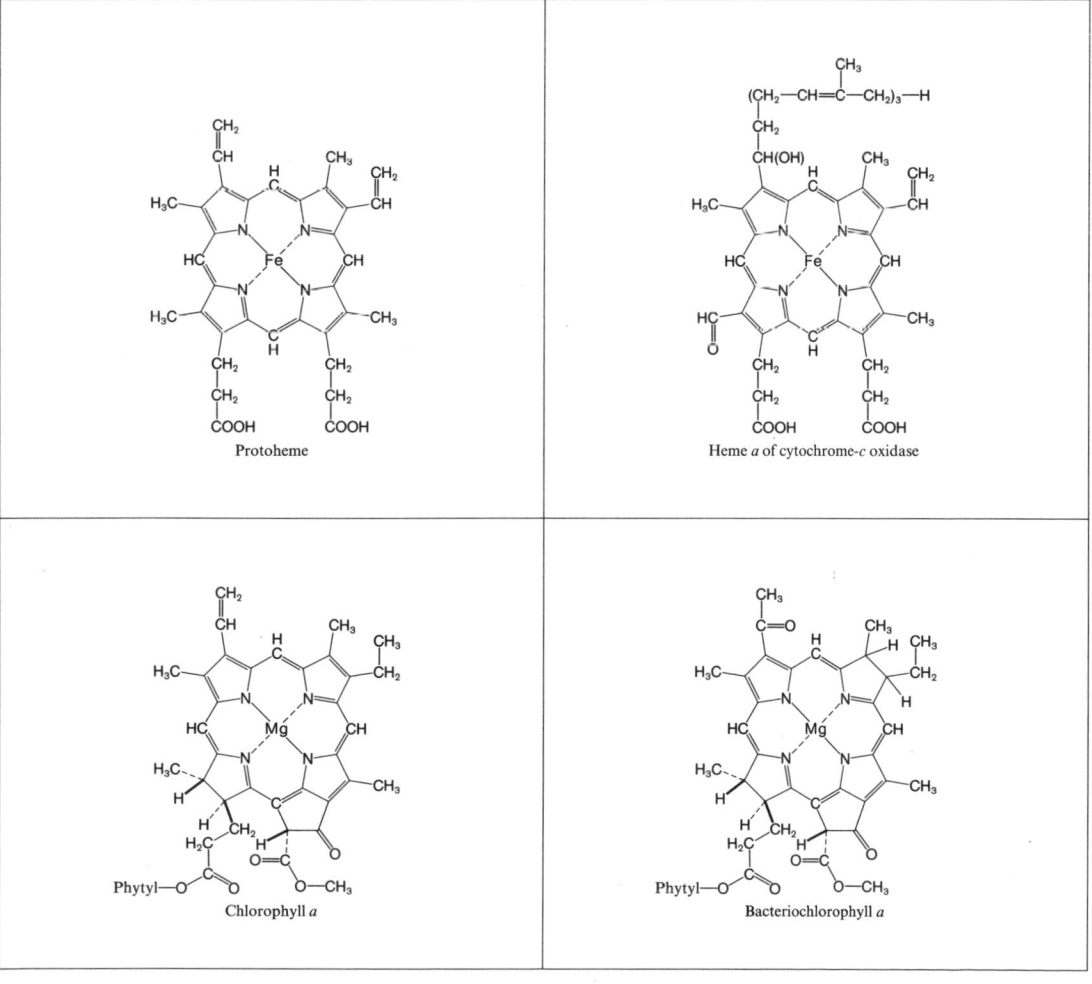

	Products of porphyrin metabolism	

Isocoproporphyrin
$C_{37}H_{40}N_4O_8$ (M_r 668.75)

Mesoporphyrin
$C_{34}H_{38}N_4O_4$ (M_r 566.70)

Table 2   *Metalloporphyrins of biological importance*

Protoheme

Heme *a* of cytochrome-*c* oxidase

Chlorophyll *a*

Bacteriochlorophyll *a*

Table 3 *Iron porphyrins and hemoproteins of biological importance*

Compound	General characteristics	Spectral data		Remarks
		Solvent	Absorption maxima nm	
Protoheme (ferroprotoheme) $C_{34}H_{32}N_4O_4Fe$ M_r 616.50	Iron(II) complex of protoporphyrin IX. Very unstable. Readily oxidized to hematin	Phosphate buffer pH 7	575 550 415	Prosthetic group of hemoglobin. Combines with many nitrogenous bases to form hemochromes
Hematin $C_{34}H_{32}N_4O_5Fe(OH)$ M_r 633.51	Iron(III) complex of protoporphyrin IX. Fairly stable	Acetic acid .... NaOH 10% .... Ether..............	625 540 510 400 580 650	Formed in blood from hemoglobin under extremely diverse conditions. The pigment of *Plasmodium malariae* consists of hematin
Hemoglobin .... M_r 64 500	4 protoheme groups bound to globin. The iron is divalent and can be readily oxidized. The globin component consists of 2 pairs of identical polypeptide chains. Differences in the amino-acid sequence or a varying combination of the chains are the cause of the large number of abnormal hemoglobins	Water	560 430	O_2 carrier in erythrocytes of all vertebrates. Combines reversibly with O_2 to form oxyhemoglobin, and with CO to form carboxyhemoglobin (affinity for CO over 100 times that for O_2)
Oxyhemoglobin.............	Compound of 1 hemoglobin molecule and 4 molecules of metabolically available O_2. The iron is divalent	Water	577 540 412	Present in fresh blood of all vertebrates (see also 'Hemoglobin', above)
Carboxyhemoglobin.........	Compound in which 4 molecules of CO are bound to the 4 Fe atoms of the hemoglobin	Water	570 538 418	Rapidly formed in the body during exposure to CO, resulting in failure of O_2 transport (see also 'Hemoglobin', above)
Hemiglobin (methemoglobin) ..	Like hemoglobin, except that the iron is trivalent	Acid solution ...... Alkaline solution	630 500 405 577 540 411	Reversible formation from hemoglobin by oxidation (ferricyanide, nitrites, nitrates, chlorates and quinones). An indirect effect is postulated for certain aromatic amino and nitro compounds. Occurs in erythrocytes in larger amounts in some pathological conditions
Sulfhemoglobin (verdoglobin S)	An iron(II) compound with 1 S atom attached to each heme group	Water	620	Formation by irreversible reaction of hemoglobin with hydrogen sulfide. Present in erythrocytes after ingestion of sulfur, sulfonamides, aromatic amines, occasionally trinitrotoluene; also in septicemia (especially *Clostridium perfringens*), severe constipation and after exposure to polluted air
Myoglobin (myohemoglobin) .. M_r 17800	1 protoheme group bound to 1 polypeptide chain of 153 amino acids. The iron is divalent	Water	555 435	Found in muscles of higher vertebrates, nematodes and mollusks, where its main function is O_2 storage. Completely saturated with O_2 at low pO_2
Catalase .... M_r 225000	4 hematin groups per enzyme molecule	Water	629 544 506 409 280	Found in breathing cells; highly active in liver, erythrocytes, etc. Catalytic activity inhibited by cyanide, hydrogen sulfide, hydroxylamine, azides, aminophenols and 2,4-dichlorophenol. The enzyme (1.11.1.6) catalyzes the reaction $H_2O_2 + H_2O_2 \longrightarrow O_2 + 2H_2O$

	Prosthetic group	Solubility	Absorption maxima	Function / Reaction
Cytochrome-c peroxidase M_r 49000	1 heme group per enzyme molecule	—	—	In yeast. The enzyme (1.11.1.5) catalyzes the reaction 2 ferrocytochrome c + H_2O_2 → 2 ferricytochrome c + $2H_2O$
Peroxidase	Prosthetic group: hematin analogs	Weak acids	Horseradish peroxidase: 645 583 548 498	In plants (horseradish peroxidase), myelocytes (myeloperoxidase), milk (lactoperoxidase). The enzyme (1.11.1.7) catalyzes the reaction Donor + H_2O_2 → Oxidized donor + $2H_2O$
Iodide peroxidase	—	—	—	The enzyme (1.11.1.8) catalyzes the reaction Iodide + H_2O_2 → Iodine + $2H_2O$
Tryptophan 2,3-dioxygenase	Prosthetic group: protoheme	—	—	The enzyme (1.13.11.11), a hemocuproprotein, catalyzes the reaction Tryptophan + O_2 → Formylkynurenine
Indoleamine 2,3-dioxygenase	1 protoheme group per enzyme molecule. The iron is trivalent	—	—	The enzyme cleaves the indole ring analogously to the ring cleavage by tryptophan 2,3-dioxygenase, but it has an absolute requirement for superoxide anion (O_2^-) for catalytic activity
Cytochrome a group (aa_3, a_1)	The prosthetic group is a heme with a formyl side chain (heme a)	Water	Ferrocytochrome aa_3: 605 (α) 445 (γ)	Cytochrome aa_3 (aa') is identical to cytochrome-c oxidase ('Warburg's respiratory enzyme') (1.9.3.1) in the mitochondria of eukaryotes. It is a hemolipocuproprotein with a relative molecular mass of 150000–200000 with 2 Cu atoms as well as 2 inseparable heme a groups ($a + a_3$) per unit, of which, however, only the heme a_3 group reacts with O_2 and is poisoned by CN^- and CO. Cytochrome aa_3 catalyzes oxidation of the mitochondrial cytochrome c by O_2 and is autoxidizable in the reduced form. Cytochrome a_1 is contained in certain bacteria and presumably functions as a terminal oxidase
Cytochrome b group (b, b_1, b_2, b_3, b_5, b_7, 'o')	Prosthetic group: protoheme or a related heme (without formyl side chain); not covalently bound to protein	Water	Ferrocytochrome b: 563 566 (α) Ferrocytochrome b_2: 559 (α) Ferrocytochrome b_5: 554 (α): P-450: 408 (γ)	Cytochrome b: in the mitochondria of eukaryotes and in chloroplasts. b_1: in certain bacteria (for example *E. coli*). b_2: in yeast; functions – together with 1 molecule of flavin mononucleotide as 2nd prosthetic group – as a lactate dehydrogenase (1.1.2.3). b_3: in the microsomes of nonphotosynthetic plant tissue. b_5: in animal microsomes; is reduced by NADH in the presence of cytochrome b_5 reductase (dehydrogenation of higher fatty acids as well as hydroxylations or detoxifications). b_7: in the spadices of *Arum* species. 'o': terminal oxidase in prokaryotes and also in some protozoa.
Cytochrome c group (c, c_1, c_2, c_3, c_5, c_6)	Prosthetic group is protoheme, whose side chains are linked covalently to protein. In cytochrome c, this takes place by means of a thioether bridge with the cysteine of the protein and with saturation of the vinyl side chain	Water	Ferrocytochrome c: 550 (α) 520 (β) 415 (γ) Ferrocytochrome c_1: 553 (α)	c and c_1: in mitochondria of eukaryotes. c: substrate for the terminal oxidase in oxidative phosphorylation. c_1: electron donor to c in the mitochondrial respiratory chain. c_2: in bacteria. c_3: in bacteria and algae. c_5: in facultative anaerobic species of *Pseudomonas* for nitrate assimilation, moreover in strictly anaerobic, nitrogen-fixing *Azotobacter*
Cytochrome d group (d [a_2], cd)	Prosthetic group is an iron–tetrapyrrole complex in which the number of conjugated double bonds is smaller than in porphyrin (for example dihydroporphyrin)	Water	Ferrocytochrome d: 630	In several species of bacteria (for example *E. coli*, *Acetobacter peroxidans*). The ferro form is autoxidizable and has a strong affinity for CO

Table 4   *Trivial names of iron porphyrins*

Valence state of the Fe atom	Ligands occupying 5th and 6th coordination sites		Authors		
			LEMBERG and LEGGE[7]	PAULING and CORYELL[8], BARRON[9]	ANSON[10], KEILIN[11]
2..............	H_2O	H_2O	Heme	Ferroheme	Heme
3..............	OH	H_2O	Hematin	Ferriheme hydroxide	Hematin
3..............	Cl	–	Hemin	Ferriheme chloride	Hemin
2..............	N compound	N compound	Hemochrome	Ferrohemochromogen	Hemochromogen
3..............	N compound	N compound	Hemichrome	Ferrihemochromogen	Parahematin
2..............	Globin	H_2O	Hemoglobin	Hemoglobin	Hemoglobin
2..............	Globin	O_2	Oxyhemoglobin	Oxyhemoglobin	Oxyhemoglobin
3..............	Globin	H_2O	Hemiglobin	Ferrihemoglobin	Acid methemoglobin
3..............	Globin	OH	Hemiglobin hydroxide	Ferrihemoglobin hydroxide	Alkaline methemoglobin
2..............	Globin	CO	Carboxyhemoglobin	Carbon monoxide hemoglobin	–

Table 5
Nomenclature of iron coordination complexes (IUPAC–IUB[12])

Heme	An iron porphyrin coordination complex
Ferroheme	An iron(II) porphyrin coordination complex
Ferriheme.......	An iron(III) porphyrin coordination complex
Hemochrome....	A low-spin iron porphyrin coordination complex with 1 or more strong-field axial ligands (e.g. pyridine)
Ferrohemochrome	An iron(II) hemochrome
Ferrihemochrome	An iron(III) hemochrome
Hemin..........	A chloro(porphyrinato)iron(III) coordination complex. For example: protohemin = chloro(protoporphyrinato)iron(III), or chloroiron(III) protoporphyrinate
Hematin	A hydroxo(porphyrinato)iron(III) coordination complex

porphyrins with 7, 6, 5 and 3 carboxy groups, as well as mesoporphyrin, which contains 2 carboxy groups, also occur in small amounts[4]. The concentrations of these substances are increased in various pathological conditions, such as lead poisoning and porphyrias. Furthermore, protoporphyrin IX is found in the root nodules of leguminous plants, in worms and in the shells of birds' eggs[1,5]. The isocoproporphyrin[6] detectable in porphyria cutanea tarda is probably a product of bacterial metabolism in the intestine[3].

Iron porphyrins, hemochromes and hemoproteins

Because of their natural occurrence, iron coordination complexes are associated with an extensive trivial nomenclature (Table 4; the recommendations 1978 of the IUPAC–IUB Joint Commission on Biochemical Nomenclature[12] are given in Table 5). In these recommendations, 'heme' is used as the generic term for any iron porphyrin complex; the prefix 'proto-' can be used in trivial names when the heme derives from protoporphyrin. The term 'heme' does not specify the valence state of the Fe atom. If this is desirable, 'ferro-' or 'ferri-' may be used as prefix. Thus, 'ferroprotoheme' would be the full trivial name for the prosthetic group of hemoglobin[13].

Hemes readily react with strong-field axial ligands such as primary amines, pyridine, ammonia, imidazole derivatives (for example histidine) and hydrazine to form the so-called *hemochromes*. Thus in hemoglobin and myoglobin the 5th coordination site of iron is occupied by an N atom of histidine; in the *b* cytochromes both the 5th and 6th coordination sites are occupied by an N atom of histidine. In

cytochrome *c*, the 5th coordination site is also occupied by an N atom of histidine, but the 6th is occupied by the S atom of methionine.

Proteins (including enzymes) that contain heme or an analog as a prosthetic group are referred to as 'hemoproteins'. Hemoproteins are found in practically all organisms with the exception of viruses and possibly certain obligate anaerobes such as *Entamoeba histolytica*[14].

Hemoglobin and myoglobin are hemoproteins that combine reversibly with O_2. A series of enzymes that function in cellular metabolism are likewise hemoproteins. If – as in cytochrome *c* – the 5th and 6th coordination sites of the iron are occupied, no reaction with O_2 or CO can take place. Fe^{2+} in the ferroheme compounds can be oxidized to Fe^{3+}, whereupon, for example, hemiglobin (methemoglobin) is formed from hemoglobin in a reversible reaction.

The physiologically active hemoproteins can be divided into 3 groups according to the valence state of the iron:

1. Fe remains divalent: hemoglobin, myoglobin
2. Fe as redox system: cytochromes*
3. Fe remains trivalent: catalase, peroxidases

The biochemical reactions of these hemoproteins take place at the Fe atom. The biological function of each of these groups is different, however, so that the selectivity of each reaction must be attributed to the specific structure of the protein and the nature of its bond to the prosthetic group. The physical and chemical properties of biologically important hemoproteins are compiled in Table 3 (pages 48 and 49).

---

* The heme–thiolate proteins P-450 ('cytochromes P-450') formerly included in the cytochrome *b* group are not involved in the reversible Fe^{2+}/Fe^{3+} equilibrium but are concerned with O atom transfer.

References

[1] SMITH, K. M., in SMITH, K. M. (Ed.), *Porphyrins and Metalloporphyrins*, Elsevier, Amsterdam, 1975, page 3.
[2] CARLSON et al., *Clin. Chem.*, **24**, 2009 (1978).
[3] HART and PIOMELLI, *Clin. Chem.*, **27**, 220 (1981).
[4] DOSS, M., *Verh. dtsch. Ges. inn. Med.*, **84**, 1165 (1978).
[5] DOSS, M., *Dtsch. med. Wschr.*, **106**, 911 (1981).
[6] ELDER et al., *Lancet*, **1**, 916 (1981).
[7] LEMBERG and LEGGE, *Hematin Compounds and Bile Pigments*, Interscience, New York, 1949.
[8] PAULING and CORYELL, *Proc. nat. Acad. Sci. (Wash.)*, **22**, 159 (1936).
[9] BARRON, E. S., *J. biol. Chem.*, **121**, 285 (1937).
[10] ANSON, M. L., *J. gen. Physiol.*, **23**, 239 (1939).
[11] KEILIN, D., *Proc. roy. Soc. B*, **100**, 129 (1926).
[12] IUPAC–IUB Joint Commission on Biochemical Nomenclature, *Europ. J. Biochem.*, **108**, 1 (1980).
[13] KARLSON, P., *J. clin. Chem*, **19**, 43 (1981).
[14] WEINBACH et al., *J. Parasit.*, **62**, 127 (1976).

Breakdown products of heme

Compound	Formula, M_r	Structure	Remarks
Biliverdin	$C_{33}H_{34}N_4O_6$ 582.65	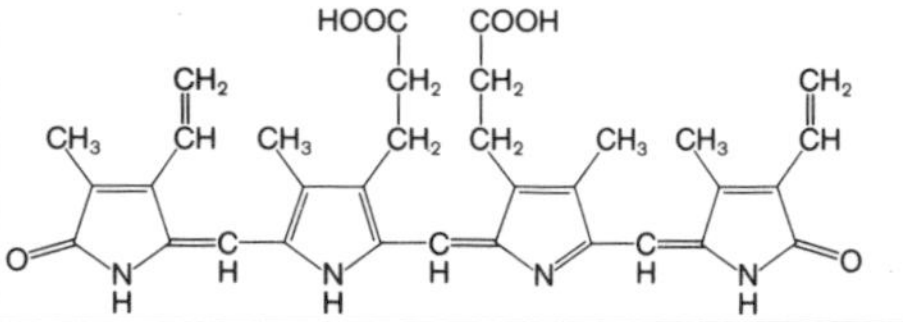	Breakdown product of hemoglobin, reduced enzymatically in liver to bilirubin. Not found in blood, but present in bile of some animals, in placenta of some mammals (uteroverdin) and in egg shells of many birds (oocyan). Also found in meconium of fetus and newborn and in bile after death
Bilirubin	$C_{33}H_{36}N_4O_6$ 584.67	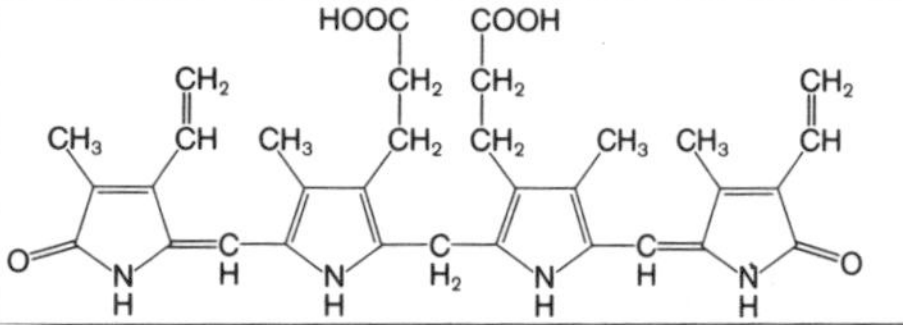	Breakdown product of hemoglobin and other heme compounds in reticuloendothelial system. Present in large amounts in serum and tissues in hemolytic jaundice. Also found in urine and feces of infants. Conjugated in liver cells with carbohydrates (mostly glucuronic acid)
Mesobilirubin	$C_{33}H_{40}N_4O_6$ 588.70	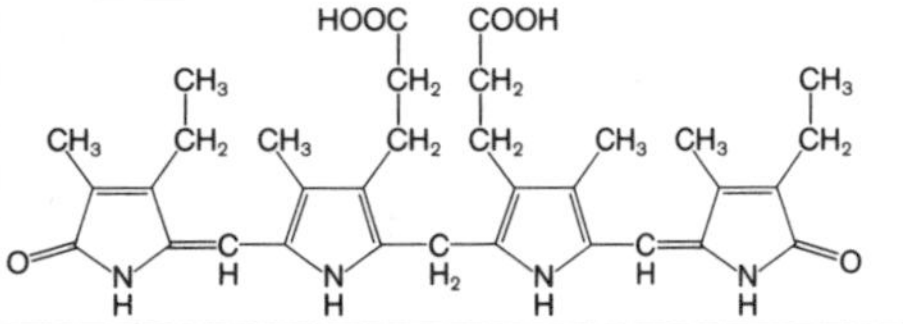	Reduction product of bilirubin
Mesobilirubinogen	$C_{33}H_{44}N_4O_6$ 592.73	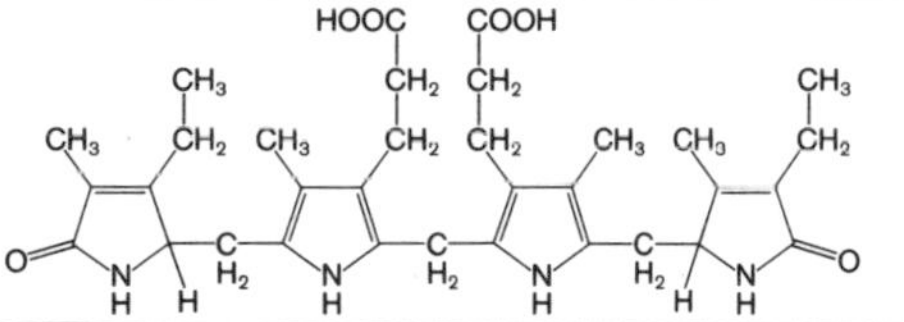	Reduction product of bilirubin in liver. Present in normal bile, urine and feces. Increased in pathological conditions
d-Urobilinogen ...	$C_{33}H_{42}N_4O_6$ 590.72	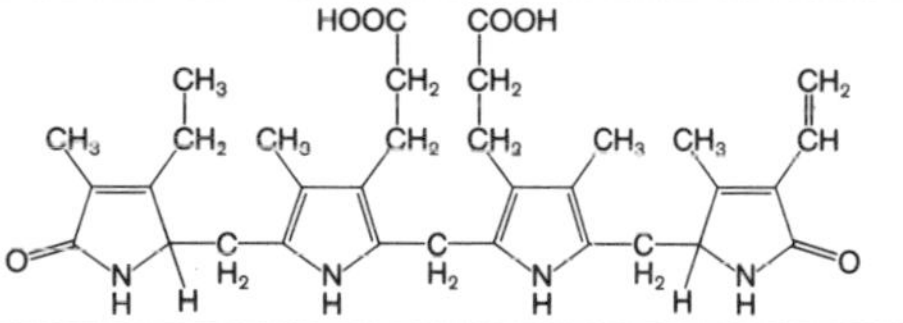	Isolated from infected bile, where it arises from bilirubin
Stercobilinogen ... (10,23-dihydro-stercobilin)	$C_{33}H_{48}N_4O_6$ 596.77	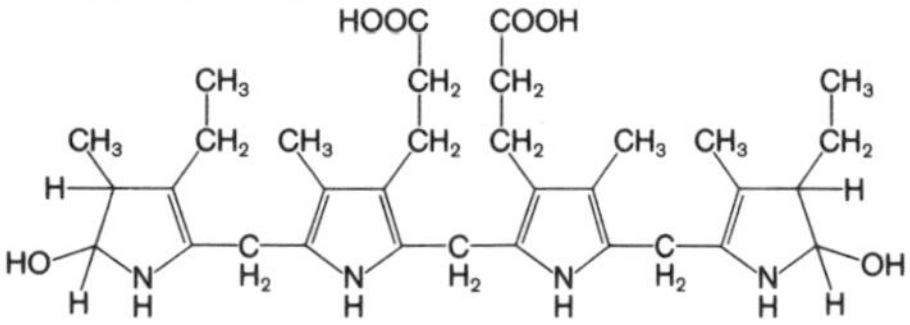	Reduction product of bilirubin. Main excretory product of hemoglobin in most vertebrates
i-Urobilin........ (urobilin IXα)	$C_{33}H_{42}N_4O_6$ 590.72	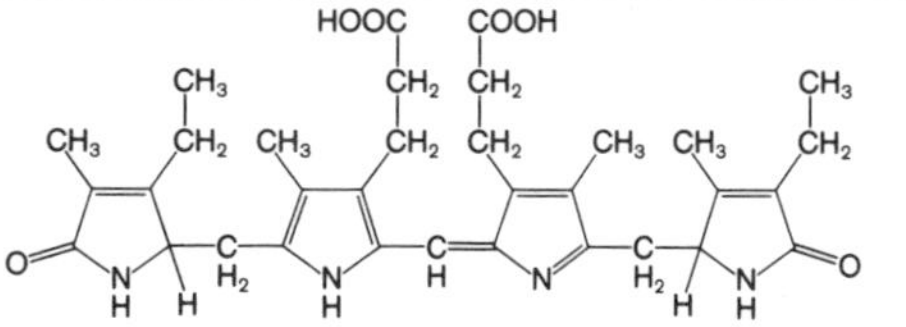	Oxidation product of mesobilirubinogen. Present in normal urine and feces
d-Urobilin	$C_{33}H_{40}N_4O_6$ 588.70	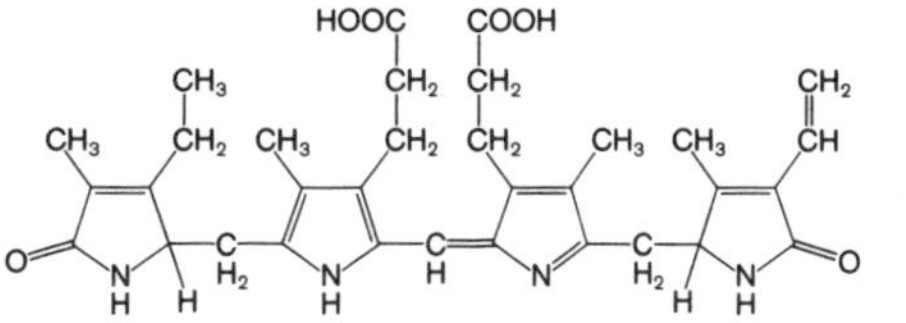	Oxidation product of *d*-urobilinogen
Stercobilin .... (*l*-urobilin)	$C_{33}H_{46}N_4O_6$ 594.75	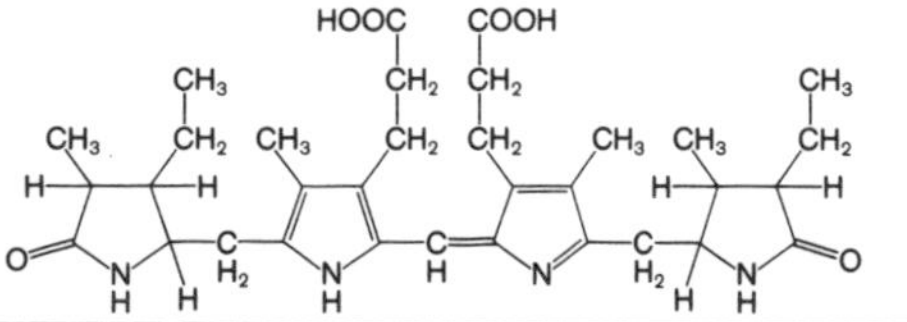	Oxidation product of stercobilinogen. Constituent of normal urine and feces

Bile pigments are linear tetrapyrroles. Their fundamental system 'bilin' is defined without oxygen substituents, and is numbered (omitting C-20) to correspond with the numbering of the unsubstituted porphyrin ring system (page 45)[1]:

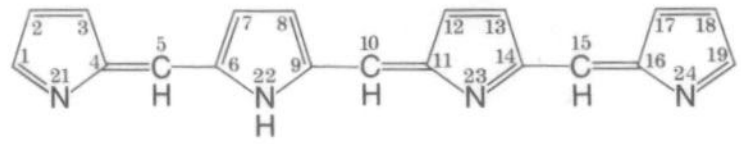

Bile pigments are breakdown products of heme compounds (page 48); in structural terms they derive from protoporphyrin IX. In vertebrates, in which the α-methene bridge is cleaved practically exclusively (page 125), the resulting bile pigments are also designated 'biliverdin IXα' and 'bilirubin IXα'. Additional bile pigments result from hydrogenation by intestinal bacteria (see Table).

The dipyrroles found in the colon are known as 'mesobilifuscins' and likewise classed with the bile pigments by some authors. They appear to be by-products of porphyrin synthesis rather than cleavage products of bile pigments[2]. Dipyrroluria is seen in unstable hemoglobin disease[3].

Bilirubin – the most important bile pigment in man – can adopt 4 configurations (see formulae), of which only the naturally occurring

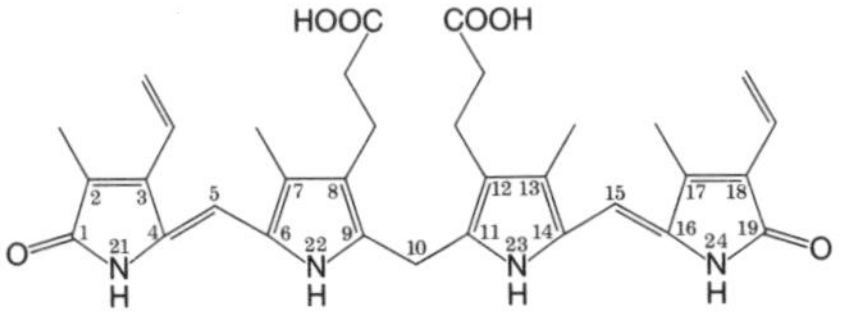

4Z,15Z isomer

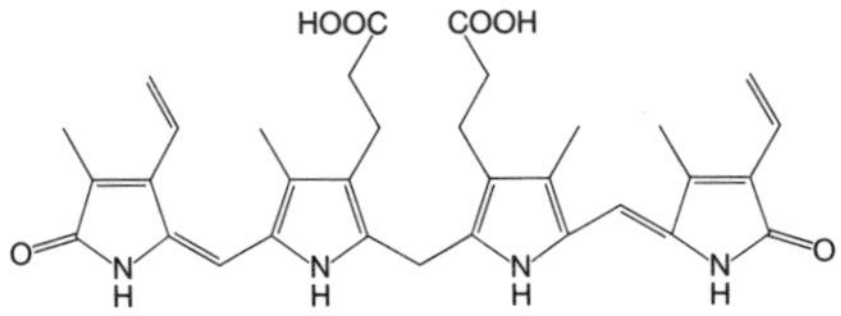

4E,15Z isomer

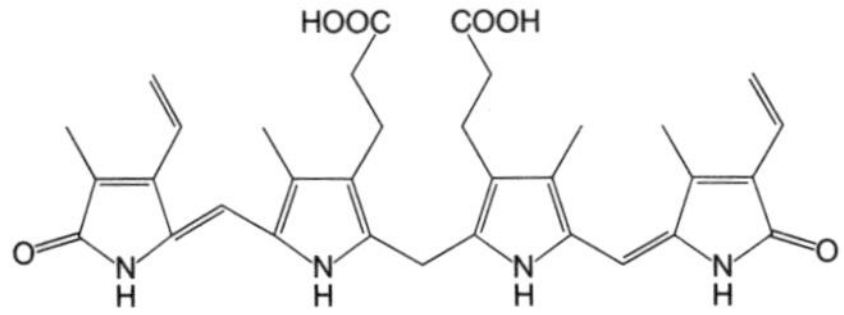

4Z,15E isomer

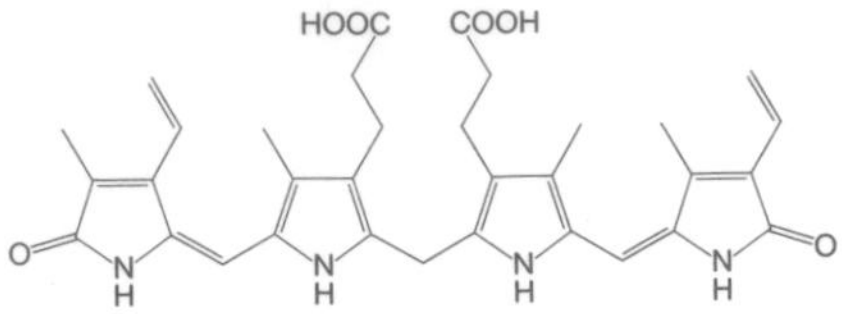

4E,15E isomer

4Z,15Z form is stable and insoluble in water, owing to the hydrogen bonding. The other forms are metastable and are formed from the stable form by the action of blue light – the basis of phototherapy in jaundice cases[4].

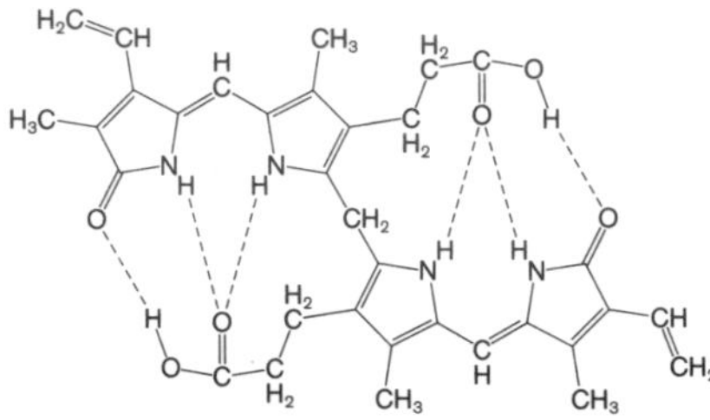

Stable form of bilirubin

In the blood of healthy persons bilirubin is almost exclusively present in conjugated form with glucuronic acid (and possibly other carbohydrates), in which case bilirubin bisglucuronide predominates.

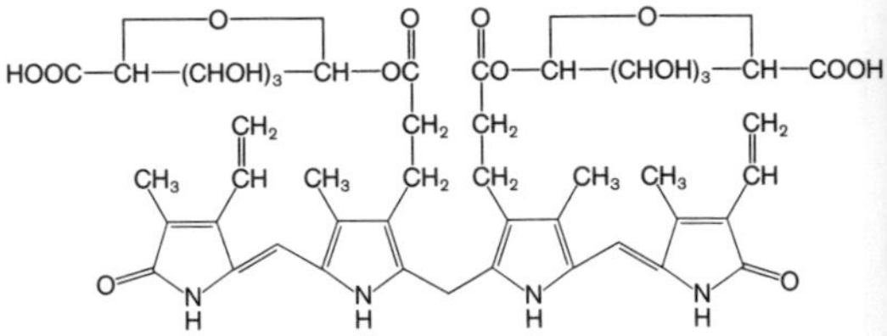

Bilirubin bisglucuronide (bilirubin diglucuronide)

References

[1] IUPAC–IUB Joint Commission on Biochemical Nomenclature, *Europ. J. Biochem.*, **108**, 1 (1980).
[2] WITH, T.K., *Bile Pigments*, Academic Press, New York, 1968.
[3] WINTROBE et al., *Clinical Hematology*, 8th ed., Lea & Febiger, Philadelphia, Pa., 1981, page 180.
[4] McDONAGH et al., *Science*, **208**, 145 (1980).

A *nucleoside* is a heterocyclic base linked to a sugar; in a *nucleotide* the sugar of the nucleoside is esterified with monophosphoric acid, diphosphoric acid or triphosphoric acid.

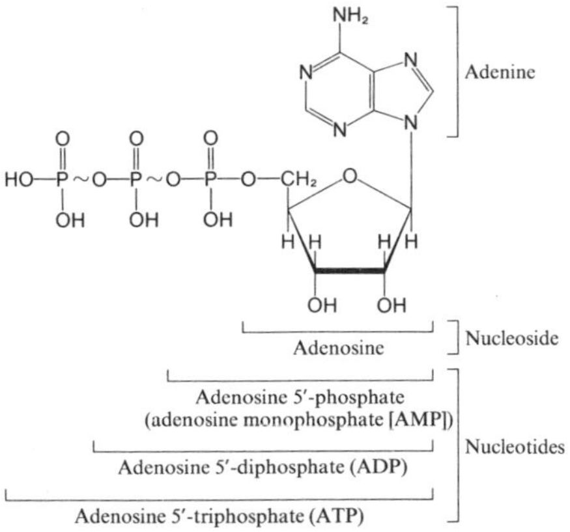

Adenine

Adenosine — Nucleoside

Adenosine 5'-phosphate (adenosine monophosphate [AMP])

Adenosine 5'-diphosphate (ADP) — Nucleotides

Adenosine 5'-triphosphate (ATP)

Dinucleotides may be formed by condensation of the phosphoric-acid groups of 2 nucleotides, thus for example nicotinamide adenine dinucleotide (NAD) and flavin adenine dinucleotide (FAD) (for structural formulae see Table 2).

The bases found in nucleosides and nucleotides are usually purines and pyrimidines, but some nucleotides with coenzyme function may include pyridines (as in NAD) or alloxazines (as in FMN or FAD). The parent compounds of these bases have the following structures:

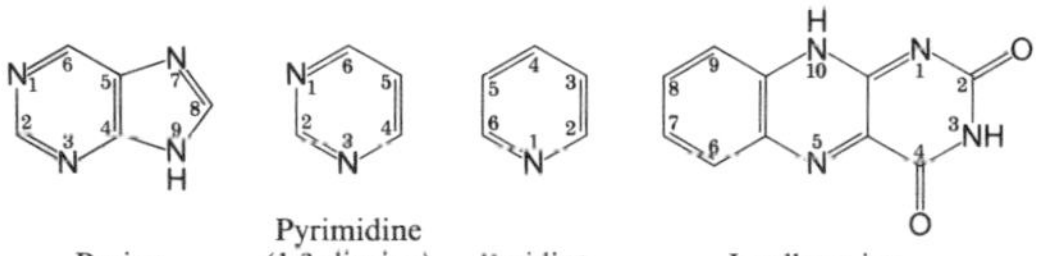

Purine   Pyrimidine (1,3-diazine)   Pyridine   Isoalloxazine

Adenine and guanine are important purine bases of nucleotides; uracil, cytosine and thymine are important pyrimidines.

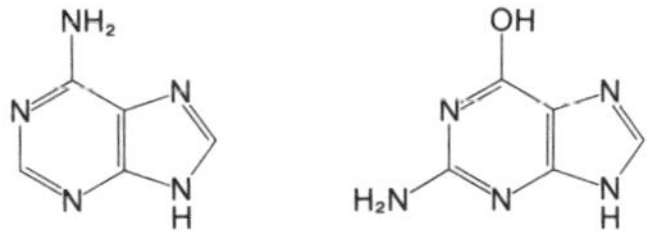

Adenine   Guanine 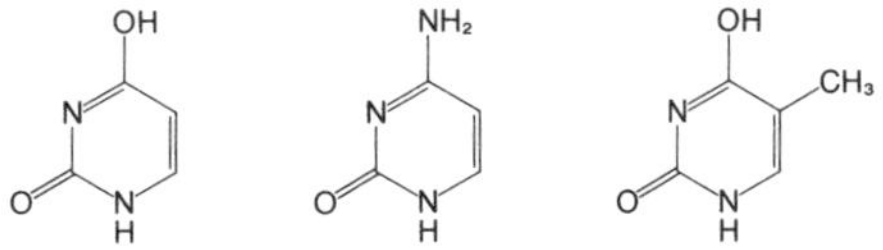   Uracil   Cytosine   Thymine

The sugars linked to the bases in nucleosides and nucleotides are most commonly either ribose or 2-deoxyribose:

Ribose (β-D-ribofuranose)   2-Deoxyribose (β-D-2-deoxyribofuranose)

The base–sugar linkage occupies the N-9 position in the case of purines and the N-3 position in the case of pyrimidines.

Symbols for purines and pyrimidines as well as for their nucleosides are listed in Table 1, and nucleotides with coenzyme functions are compiled in Table 2.

Nucleic acids are polynucleotides with a relative molecular mass of 2×10^4 to 4×10^{10}. They are built up of nucleotide units via phosphodiester linkages. In the ribonucleic acids (RNA) the sugar is ribose, in the deoxyribonucleic acids (DNA) it is deoxyribose.

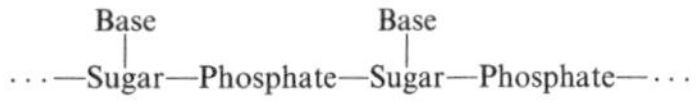

$$\cdots \text{—Sugar—Phosphate—Sugar—Phosphate—} \cdots$$

The 4 principal types of nucleotide units in RNA are:

Adenosine monophosphate (AMP)
Guanosine monophosphate (GMP)
Cytidine monophosphate (CMP)
Uridine monophosphate (UMP)

The nucleotide units in DNA are:

Deoxyadenosine monophosphate (dAMP)
Deoxyguanosine monophosphate (dGMP)
Deoxycytidine monophosphate (dCMP)
Thymidine monophosphate (dTMP)

In addition, however, a whole series of derivatives of these compounds can also occur in RNA or DNA (so-called 'minor bases').

Examples of nucleoside variants in transfer RNA:

1-Methyladenosine
N^6-Isopentenyladenosine
N^6,N^6-Dimethyladenosine
1-Methylinosine
5,6-Dihydrouridine
Pseudouridine
2'-O-Methyluridine
Ribosylthymine
1-Methylguanosine
7-Methylguanosine
N^2,N^2-Dimethylguanosine
2'-O-Methylguanosine
5-Methylcytidine
2'-O-Methylcytidine
N^4-Acetylcytidine
2-Thiocytidine

Major nucleoside variant in DNA:

5-Methyldeoxycytidine

The arrangement of the bases laterally to the basic structure of the sugar-phosphate chain in RNA and DNA is depicted on page 60.
For further details on the structure of RNA and DNA see pages 175–177.

Table 1   *Symbols* for purines and pyrimidines and their nucleosides*

Purine	Symbol	Pyrimidine	Symbol	Purine nucleoside	Symbols	Pyrimidine nucleoside◊	Symbols
Adenine	Ade	Cytosine	Cyt	Adenosine	Ado, A	Cytidine	Cyd, C
Guanine	Gua	Orotic acid	Oro	Guanosine	Guo, G	Dihydrouridine	–, D, hU
Hypoxanthine ...	Hyp	Thiouracil.......	Sur	Inosine	Ino, I	Orotidine	Ord, O
Thiohypoxanthine	Shy	Thymine	Thy	Thioinosine	Sno, M, sI	Pseudouridine	Ψrd, Ψ, Q
Xanthine........	Xan	Uracil	Ura	Xanthosine......	Xao, X	Ribosylthymine	Thd, T
Undetermined purine base	Pur	Undetermined pyrimidine base	Pyr	'Purine nucleoside'	Puo, R	Thiouridine	Srd, S, sU
				'Nucleoside'	Nuc, N	Thymidine (2'-deoxyribosylthymine)................	dThd, dT
						Uridine...................	Urd, U
						'Pyrimidine nucleoside'......	Pyd, Y

*According to the recommendations of the IUPAC–IUB Commission on Biochemical Nomenclature, *Europ. J. Biochem.*, **74**, 1 (1977).

◊ Deoxynucleosides are indicated by a prefixed d (for example dAdo or dA for deoxyadenosine).

Table 2 *Nucleotides with coenzyme function*

Name	Formula, M_r	Structure	Function
Nicotinamide mononucleotide (NMN)	$C_{11}H_{15}N_2O_8P$ 334.22	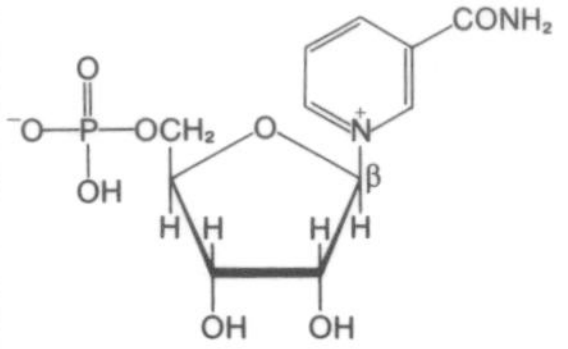	Constituent of NAD and NADP (see below)
Flavin mononucleotide (FMN) (flavin ribitylphosphate, riboflavin 5'-phosphate)	$C_{17}H_{21}N_4O_9P$ 456.35	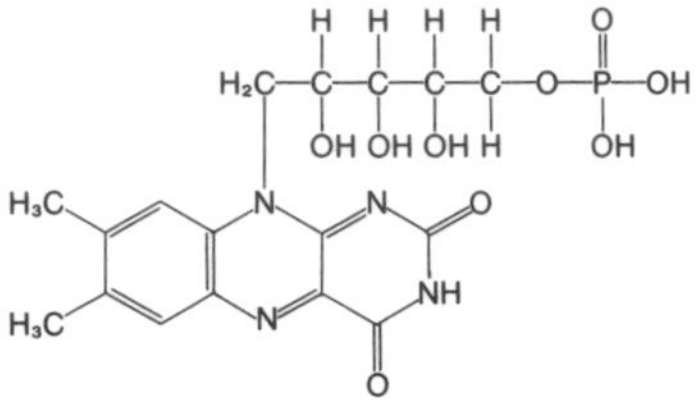	Hydrogen and electron transfer (page 76)
		Nucleotides containing adenine	
Nicotinamide adenine dinucleotide (NAD) (diphosphopyridine nucleotide [DPN], codehydrogenase I, coenzyme I [Co I], cozymase)	$C_{21}H_{27}N_7O_{14}P_2$ 663.43	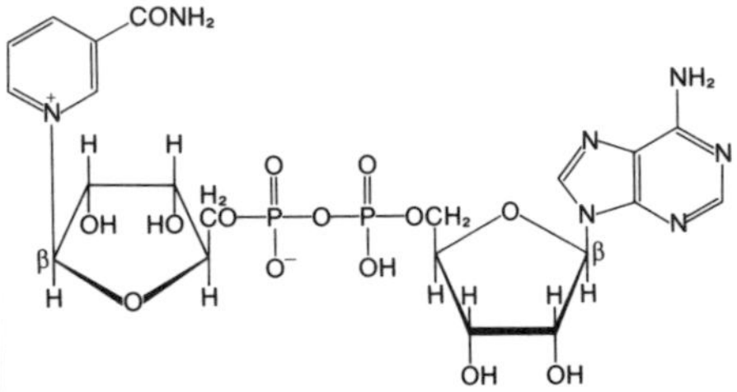	Hydrogen and electron transfer (page 75)
Nicotinamide adenine dinucleotide phosphate (NADP) (triphosphopyridine nucleotide [TPN], codehydrogenase II, coenzyme II [Co II], phosphocozymase)	$C_{21}H_{28}N_7O_{17}P_3$ 743.41	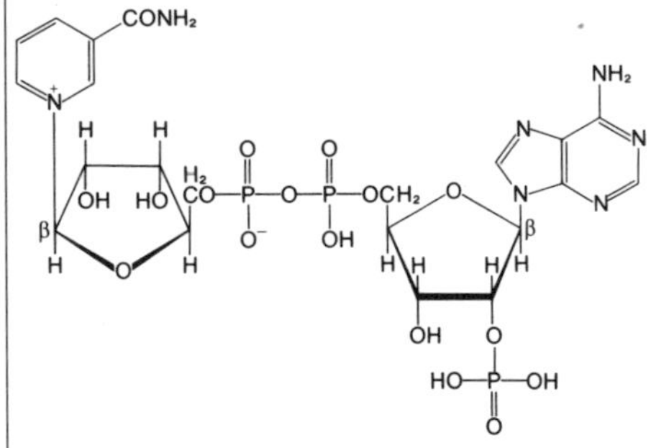	Hydrogen and electron transfer (page 75)
Flavin adenine dinucleotide (FAD)	$C_{27}H_{33}N_9O_{15}P_2$ 785.56	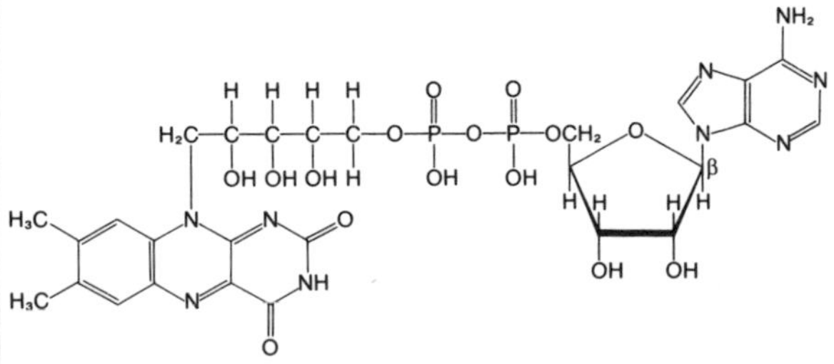	Hydrogen and electron transfer (page 76)

Table 2   *Nucleotides with coenzyme function (continued)*

Name	Formula, M_r	Structure	Function
Coenzyme A (CoA, HSCoA)	$C_{21}H_{36}N_7O_{16}P_3S$ 767.54	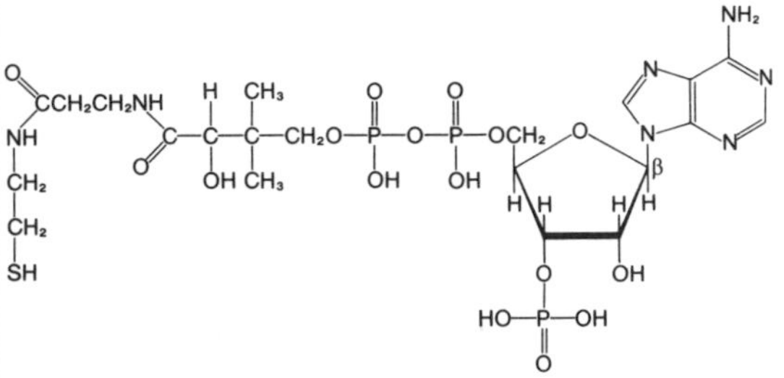	Transfer of acyl groups
Adenosine 5'-triphosphate (ATP)	$C_{10}H_{16}N_5O_{13}P_3$ 507.18	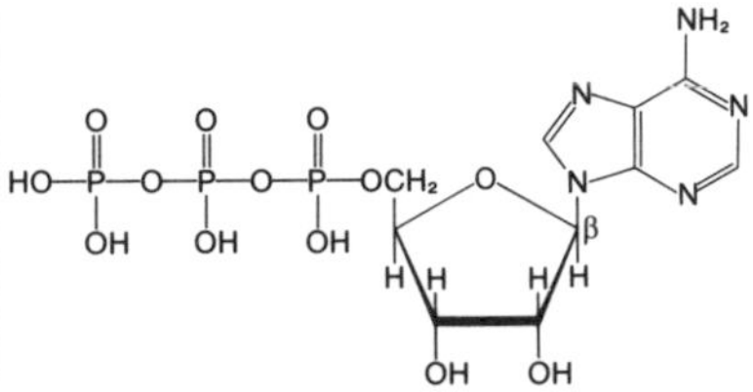	Energy transfer (page 78)
Adenosine 3',5'-phosphate (cyclic adenosine monophosphate [cAMP])	$C_{10}H_{12}N_5O_6P$ 329.21	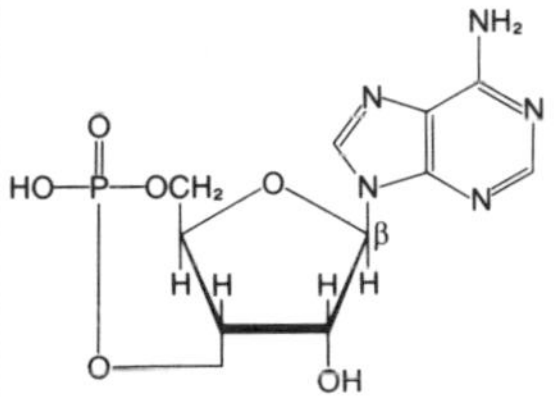	Mediator of the action of hormones ('second messenger') (page 79); activates and regulates many metabolic systems
Acyladenosine monophosphates (acyladenylates)	—	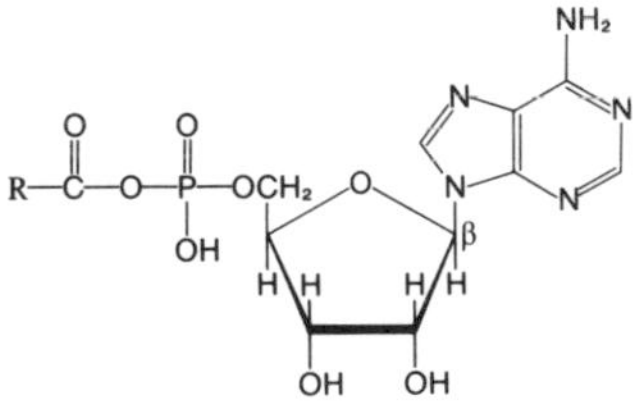 R: $CH_3(CH_2)_n-$	Formed from the following reaction: Fatty acid + ATP → Acyl-AMP + pyrophosphate. Activation of fatty acids (page 100)
Aminoacyladenosine monophosphates	—	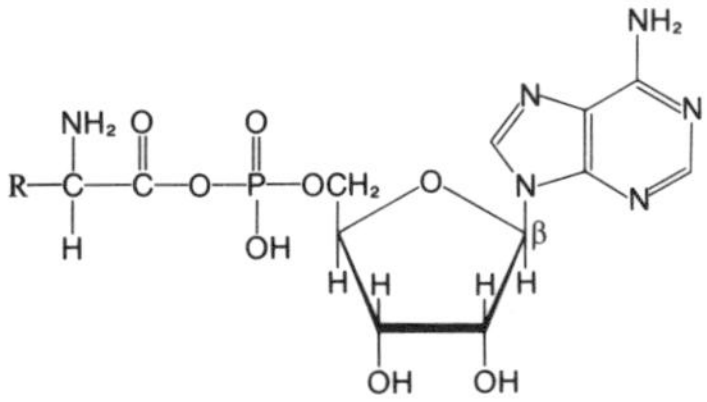 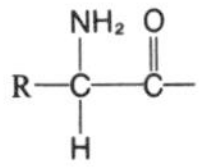 Amino-acid residue	Activation of amino acids for protein synthesis (see page 179)
Adenosine 5'-phosphosulfate (APS)	$C_{10}H_{14}N_5O_{10}PS$ 427.29	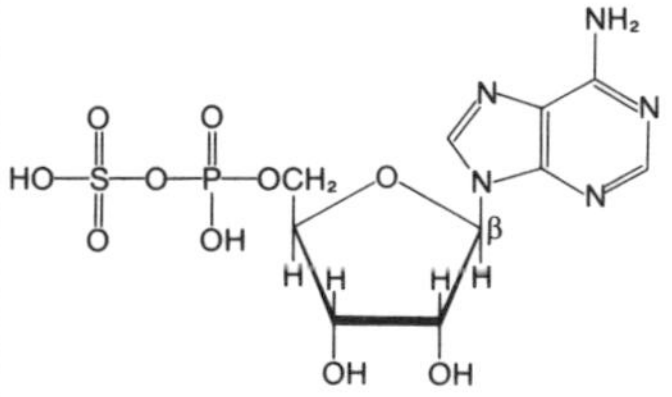	Formed from ATP and inorganic sulfate. Intermediate in the synthesis of PAPS (see next page)

Table 2 *Nucleotides with coenzyme function (continued)*

Name	Formula, M_r	Structure	Function
Adenosine 3'-phosphate 5'-phosphosulfate (PAPS) (3'-phosphoadenosine 5'-phosphosulfate)	$C_{21}H_{36}N_7O_{16}P_3S$ 767.54	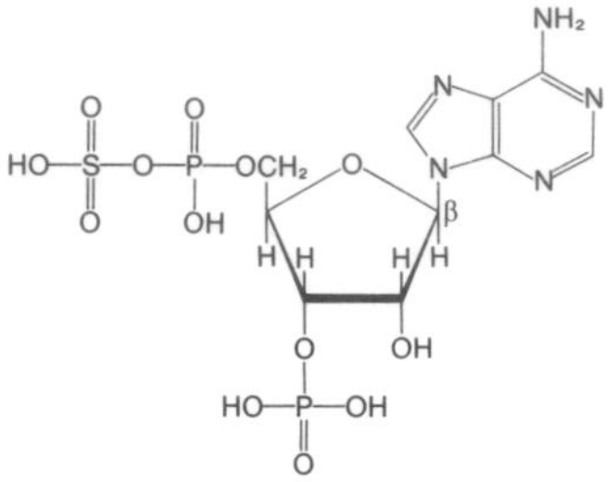	Formed from APS (see previous page) and ATP; sulfate-group donor in the formation of sulfuric-acid esters (such as chondroitin sulfate, heparin, keratan sulfate, steroid sulfates and phenol sulfates)
Adenosine diphosphoglucose	$C_{16}H_{25}N_5O_{15}P_2$ 689.35	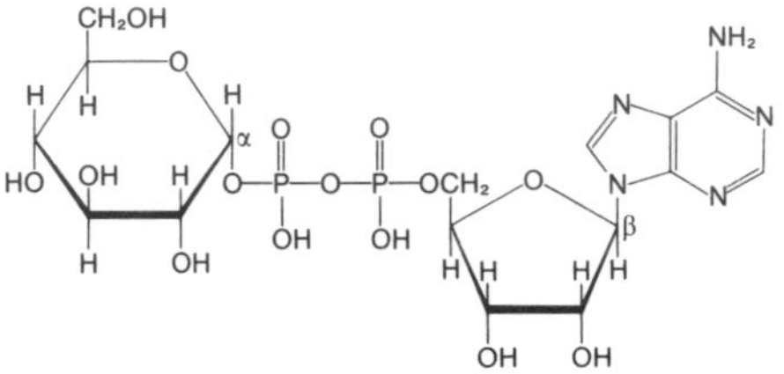	Formation of starch and glycogen

Nucleotides containing guanine

Guanosine 3',5'-phosphate (cyclic guanosine monophosphate [cGMP])	$C_{10}H_{12}N_5O_7P$ 345.21	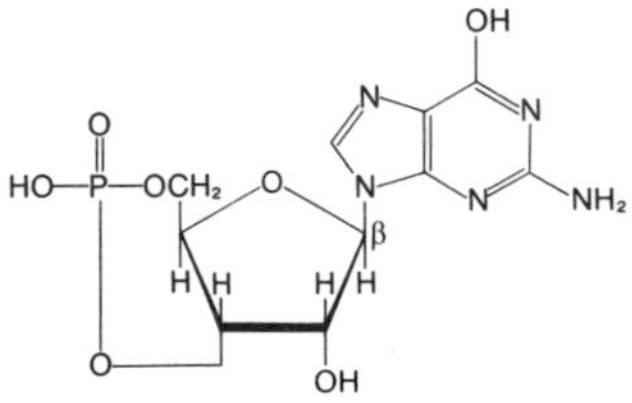	Activates and regulates many metabolic systems. Indirect mediator of the action of hormones (?)
Guanosine diphosphomannose (GDPMan)	$C_{16}H_{25}N_5O_{16}P_2$ 605.35	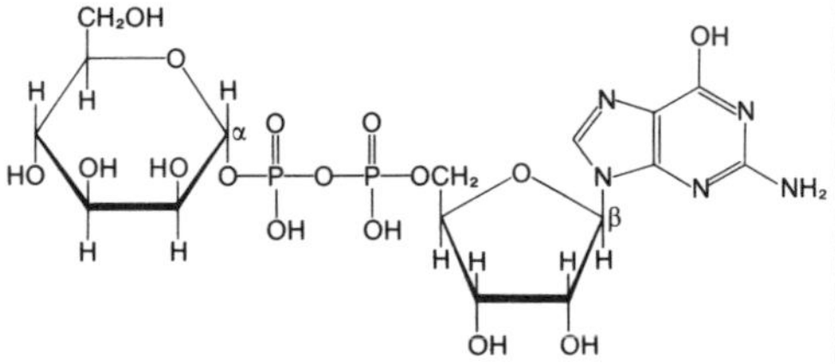	Formation of mannose-containing oligosaccharide chains of glycoproteins and proteoglycans
Guanosine diphospho-L-fucose (GDPFuc)	$C_{16}H_{25}N_5O_{15}P_2$ 589.35	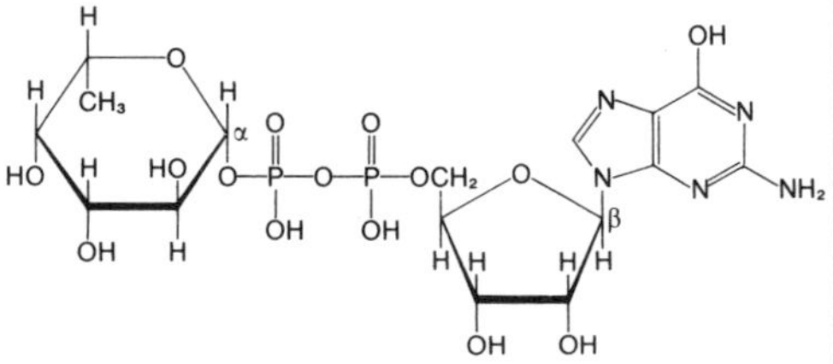	Formation of oligosaccharides in milk; formation of glycoproteins and blood-group substances

Nucleotides containing uracil

Uridine diphosphoglucose (UDPGlc, UDPG)	$C_{15}H_{24}N_2O_{17}P_2$ 566.31	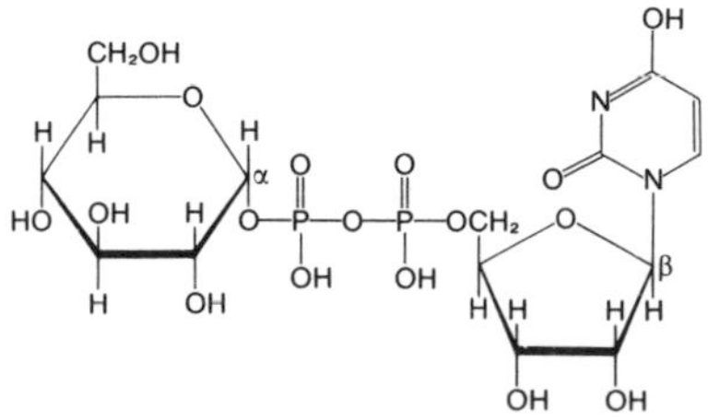	Intermediate in the reversible conversion of glucose to galactose (page 91); formation of glycogen and starch

Table 2   *Nucleotides with coenzyme function (continued)*

Name	Formula, M_r	Structure	Function
Uridine diphosphogalactose (UDPGal)	$C_{15}H_{24}N_2O_{17}P_2$ 566.31	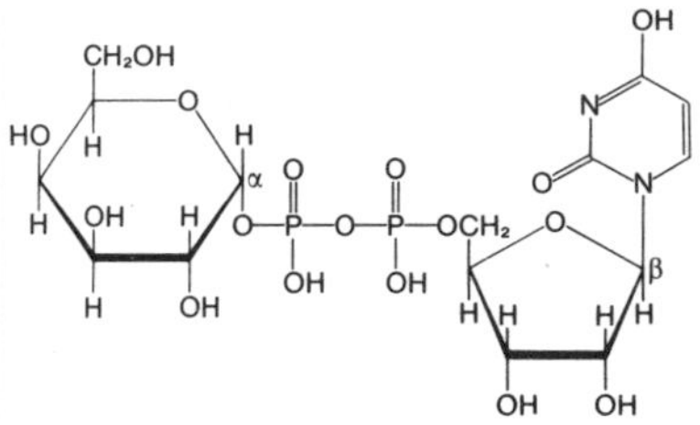	Intermediate in the reversible conversion of glucose to galactose; formation of lactose, cerebrosides, chondroitin sulfate, keratan sulfate
Uridine diphosphogalactose sulfate	$C_{15}H_{24}N_2O_{20}P_2S$ 646.36	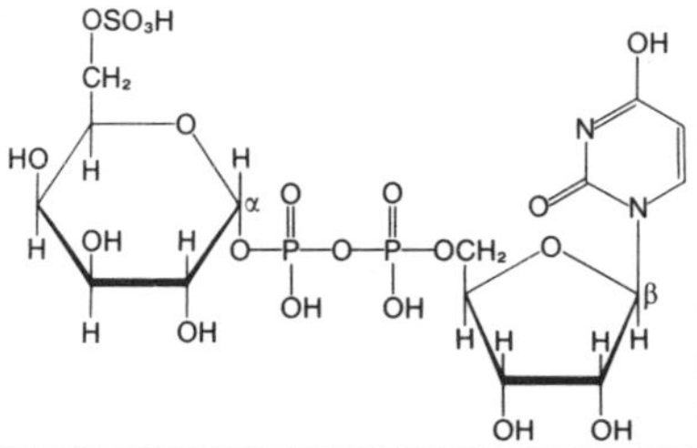	Formation of keratan sulfate (?)
Uridine diphosphoglucosamine (UDPGlcN)	$C_{15}H_{25}N_3O_{16}P_2$ 565.32	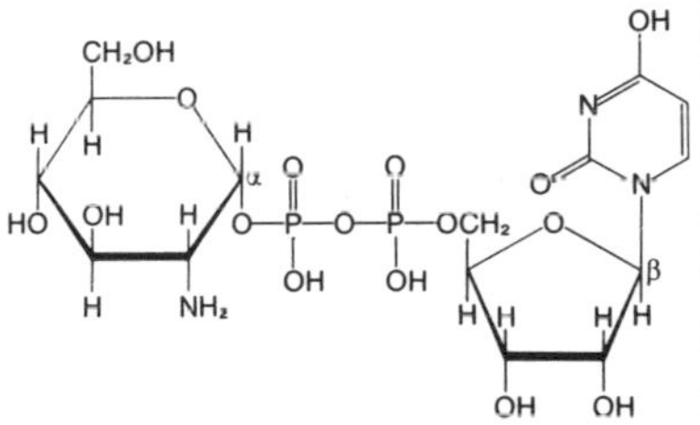	Formation of proteoglycans and glycoproteins
Uridine diphospho-N-acetyl-glucosamine (UDPGlcNAc)	$C_{17}H_{27}N_3O_{17}P_2$ 607.36	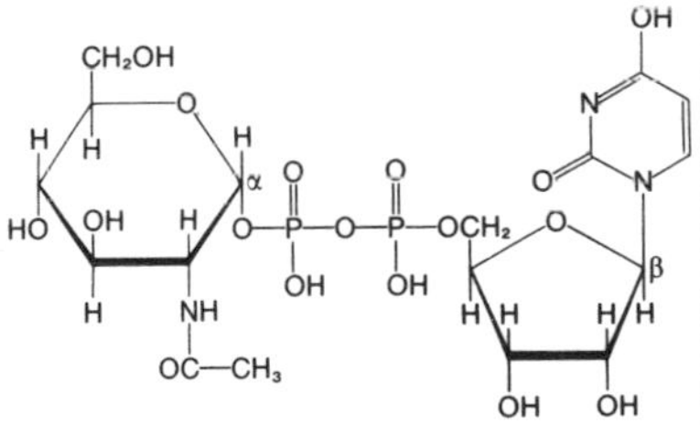	Formation of chitin, hyaluronic acid, heparin and other proteoglycans, as well as glycoproteins
Uridine diphospho-N-acetyl-glucosamine sulfate	$C_{17}H_{27}N_3O_{20}P_2S$ 687.42	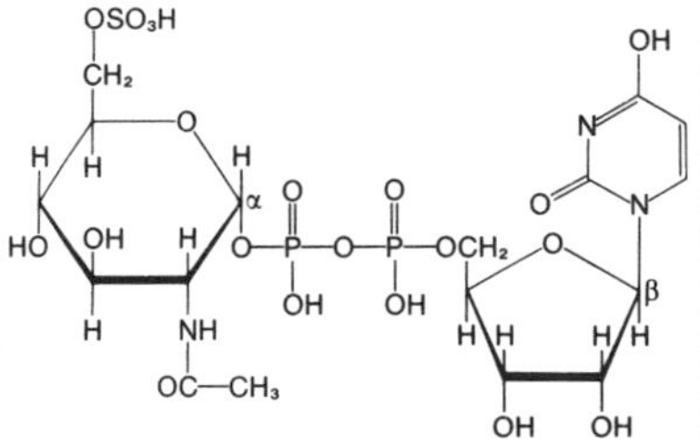	Formation of keratan sulfate (?)
Uridine diphosphoglucuronic acid (UDPGlcA, UDPGlcUA)	$C_{15}H_{22}N_2O_{18}P_2$ 580.29	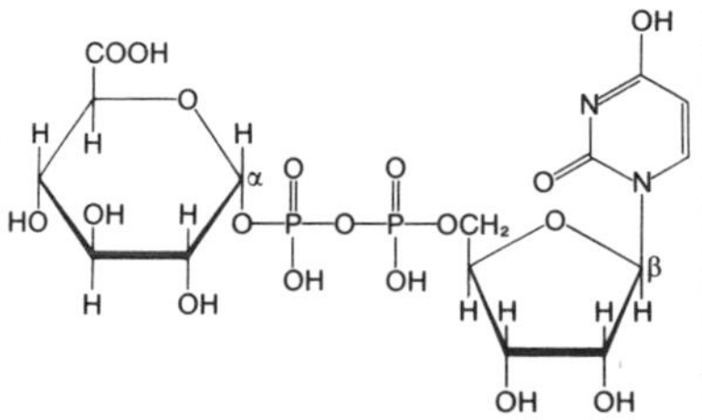	Formation of hyaluronic acid, heparin, chondroitin sulfate; glucuronide conjugation of bilirubin and xenobiotics

Table 2   *Nucleotides with coenzyme function (continued)*

Name	Formula, M_r	Structure	Function
Uridine diphospho-N-acetyl-galactosamine (UDPGalNAc)	$C_{17}H_{27}N_3O_{17}P_2$ 607.36	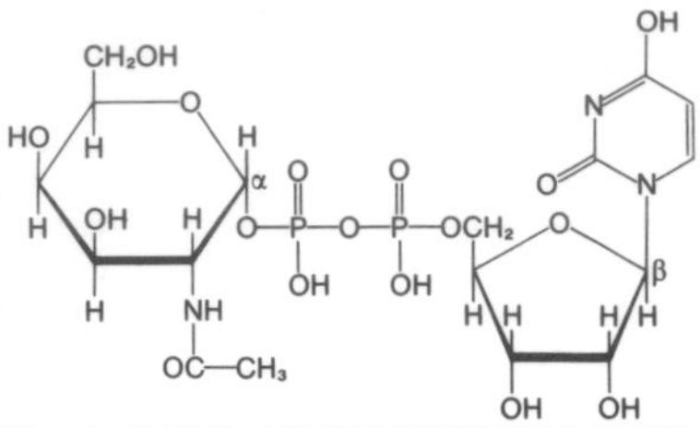	Formation of chondroitin sulfate and dermatan sulfate
Uridine diphospho-N-acetyl-galactosamine sulfate	$C_{17}H_{27}N_3O_{20}P_2S$ 687.42	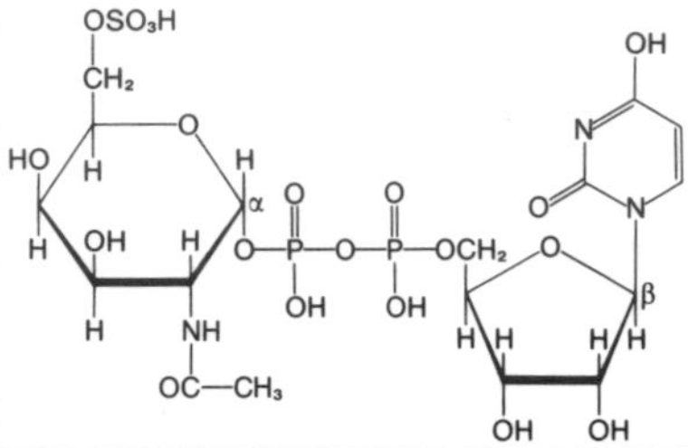	Formation of chondroitin sulfate and dermatan sulfate (?)
Uridine diphosphogalacturonic acid (UDPGalA, UDPGalUA)	$C_{15}H_{22}N_2O_{18}P_2$ 580.29	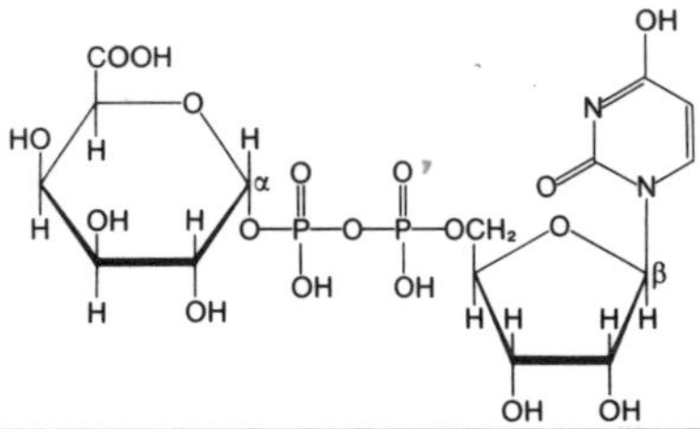	Formation of pectin
Uridine diphosphoiduronic acid (UDPIdoA, UDPIdoUA)	$C_{15}H_{22}N_2O_{18}P_2$ 580.29	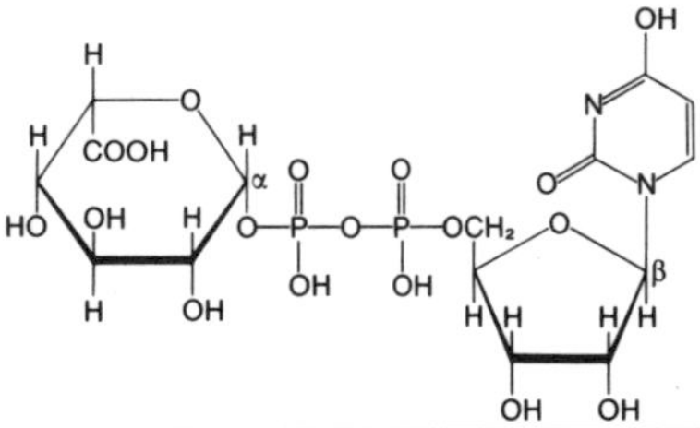	Formation of heparin and of dermatan sulfate (?)
Uridine diphospho-N-acetyl-muramic acid	$C_{20}H_{32}N_3O_{22}P_2$ 728.43	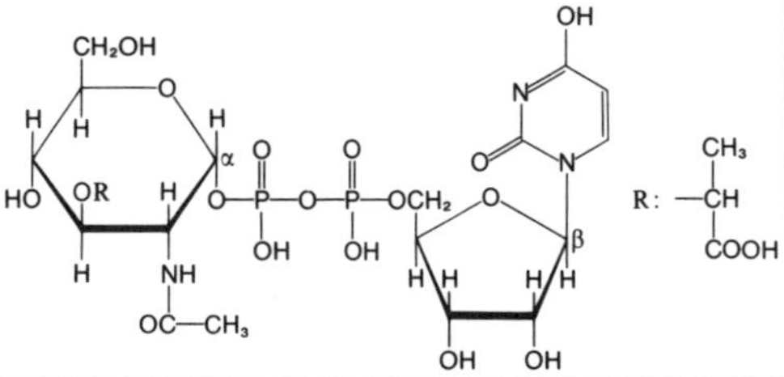 R: —CH with CH₃ and COOH	Formation of peptidoglycans in cell walls of primarily gram-positive bacteria
		Nucleotides containing thymine	
Thymidine diphosphorhamnose	$C_{16}H_{26}N_2O_{15}P_2$ 548.33	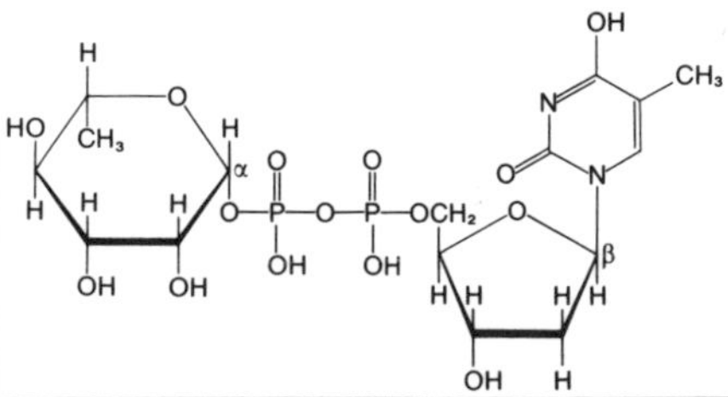	Formation of 0 antigens on surface of bacteria

Table 2 *Nucleotides with coenzyme function (continued)*

Name	Formula, M_r	Structure	Function
		Nucleotides containing cytosine	
Cytidine diphosphoglycerol	$C_{12}H_{21}N_3O_{13}P_2$ 477.26	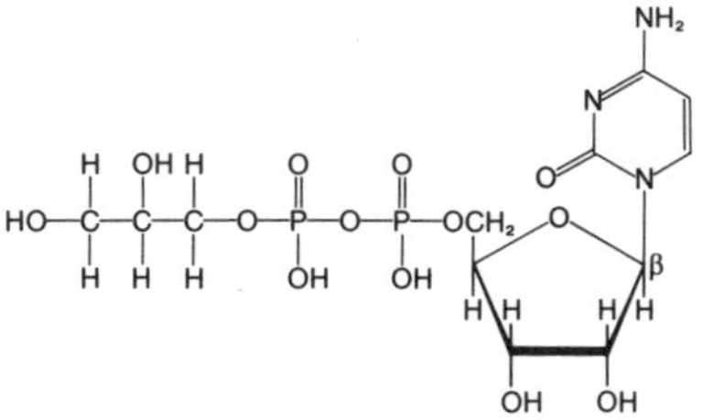	Formation of teichoic acid in membranes and cell walls of gram-positive bacteria
Cytidine diphosphoribitol	$C_{14}H_{25}N_3O_{15}P_2$ 537.31	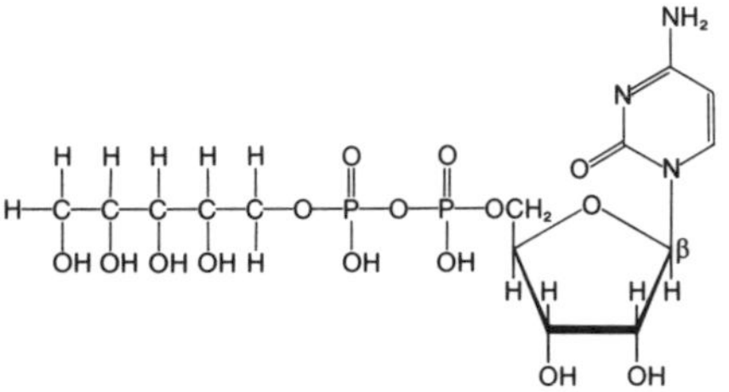	Formation of teichoic acid in membranes and cell walls of gram-positive bacteria
Cytidine diphosphocholine	$C_{11}H_{20}N_4O_{11}P_2$ 446.25	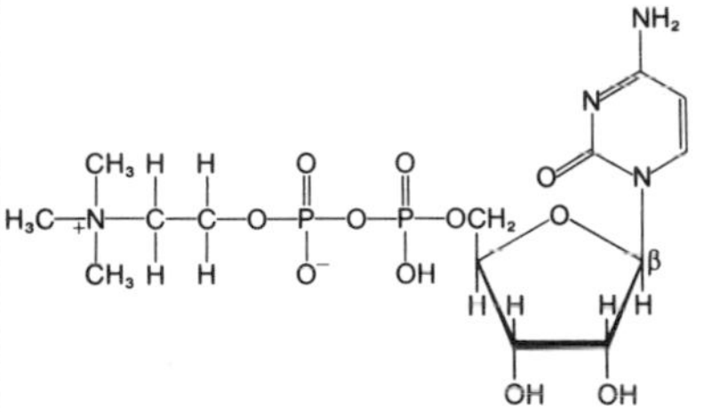	Formation of phosphatidyl-choline and choline plasmalogen
Cytidine diphosphoethanol-amine	$C_{14}H_{26}N_4O_{11}P_2$ 488.33	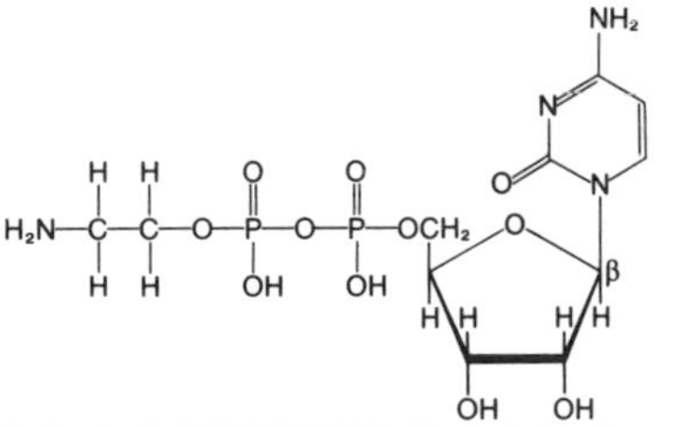	Formation of phosphatidyl-ethanolamine and ethanol-amine plasmalogen
Cytidine diphosphodiacyl-glycerol	–	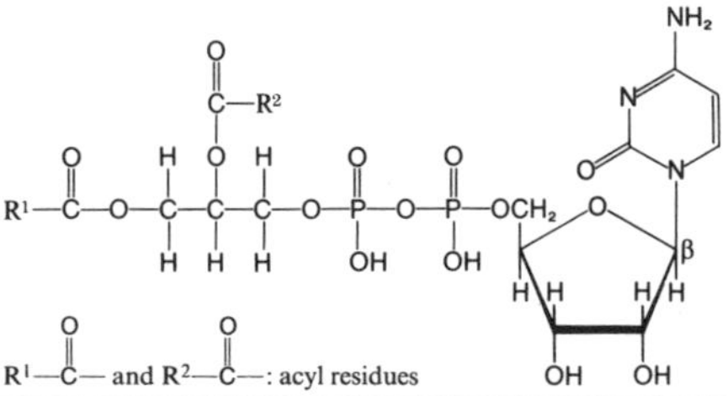 R^1—C— and R^2—C—: acyl residues	Formation of phosphatidyl-inositol, phosphatidylglycerol and cardiolipin
Cytidine monophosphate N-acetylneuraminic acid (CMPNeuAc)	$C_{20}H_{31}N_4O_{16}P$ 614.46	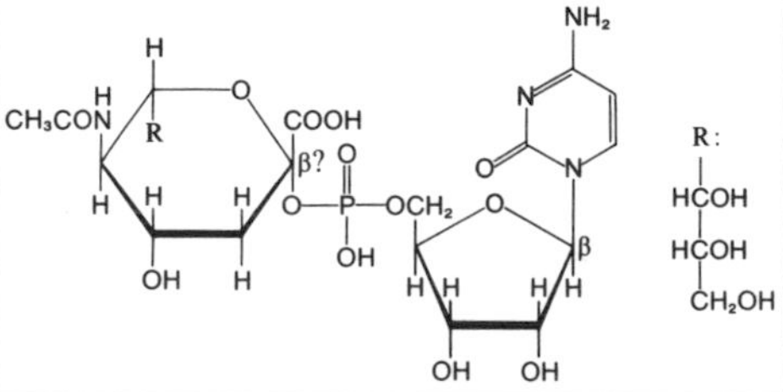	Formation of oligosaccharides of milk, as well as mucopro-teins, glycolipids and sialic acid

Partial sequences of RNA and DNA

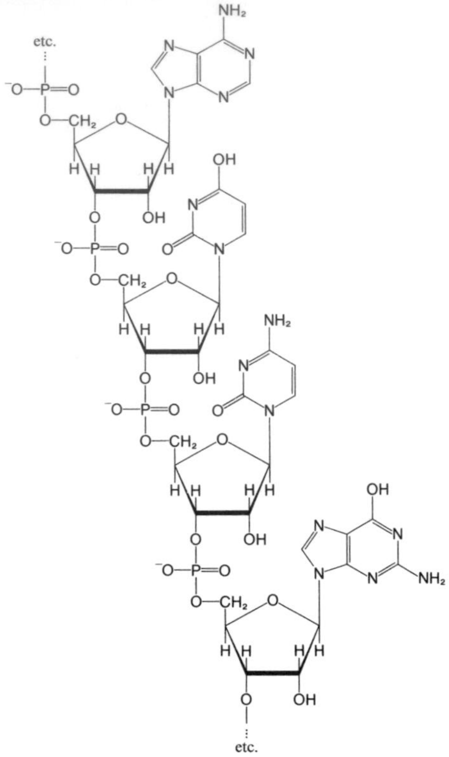

Ribonucleic acid

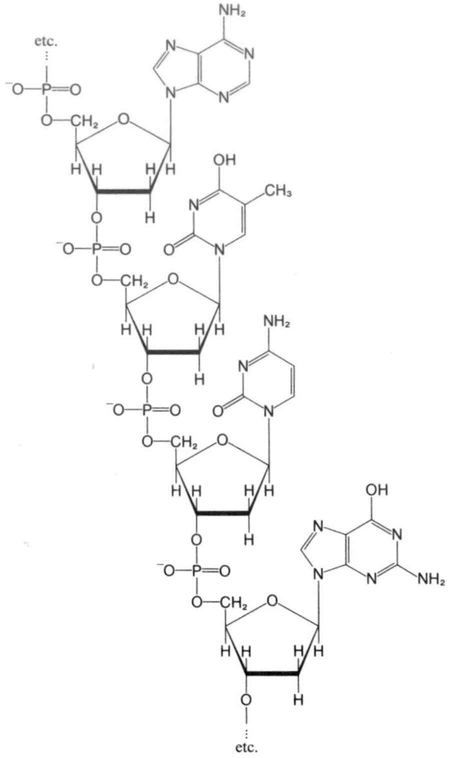

Deoxyribonucleic acid

Vitamins – originally divided into a fat-soluble group A and a water-soluble group B – are essential food components that are organic in nature but which, in contrast to the essential amino acids of the human body, are needed only in small amounts. According to this definition, ascorbic acid (page 12) and nicotinic acid can be only conditionally classed with the vitamins.

The ubiquinones and pteridines are related to the vitamins but are synthesized by human beings.

The water-soluble vitamins are coenzymes or constituents thereof.

The mechanism of action of the fat-soluble vitamins on the molecular level is largely unknown. In the form of its hydroxylated metabolites, vitamin D acts in a steroid-hormone-like manner, and also a part of the reactions of vitamin A compounds seems to take place via nuclear receptors such as are known for steroid hormones. Vitamin E acts primarily as a lipid antioxidant and free-radical scavenger.

Vitamin K is required as cosubstrate in the posttranslational 4-carboxylation of glutamic residues in peptides (see chapter on 'Coenzyme Function', page 75).

Vitamin requirement and vitamin-deficiency symptoms in human beings

Vitamin	Daily requirement[1]	Deficiency symptom
Fat-soluble vitamins		
A Retinol	1.0 mg	Night blindness, xerophthalmia
D Calciferol	5 µg (synthesis in the skin)	Rickets
E Tocopherol	10 mg	Muscle weakness, hemolysis
K Menaquinone.	1.4 mg (synthesis in the body by intestinal bacteria)	Delayed blood coagulation
Q Ubiquinone	Synthesis in the body	–
Water-soluble vitamins		
B_1 Thiamin	1.4 mg	Polyneuritis (beriberi)
B_2 Riboflavin	1.7 mg	Dermatitis
Niacin	18 mg (synthesis in the body from tryptophan)	Pellagra
Pantothenic acid	7 mg	Paresthesias and cramps in the extremities
Folacin	0.4 mg	Megaloblastic anemia
Pteridine (biopterin)	Synthesis in the body	–
B_6 Pyridoxal	2.2 mg	Dermatitis, psychic disturbances
B_{12} Cobalamin	3.0 µg	Pernicious anemia, neuropathy
C Ascorbic acid	60 mg	Scurvy
H Biotin	0.15 mg (synthesis in the body by intestinal bacteria)	Dermatitis

Reference   [1] *Geigy Scientific Tables*, 8th ed., Volume 1, CIBA-GEIGY Limited, Basle, 1981, page 235.

Structure and properties of vitamin A and related compounds

Vitamin A

Compound	Formula, M_r	Structure	Occurrence	Activity
		(old numbering) (new numbering*) all-*trans*-Retinol		
Retinol (all-*trans*) (vitamin A₁, axerophthol)	$C_{20}H_{30}O$ 286.46		Milk, eggs, liver (mainly fish liver)	100
3′-*cis*-Retinol (9-*cis*, iso-a)	$C_{20}H_{30}O$ 286.46	Like all-*trans*-retinol, but with double bond at C-3′ in the *cis* configuration	Liver, kidneys, plasma	21
5′-*cis*-Retinol (11-*cis*, neo-b)	$C_{20}H_{30}O$ 286.46	Like all-*trans*-retinol, but with double bond at C-5′ in the *cis* configuration	Retina	23
7′-*cis*-Retinol (13-*cis*, neo-a)	$C_{20}H_{30}O$ 286.46	Like all-*trans*-retinol, but with double bond at C-7′ in the *cis* configuration	Fish liver	75
Retinylphosphate	$C_{20}H_{31}O_4P$ 366.44		Cell membranes of mammals	–

*Recommendation of the IUPAC–IUB Commission on Biochemical Nomenclature, *Europ. J. Biochem.*, **2**, 1 (1967).   °Relative activity, referred to retinol (= 100).

(Vitamin A, continued)

Compound	Formula, M_r	Structure	Occurrence	Activity
β-Mannosylretinyl phosphate	$C_{26}H_{40}O_9P$ 527.57	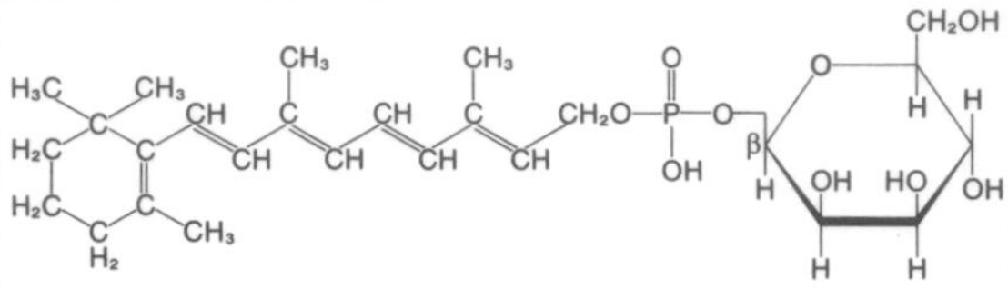 *(structure)*	Intermediate in oligosaccharide synthesis: mannose donor for glycoproteins	–
Retinal (all-*trans*) (retinaldehyde, retinene, vitamin A₁ aldehyde)	$C_{20}H_{28}O$ 284.45	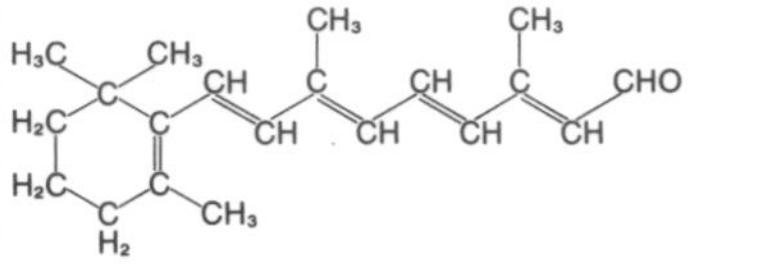 *(structure)*	Citrus fruits, green vegetables, liver, eggs, retina	91
5'-*cis*-Retinal (11-*cis*, neo-b)	$C_{20}H_{28}O$ 284.45	Like all-*trans*-retinal, but double bond at C-5' in the *cis* configuration	Retina	48
7'-*cis*-Retinal (13-*cis*, neo-a)	$C_{20}H_{28}O$ 284.45	Like all-*trans*-retinal, but double bond at C-7' in the *cis* configuration	–	93
Retinoic acid (all-*trans*) (vitamin A₁ acid)	$C_{20}H_{28}O_2$ 300.44	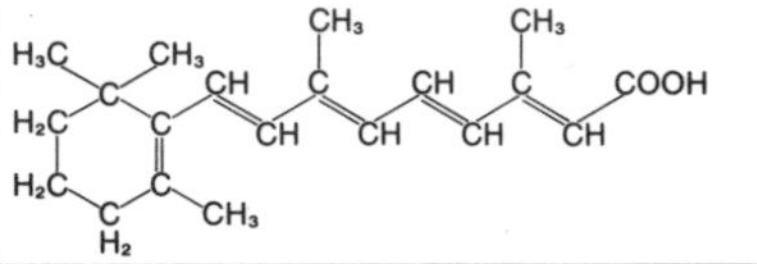 *(structure)*	Liver, kidneys (intermediate)	~65
3-Dehydroretinol (vitamin A₂)	$C_{20}H_{28}O$ 284.45	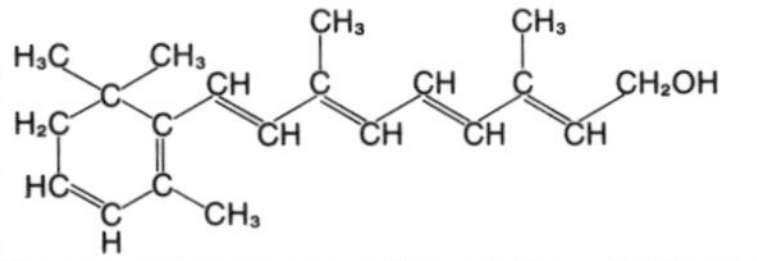 *(structure)*	Human skin and liver of freshwater fish	40
3-Dehydroretinal (3-dehydroretinaldehyde, vitamin A₂ aldehyde, retinene-2)	$C_{20}H_{26}O$ 282.43	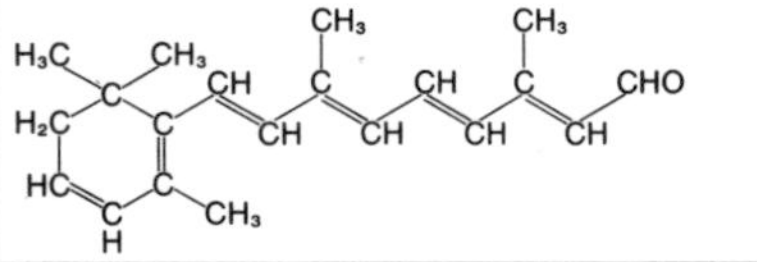 *(structure)*	Retina of freshwater fish	–
3-Dehydroretinoic acid (vitamin A₂ acid)	$C_{20}H_{26}O_2$ 298.43	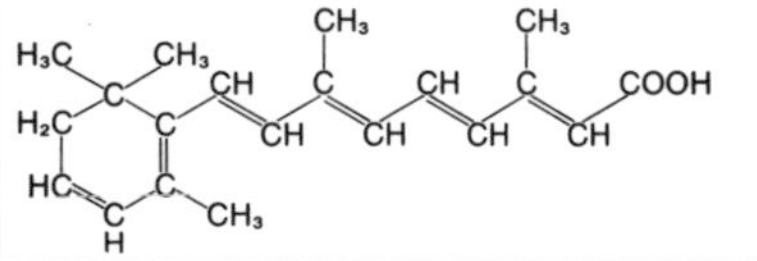 *(structure)*	–	–

Relative activity, referred to retinol (= 100).

Carotenes

Compound	Formula, M_r	Structure	Occurrence	Activity*
α-Carotene	$C_{40}H_{56}$ 536.88	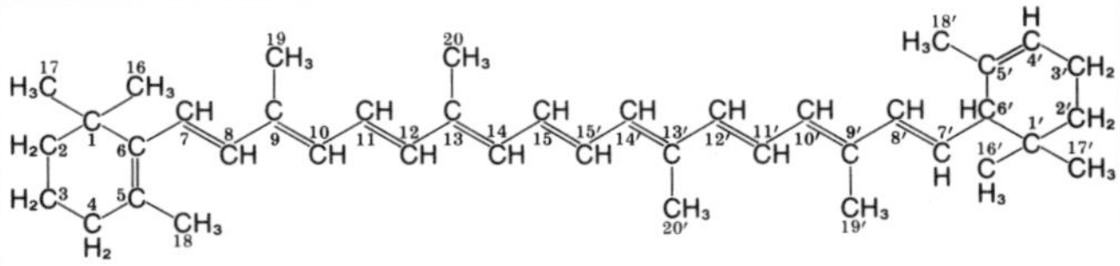 *(structure)*	Palm oil, mountain ash berries	55
β-Carotene	$C_{40}H_{56}$ 536.88	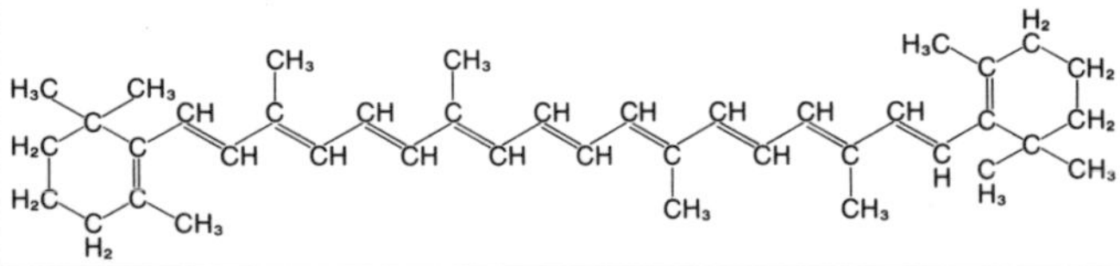 *(structure)*	Plants, fruits	100

*Theoretical relative activity, referred to retinol (= 100); under physiological conditions only about half.

(Carotenes, continued)

Compound	Formula, M_r	Structure	Occurrence	Activ-ity*
γ-Carotene	$C_{40}H_{56}$ 536.88	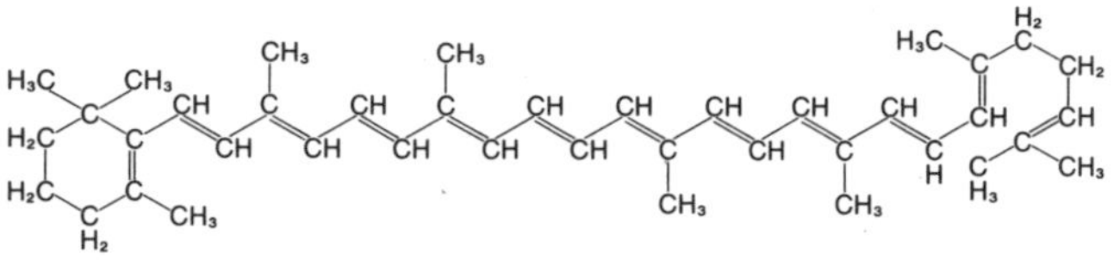	Bacteria, fungi, plants	43
Cryptoxanthin (3-hydroxy-β-carotene)	$C_{40}H_{56}O$ 552.89	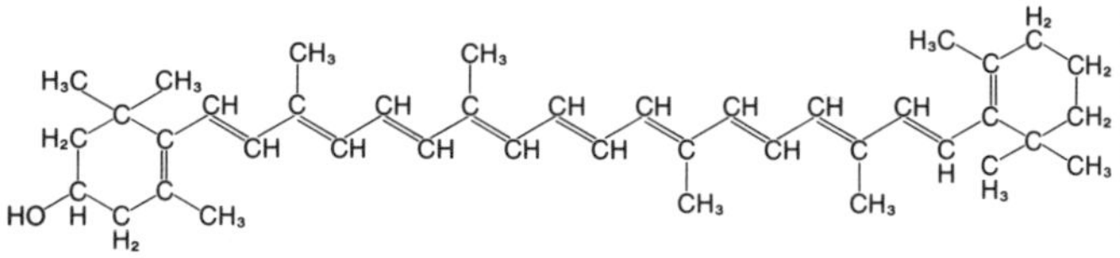	Corn, some fruits	57
β-Zeacarotene	$C_{40}H_{60}$ 540.91	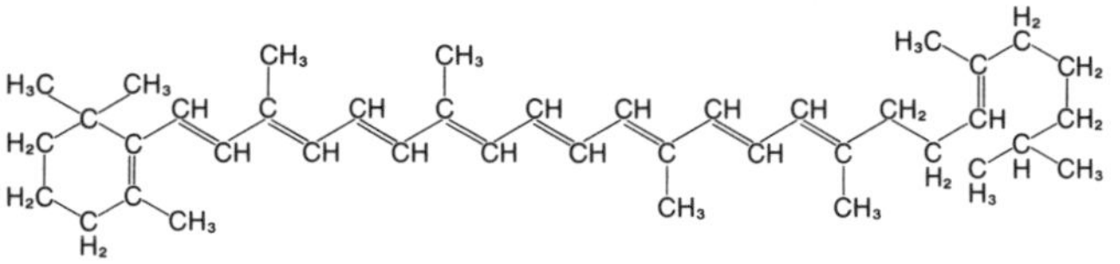	Corn	50

*Theoretical relative activity, referred to retinol (= 100); under physiological conditions only about half.

Structure and properties of vitamin D and its metabolites

Compound	Formula, M_r	Structure	Occurrence and activity
Ergosterol (provitamin D$_2$, 5,7,22-ergostatrien-3β-ol)	$C_{28}H_{44}O$ 396.66	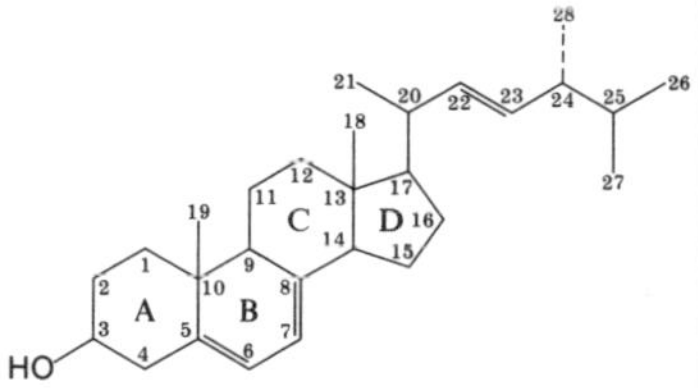	In fungi, also in yeasts. No activity
Ergocalciferol* [vitamin D$_2$, ercalciol*, 9,10-seco-5,7,10(19)22-ergosta-tetraen-3β-ol]	$C_{28}H_{44}O$ 396.66	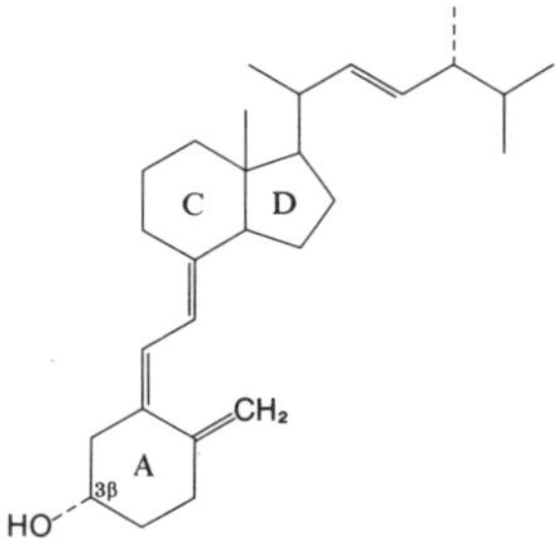	In vegetable oils. Formed by irradiation of ergosterol. Antirachitic activity; slight bone-mobilizing activity
7-Dehydrocholesterol (provitamin D$_3$, 5,7-cholestadien-3β-ol)	$C_{27}H_{44}O$ 384.64	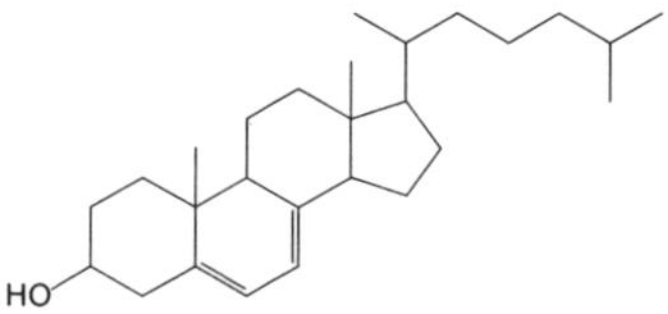	In mollusks, higher animals and in man (primarily in epidermis and dermis). No activity

*Names recommended by the IUPAC–IUB Joint Commission on Biochemical Nomenclature, *Europ. J. Biochem.*, **124**, 223 (1982).

(Structure and properties of vitamin D and its metabolites, continued)

Compound	Formula, M_r	Structure	Occurrence and activity
Cholecalciferol* [vitamin D$_3$, calciol*, 9,10-seco-5,7,10(19)-cholesta-trien-3β-ol]	C$_{27}$H$_{44}$O 384.64	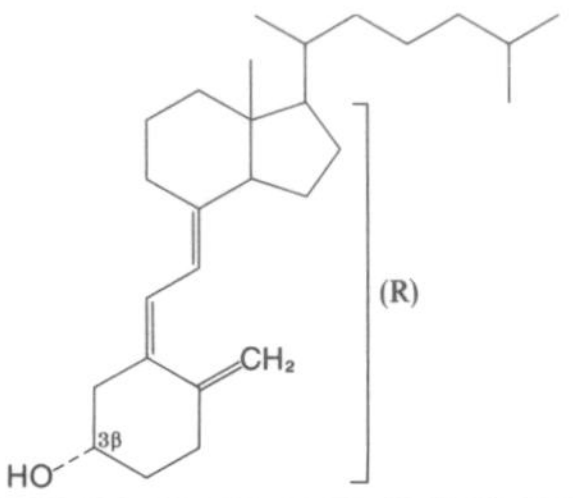 (R)	In fish-liver oils, egg yolk, milk fat. Antirachit-ic and bone-mobilizing activity
Vitamin D$_4$ [22,23-dihydroercalciol*, (24S)-methylcalciol*, 9,10-seco-24α-methyl-5,7,10(19)-cholestatrien-3β-ol]	C$_{28}$H$_{46}$O 398.67	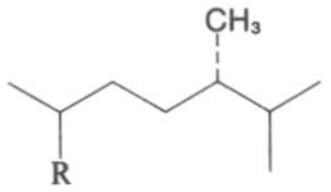 CH$_3$ R: see Cholecalciferol	Formation from 22,23-dihydroergosterol. Syn-thetic; does not occur in nature. Antirachitic activity
Vitamin D$_5$ [(24S)-ethylcalciol*, 9,10-seco-24α-ethyl-5,7,10(19)-cholestatrien-3β-ol]	C$_{29}$H$_{48}$O 412.70	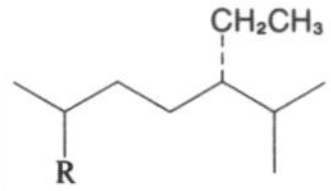 CH$_2$CH$_3$ R: see Cholecalciferol	Formation from 7-dehydrositosterol. Slight antirachitic activity
Vitamin D$_6$ [(22E)-(24R)-ethyl-22,23-didehydrocalciol*, 9,10-seco-24α-ethyl-5,7,10(19)22-cholestatetraen-3β-ol]	C$_{29}$H$_{46}$O 410.68	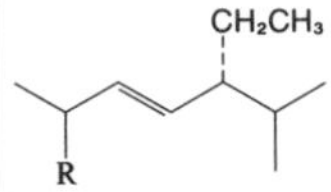 CH$_2$CH$_3$ R: see Cholecalciferol	Formation from 7-dehydrostigmasterol. No antirachitic activity
Vitamin D$_7$ [9,10-seco-24β-methyl-5,7,10(19)-cholestatrien-3β-ol]	C$_{28}$H$_{46}$O 398.67	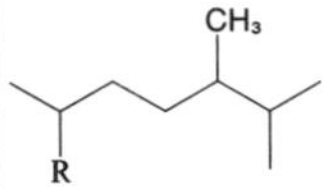 CH$_3$ R: see Cholecalciferol	Formation from 7-dehydrocampesterol. Slight antirachitic activity
25-Hydroxycholecalciferol (calcidiol*, calcifediol)	C$_{27}$H$_{44}$O$_2$ 400.64	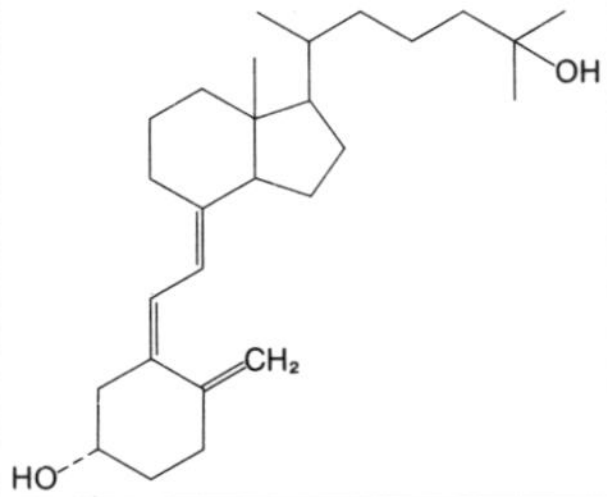	Formation in the liver from cholecalciferol by a microsomal hydroxylation system. Antira-chitic activity 1.4 × D$_3$
1α,25-Dihydroxycholecalciferol (calcitriol*)	C$_{27}$H$_{44}$O$_3$ 416.64	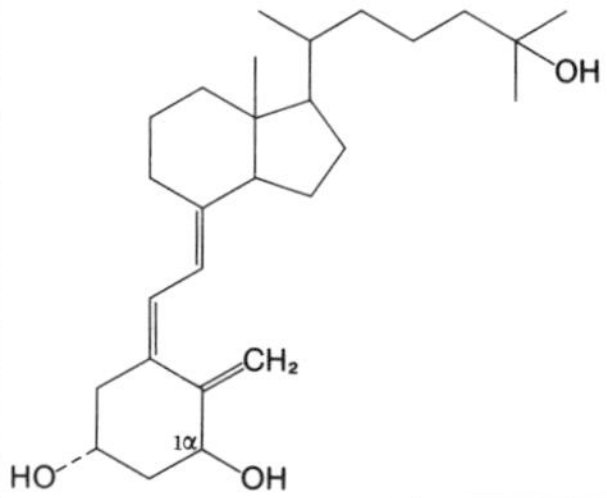	Formed in the kidneys. Activity 3 to 5 times higher than that of cholecalciferol
24(R),25-Dihydroxycholecalciferol [(24R)-hydroxycalcidiol*]	C$_{27}$H$_{44}$O$_3$ 416.64	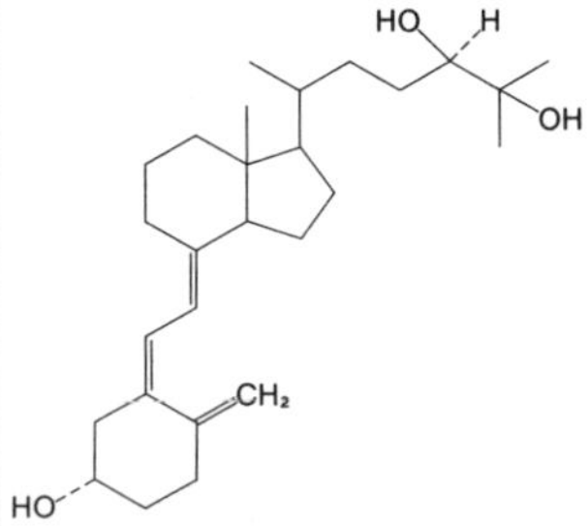	Formed in the kidneys

*Names recommended by the IUPAC IUB Joint Commission on Biochemical Nomenclature, *Europ. J. Biochem.*, **124**, 223 (1982).

Structure and properties of vitamin E and related compounds

Compound	Formula, M_r	Structure	Most important occurrence	Activity*
		Tocols 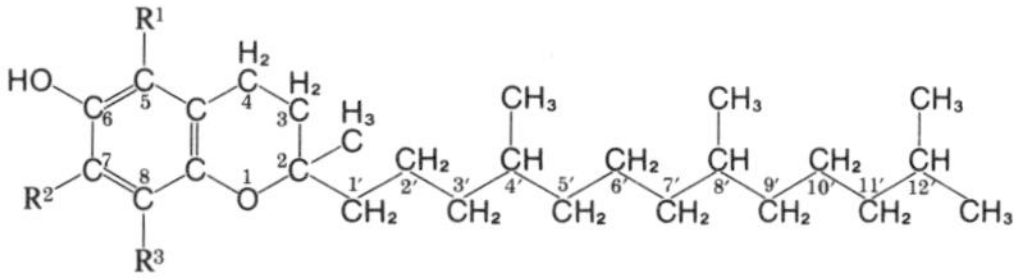		
Tocol	$C_{26}H_{44}O_2$ 388.64	R^1: H R^2: H R^3: H	Synthetic	Inactive
8-Methyltocol (δ-tocopherol)	$C_{27}H_{46}O_2$ 402.67	R^1: H R^2: H R^3: CH₃	Soybean oil	1
5,8-Dimethyltocol (β-tocopherol)	$C_{28}H_{48}O_2$ 416.69	R^1: CH₃ R^2: H R^3: CH₃	Wheat-germ oil	33
7,8-Dimethyltocol (γ-tocopherol)	$C_{28}H_{48}O_2$ 416.69	R^1: H R^2: CH₃ R^3: CH₃	Corn oil	10
5,7,8-Trimethyltocol (α-tocopherol)	$C_{29}H_{50}O_2$ 430.72	R^1: CH₃ R^2: CH₃ R^3: CH₃	Corn oil, wheat-germ oil, etc., adipose tissue	100
		Tocotrienols 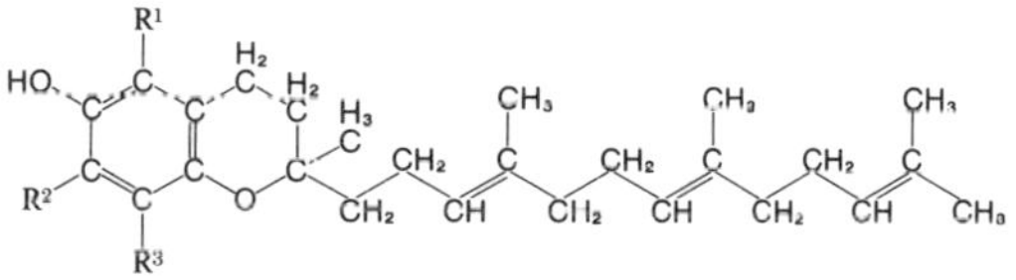		
8-Methyltocotrienol (δ-tocotrienol)	$C_{27}H_{40}O_2$ 396.62	R^1: H R^2: H R^3: CH₃	Palm oil	—
5,8-Dimethyltocotrienol (ε-tocopherol, β-tocotrienol)	$C_{28}H_{42}O_2$ 410.65	R^1: CH₃ R^2: H R^3: CH₃	Wheat	5
7,8-Dimethyltocotrienol (γ-tocotrienol, plastochromatonol-3)	$C_{28}H_{42}O_2$ 410.65	R^1: H R^2: CH₃ R^3: CH₃	Rice	—
5,7,8-Trimethyltocotrienol (ζ₁-tocopherol, α-tocotrienol, tocochromanol-3)	$C_{29}H_{44}O_2$ 424.67	R^1: CH₃ R^2: CH₃ R^3: CH₃	Wheat	30
		Tocopherol-like compounds		
α-Tocopherolquinone (α-tocopherylquinone)	$C_{29}H_{50}O_3$ 446.72	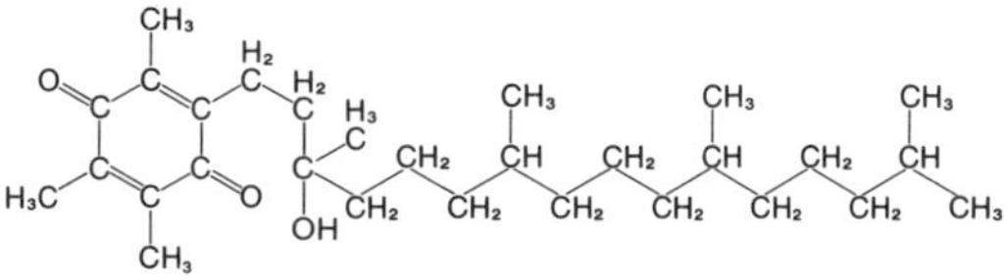	Green plants. Oxidation product of α-tocopherol	Active
Ubiquinone-n ($n = 6$–10) (coenzyme Q)	—	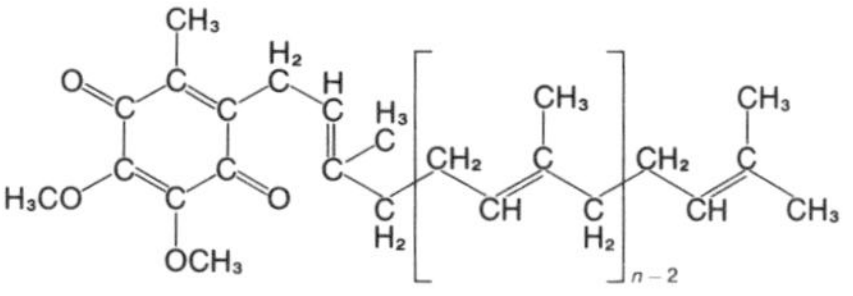	Ubiquinone-9(ubiquinone-45, coenzyme Q₉): leaves Ubiquinone-10 (ubiquinone-50, coenzyme Q₁₀): liver, yeast	—

*Relative activity in antisterility test in rats.

(Structure and properties of vitamin E and related compounds, continued)

Compound	Formula, M_r	Structure	Most important occurrence	Activity
Ubichromenol-$(n-1)$ $n = 10$: Ubichromenol-9	–	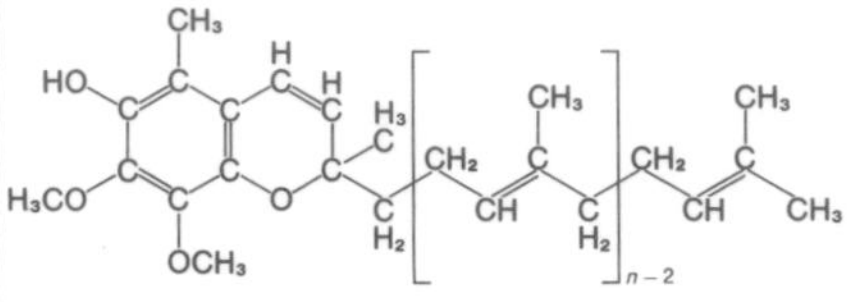	Like the corresponding ubiquinones	Active
Plastoquinone-n $(n = 9)$	$C_{53}H_{82}O_2$ 751.23	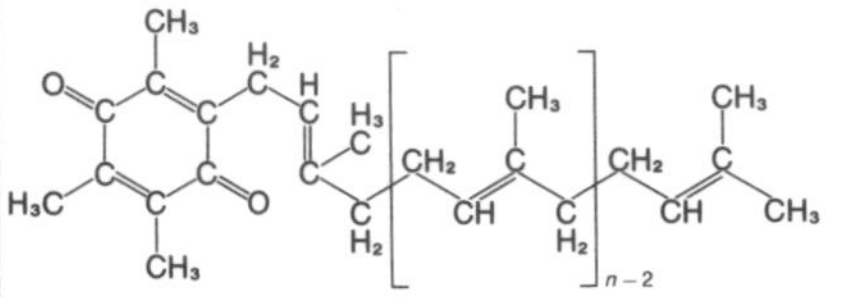	Chloroplasts	–

Structure and properties of vitamin K and related compounds

Compound	Formula, M_r	Structure	Occurrence and function	Activity*
Menadione (vitamin K_3, 2-methyl-1,4-naphtho-quinone)	$C_{11}H_8O_2$ 172.18	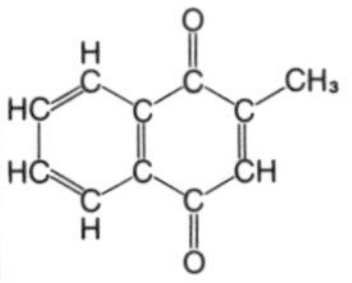	Provitamin	~ 100
Phylloquinone [vitamin $K_1(20)$, 2-methyl-3-phytyl-1,4-naphtho-quinone]	$C_{31}H_{46}O_2$ 450.70	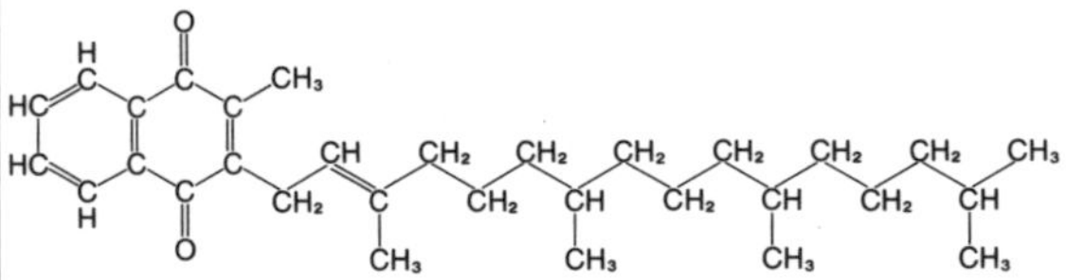	In green plants, tomatoes, some species of bacteria. Coenzyme of post-translational carboxylation of glutamic acid to the 4-carboxyglutamic acid (page 77) in prothrombin, coagulation factors VII, IX and X, osteocalcin of bones, as well as in other proteins, primarily of the kidney	100
Menaquinone-n $(n = 4–13)$ $n = 6$: Vitamin $K_2(30)$	$C_{41}H_{56}O_2$ 580.89		In animals and bacteria Function like phylloquinone	100
$n = 7$: Vitamin $K_2(35)$	$C_{46}H_{64}O_2$ 649.01		Function like phylloquinone	70
$n = 9$: Vitamin $K_2(45)$	$C_{56}H_{80}O_2$ 785.25		In mycobacteria	–
Dicoumarol	$C_{19}H_{12}O_6$ 336.30	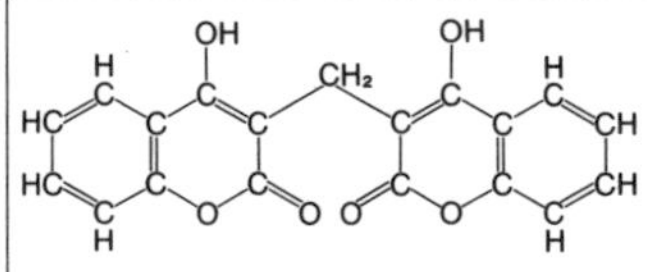	In plants. Vitamin K antagonist	–
Warfarin	$C_{19}H_{16}O_4$ 308.33	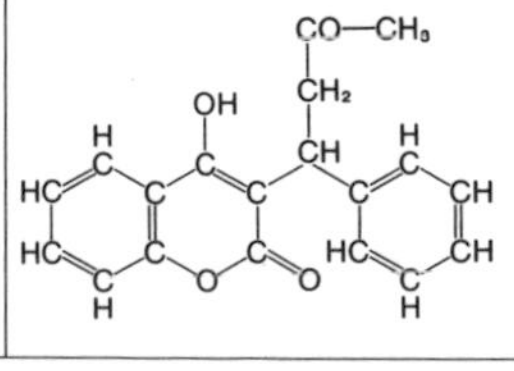	Synthetic. Anticoagulant. Inhibits reduction of the epoxide form of vitamin K in the vitamin K cycle (page 77)	–

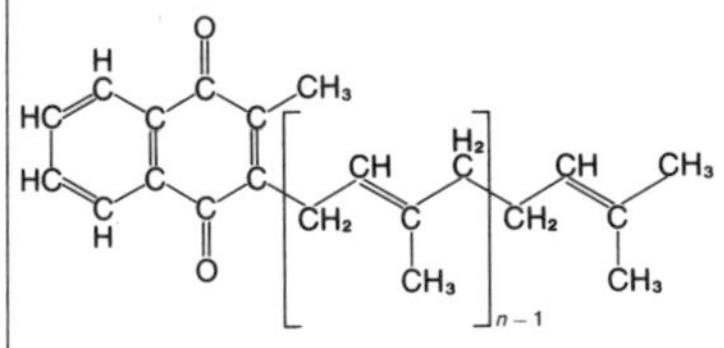

*Relative activity, determined in chicks with vitamin K deficiency.

Structure and properties of the vitamins of the B group

Thiamin

Compound	Formula, M_r	Structure	Occurrence and function
Thiamin (vitamin B$_1$, aneurin)	Cation: C$_{12}$H$_{17}$N$_4$OS 265.36 Hydrochloride: C$_{12}$H$_{18}$N$_4$OSCl$_2$ 337.27	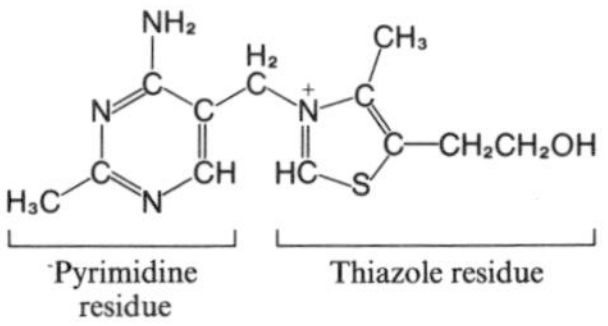 Pyrimidine residue — Thiazole residue	In plants. Active after enzymatic conversion to thiamin diphosphate
Thiamin diphosphate (diphosphothiamin [DPT])	C$_{12}$H$_{18}$N$_4$O$_7$P$_2$S 424.31	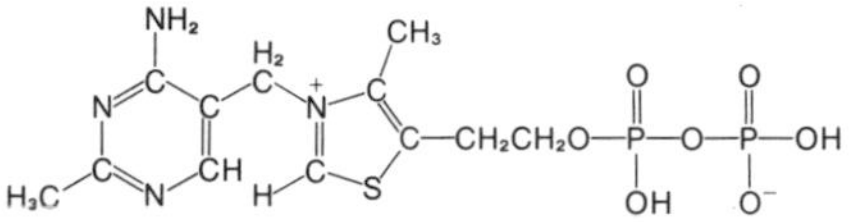	In animals. For function see page 80
Thiamin triphosphate	C$_{12}$H$_{19}$N$_4$O$_{10}$P$_3$S 504.28	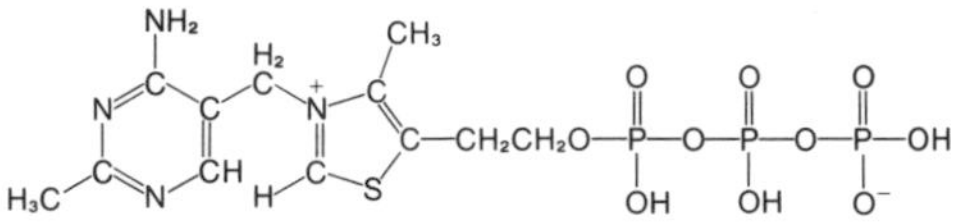	In animal tissues. Formation from thiamin diphosphate and ATP. Involved in neural conduction and transmission (?)
2-Hydroxyethylthiamin diphosphate	C$_{14}$H$_{22}$N$_4$O$_8$P$_2$S 468.37	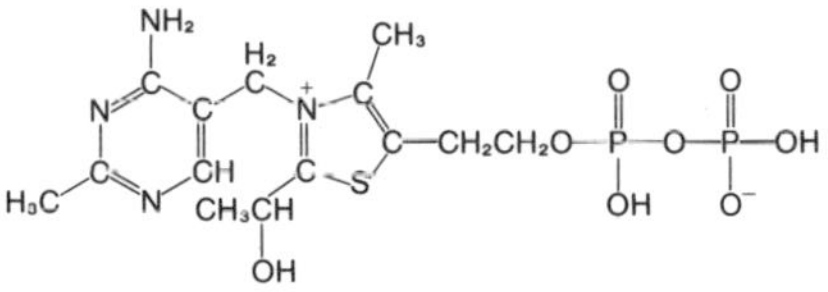	In microorganisms (in *Escherichia coli* making up 60% of the total thiamin). Active acetaldehyde (see page 76)

Riboflavin

Compound	Formula, M_r	Structure	Occurrence and function
Riboflavin [vitamin B$_2$, lactoflavin, 7,8-dimethyl-10-(D-ribityl)-isoalloxazine]	C$_{17}$H$_{20}$N$_4$O$_6$ 376.37	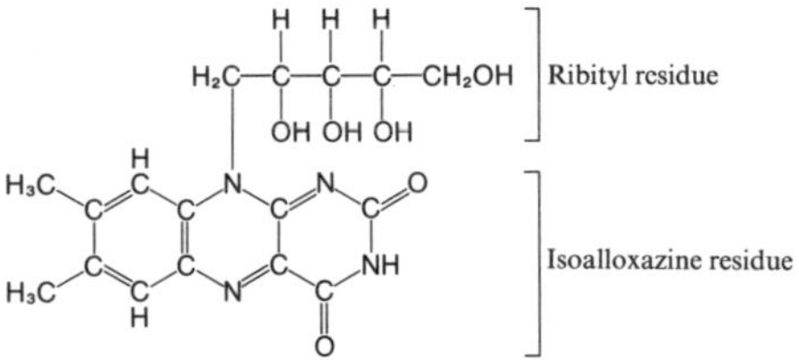 Ribityl residue — Isoalloxazine residue	Constituent of FMN and FAD. In free form in some microorganisms. Makes up 0.5–2% of total riboflavin in animal organs
Flavin mononucleotide (FMN) (riboflavin 5'-phosphate)	C$_{17}$H$_{21}$N$_4$O$_9$P 456.35	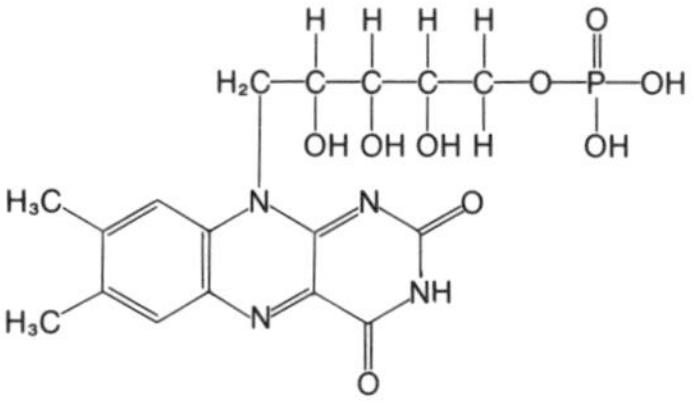	As active group of flavoproteins in microorganisms, plants and animals. Makes up 5–30% of the total riboflavin in animal organs
Flavin adenine dinucleotide (FAD)	C$_{27}$H$_{33}$N$_9$O$_{15}$P$_2$ 785.56	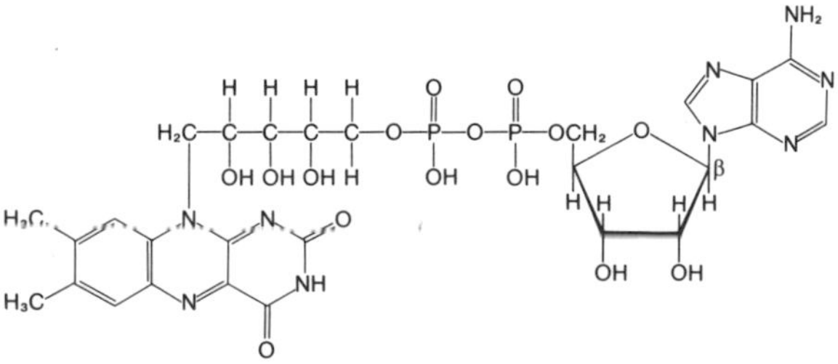	As active group of flavoproteins in microorganisms, plants and animals. Makes up 70–90% of the total riboflavin in animal organs

Vitamin B$_6$

Compound	Formula, M_r	Structure	Occurrence and activity
Pyridoxine (pyridoxol, adermine)	$C_8H_{11}NO_3$ 169.18 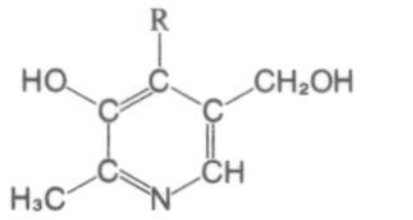	R: CH$_2$OH	Particularly in plant tissues. Vitamin B$_6$ activity for higher animals and yeast; only slight activity for bacteria
Pyridoxamine	$C_8H_{12}N_2O_2$ 168.20 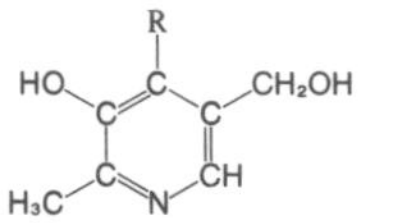	R: CH$_2$NH$_2$	Particularly in animal tissues. Vitamin B$_6$ activity for microorganisms and higher animals
Pyridoxal	$C_8H_9NO_3$ 167.17	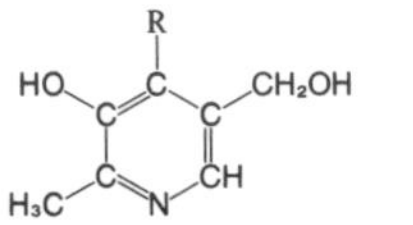 R: CHO	Particularly in animal tissues. Vitamin B$_6$ activity for microorganisms and higher animals
Pyridoxamine phosphate	$C_8H_{13}N_2O_5P$ 248.18 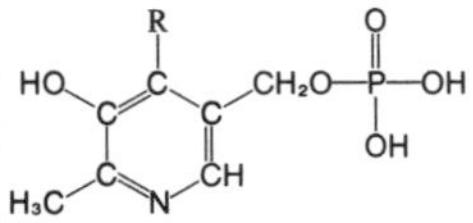	R: CH$_2$NH$_2$	Coenzyme in transaminations (page 80)
Pyridoxal phosphate (codecarboxylase)	$C_8H_{10}NO_6P$ 247.15	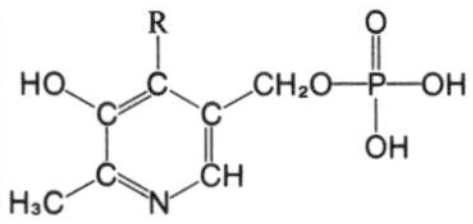 R: CHO	Particularly in muscle. Coenzyme in decarboxylations, transaminations, racemizations (page 80)
Pyridoxic acid (4-pyridoxic acid)	$C_8H_9NO_4$ 183.17	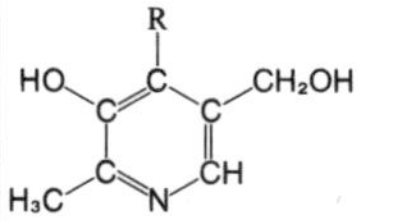 R: COOH	Particularly in urine (breakdown product). No vitamin B$_6$ activity

Niacin

Compound	Formula, M_r	Structure	Occurrence and function
Nicotinic acid (niacin, pyridine-3-carboxylic acid, vitamin PP)	$C_6H_5NO_2$ 123.11	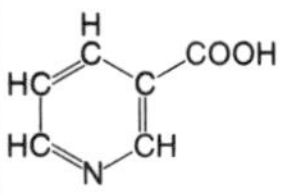	In plant and animal tissues. Constituent of NAD and NADP
Nicotinamide (nicotinic acid amide, niacinamide, pyridine-3-carboxylic acid amide, vitamin PP)	$C_6H_6N_2O$ 122.13	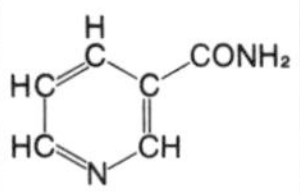	In plant and animal tissues. Constituent of NAD and NADP
Nicotinamide adenine dinucleotide (NAD)	$C_{21}H_{27}N_7O_{14}P_2$ 663.43	See page 54	In all animal and plant cells. Coenzyme of many dehydrogenases
Nicotinamide adenine dinucleotide phosphate (NADP)	$C_{21}H_{28}N_7O_{17}P_3$ 743.41	See page 54	In all animal and plant cells. Coenzyme of many dehydrogenases

Pantothenic acid

Compound	Formula, M_r	Structure	Occurrence and activity
Pantothenic acid [D-(+)-N-(2,4-dihydroxy-3,3-dimethylbutyryl)-β-alanine]	$C_9H_{17}NO_5$ 219.24	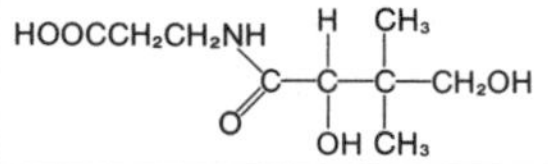 HOOCCH₂CH₂NH ...	Widely distributed in plants and animals. Growth factor for yeasts and many other microorganisms, as well as for all higher animals. Constituent of coenzyme A (page 82)
Panthenyl alcohol (panthenol, N-pantoyl-3-propanolamine)	$C_9H_{19}NO_4$ 205.26	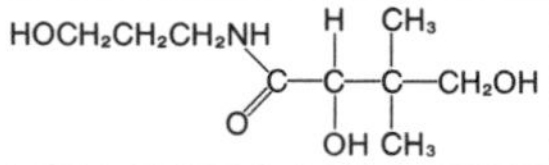 HOCH₂CH₂CH₂NH ...	Synthetic. Shows 86% of activity of pantothenic acid in the chick test
Pantetheine (N-pantothenylcysteamine)	$C_{11}H_{22}N_2O_4S$ 278.37	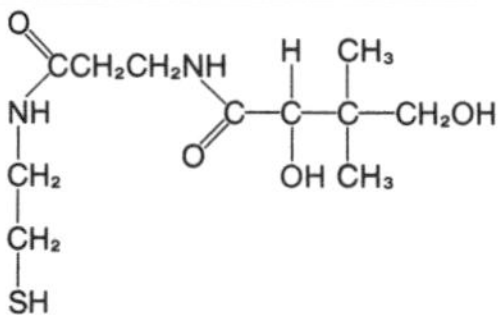 CCH₂CH₂NH ... SH	Growth factor for *Lactobacillus bulgaricus*

Biotin

Compound	Formula, M_r	Structure	Occurrence and activity
Biotin (vitamin H)	$C_{10}H_{16}N_2O_3S$ 244.31	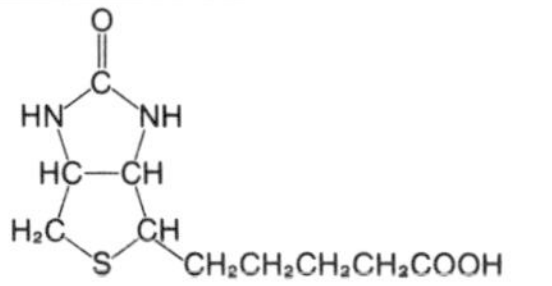 CH₂CH₂CH₂CH₂COOH	In various microorganisms (for example yeasts), in animal tissues (primarily liver), in egg yolk and in plants. Growth factor for many bacteria, protozoa and probably all higher animals
6-N-Biotinyl-L-lysine (biocytin)	$C_{16}H_{28}N_4O_4S$ 372.49	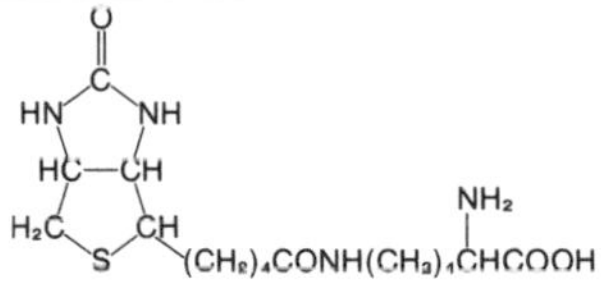 (CH₂)₄CONH(CH₂)₄CHCOOH	In yeasts. Growth factor for various microorganisms
Biotin sulfoxide (AN factor)	$C_{10}H_{16}N_2O_4S$ 260.31	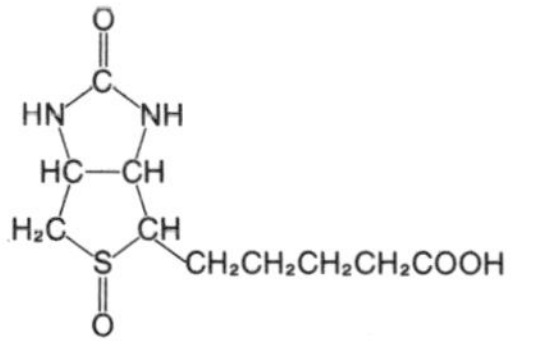 CH₂CH₂CH₂CH₂COOH	Cultures of *Aspergillus niger* and *Phycomyces blakesleeanus*. Growth factor for *Neurospora crassa*
Oxybiotin (oxobiotin)	$C_{10}H_{16}N_2O_4$ 228.25	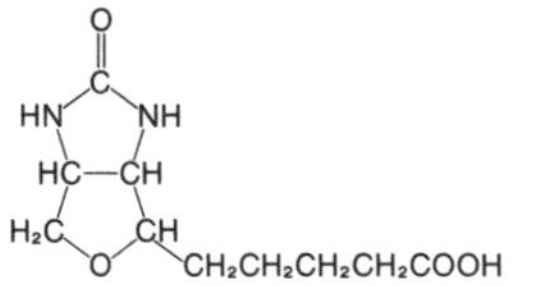 CH₂CH₂CH₂CH₂COOH	Synthetic. Shows 5–30% of activity of biotin

Vitamin B$_{12}$

Compound	Formula, M_r	Structure	Occurrence and activity
Cyanocobalamin (vitamin B$_{12}$, 5,6-dimethylbenzimidazoloylcyanocobamide)	$C_{63}H_{88}N_{14}O_{14}PCo$ 1355.40	See page 83	Can be isolated from many species of bacteria, sewage sludge, activated sludge. No physiological importance in this form for human beings
Aquocobalamin (vitamin B$_{12b}$, 5,6-dimethyl-benzimidazoloylaquacobamide)	$C_{62}H_{90}N_{13}O_{15}PCo$ 1347.38	See page 83	Depot form in the human body (erythrocytes, liver)
Hydroxocobalamin (vitamin B$_{12a}$, 5,6-dimethyl-benzimidazoloylhydroxocobamide)	$C_{62}H_{89}N_{13}O_{15}PCo$ 1346.37		
Adenosylcobalamin (5'-deoxyadenosylcobalamin, coenzyme B$_{12}$)	$C_{72}H_{100}N_{18}O_{17}PCo$ 1579.60	See page 83	In many species of bacteria and in animal tissues (primarily liver). Biochemically active form of vitamin B$_{12}$. Growth-promoting activity for microorganisms and chicks; depot form in the human body (erythrocytes, liver, kidneys); active against pernicious anemia
Methylcobalamin	$C_{63}H_{91}N_{13}O_{14}PCo$ 1344.40	See page 83	In animal tissues (liver). Main component of cobalamins in human plasma. Coenzyme function

Folic acids (biological active forms: folacin)

Compound	Formula, M_r	Structure	Occurrence and activity
		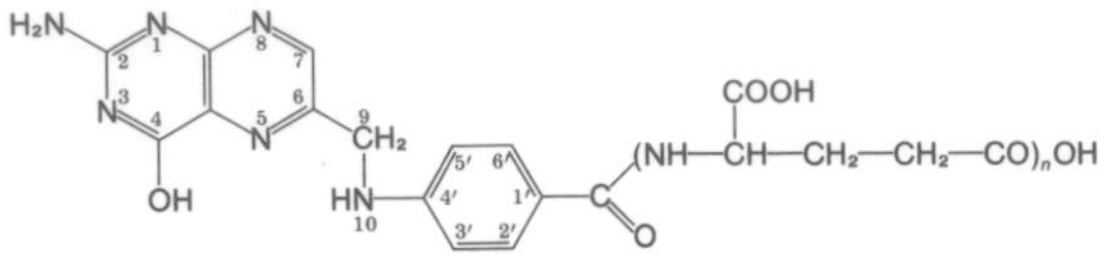 H_2N ... COOH ... $(NH-CH-CH_2-CH_2-CO)_nOH$ (pteroylglutamic acid structure with pteridine ring positions 1–8, OH at 4, CH_2 at 9, HN at 10, benzoyl ring 1′–6′, glutamyl 1″–3″)	
Pteroylglutamic acid (PteGlu) (folic acid, vitamin B_c, N-[2-amino-4-hydroxypteridin-6-ylmethyl]-4′-aminobenzoyl-L-glutamic acid)	$C_{19}H_{19}N_7O_6$ 441.40	$n = 1$	Does not occur in nature in this form. Biochemically inactive. Polyglutamyl derivatives intracellular in all investigated species, such as lichens, algae, yeast, bacteria, bacteriophages, plants and animals
Pteroylpolyglutamic acid (PteGlu$_n$) (conjugated folic acid)	–	$n = 2–8$	
Dihydropteroylglutamic acid (H_2PteGlu$_n$) (dihydrofolic acid [FH$_2$])	–	Reduced at positions 7 and 8	Formed in the biosynthesis of thymidine monophosphate (page 174) and is reduced to FH$_4$
Tetrahydropteroylglutamic acid (H_4PteGlu$_n$) (tetrahydrofolic acid [FH$_4$])	–	Reduced at positions 5, 6, 7 and 8	Coenzyme in one-carbon-group transfer. For active forms see page 84
Methotrexate (4-amino-N^{10}-methylpteroylglutamic acid)	$C_{20}H_{22}N_8O_5$ 466.46	$n = 1$; $-NH_2$ substitution at C-4, $-CH_3$ substitution at N-10	Antagonist of folic acid; inhibits synthesis of purine nucleotides, thymidine monophosphate and thereby that of RNA and DNA. Cytostaticum

Pteridines

Compound	Formula, M_r	Structure	Occurrence and activity
L-*erythro*-6,7-Dihydrobiopterin (quinoid form)	$C_9H_{13}N_5O_3$ 239.23	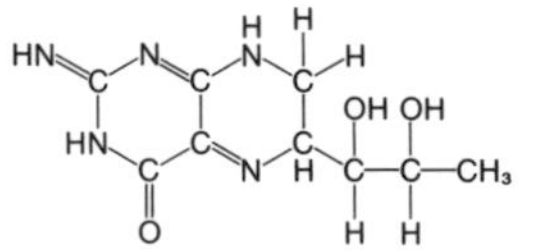 *(structure)*	In the liver. Formed by oxidation of L-*erythro*-5,6,7,8-tetrahydrobiopterin. Regenerated by dihydropteridine reductase to yield tetrahydrobiopterin
L-*erythro*-5,6,7,8-Tetrahydrobiopterin	$C_9H_{15}N_5O_3$ 241.25	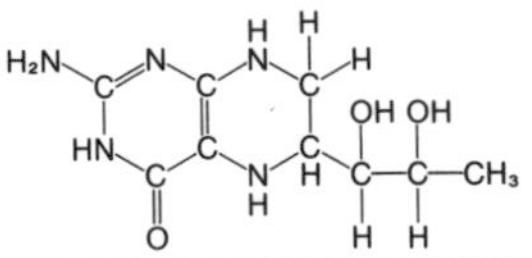 *(structure)*	In the liver. Hydrogen donor in the hydroxylation of aromatic amino acids
L-*erythro*-Biopterin (2-amino-6-[L-*erythro*-1,2-dihydroxypropyl]-4[3H]-pteridinone)	$C_9H_{11}N_5O_3$ 237.22	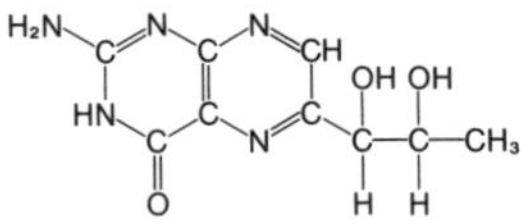 *(structure)*	In urine; also in the royal jelly of queen bee larvae
L-*erythro*-7,8-Dihydrobiopterin	$C_9H_{13}N_5O_3$ 239.23	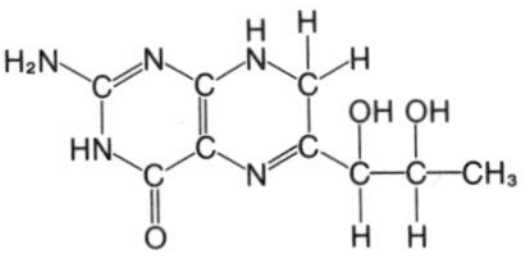 *(structure)*	Inactive form in urine
D-*erythro*-Neopterin	$C_9H_{11}N_5O_4$ 253.22	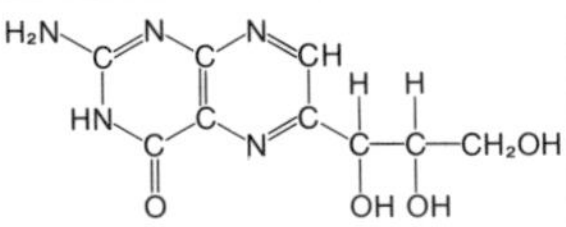 *(structure)*	Inactive form in urine. Excretion increased in patients with malignant diseases
Xanthopterin	$C_6H_5N_5O_2$ 179.14	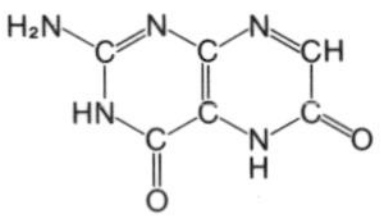 *(structure)*	In urine

Enzymes form a special class of proteins that catalyze biological reactions. Although they participate in the chemical steps of the reactions, they finally emerge unchanged. The rate of enzymatically catalyzed reactions exceeds that of uncatalyzed reactions by factors of 10^8 to 10^{14} for standard states of 1 mol L^{-1}, or even greater factors in more realistic states of 10^{-6} mol L^{-1} [1]. Enzymes do not affect the final equilibrium of reactions.

Enzymes can be isolated using standard methods of protein isolation; their properties are summarized in relevant publications[2, 3], the relative molecular mass ranging between about 13000 and several million.

Since 1963, when the complete amino-acid sequence of bovine ribonuclease was elucidated[4], the primary structure of a whole series of enzymes has become known[5]. In 1969 the first total synthesis of an enzyme – that of ribonuclease – was also achieved[6]. The three-dimensional structure of enzymes in the crystalline state has been determined by X-ray diffraction, thus providing an aid to the understanding of enzyme action. About 60 tertiary enzyme structures have been determined, for example: lysozyme[7], carboxypeptidase A[8, 9], ribonuclease[8], various serine proteinases[10] (chymotrypsin, trypsin, elastase), phosphorylase a[11], phosphorylase b[12], alcohol dehydrogenase[9, 13], and carbonate dehydratase[9].

Nomenclature of enzymes

The name of an enzyme usually specifies both the principal substrate and the reaction catalyzed (e.g. malate dehydrogenase). Many enzymes have, however, been given trivial names which often lead to confusion. To avoid this, the Nomenclature Committee of the International Union of Biochemistry on the Nomenclature and Classification of Enzymes has worked out a systematic nomenclature based on the reaction catalyzed in each case and has classified and numbered the enzymes (pages 72–74)[14]. The trivial names recommended by this commission are used in this book.

Most enzymes – but not, for example, the hydrolases – consist of a protein together with an additional component that cannot readily be removed without denaturing the protein. These components, usually referred to as 'cofactors'[15], can be either organic compounds of low molecular mass or inorganic ions: coenzymes are organic compounds that are indispensable for the enzymatic action. The coenzyme-free enzyme protein is denoted by the term 'apoenzyme', and the coenzyme-containing protein by 'holoenzyme'. As to the coenzymes, a distinction is made between cosubstrates and prosthetic groups. A cosubstrate may be a hydrogen donor (for example NADH + H$^+$) or a group donor (for example ATP) whose catalytic action takes place only by coupling with 2 enzymes in an enzyme system. Group donors are also called 'transfer metabolites'. Prosthetic groups, on the other hand, are tightly bound to the enzyme protein (for example, enzymes containing FAD), and the reaction with 2 different substrates takes place on the enzyme. Inorganic cofactors, also designated 'inorganic complements', are necessary for accomplishing specific enzymatic catalyses, even though differentiation from the 'activators' – which are needed by some enzymes for development of their full catalytic activity – is occasionally difficult.

Multiple forms. The term 'multiple forms of the enzyme …' should be used as a broad term covering all proteins catalyzing the same reaction and occurring naturally in a single species. The term 'isoenzyme' or 'isozyme' should only apply to multiple forms of enzymes arising from genetically determined differences in the primary protein structure and *not* to those derived by modification of the same primary sequence.

Enzyme specificity

Although almost all the reactions of intermediary metabolism are catalyzed by their own characteristic enzymes, few of these enzymes have absolute specificity for the structure of their substrates. Most enzymes can also act on closely related structural analogs of their physiological substrates – although usually with considerable reduction of the reaction rate. Some few enzymes, however, can act on a relatively wide group of substrates.

There are no consistently applicable rules for enzyme specificity because different parts of the substrate molecule seem to be important in different enzyme systems. Thus, although the lipases require an ester bond in their substrates, considerable variation can occur in the structures of the groups adjoining this susceptible bond. On the other hand, chymotrypsin and trypsin require certain configurations in the vicinity of the bond to be acted upon, but the nature of the bond itself can vary. For example, these enzymes hydrolyze peptide bonds in protein substrates but can also hydrolyze ester bonds in certain synthetic substrates (e.g. methyl cinnamate).

A further complication is that those hydrolytic enzymes which can act on several substrates are also usually capable of catalyzing a transfer reaction in which an alcohol or an amine replaces the water. Many of these transfer reactions are unlikely to be of physiological significance because of the prevalence of water molecules under physiological conditions.

Many enzymes show stereochemical specificity[16] in that they act upon only one form of those molecules that possess chirality or *cis-trans* isomerism. A few enzymes, such as esterases, however, attack stereochemical isomers, although usually at reduced rates.

The full catalytic activity of an enzyme depends on the integrity of the secondary and tertiary structure of the folded polypeptide chain. Denaturation of the enzyme with concomitant destruction of the three-dimensional chain structure usually leads to a decrease or loss of catalytic activity. The surface formed by the folding of the chain in the native structure thus enables the enzyme to interact at one or more points with the substrate molecule[1]. Those amino-acid residues that take part in the formation of the enzyme–substrate complex and the catalytic process constitute the 'active site(s)' of the enzyme. The folding of the peptide chain thus brings these amino-acid residues – which may be remote from each other in sequence – into close juxtaposition to form an active site.

Some enzymes – the so-called 'allosteric enzymes'[9, 17] – have 2 (or more) active sites, one for linkage to the substrate and another (allosteric site) for combining with an effector (usually an inhibitor), which regulates the activity of the enzyme. Linkage of the inhibitor to the allosteric site alters the structure of the enzyme protein, so that its active site may no longer be able to combine with the substrate.

Various possibilities for the reaction mechanism of an enzyme have been suggested[18, 19]. The most obvious ones involve the formation of a covalently bound enzyme–substrate complex in which nucleophilic or electrophilic attack on the substrate moiety is facilitated by the enzyme.

Enzyme kinetics[20, 21]

When an enzyme is added to a suitable reaction mixture, a constant reaction rate is obtained after a very short initial lag, which is too short to be determined by measurements made at intervals of 1 minute or longer. Once the maximum reaction rate has been reached, it remains constant, sometimes for several hours, but often only for a few minutes. As the substrate concentration decreases or end products accumulate, the rate of reaction starts to decrease. This

Multiple forms of enzymes

	Reason of multiplicity	Example
Group 1	Genetically independent proteins*	Malate dehydrogenase in mitochondria and cytosol
Group 2	Heteropolymers (hybrids) of 2 or more noncovalently bound polypeptide chains*	Hybrid forms of lactate dehydrogenase
Group 3	Genetic variants (allelozymes)*	Glucose-6-phosphate dehydrogenases in man
Group 4	Conjugated or derived proteins:	
	(a) Proteins conjugated with other groups	Phosphorylase b, glycogen synthase a
	(b) Proteins derived from single polypeptide chains	The family of chymotrypsins arising from chymotrypsinogen
Group 5	Polymers of a single polypeptide subunit	Glutamate dehydrogenase of M_r 1 000 000 and M_r 250 000
Group 6	Conformationally different forms	All allosteric modifications of enzymes

*These classes fall into the category of isoenzymes.

Reference
IUPAC–IUB Commission on Biochemical Nomenclature, *Europ. J. Biochem.*, **82**, 1 (1978).

decline of the reaction rate is difficult to analyze mathematically, so that only the constant reaction rate is usually investigated, as is the case in the following text.

If an enzyme is susceptible to inhibition by excess substrate (see below), the rate may at first increase as the inhibition is relieved by removal of the substrate.

Enzyme concentration. The reaction rate is usually proportional to the enzyme concentration. It is not always possible experimentally to achieve strict linearity because, for example, the enzyme preparation may contain a dissociable activator or inhibitor, or the enzyme may be unstable at low concentrations. Alternatively, at very high enzyme concentrations the reaction may have proceeded so far that the rate has already begun to fall again.

Hydrogen ion concentration. Most enzymes have well-defined pH optima with appreciable activity over a range of only 2–3 pH units. Some enzymes are inhibited by one or other of the buffers in common use. It is therefore often worthwhile to compare the results in one buffer with those obtained in another buffer solution of the same pH range.

Temperature. The rate of an enzyme-catalyzed reaction usually increases by a factor of between 1.5 and 3 for each 10°C increase in temperature. There is, however, an optimum temperature above which further increase reduces the amount of substrate reacting because the enzyme becomes inactivated. In many cases the optimum temperature for short-term experiments (e.g. of 1 hour's duration) is about 50°C. However, since most mammalian enzymes show little inactivation in the presence of their cofactors and substrates at 37°C, this is usually a suitable temperature to study enzymatic reactions. It is not desirable to increase the temperature to the optimum because the rate of enzyme inactivation, and therefore the optimum temperature, is often greatly influenced by slight changes in the experimental conditions.

Substrate concentration. The cellular enzyme concentration is limited, whereas that of the substrate may vary considerably, depending on the environment. At a very low substrate concentration, doubling it will double the probability of collision of the substrate molecules with its enzyme molecules and hence double the concentration of the product. At higher substrate concentrations, however, the reaction rate may become virtually independent of it. This relation can be substantiated theoretically by considering a mechanism such as the following (E: enzyme; S: substrate; ES: enzyme–substrate complex; k_1, k_{-1}, k_2: rate constants of the three reactions; P: reaction products).

$$E + S \underset{k_{-1}}{\overset{k_1}{\rightleftharpoons}} ES \overset{k_2}{\longrightarrow} E + P$$

The constant steady-state reaction rate v is expressed by the following equation:

$$v = \frac{V[S]}{K_m + [S]}$$

V is the maximum reaction rate at high substrate concentrations, [S] is the substrate concentration, and K_m is a quantity termed the 'Michaelis constant' (this is equivalent to the substrate concentration at which the reaction rate is half the maximum and thus has the dimension mol L⁻¹). [S] is strictly the concentration only of the substrate which is not combined with the enzyme, but the amount of enzyme is usually so low that there is virtually no difference between the concentrations of free and total substrate. Mathematically, V is given by $k_2 e$, where e is the total enzyme concentration present. K_m is given by $(k_{-1} + k_2)/k_1$. It is a useful measure of the affinity (combining power) of the substrate for a given enzyme; the smaller K_m, the greater the affinity. Hence knowledge of K_m values makes possible an assessment of the efficiency of individual metabolic reactions in an environment containing different substrates of known concentration.

Enzyme inhibition. Inhibition of the catalyzed reaction always occurs when the active site of the enzyme is disturbed, whether by combining with a compound similar to the substrate or by a nonspecific alteration of the steric configuration of the enzyme protein. In competitive inhibition, a substance which has a structure similar to that of the substrate (substrate analog) binds to the active site. In noncompetitive inhibition, the inhibitor binds not only to the free enzyme, but also to the enzyme–substrate complex, and thus prevents the reaction (the ternary enzyme–substrate–inhibitor complex is also termed 'dead-end complex').

References

[1] LIPSCOMB, W. N., *Ciba Found. Symp.*, NS **60**, 1 (1978).
[2] BOYER, P. D. (Ed.), *The Enzymes*, 3rd ed., Volumes 1–15, Academic Press, New York, 1970–1982.
[3] BARMAN, T. E., *Enzyme Handbook*, 2 volumes, Springer, Berlin, 1969, and Suppl. I, 1974.
[4] SMITH et al., *J. biol. Chem.*, **238**, 227 (1963).
[5] DAYHOFF, M. O., *Atlas of Protein Sequence and Structure*, Volume 5, National Biomedical Research Foundation, Silver Spring, Md., 1972, and Suppl. 1–3, 1973, 1976, 1978.
[6] GUTTE and MERRIFIELD, *J. Amer. chem. Soc.*, **91**, 501 (1969); DENKEWALTER et al., *J. Amer. chem. Soc.*, **91**, 503 (1969).
[7] BLAKE et al., *Nature*, **206**, 757 (1965); BLAKE et al., *Ciba Found. Symp.*, NS **60**, 137 (1978).
[8] BLOW and STEITZ, *Ann. Rev. Biochem.*, **39**, 63 (1970).
[9] LIPSCOMB, W. N., *Ann. Rev. Biochem.*, **52**, 17 (1983).
[10] KRAUT, J., *Ann. Rev. Biochem.*, **46**, 331 (1977).
[11] JOHNSON et al., *J. molec. Biol.*, **90**, 703 (1974).
[12] FLETTERICK and MADSEN, *Ann. Rev. Biochem.*, **49**, 31 (1980).
[13] EKLUND et al., *J. molec. Biol.*, **102**, 27 (1976).
[14] International Union of Biochemistry, *Report of the Commission on Enzymes*, Pergamon Press, Oxford, 1961; International Union of Biochemistry, *Enzyme Nomenclature 1984*, Academic Press, Orlando, Fla., 1984.
[15] HOFFMANN-OSTENHOF, O., *Enzymologie*, Springer, Vienna, 1954.
[16] HANSON, K. R., *Ann. Rev. Biochem.*, **45**, 307 (1976).
[17] MONOD et al., *J. molec. Biol.*, **12**, 88 (1965).
[18] MILDVAN, A. S., *Ann. Rev. Biochem.*, **43**, 357 (1974).
[19] WIMMER and ROSE, *Ann. Rev. Biochem.*, **47**, 1031 (1979).
[20] CORNISCH-BOWDEN, A., *Principles of Enzyme Kinetics*, Butterworth, London, 1976.
[21] FERSHT, A., *Enzyme Structure and Mechanism*, 2nd ed., Freeman, New York, 1985.

Classification and numbering of enzymes[14]

1. Oxidoreductases

To this class belong all enzymes catalyzing oxidoreductions. The substrate oxidized is regarded as hydrogen or electron donor. The classification is based on 'donor:acceptor oxidoreductase'. The recommended name is 'dehydrogenase', wherever this is possible; as an alternative, 'acceptor reductase' can be used. 'Oxidase' is used only in cases where O_2 is an acceptor. Classification is difficult in some cases because of the lack of specificity towards the acceptor.

1.1 Acting on the CH—OH group of donors
    1.1.1   With NAD⁺ or NADP⁺ as acceptor
    1.1.2   With a cytochrome as acceptor
    1.1.3   With O_2 as acceptor
    1.1.5   With a quinone or related compound as acceptor
    1.1.99 With other acceptors

1.2 Acting on the aldehyde or oxo group of donors
    1.2.1   With NAD⁺ or NADP⁺ as acceptor
    1.2.2   With a cytochrome as acceptor
    1.2.3   With O_2 as acceptor
    1.2.4   With a disulfide compound as acceptor
    1.2.7   With an iron–sulfur protein as acceptor
    1.2.99 With other acceptors

1.3 Acting on the CH—CH group of donors
    1.3.1   With NAD⁺ or NADP⁺ as acceptor
    1.3.2   With a cytochrome as acceptor
    1.3.3   With O_2 as acceptor
    1.3.5   With a quinone or related compound as acceptor
    1.3.7   With an iron–sulfur protein as acceptor
    1.3.99 With other acceptors

1.4 Acting on the CH—NH₂ group of donors
    1.4.1   With NAD⁺ or NADP⁺ as acceptor
    1.4.2   With a cytochrome as acceptor
    1.4.3   With O_2 as acceptor
    1.4.4   With a disulfide compound as acceptor
    1.4.7   With an iron–sulfur protein as acceptor
    1.4.99 With other acceptors

1.5 Acting on the CH—NH group of donors
    1.5.1   With NAD⁺ or NADP⁺ as acceptor
    1.5.3   With O_2 as acceptor
    1.5.99 With other acceptors

1.6 Acting on NADH or NADPH
    1.6.1   With NAD⁺ or NADP⁺ as acceptor
    1.6.2   With a cytochrome as acceptor

1.6.4   With a disulfide compound as acceptor
1.6.5   With a quinone or related compound as acceptor
1.6.6   With a nitrogenous group as acceptor
1.6.8   With a flavin as acceptor
1.6.99 With other acceptors

1.7   Acting on other nitrogenous compounds as donors
1.7.2   With a cytochrome as acceptor
1.7.3   With O_2 as acceptor
1.7.7   With an iron–sulfur protein as acceptor
1.7.99 With other acceptors

1.8   Acting on a sulfur group of donors
1.8.1   With NAD^+ or $NADP^+$ as acceptor
1.8.2   With a cytochrome as acceptor
1.8.3   With O_2 as acceptor
1.8.4   With a disulfide compound as acceptor
1.8.5   With a quinone or related compound as acceptor
1.8.7   With an iron–sulfur protein as acceptor
1.8.99 With other acceptors

1.9   Acting on a heme group of donors
1.9.3   With O_2 as acceptor
1.9.6   With a nitrogenous group as acceptor
1.9.99 With other acceptors

1.10 Acting on diphenols and related substances as donors
1.10.1 With NAD^+ or $NADP^+$ as acceptor
1.10.2 With a cytochrome as acceptor
1.10.3 With O_2 as acceptor
1.10.99 With other acceptors

1.11 Acting on H_2O_2 as acceptor

1.12 Acting on hydrogen as donor
1.12.1 With NAD^+ or $NADP^+$ as acceptor
1.12.2 With a cytochrome as acceptor

1.13 Acting on single donors with incorporation of molecular oxygen (oxygenases)
1.13.11 With incorporation of 2 O atoms
1.13.12 With incorporation of 1 O atom (internal monooxygenases or internal mixed function oxidases)
1.13.99 Miscellaneous (requires further characterization)

1.14 Acting on paired donors with incorporation of molecular oxygen
1.14.11 With 2-oxoglutarate as one donor, and incorporation of 1 O atom each into both donors
1.14.12 With NADH or NADPH as one donor, and incorporation of 2 O atoms into one donor
1.14.13 With NADH or NADPH as one donor, and incorporation of 1 O atom
1.14.14 With reduced flavin or flavoprotein as one donor, and incorporation of 1 O atom
1.14.15 With a reduced iron–sulfur protein as one donor, and incorporation of 1 O atom
1.14.16 With reduced pteridine as one donor, and incorporation of 1 O atom
1.14.17 With ascorbate as one donor, and incorporation of 1 O atom
1.14.18 With another compound as one donor, and incorporation of 1 O atom
1.14.99 Miscellaneous (requires further characterization)

1.15 Acting on superoxide radicals as acceptor

1.16 Oxidizing metal ions
1.16.1 With NAD^+ or $NADP^+$ as acceptor
1.16.3 With O_2 as acceptor

1.17 Acting on CH_2 groups
1.17.1 With NAD^+ or $NADP^+$ as acceptor
1.17.3 With O_2 as acceptor
1.17.4 With a disulfide compound as acceptor
1.17.99 With other acceptors

1.18 Acting on reduced ferredoxin as donor
1.18.1 With NAD^+ or $NADP^+$ as acceptor
1.18.6 With N_2 as acceptor
1.18.99 With H^+ as acceptor

1.19 Acting on reduced flavodoxin as donor
1.19.6 With N_2 as acceptor

1.97 Other oxidoreductases

2. Transferases

Transferases are enzymes transferring a group, for example the methyl group or a glycosyl group, from one compound (generally regarded as donor) to another compound (generally regarded as acceptor). The classification is based on the scheme 'donor:acceptor grouptransferase'. The recommended names are normally formed as 'acceptor grouptransferase' or 'donor grouptransferase'. In many cases, the donor is a cofactor (coenzyme), carrying the group to be transferred. The aminotransferases constitute a special case (subclass 2.6).

2.1   Transferring one-carbon groups
2.1.1   Methyltransferases
2.1.2   Hydroxymethyl-, formyl- and related transferases
2.1.3   Carboxyl- and carbamoyltransferases
2.1.4   Amidinotransferases

2.2   Transferring aldehyde or ketone residues

2.3   Acyltransferases
2.3.1   Acyltransferases
2.3.2   Aminoacyltransferases

2.4   Glycosyltransferases
2.4.1   Hexosyltransferases
2.4.2   Pentosyltransferases
2.4.99 Transferring other glycosyl groups

2.5   Transferring alkyl or aryl groups, other than methyl groups

2.6   Transferring nitrogenous groups
2.6.1   Aminotransferases
2.6.3   Oximinotransferases
2.6.99 Transferring other nitrogenous groups

2.7   Transferring phosphorus-containing groups
2.7.1   Phosphotransferases with an alcohol group as acceptor
2.7.2   Phosphotransferases with a carboxy group as acceptor
2.7.3   Phosphotransferases with a nitrogenous group as acceptor
2.7.4   Phosphotransferases with a phosphate group as acceptor
2.7.6   Diphosphotransferases
2.7.7   Nucleotidyltransferases
2.7.8   Transferases for other substituted phosphate groups
2.7.9   Phosphotransferases with paired acceptors

2.8   Transferring sulfur-containing groups
2.8.1   Sulfurtransferases
2.8.2   Sulfotransferases
2.8.3   CoA-transferases

3. Hydrolases

These enzymes catalyze the hydrolysis of various bonds. Some of these enzymes pose problems because they have a very wide specificity, and it is not easy to decide if two preparations described by different authors are the same, or if they should be listed under different entries. While the systematic name always includes 'hydrolase', the recommended name is, in most cases, formed by the name of the substrate with the suffix *-ase*. It is understood that the name of the substrate with this suffix means a hydrolytic enzyme.

3.1   Acting on ester bonds
3.1.1   Carboxylic ester hydrolases
3.1.2   Thiolester hydrolases
3.1.3   Phosphoric monoester hydrolases
3.1.4   Phosphoric diester hydrolases
3.1.5   Triphosphoric monoester hydrolases
3.1.6   Sulfuric ester hydrolases
3.1.7   Diphosphoric monoester hydrolases
3.1.11 Exodeoxyribonucleases producing 5′-phosphomonoesters
3.1.13 Exoribonucleases producing 5′-phosphomonoesters
3.1.14 Exoribonucleases producing other than 5′-phosphomonoesters
3.1.15 Exonucleases active with either ribo- or deoxyribonucleic acids and producing 5′-phosphomonoesters
3.1.16 Exonucleases active with either ribo- or deoxyribonucleic acids and producing other than 5′-phosphomonoesters
3.1.21 Endodeoxyribonucleases producing 5′-phosphomonoesters
3.1.22 Endodeoxyribonucleases producing other than 5′-phosphomonoesters

3.1.25 Site-specific endodeoxyribonucleases: specific for altered bases
3.1.26 Endoribonucleases producing 5'-phosphomonoesters
3.1.27 Endoribonucleases producing other than 5'-phospho-monoesters
3.1.30 Endonucleases active with either ribo- or deoxyribo-nucleic acids and producing 5'-phosphomonoesters
3.1.31 Endonucleases active with either ribo- or deoxyribo-nucleic acids and producing other than 5'-phospho-monoesters

3.2 Glycosidases
3.2.1 Hydrolyzing O-glycosyl compounds
3.2.2 Hydrolyzing N-glycosyl compounds
3.2.3 Hydrolyzing S-glycosyl compounds

3.3 Acting on ether bonds
3.3.1 Thioether hydrolases
3.3.2 Ether hydrolases

3.4 Acting on peptide bonds (peptide hydrolases)
3.4.11 2-Aminoacylpeptide hydrolases
3.4.13 Dipeptide hydrolases
3.4.14 Dipeptidylpeptide hydrolases
3.4.15 Peptidyldipeptide hydrolases
3.4.16 Serine carboxypeptidases
3.4.17 Metallocarboxypeptidases
3.4.18 Cysteine carboxypeptidases
3.4.19 Omega peptidases
3.4.21 Serine proteinases
3.4.22 Cysteine proteinases
3.4.23 Aspartic proteinases
3.4.24 Metalloproteinases
3.4.99 Proteinases of unknown catalytic mechanism

3.5 Acting on C—N bonds, other than peptide bonds
3.5.1 In linear amides
3.5.2 In cyclic amides
3.5.3 In linear amidines
3.5.4 In cyclic amidines
3.5.5 In nitriles
3.5.99 In other compounds

3.6 Acting on acid anhydrides
3.6.1 In phosphorus-containing anhydrides
3.6.2 In sulfonyl-containing anhydrides

3.7 Acting on C—C bonds
3.7.1 In ketonic substances

3.8 Acting on halide bonds
3.8.1 In C-halide compounds
3.8.2 In P-halide compounds

3.9 Acting on P—N bonds

3.10 Acting on S—N bonds

3.11 Acting on C—P bonds

4. Lyases

Lyases are enzymes cleaving C—C, C—O, C—N and other bonds by other means than by hydrolysis or oxidation. They differ from other enzymes in that two substrates are involved in one reaction direction, but only one in the other direction. When acting on the single substrate, a molecule is eliminated leaving an unsaturated residue. The systematic name is formed according to 'substrate group-lyase'. In recommended names, expressions like 'decarboxylase', 'aldolase', etc. are used. 'Dehydratase' is used for those enzymes eliminating water. In cases where the reverse reaction is the more important, or the only one to be demonstrated, 'synthase' may be used in the name.

4.1 C—C lyases
4.1.1 Carboxy-lyases
4.1.2 Aldehyde-lyases
4.1.3 Oxo-acid-lyases
4.1.99 Other C—C lyases

4.2 C—O lyases
4.2.1 Hydro-lyases
4.2.2 Acting on polysaccharides
4.2.99 Other C—O lyases

4.3 C—N lyases
4.3.1 Ammonia-lyases
4.3.2 Amidine-lyases

4.4 C—S lyases

4.5 C-halide lyases

4.6 P—O lyases

4.99 Other lyases

5. Isomerases

These enzymes catalyze changes within 1 molecule.

5.1 Racemases and epimerases
5.1.1 Acting on amino acids and derivatives
5.1.2 Acting on hydroxy acids and derivatives
5.1.3 Acting on carbohydrates and derivatives
5.1.99 Acting on other compounds

5.2 *cis-trans*-Isomerases

5.3 Intramolecular oxidoreductases
5.3.1 Interconverting aldoses and ketoses
5.3.2 Interconverting oxo and enol groups
5.3.3 Transposing C=C bonds
5.3.4 Transposing S—S bonds
5.3.99 Other intramolecular oxidoreductases

5.4 Intramolecular transferases
5.4.1 Transferring acyl groups
5.4.2 Phosphotransferases
5.4.3 Transferring amino groups
5.4.99 Transferring other groups

5.5 Intramolecular lyases

5.99 Other isomerases

6. Ligases (synthetases)

Ligases are enzymes catalyzing the joining of 2 molecules with concomitant hydrolysis of the pyrophosphate bond in ATP or a similar triphosphate. The bonds formed are often 'high-energy' bonds. 'Ligase' is commonly used for the recommended name, but in a few cases 'synthase' or 'carboxylase' is used. 'Synthetase' may be used in place of 'synthase' for enzymes in this class.

6.1 Forming C—O bonds
6.1.1 Ligases forming aminoacyl-tRNA and related compounds

6.2 Forming C—S bonds
6.2.1 Acid–thiol ligases

6.3 Forming C—N bonds
6.3.1 Acid–ammonia (or amine) ligases (amide synthases)
6.3.2 Acid–amino-acid ligases (peptide synthases)
6.3.3 Cyclo-ligases
6.3.4 Other C—N ligases
6.3.5 C—N ligases with glutamine as amido-N donor

6.4 Forming C—C bonds

6.5 Forming phosphoric ester bonds

Table 1   *Classification and metabolic function of the coenzymes*

Coenzyme	Symbol	Function	Related vitamin
Oxidoreduction coenzymes			
Nicotinamide adenine dinucleotide	NAD	Hydrogen and electron transfer	Nicotinic acid
Nicotinamide adenine dinucleotide phosphate	NADP	Hydrogen and electron transfer	Nicotinic acid
Flavin mononucleotide....................	FMN	Hydrogen and electron transfer	Riboflavin
Flavin adenine dinucleotide	FAD	Hydrogen and electron transfer	Riboflavin
Lipoic acid	–	Hydrogen and acyl transfer	–
Vitamin K_1.............................	–	Electron transfer (?)	Vitamin K
Ubiquinone	CoQ	Hydrogen and electron transfer	–
Cytochromes	–	Electron transfer (page 96)	–
Tetrahydrobiopterin	–	Hydrogen donor	–
Iron–sulfur proteins (e.g. ferredoxins).......	(Fd)	Electron transfer, hydrogen activation	–
Thioredoxins	–	Hydrogen transfer..................................	–
Group-transfer coenzymes			
Biotin or carboxybiotin	–	Carboxylation, transcarboxylation, decarboxylation	Biotin
Cytidine monophosphate.................	CMP	Transfer of N-acetylneuraminic acid (page 133)..........	–
Nucleoside diphosphates	–	UDP, GDP: transfer of sugars and uronic acids (pages 182 and 187); CDP: transfer of substituted phosphate groups (page 138).......................................	–
Adenosine 3'-phosphate 5'-phosphosulfate ..	PAPS	Sulfate transfer	–
Adenosine triphosphate	ATP	Phosphorylation, transfer of pyrophosphate and adenosyl groups......................................	–
S-Adenosyl-L-methionine.................	–	Transmethylation (page 121)	(Methionine)
Pyridoxal phosphate	–	Decarboxylation, transamination, racemization, etc.	Vitamin B_6
Thiamin diphosphate	–	Decarboxylation, C_1- and C_2-group transfer.............	Thiamin
Coenzyme A...........................	CoA	Acyl transfer	Pantothenic acid
Acyl-carrier protein.....................	ACP	Acyl transfer in fatty-acid synthesis (page 136)	Pantothenic acid
Tetrahydrofolic acid and conjugates	FH_4	Transfer of formyl, hydroxymethyl and methyl groups.....	Folic acid
Methylcobalamin	–	Transfer of methyl groups	Vitamin B_{12}
Isomerization coenzymes			
Adenosylcobalamin	–	Intramolecular shift of groups	Vitamin B_{12}
Uridine diphosphate	UDP	Sugar isomerization (page 91)	–
Second messengers			
Adenosine 3',5'-phosphate	cAMP	Mediation of the action of several hormones	–
Guanosine 3',5'-phosphate...............	cGMP	Mediation of the action of several hormones	–

Coenzymes play a vital role in many enzyme-catalyzed reactions. They are the dissociable active enzyme moieties (cosubstrates) which transfer chemical groups, e.g. carbon dioxide, phosphate, amino groups, acyl and one-carbon groups (such as methyl and formyl groups) or electrons or hydrogen from a donor molecule to a recipient molecule; they couple two otherwise independent reactions and can thus be regarded as transport metabolites. Coenzymes are complex organic compounds of low relative molecular mass, able to pass through most membranes. Usually they are thermostable.

In the wider sense coenzymes may be any catalytically active, low-molecular-mass enzyme component, including covalently bound substances (prosthetic groups). Many coenzymes in this broader sense are synthesized from vitamins; other coenzymes, such as biotin and folic acid, are themselves vitamins (Table 1).

Nicotinamide adenine dinucleotide (phosphate) [NAD(P)]

Structure

For structural formula see page 54.

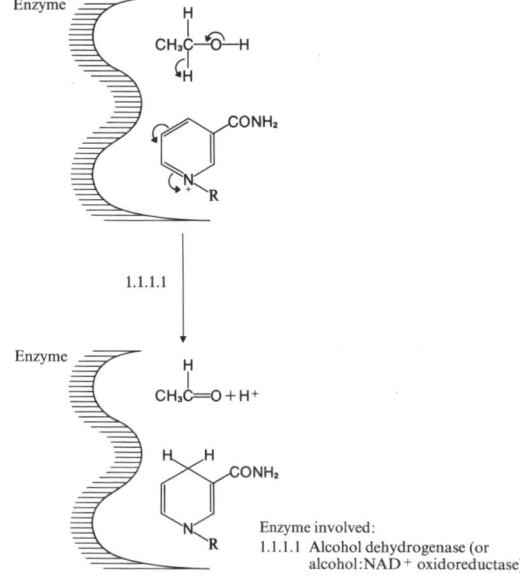

Function

Hydrogen and electron transfer
Coenzymes for oxidoreductases (dehydrogenases)

Typical reactions

The ability of NAD and NADP to accept hydrogen depends on the tendency of the positively charged N atom in the pyridine ring to

withdraw electrons and so create an electrophilic site at C-4 of the pyridine nucleus. A hydrogen atom then appears to be transferred from the substrate to this site in the form of a hydride ion (a proton with an electron pair). At the same time the substrate loses a second hydrogen atom as a proton.

Enzyme involved:
1.1.1.1 Alcohol dehydrogenase (or alcohol:NAD⁺ oxidoreductase)

Flavins

Structure

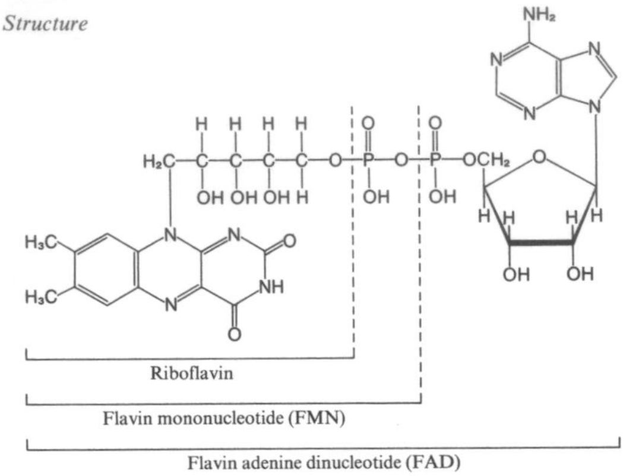

Riboflavin

Flavin mononucleotide (FMN)

Flavin adenine dinucleotide (FAD)

FMN and FAD are prosthetic groups of a wide variety of enzymes and are often associated with other cofactors, such as metals, non-heme iron compounds, sulfur compounds, in highly composite complexes. Two or more molecules of one or of both the flavins may be present in the same enzyme system. The flavin proteins are usually yellow in color, but radicals may be blue or red. Succinate dehydrogenase (1.3.99.1) is a typical flavin enzyme in which the flavin is covalently bound to the enzyme via a histidyl group and the enzyme firmly bound to the cristae of mammalian mitochondria. In liver amine oxidase (flavin-containing) (1.4.3.4), the flavin is coupled to a cysteinyl group. Some reduced flavins are re-oxidized by reaction with other coenzymes, whereas others, such as D-amino-acid oxidase (1.4.3.3), react directly with dioxygen.

Function

Dehydrogenation, hydrogen and electron transfer

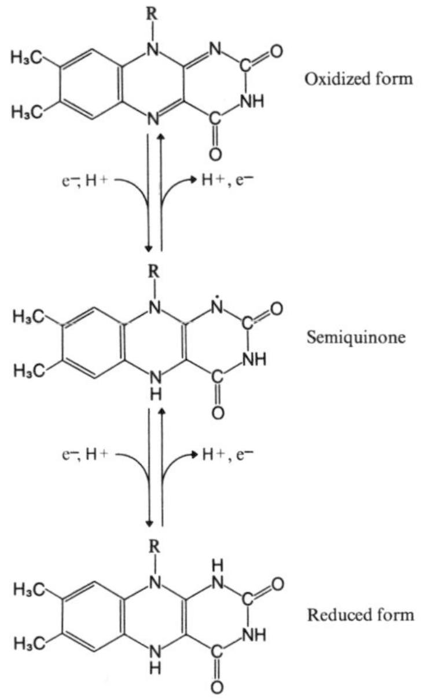

Oxidized form

Semiquinone

Reduced form

The transfer of 2 protons and 2 electrons from donor to flavin may involve a two-fold step in which a semiquinone is formed as an intermediate. This contains a N atom possessing an unpaired electron.

Typical reactions

1. Oxidation of reduced NAD(P). Example:

$$\text{NAD(P)H} + \text{H}^+ + \text{acceptor} \xrightarrow[\text{1.6.99.1-3}]{\text{Flavoprotein}} \text{NAD(P)} + + \text{reduced acceptor}$$

Enzymes involved:
1.6.99.1–3 NAD(P)H dehydrogenases

2. Removal of 2 hydrogen atoms from adjacent C atoms to form a double bond. Example:

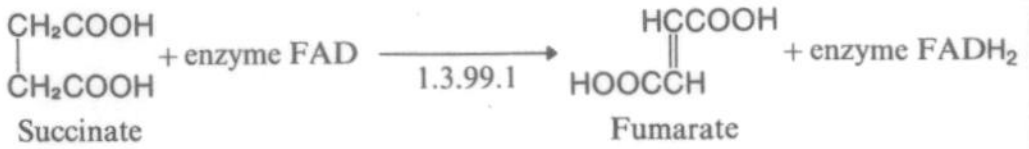

Enzyme involved:
1.3.99.1 Succinate dehydrogenase

3. Transfer of hydrogen to dioxygen. Example:

$$\text{Xanthine} + \text{H}_2\text{O} + \text{O}_2 \xrightarrow{\text{1.1.3.22}} \text{Urate} + \text{H}_2\text{O}_2$$

Enzyme involved:
1.1.3.22 Xanthine oxidase

The enzyme xanthine:oxygen oxidoreductase (xanthine oxidase) is an iron–molybdenum flavoprotein (FAD).

Lipoic acid

Structure

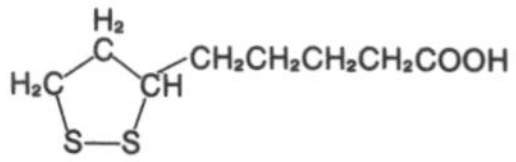

Lipoic acid (1,2-dithiolane-3-valeric acid)

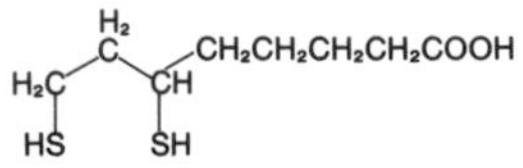

Dihydrolipoic acid (6,7-dimercaptooctanoic acid)

It may be bonded to the enzyme through an amide link formed by condensation with the 6-amino group of a lysine residue.

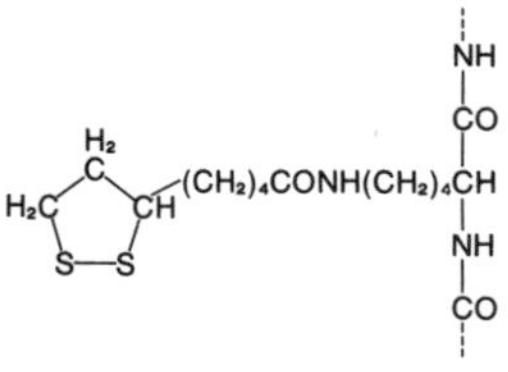

Function

Acyl transfer (in the reduced form).
Hydrogen transfer from the reduced form to regenerate the oxidized form, which is required for further acyl transfer.

Typical reaction

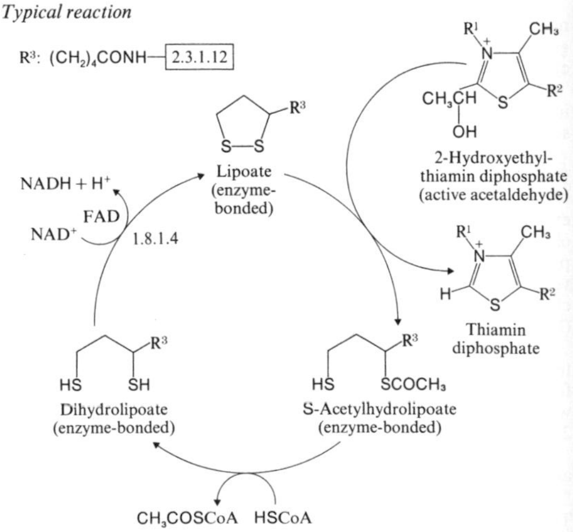

Enzymes involved:
1.8.1.4 Dihydrolipoamide dehydrogenase (dihydrolipoamide:NAD⁺ oxidoreductase)
2.3.1.12 Dihydrolipoamide acetyltransferase (acetyl-CoA:dihydrolipoamide S-acetyltransferase)

Ubiquinone (coenzyme Q)

Structure

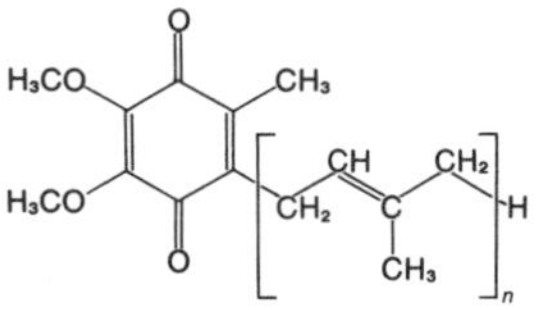

Ubiquinone-n (coenzyme Q_n)

Ubiquinones are substituted benzoquinones having a side chain of 6 to 10 isoprene units. Thus ubiquinone with 10 isoprene units is designated ubiquinone-10 or coenzyme Q_{10} (UQ_{10} or CoQ_{10}).

Function

Ubiquinones are vital intermediates in the electron transfer system, situated at the point at which reduced NAD(P) and reduced flavoproteins converge (see Fig. 3, page 98). $FADH_2$ and $FMNH_2$ may both be oxidized.

Reaction mechanism

Quinones may be reversibly reduced to the corresponding quinol in 3 steps. The first step involves electron transfer and results in the formation of the semiquinone or quinol radical. Another electron is then transferred, resulting in the formation of the quinol anion or phenolate. This finally reacts with 2 protons to form the quinol.

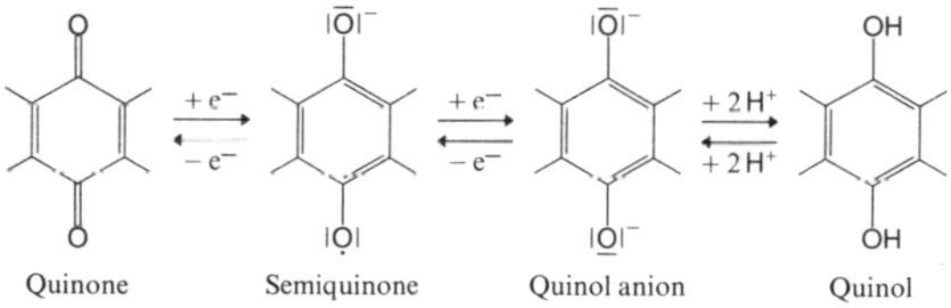

Quinone   Semiquinone   Quinol anion   Quinol

Iron–sulfur proteins

Structure

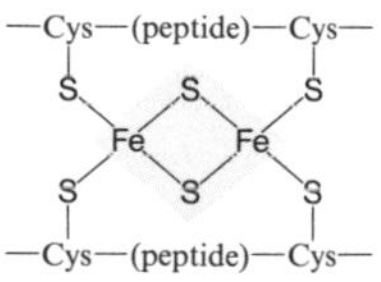

2Fe–2S cluster

These are sulfur-containing non-heme iron proteins of low relative molecular mass. Ferredoxins and related compounds belong to this group of coenzymes. The active site of the protein consists of non-cystein sulfur ('labile' sulfur) linked to Fe atoms in 1:1 ratio. These 'iron–sulfur clusters' may be 2Fe–2S, 4Fe–4S, or 8Fe–8S, depending on function and species. On acidification below pH 1, the labile sulfur is liberated as H_2S.

Function

Iron–sulfur proteins are involved in electron transfer from one enzyme system to another. An iron–sulfur cluster can transfer 1 electron: in taking up the electron, Fe^{3+} is reduced to Fe^{2+}. These proteins possess a wide range of redox potentials, varying from the very low – i.e. highly reducing ($E^0 = -410\,mV$) – in the case of clostridial ferredoxin to the high-potential iron–sulfur proteins (HiPIP) ($E^0 = +350\,mV$) in some photosynthetic bacteria.

Iron–sulfur proteins are intermediates in the electron transfer system (page 96). Ferredoxin is involved in enzymatic hydroxylations, for example in 1α-hydroxylation of 25-hydroxycholecalciferol, as well as in formation of 2-oxo acids by action of pyruvate synthase, 2-oxobutyrate synthase, 2-oxoglutarate synthase (1.2.7.1–3).

Iron–sulfur proteins are involved in such fundamental processes as photosynthesis and nitrogen fixation.

Thioredoxin

Structure

Thioredoxin is a nonmetallic protein consisting of about 109 amino-acid residues. The function groups are 2 cysteine residues which are separated by 10 amino acids and form a disulfide bridge.

Function

Thioredoxin is involved in the reduction of ribonucleoside phosphates to the corresponding deoxyriboside phosphate, usually at the di- or – more rarely – the triphosphate level.

Reduced thioredoxin takes part in the enzymatic reaction of ribonucleoside-diphosphate reductase (1.17.4.1), which reduces ribonucleosides to deoxyribonucleosides. The oxidized thioredoxin then undergoes reduction by reduced NADP and thioredoxin reductase (NADPH) (1.6.4.5), which is a flavoprotein (FAD).

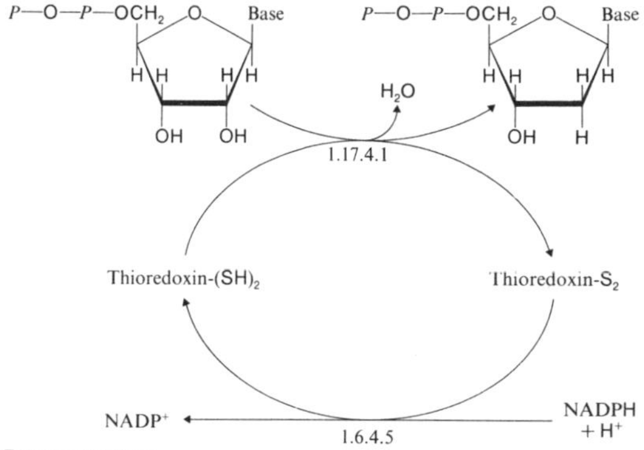

Enzymes involved:
1.6.4.5 Thioredoxin reductase (NADPH)
1.17.4.1 Ribonucleoside-diphosphate reductase

Vitamin K

Structure

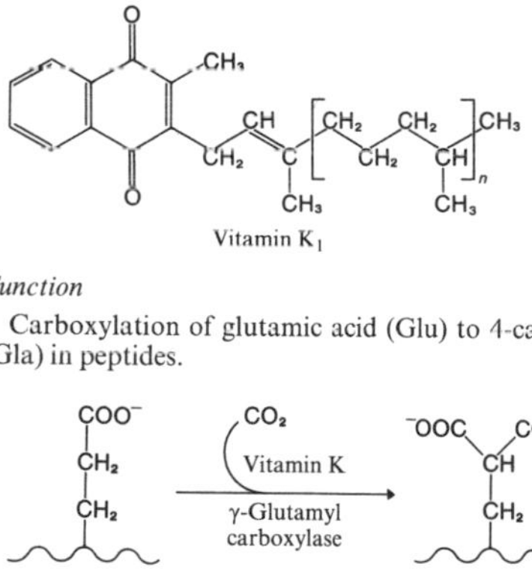

Vitamin K_1

Function

Carboxylation of glutamic acid (Glu) to 4-carboxyglutamic acid (Gla) in peptides.

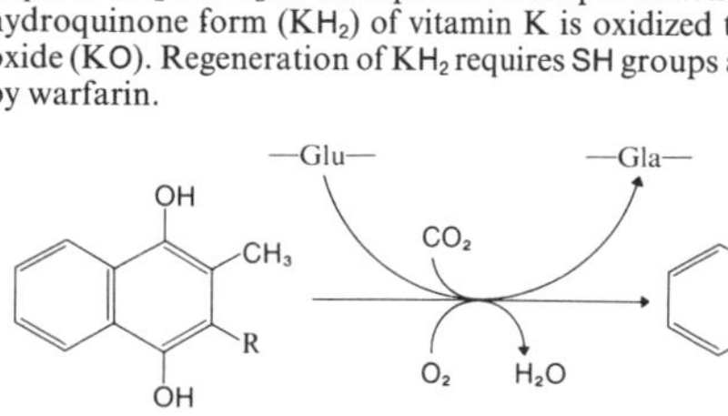

Glu in peptides   Gla in peptides

Reaction mechanism

The exact reaction mechanism is not yet known. Carboxylation requires CO_2 and O_2. It takes place in a coupled reaction in which the hydroquinone form (KH_2) of vitamin K is oxidized to yield the epoxide (KO). Regeneration of KH_2 requires SH groups and is inhibited by warfarin.

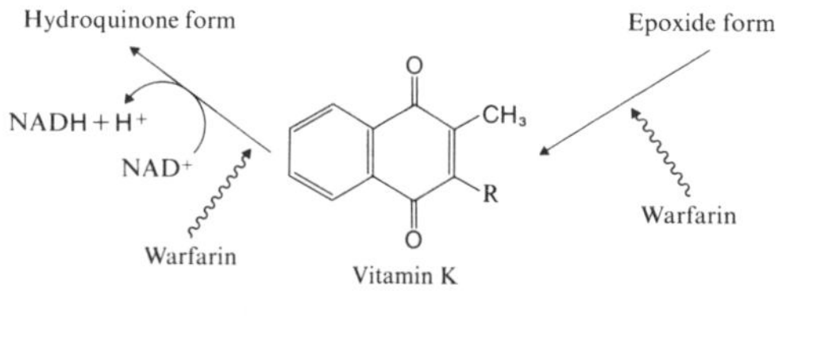

Hydroquinone form   Epoxide form

Warfarin   Vitamin K

Biotin

Structure

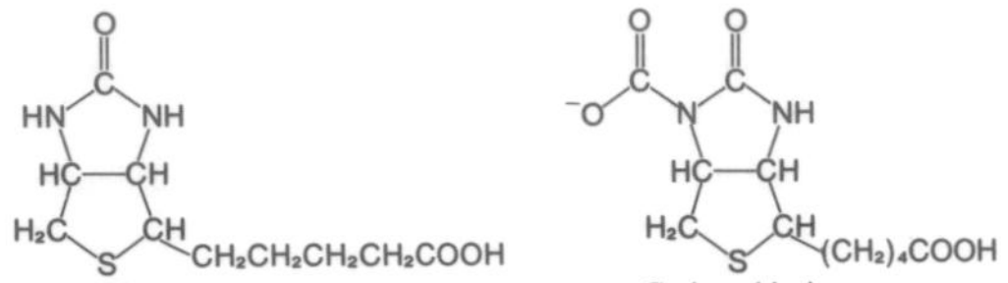

$CH_2CH_2CH_2CH_2COOH$
Biotin

$(CH_2)_4COOH$
Carboxybiotin

Enzyme-bound by condensation with the 6-amino group of a lysine residue.

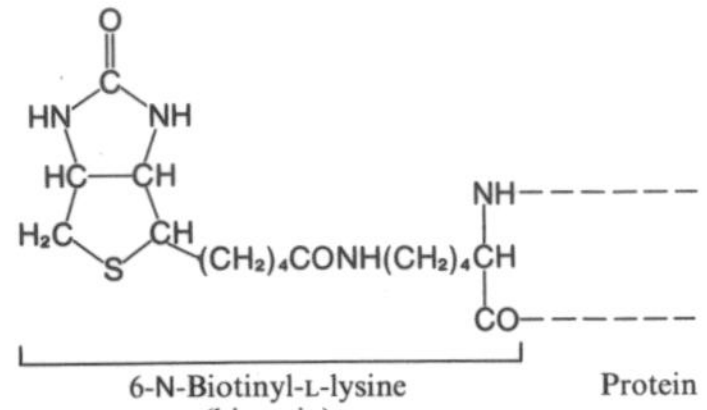

$(CH_2)_4CONH(CH_2)_4CH$

6-N-Biotinyl-L-lysine   Protein
(biocytin)

Function

Carboxylation

Reaction mechanism

Carboxylations require 'activated' CO_2 (or carbonic acid). Free energy of cleavage of carboxybiotin enzymes is sufficient to make carboxylations possible. The formation of carboxybiotin therefore requires the participation of ATP.

$HCO_3^- + \text{biotin enzyme} + ATP \longleftrightarrow \text{Carboxybiotin enzyme} + ADP + P_i$
$\text{Carboxybiotin enzyme} + \text{acceptor} \longleftrightarrow \text{Carboxylated acceptor} + \text{biotin}$

Typical reaction

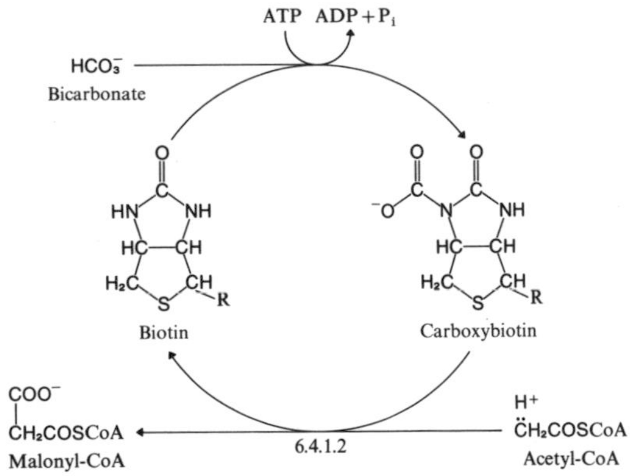

ATP   ADP + P_i

HCO_3^-
Bicarbonate

Biotin

Carboxybiotin

COO^-
$CH_2COSCoA$ 6.4.1.2
Malonyl-CoA

H^+
$CH_2COSCoA$
Acetyl-CoA

Enzyme involved:
6.4.1.2 Acetyl-CoA carboxylase (acetyl-CoA:carbon-dioxide ligase [ADP-forming])

Adenosine triphosphate (ATP)

Structure

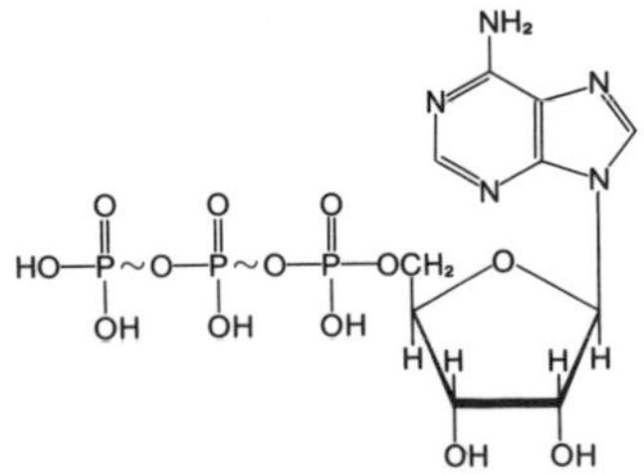

NH_2

$HO-\overset{O}{\underset{OH}{P}}\sim O-\overset{O}{\underset{OH}{P}}\sim O-\overset{O}{\underset{OH}{P}}-OCH_2$

OH OH

Adenosine triphosphate

Hydrolysis of the pyrophosphate bonds of ATP releases approximately 3 times as much energy as does hydrolysis of the bonds of phosphoric acid esters such as glycerol 1-phosphate or 3-phosphoglycerate. They are often, though inaccurately, called 'high-energy bonds' and are denoted by the sign $\sim$.

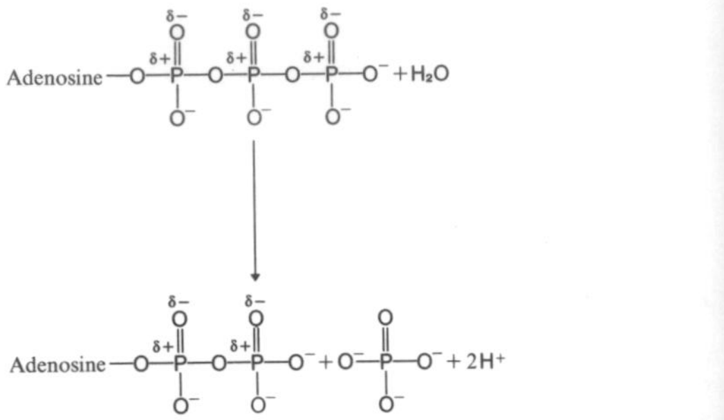

$\text{Adenosine}-O-\overset{\delta-}{\underset{O^-}{\overset{O}{P}}}-O-\overset{\delta-}{\underset{O^-}{\overset{O}{P}}}-O-\overset{\delta-}{\underset{O^-}{\overset{O}{P}}}-O^- + H_2O$

$\text{Adenosine}-O-\overset{\delta-}{\underset{O^-}{\overset{O}{P}}}-O-\overset{\delta-}{\underset{O^-}{\overset{O}{P}}}-O^- + O=\overset{O}{\underset{O^-}{P}}-O^- + 2H^+$

$ATP + H_2O \longrightarrow ADP + P_i + \text{free energy } (\Delta G)$

For removal of orthophosphate the free energy of hydrolysis ΔG^0 is $-34.5 \text{ kJ mol}^{-1}$ (measured under standard conditions at $25°C$ and pH 7); for conditions in biological systems, the energy released will amount to $40–50 \text{ kJ mol}^{-1}$.

The high free energy of hydrolysis depends upon two principal factors:

- The close proximity of the negative charges on the oxygen atoms subjects the molecule to a stress which is relieved by hydrolysis. The forces of electrostatic repulsion contribute to the energy released.
- When the orthophosphate ion separates, the number of possible resonance forms is increased: in other words, the reaction products of the group transfer are more stable than ATP. The increase in stability by resonance also contributes towards the energy released.

Function

Energy transfer. Part of the molecule (especially orthophosphate) may be transferred to an acceptor molecule to increase its energy content [see reactions (a) to (d) below].

Typical reactions

The ATP molecule can be cleaved at several sites, and at least 4 different fragments can be transferred to acceptor molecules:

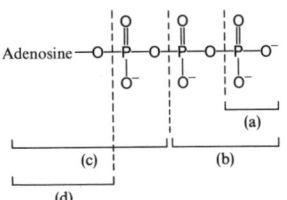

(a) Transfer of the terminal orthophosphate group by a large number of kinases (phosphotransferases, 2.7.1). Example:

$ATP + \text{glucose} \xrightarrow{2.7.1.2} ADP + \text{glucose 6-phosphate}$

(b) Transfer of the pyrophosphate group by pyrophosphokinases (diphosphotransferases, 2.7.6). Example:

$ATP + \text{D-ribose 5-phosphate} \xrightarrow{2.7.6.1} AMP + \text{5-phosphoribose 1-diphosphate}$

(c) Transfer of AMP with the aid of nucleotidyltransferases (2.7.7), leaving pyrophosphate. Example:

$ATP + \text{nicotinamide ribonucleotide} \xrightarrow{2.7.7.1} PP_i + NAD^+$

(d) Transfer of adenosine with formation of orthophosphate and pyrophosphate. Example:

$ATP + \text{L-methionine} + H_2O \xrightarrow{2.5.1.6} P_i + PP_i + \text{S-adenosyl-L-methionine}$

Enzyme involved:
2.5.1.6 Methionine adenosyltransferase

(e) The free energy of hydrolysis of ATP may be utilized by ligases (synthetases) to link other molecules together. A phosphorylated intermediate usually formed is not shown in the overall equation:

$$\text{ATP} + \text{acetate} + \text{CoA} \xrightarrow[6.2.1.1]{} \text{AMP} + \text{PP}_i + \text{acetyl-CoA}$$

or

$$\text{ATP} + \text{succinate} + \text{CoA} \xrightarrow[6.2.1.5]{} \text{ADP} + \text{P}_i + \text{succinyl-CoA}$$

Enzymes involved:
6.2.1.1 Acetate–CoA ligase
6.2.1.5 Succinate–CoA ligase (ADP-forming)

Cyclic adenosine monophosphate (cAMP)

Structure

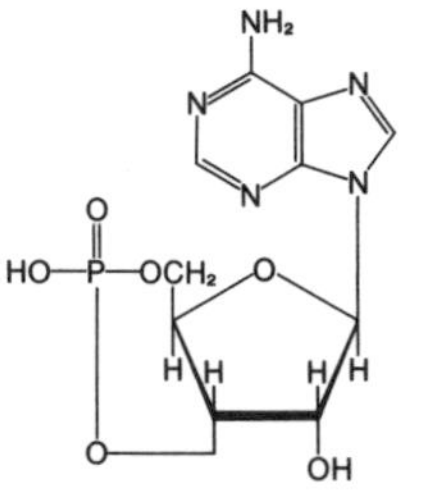

Cyclic adenosine monophosphate
(adenosine 3′,5′-phosphate)

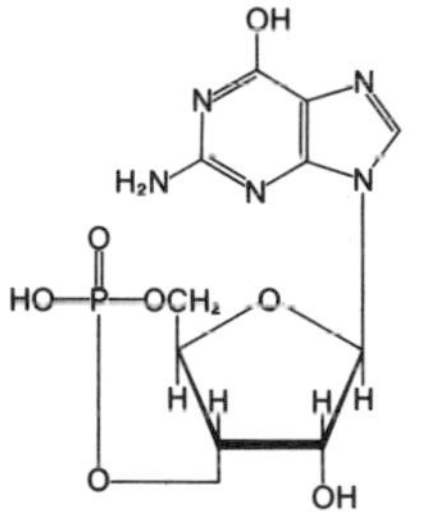

Cyclic guanosine monophosphate
(guanosine 3′,5′-phosphate)

Function

Cyclic AMP mediates the action of several hormones ('second messenger').

Reaction mechanism

Via specific receptors the hormones stimulate the enzyme adenylate cyclase (4.6.1.1), which brings about the formation of cAMP from ATP.

$$\text{ATP} \xrightarrow[4.6.1.1]{} \text{cAMP} + \text{PP}_i$$

In a further step cAMP activates an inactive protein kinase (a). The active form of this enzyme then starts up – via phosphorylated enzymes – the subsequent steps of the reaction sequence (b), which lead to the end-product of the hormone action.

(a) $\text{B}_2\text{A}_2 + 4\,\text{cAMP} \longleftrightarrow \text{B}_2(\text{cAMP})_4 + 2\,\text{A}$

(b) $\text{Enzyme} + n\,\text{ATP} \xrightarrow{\text{A}} \text{Enzyme}\,P_n + n\,\text{ADP}$

[B_2A_2: inactive holoenzyme; A: active catalytic subunit]

The most important hormones, which act by stimulation of cAMP formation, can be seen in the table below. For details on the regulation of glycogen metabolism see page 199.

Cyclic GMP acts similarly to cyclic AMP, at least in some reaction procedures. Activation of protein kinase probably takes place as follows:

$\text{E}_2 + 2\,\text{cGMP} \longleftrightarrow \text{E}_2(\text{cGMP})_2$

[E_2: inactive enzyme; $\text{E}_2(\text{cGMP})_2$: active enzyme]

Adenosine 3′-phosphate 5′-phosphosulfate (phosphoadenosine phosphosulfate [PAPS])

Structure

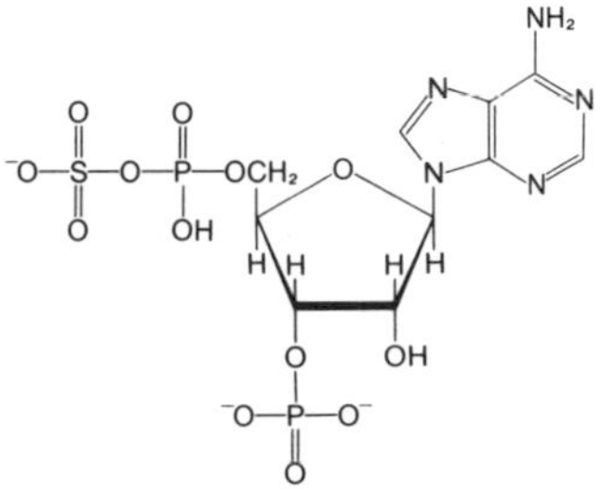

Adenosine 3′-phosphate 5′-phosphosulfate

Function

PAPS is a coenzyme which is involved in sulfate transfer. Sulfate is 'activated' by reaction with ATP using sulfate adenylyltransferase as enzyme. This results in the formation of adenosine 5′-phosphosulfate (APS), which is then further 'activated' by reaction with another molecule of ATP.

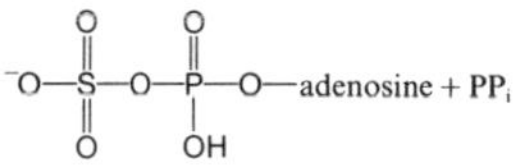

Adenosine 5′-phosphosulfate

Enzymes involved:
2.7.1.25 Adenylylsulfate kinase
2.7.7.4 Sulfate adenylyltransferase

Adenosine 3′-phosphate 5′-phosphosulfate then reacts with a suitable acceptor, catalyzed by sulfotransferases (2.8.2), to form the acceptor sulfate and adenosine 3′,5′-bisphosphate (PAP).

Table 2   *Some hormones that act via the 'second messenger' cAMP*

Hormone	Target organ	Biochemical action	Physiological action
Epinephrine	Liver, muscle	Stimulation of glycogen phosphorylase	Elevation of blood-glucose level
	Fatty tissue	Stimulation of lipase	Lipolysis
Glucagon	Muscle	Influence on muscle phosphorylase	Contraction of smooth muscles
	Liver	Stimulation of glycogen phosphorylase	Elevation of blood-glucose level
	Fatty tissue	Stimulation of triacylglycerol lipase	Lipolysis
Corticotropin.	Adrenal cortex	Activation of cholesterol esterase and cholesterol monooxygenase (side-chain-cleaving) (?)	Increase in cortisol production
	Fatty tissue	Stimulation of triacylglycerol lipase	Lipolysis
Gonadotropin	Testes	Activation of cholesterol esterase and cholesterol monooxygenase (side-chain-cleaving) (?)	Increase in androgen production
Thyrotropin	Thyroid gland	Stimulation of thyroglobulin hydrolysis	Increase in thyroxin release

Pyridoxal phosphate

Structure

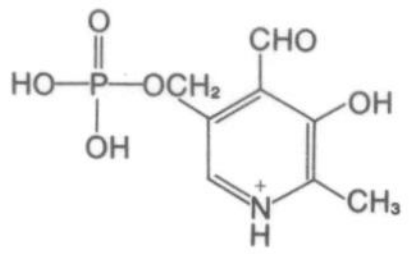

Pyridoxal phosphate

Active form

The active form is a Schiff's base formed by the condensation of the aldehyde group with the 6-amino group of a lysine residue on an enzyme. This reacts with an amino acid, with which it forms a Schiff's base, and liberates a free 6-amino group on the lysine residue.

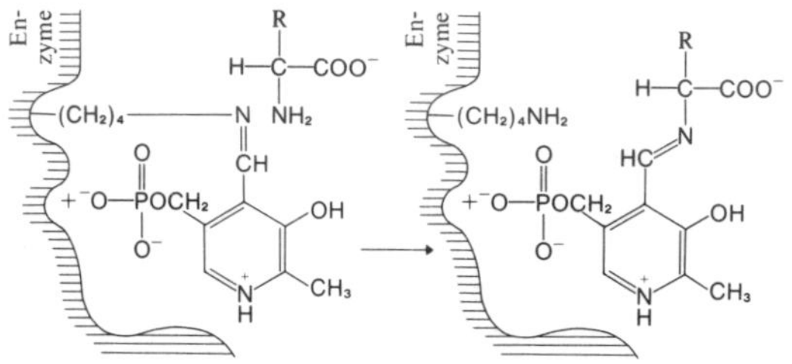

Function

Decarboxylation, transamination and racemization of amino acids. It also catalyzes the condensation of indole and serine to form tryptophan, the 2,3-dehydration of serine, the 3,4-desulfurization of homocysteine, and the formation of serine from glycine.

Reactions

The starting point of each reaction is the Schiff's base formed between the aldehyde group of pyridoxal phosphate and the amino group of the amino acid (see Fig. 1).

Thiamin diphosphate

Structure

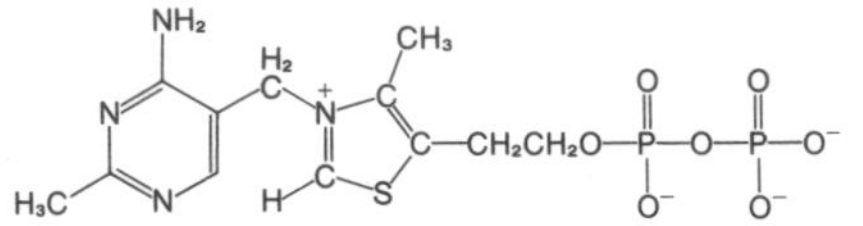

The C-2 atom of the thiazole ring of the molecule ionizes to give a carbanion and a proton.

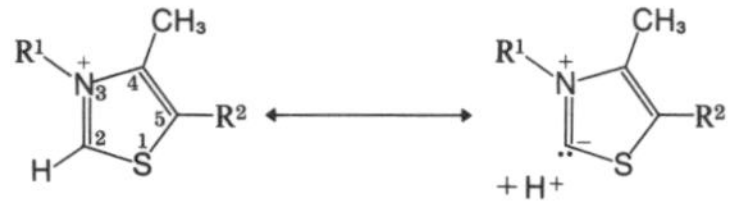

(Continued on page 82)

Fig. 1　Reactions of pyridoxal phosphate

Decarboxylation

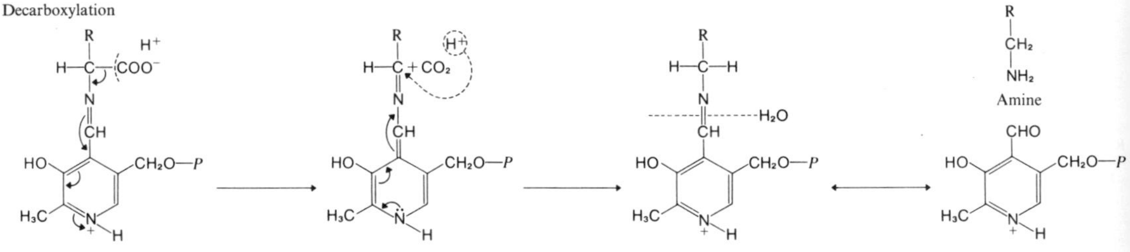

Net result:　$RCH(NH_2)COOH \longrightarrow RCH_2NH_2 + CO_2$

Transamination

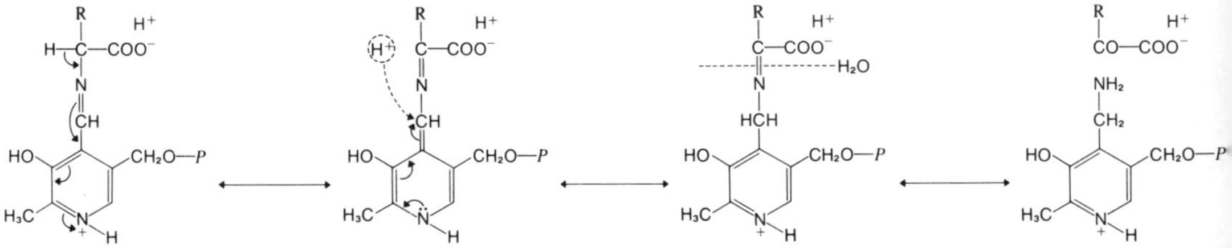

Net result:　Donor amino acid + pyridoxal phosphate $\longrightarrow$ Product oxo acid + pyridoxamine phosphate
　　　　　　　　(Schiff's base)
　　or
　　　　Product amino acid + pyridoxal phosphate $\longleftarrow$ Donor oxo acid + pyridoxamine phosphate
　　　　　　　(Schiff's base)

Racemization

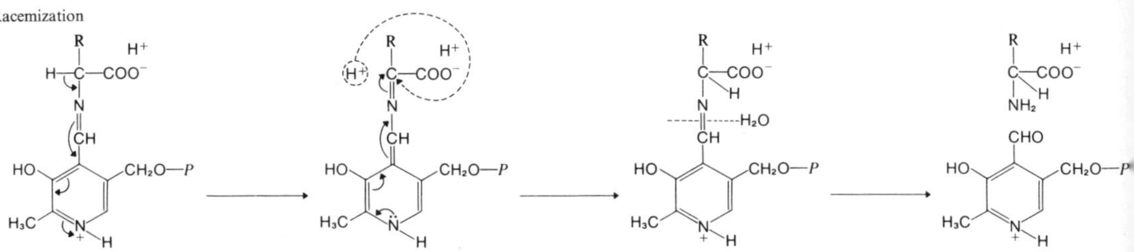

Net result:　$H-\underset{NH_2}{\overset{R}{C}}-COO^- \longleftrightarrow H_2N-\underset{H}{\overset{R}{C}}-COO^-$

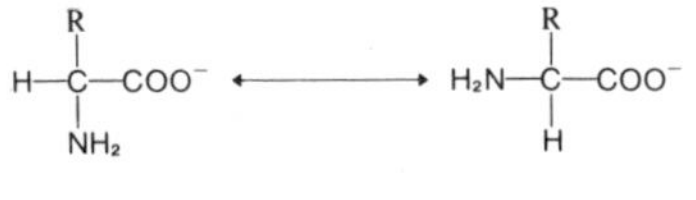

Fig. 2   *Typical reactions with thiamin diphosphate as coenzyme*

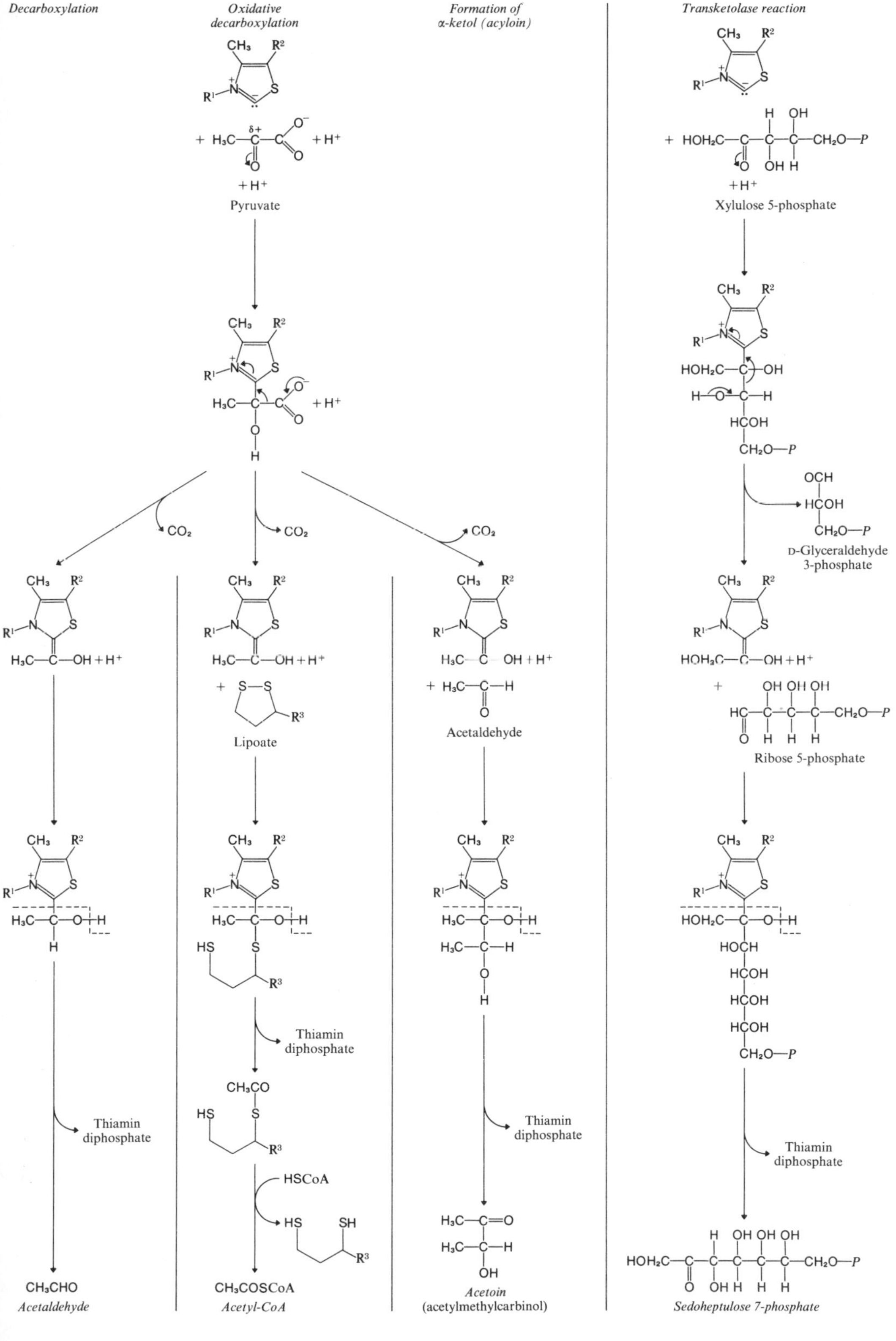

Function

Decarboxylation, oxidative decarboxylation, formation of α-ketol (acyloin), transketolase reaction.

Reaction mechanism

The carbanion reacts with the (δ +) carbon of a carbonyl group. Cleavage then takes place of the bond between this C atom and an adjacent C atom of the substrate. This results in the formation of an 'active' aldehyde and either carbon dioxide or a stable aldehyde.

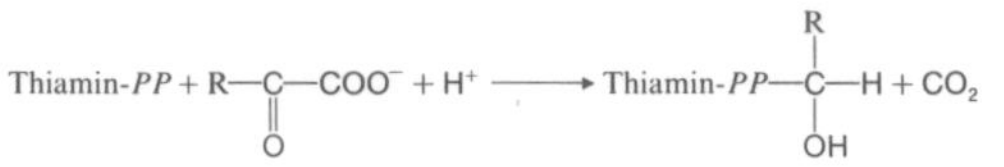

$$\text{Thiamin-}PP + R\!-\!\underset{\overset{\|}{O}}{C}\!-\!COO^- + H^+ \longrightarrow \text{Thiamin-}PP\!-\!\underset{\overset{|}{OH}}{\overset{R}{C}}\!-\!H + CO_2$$

or

$$\text{Thiamin-}PP + R^1\!-\!\underset{\overset{|}{O}}{\overset{H}{C}}\!-\!\underset{\overset{|}{OH}}{C}\!-\!R^2 + H^+ \longrightarrow \text{Thiamin-}PP\!-\!\underset{\overset{|}{OH}}{\overset{R^1}{C}}\!-\!H + R^2CHO$$

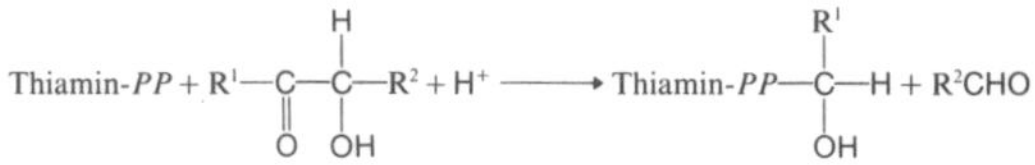

Typical reactions

See Figure 2.

Coenzyme A

Structure

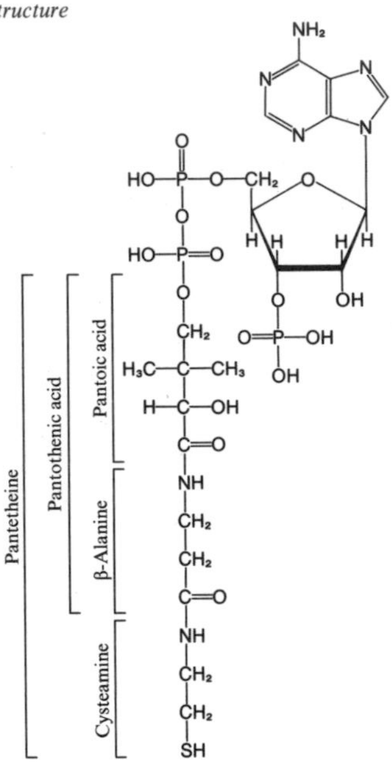

Coenzyme A

Active form

RCH₂COSCoA (acyl CoA)

Function

Acyl transfer

Reaction mechanism

The stability of normal (oxygen) esters is due to resonance between the forms

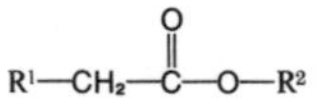

$$R^1\!-\!CH_2\!-\!\underset{\overset{\|}{O}}{C}\!-\!O\!-\!R^2$$

and

$$R^1\!-\!CH_2\!-\!\underset{\overset{\|}{O^-}}{C}\!=\!\overset{+}{O}\!-\!R^2$$

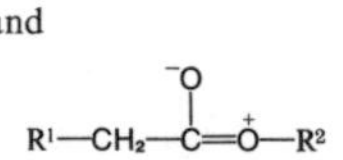

This resonance increases the stability of the molecule and minimizes the yield of free energy released upon hydrolysis. In *thioesters*, the S atom shows no tendency to form a double bond with the C atom, so that a structure such as the second form (see formula above) does not

contribute to resonance. The chemical stability of the molecule is therefore comparatively low, and the energy yielded upon hydrolysis is comparatively high. Thioesters can thus be regarded as 'energy-rich'.

The inability of thioesters to produce resonance forms increases the importance of the carbonyl group, whose C atom possesses a partial positive charge:

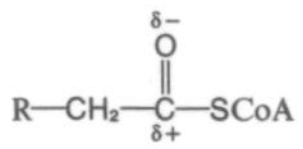

$$R\!-\!CH_2\!-\!\underset{\delta+}{\overset{\overset{\delta-}{O}}{\overset{\|}{C}}}\!-\!SCoA \tag{a}$$

Since no double bond can be formed with the S atom, there is a tendency toward dissociation of the adjacent 2-methylene or 2-methyl group, and thus toward the formation of a carbanion and a proton.

$$R\!-\!\overset{H\cdots O}{\underset{}{CH}}\!-\!\overset{\overset{\|}{O}}{C}\!-\!SCoA \longrightarrow R\!-\!\overset{-}{CH}\!-\!\overset{\overset{\|}{O}}{C}\!-\!SCoA + H^+ \tag{b}$$

Acyl-CoA can therefore exist in 2 forms:

- An *electrophilic form* (a), in which the positively charged carbonyl carbon is open to attack by nucleophilic (negatively charged) compounds.
- A *nucleophilic form* (b) in which the negatively charged methylene group is open to attack by electrophilic (positively charged) compounds.

Typical reactions

(a) Electrophilic form

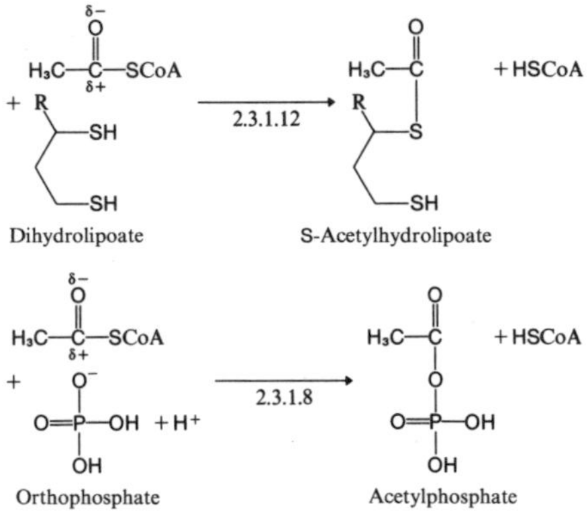

Dihydrolipoate   S-Acetylhydrolipoate

Orthophosphate   Acetylphosphate

Enzymes involved:
2.3.1.8   Phosphate acetyltransferase
2.3.1.12 Dihydrolipoamide acetyltransferase

(b) Nucleophilic form

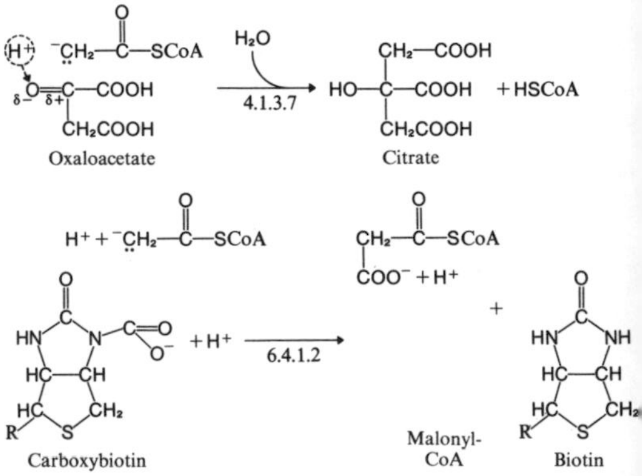

Oxaloacetate   Citrate

Carboxybiotin   Malonyl-   Biotin
                                 CoA

Enzymes involved:
4.1.3.7 Citrate (si)-synthase
6.4.1.2 Acetyl-CoA carboxylase

(c) Electrophilic *and* nucleophilic form

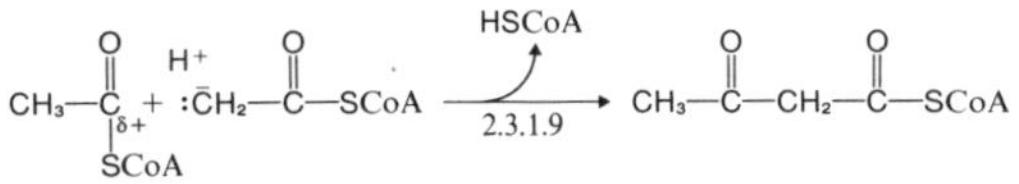

$$CH_3-\underset{\underset{SCoA}{|}}{\overset{\overset{O}{\|}}{C}}\overset{\delta+}{} + :\overset{-}{C}H_2-\overset{\overset{O}{\|}}{C}-SCoA \xrightarrow[2.3.1.9]{H^+ \quad HSCoA} CH_3-\overset{\overset{O}{\|}}{C}-CH_2-\overset{\overset{O}{\|}}{C}-SCoA$$

2 acetyl-CoA   Acetoacetyl-CoA

Enzyme involved:
2.3.1.9 Acetyl-CoA acetyltransferase

Folic-acid derivatives

See Figures 5 and 6.

Tetrahydrobiopterin (tetrahydropteridine)

Structure

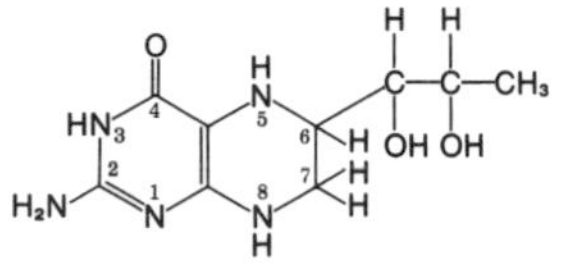

L-*erythro*-5,6,7,8-Tetrahydrobiopterin

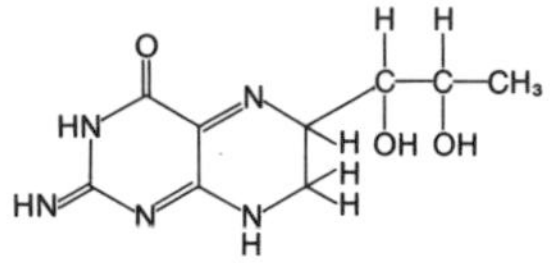

L-*erythro*-6,7-Dihydrobiopterin (quinoid form)

Function

Hydrogen donor in some hydroxylations (coenzyme of monooxygenases).

Typical reactions

Hydroxylation of the aromatic amino acids phenylalanine (page 155), tyrosine (page 161) and tryptophan (page 161).

Cobalamin coenzymes: adenosylcobalamin and methylcobalamin

Structure

See Figure 3.

Function of adenosylcobalamin

Rearrangement reactions in which hydrogen and organic groups change places:

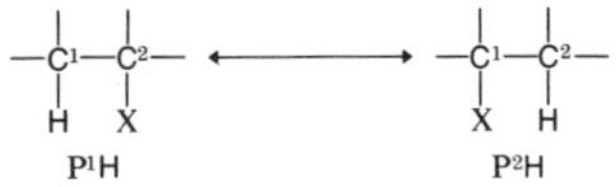

Fig. 3   *Structure of the cobalamins*

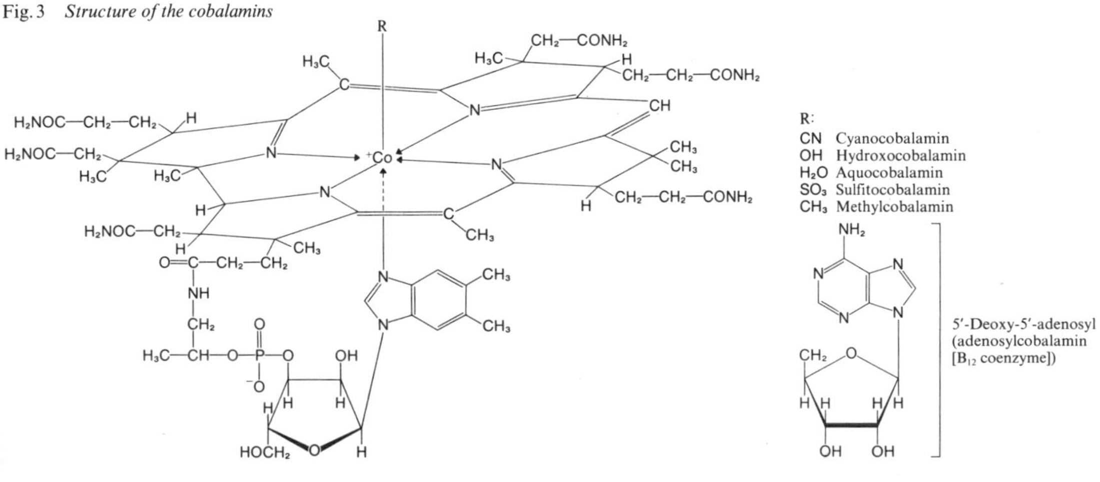

Fig. 4

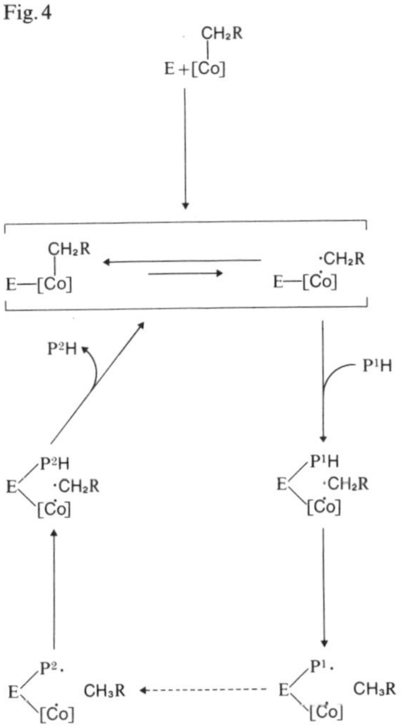

CH₂R Adenosyl residue   ←-- Intramolecular rearrangement mechanism
E   Enzyme   unknown
[Co]   Cobalamin molecule

Reaction mechanism of adenosylcobalamin

The reactive group is the organometallic bond of the Co atom with C-5 of 5'-deoxyadenosine, which is homolytically cleaved (Fig. 4).
The isomerization of methylmalonyl-CoA to form succinyl-CoA (page 102) is the sole adenosylcobalamin-dependent rearrangement in man and in higher animals.

Function of methylcobalamin

Transfer of methyl groups. The methyl group may be transferred as a carbanion (CH_3^-), a radical (CH_3) or a carbonium ion (CH_3^+).

Reaction mechanism of methylcobalamin

Not yet known.

Typical reaction due to action of methylcobalamin

$$\text{5-Methyl-FH}_4 + \text{homocysteine} \xrightarrow{2.1.1.13} \text{FH}_4 + \text{methionine}$$

Enzyme involved:
2.1.1.13 5-Methyltetrahydrofolate–homocysteine methyltransferase

Fig. 5 *Structure of active forms of folic acid and typical reactions*

Structure of folic acid

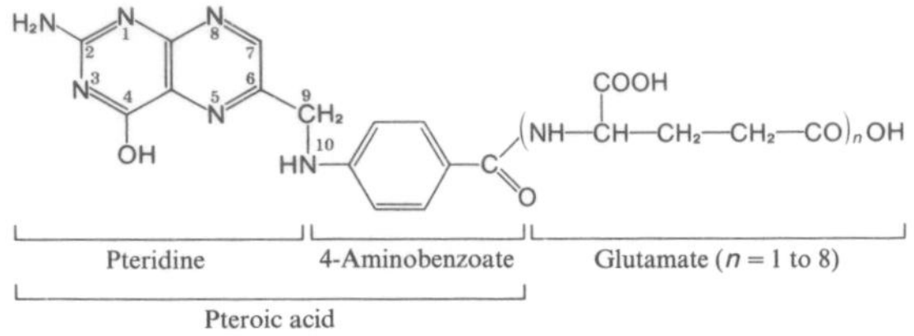

Function
Transfer of one-carbon units

| Pteridine | 4-Aminobenzoate | Glutamate (n = 1 to 8) |

Pteroic acid

Dihydrofolate (FH$_2$) is reduced at positions 7 and 8.
Tetrahydrofolate (FH$_4$) is reduced at positions 5, 6, 7 and 8.

Structure of active forms　　　*Typical reactions*

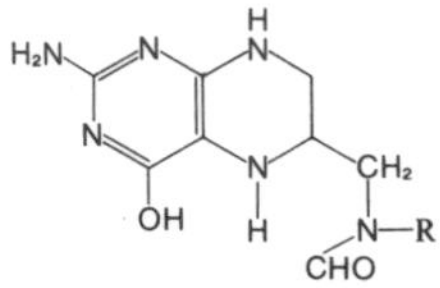

10-Formyltetrahydrofolate

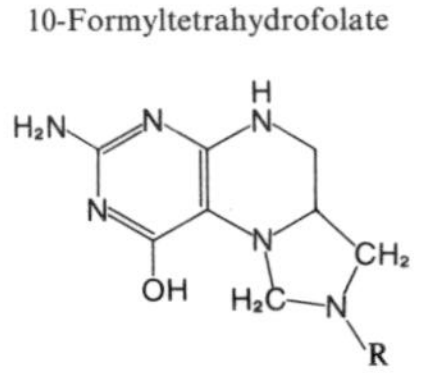

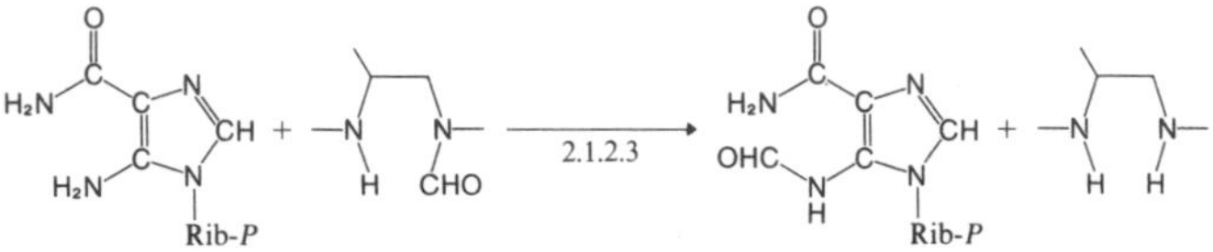

5'-Phosphoribosyl-5-amino-4-imidazolecarboxamide
+ 10-formyl-FH$_4$
　　　⟶　　5'-Phosphoribosyl-5-formamido-4-imidazole-
carboxamide + FH$_4$

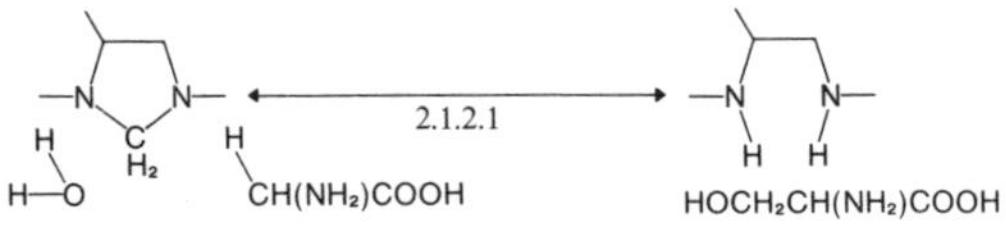

5,10-Methylenetetrahydrofolate

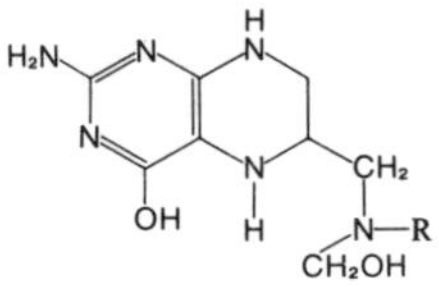

5,10-Methylene-FH$_4$ + H$_2$O + glycine ⟷ FH$_4$ + serine

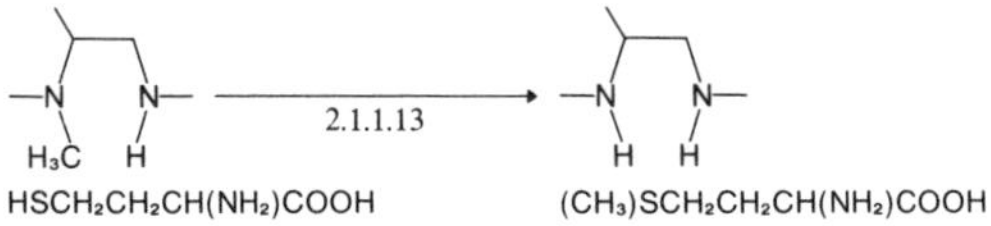

10-Hydroxymethyltetrahydrofolate

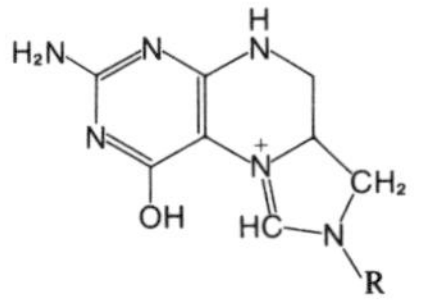

5,10-Methenyltetrahydrofolate

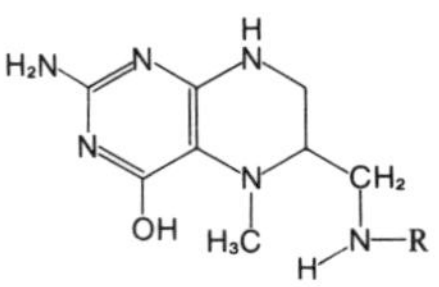

5-Methyltetrahydrofolate

5-Methyl-FH$_4$ + homocysteine ⟶ FH$_4$ + methionine

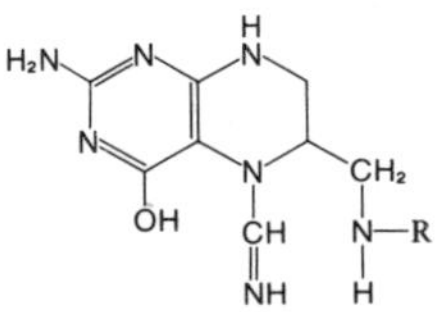

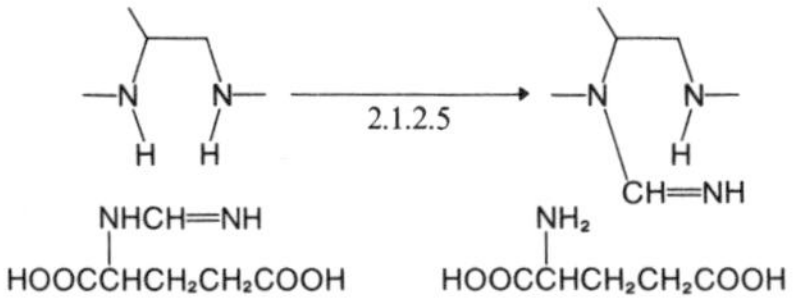

5-Formiminotetrahydrofolate

Formiminoglutamate + FH$_4$ ⟶ 5-Formimino-FH$_4$ + glutamate

Enzymes involved:
2.1.1.13 5-Methyltetrahydrofolate–homocysteine methyltransferase
2.1.2.1 Glycine hydroxymethyltransferase
2.1.2.3 Phosphoribosylaminoimidazolecarboxamide formyltransferase
2.1.2.5 Glutamate formiminotransferase

Fig. 6 *Relationships between active forms of tetrahydrofolate*

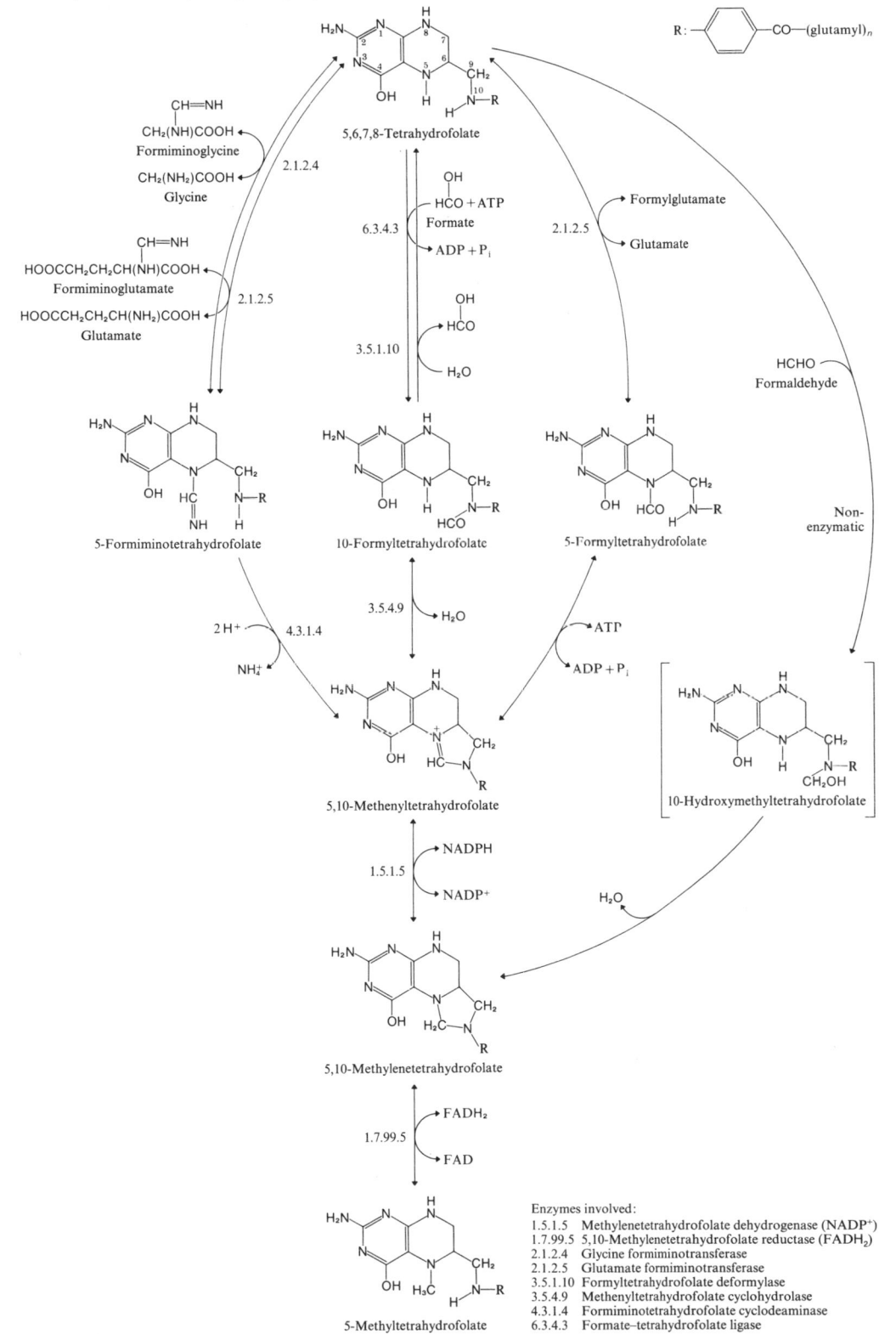

Enzymes involved:
1.5.1.5   Methylenetetrahydrofolate dehydrogenase (NADP⁺)
1.7.99.5 5,10-Methylenetetrahydrofolate reductase (FADH₂)
2.1.2.4   Glycine formiminotransferase
2.1.2.5   Glutamate formiminotransferase
3.5.1.10 Formyltetrahydrofolate deformylase
3.5.4.9   Methenyltetrahydrofolate cyclohydrolase
4.3.1.4   Formiminotetrahydrofolate cyclodeaminase
6.3.4.3   Formate–tetrahydrofolate ligase

Reviews

· HOLMGREN, A., Thioredoxin, *Ann. Rev. Biochem.*, **54**, 237 (1985).
· SUTTIE, J. W., Vitamin K-dependent carboxylase, *Ann. Rev. Biochem.*, **54**, 459 (1985).
· ZAGALAK, B., Vitamin B_{12} als biologisch aktive Modellsubstanz, *Naturwissenschaften*, **69**, 63 (1982).
· YAMAMURA et al. (Eds.), *Biomedical and Clinical Aspects of Coenzyme Q*, Volume 2, Elsevier/North Holland, Amsterdam, 1980.
· SUTTIE, J. W., Mechanism of action of vitamin K: synthesis of γ-carboxy-glutamic acid, *Crit. Rev. Biochem.*, **8**, 191 (1980).

· BENKOVIC, S. J., On the mechanism of action of folate- and biopterin-requiring enzymes, *Ann. Rev. Biochem.*, **49**, 227 (1980).
· BABIOR and KROUWER, The mechanism of adenosylcobalamin-dependent reactions, *Crit. Rev. Biochem.*, **6**, 35 (1979).
· WIMMER and ROSE, Mechanisms of enzyme-catalyzed group transfer reactions, *Ann. Rev. Biochem.*, **47**, 1031 (1978).
· WOOD, H. G., Biotin enzymes, *Ann. Rev. Biochem.*, **46**, 385 (1977).
· DAGLEY and NICHOLSON, *An Introduction to Metabolic Pathways*, Blackwell, Oxford, 1970.

Chemical changes taking place in living organisms are commonly referred to as *metabolism*. This may involve *anabolism*, which is the building up of complex molecules characteristic of living matter from simple building blocks. The latter are obtained chiefly by the breakdown or *catabolism* of large food molecules. Anabolism, as with all building operations, needs not only raw materials but also energy. One of the major functions of catabolism is to supply this energy, primarily by oxidation reactions. Catabolism must therefore precede anabolism, and evolution has ensured a very efficient interrelationship between the two processes.

The complexity of metabolism varies with different organisms. It is generally accepted that the metabolic capabilities of higher organisms – such as man – are much greater than those of simpler organisms. This, however, is only partially true. Some bacteria, for example, can live and multiply on a diet of glucose and a few inorganic salts. They can absorb these simple raw materials and use them to produce all the carbohydrates, lipids, purines, pyrimidines, and other compounds which are the building blocks of the complex molecules characteristic of living organisms. From half a dozen simple compounds they can form thousands of new and different molecules in the space of a few minutes. The ability of bacteria to reproduce every 20 minutes is a marvel of organization and control of which metabolism is capable. Although man is a far more complex creature, in most ways he has a biosynthetic ability inferior to many bacteria. As a result he has to be provided in his food with many of the basic small molecules that most bacteria can make for themselves. Thus human protein is built up from amino acids most of which have been obtained by the breakdown of animal or vegetable proteins.

Respiration and fermentation rates of animal tissues*

Tissue	Species	Dioxygen consumption**, relative to dry mass of the tissue (Q_{O_2})		Anaerobic lactate formation, relative to dry mass of the tissue ($Q_L^{N_2}$)	
		$mL\,h^{-1}\,g^{-1}$	$mmol\,h^{-1}\,g^{-1}$	$mL\,h^{-1}\,g^{-1}$	$mmol\,h^{-1}\,g^{-1}$
Connective tissue (renal capsule)	Goat	− 1	− 0.04	−	−
Blood cells:					
Erythrocytes	Rat	− 0.6	− 0.03	0.35	0.016
Leukocytes	Rat	− 9	− 0.40	−	−
	Rabbit	−	−	22°	0.98
Platelets	Rat	− 7	− 0.31	26	1.1
Embryo	Rat	−	−	12	0.54
Adipose tissue°°	Rat	− 0.5	− 0.02	0.7	0.03
Glandular tissues:					
Glandula submandibularis	Rat	− 12	− 0.54	5	0.22
Hypophysis	Rat	− 12	− 0.54	13	0.58
Liver	Rat	− 13	− 0.58	3	0.13
Spleen	Rat	− 12	− 0.54	8	0.36
Adrenal gland	Rat	− 10	− 0.45	4	0.18
Renal medulla	Guinea pig	− 8	− 0.36	28	1.3
Renal cortex	Rat	− 25	− 1.1	3	0.13
Pancreas	Rat	− 4	− 0.18	−	−
	Rabbit	−	−	3.5	0.16
Thyroid	Guinea pig	− 8	− 0.36	−	−
Testes	Rat	− 10	− 0.45	8	0.36
Thymus	Rat	− 5	− 0.22	8	0.36
Skin	Rat	− 1	− 0.04	7	0.31
Cerebral cortex	Rat	− 12	− 0.53	18	0.80
Brain, white substance	Rat	− 6	− 0.27	−	−
Bone marrow, red	Rat	− 10	− 0.45	21	0.94
Cartilage (ribs)	Rat	− 0.5	− 0.02	1.5	0.07
Lungs	Rat	− 8	− 0.36	−	−
	Rat embryo	−	−	10	0.45
Mucosa:					
Intestine	Rat	− 12	− 0.54	14	0.63
Colon	Rat	− 10	− 0.45	−	−
Muscle tissues:					
Diaphragm	Rat	− 7	− 0.31	−	−
Heart, minced	Sheep	− 18	− 0.80	−	−
M. gastrocnemius	Rat	− 3	− 0.13	−	−
M. pectoralis, minced	Pigeon	− 40	− 1.9	−	−
Gizzard	Pigeon	− 4	− 0.18	−	−
Retina	Rat	− 30	− 1.3	88	3.9
	Pigeon	−	−	180	8.0
Tumors:					
Flexner carcinoma	Rat	− 8	− 0.36	30	1.3
Jensen sarcoma	Rat	− 11	− 0.49	32	1.4
Rous sarcoma	Chicken	− 5	− 0.22	30	1.3

References

KREBS and JOHNSON, *Tab. biol. (Amst.)*, **19**, 100 (1948); ALBRITTON, E. C. (Ed.), *Standard Values in Nutrition and Metabolism*, Saunders, Philadelphia, 1954; RAUEN, H. M. (Ed.), *Biochemisches Taschenbuch*, Part 2, 2nd ed., Springer, Berlin, 1964; ALTMAN and DITTMER, *Metabolism*, Federation of American Societies for Experimental Biology, Bethesda, Md., 1968.

* Typical values, measured on isolated tissues; ordinary sections in glucose–salt solution at 38–40 °C. (The consumption of a substance is usually represented by a − sign, the formation either without a sign or by a + sign. Anaerobic and aerobic conditions are indicated by the indices N_2 or O_2, for example $Q_L^{N_2}, Q_L^{O_2}$.)

** 1 mmol corresponds to 22.4 mL gas.

° Polymorphonuclear and mononuclear.

°° Calculated as dry mass minus ether-soluble substance.

Energy metabolism

The need for energy springs from the fact that living matter is a thermodynamically unstable system which cannot be maintained without continuous input of energy. Moreover, living matter is constantly engaged in performing work of various kinds, such as motion, chemical syntheses and transporting substances against concentration gradients. Activities of this kind cannot take place unless there is a supply of energy. Warm-blooded organisms need energy also to maintain the body temperature.

Energy is obtained by the breakdown of foodstuffs. The first stage either for the supply of energy or for other purposes consists of a hydrolytic cleavage of the large molecules of food to small constituent units. Proteins are converted to amino acids, polysaccharides to hexoses, fats to glycerol and fatty acid, nucleic acids to the constituent bases, pentoses and phosphate. This hydrolytic cleavage – a prerequisite for absorption by the intestine – is commonly referred to as *digestion*. Processes very similar to digestion in the intestine also occur in most tissues when reserve materials are mobilized to serve as a source of energy, or when damaged tissues are subject to 'autolysis'. In higher organisms the end result of this breakdown is essentially an oxidation of the organic substance to carbon dioxide and water. This result is the sum total of hundreds of individual chemical reactions, many of which are known in considerable detail.

Energy can also be obtained anaerobically from glucose and other hexoses by certain special degradation reactions. Such reactions are referred to as 'fermentations' or 'glycolyses'. The main form of fermentation occurring in animal tissues is lactic acid fermentation, by which 1 molecule of glucose is split into 2 molecules of lactic acid:

$$C_6H_{12}O_6 \longrightarrow 2CH_3CH(OH)COOH$$

Microorganisms show many types of fermentation, among which the most important is the alcoholic fermentation:

$$C_6H_{12}O_6 \longrightarrow 2CH_3CH_2OH + 2CO_2$$

The energy made available by fermentations is only a small fraction of that liberated by the oxidation of glucose. The complete oxidation of 1 mol of glucose yields about 2870 kJ of free energy, whilst the fermentation of the same amount of glucose to lactic acid yields only about 188 kJ. Thus to obtain the same amount of energy by fermentation, 15 times more glucose has to be decomposed.

In most tissues of higher organisms, lactic-acid fermentation is low in the presence of dioxygen but may become high in the absence of dioxygen. The suppression of fermentation by dioxygen, first observed by PASTEUR in yeast cells, is known as the Pasteur effect.

Cell metabolism

Metabolism of the body as a whole is the result of the metabolic activities in the component tissues. Within the last fifty years methods have become available for studying the metabolic activities of isolated tissues. A few representative data on rates of respiration and lactic-acid fermentation in animal tissues are given in the table on page 87.

There are wide variations in the metabolic activities of different materials. The highest rates of respiration and fermentation are found among microorganisms. *Azotobacter*, for example, at 38°C can show Q_{O_2} values of over 350 mmol h^{-1} g^{-1}, while the normal rates for bacteria are about 4.5–9.0 mmol h^{-1} g^{-1}. Anaerobic fermentation rates of up to 18 mmol h^{-1} g^{-1} are measured in microorganisms. The maximum rate of lactic-acid production in muscle can probably reach $Q_L^{N_2}$ values of well over 4.5 mmol h^{-1} g^{-1} for short periods. Avian retina gives the highest continuous rate of lactic-acid production among animal tissues (pigeon retina: $Q_L^{N_2} = 8$ mmol h^{-1} g^{-1}).

Low metabolic rates are generally found in tissues with relatively low physiological activity. This holds true for resting glands or muscles and in particular for tissues whose function, like that of connective tissue or bone, is largely structural or, like that of adipose tissue, is concerned with the storage of metabolically inert material.

The rates of respiration and fermentation increase with temperature, like the majority of other chemical reactions. At a critical temperature – which is about 40°C for warm-blooded animals and somewhat below this temperature for cold-blooded animals – a further rise in temperature reduces metabolism. In exceptional cases, as with thermophilic bacteria, the critical temperature may be as high as 80°C.

Among the factors which affect energy production in the intact warm-blooded animal, body size has long been recognized as being of major importance. The differences in the dioxygen consumption of intact animals of different size are not, however, exactly reflected in the rates of respiration of individual tissues. In general, the tissues of larger species have a somewhat lower metabolism than the tissues of smaller species, but the differences between the Q_{O_2} values of, for example, brain, kidney, liver, spleen and lung of different species are relatively small. The characteristic differences in the basal metabolic rate of animals of different size seem to be due mainly to differences in the resting metabolism of the musculature.

Fig. 1   *Breakdown of glycogen and disaccharides*

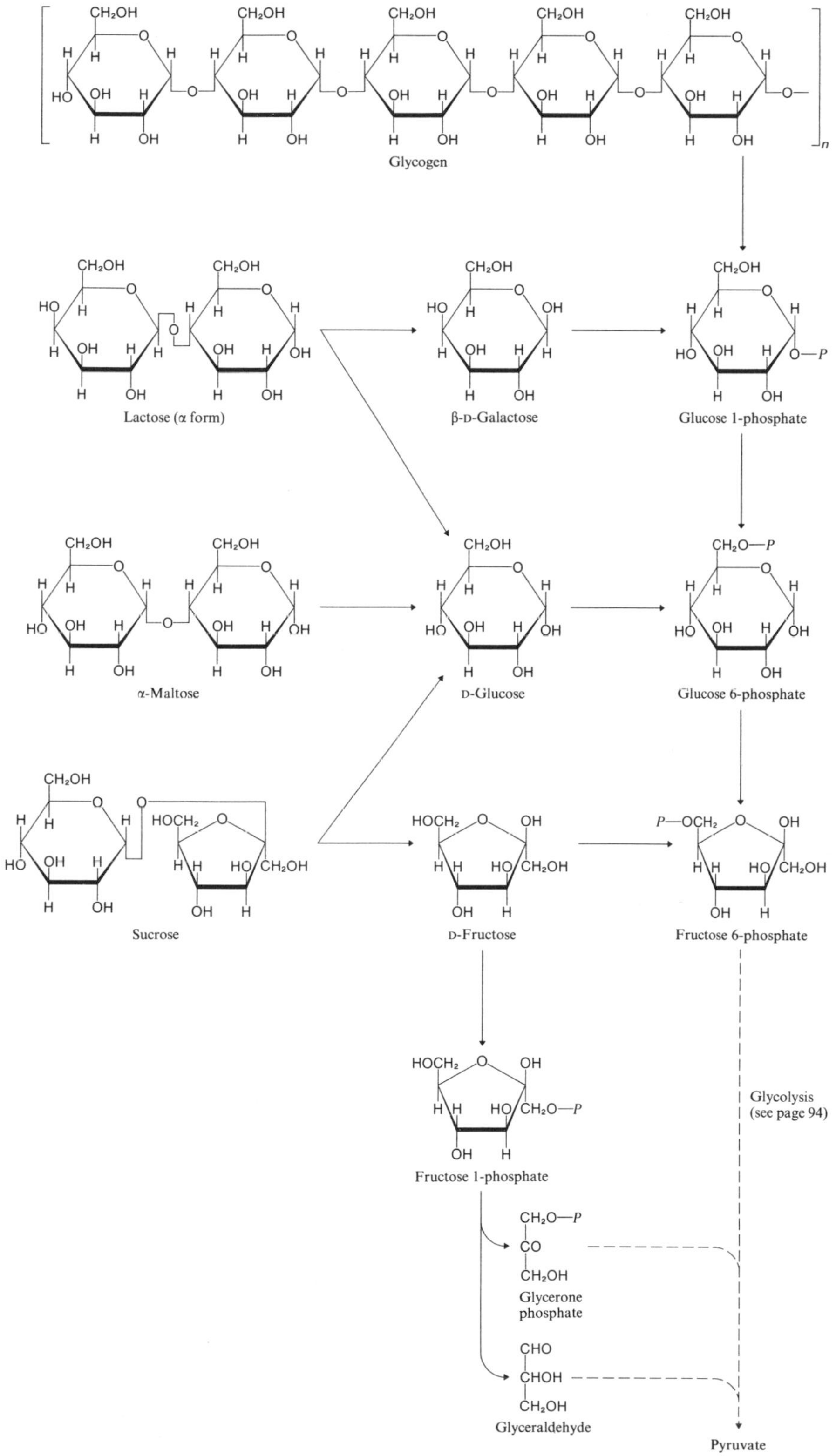

Glycogen

Lactose (α form)

β-D-Galactose

Glucose 1-phosphate

α-Maltose

D-Glucose

Glucose 6-phosphate

Sucrose

D-Fructose

Fructose 6-phosphate

Fructose 1-phosphate

Glycerone
phosphate

Glyceraldehyde

Glycolysis
(see page 94)

Pyruvate

In the digestion of a wide variety of food constituents, and also in the breakdown of constituents of the body itself, a whole series of carbohydrates in addition to glucose may be formed. These include fructose (from sucrose), galactose (from lactose), uronic acids and amino sugars (from proteoglycans), and mannose, fucose and xylose (from glycoproteins and glycolipids). Ribose and deoxyribose are formed by hydrolysis of nucleic acids, and *myo*-inositol is a breakdown product of phosphatidylinositols.

Intestinal breakdown of poly- and oligosaccharides (Fig. 1)

In an ordinary Western European diet starch constitutes about 60%, sucrose about 30%, and lactose about 10% of the carbohydrates. Oligosaccharides such as raffinose and stachyose, which are contained in small amounts in legumes, are broken down by intestinal bacteria. Amylose, amylopectin – the two constituents of starch (page 21) – and glycogen are hydrolyzed by α-amylase in the lumen of the small intestine and top part of the jejunum. Since α-amylase can split only the 1,4 bond between 2 glucose residues outside of branchings, but not the 1,6 bond, maltotriose and branched-chain oligosaccharides, the so-called 'α-limit dextrins', are also formed from amylopectin and glycogen along with glucose and maltose. The disaccharides lactose, maltose and sucrose as well as the oligosaccharides consisting of glucose residues are split in the brush border of the mucosa of the small intestine by specific disaccharidases and oligosaccharidases to yield the corresponding monosaccharides. Since the monosaccharide molecules are too big to be able to diffuse through the intestinal membrane, special transport mechanisms are needed. The transport of glucose and galactose seems to take place via the same Na^+-dependent mechanism, whereas the transport of fructose is independent of Na^+.

Degradation of glucose

The degradation of glucose is described in the section 'Glycolysis' (page 95). Glucose can be reduced to sorbitol in the seminal vesicles (page 131).

Degradation of fructose (Fig. 2)

Two routes whereby fructose may be broken down to intermediates of the glycolytic pathway are possible. In the first and less important one, fructose is phosphorylated at position 6 by fructokinase and enters the glycolytic pathway directly. The alternative – and more important – pathway involves phosphorylation at position 1 and the subsequent cleavage of the fructose 1-phosphate into glyc-

eraldehyde and glycerone phosphate, both of which are readily metabolized. The pathway via fructose 6-phosphate in the spermatozoa is used to produce energy.

Metabolism of glucosamine

Glucosamine is phosphorylated to yield glucosamine 6-phosphate, which is then converted to fructose 6-phosphate, an intermediate of the glycolytic pathway. This conversion involves a reversal of the first step of the reaction pathway described on page 132.

Degradation of glucuronic acid, *myo*-inositol and D-xylose

D-Glucuronic acid is reduced in a first step to L-gulonic acid and then oxidized to 3-dehydro-L-gulonic acid. This compound is decarboxylated at position C-6 to yield L-xylulose. The subsequent steps up to the formation of xylulose 5-phosphate, which appears in the pentose phosphate cycle, can be seen in Figure 3.

myo-Inositol is oxidized to glucuronic acid, which is then metabolized as indicated above.

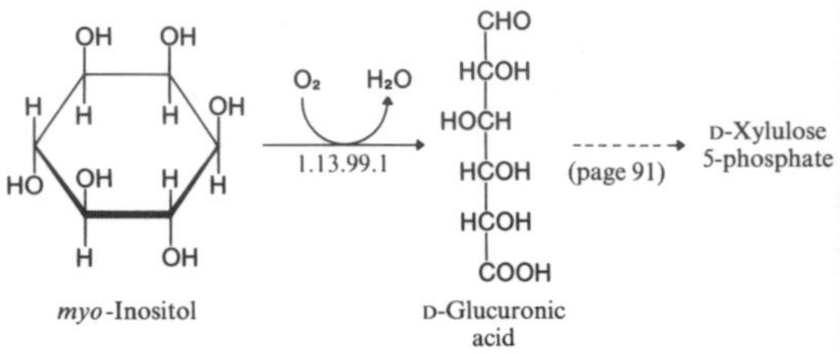

Enzyme involved:
1.13.99.1 *myo*-Inositol oxygenase

D-Xylose is converted to D-xylulose, an intermediate product in the degradation of glucuronic acid.

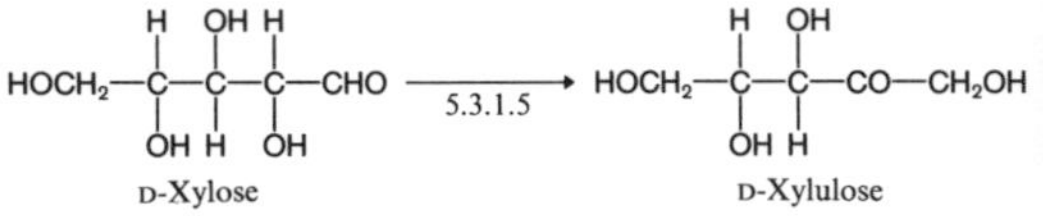

Enzyme involved:
5.3.1.5 Xylose isomerase

Fig. 2 *Degradation of fructose*

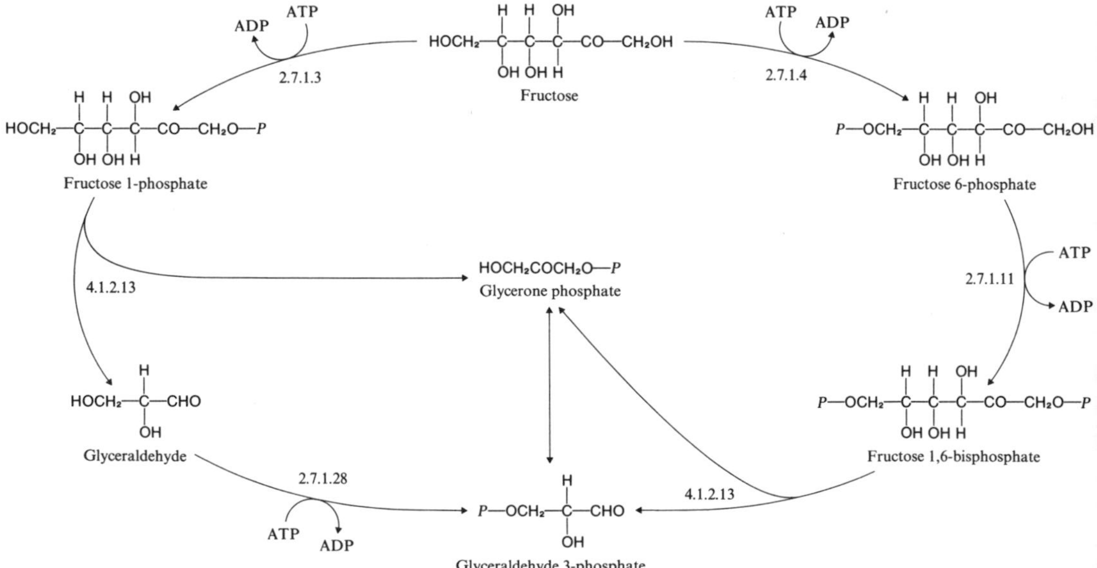

Enzymes involved:
2.7.1.3 Ketohexokinase
2.7.1.4 Fructokinase
2.7.1.11 6-Phosphofructokinase
2.7.1.28 Triokinase
4.1.2.13 Fructose-bisphosphate aldolase

Fig. 3 *Degradation of D-glucuronic acid*

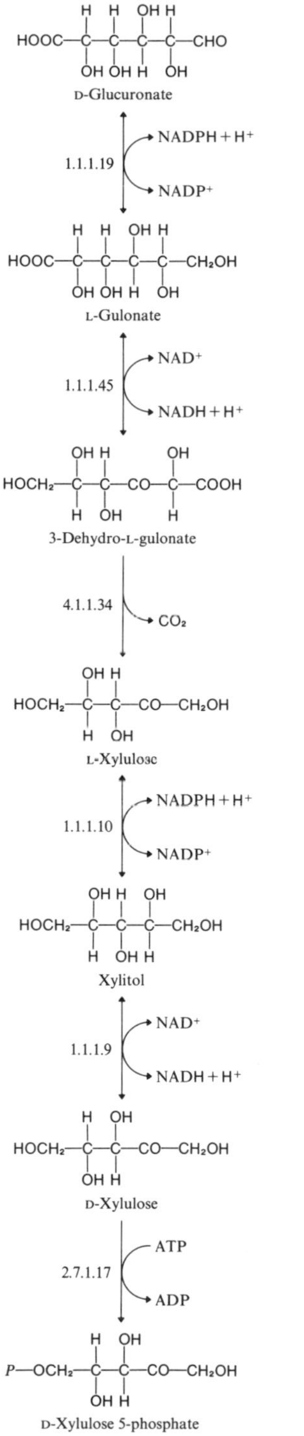

```
        H  H  OH H
HOOC—C—C—C—C—CHO
        OH OH H  OH
```
D-Glucuronate

↓ 1.1.1.19 (NADPH + H⁺ → NADP⁺)

```
        H  H  OH H
HOOC—C—C—C—C—CH₂OH
        OH OH H  OH
```
L-Gulonate

↓ 1.1.1.45 (NAD⁺ → NADH + H⁺)

```
        OH H        OH
HOCH₂—C—C—CO—C—COOH
        H  OH       H
```
3-Dehydro-L-gulonate

↓ 4.1.1.34 (→ CO₂)

```
        OH H
HOCH₂—C—C—CO—CH₂OH
        H  OH
```
L-Xylulose

↓ 1.1.1.10 (NADPH + H⁺ → NADP⁺)

```
        OH H  OH
HOCH₂—C—C—C—CH₂OH
        H  OH H
```
Xylitol

↓ 1.1.1.9 (NAD⁺ → NADH + H⁺)

```
        H  OH
HOCH₂—C—C—CO—CH₂OH
        OH H
```
D-Xylulose

↓ 2.7.1.17 (ATP → ADP)

```
        H  OH
P—OCH₂—C—C—CO—CH₂OH
        OH H
```
D-Xylulose 5-phosphate

Enzymes involved:
1.1.1.9   D-Xylulose reductase
1.1.1.10 L-Xylulose reductase
1.1.1.19 Glucuronate reductase
1.1.1.45 L-Gulonate dehydrogenase
2.7.1.17 Xylulokinase
4.1.1.34 Dehydro-L-gulonate decarboxylase

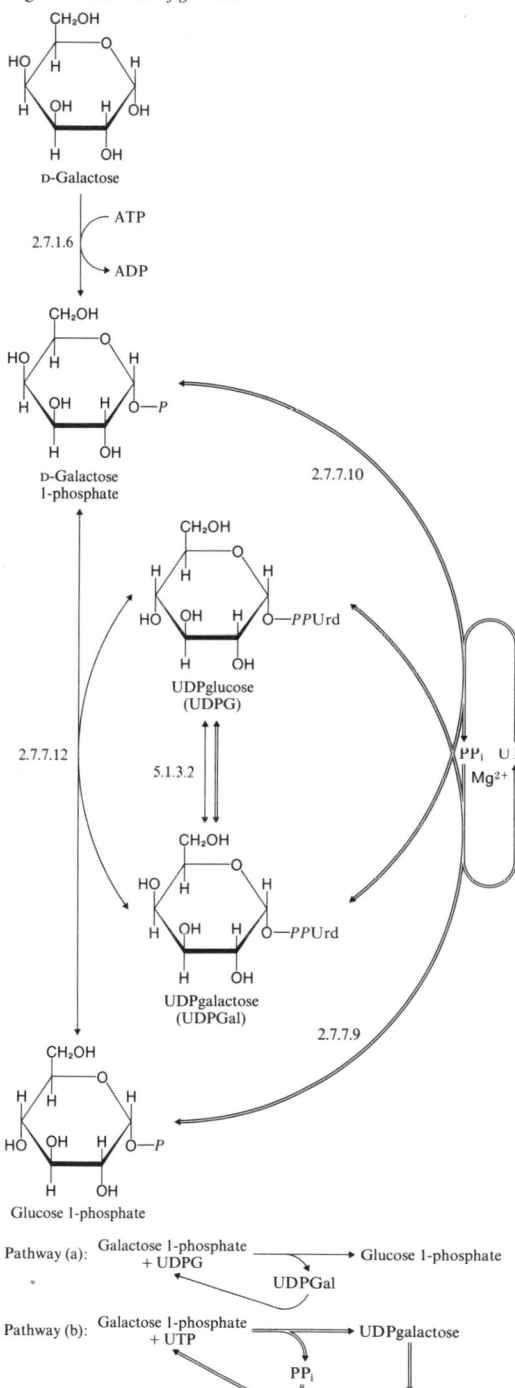

Fig. 4 *Metabolism of galactose*

D-Galactose

↓ 2.7.1.6 (ATP → ADP)

D-Galactose 1-phosphate

2.7.7.12

UDPglucose (UDPG)

5.1.3.2

UDPgalactose (UDPGal)

2.7.7.10   2.7.7.9   PPᵢ UTP Mg²⁺

Glucose 1-phosphate

Pathway (a): Galactose 1-phosphate + UDPG → Glucose 1-phosphate / UDPGal

Pathway (b): Galactose 1-phosphate + UTP → UDPgalactose / PPᵢ → UDPglucose → Glucose 1-phosphate

Enzymes involved:
2.7.1.6   Galactokinase
2.7.7.9   UTP–glucose-1-phosphate uridylyltransferase
2.7.7.10 UTP–hexose-1-phosphate uridylyltransferase
2.7.7.12 UDPglucose–hexose-1-phosphate uridylyltransferase
5.1.3.2   UDPglucose 4-epimerase

Fig. 5 *Metabolism of mannose*

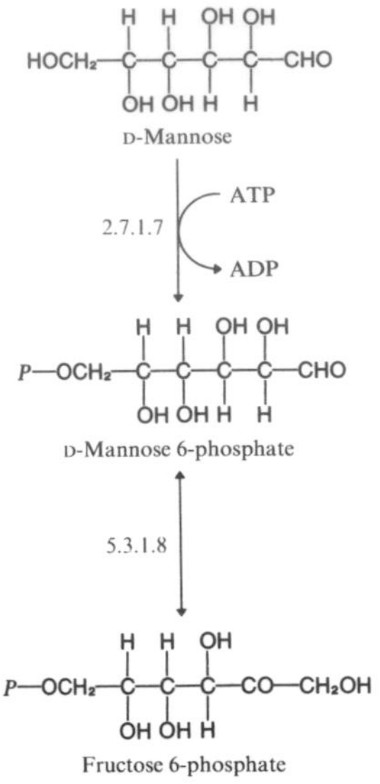

H H OH OH
HOCH₂—C—C—C—C—CHO
OH OH H H
D-Mannose

2.7.1.7 ⟍ ATP
         ⟍ ADP

H H OH OH
P—OCH₂—C—C—C—C—CHO
OH OH H H
D-Mannose 6-phosphate

5.3.1.8

H H OH
P—OCH₂—C—C—C—CO—CH₂OH
OH OH H
Fructose 6-phosphate

Enzymes involved:
2.7.1.7 Mannokinase
5.3.1.8 Mannose-6-phosphate isomerase

Fig. 6 *Metabolism of L-fucose in mammals*

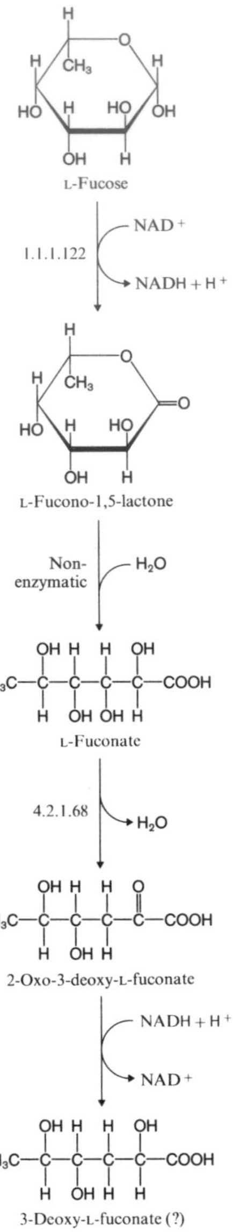

L-Fucose

1.1.1.122 ⟍ NAD+
           ⟍ NADH + H+

L-Fucono-1,5-lactone

Non-enzymatic ⟍ H₂O

OH H H OH
H₃C—C—C—C—C—COOH
H OH OH H
L-Fuconate

4.2.1.68 ⟍ H₂O

OH H H O
H₃C—C—C—C—C—COOH
H OH H
2-Oxo-3-deoxy-L-fuconate

⟍ NADH + H+
⟍ NAD+

OH H H OH
H₃C—C—C—C—C—COOH
H OH H H
3-Deoxy-L-fuconate (?)

Enzymes involved:
1.1.1.122 D-*threo*-Aldose dehydrogenase
4.2.1.68 L-Fuconate dehydratase

Metabolism of galactose (Fig. 4)

The metabolism of galactose proceeds via an epimerization of the hydroxy group at position 4. Galactose is first phosphorylated to galactose 1-phosphate and then converted to glucose 1-phosphate by one of two possible pathways. Glucose 1-phosphate may then enter the glycolytic pathway.

Another reaction – which seems to be of importance in the lens of the eye – consists in the reduction of galactose to galactitol with the aid of aldose reductase, a reaction which is analogous to the reduction of glucose to sorbitol (page 131).

Metabolism of mannose (Fig. 5)

Mannose is possibly formed – by the action of an α-mannosidase in the gastrointestinal tract – from food glycoproteins. After phosphorylation to mannose 6-phosphate a conversion takes place either to mannose 1-phosphate (Fig. 3, page 133) or to fructose 6-phosphate, which enters the glycolytic pathway.

Metabolism of fucose (Fig. 6)

Fucose is possibly formed – by the action of an α-fucosidase in the gastrointestinal tract – from food glycoproteins. Fucose metabolism in mammals, in contrast to fucose metabolism in bacteria, is known only in part. The first step – the formation of L-fuconic acid by dehydrogenation of fucose – probably proceeds via the lactone, which splits spontaneously.

Degradation of ribose and 2-deoxyribose

Both of these pentoses are first phosphorylated at position 5 by the action of ribokinase (2.7.1.15). Ribose 5-phosphate is converted to glucose 6-phosphate and triose phosphate in the pentose phosphate cycle (Fig. 1, page 134), while 2-deoxyribose 5-phosphate is split by deoxyribose-phosphate aldolase (4.1.2.4) to acetaldehyde and glyceraldehyde 3-phosphate:

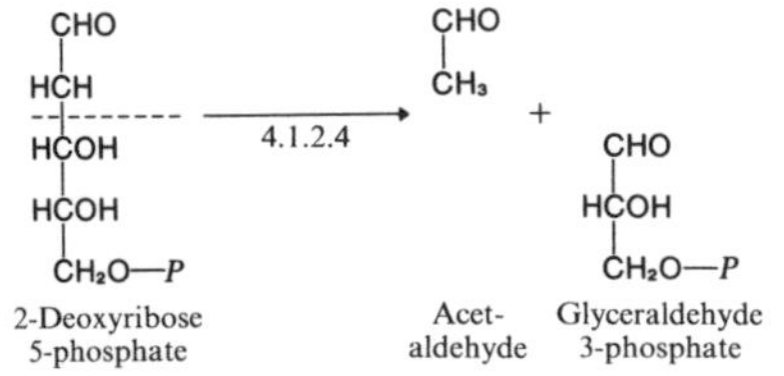

CHO   CHO
HCH   CH₃
HCOH   4.1.2.4   +   CHO
HCOH   HCOH
CH₂O—P   CH₂O—P

2-Deoxyribose   Acet-   Glyceraldehyde
5-phosphate   aldehyde   3-phosphate

Acetyl-CoA can then be formed from acetaldehyde.

Formation of oxalic acid

Oxalic acid can be formed in the body in two different ways: either as a metabolic product of dietary ascorbic acid (Fig. 7) or from endogenously formed glyoxylic acid or glycolic acid (Fig. 8). The latter two compounds may derive from a series of starting materials, so that the origin of the final product – oxalic acid – is hard to trace.

Importance of carbohydrate degradation

The monosaccharides formed by digestion in the intestinal tract are absorbed and reach the various tissues through the blood circulation. The main pathway by which hexoses are degraded is the anaerobic fermentation to yield lactic acid, a process referred to as 'glycolysis'. As a rule, products of glycolysis are subsequently oxidized to CO_2 and water in the tricarboxylic acid cycle (Krebs cycle). An alternative pathway of oxidation exists in which glucose is oxidized without first undergoing fission to C_3 compounds. This pathway – the 'pentose phosphate cycle' (see page 134) – is not, however, a major source of energy in higher animals. Its main function is to yield reduced NADP, as well as to produce the intermediates necessary for biosynthesis.

Fig. 7 *Probable reactions of the degradation of L-ascorbic acid*

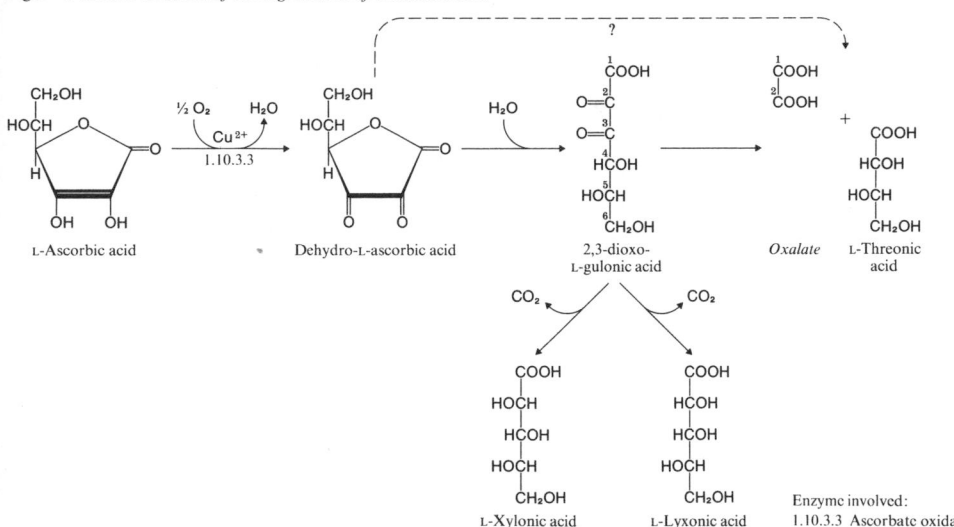

L-Ascorbic acid → Dehydro-L-ascorbic acid → 2,3-dioxo-L-gulonic acid → Oxalate + L-Threonic acid

L-Xylonic acid   L-Lyxonic acid

Enzyme involved:
1.10.3.3 Ascorbate oxidase

Fig. 8 *Endogenous formation of oxalate*

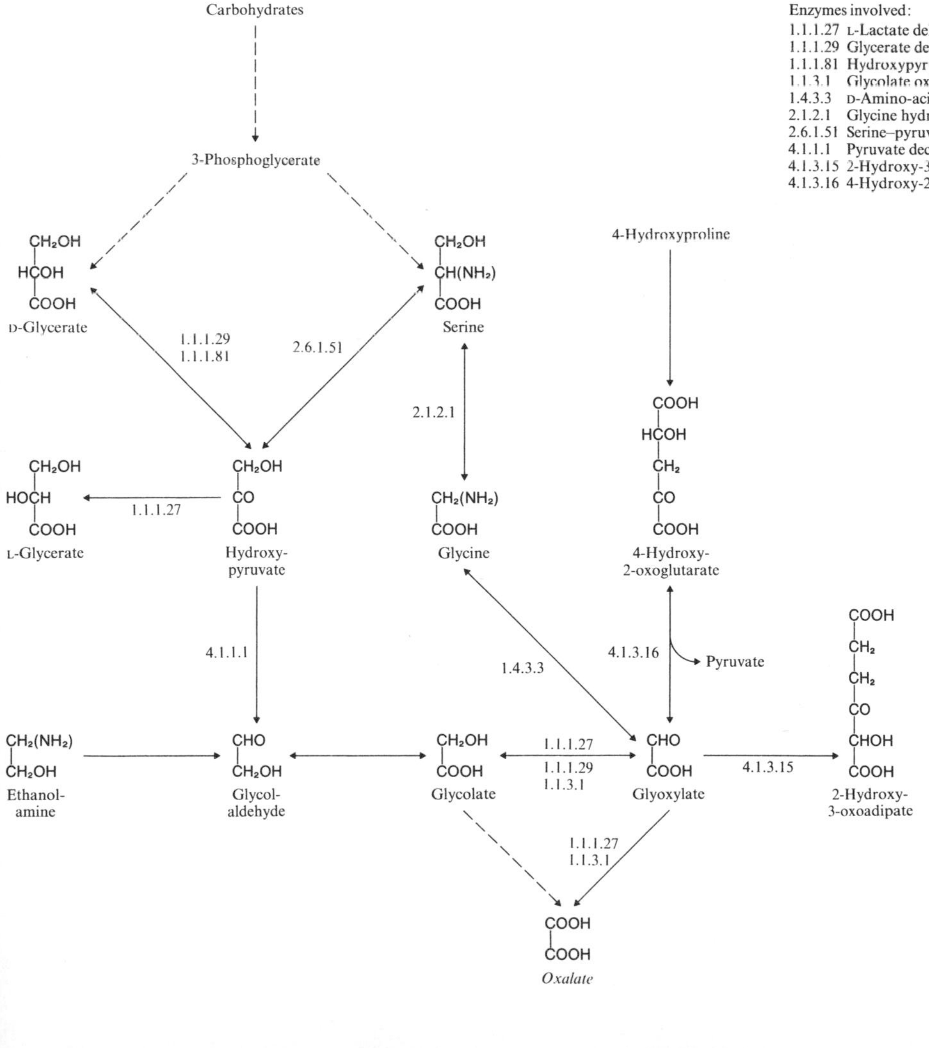

Enzymes involved:
1.1.1.27 L-Lactate dehydrogenase
1.1.1.29 Glycerate dehydrogenase
1.1.1.81 Hydroxypyruvate reductase
1.1.3.1 Glycolate oxidase
1.4.3.3 D-Amino-acid oxidase
2.1.2.1 Glycine hydroxymethyltransferase
2.6.1.51 Serine–pyruvate aminotransferase
4.1.1.1 Pyruvate decarboxylase
4.1.3.15 2-Hydroxy-3-oxoadipate synthase
4.1.3.16 4-Hydroxy-2-oxoglutarate aldolase

Carbohydrates

3-Phosphoglycerate

D-Glycerate   Serine   4-Hydroxyproline

1.1.1.29
1.1.1.81   2.6.1.51   2.1.2.1

L-Glycerate   Hydroxypyruvate   Glycine   4-Hydroxy-2-oxoglutarate

1.1.1.27

4.1.1.1   1.4.3.3   4.1.3.16 → Pyruvate

Ethanolamine   Glycolaldehyde   Glycolate   Glyoxylate   2-Hydroxy-3-oxoadipate

1.1.1.27
1.1.1.29
1.1.3.1

4.1.3.15

1.1.1.27
1.1.3.1

Oxalate

Fig. 9 *Glycolysis*

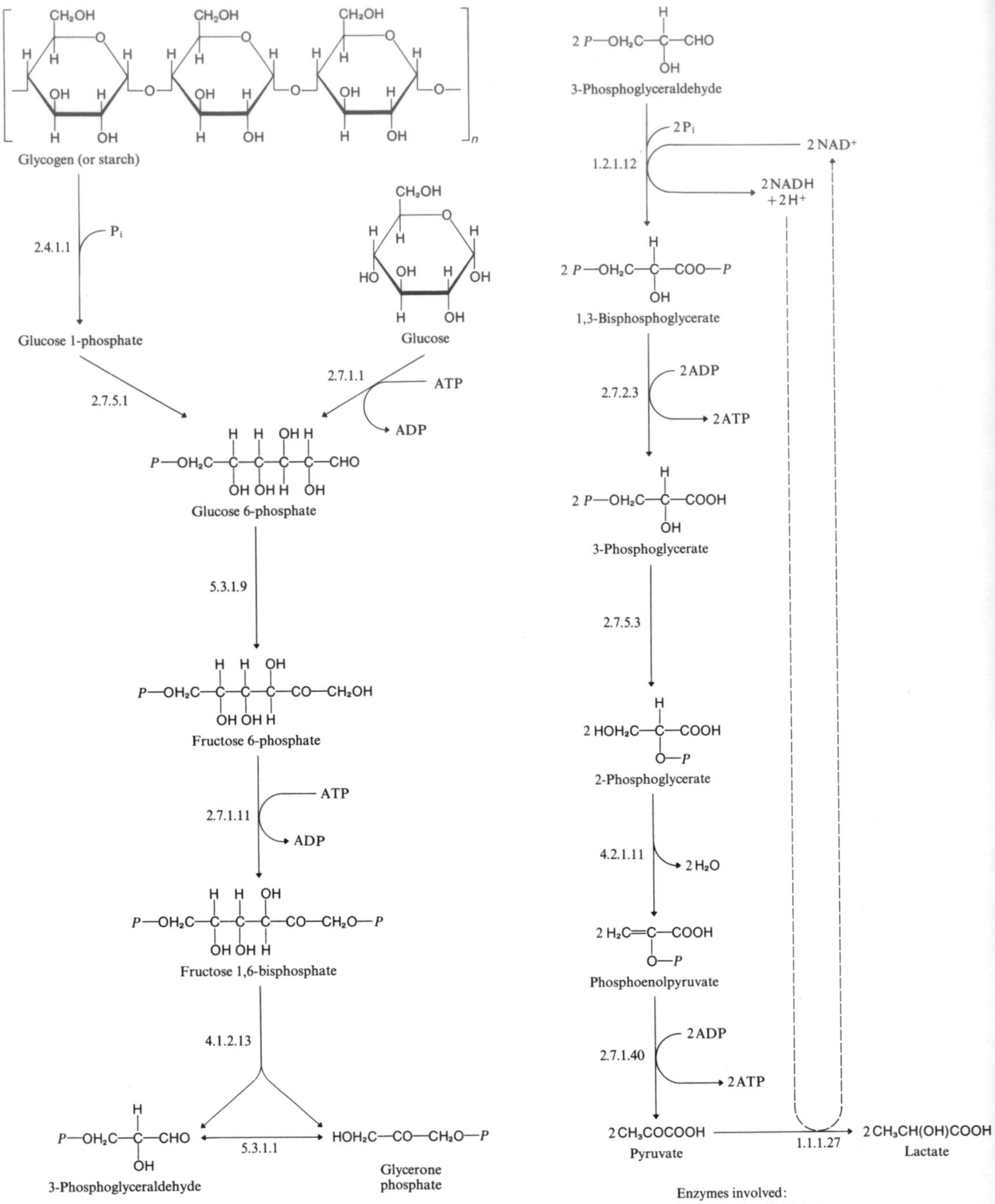

CH_2OH ... Glycogen (or starch)

Glucose 1-phosphate

2.4.1.1 P_i

2.7.5.1

CH_2OH ... Glucose

2.7.1.1 ATP

ADP

$P{-}OH_2C{-}C{-}C{-}C{-}C{-}CHO$
Glucose 6-phosphate

5.3.1.9

$P{-}OH_2C{-}C{-}C{-}C{-}CO{-}CH_2OH$
Fructose 6-phosphate

2.7.1.11 ATP

ADP

$P{-}OH_2C{-}C{-}C{-}C{-}CO{-}CH_2O{-}P$
Fructose 1,6-bisphosphate

4.1.2.13

$P{-}OH_2C{-}C{-}CHO$
OH
3-Phosphoglyceraldehyde

5.3.1.1

$HOH_2C{-}CO{-}CH_2O{-}P$
Glycerone phosphate

(Continued on the right side)

$2\ P{-}OH_2C{-}C{-}CHO$
OH
3-Phosphoglyceraldehyde

1.2.1.12 2 P_i

2 NAD^+

2 NADH + 2H^+

$2\ P{-}OH_2C{-}C{-}COO{-}P$
OH
1,3-Bisphosphoglycerate

2.7.2.3 2 ADP

2 ATP

$2\ P{-}OH_2C{-}C{-}COOH$
OH
3-Phosphoglycerate

2.7.5.3

$2\ HOH_2C{-}C{-}COOH$
$O{-}P$
2-Phosphoglycerate

4.2.1.11 2 H_2O

$2\ H_2C{=}C{-}COOH$
$O{-}P$
Phosphoenolpyruvate

2.7.1.40 2 ADP

2 ATP

2 $CH_3COCOOH$
Pyruvate

1.1.1.27

2 $CH_3CH(OH)COOH$
Lactate

Net result of glycolysis from glucose:
$C_6H_{12}O_6 + 2P_i + 2ADP \longrightarrow 2CH_3CH(OH)COOH + 2ATP + 2H_2O$
or
$C_6H_{12}O_6 + 2P_i + 2ADP + 2NAD^+ \longrightarrow 2CH_3COCOOH + 2ATP + 2H_2O + 2NADH + 2H^+$

Net result of glycolysis from glycogen:
$[\alpha\text{-}1,4\text{-Glycosyl}]_n + 3P_i + 3ADP \longrightarrow 2CH_3CH(OH)COOH + 3ATP + 2H_2O + [\alpha\text{-}1,4\text{-Glycosyl}]_{n-1}$

Enzymes involved:
1.1.1.27 L-Lactate dehydrogenase
1.2.1.12 Glyceraldehyde-3-phosphate dehydrogenase
2.4.1.1 Glycogen phosphorylase
2.7.1.1 Hexokinase
2.7.1.11 6-Phosphofructokinase
2.7.1.40 Pyruvate kinase
2.7.2.3 Phosphoglycerate kinase
2.7.5.1 Phosphoglucomutase
2.7.5.3 Phosphoglyceromutase
4.1.2.13 Fructose-bisphosphate aldolase
4.2.1.11 Enolase
5.3.1.1 Triose-phosphate isomerase
5.3.1.9 Glucose-6-phosphate isomerase

Glycolysis (anaerobic lactic-acid fermentation) (Fig. 9)

Glycolysis, together with the tricarboxylic acid cycle and the electron transfer system (ETS), provides the 'backbone' of the body's biochemistry, through which interrelationships between carbohydrates, lipids, amino acids, purines and pyrimidines are established. From this backbone many metabolites arise, and to it they return on degradation.

In this glycolytic pathway, glucose is broken down into lactic acid or – in the case of yeasts – to ethanol. The most important reaction is the oxidation of 3-phosphoglyceraldehyde to 1,3-bisphosphoglycerate. Biological oxidations are mostly dehydrogenations, and NAD is usually the hydrogen carrier (see page 75). There is, however, a limited amount of NAD available in the cell, so that continuous oxidation depends on reoxidation of the reduced NAD. In glycolytic fermentation, the hydrogen acceptor is pyruvate or decarboxylated pyruvate (acetaldehyde), from which lactic acid or ethanol is formed. Thus a linked, purely anaerobic oxidation–reduction system is active within the pathway. Oxidations are exothermic reactions, and part of the energy released is harnessed in the biologically utilizable form of ATP. The first product of oxidation is 1,3-bisphosphoglycerate, which contains a mixed acid anhydride bond ($-COO-P$). For reasons explained under ATP (page 78), acid anhydride bonds release a high amount of energy in hydrolysis, and the next reaction with ADP makes possible the formation of ATP.

The net result of glycolysis is the formation of 2 mol lactic acid and 2 mol ATP from 1 mol glucose. It is not an efficient means of ATP synthesis since the major products are still highly reduced and therefore contain much potential energy. In order to release this energy, pyruvate must not be fermented to lactic acid but must be completely oxidized to CO_2 and water, a process that takes place in the tricarboxylic acid cycle and the electron transfer system (see next chapter). In the aerobic oxidation of 1 mol glucose, 38 mol ATP are formed, compared with only 2 mol ATP in the case of glycolytic fermentation.

Reviews

· STANBURY et al., *The Metabolic Basis of Inherited Disease*, 5th ed., Part 2: Disorders of carbohydrate metabolism, McGraw-Hill, New York, 1983.
· HERS and HUE, Gluconeogenesis and related aspects of glycolysis, *Ann. Rev. Biochem.*, **52**, 617 (1983).
· COLOWICK, S. P., The hexokinases, in BOYER, P. D. (Ed.), *The Enzymes*, 4th ed., Volume 9, Academic Press, New York, 1973, page 1.
· PURICH et al., The hexokinases; kinetic, physical, and regulatory properties, *Advanc. Enzymol.*, **39**, 249 (1973).
· VILLAR-PALASI and LARNER, Glycogen metabolism and glycolytic enzymes, *Ann. Rev. Biochem.*, **39**, 639 (1970).
· FISCHER et al., The structure, function and control of glycogen phosphorylase, *Essays Biochem.*, **6**, 23 (1970).
· PONTREMOLI and GRAZI, Hexose-monophosphate oxidation, *Comprehens. Biochem.*, **17**, 163 (1969).
· DICKENS et al., *Carbohydrate Metabolism and Its Disorders*, Volumes 1 and 2, Academic Press, London, 1968.
· AXELROD, B., Glycolysis, in GREENBERG, D. M. (Ed.), *Metabolic Pathways*, 3rd ed., Volume 1, Academic Press, New York, 1967, page 112.

Aerobic respiration · Tricarboxylic acid cycle

Before pyruvate can be utilized in the tricarboxylic acid cycle it must first be converted to acetyl-CoA by oxidative decarboxylation. The reaction is catalyzed by the pyruvate-dehydrogenase complex, and 5 cofactors are utilized: thiamin diphosphate, lipoic acid, coenzyme A, FAD and NAD; Mg^{2+} is also required. The overall reaction is catalyzed by 3 enzymes in an ordered sequence: pyruvate dehydrogenase (lipoamide) (1.2.4.1), the core enzyme dihydrolipoamide acetyltransferase (2.3.1.12), and dihydrolipoamide dehydrogenase (1.8.1.4).

In the first step, pyruvate reacts with thiamin diphosphate, yielding 2-hydroxyethylthiamin diphosphate and releasing CO_2. The α unit of the enzyme – a tetramer with the structure $\alpha_2\beta_2$ – binds thiamin diphosphate tightly but not covalently. In the subsequent step the core enzyme catalyzes transfer and simultaneous oxidation of the C_2 fragment of 2-hydroxyethylthiamin diphosphate, forming acetyl-CoA. In this process, the disulfide bond of lipoic acid is re-

duced to the dihydro form, and at the same time an acetaldehyde equivalent is oxidized to an acetyl equivalent. Lipoic acid is covalently bound to a lysine residue of the core enzyme. In the final step, the reduced lipoic acid is reoxidized by interreaction with NAD. The reaction sequence is displayed in Figure 1.

The oxidative decarboxylation of 2-oxoglutaric acid and of the 2-oxo acids formed from valine, leucine and isoleucine proceeds by the same reaction mechanism involving the 2-oxoglutarate dehydrogenase complex (page 97) and the branched-chain-2-oxo-acid dehydrogenase complex, respectively (page 114).

Acetyl-CoA is completely oxidized in the tricarboxylic acid cycle. The first step consists in the formation of citric acid by the condensation of acetyl-CoA with oxaloacetic acid. The citric acid then undergoes a series of reactions that are, on balance, oxidative and in which other tricarboxylic and dicarboxylic acids arise. Finally there is a regeneration of the oxaloacetic acid, which is then available for another turn of the cycle.

The tricarboxylic acid cycle (Fig. 2) has 2 functions: It makes possible the oxidation of acetyl-CoA, with the formation of CO_2, as well as reduced NAD and FAD. These reduced coenzymes then enter the electron transfer system, where the hydrogen is completely oxidized to water, with the formation of ATP. In the tricarboxylic acid cycle itself, only 1 mol GTP, but no ATP, is formed from 1 mol of substrate. The other function of the cycle is to provide a series of intermediates. The most important of these is 2-oxoglutaric acid, the precursor of glutamic acid and hence other amino acids (see page 154). Aspartic acid, from which further amino acids as well as the pyrimidines are derived, is formed from oxaloacetic acid (see page 155). Succinyl-CoA is the precursor of heme (see page 166).

The link between the tricarboxylic acid cycle and glycolysis is acetyl-CoA, which is formed from pyruvate by oxidative decarboxylation. If the net result of these reactions (Fig. 1) is added to that of the tricarboxylic acid cycle (page 97), the complete oxidation of the pyruvate to carbon dioxide and water with simultaneous reduction of the coenzymes becomes evident:

$$CH_3COCOOH + GDP + P_i + 4\,NAD^+ \longrightarrow 3\,CO_2 + GTP + 4\,NADH$$
$$+ FAD + 2\,H_2O \qquad\qquad\qquad + 4\,H^+ + FADH_2$$

Electron transfer system (ETS)

The reduced coenzymes derived from glycolysis and the tricarboxylic acid cycle still contain considerable amounts of potential energy. The function of the ETS is to convert part of this energy to the biologically utilizable form of ATP, the importance of which was discussed on page 78. ATP is formed by the condensation of ADP with inorganic phosphate, with the formation of an energy-rich acid anhydride bond. The energy required for this is supplied by specific redox reactions of the ETS. When the reduced coenzymes are oxidized in the ETS, enough energy is released in certain steps to make it possible for the mitochondrial ATP synthase complex (also called 'proton ATPase'), comprising the coupling factors F_0 and F_1, to form ATP from ADP and inorganic phosphate. This process is also called 'oxidative phosphorylation' and is strongly endergonic.

The stepwise release of energy in the mitochondrial inner membrane is made possible by the transfer of hydrogen or electrons from one carrier to another, which are therefore alternately oxidized and reduced (Fig. 3).

In the first reaction the reduced NAD is oxidized by NADH dehydrogenase. This enzyme contains flavin mononucleotide (FMN) as a prosthetic group (see page 76), and also iron, which participates in the electron transfer. Thus NADH dehydrogenase is a non-heme iron protein. The reduced FMN formed in this reaction then passes its H atoms to an iron–sulfur protein and thence to ubiquinone (coenzyme Q), which is reduced to ubiquinol (see page 77). In the conversion of succinate to fumarate, reduced FAD ($FADH_2$) is formed, which enters the ETS and gives up its H atoms to ubiquinone via a similar iron–sulfur protein.

In the redox reactions so far considered, hydrogen atoms (protons and electrons) are transferred, whereas in the subsequent redox reactions – via the cytochrome system – only electrons are transferred. Cytochromes are proteins with a heme group, the iron of which alternates between the oxidized form (ferri stage) and the reduced form (ferro stage). Thus energy-rich electrons are passed from one cytochrome to another; in each step they give up a certain amount of their energy. Properties of the cytochromes are presented on page 49.

It follows from Figure 3 that the hydrogen or electron carriers in the ETS possess a decreasing reducing power. Reduced NAD ($NADH + H^+$) reduces FMN; $FMNH_2$ (or $FADH_2$) reduces ubiquinone and so on. These relative reducing powers may be quantified by their redox potentials. The redox potential of a strongly reducing

Fig. 1   *Formation of acetyl-CoA*

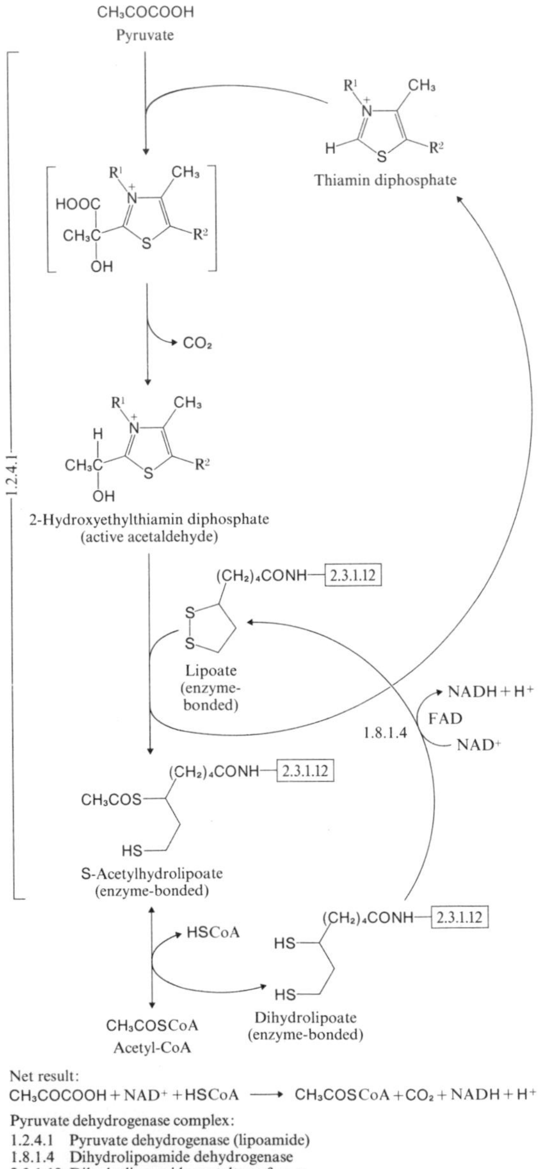

CH₃COCOOH
Pyruvate

Thiamin diphosphate

CO₂

2-Hydroxyethylthiamin diphosphate
(active acetaldehyde)

Lipoate
(enzyme-bonded)

NADH + H⁺
FAD
1.8.1.4
NAD⁺

S-Acetylhydrolipoate
(enzyme-bonded)

HSCoA

Dihydrolipoate
(enzyme-bonded)

CH₃COSCoA
Acetyl-CoA

Net result:
$$CH_3COCOOH + NAD^+ + HSCoA \longrightarrow CH_3COSCoA + CO_2 + NADH + H^+$$

Pyruvate dehydrogenase complex:
1.2.4.1   Pyruvate dehydrogenase (lipoamide)
1.8.1.4   Dihydrolipoamide dehydrogenase
2.3.1.12   Dihydrolipoamide acetyltransferase

Fig. 2 *Tricarboxylic acid cycle (citrate cycle)*

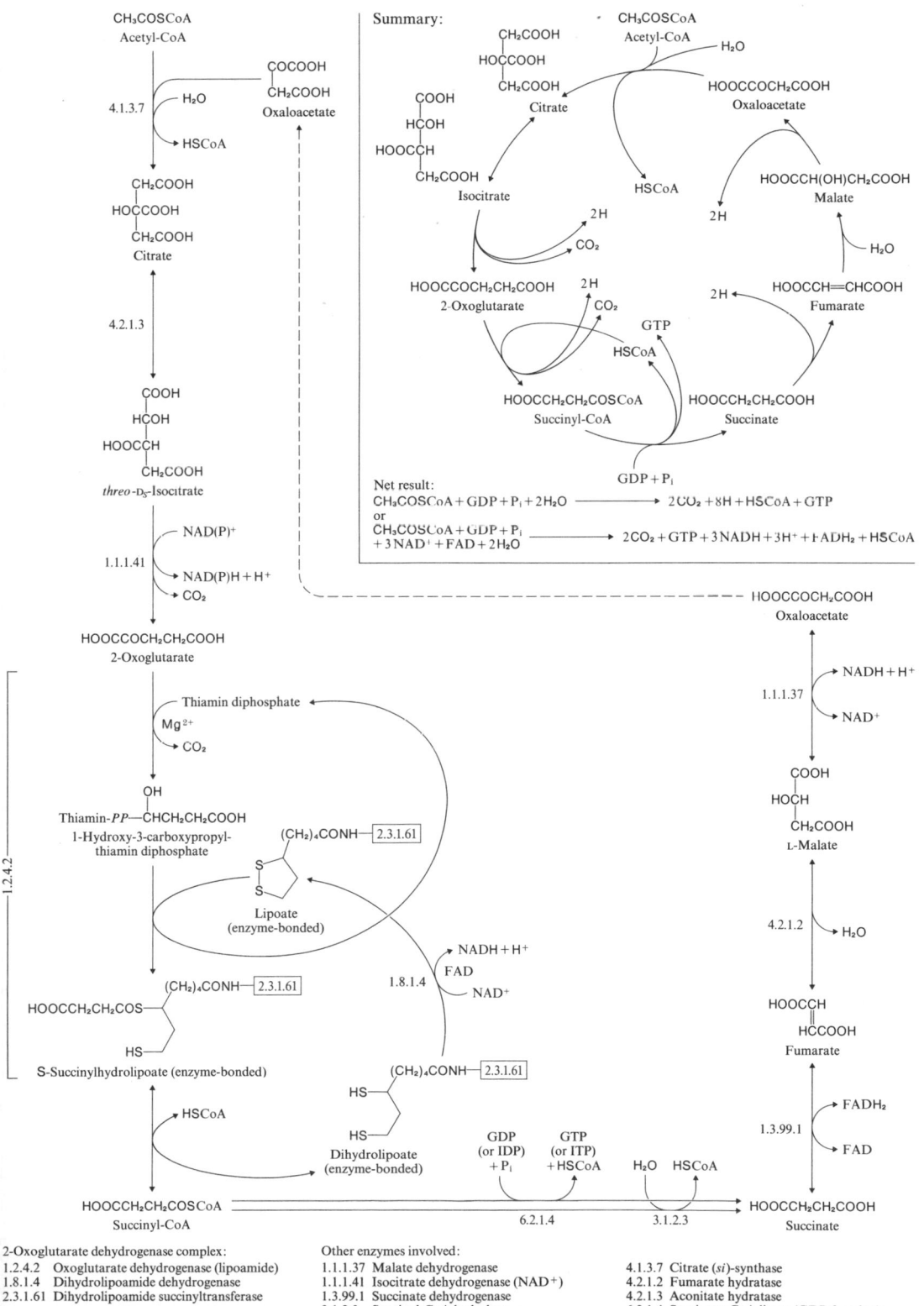

2-Oxoglutarate dehydrogenase complex:
1.2.4.2 Oxoglutarate dehydrogenase (lipoamide)
1.8.1.4 Dihydrolipoamide dehydrogenase
2.3.1.61 Dihydrolipoamide succinyltransferase

Other enzymes involved:
1.1.1.37 Malate dehydrogenase
1.1.1.41 Isocitrate dehydrogenase (NAD+)
1.3.99.1 Succinate dehydrogenase
3.1.2.3 Succinyl-CoA hydrolase

4.1.3.7 Citrate (si)-synthase
4.2.1.2 Fumarate hydratase
4.2.1.3 Aconitate hydratase
6.2.1.4 Succinate–CoA ligase (GDP-forming)

Fig. 3   *Electron transfer system (respiratory chain)*

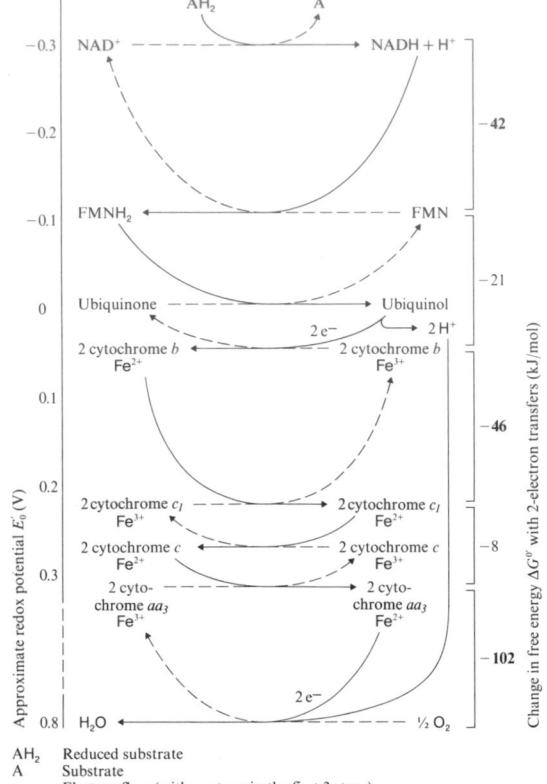

AH₂   Reduced substrate
A   Substrate
———   Electron flow (with protons in the first 3 steps)
– – –   Utilization and regeneration of oxidized coenzymes

about 0.2 volt. 2 hydrogen atoms and hence also 2 electrons take part in the reaction, so that $n = 2$ and

$$\Delta G^{0\prime} = -2 \times 96485 \times 0.2 = 38.6\,\text{kJ}$$

The energies released in the subsequent steps are shown at the right side of Figure 3. The formation of 1 mol ATP from 1 mol each of ADP and inorganic phosphate (P_i) requires at least 35 kJ. This amount of energy is released in each of the following 3 reactions:

1. Reaction between reduced NAD and FMN
2. Reaction between cytochrome b and cytochrome c_l
3. Reaction between cytochrome aa_3 and dioxygen

Hence it follows that 3 ATP molecules can be formed for each reduced NAD molecule entering the system, and 2 ATP molecules can be formed for each $FADH_2$ molecule.

The sequence of oxidation and reduction reactions, which characterizes the ETS, is in reality a far more complex process than has been described. Some of the reactions – such as that involving ubiquinone – result in the transfer of protons or electrons across the mitochondrial membrane. This sets up a potential which is a source of energy for phosphorylation, but the exact process is still uncertain.

The superiority of *aerobic respiration* using dioxygen as the ultimate electron acceptor, compared with glycolysis, which uses an organic substance as the ultimate electron acceptor, can – as is shown below – be quantified. The overall equation for the complete oxidation of glucose is obtained by adding the equations applicable to the following steps:

1. Glucose to pyruvate:

$C_6H_{12}O_6 + 2\,ADP$ $\longrightarrow$ $2\,CH_3COCOOH + 2\,ATP + 2\,NADH + 2\,H^+$
$+ 2\,P_i + 2\,NAD^+$ $+ 2\,H_2O$

2. Pyruvate to acetyl-CoA:

$2\,CH_3COCOOH + 2\,NAD^+$ $\longrightarrow$ $2\,CH_3COSCoA + 2\,CO_2 + 2\,NADH$
$+ 2\,HSCoA$ $+ 2\,H^+$

3. Acetyl-CoA to CO_2 and reduced coenzymes:

$2\,CH_3COSCoA + 2\,GDP + 2\,P_i$ $\longrightarrow$ $4\,CO_2 + 2\,GTP + 6\,NADH$
$+ 6\,NAD^+ + 2\,FAD + 4\,H_2O$ $+ 6\,H^+ + 2\,FADH_2 + 2\,HSCoA$

Addition yields

$C_6H_{12}O_6 + 2\,ADP + 2\,GDP + 4\,P_i$ $\longrightarrow$ $6\,CO_2 + 2\,ATP + 2\,GTP$
$+ 10\,NAD^+ + 2\,FAD + 4\,H_2O$ $+ 10\,NADH + 10\,H^+ + 2\,FADH_2$

Thus from the complete *oxidation* of 1 mol glucose a total of 36 mol ATP + 2 mol GTP (this corresponds to 38 mol ATP) arise – compared to 2 mol ATP produced by *fermentation* of 1 mol glucose to lactic acid.

Reviews

· HATEFI, Y., The mitochondrial electron transport and oxidative phosphorylation system, *Ann. Rev. Biochem.*, **54**, 1015 (1985).
· AMZEL and PEDERSEN, Proton ATPases: structure and mechanism, *Ann. Rev. Biochem.*, **52**, 801 (1983).
· WIKSTRÖM et al., *Cytochrome Oxidase*, Academic Press, New York, 1981.
· RACKER, E., Inner mitochondrial membranes: basic and applied aspects, *Hosp. Pract.*, **9**, 87 (1974).
· SINGER et al., Succinate dehydrogenase, *Advanc. Enzymol.*, **37**, 189 (1973).
· LOWENSTEIN, J. M., The pyruvate dehydrogenase complex and the citric acid cycle, *Comprehens. Biochem.*, **18S**, 1 (1971).
· KREBS, H. A., The history of the tricarboxylic acid cycle, *Perspect. Biol. Med.*, **14**, 154 (1970).
· LOWENSTEIN, J. M. (Ed.), *Citric Acid Cycle: Control and Compartmentation*, Dekker, New York, 1969.

substance is highly negative; that of a strongly oxidizing substance is correspondingly positive, as is evident from Figure 3. The loss of electrons (oxidation) results in the release of energy, the amount of which depends on the change in the redox potential. It is expressed by the equation

$$\Delta G^{0\prime} = -n\,F\Delta E_0^{\prime}$$

(n: number of electrons transferred; F [amount of charge in coulombs for 1 mol]: 96 485 $C\,mol^{-1}$; $E_0^{\prime}$: difference in the redox potentials of the reacting carriers at pH 7). For example, the change in the redox potential ($\Delta E_0^{\prime}$) in the reduction of FMN by reduced NAD is

---

*Figure 3 represents a simplified version of the respiratory chain and does not show all the cofactors known to be involved; for example an iron–sulfur protein is an intermediate in the transfer of electrons from reduced flavoproteins to ubiquinone, and a similar cofactor is active between cytochrome b and cytochrome c_l.

Absorption of acylglycerols

The fats ingested by the animal organism are emulsified in the duodenum with monoacylglycerols and polar lipids, such as phosphatidylcholine and lysophosphatidylcholine, under the influence of pancreatic lipase. Triacylglycerols are hydrolyzed in the emulsion by pancreatic triacylglycerol lipase (3.1.1.3) to yield free fatty acids and 2-acylglycerol. In man, 2-acylglycerol is the major compound absorbed. Partial isomerization of 2-acylglycerol may take place to form 1-acylglycerol, which may undergo further hydrolysis to glycerol and fatty acid, catalyzed by acylglycerol lipase (3.1.1.23). The lipids in the intestinal lumen are present as colloid particles (micelles), which consist mainly of salts of bile acids, monoacylglycerols and free fatty acids. The constituents of the micelles separate before absorption. Monoacylglycerols and free fatty acids diffuse through the lipoprotein membrane of the epithelial cells of the small intestine and are rapidly resynthesized in the endoplasmic reticulum to yield triacylglycerols. The resynthesis of triacylglycerols is not a random process, and certain fatty acids are preferred in given positions of the glycerol molecule.

$$\text{Acylglycerol} + \text{acyl-CoA} \xrightarrow[2.3.1.22]{} \text{1,2-Diacylglycerol} + \text{CoA}$$

$$\text{1,2-Diacylglycerol} + \text{acyl-CoA} \xrightarrow[2.3.1.20]{} \text{Triacylglycerol} + \text{CoA}$$

Enzymes involved:
2.3.1.20 Diacylglycerol acyltransferase
2.3.1.22 Acylglycerol palmitoyltransferase

Fatty acids of medium chain length (C_6 to C_{12}) are not reesterified in the intestinal wall but are transported via the portal circulation to the liver, where they are oxidized. Also part of the oleic acid is not reesterified and arrives directly in the liver. The newly formed triacylglycerols enter the venous blood stream via the lymphatic vessels combined with apolipoproteins, cholesterol and phospholipids in the form of fine droplets (chylomicrons). In the capillary bed of peripheral tissues (primarily adipose tissue and muscle), chylomicrons are broken down by the action of lipoprotein lipase (3.1.1.34), which catalyzes the hydrolysis of triacylglycerol to diacylglycerol and free fatty acid. Diacylglycerol can be further hydrolyzed by this enzyme, yielding 2-acylglycerol and free fatty acid. While chylomicron surface materials, including phospholipids, free cholesterol and apolipiprotein C, are transferred to HDL_3, the residues of the chylomicrons ('core remnants'), including cholesterol esters and apolipoprotein E, are recognized by hepatic apolipoprotein E receptors and absorbed by the liver.

The principal location of depot fat in the body are subcutaneous, intramuscular, in the omentum, and in association with various organs such as the heart, kidneys, mesentery, ovaries, etc. Their main function is that of an energy reserve. In many species, including man, the triacylglycerols are the most important energy source for skeletal muscle activity. In warm-blooded animals, subcutaneous fat often serves as a vital insulation against heat loss. Adipose tissue in addition acts as a protective cushion against mechanical insults to vital organs.

Absorption of cholesterol

Cholesterol in the intestinal lumen comes from 3 sources: diet, bile and desquamated cells. Prior to absorption, cholesterol esters have to be hydrolyzed with the aid of pancreatic cholesterol esterase (3.1.1.13), which requires cholic acid or its conjugates as cofactors. Nonesterified cholesterol is transported to mucosal cells in mixed micelles, with bile acids or their salts as a prerequisite. In addition to absorption, mucosal cells obtain cholesterol by de novo synthesis (page 144) and from circulating lipoproteins. Cholesterol is used to make new cellular membranes and the surfaces of newly formed chylomicrons. Excess cholesterol is esterified with the aid of cholesterol acyltransferase (page 146) and transported away with triacylglycerols in the core of chylomicrons.

Absorption and breakdown of phospholipids

Prior to absorption, the major part of dietary phospholipids is split in the intestinal lumen by pancreatic phospholipase A_2 (3.1.1.4), yielding free fatty acids and lysophospholipids, but also some unhydrolyzed phospholipids may be absorbed by the mucosal cells. Lysophospholipids are reacylated in the intestinal mucosa. The phospholipids are then incorporated into the chylomicrons, which enter the circulation.

In the organism several enzymes are present which can split phospholipids at all sites that are accessible to hydrolysis.

Phospholipase A_2 (3.1.1.4) – first isolated from snake venom, but found in many tissues – splits the fatty-acid residue at the C-2 position of the glycerol molecule. This enzyme has a special affinity to lipids containing unsaturated fatty acids and plays an important part in the conversion of lipids into types needed by the cell. Like the triacylglycerol lipase (3.1.1.3) of the pancreas, phospholipase A_1 (3.1.1.32) splits off the fatty-acid residues at the C-1 position of the

Phosphatidylcholine (lecithin)

glycerol molecule, and it is probably also involved in the conversion of lipids. Phospholipase A_2 is of importance for the release of arachidonic acid, the starting material for the prostaglandins, leukotrienes and related compounds (page 142).

From lysolecithins the fatty-acid residues are split off with the aid of lysophospholipase (3.1.1.5) (phospholipase B), whereupon glycerophosphocholine is formed.

Lysolecithins

Phospholipase C (3.1.4.3) is primarily a bacterial enzyme (Clostridium toxin) and hydrolyzes phosphatidylcholine to 1,2-diacylglycerol and choline phosphate.

1,2-Diacylglycerol   Choline phosphate

Phospholipase D (3.1.4.4) has as yet been detected only in plants and hydrolyzes phosphatidylcholine to phosphatidic acid and choline.

These enzymes may not only act on phosphatidylcholine, but also on phosphatidylethanolamine.

Phosphatidate phosphatase (3.1.3.4) acts on 1,2-diacylglycerol 3-phosphate to yield 1,2-diacylglycerol and plays an important part in the synthesis of triacylglycerol (page 139).

Choline phosphate can be split off from sphingomyelin by phospholipase C (3.1.4.3) as well as by sphingomyelin phosphodiesterase (3.1.4.12).

Sphingomyelin phosphodiesterase
Phospholipase C

$(CH_3)_3\overset{+}{N}CH_2CH_2O$—P—$\overset{O}{\parallel}$—$OCH_2$

HC—NH—COR

HC—OH

HC

CH

$(CH_2)_{12}$

CH$_3$

Sphingomyelin

With the aid of acylsphingosine deacylase (3.5.1.23) (ceramidase) the fatty-acid residue is split off from the N-acylsphingosine also formed in this process.

Acylsphingosine deacylase

HOCH$_2$

HC—NH—COR

HC—OH

HC

CH

$(CH_2)_{12}$

CH$_3$

Ceramide
(N-acylsphingosine)

Oxidative degradation of acylglycerols

Triacylglycerols are better sources of energy than carbohydrates or proteins because they are more highly reduced. In addition, they are nonpolar substances and therefore bind much less water, so that a mass unit of tissue fat can supply up to 6 times the amount of energy than the corresponding mass unit of glycogen.

Prior to oxidation, triacylglycerols are hydrolyzed to free fatty acids and glycerol. The first step in hydrolysis of triacylglycerols in adipose tissue is catalyzed by the specific hormone-sensitive triacylglycerol lipase (3.1.1.3), which splits off 1 fatty acid residue, leaving diacylglycerol (page 200). This reaction proceeds rather slowly and is rate-limiting. Acylglycerol lipase (3.1.1.23) hydrolyzes 1- and 2-acylglycerols, and it is probably also responsible for the hydrolysis of the diacylglycerols. Lipoprotein lipase (3.1.1.34) acts on chylomicrons and triacylglycerol-rich lipoproteins (VLDL), from which 2-acylglycerols and free fatty acids are ultimately formed.

The glycerol is converted to sn-glycerol 3-phosphate, which is then oxidized to glycerone phosphate, an intermediate in the glycolytic pathway:

CH$_2$OH $\quad$ ATP $\;$ ADP $\qquad$ CH$_2$OH $\quad$ NAD$^+$ +H$^+$ $\qquad$ CH$_2$OH

HOCH $\qquad\qquad$ HOCH $\qquad\qquad$ CO

CH$_2$OH $\qquad$ 2.7.1.30 $\qquad$ CH$_2$O—P $\qquad$ 1.1.1.8 $\qquad$ CH$_2$O—P

Glycerol $\qquad\qquad$ sn-Glycerol $\qquad\qquad$ Glycerone
$\qquad\qquad\qquad$ 3-phosphate $\qquad\qquad$ phosphate

Enzymes involved:
1.1.1.8   Glycerol-3-phosphate dehydrogenase (NAD$^+$)
2.7.1.30 Glycerol kinase

Since the enzymes involved in the *oxidation of fatty acids* are located in the matrix of the mitochondria, the fatty acids must first be transported there from the site of their formation, the cytosol. Mitochondria have 2 membranes, a smooth outer one and an inner one that invaginates to form folds (cristae). Transport of the fatty acids from the cytosol into the interior of the mitochondria takes place in 3 stages. The first stage, which occurs on the outer membrane, involves the 'activation' of fatty acid by coenzyme A (CoA) at the expense of ATP:

$$RCOOH + ATP + HSCoA \xrightarrow[6.2.1.3]{} RCOSCoA + AMP + PP_i$$

The reaction – catalyzed by long-chain-fatty-acid–CoA ligase (6.2.1.3) – is driven forward by the hydrolysis of pyrophosphate and its consequent release of energy. In the first step, a fatty acid reacts with ATP to give an acyladenylate:

$$RCOOH + ATP \longrightarrow RCO\text{-}AMP + PP_i$$

In the second step, the acyladenylate reacts with CoA to give acyl-CoA:

$$RCO\text{-}AMP + HSCoA \longrightarrow RCOSCoA + AMP$$

Long-chain acyl-CoA molecules – in contrast to medium-chain ones – cannot cross the inner mitochondrial membrane; the transfer takes place rather in the form of acylcarnitine, which is synthesized by the transfer of the acyl group from acyl-CoA to carnitine (second stage). Having reached the mitochondrial matrix, the acyl group is transferred back to CoA by the reversal of the reaction below (third

$$R\overset{O}{\overset{\parallel}{-}}C\text{—SCoA} + HO\text{—CH—CH}_2\text{—}\overset{+}{N}\text{—CH}_3$$

Acyl-CoA $\qquad\qquad\qquad$ CH$_2$ $\quad$ CH$_3$
(activated $\qquad\qquad\qquad$ COO$^-$
fatty acid)

2.3.1.21 $\qquad\qquad$ Carnitine

$$R\overset{O}{\overset{\parallel}{-}}C\text{—O—CH—CH}_2\text{—}\overset{+}{N}\text{—CH}_3 + HSCoA$$

CH$_2$ $\qquad$ CH$_3$
COO$^-$

Acylcarnitine

Enzyme involved:
2.3.1.21 Carnitine palmitoyltransferase

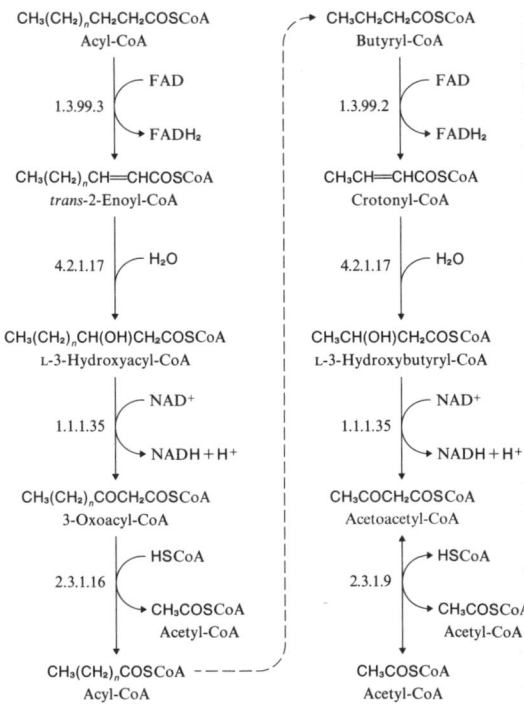

Fig. 1   *Degradation of fatty acids*

Enzymes involved:
1.1.1.35 3-Hydroxyacyl-CoA dehydrogenase
1.3.99.2 Butyryl-CoA dehydrogenase
1.3.99.3 Acyl-CoA dehydrogenase
2.3.1.9   Acetyl-CoA acetyltransferase
2.3.1.16 Acetyl-CoA acyltransferase
4.2.1.17 Enoyl-CoA hydratase

Fig. 2 *'Spiral diagram' of fatty-acid oxidation*

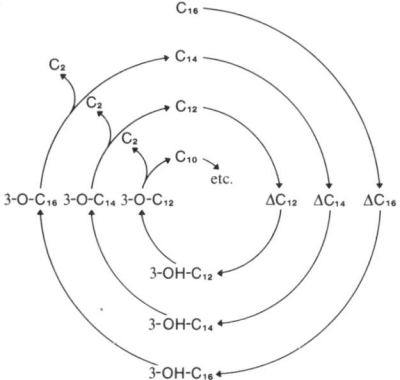

C₁₆, C₁₄, etc.: acyl-CoA
ΔC₁₆, ΔC₁₄, etc.: unsaturated acyl-CoA
3-OH-C₁₆, 3-OH-C₁₄, etc.: 3-hydroxyacyl-CoA
3-O-C₁₆, 3-O-C₁₄, etc.: 3-oxoacyl-CoA
C₂: acetyl-CoA
The subscripts indicate the length of the carbon chain.

stage) leaving acyl-CoA available for the β-oxidation of fatty acids. This is so called because the oxidation occurs at the C-3(β) atom of the chain, leading to stepwise removal of C₂ units in the form of acetyl-CoA. One reaction sequence comprises 4 steps (Fig. 1). The first is the dehydrogenation in the 2,3 position; the second, the addition of water to the double bond and the formation of a 3-hydroxy acid which is then dehydrogenated to the 3-oxo acid in a third step. The last step is a thioclastic one, that is, it consists in a cleavage of the carbon chain effected by the HS group of CoA. This reaction results in the formation of 1 molecule of acetyl-CoA and 1 molecule of an acyl-CoA derivative whose fatty-acid residue is shorter by 2 C atoms than the chain of the starting material. The shortened chain then repeatedly undergoes the same sequence of reactions until it is reduced to a fragment of less than 4 C atoms. In the case of chains with even numbers of C atoms the final fragment is acetyl-CoA, in the case of those with odd numbers it is propionyl-CoA.

The great majority of naturally occurring fatty acids contain an even number of C atoms and therefore yield acetyl-CoA as the only product. The propionyl-CoA formed from odd-numbered chains is known to enter a CO₂-fixation reaction leading to succinyl-CoA (see next page).

Fig. 3 *Degradation of oleic acid*

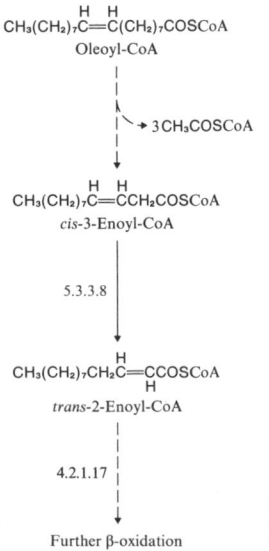

Enzymes involved:
4.2.1.17 Enoyl-CoA hydratase
5.3.3.8 Dodecenoyl-CoA Δ-isomerase

Although the reaction sequence by which the fatty acids are oxidized has been referred to as the 'fatty-acid cycle', it is not really a cycle since the starting material is not regenerated by a full turn of the 'cycle'. What happens is a periodic repetition of the same *types* of reaction, but not of the same reactions. This is shown diagrammatically in Figure 2, from which it can be seen that the mechanism is a 'spiral' rather than a 'cycle'.

Unsaturated fatty acids are also degraded by β-oxidation, but one or two additional enzymes are required. The double bonds of naturally occurring unsaturated fatty acids are of the *cis* configuration instead of the *trans* configuration, which is used in the hydration step of β-oxidation. In addition, the successive removal of C₂ fragments results in an unsaturated acyl-CoA compound (enoyl-CoA) with a double bond between C-3 and C-4. However, a substrate with a double bond between C-2 and C-3 is necessary for further β-oxidation. Aconitate Δ-isomerase (5.3.3.7) converts the *cis*-3 double bond to a *trans*-2 double bond. The sequence of reactions in the case of oleic acid, for example, is represented in Figure 3.

The oxidation of polyunsaturated fatty acids poses a further problem. Linoleic acid, for example, will undergo 3 rounds of degradation and result in *cis,cis*-3,6-enoyl-CoA, which is then converted by aconitate Δ-isomerase to *trans*-2-*cis*-6-enoyl-CoA. This is then hy-

Fig. 4 *Degradation of polyunsaturated fatty acids*

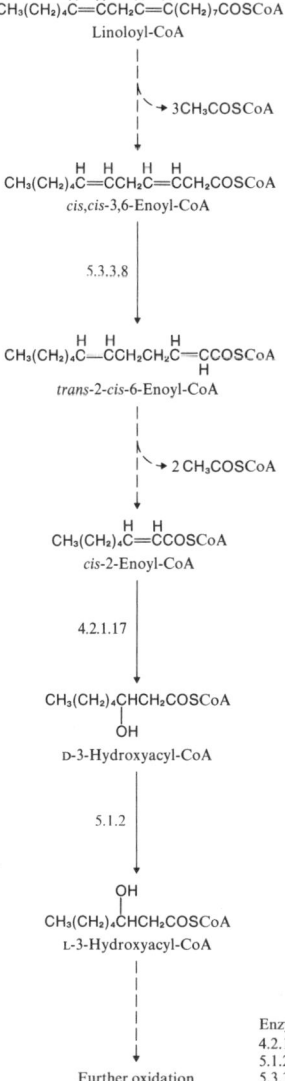

Enzymes involved:
4.2.1.17 Enoyl-CoA hydratase
5.1.2 3-Hydroxyacyl epimerase
5.3.3.8 Dodecenoyl-CoA Δ-isomerase

drated normally, and a further two C_2 fragments are lost, which leaves *cis*-2-enoyl-CoA. This compound is then converted by enoyl-CoA hydratase (4.2.1.17), but the hydration product is the D-isomer of 3-hydroxyacyl-CoA instead of the L-isomer, which is the substrate for the 3-hydroxyacyl-CoA dehydrogenase (1.1.1.35). Hence an inversion or epimerization is necessary, and this is made possible by an additional enzyme, an epimerase. The sequence of reactions is thus the one shown in Figure 4.

The β-oxidation pathway does not only work in mitochondria, but also in *peroxisomes*. The long-chain-fatty-acid–CoA ligase of peroxisomes is identical to that of mitochondria (6.2.1.3). A special enzyme of peroxisomes – acyl-CoA oxidase – is responsible for the dehydrogenation of acyl-CoA to enoyl-CoA. The reaction is coupled with the consumption of O_2 and the formation of H_2O_2. In mitochondria, 2 specific enzymes catalyze the hydration of enoyl-CoA and the subsequent dehydrogenation of 3-hydroxyacyl-CoA. In peroxisomes, however, these reactions are catalyzed by a bifunctional protein consisting of 1 polypeptide chain. The final enzyme of the β-oxidation pathway – acetyl-CoA acyltransferase (2.3.1.16) – differs in molecular and catalytic properties between mitochondria and peroxisomes. The peroxisomal β-oxidation system is almost inactive toward acyl moieties of 8 C atoms or less; very-long-chain fatty acids (e.g. lignoceric acid), however, are mainly oxidized in peroxisomes.

Formation of succinyl-CoA from propionyl-CoA

As mentioned on the preceding page, the propionyl-CoA formed from fatty acids with odd-numbered carbon chains yields succinyl-CoA. This involves a CO_2 fixation followed by racemization and rearrangement of methylmalonyl-CoA in accordance with the reaction sequence shown in Figure 5. The succinyl-CoA formed in this manner feeds into the tricarboxylic acid cycle and is oxidized. The total amount of succinyl-CoA arising in this way is normally very small, since fatty acids with odd numbers of C atoms are uncommon in nature. The reason for this is that fatty-acid chains are usually synthesized from C_2 units (see page 136).

Ketone bodies

Acetyl-CoA, the end-product of fat metabolism, normally enters the tricarboxylic acid cycle, where it is oxidized to CO_2 with the formation of reduced NAD and FAD. The reduced coenzymes then serve as a source of energy for the formation of ATP or GTP in the electron transfer system (page 96). However, the amount of acetyl-CoA that can be dealt with in this way is limited. Its utilization depends on an adequate supply of oxaloacetate to make possible the formation of citrate. If, therefore, the supply of oxaloacetate is diverted to biosynthetic purposes, further metabolism through the tricarboxylic acid cycle becomes impossible. In the case of acetyl-CoA derived from carbohydrate metabolism, this problem can be rectified by the production of more oxaloacetate by carboxylation of pyruvate. Pyruvate is not, however, an intermediate in the degradation of fats. This means that animals are unable to convert fats into carbohydrates, though of course the reverse conversion is possible. It therefore follows that if too much fat or too little carbohydrate is being metabolized, an excess of acetyl-CoA will build up, and this must be dealt with in another way, namely by ketogenesis.

The first step in the formation of ketone bodies consists in the reversal of the final step in the degradation of fatty acids: 2 molecules of acetyl-CoA give rise to 1 molecule of acetoacetyl-CoA. This reacts with another molecule of acetyl-CoA to form 3-methyl-3-hydroxyglutaryl-CoA, which then undergoes cleavage to acetyl-CoA and acetoacetate. The acetoacetate may be further reduced to 3-hydroxybutyrate if NADH is available, or it may be subject to a nonenzymatic decarboxylation to form acetone.

The formation of ketone bodies is shown in Figure 6.

Fig. 5   *Utilization of propionyl-CoA*

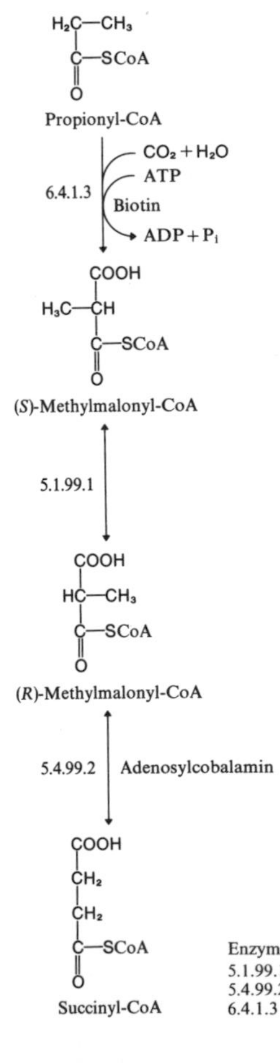

Enzymes involved:
5.1.99.1   Methylmalonyl-CoA epimerase
5.4.99.2   Methylmalonyl-CoA mutase
6.4.1.3   Propionyl-CoA carboxylase

Fig. 6   *Formation of ketone bodies (Lynen cycle)*

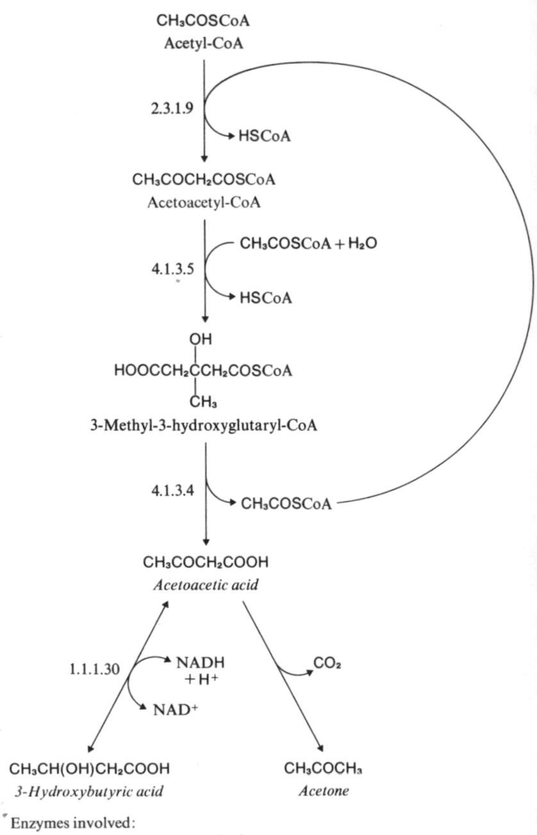

Enzymes involved:
1.1.1.30   3-Hydroxybutyrate dehydrogenase
2.3.1.9   Acetyl-CoA acetyltransferase (thiolase)
4.1.3.4   Hydroxymethylglutaryl-CoA lyase
4.1.3.5   Hydroxymethylglutaryl-CoA synthase

Fig. 7   *Utilization of acetoacetate*

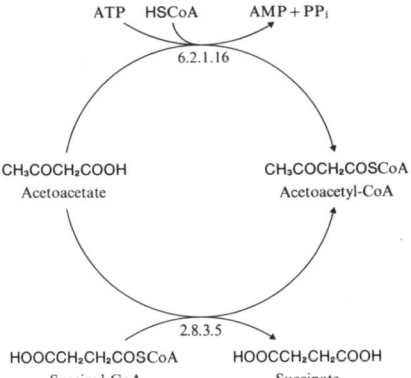

Enzymes involved:
2.8.3.5   3-Oxoacid CoA-transferase
6.2.1.16 Acetoacetate–CoA ligase (thiokinase)

Ketone body production is restricted to the liver because hydroxy-methylglutaryl-CoA synthase, the rate-limiting enzyme, is present in large quantities only in this organ. Re-formation of acetoacetyl-CoA cannot take place in the liver, however, because the enzymes needed for that are lacking. The ketone bodies therefore diffuse into the blood and hence to tissues, where they are normally present in low concentrations. Acetoacetate and/or 3-hydroxybutyrate are good suppliers of energy and, for example, are utilized by the heart muscle in preference to glucose. If they are going to be used for such purposes, acetoacetyl-CoA must be regenerated preliminary to oxidation. This may be brought about by a transfer of CoA, either directly or from succinyl-CoA (Fig. 7). The acetoacetyl-CoA is then cleaved by acetyl-CoA acetyltransferase (2.3.1.9) into 2 acetyl-CoA molecules, which may be oxidized in the tricarboxylic acid cycle.

The concentration of ketone bodies in the blood is an indicator for the equilibrium between formation in the liver and utilization by the peripheral tissues. With a balanced food intake the concentration is low (about 0.1 mmol/L), while in the fasting state, in late pregnancy, in untreated diabetes mellitus (up to 25 mmol/L) and in some inherited disorders of carbohydrate metabolism (glycogenoses) it is increased.

Reviews

· BREMER and OSMUNDSEN, in NUMA, S. (Ed.), *Fatty Acid Metabolism and Its Regulation*, Elsevier, Amsterdam, 1984, page 113.
· NORUM et al., Transport of cholesterol, *Physiol. Rev.*, **63**, 1343 (1983).
· MCGARRY and FOSTER, Regulation of hepatic fatty acid oxidation and ketone body production, *Ann. Rev. Biochem.*, **49**, 395 (1980).
· FULCO, A. J., Metabolic alterations of fatty acids, *Ann. Rev. Biochem.*, **43**, 215 (1974).
· NEWSHOLME and START, *Regulation in Metabolism*, Wiley, New York, 1973, pages 146 and 293.
· WAKIL and BARNES, Fatty acid metabolism, *Comprehens. Biochem.*, **18S**, 57 (1971).
· BRESSLER, R., Fatty acid oxidation, *Comprehens. Biochem.*, **18**, 331 (1970).
· STUMPF, P. K., Metabolism of fatty acids, *Ann. Rev. Biochem.*, **38**, 159 (1969).
· GREVILLE and TUBBS, The catabolism of long-chain fatty acids in mammalian tissues, *Essays Biochem.*, **4**, 155 (1968).

Metabolism of Bile Acids*

Fig. 1   *Biosynthesis of bile acids*

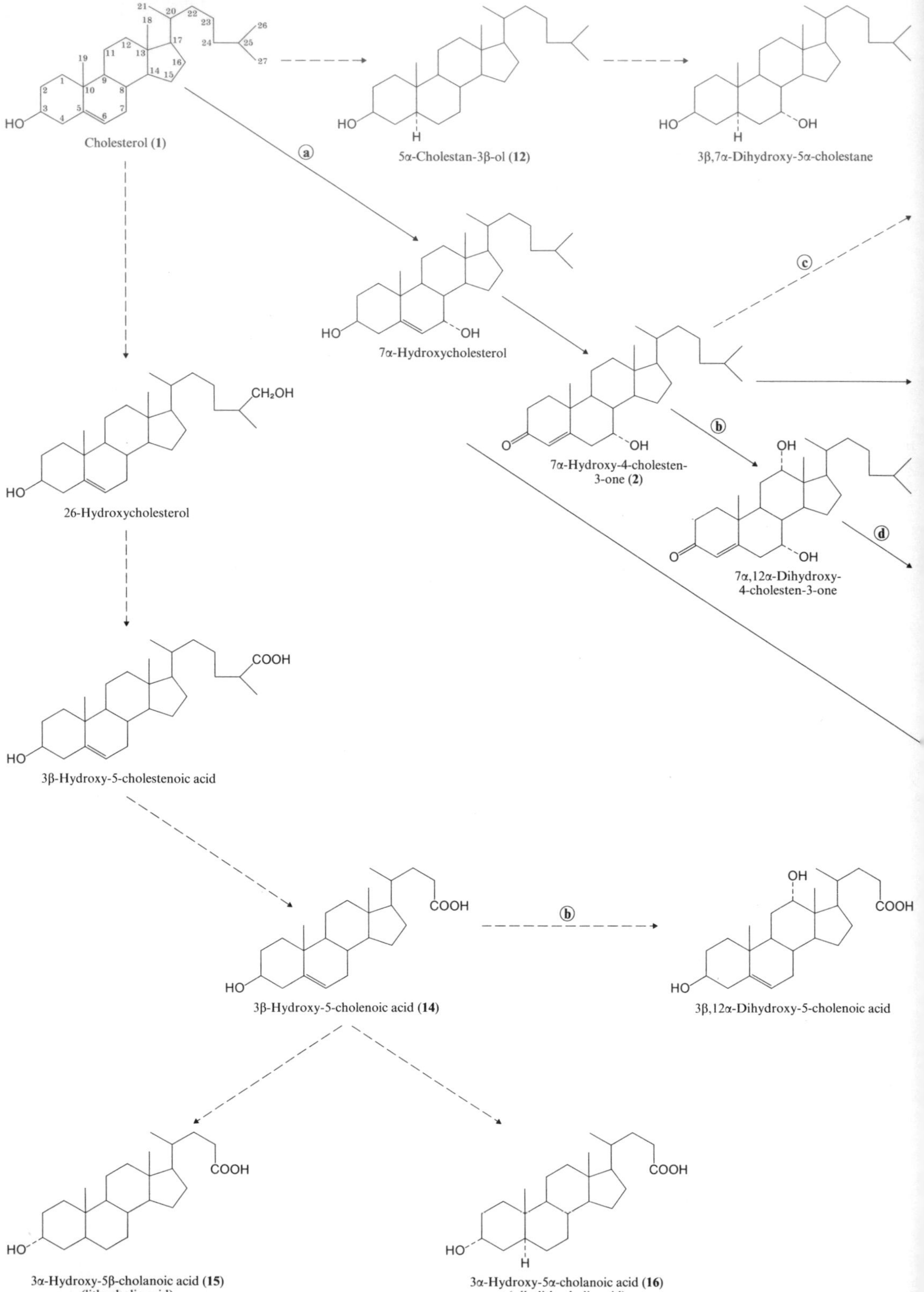

Cholesterol (**1**)

5α-Cholestan-3β-ol (**12**)

3β,7α-Dihydroxy-5α-cholestane

7α-Hydroxycholesterol

7α-Hydroxy-4-cholesten-
3-one (**2**)

7α,12α-Dihydroxy-
4-cholesten-3-one

26-Hydroxycholesterol

3β-Hydroxy-5-cholestenoic acid

3β-Hydroxy-5-cholenoic acid (**14**)

3β,12α-Dihydroxy-5-cholenoic acid

3α-Hydroxy-5β-cholanoic acid (**15**)
(lithocholic acid)

3α-Hydroxy-5α-cholanoic acid (**16**)
(*allo*-lithocholic acid)

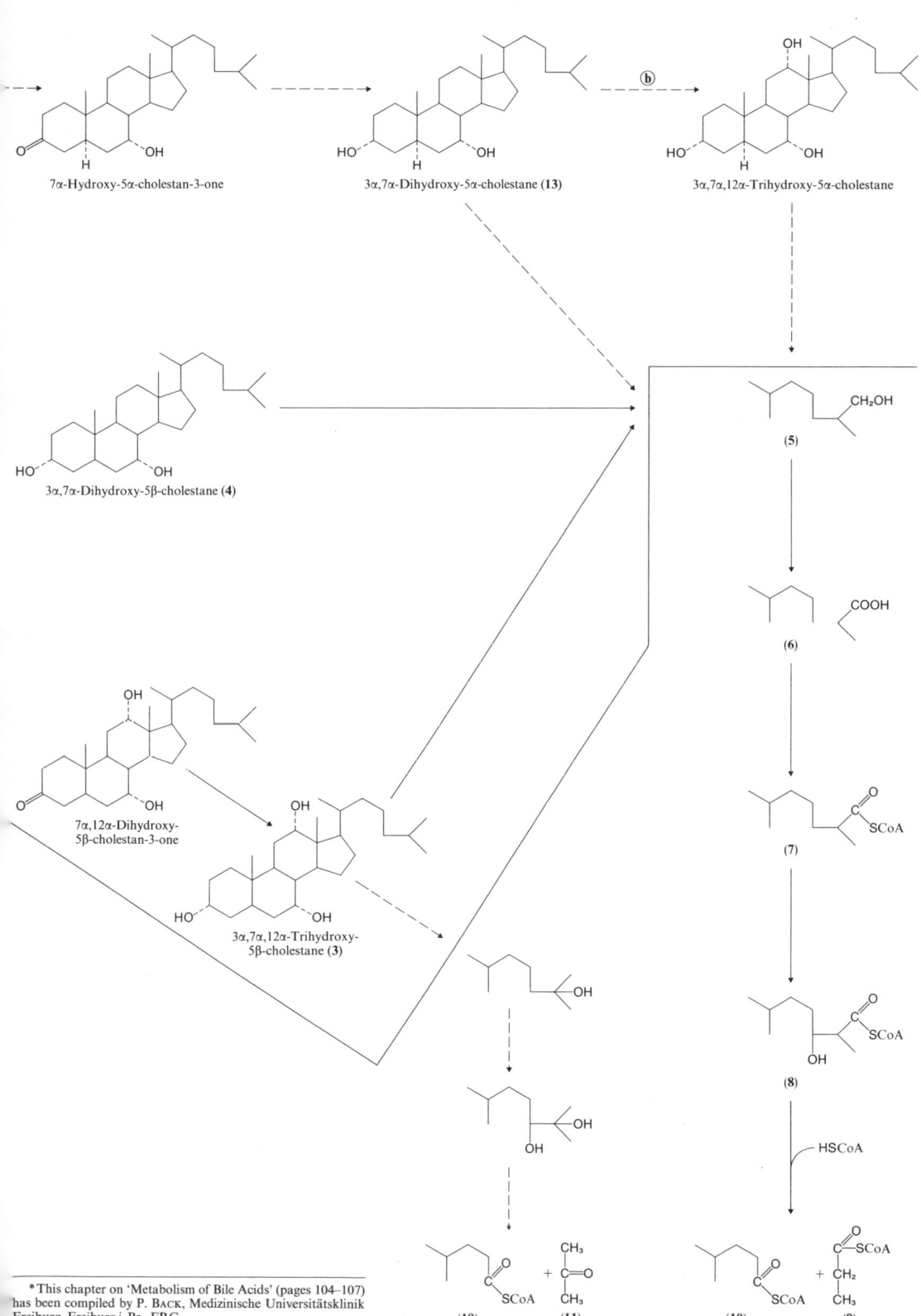

7α-Hydroxy-5α-cholestan-3-one

3α,7α-Dihydroxy-5α-cholestane (13)

(b)

3α,7α,12α-Trihydroxy-5α-cholestane

3α,7α-Dihydroxy-5β-cholestane (4)

(5)

(6)

7α,12α-Dihydroxy-
5β-cholestan-3-one

(7)

3α,7α,12α-Trihydroxy-
5β-cholestane (3)

(8)

HSCoA

(10)   (11)

(10)   (9)

* This chapter on 'Metabolism of Bile Acids' (pages 104–107)
has been compiled by P. BACK, Medizinische Universitätsklinik
Freiburg, Freiburg i. Br., FRG.

Fig. 2   *Atypical bile acids*

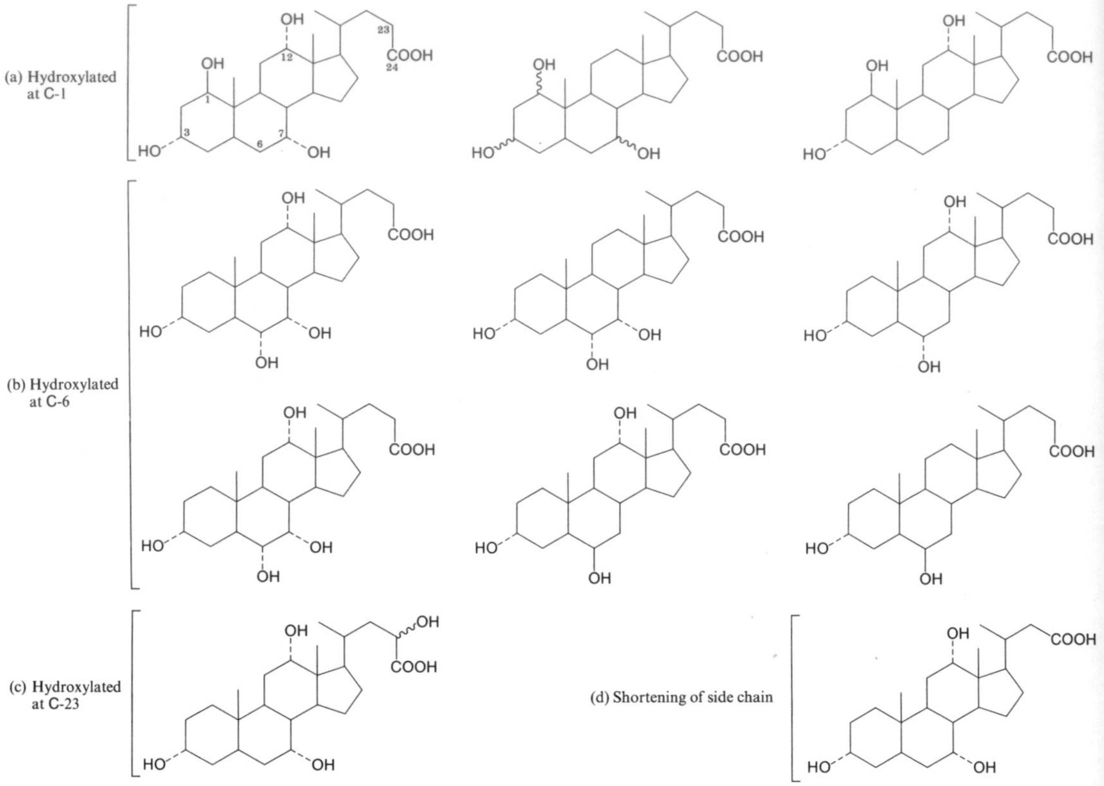

(a) Hydroxylated
    at C-1

(b) Hydroxylated
    at C-6

(c) Hydroxylated
    at C-23

(d) Shortening of side chain

Fig. 3   *Primary, secondary and tertiary bile acids*

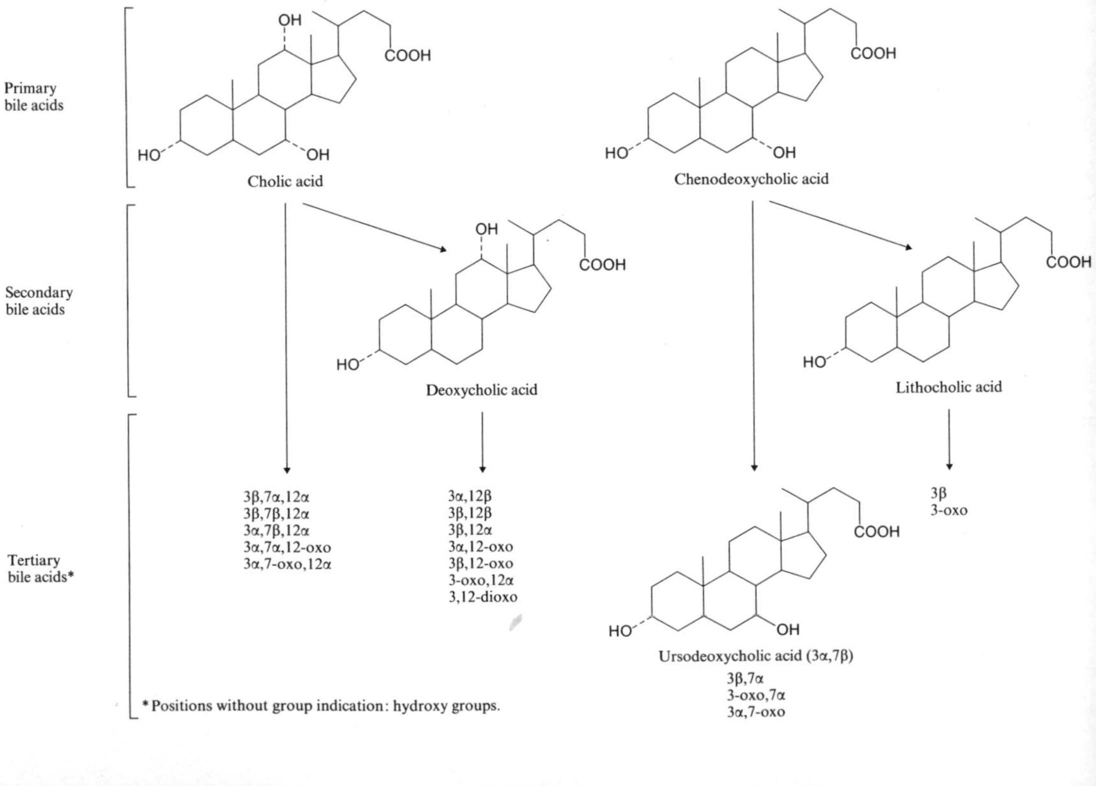

Primary
bile acids

Cholic acid

Chenodeoxycholic acid

Secondary
bile acids

Deoxycholic acid

Lithocholic acid

Tertiary
bile acids*

3β,7α,12α
3β,7β,12α
3α,7β,12α
3α,7α,12-oxo
3α,7-oxo,12α

3α,12β
3β,12β
3β,12α
3α,12-oxo
3β,12-oxo
3-oxo,12α
3,12-dioxo

3β
3-oxo

Ursodeoxycholic acid (3α,7β)

3β,7α
3-oxo,7α
3α,7-oxo

* Positions without group indication: hydroxy groups.

Bile acids are specific hepatic catabolites of cholesterol. In the initial reactions during the conversion of cholesterol (1) to bile acids, mainly microsomal enzymes are involved[1] (Fig. 1); the rate-limiting step in the biosynthesis is the hydroxylation of cholesterol by cholesterol 7α-monooxygenase (1.14.13.17) ⓐ. The activity of this enzyme exhibits a circadian rhythm, as does the biosynthesis of cholesterol itself. The enzyme is inhibited to a varying degree in its activity by the end-products of cholesterol catabolism, the bile acids.

Increasingly hydrophilic intermediates are derived from subsequent reactions: 5β-cholestanediols and -triols, which represent the initial substrates (3, 4) for side-chain oxidation, are formed by oxidoreduction steps and hydroxylation of the steroid nucleus, respectively. Cholestenone 5β-reductase (1.3.1.23) ⓓ is localized in the cytosolic compartment, whereas cholestenone 5α-reductase (1.3.1.22) ⓒ is a microsomal enzyme. 12α-Hydroxylation ⓑ, which represents the branching point in the synthesis of cholic acid, needs coplanar steroids as substrates[2]; the same enzyme is probably active in the hydroxylation of 7α-hydroxy-4-cholesten-3-one (2), 3α,7α-dihydroxy-5α-cholestane (13), and 3β-hydroxy-5-cholenoic acid (14).

In man, oxidation of the side chain at C-26 is performed by mitochondrial 26-hydroxylase. 26-Hydroxylated 3α,7α,12α-trihydroxy-5β-cholestanol (5) was found to be the main precursor of cholyl-CoA or cholic acid. The further conversion of the polyhydroxycholestanols involves several enzymatic steps, including the formation of di- and trihydroxycoprostanoic acids (6), the formation of CoA derivatives (7), the intermediary peroxisomal introduction of a 24-hydroxy group [(8); the 3α,7α,12α,24-tetrahydroxy derivative is called 'varanyl-CoA'], and finally a cleavage similar to the thioclastic step in β-oxidation of fatty acids to yield propionyl-CoA (9) and cholanoyl-CoA (10).

Alternatively microsomal 25 hydroxylation followed by cytosolic 24β(S)-hydroxylation seems to be possible, resulting in the formation of a cholestanetetrol and pentol, respectively[3]. Only these isomers – probably after the splitting off of acetone (11) – are converted to cholic acid without coprostanoic acids being involved as intermediates.

As activated CoA compounds, the bile acids are linked to glycine and taurine, usually in a ratio of 3:1. Taurine conjugation and esterification with sulfuric acid at position C-3 are predominant in the prenatal period. A similar condition is encountered in the case of cholestasis, where taurine conjugates, sulfate esters and even glucuronides occur. The latter two groups of compounds are readily eliminated via the kidneys, while taurine- and glycine-conjugated bile acids have a low renal clearance.

Further pathways of bile-acid synthesis which can be of importance in hepatobiliary disease consist in the primary formation of 5α-cholanoic acids, starting from 5α-cholestan-3β-ol (12), and also

of the action of cholestenone 5α-reductase ⓒ on 7α-hydroxy-4-cholesten-3-one (2).

Furthermore, mitochondrial primary side-chain oxidation of cholesterol seems possible as an alternative pathway of catabolism in liver disease, so that 3β-hydroxy-5-cholenoic acid (14) is formed, which still contains the cholesterol nucleus. This compound may serve as a precursor of the saturated monohydroxy bile acids 3α-hydroxy-5β-cholanoic acid (15) and 3α-hydroxy-5α-cholanoic acid (16) in conditions of severe cholestasis. However, 12α-hydroxylation ⓑ of 3β-hydroxy-5-cholenoic acid (14) seems to be preferred.

In hepatobiliary disease there is a series of 'atypical' bile acids in plasma and urine[4] (Fig. 2) that usually do not appear in the biliary bile-acid spectrum of the healthy adult, but can also be detected in the meconium as an expression of a different mode of prenatal bile-acid metabolism[5]. Besides the usual bile acids, considerable amounts of 1-hydroxylated (a) and 6-hydroxylated (b) tri- and tetrahydroxycholanoic acids can be found. In intrahepatic cholestasis their formation can be induced by phenobarbital[6]. 1-Hydroxylated bile acids have a high renal clearance that exceeds that of bile-acid sulfate, probably as a consequence of the more extended hydration envelope. In the adult they are present almost exclusively in the urine. In conditions of liver disease, side-chain hydroxylation of bile acids in position C-23 (c) and a shortening of the side chain (d), which leads to the formation of 24-norcholic acid, has been demonstrated.

In normal conditions, secondary and tertiary bile acids appear along with the primary bile acids of bile-acid metabolism (Fig. 3); in part they circulate enterohepatically, but mostly they are excreted with the feces.

The most important secondary bile acids are lithocholic acid and deoxycholic acid, which are formed by bacterial 7α-dehydroxylation in the colon after previous deconjugation. Together with these principal catabolites, ursodeoxycholic acid (3α,7β-dihydroxy-5β-cholanoic acid) and a wide range of epimeric and oxo bile acids substituted at C-3, C-7, and C-12 are found, the diverse structures of which reflect how far-reaching possibilities of enterobacterial oxidoreductions can be[7].

References

[1] DANIELSSON, H., in NAIR and KRITCHEVSKY (Eds.), *The Bile Acids*, Volume 2, Plenum, New York, 1973, page 1.
[2] ELLIOTT, W. H., in MATERN et al. (Eds.), *Advances in Bile Acid Research*, Schattauer, Stuttgart, 1975, page 31.
[3] MOSBACH et al., in PAUMGARTNER and STIEHL (Eds.), *Bile Acid Metabolism in Health and Disease*, MTP Press, Lancaster, 1977, page 11
[4] ALMÉ et al., *J. Lipid Res.*, **18**, 339 (1977).
[5] BACK and WALTER, *Gastroenterology*, **78**, 671 (1980).
[6] BACK et al., *Hoppe-Seyler's Z. physiol. Chem.*, **365**, 479 (1984).
[7] ENEROTH et al., *J. Lipid Res.*, **7**, 524 (1966).

Enzymes of protein breakdown

As a consequence of the remarkably high specificity of the individual enzymes involved in protein breakdown a whole series of them is necessary to break the peptide chain completely down to amino acids.

In accordance with the recommendations of the International Union of Biochemistry (IUB) the enzymes involved in protein breakdown, the peptide hydrolases (3.4), are divided into 2 sets of sub-sub-classes: peptidases (exopeptidases, 3.4.11–19), and proteinases (3.4.21–24). The peptidases are divided according to their specificity into those hydrolyzing single amino acids from the N terminus of the peptide chain (3.4.11), those hydrolyzing single residues from the C terminus (3.4.16–17), those specific for dipeptide substrates (3.4.13), and those splitting off dipeptide units either from the N terminus (3.4.14) or the C terminus (3.4.15). The group hydrolyzing single residues from the C terminus is subdivided into 3 distinct classes. One class displays maximum activity in the acid range and is inhibited by

Classification of the proteinases

	Sub-subclasses			
	3.4.21	3.4.22	3.4.23	3.4.24
	Serine proteinases	Cysteine proteinases	Aspartic proteinases	Metalloproteinases
Examples	Chymotrypsin (3.4.21.1) Trypsin (3.4.21.4) Thrombin (3.4.21.5) Plasmin (3.4.21.7) Enteropeptidase (3.4.21.9) Acrosin (3.4.21.10) Pancreatic elastase (3.4.21.36) Leukocyte elastase (3.4.21.37)	Cathepsin B (3.4.22.1) Cathepsin L (3.4.22.15) Cathepsin H (3.4.22.16)	Pepsin A, B, C (3.4.23.1–3) Chymosin (3.4.23.4) Cathepsin D (3.4.23.5)	Lens neutral proteinase (3.4.24.5) Vertebrate collagenase (3.4.24.7) Immunoglobulin A_1 proteinase (3.4.24.13)
pH range of enzyme activity	7–9	3–8	2–7	7–9
Inhibitors used for identification	Diisopropyl fluoro-phosphate	Iodoacetate 4-Chloromercuri-benzoate	Pepstatin	1,10-Phenanthroline EDTA 1,4-Dithiothreitol

References   KAY, J., *Biochem. Soc. Trans.*, **10**, 277 (1982); BARRETT, A. J., *Ciba Found. Symp.*, NS **75**, 1 (1980).

Protein breakdown in the gastrointestinal tract of nonruminant mammals

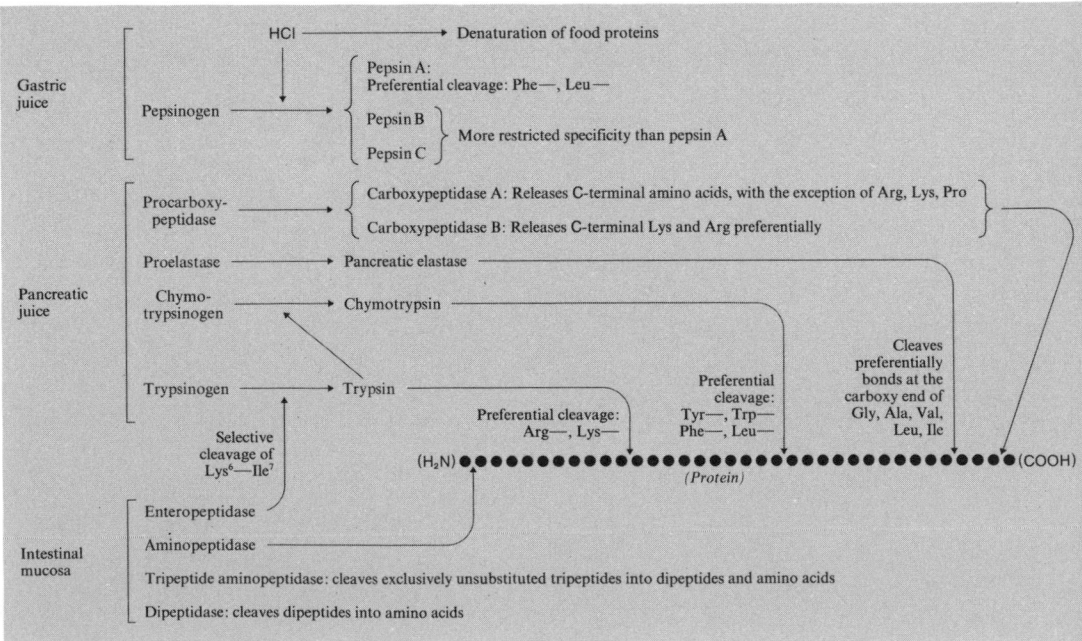

the substitution of a serine residue by organic fluorophosphates (serine carboxypeptidases, 3.4.16), the second class requires for activity divalent cations (metallocarboxypeptidases, 3.4.17), the third class is thiol-dependent (cysteine carboxypeptidases, 3.4.18). A separate category (omega peptidases, 3.4.19) includes enzymes removing substituted N- and C-terminal amino-acid residues.

The proteinases (proteolytic enzymes, endopeptidases, peptidyl-peptide hydrolases) are divided into sub-subclasses on the basis of the catalytic mechanism, as shown by active-center studies or the effect of pH. The enzymes of sub-subclasses 3.4.21 ('serine proteinases') have an active center histidine and serine involved in the catalytic process; those of 3.4.22 ('cysteine proteinases') have a cysteine in the active center; those of 3.4.23 have a pH optimum below 5, due to the involvement of an acidic residue in the catalytic process ('aspartic proteinases'), and those of 3.4.24 are metallo-proteins using a metal ion (e.g. Ca^{2+}, Zn^{2+}) in the catalytic mechanism ('metalloproteinases').

The serine proteinases are the largest group of proteinases. At least 50 such enzymes are known in mammals, among them a whole series in the plasma (coagulation factors and complement components).

The most common mechanism of cleavage of peptide bonds involves polarization of the peptide bond by nucleophilic attack on the $C=O$ bond (either directly or mediated by a water molecule), assisted by the donation of a proton to the N atom of the peptide bond.

Gastrointestinal breakdown of proteins

Proteins coming from the most diverse sources are broken down to free amino acids as well as di- and tripeptides in the lumen of the small intestine. Main sources are the diet (the adult needs a daily intake of about 0.5–0.8 g protein for 1 kg body mass), the gastrointestinal secretions (about 10–30 g protein daily) and desquamated cells (about 25 g protein daily); furthermore, some proteins (mostly albumin) derive from plasma.

Gastric juice is not absolutely necessary for protein breakdown. At best 10–15% of the protein ingested with food is hydrolyzed in the stomach.

About 10% of the proteins in the gastrointestinal tract escape hydrolysis and appear as mucoproteins, desquamated cells and bacteria in the feces. Unattacked proteins enter the portal blood at most in traces. In the newborn, however, considerable amounts of protein are absorbed from the colostrum by pinocytosis in the first 36 hours of life.

The scheme on the preceding page gives a summary of the protein breakdown in the gastrointestinal tract.

For the transport of free amino acids into the brush-border cells, 4 mechanisms are available: one for most neutral amino acids – a separate one for proline, hydroxyproline and glycine –, one for basic amino acids, and one for the two acidic amino acids, glutamic acid and aspartic acid. By another mechanism, di- and tripeptides are transported into the membrane and the interior of the brush-border cells, where the peptides are hydrolyzed to yield the free amino acids.

Intracellular breakdown of proteins

Most cellular proteins are in a state of constant turnover, which has to be highly specific. On the one hand, undesirable proteins formed, for example, by denaturation or mutation are removed; on the other hand, the breakdown of enzymes within the cell makes it possible to adapt rapidly to an altered metabolic situation by modifying the synthesis of enzymes from the amino acids obtained in order to meet the new demand. Finally, cell proteins represent an energy reserve which can be mobilized in case of an inadequate energy supply. In the rat, tissues such as liver, intestinal epithelium, thymus and kidney lose considerable portions of their cellular protein in the early stage of deprivation, whereas the mass of skeletal muscle protein remains relatively stable. In prolonged starvation,

however, muscle loss accelerates and is the major source of amino acids.

The turnover rates of various proteins vary considerably, enzymes especially being broken down rapidly. Half-lives in rat liver, for example, range from about 12 minutes (in the case of ornithine decarboxylase) to 1 or more days for the majority of cytosolic proteins. Based on the differences in the turnover rate, 2 general classes of protein can be distinguished. The first class, termed 'short-lived' proteins, comprises only a small fraction of total protein (less than 1% in the liver) and has an average $T_{1/2}$ of less than 60 minutes. The second class, termed 'long-lived' or 'resident' proteins, includes all the remaining proteins of the cell. The degradation of the latter is thought to be carried out by lysosomal processes. In hepatocytes, cytoplasmic proteins are continuously internalized and degraded by 2 lysosomal processes: (a) overt or macroautophagy, and (b) microautophagy involving dense bodies. Macroautophagy is finely regulated by amino acids, insulin and glucagon, and is initiated as double-walled vacuoles that are rapidly transformed to degradative vacuoles. The mechanism of microautophagy – the basal degradation mechanism – and its regulation are less well known.

Glycoproteins from the blood – almost all plasma proteins are glycoproteins – can be absorbed by cells only when the terminal neuraminyl residues are split off by sialidase (3.2.1.18) (neuraminidase). Absorption takes place via specific receptors for certain monosaccharides.

A series of intracellular proteinases plays a part in joint diseases. Cathepsin D (3.4.23.5), a lysosomal enzyme, breaks down the proteoglycans of cartilage at an optimum pH of about 5 and is linked with the onset of inflammations. Cathepsin B (3.4.22.1) takes part in the breakdown of collagen. Vertebrate collagenase (3.4.24.7) displays specificity for the substrate collagen. The lysosomal elastase of the polymorphonuclear leukocytes (leukocyte elastase, 3.4.21.37) and the pancreatic elastase (3.4.21.36) not only split elastin, but also act on proteoglycans.

Along with the breakdown of intracellular protein by lysosomal enzymes there is a nonlysosomal proteolytic system which is energy-dependent. The system investigated in reticulocytes is highly active in the degradation of abnormal globin chains, whereas normal hemoglobin is stable. It consists of several components, one of these is ubiquitin – apparently identical with APF-1 (ATP-dependent proteolysis factor I) – a ubiquitously occurring, heat-stable polypeptide of low molecular mass. Ubiquitin is conjugated with the substrate protein in a reaction that is ATP-dependent. This complex, consisting of several molecules of ubiquitin and 1 molecule of protein, is then rapidly broken down, releasing small peptides and free ubiquitin.

Reviews

· International Union of Biochemistry, *Enzyme Nomenclature 1984*, Academic Press, Orlando, Fla., 1984.
· NEURATH, H., Evolution of proteolytic enzymes, *Science*, **224**, 350 (1984).
· MORTIMORE and PÖSÖ, Lysosomal pathways in hepatic protein degradation: regulatory role of amino acids, *Fed. Proc.*, **43**, 1289 (1984).
· CIECHANOVER et al., The ubiquitin-mediated proteolytic pathway and mechanisms of energy-dependent intracellular protein degradation, *J. cell. Biochem.*, **24**, 27 (1984).
· MORTIMORE, G. E., Mechanisms of cellular protein catabolism, *Nutr. Rev.*, **40**, 1 (1982).
· HERSHKO and CIECHANOVER, Mechanisms of intracellular protein breakdown, *Ann. Rev. Biochem.*, **51**, 335 (1982).
· ASHWELL and STEER, Hepatic recognition and catabolism of serum glycoproteins, *J. Amer. med. Ass.*, **246**, 2358 (1981).
· Protein degradation in health and disease, *Ciba Found. Symp.*, NS **75** (1980).
· HOLZER and HEINRICH, Control of proteolysis, *Ann. Rev. Biochem.*, **49**, 63 (1980).
· GOLDBERG and ST. JOHN, Intracellular protein degradation in mammalian and bacterial cells, Part 2, *Ann. Rev. Biochem.*, **45**, 747 (1976).
· MATTHEWS, D. M., Intestinal absorption of peptides, *Physiol. Rev.*, **55**, 537 (1975).

The proteins of the body are subject to a constant synthesis and breakdown. Protein synthesis is only possible when all the amino acids are present in adequate amounts; the essential amino acids (page 154) must be ingested with the food. Excess amino acids are not stored and are excreted only in small amounts, any excess being used as a source of energy. Degradation usually involves the initial removal of the amino groups. The remaining carbon skeletons then undergo a series of reactions which ultimately lead to the formation of pyruvate, acetyl-CoA, acetoacetyl-CoA or an intermediate of the tricarboxylic acid cycle. In this way protein breakdown may be linked with the synthesis of fatty acids and carbohydrates or, in some cases, of ketone bodies.

Removal and subsequent utilization of amino groups

The α-amino group (at the C-2 position) is transferred from most amino acids to a 2-oxo acid by transamination. This transamination usually leads to glutamic acid, from which NH_3 is split off by oxidative deamination. Most of the NH_3 is removed in the urea cycle, but it can also be combined with glutamic acid to yield glutamine and thus be transported from peripheral tissues with the blood to the liver, where NH_3 – after splitting off from glutamine – is likewise available for the synthesis of urea.

Transamination

Transamination is a reversible reaction between 2-amino acids and 2-oxo acids in which the amino group and oxo group are exchanged.

2-Oxo acid A + 2-amino acid B $\longleftrightarrow$ 2-Amino acid A + 2-oxo acid B

The following are important transaminations:

– Alanine–oxo-acid aminotransferase (2.6.1.12) catalyzes the reaction of a 2-amino acid with pyruvate, in which alanine and the 2-oxo acid corresponding to the 2-amino acid result.

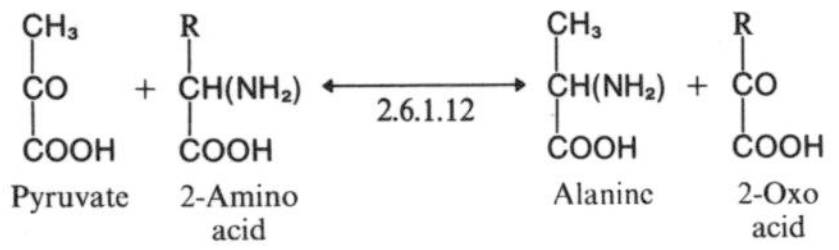

In the reaction catalyzed by alanine aminotransferase (2.6.1.2) the amino group of alanine is transferred to 2-oxoglutarate, whereupon glutamic acid is formed.

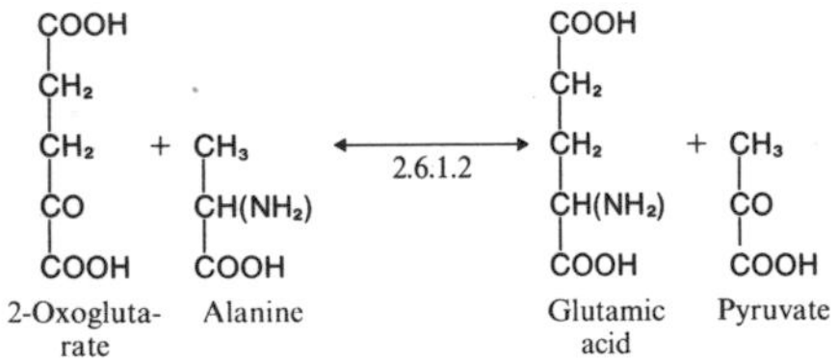

– In the reaction catalyzed by aspartate aminotransferase (2.6.1.1) the amino group of glutamic acid is transferred to oxaloacetate, yielding aspartic acid, which enters the urea cycle.

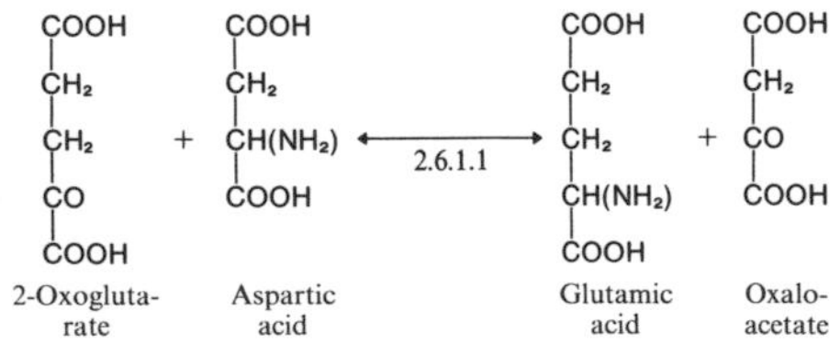

The removal of the amino group of a series of amino acids – in the form of urea – is made possible by coupling these transamination steps.

All these transaminations need pyridoxal phosphate (vitamin B_6) as a coenzyme (page 80).

Aminotransferases (transaminases) occur in many tissues. High aspartate aminotransferase activities are found in the heart muscle, skeletal muscle and liver. The alanine aminotransferase activity is also high in the liver.

Oxidative deamination

Oxidative deamination is a very important reaction. Having concentrated amino groups from various amino acids into amino groups of glutamic acid, this compound may undergo oxidative deamination, resulting in the release of NH_3. In the mitochondria, NH_3 is incorporated into carbamoyl phosphate, which enters the urea cycle (Fig. 1).

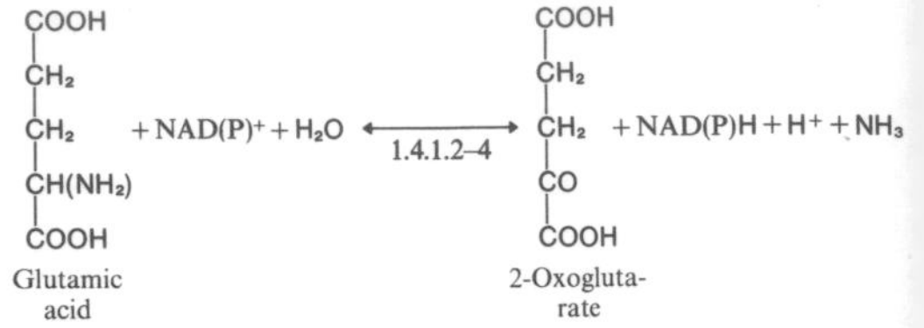

This reaction is catalyzed by glutamate dehydrogenases (1.4.1.2 to 1.4.1.4), which are able to use NAD or NADP as hydrogen acceptor. Glutamate dehydrogenase will also catalyze the release of NH_3 – at a lower rate – from alanine, leucine, isoleucine, valine and methionine, but not from aspartic acid.

The glutamate dehydrogenases consist of 4 subunits and contain zinc. The activity is reduced by dissociation of the tetrameric enzyme; this can be stopped by ADP or GDP. An ATP-poor and therefore ADP-rich environment hence accelerates the oxidation of amino acids and the formation of reduced NAD with the result of an increased ATP synthesis in the electron transfer system. This is a possible control mechanism of oxidative deamination. If NADP is the hydrogen acceptor the reduced NADP can be used as a reducing agent in biosynthetic processes.

In addition to the oxidative deamination of glutamic acid described above, some amino acids can be deaminated as shown in the following reaction:

$$RCH(NH_2)COOH + \text{flavoprotein} + H_2O \xrightarrow{\text{Oxidase}} RCOCOOH + \text{reduced flavoprotein} + NH_3$$

L-Amino acids are oxidized by L-amino-acid oxidase (1.4.3.2) with FMN as hydrogen acceptor, D-amino acids by D-amino-acid oxidase (1.4.3.3), with FAD as hydrogen acceptor.

The reduced flavoproteins can react directly with dioxygen, whereupon hydrogen peroxide is formed, which is then decomposed by catalase (1.11.1.6):

$$\text{Enzyme-FADH}_2 + O_2 \xrightarrow{1.4.3.2} \text{Enzyme-FAD} + H_2O_2$$
or
$$\text{Enzyme-FMNH}_2 + O_2 \xrightarrow{1.4.3.3} \text{Enzyme-FMN} + H_2O_2$$

$$H_2O_2 \xrightarrow{1.11.1.6} H_2O + \tfrac{1}{2}O_2$$

The liver and kidneys contain both L-amino-acid oxidase and D-amino-acid oxidase, but they are probably of minor importance in amino-acid metabolism.

The hydroxy amino acids serine (page 113) and threonine (page 113) are subject to another form of deamination.

Urea cycle

Most terrestrial vertebrates utilize the urea cycle as a means of removing free ammonia – that is, of keeping the ammonia concentration low in tissues and body fluids.

Ammonia arises from various sources: from excess amino acids from glutamine, and from the breakdown of nucleic acids. Even bacteria in the gastrointestinal tract can form ammonia, for example from uric acid and urea, which are end-products of nitrogen metabolism.

Ammonia (NH_3, NH_4^+) is highly toxic, in part because it can so readily combine with 2-oxoglutarate by a process of reductive amination. This is the reverse of the oxidative deamination already discussed; the equilibrium under physiological conditions is usually in the direction of ammonia utilization. This removal of 2-oxoglutarate, a vital intermediate in the tricarboxylic acid cycle, causes considerable disorganization of cell respiration and the production of excessive amounts of ketone bodies.

In a preliminary reaction of the urea cycle, ammonia combines with bicarbonate and ATP to form carbamoyl phosphate. The reaction is catalyzed by carbamoyl-phosphate synthase (ammonia

Fig. 1 *Urea cycle*

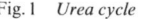

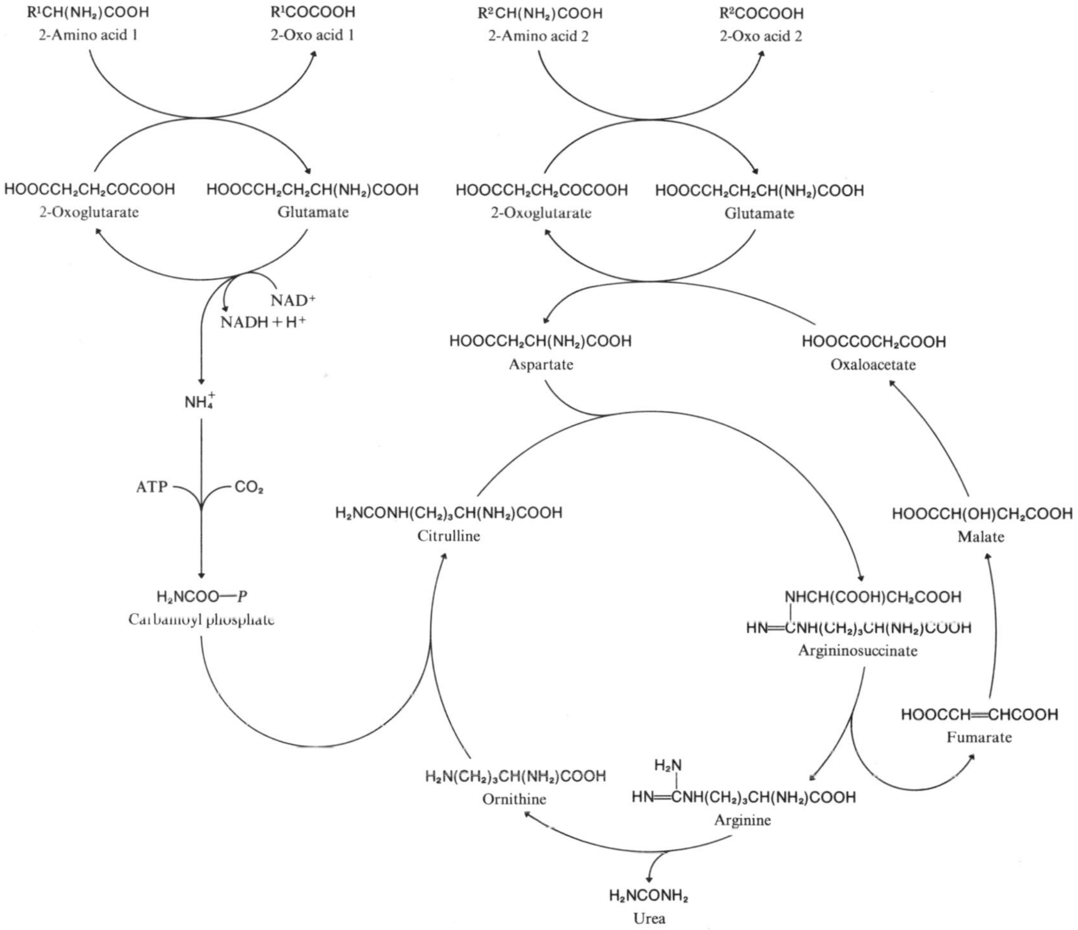

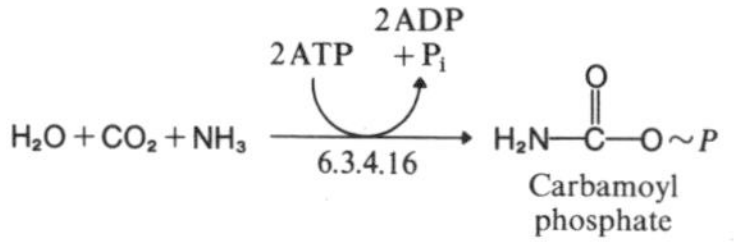

R¹CH(NH₂)COOH
2-Amino acid 1

R¹COCOOH
2-Oxo acid 1

R²CH(NH₂)COOH
2-Amino acid 2

R²COCOOH
2-Oxo acid 2

HOOCCH₂CH₂COCOOH
2-Oxoglutarate

HOOCCH₂CH₂CH(NH₂)COOH
Glutamate

HOOCCH₂CH₂COCOOH
2-Oxoglutarate

HOOCCH₂CH₂CH(NH₂)COOH
Glutamate

NAD⁺
NADH + H⁺

HOOCCH₂CH(NH₂)COOH
Aspartate

HOOCCOCH₂COOH
Oxaloacetate

NH₄⁺

ATP — CO₂

H₂NCONH(CH₂)₃CH(NH₂)COOH
Citrulline

HOOCCH(OH)CH₂COOH
Malate

H₂NCOO—P
Carbamoyl phosphate

NHCH(COOH)CH₂COOH
HN=CNH(CH₂)₃CH(NH₂)COOH
Argininosuccinate

HOOCCH=CHCOOH
Fumarate

H₂N(CH₂)₃CH(NH₂)COOH
Ornithine

H₂N
HN=CNH(CH₂)₃CH(NH₂)COOH
Arginine

H₂NCONH₂
Urea

$$2\,ATP \xrightarrow[6.3.4.16]{\quad 2\,ADP + P_i \quad} $$

$$H_2O + CO_2 + NH_3 \longrightarrow H_2N\!-\!\overset{O}{\overset{\|}{C}}\!-\!O \sim P$$

Carbamoyl phosphate

age of ATP to yield AMP + pyrophosphate and finally the cleavage of pyrophosphate to orthophosphate.

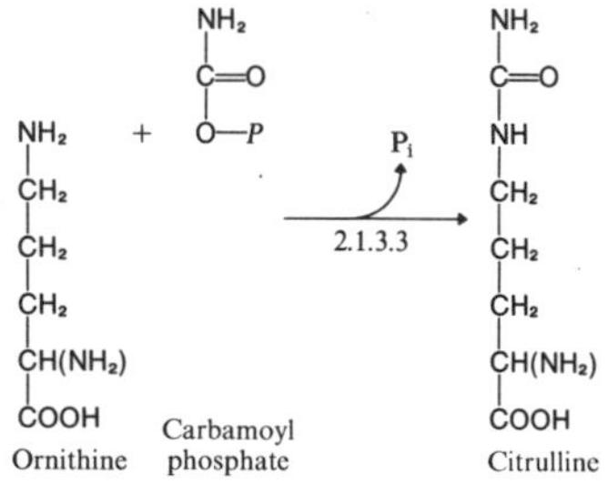

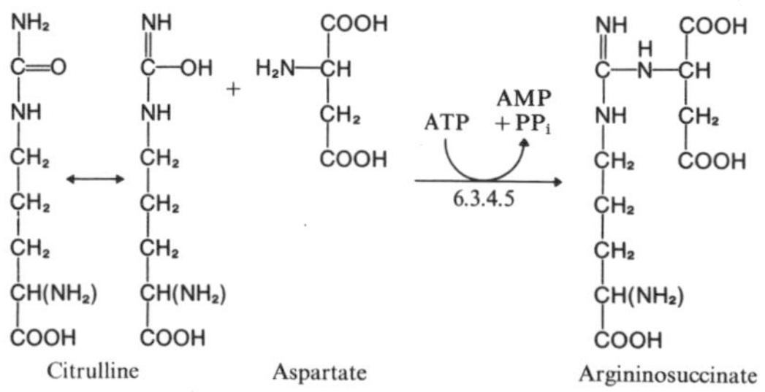

6.3.4.16), an enzyme localized in the mitochondria. Another carbamoyl-phosphate synthase (glutamine-hydrolyzing) (6.3.5.5) is present in the cytosol; this enzyme transfers the NH₂ group of glutamine, and the carbamoyl phosphate formed in the cytosol reacts further to yield pyrimidines (page 172) and not urea. The synthesis of 1 molecule of carbamoyl phosphate requires the hydrolysis of 2 molecules of ATP; thus the reaction is practically irreversible. Mitochondrial carbamoyl-phosphate synthase is activated by N-acetyl-glutamate. This compound is formed, with the aid of mitochondrial amino-acid acetyltransferase (2.3.1.1), from glutamate and acetyl-CoA in a reaction that is stimulated by arginine.

In the first step of the actual synthesis of urea, carbamoyl phosphate reacts with ornithine to give citrulline – a reaction which is catalyzed by ornithine carbamoyltransferase (2.1.3.3). NH₃-dependent carbamoyl-phosphate synthase and ornithine carbamoyltransferase are both mitochondrial liver enzymes, so the formation of urea takes place mainly in the liver.

In the next reaction a second amino group enters the cycle in the form of aspartic acid, which in turn arises from glutamic acid or other amino acids by transamination. After migration into the cytosol, citrulline reacts with aspartate in the presence of argininosuccinate synthase (6.3.4.5) to form argininosuccinate. The reaction equilibrium is shifted in the direction of urea synthesis by the cleav-

NH₂
CH₂
CH₂
CH₂
CH(NH₂)
COOH
Ornithine

+

NH₂
C=O
O—P
Carbamoyl phosphate

→ 2.1.3.3 → Pᵢ

NH₂
C=O
NH
CH₂
CH₂
CH₂
CH(NH₂)
COOH
Citrulline

NH₂
C=O
NH
CH₂
CH₂
CH₂
CH(NH₂)
COOH
Citrulline

+

NH
C—OH
NH
CH₂
CH₂
CH₂
CH(NH₂)
COOH
Citrulline

+

COOH
H₂N—CH
CH₂
COOH
Aspartate

ATP → AMP + PPᵢ → 6.3.4.5 →

NH   COOH
C—N—CH
| H
NH   CH₂
CH₂   COOH
CH₂
CH₂
CH(NH₂)
COOH
Argininosuccinate

Argininosuccinate then splits in a reaction catalyzed by argininosuccinate lyase (4.3.2.1), in which the aspartate portion releases its amino group and arginine and fumarate are formed.

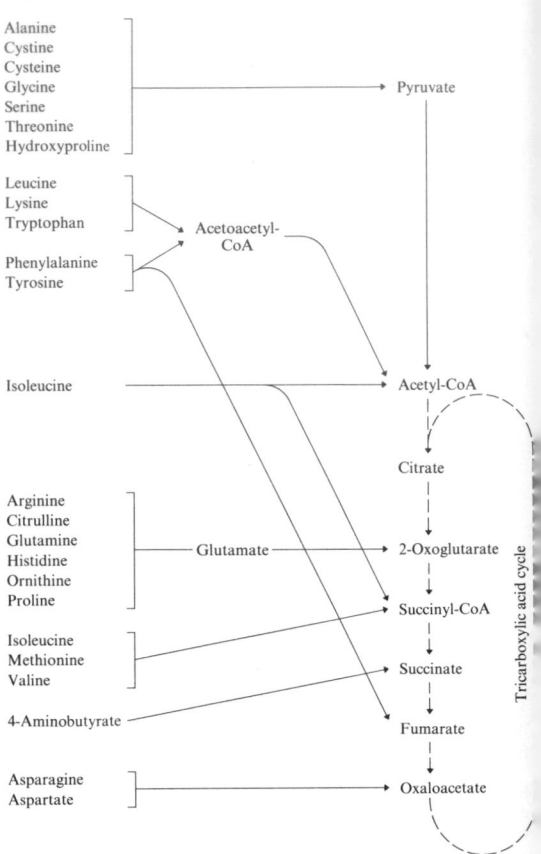

Fig. 2   *Breakdown of the carbon skeleton of amino acids*

NH   COOH
‖ H
C—N—CH
| |
NH   CH₂
| |
CH₂   COOH
|
CH₂   4.3.2.1
|
CH₂
|
CH(NH₂)
|
COOH

Argininosuccinate

NH   COOH
‖
C—NH₂   CH   +
| |
NH   CH
| |
CH₂   COOH
|
CH₂
|
CH₂
|
CH(NH₂)
|
COOH

Arginine   Fumarate

In the final reaction arginine is hydrolyzed to urea and ornithine by arginase (3.5.3.1), an enzyme which occurs in all tissues, but especially in the liver. Arginase is activated by Mn^{2+}. The ornithine thus formed then reacts – after transfer by means of a specific mechanism into the mitochondria – with another molecule of carbamoyl phosphate and initiates the next turn of the cycle (summarized in Fig. 1).

NH
‖
C—NH₂
|
NH   H₂O
|
CH₂
| 3.5.3.1
CH₂
|
CH₂
|
CH(NH₂)
|
COOH

Arginine

NH₂
|
O=C—NH₂   +
|
           NH₂
           |
           CH₂
           |
           CH₂
           |
           CH₂
           |
           CH(NH₂)
           |
           COOH

Urea   Ornithine

Decarboxylation of amino acids

The decarboxylation of amino acids is represented by the general formula:

R
|
CHNH₂   ⟶   CH₂NH₂ + CO₂
|
COOH

2-Amino acid   Primary amine

Decarboxylases (4.1.1) occur in animal tissues and in many microorganisms, but not every amino acid can be enzymatically decarboxylated. Decarboxylation products are listed on pages 42–43. Decarboxylations occurring in animal tissues are of importance in the formation of essential metabolites such as, for example, taurine (needed for the conjugation of bile acids) as well as 4-aminobutyric acid and serotonin (neurotransmitters). In decarboxylation of amino acids, pyridoxal phosphate acts as the coenzyme (page 80), but not in the decarboxylation of histidine in bacteria.

Breakdown of individual amino acids

After deamination of amino acids described previously (page 110), the carbon skeletons remaining are usually broken down further to pyruvate, acetyl-CoA or intermediates of the tricarboxylic acid cycle (Fig. 2).

Those amino acids from which acetoacetyl-CoA or acetyl-CoA derive are referred to as *ketogenic* amino acids because they can be converted to ketone bodies; the others are described as *glucogenic* amino acids on account of their possible conversion to glucose via phosphoenol pyruvate.

Breakdown of amino acids via pyruvate

L-*Alanine*. Pyruvate is formed directly from alanine either by oxidative deamination or by transamination.

L-*Cysteine*. This amino acid is at the center of a wide range of reaction pathways (Fig. 3) and is, of course, a precursor in the formation of glutathione and of coenzyme A. There are two major pathways of metabolism – one involving initial transamination and the other, the more important, involving initial oxidation (Fig. 4).

Cysteine sulfinate pathway. Sulfinoalanine (cysteine sulfinate) is formed from cysteine by combination with dioxygen, which is catalyzed by cysteine dioxygenase (1.13.11.20). This product may then react in 3 ways:

1. Transamination leads to the formation of 3-sulfinopyruvate, the enzyme involved being similar to or identical with aspartate aminotransferase (2.6.1.1). The 3-sulfinopyruvate rapidly loses its sulfur (with or without an enzyme) to form pyruvate and sulfite. This is then oxidized to sulfate by sulfite dehydrogenase (1.8.2.1) (also called 'sulfite oxidase'), a mitochondrial enzyme that contains molybdenum and a heme of the cytochrome b_5 type.

Fig. 3   *Reactions of cysteine*

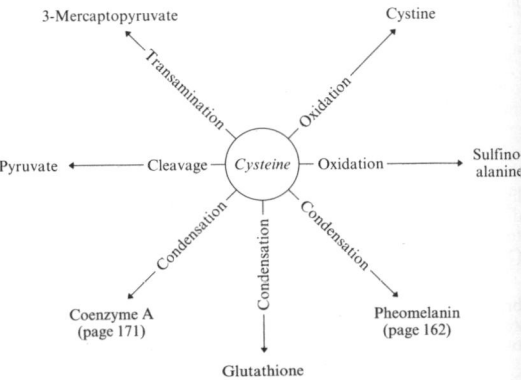

Fig. 4 *Major pathways of cysteine breakdown*

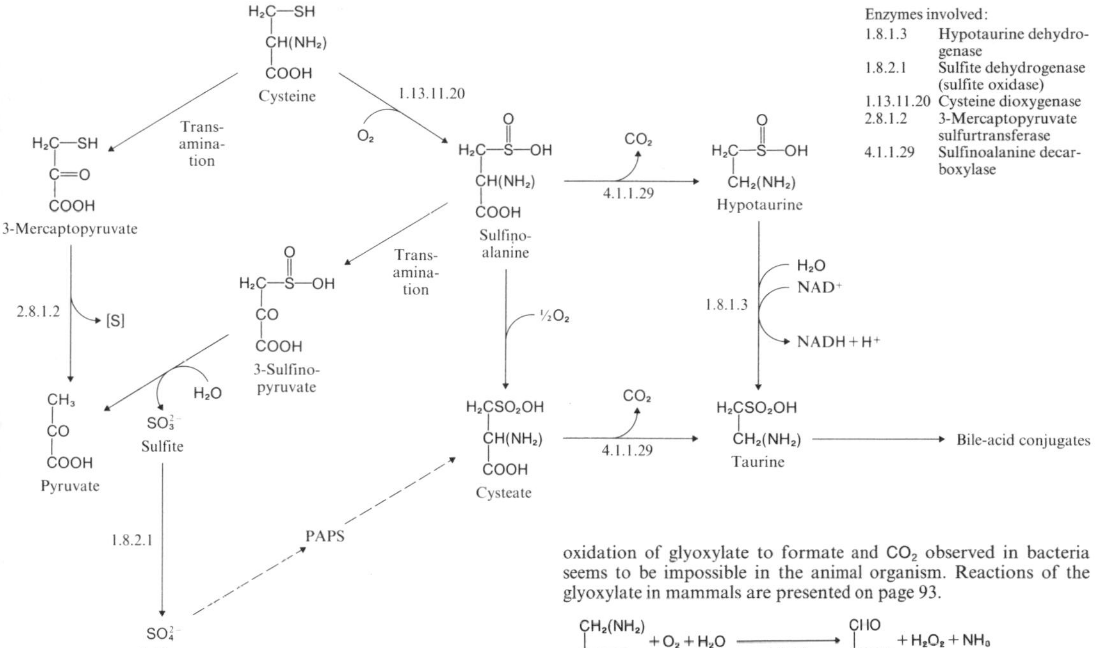

Enzymes involved:

1.8.1.3	Hypotaurine dehydrogenase
1.8.2.1	Sulfite dehydrogenase (sulfite oxidase)
1.13.11.20	Cysteine dioxygenase
2.8.1.2	3-Mercaptopyruvate sulfurtransferase
4.1.1.29	Sulfinoalanine decarboxylase

(Fig. 4 diagram showing cysteine breakdown pathways: Cysteine → via transamination → 3-Mercaptopyruvate; via 1.13.11.20 with O_2 → Sulfinoalanine; 3-Mercaptopyruvate via 2.8.1.2 [S] → mercaptopyruvate intermediates → Pyruvate + Sulfite (1.8.2.1) → Sulfate; Sulfinoalanine → Hypotaurine via 4.1.1.29 with CO_2 → Taurine via 1.8.1.3 → Bile-acid conjugates; Sulfinoalanine → via transamination → 3-Sulfinopyruvate → Cysteate via $\frac{1}{2}O_2$; Cysteate via 4.1.1.29 with CO_2 → Taurine. PAPS/PAPS pathway to Sulfate.)

oxidation of glyoxylate to formate and CO_2 observed in bacteria seems to be impossible in the animal organism. Reactions of the glyoxylate in mammals are presented on page 93.

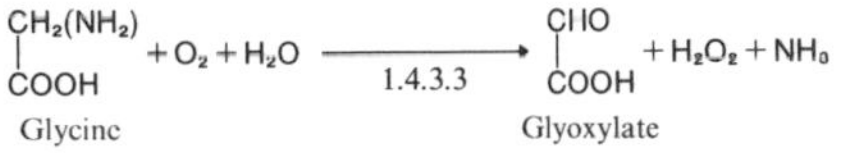

$$CH_2(NH_2)\text{-}COOH \xrightarrow[1.4.3.3]{+O_2+H_2O} CHO\text{-}COOH + H_2O_2 + NH_3$$

Glycine → Glyoxylate

Glycine is an important cell constituent for detoxication mechanisms (page 212). For example, it reacts with benzoic acid to form hippuric acid, which can then be excreted. Glycine is also involved in the synthesis of purines (page 170), glutathione (page 154) and creatine (page 158).

L *Serine.* Serine can be nonoxidatively deaminated to form pyruvate in the presence of L-serine dehydratase (4.2.1.13), a reaction closely analogous to the conversion of cysteine to pyruvate.

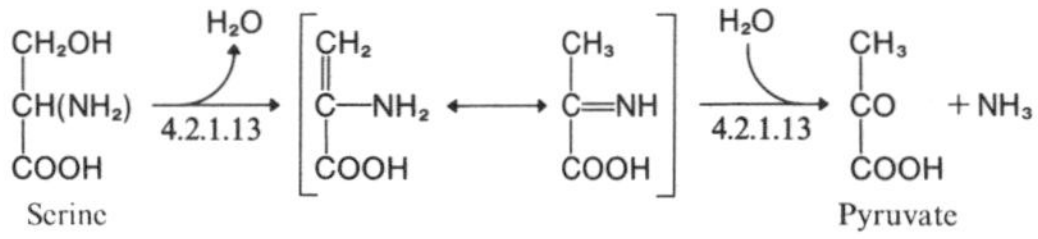

$$\text{Serine} \xrightarrow[4.2.1.13]{H_2O} \rightleftharpoons \xrightarrow[4.2.1.13]{H_2O} \text{Pyruvate} + NH_3$$

Owing to the influence of glycine hydroxymethyltransferase (2.1.2.1), serine is in equilibrium with glycine, so that the reactions described above in the section on 'Glycine' also hold true for serine. Serine moreover passes through the one-carbon unit cycle (page 159).

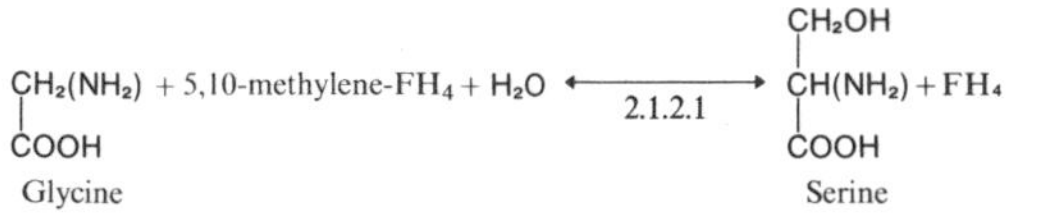

$$CH_2(NH_2)\text{-}COOH + 5,10\text{-methylene-}FH_4 + H_2O \underset{2.1.2.1}{\rightleftharpoons} CH_2OH\text{-}CH(NH_2)\text{-}COOH + FH_4$$

Glycine → Serine

2. Of lesser importance is the pathway in which sulfinoalanine is first oxidized to cysteate, which is then decarboxylated (using sulfinoalanine decarboxylase, 4.1.1.29) to form taurine.

3. A much more important route to taurine involves the decarboxylation of sulfinoalanine to hypotaurine, using sulfinoalanine decarboxylase (4.1.1.29). The hypotaurine is then oxidized to taurine, using hypotaurine dehydrogenase (1.8.1.3).

3-Mercaptopyruvate pathway. 3-Mercaptopyruvate is formed from cysteine by transamination and can then react in 3 ways:

1. Oxidative decarboxylation forms mercaptoacetate, which can then react with a molecule of cysteine to form mixed disulfide of mercaptoacetate and cysteine.

2. Reduction results in the formation of 3-mercaptolactate, which can then react with cysteine in a similar way to form mixed disulfide of 3-mercaptolactate and cysteine.

3. Transsulfuration may occur with the formation of pyruvate. The sulfur may appear as elemental sulfur or may be transferred to sulfite to form thiosulfate, to sulfinoalanine to form alanine thiosulfonate, or (surprisingly) to cyanide to form thiocyanate.

The cleavage of cysteine to yield hydrogen sulfide, ammonia and pyruvate proceeds analogously to the cleavage of cystathionine (see Fig. 15, page 122) and is catalyzed by cystathionine γ-lyase (4.4.1.1). It is, however, questionable whether it is of significance in mammalian tissues.

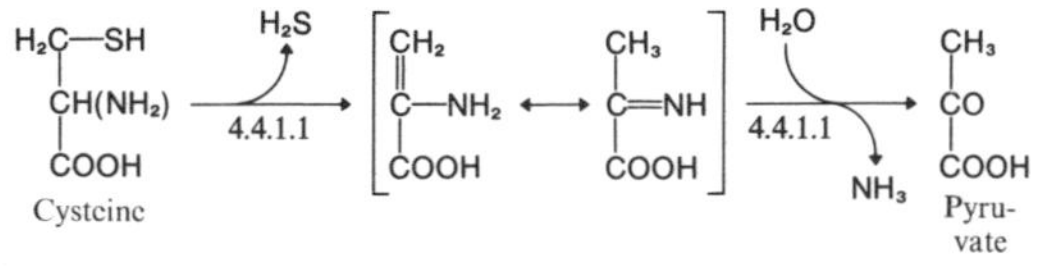

$$\text{Cysteine} \xrightarrow[4.4.1.1]{H_2S} \rightleftharpoons \xrightarrow[4.4.1.1]{H_2O} \text{Pyruvate} + NH_3$$

Cystine and *oxidized glutathione* (glutathione disulfide). In the liver, cystine is reduced to cysteine in the presence of cystine reductase (NADH) (1.6.4.1), and/or oxidized glutathione is reduced to glutathione in the presence of glutathione reductase (1.6.4.2) (NADPH).

Glycine. This amino acid has no asymmetric C atom and cannot be broken down by L-amino-acid oxidase. A specific flavoprotein enzyme is necessary for its oxidation. This is probably identical with D-amino-acid oxidase (1.4.3.3).

The glyoxylate thus formed is the oxo acid corresponding to glycine and can also be formed from glycine by transamination. The

L-*Threonine.* Threonine aldolase (4.1.2.5) – an enzyme containing pyridoxal phosphate – may split threonine to give acetaldehyde and glycine. The acetaldehyde is oxidized to acetyl-CoA, the glycine is converted to serine and metabolized to pyruvate, as described above in the section on 'Glycine'.

$$\text{Threonine} \xrightarrow{4.1.2.5} \text{Glycine} + \text{Acetaldehyde} \xrightarrow[HSCoA]{NAD^+ + H^+ \;\; NADH} \text{Acetyl-CoA}$$

$$\cdots\cdots\rightarrow CH_3COCOOH \;(\text{Pyruvate})$$

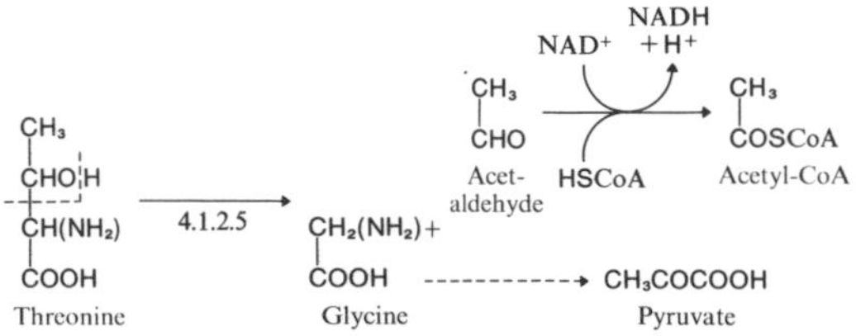

Fig. 5   *Degradation of branched-chain amino acids* (see below and page 121)

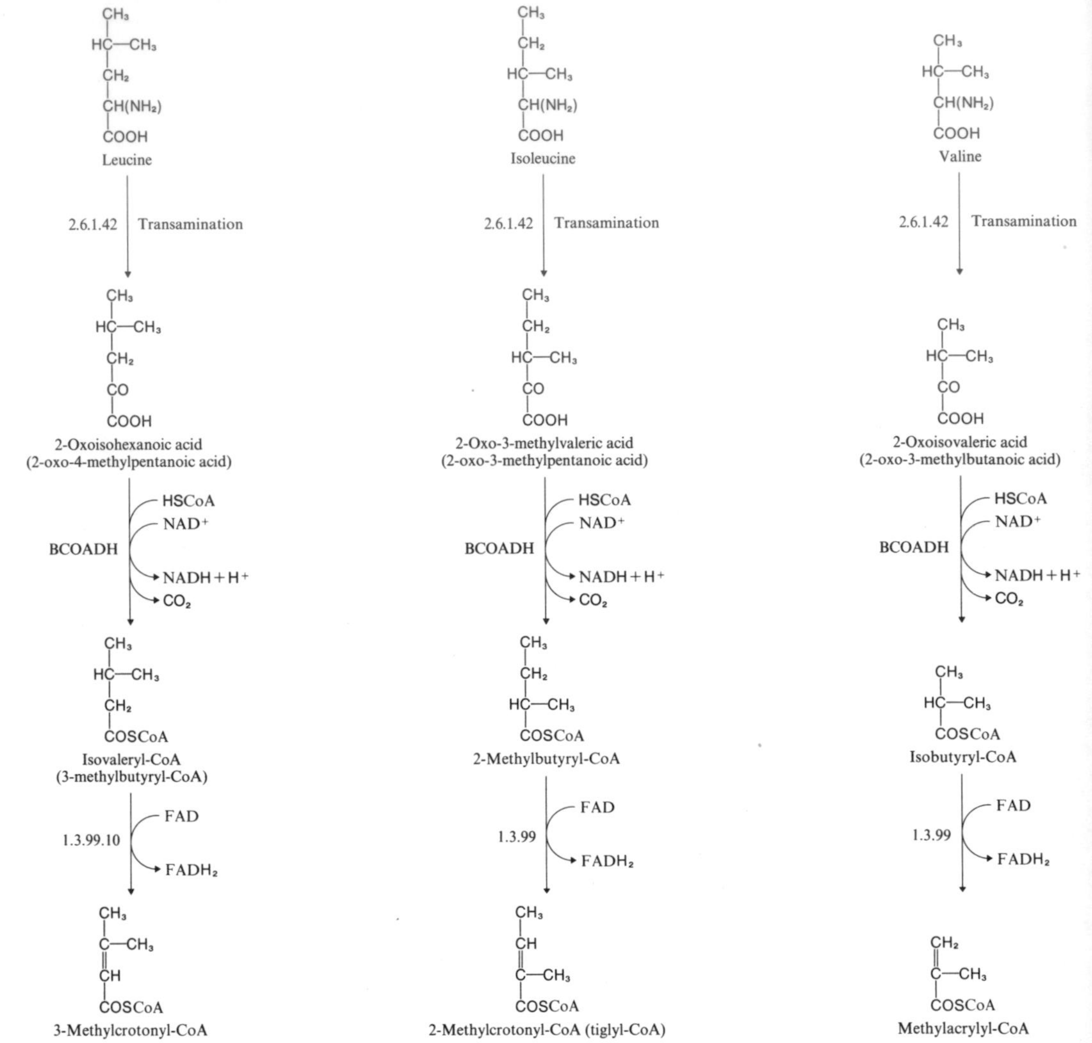

Leucine column:

CH₃ — HC—CH₃ — CH₂ — CH(NH₂) — COOH
Leucine

2.6.1.42 | Transamination

CH₃ — HC—CH₃ — CH₂ — CO — COOH
2-Oxoisohexanoic acid
(2-oxo-4-methylpentanoic acid)

BCOADH   HSCoA, NAD⁺ → NADH+H⁺, CO₂

CH₃ — HC—CH₃ — CH₂ — COSCoA
Isovaleryl-CoA
(3-methylbutyryl-CoA)

1.3.99.10   FAD → FADH₂

CH₃ — C—CH₃ — CH — COSCoA
3-Methylcrotonyl-CoA

Isoleucine column:

CH₃ — CH₂ — HC—CH₃ — CH(NH₂) — COOH
Isoleucine

2.6.1.42 | Transamination

CH₃ — CH₂ — HC—CH₃ — CO — COOH
2-Oxo-3-methylvaleric acid
(2-oxo-3-methylpentanoic acid)

BCOADH   HSCoA, NAD⁺ → NADH+H⁺, CO₂

CH₃ — CH₂ — HC—CH₃ — COSCoA
2-Methylbutyryl-CoA

1.3.99   FAD → FADH₂

CH₃ — CH — C—CH₃ — COSCoA
2-Methylcrotonyl-CoA (tiglyl-CoA)

Valine column:

CH₃ — HC—CH₃ — CH(NH₂) — COOH
Valine

2.6.1.42 | Transamination

CH₃ — HC—CH₃ — CO — COOH
2-Oxoisovaleric acid
(2-oxo-3-methylbutanoic acid)

BCOADH   HSCoA, NAD⁺ → NADH+H⁺, CO₂

CH₃ — HC—CH₃ — COSCoA
Isobutyryl-CoA

1.3.99   FAD → FADH₂

CH₂ — C—CH₃ — COSCoA
Methylacrylyl-CoA

(Subsequent course of reactions see next page)

Threonine may also undergo nonoxidative deamination in the presence of threonine dehydratase (4.2.1.16), yielding 2-oxobutyrate and ammonia.

CH₃ — CHOH — CH(NH₂) — COOH
Threonine

H₂O ↘ 4.2.1.16

[CH₃ — CH — C—NH₂ — COOH] ↔ [CH₃ — CH₂ — C=NH — COOH]

H₂O ↘ 4.2.1.16 → + NH₃

CH₃ — CH₂ — CO — COOH
2-Oxobutyrate

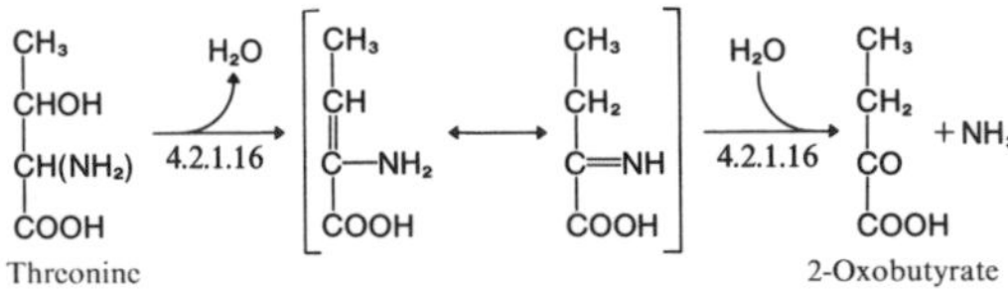

The 2-oxobutyrate is then oxidatively decarboxylated to yield propionyl-CoA – a precursor of succinyl-CoA. The initial reaction proceeds in the presence of 2-oxobutyrate synthase (1.2.7.2) and

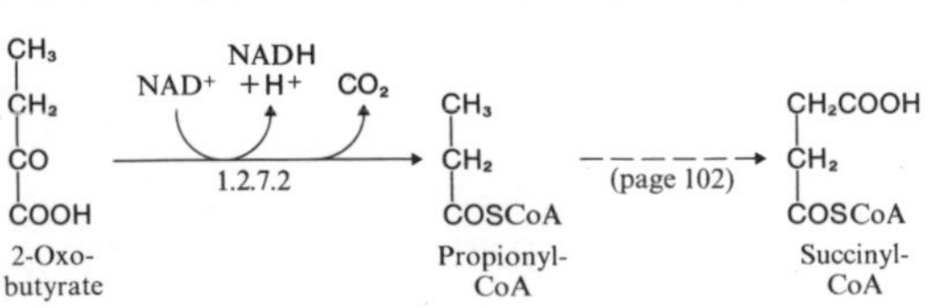

CH₃ — CH₂ — CO — COOH
2-Oxo-butyrate

NADH, NAD⁺ +H⁺, CO₂ ↘ 1.2.7.2

CH₃ — CH₂ — COSCoA
Propionyl-CoA

- - - (page 102) - - →

CH₂COOH — CH₂ — COSCoA
Succinyl-CoA

ferredoxin. The subsequent conversion of propionyl-CoA to succinyl-CoA is described in detail on page 102.

While the cleavage of threonine to 2-oxobutyrate and ammonia takes place in the cytosol, 2-amino-3-oxobutyrate (which spontaneously decarboxylates to aminoacetone) can be formed from threonine with the aid of mitochondrial L-threonine 3-dehydrogenase (1.1.1.103).

L-*4-Hydroxyproline* (Fig. 12, page 121). The degradation of 4-hydroxyproline is analogous to that of proline (see Fig. 13, page 121), except for the last cleavage reaction. 4-Hydroxyproline dehydrogenase is not, however, identical with the proline dehydrogenase (1.5.99.8).

L-*3-Hydroxyproline*. The breakdown pathway has not been fully characterized, but it does not proceed analogously to that of 4-hydroxyproline.

Breakdown of amino acids via acetyl-CoA

L-*Leucine* and L-*isoleucine* (Fig. 5). Initiated by transamination, the first 3 reactions proceed analogously. The further breakdown of leucine yields 3 molecules of acetyl-CoA, that of isoleucine yields 1 molecule of acetyl-CoA and 1 molecule of succinyl-CoA.

(Continued on page 119)

(to Fig. 5)

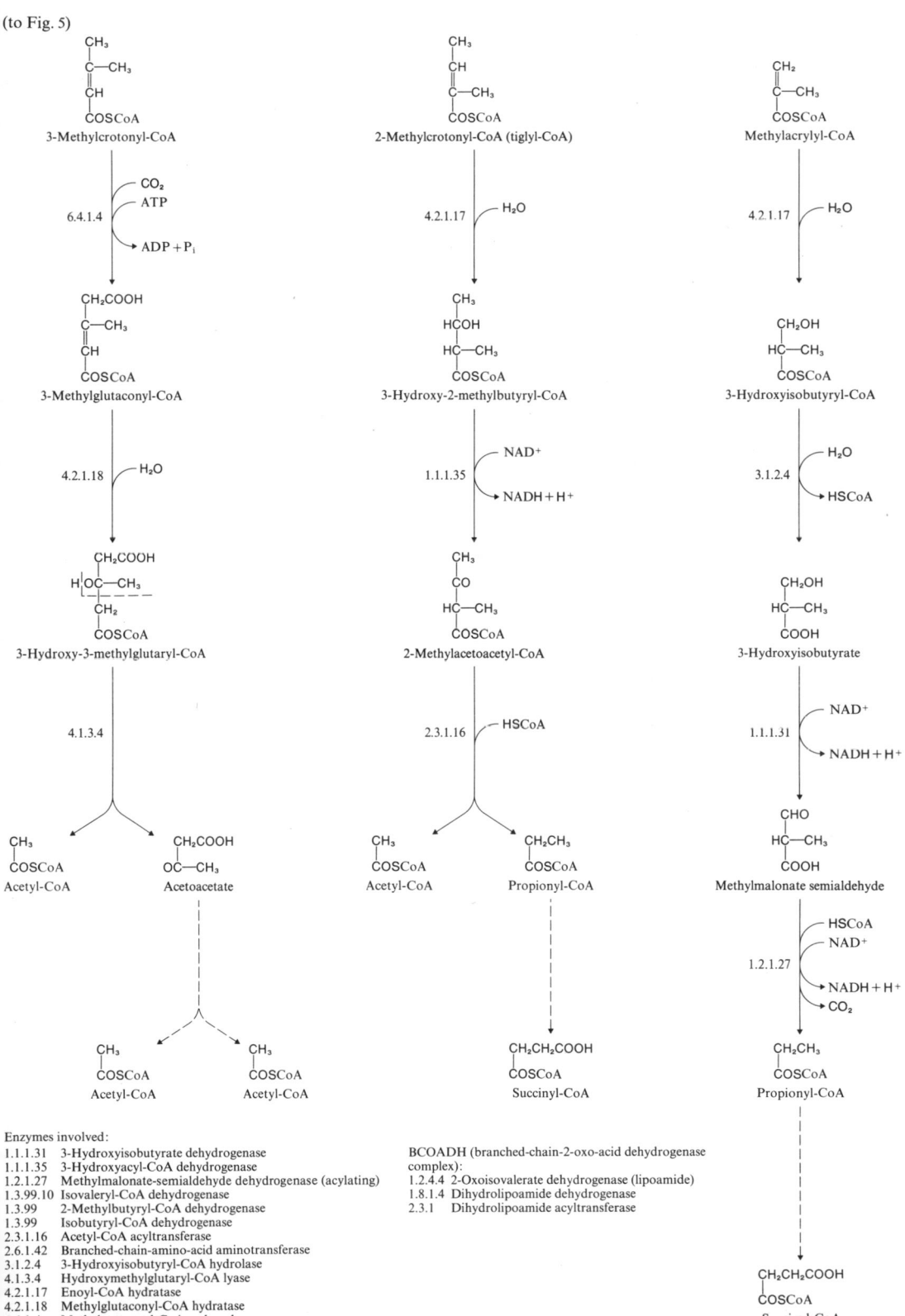

Enzymes involved:
1.1.1.31   3-Hydroxyisobutyrate dehydrogenase
1.1.1.35   3-Hydroxyacyl-CoA dehydrogenase
1.2.1.27   Methylmalonate-semialdehyde dehydrogenase (acylating)
1.3.99.10 Isovaleryl-CoA dehydrogenase
1.3.99   2-Methylbutyryl-CoA dehydrogenase
1.3.99   Isobutyryl-CoA dehydrogenase
2.3.1.16   Acetyl-CoA acyltransferase
2.6.1.42   Branched-chain-amino-acid aminotransferase
3.1.2.4   3-Hydroxyisobutyryl-CoA hydrolase
4.1.3.4   Hydroxymethylglutaryl-CoA lyase
4.2.1.17   Enoyl-CoA hydratase
4.2.1.18   Methylglutaconyl-CoA hydratase
6.4.1.4   Methylcrotonoyl-CoA carboxylase

BCOADH (branched-chain-2-oxo-acid dehydrogenase complex):
1.2.4.4   2-Oxoisovalerate dehydrogenase (lipoamide)
1.8.1.4   Dihydrolipoamide dehydrogenase
2.3.1   Dihydrolipoamide acyltransferase

Fig. 6   *Degradation of lysine* (page 119)

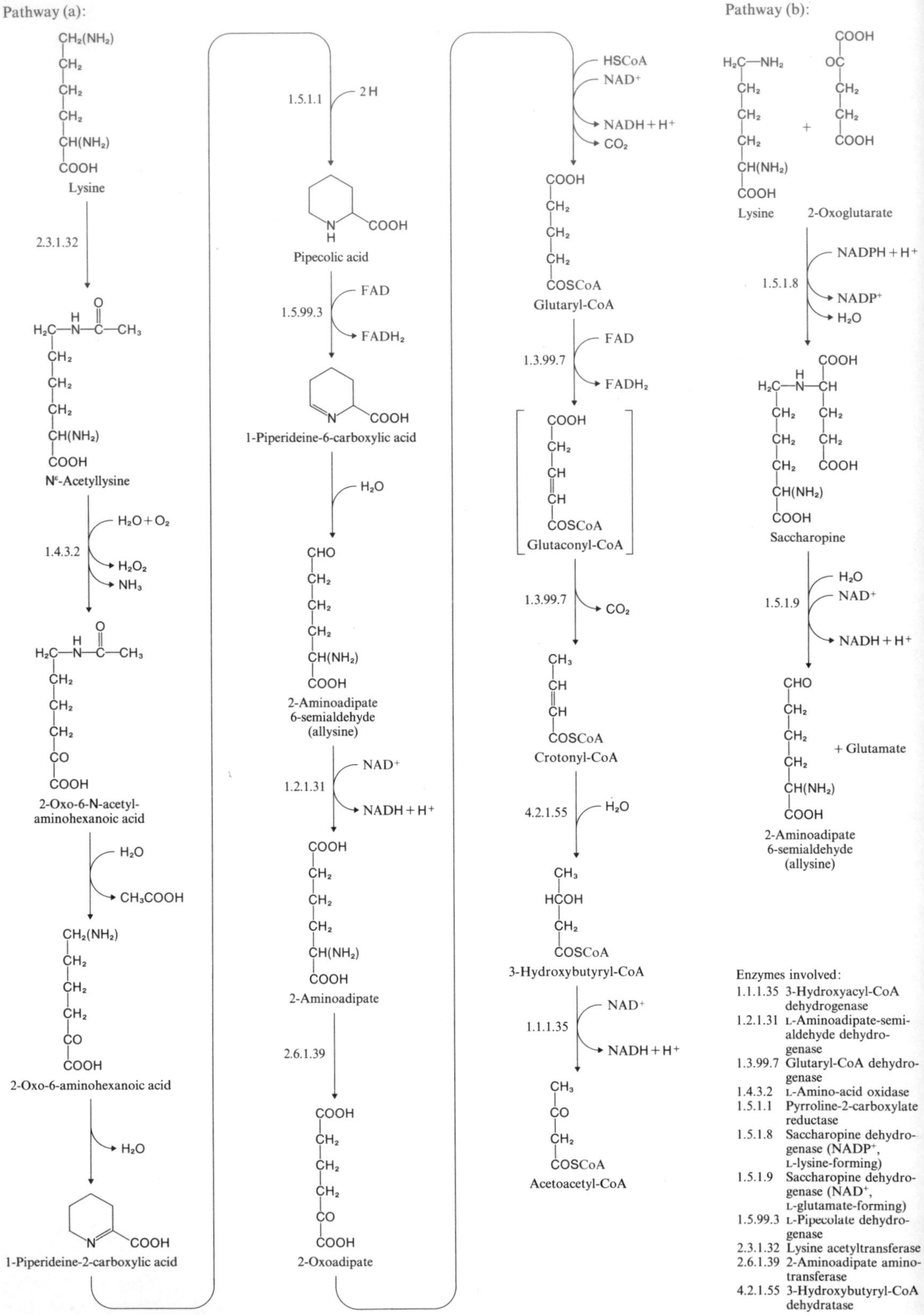

Pathway (a):

Lysine

2.3.1.32

N^ε-Acetyllysine

1.4.3.2 $H_2O + O_2$ → H_2O_2, NH_3

2-Oxo-6-N-acetyl-aminohexanoic acid

→ H_2O → CH_3COOH

2-Oxo-6-aminohexanoic acid

→ H_2O

1-Piperideine-2-carboxylic acid

1.5.1.1   2 H

Pipecolic acid

1.5.99.3   FAD → FADH₂

1-Piperideine-6-carboxylic acid

→ H_2O

2-Aminoadipate 6-semialdehyde (allysine)

1.2.1.31   NAD⁺ → NADH + H⁺

2-Aminoadipate

2.6.1.39

2-Oxoadipate

HSCoA, NAD⁺ → NADH + H⁺, CO₂

Glutaryl-CoA

1.3.99.7   FAD → FADH₂

Glutaconyl-CoA

1.3.99.7   → CO₂

Crotonyl-CoA

4.2.1.55 H_2O

3-Hydroxybutyryl-CoA

1.1.1.35   NAD⁺ → NADH + H⁺

Acetoacetyl-CoA

Pathway (b):

Lysine   2-Oxoglutarate

1.5.1.8   NADPH + H⁺ → NADP⁺, H_2O

Saccharopine

1.5.1.9 H_2O, NAD⁺ → NADH + H⁺

2-Aminoadipate 6-semialdehyde (allysine)   + Glutamate

Enzymes involved:
1.1.1.35 3-Hydroxyacyl-CoA dehydrogenase
1.2.1.31 L-Aminoadipate-semi-aldehyde dehydro-genase
1.3.99.7 Glutaryl-CoA dehydro-genase
1.4.3.2 L-Amino-acid oxidase
1.5.1.1 Pyrroline-2-carboxylate reductase
1.5.1.8 Saccharopine dehydro-genase (NADP⁺, L-lysine-forming)
1.5.1.9 Saccharopine dehydro-genase (NAD⁺, L-glutamate-forming)
1.5.99.3 L-Pipecolate dehydro-genase
2.3.1.32 Lysine acetyltransferase
2.6.1.39 2-Aminoadipate amino-transferase
4.2.1.55 3-Hydroxybutyryl-CoA dehydratase

Fig. 7 *End-products of tryptophan metabolism after decarboxylation, transamination and 5-hydroxylation* (page 119)

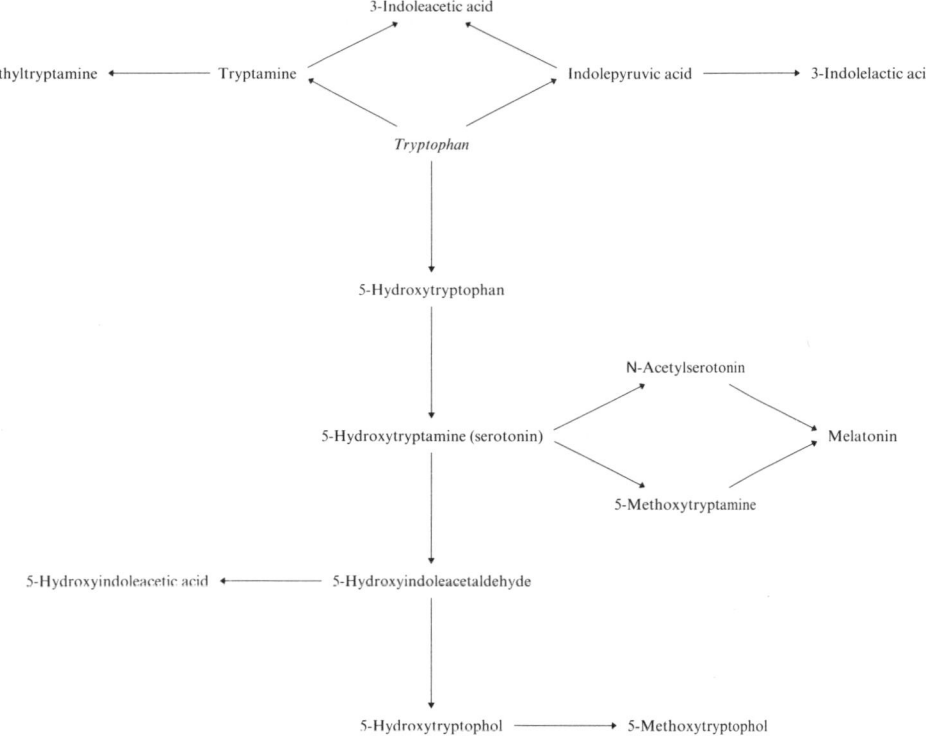

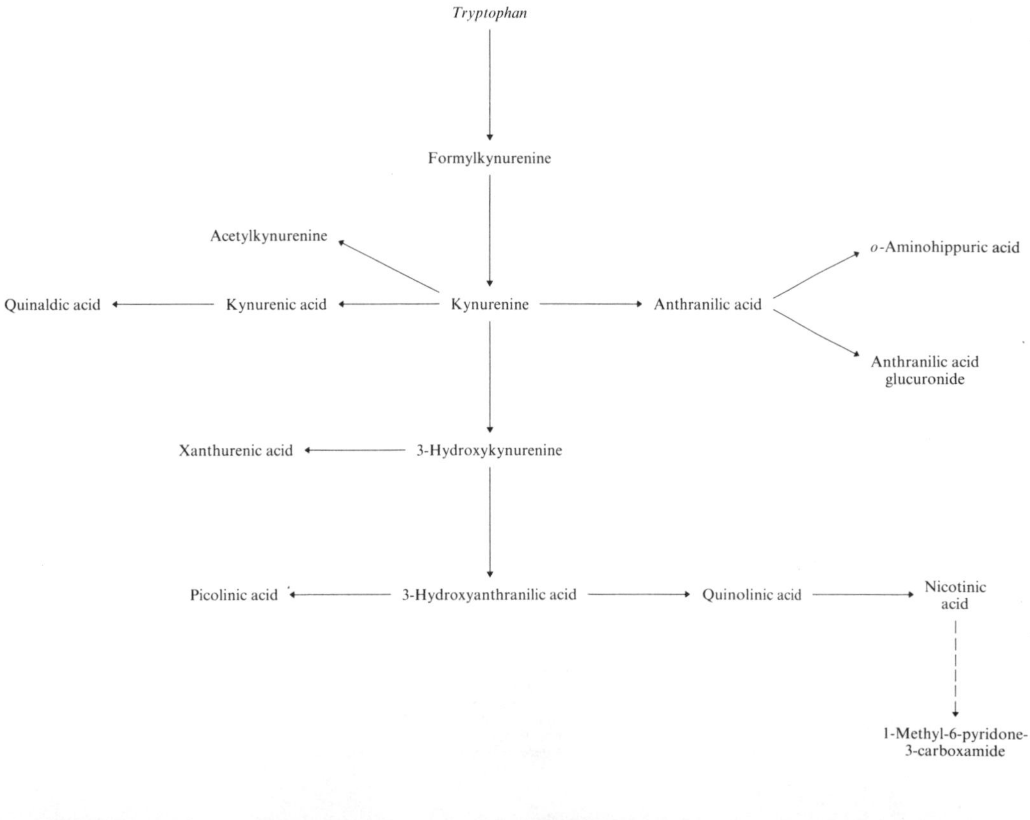

Fig. 8 *End-products of the kynurenine pathway in tryptophan degradation* (page 119)

Fig. 9 *Tryptophan degradation and formation of nicotinic acid* (page 119)

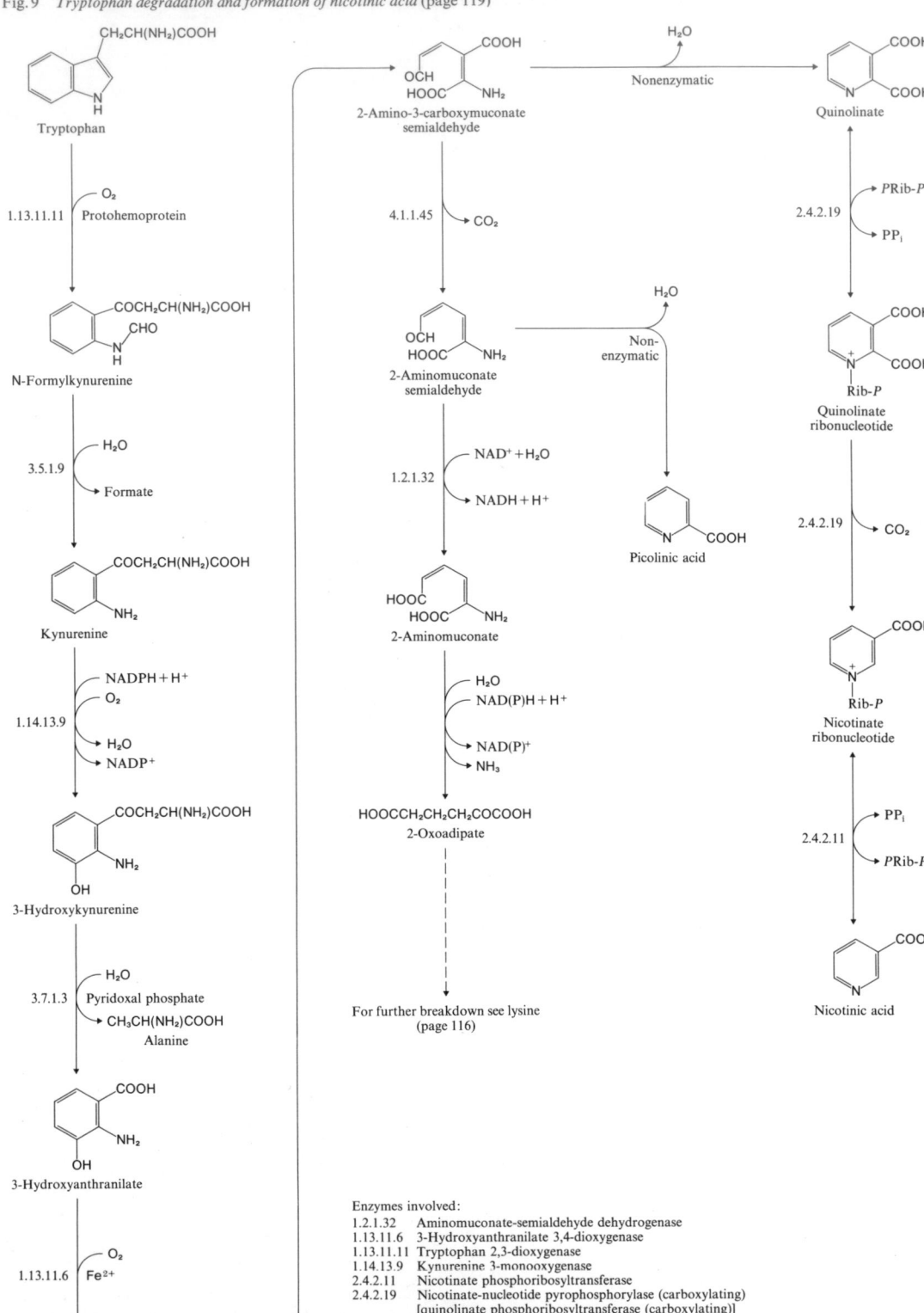

Enzymes involved:
1.2.1.32   Aminomuconate-semialdehyde dehydrogenase
1.13.11.6   3-Hydroxyanthranilate 3,4-dioxygenase
1.13.11.11 Tryptophan 2,3-dioxygenase
1.14.13.9   Kynurenine 3-monooxygenase
2.4.2.11   Nicotinate phosphoribosyltransferase
2.4.2.19   Nicotinate-nucleotide pyrophosphorylase (carboxylating)
            [quinolinate phosphoribosyltransferase (carboxylating)]
3.5.1.9   Arylformamidase
3.7.1.3   Kynureninase
4.1.1.45   Aminocarboxymuconate-semialdehyde decarboxylase

L-*Lysine*. This amino acid undergoes a complex series of degradation reactions [Fig. 6 (page 116), reaction pathway (a)], in which 2 C atoms are split off and the remaining 4 C atoms are converted to 1 molecule of acetoacetyl-CoA or 2 molecules of acetyl-CoA. The initial stages of degradation are unusual. The 6-amino group is first acetylated and the 2-amino group then converted to the oxo group not by transamination but by L-amino-acid oxidase. Another pathway to 2-aminoadipate 6-semialdehyde [Fig. 6 (page 116), reaction pathway (b)] predominates in the liver; it consists in a partial reversal of the biosynthesis of aminoadipate.

L-*Tryptophan*. This amino acid is incompletely oxidized in man and in most animals. End-products of the tryptophan degradation excreted in small amounts in the urine can be seen from Figures 7 and 8.

Transamination. This reaction yields indolepyruvate and is catalyzed by tryptophan aminotransferase (2.6.1.27).

Decarboxylation. This reaction yields tryptamine and is catalyzed by aromatic-L-amino-acid decarboxylase (4.1.1.28). Tryptamine is then methylated with the aid of arylamine N-methyltransferase (2.1.1.49) and S-adenosylmethionine as methyl-group donor.

Hydroxylation in position 5 is the starting reaction for the synthesis of serotonin and melatonin (page 161).

The main catabolic pathway of tryptophan leads to nicotinate ribonucleotide, the precursor of NAD (page 170). In this pathway (Fig. 9), tryptophan is first oxidized by the liver enzyme tryptophan 2,3-dioxygenase (1.13.11.11) to form N-formylkynurenine. In a further reaction, the side chain is split off with the aid of the pyridoxal-phosphate-requiring enzyme kynureninase (3.7.1.3). The conversion of the aromatic ring to the pyridine ring takes place first by cleavage of the benzene ring of 3-hydroxyanthrilic acid, whereupon the

pyridine ring is formed, using the NH_2 group of the 3-hydroxyanthranilic acid.

The usual tryptophan content of the diet does not seem to be sufficient to guarantee an adequate synthesis of nicotinic acid, so that a dietary supply of nicotinic acid is indispensable. In urine, quantitatively the main product of tryptophan, NAD and nicotinic-acid metabolism is 1-methyl-6-pyridone-3-carboxamide (1-methyl-2-pyridone-5-carboxamide) (Fig. 10). The compound is synthesized via the N-methylated derivative of nicotinamide, using S-adenosyl-methionine as methyl-group donor.

L-*Phenylalanine* and L-*tyrosine* (Fig. 11). Phenylalanine is oxidized to tyrosine by the reaction mechanism described on page 155. In the principal pathway of the breakdown of tyrosine depicted in Figure 11, fumarate and acetoacetate are specified as end-products. Both these compounds, however, are subject to further metabolic reactions. (In man 99% of the tyrosine is metabolized in this way.) Ascorbic acid is the cofactor in the formation of homogentisate, which includes a rearrangement of the side chain of 4-hydroxyphenylpyruvate.

Phenylalanine and tyrosine can also be decarboxylated to yield the corresponding amines (Fig. 11, alternate pathway). The octopamine formed from p-tyramine is an important constituent of the nervous system in invertebrates, and a 'false' neurotransmitter in humans.

The formation of catecholamines (page 161), ubiquinone (page 165) and melanins (page 162) and thyroid hormones (page 165) depends on tyrosine as precursor.

Breakdown of amino acids via 2-oxoglutarate

Arginine (or ornithine), proline, histidine and glutamine are all broken down to glutamic acid, which then enters the tricarboxylic acid cycle as 2-oxoglutaric acid. Glutamic acid in addition is regenerated by the metabolism of glutathione (page 154).

L-*Glutamine*. Glutamine is hydrolyzed by glutaminase (3.5.1.2) to glutamic acid, which is converted to 2-oxoglutarate either by trans-

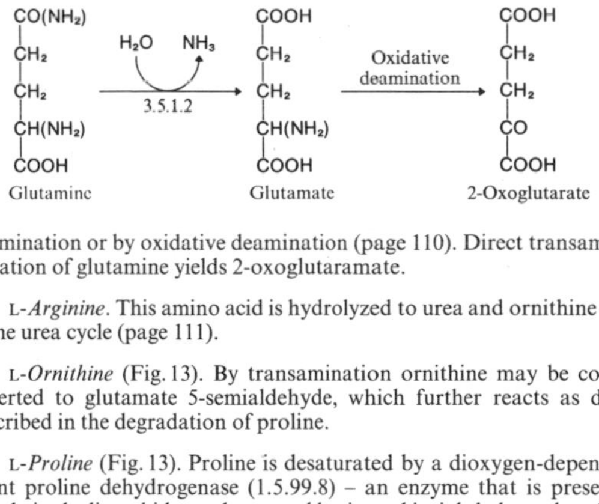

Fig. 10   *Degradation of NAD+*

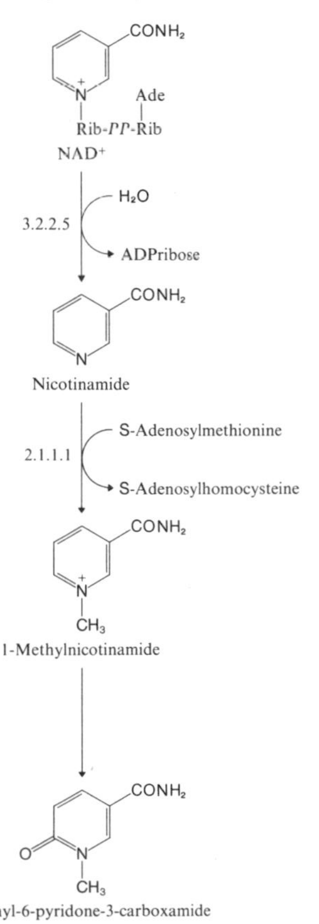

CONH₂

⁺N   Ade

Rib-*PP*-Rib

NAD⁺

— H₂O

3.2.2.5

→ ADPribose

CONH₂

N

Nicotinamide

— S-Adenosylmethionine

2.1.1.1

→ S-Adenosylhomocysteine

CONH₂

⁺N

CH₃

1-Methylnicotinamide

CONH₂

O   N

CH₃

1-Methyl-6-pyridone-3-carboxamide

Enzymes involved:
2.1.1.1 Nicotinamide methyltransferase
3.2.2.5 NAD⁺ nucleosidase

CO(NH₂) | H₂O NH₃ | COOH | Oxidative | COOH
CH₂ | | CH₂ | deamination | CH₂
CH₂ | 3.5.1.2 | CH₂ | → | CH₂
CH(NH₂) | | CH(NH₂) | | CO
COOH | | COOH | | COOH
Glutamine | | Glutamate | | 2-Oxoglutarate

amination or by oxidative deamination (page 110). Direct transamination of glutamine yields 2-oxoglutaramate.

L-*Arginine*. This amino acid is hydrolyzed to urea and ornithine in the urea cycle (page 111).

L-*Ornithine* (Fig. 13). By transamination ornithine may be converted to glutamate 5-semialdehyde, which further reacts as described in the degradation of proline.

L-*Proline* (Fig. 13). Proline is desaturated by a dioxygen-dependent proline dehydrogenase (1.5.99.8) – an enzyme that is present only in the liver, kidneys, heart and brain and is tightly bound to the inner mitochondrial membrane – to yield 1-pyrroline-5-carboxylate. 1-Pyrroline-5-carboxylate dehydrogenase (1.5.1.12), which oxidizes 1-pyrroline-5-carboxylate to glutamate, is found in most tissues, but not in erythrocytes.

L-*Histidine* (Fig. 14, page 122). This amino acid is converted to glutamic acid by a liver enzyme complex that includes tetrahydrofolic acid (FH_4) as cofactor. The conversion of formimino-FH_4 to 5,10-methenyl-FH_4 and 10-formyl-FH_4, as well as the reactions subsequent thereto, are presented on page 85.

Oxidative deamination or transamination of histidine yields imidazolepyruvic acid, which may be further converted to imidazolelactic acid and imidazoleacetic acid.

A similar pathway of histidine degradation to glutamic acid has been shown in bacteria, although tetrahydrofolic acid does not appear to be involved.

The 4-imidazolone-5-propionate may also be oxidized by a flavoprotein enzyme to hydantoin-5-propionate, which is excreted.

Small amounts of histidine are decarboxylated to histamine (for formula see page 42) by action of histidine decarboxylase (4.1.1.22), an enzyme present in many tissues.

Fig. 11   *Main and alternate pathways of the breakdown of phenylalanine and tyrosine* (page 119)

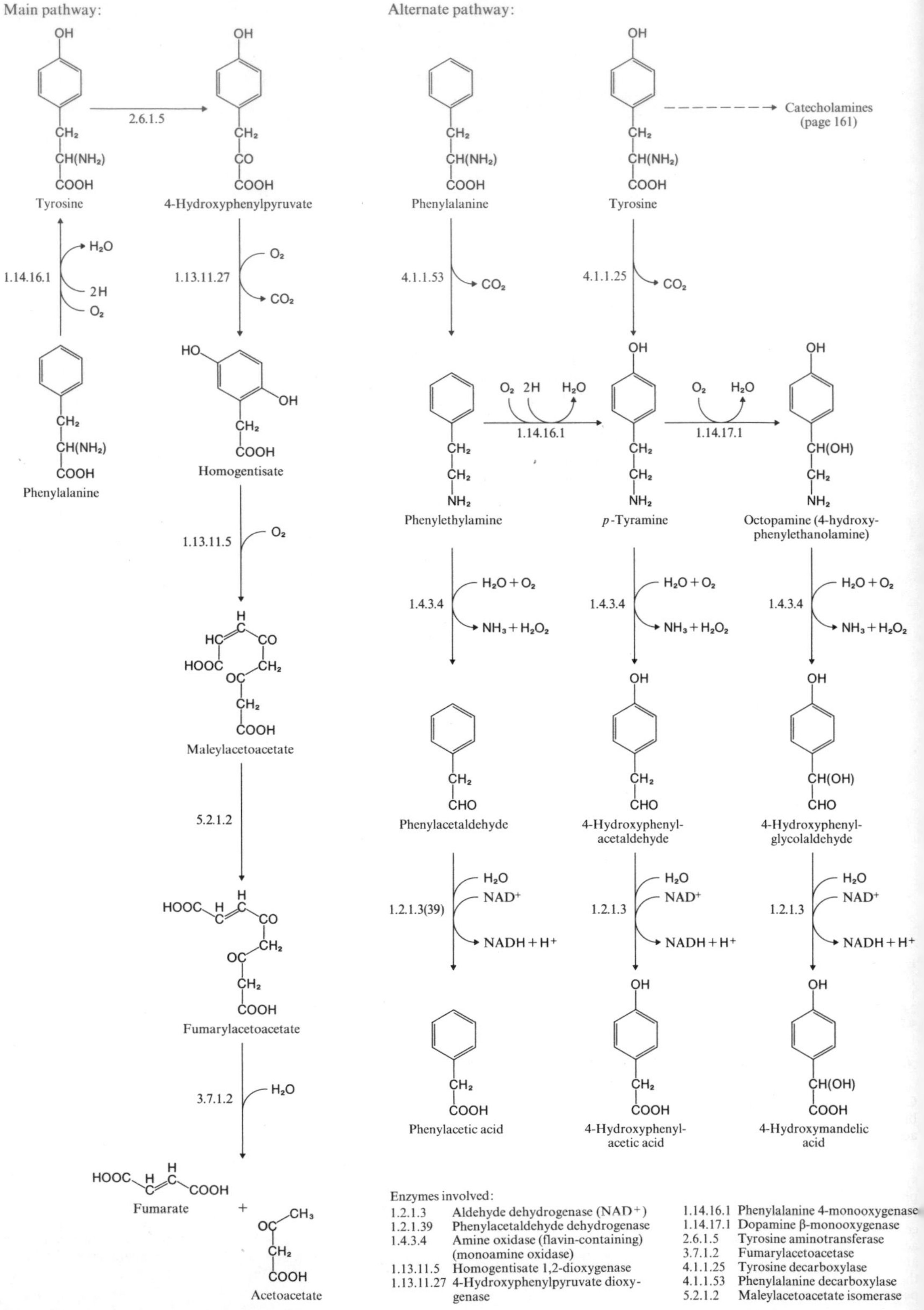

Main pathway:

Tyrosine → (2.6.1.5) → 4-Hydroxyphenylpyruvate

Tyrosine: OH–⬡–CH₂–CH(NH₂)–COOH
4-Hydroxyphenylpyruvate: OH–⬡–CH₂–CO–COOH

1.14.16.1 (H₂O, 2H, O₂) → Phenylalanine
1.13.11.27 (O₂ → CO₂) → Homogentisate

Phenylalanine: ⬡–CH₂–CH(NH₂)–COOH
Homogentisate: HO–⬡(OH)–CH₂–COOH

1.13.11.5 (O₂) → Maleylacetoacetate

5.2.1.2 → Fumarylacetoacetate

3.7.1.2 (H₂O) → Fumarate + Acetoacetate

Alternate pathway:

Phenylalanine: ⬡–CH₂–CH(NH₂)–COOH
Tyrosine: OH–⬡–CH₂–CH(NH₂)–COOH ----→ Catecholamines (page 161)

4.1.1.53 (CO₂)
4.1.1.25 (CO₂)

Phenylethylamine: ⬡–CH₂–CH₂–NH₂
1.14.16.1 (O₂ 2H, H₂O)
p-Tyramine: OH–⬡–CH₂–CH₂–NH₂
1.14.17.1 (O₂, H₂O)
Octopamine (4-hydroxyphenylethanolamine): OH–⬡–CH(OH)–CH₂–NH₂

1.4.3.4 (H₂O + O₂ → NH₃ + H₂O₂)

Phenylacetaldehyde: ⬡–CH₂–CHO
4-Hydroxyphenylacetaldehyde: OH–⬡–CH₂–CHO
4-Hydroxyphenylglycolaldehyde: OH–⬡–CH(OH)–CHO

1.2.1.3(39) / 1.2.1.3 (H₂O, NAD⁺ → NADH + H⁺)

Phenylacetic acid: ⬡–CH₂–COOH
4-Hydroxyphenylacetic acid: OH–⬡–CH₂–COOH
4-Hydroxymandelic acid: OH–⬡–CH(OH)–COOH

Enzymes involved:

1.2.1.3	Aldehyde dehydrogenase (NAD⁺)	
1.2.1.39	Phenylacetaldehyde dehydrogenase	
1.4.3.4	Amine oxidase (flavin-containing) (monoamine oxidase)	
1.13.11.5	Homogentisate 1,2-dioxygenase	
1.13.11.27	4-Hydroxyphenylpyruvate dioxygenase	
1.14.16.1	Phenylalanine 4-monooxygenase
1.14.17.1	Dopamine β-monooxygenase
2.6.1.5	Tyrosine aminotransferase
3.7.1.2	Fumarylacetoacetase
4.1.1.25	Tyrosine decarboxylase
4.1.1.53	Phenylalanine decarboxylase
5.2.1.2	Maleylacetoacetate isomerase

Fig. 12   *Degradation of 4-hydroxyproline* (page 114)

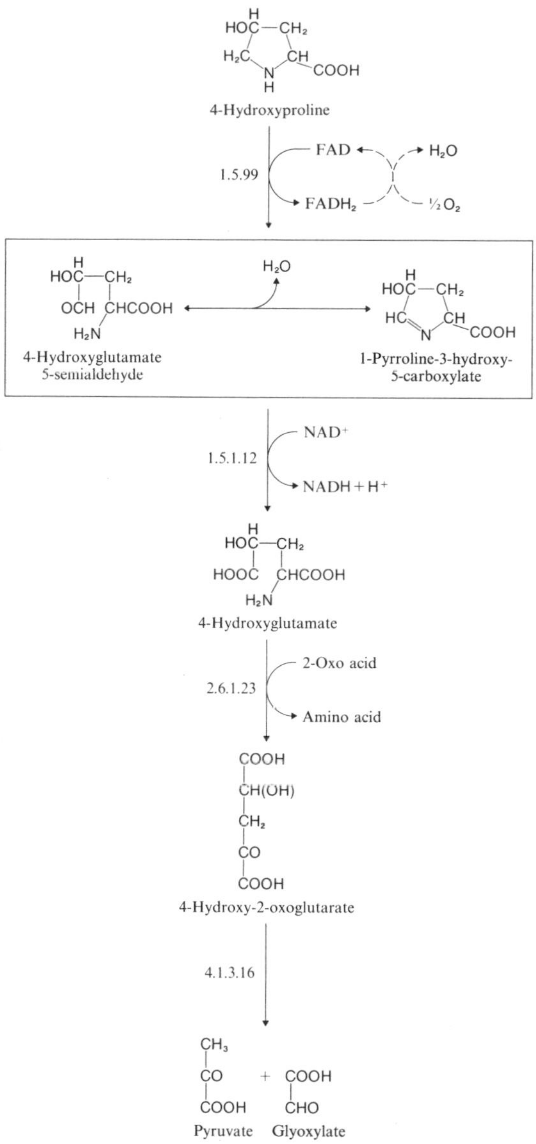

$$
\begin{array}{c}
\text{H} \\
\text{HOC—CH}_2 \\
\text{H}_2\text{C}\quad\text{CH} \\
\text{N}\quad\text{COOH} \\
\text{H}
\end{array}
$$

4-Hydroxyproline

1.5.99   FAD ← → H$_2$O   FADH$_2$ → → ½O$_2$

$$
\begin{array}{c}
\text{H} \\
\text{HOC—CH}_2 \\
\text{OCH CHCOOH} \\
\text{H}_2\text{N}
\end{array}
\quad\leftarrow\quad \text{H}_2\text{O} \quad
\begin{array}{c}
\text{H} \\
\text{HOC—CH}_2 \\
\text{HC}\quad\text{CH} \\
\text{N}\quad\text{COOH}
\end{array}
$$

4-Hydroxyglutamate 5-semialdehyde   1-Pyrroline-3-hydroxy-5-carboxylate

1.5.1.12   NAD$^+$ → NADH + H$^+$

$$
\begin{array}{c}
\text{H} \\
\text{HOC—CH}_2 \\
\text{HOOC CHCOOH} \\
\text{H}_2\text{N}
\end{array}
$$

4-Hydroxyglutamate

2.6.1.23   2-Oxo acid → Amino acid

$$
\begin{array}{c}
\text{COOH} \\
\text{CH(OH)} \\
\text{CH}_2 \\
\text{CO} \\
\text{COOH}
\end{array}
$$

4-Hydroxy-2-oxoglutarate

4.1.3.16

$$
\begin{array}{c}
\text{CH}_3 \\
\text{CO} \\
\text{COOH}
\end{array}
\quad + \quad
\begin{array}{c}
\text{COOH} \\
\text{CHO}
\end{array}
$$

Pyruvate   Glyoxylate

Enzymes involved:
1.5.1.12 1-Pyrroline-5-carboxylate dehydrogenase
1.5.99   4-Hydroxyproline dehydrogenase
2.6.1.23 4-Hydroxyglutamate aminotransferase
4.1.3.16 4-Hydroxy-2-oxoglutarate aldolase

Amino-acid breakdown via succinyl-CoA

Methionine, valine and isoleucine are degraded via propionyl-CoA, which enters the tricarboxylic acid cycle. (The breakdown of isoleucine has been discussed on page 114, since acetyl-CoA is also formed from isoleucine, as well as succinyl-CoA.)

L-*Methionine* (Fig. 15). Methionine is first converted to S-adenosylmethionine with the release of inorganic phosphate and pyrophosphate of ATP; the reaction is thus practically irreversible. S-Adenosylmethionine is the most important methyl-group donor in cellular metabolism and may transfer the methyl group to various acceptors. The transmethylation gives rise not only to the methylated product, but also to S-adenosylhomocysteine (see for example the synthesis of creatine [see page 158] and phosphatidylcholine [see page 139]). The bulk of the S-adenosylmethionine is used for trans-

Fig. 13   *Degradation of ornithine and proline* (page 119)

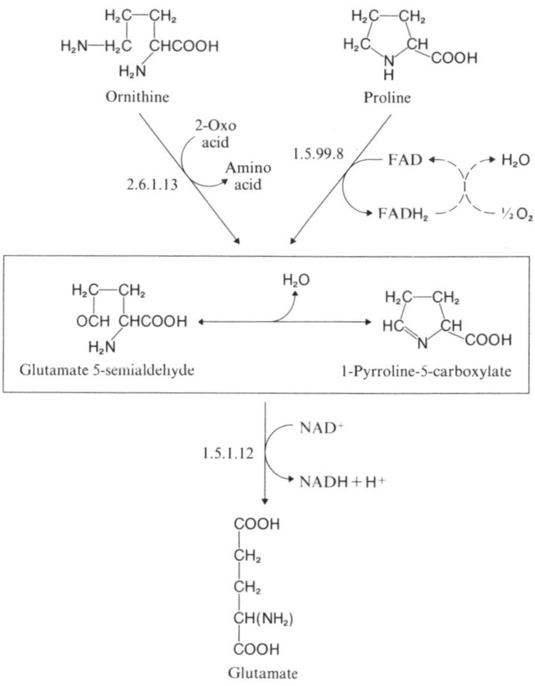

$$
\begin{array}{c}
\text{H}_2\text{C—CH}_2 \\
\text{H}_2\text{N—H}_2\text{C CHCOOH} \\
\text{H}_2\text{N}
\end{array}
\qquad
\begin{array}{c}
\text{H}_2\text{C—CH}_2 \\
\text{H}_2\text{C}\quad\text{CH} \\
\text{N}\quad\text{COOH} \\
\text{H}
\end{array}
$$

Ornithine   Proline

2.6.1.13   2-Oxo acid → Amino acid

1.5.99.8   FAD ← → H$_2$O   FADH$_2$ → → ½O$_2$

$$
\begin{array}{c}
\text{H}_2\text{C—CH}_2 \\
\text{OCH CHCOOH} \\
\text{H}_2\text{N}
\end{array}
\quad\leftarrow\quad \text{H}_2\text{O} \quad
\begin{array}{c}
\text{H}_2\text{C—CH}_2 \\
\text{HC}\quad\text{CH} \\
\text{N}\quad\text{COOH}
\end{array}
$$

Glutamate 5-semialdehyde   1-Pyrroline-5-carboxylate

1.5.1.12   NAD$^+$ → NADH + H$^+$

$$
\begin{array}{c}
\text{COOH} \\
\text{CH}_2 \\
\text{CH}_2 \\
\text{CH(NH}_2) \\
\text{COOH}
\end{array}
$$

Glutamate

Enzymes involved:
1.5.1.12 1-Pyrroline-5-carboxylate dehydrogenase
1.5.99.8 Proline dehydrogenase
2.6.1.13 Ornithine–oxo-acid aminotransferase

methylations; a small portion, however, is used for the synthesis of polyamines (page 159). S-adenosylhomocysteine is cleaved to adenosine and homocysteine in a reversible reaction.

Homocysteine can be reconverted to methionine with betaine as the methyl-group donor or condensed with serine in an irreversible reaction to yield cystathionine, which can be split into cysteine and 2-oxobutyrate.

The oxidative decarboxylation of 2-oxobutyrate to yield propionyl-CoA is described in the degradation of threonine (page 114), the subsequent conversion to succinyl-CoA on page 102. For reactions of cysteine see page 112.

Impairment of the transsulfuration pathway (in liver disease, portacaval shunting and some forms of hypermethioninemia) may lead to a relative increase in the transamination pathway of methionine metabolism (Fig. 16). However, there are dangers in this pathway, since such highly toxic substances as methylmercaptan and H$_2$S are intermediates.

A salvage pathway for methionine from 5′-methylthioadenosine (a by-product in polyamine synthesis; see page 160) has been postulated as existing in mammals. 5′-Methylthioadenosine is first converted to 5-methylthioribose 1-phosphate and adenine in a reaction catalyzed by 5′-methylthioadenosine phosphorylase (2.4.2.28). 5-Methylthioribose 1-phosphate is then converted to 4-methylthio-2-oxobutyrate by a mechanism not yet elucidated, and this product can then undergo transamination (especially with glutamine or asparagine) to give methionine.

L-*Valine* (Fig. 5, page 114). The first 3 steps of the degradation of valine, leucine and isoleucine proceed analogously. In the further degradation of valine and isoleucine, succinyl-CoA is formed, although by different pathways.

L-*4-Aminobutyric acid* (γ-aminobutyric acid) (Fig. 17). This compound is transaminated to succinate semialdehyde by the action of 4-aminobutyrate aminotransferase (2.6.1.19). The enzyme is found not only in the nervous system, but also in the liver, kidneys and platelets. Succinate semialdehyde can be oxidized to succinate or reduced via an alternate route to 4-hydroxybutyrate, which is then subject to β-oxidation.

Fig. 14   *Degradation of histidine* (page 119)

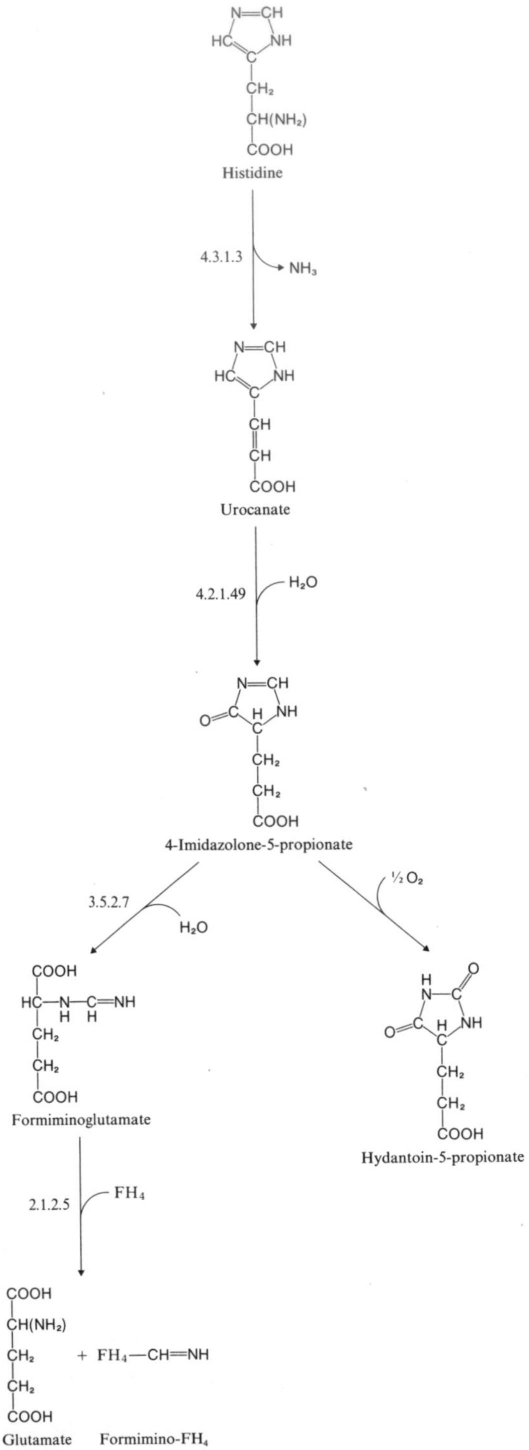

$$\text{Histidine}$$

N=CH
HC NH
  CH_2
  CH(NH_2)
  COOH
Histidine

4.3.1.3 → NH_3

N=CH
HC NH
  CH
  CH
  COOH
Urocanate

4.2.1.49 → H_2O

N=CH
O=C H NH
  CH_2
  CH_2
  COOH
4-Imidazolone-5-propionate

3.5.2.7 ← H_2O ½ O_2

COOH
HC—N—C=NH
  H H
  CH_2
  CH_2
  COOH
Formiminoglutamate

2.1.2.5 ← FH_4

COOH
CH(NH_2)
  CH_2   + FH_4—CH=NH
  CH_2
  COOH
Glutamate   Formimino-FH_4

H
N—C=O
O=C H NH
  CH_2
  CH_2
  COOH
Hydantoin-5-propionate

Enzymes involved:
2.1.2.5   Glutamate formiminotransferase
3.5.2.7   Imidazolonepropionase
4.2.1.49   Urocanate hydratase
4.3.1.3   Histidine ammonia-lyase (histidase)

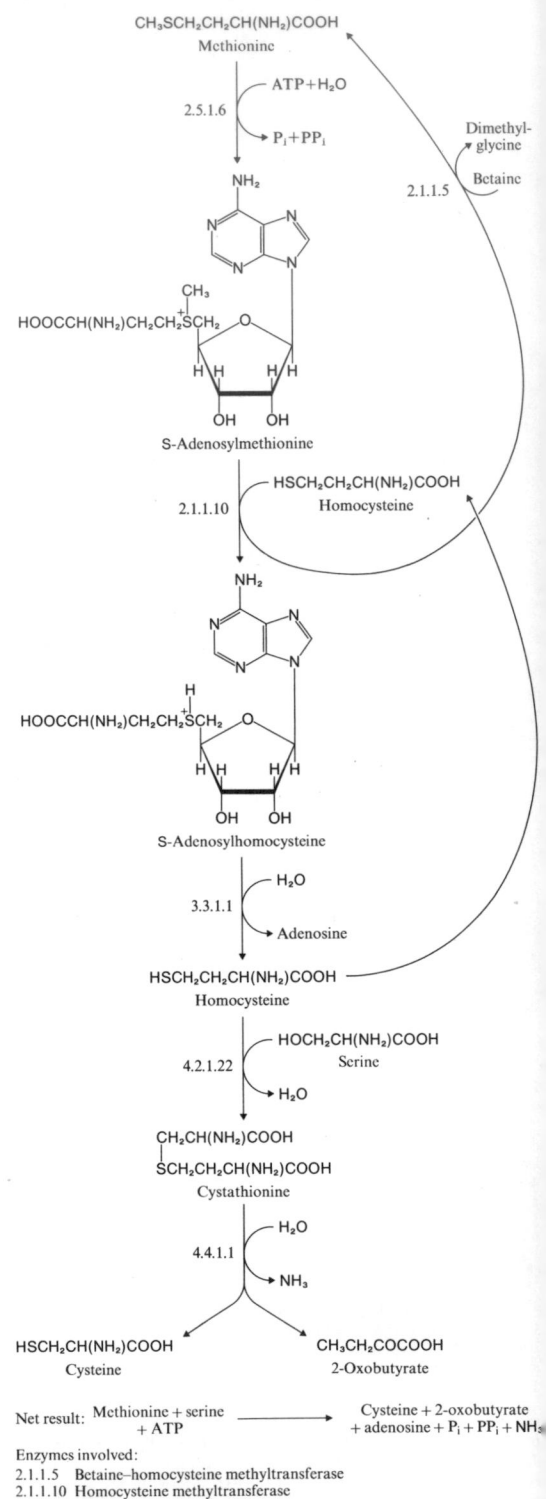

Fig. 15   *Transsulfuration pathway of methionine degradation*

Net result: Methionine + serine + ATP → Cysteine + 2-oxobutyrate + adenosine + P_i + PP_i + NH_3

Enzymes involved:
2.1.1.5   Betaine–homocysteine methyltransferase
2.1.1.10   Homocysteine methyltransferase
2.5.1.6   Methionine adenosyltransferase
3.3.1.1   Adenosylhomocysteinase
4.2.1.22   Cystathionine β-synthase
4.4.1.1   Cystathionine γ-lyase

Fig. 16   *Transamination pathway of methionine degradation*

Fig. 17   *Transamination pathway of 4-aminobutyrate degradation*

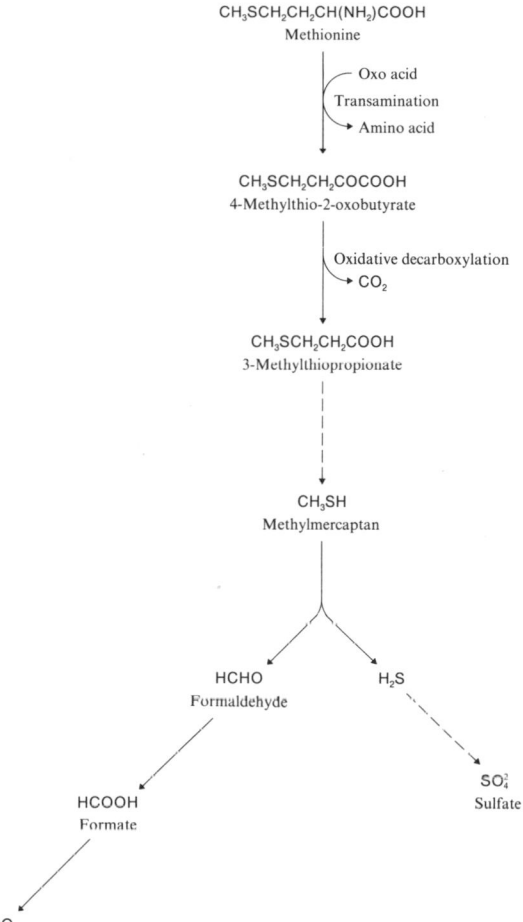

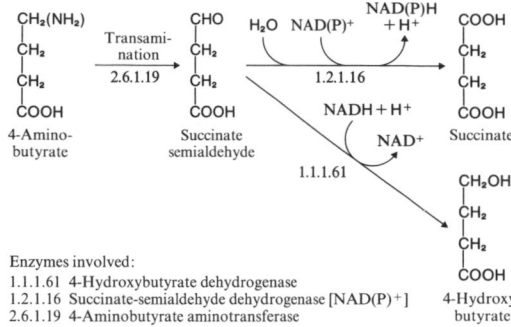

Enzymes involved:
1.1.1.61 4-Hydroxybutyrate dehydrogenase
1.2.1.16 Succinate-semialdehyde dehydrogenase [NAD(P)$^+$]
2.6.1.19 4-Aminobutyrate aminotransferase

Reviews

· STANBURY et al., *The Metabolic Basis of Inherited Disease*, 5th ed., Part 3: Disorders of amino acid metabolism, McGraw-Hill, New York, 1983.
· COOPER, A.J., Biochemistry of sulfur-containing amino acids, *Ann. Rev. Biochem.*, **52**, 187 (1983).
· HOLMES, F. L., Hans Krebs and the discovery of the ornithine cycle, *Fed. Proc.*, **39**, 216 (1980).
· ADAMS and FRANK, Metabolism of proline and the hydroxyprolines, *Ann. Rev. Biochem.*, **49**, 1005 (1980).
· SHAMBAUGH, G. E., Urea biosynthesis I. The urea cycle and relationships to the citric acid cycle, *Amer. J. clin. Nutr.*, **30**, 2083 (1977).
· SHAMBAUGH, G. E., Urea biosynthesis II. Normal and abnormal regulation, *Amer. J. clin. Nutr.*, **31**, 126 (1978).
· BENDER, D. A., *Amino Acid Metabolism*, Wiley, New York, 1975.
· BRAUNSTEIN, A. E., Amino group transfer, in BOYER, P. D. (Ed.), *The Enzymes*, 2nd ed., Volume 9, Academic Press, New York, 1973, page 379.
· RATNER, S., Enzymes of arginine and urea synthesis, *Advanc. Enzymol.*, **39**, 1 (1973).
· Metabolism of amino acids and amines, *Methods Enzymol.*, **17**, Parts A and B (1970–1971).
· MEISTER, A., *Biochemistry of the Amino Acids*, 2nd ed., Volumes 1 and 2, Academic Press, New York, 1965.

Fig. 1 *Postulated reaction sequence for the metabolism of protoheme*

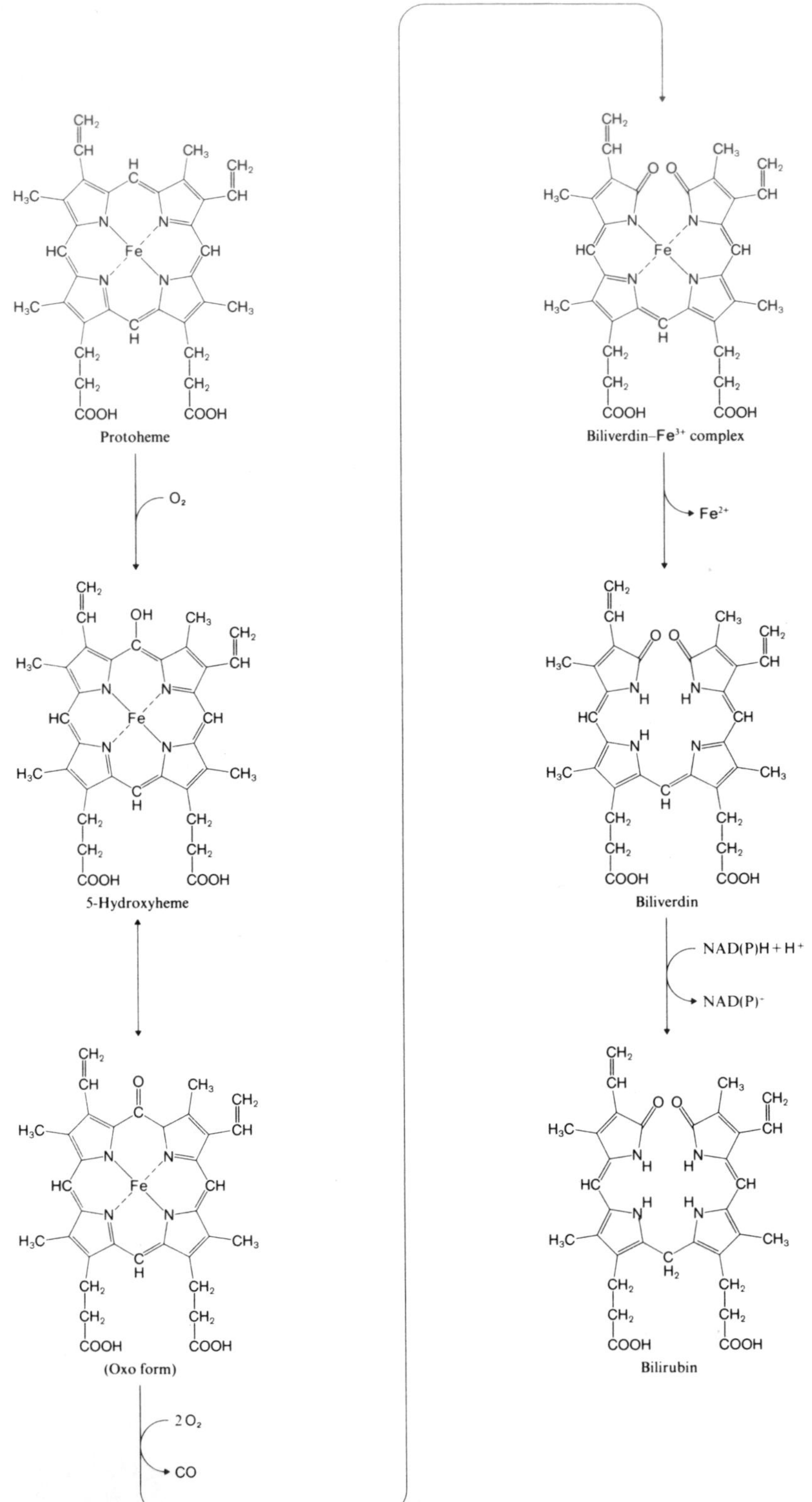
Protoheme
O_2
5-Hydroxyheme
(Oxo form)
$2\,O_2$
CO
Biliverdin–Fe^{3+} complex
Fe^{2+}
Biliverdin
NAD(P)H + H^+
NAD(P)$^-$
Bilirubin

Protoheme is released from the various hemoproteins in the intact cell by the action of proteolytic enzymes. Protoheme can be split in the microsomes of various tissues – mainly the spleen, liver and kidneys – with the aid of the heme oxygenase system, forming biliverdin and carbon monoxide. Since protoheme represents practically the only endogenous source of carbon monoxide, the rate of protoheme conversion can be determined from the measurement of carbon monoxide production.

In vertebrates the cleavage of metalloporphyrins takes place at the α-methene bridge, an exception being liver catalase, in which the β-methene bridge is cleaved. Cytochrome c, which is covalently bound to the substrate protein via thioether bridges, can only be split after breakdown of the protein moiety. Hemoproteins containing heme a yield a biliverdin analog with the side chains characteristic of heme a.

The oxidation of the C atom in the α-methene bridge is catalyzed by the microsomal heme oxygenase (decyclizing) (1.14.99.3), which exhibits an absolute requirement for NADPH–ferrihemoprotein reductase (1.6.2.4). The reaction consumes dioxygen and reduced NADP. A possible mechanism of the cleavage is shown in Figure 1. For the release of iron from the biliverdin–iron complex, iron may have to be reduced to the ferrous state. The iron released enters the body's iron pool for reuse or storage in the form of the iron-containing proteins, hemosiderin and ferritin.

Biliverdin is excreted by most nonmammals as an end-product of heme metabolism, while in mammals it is reduced to bilirubin with the aid of biliverdin reductase (1.3.1.24). This enzyme utilizes reduced NADP as cofactor rather than reduced NAD.

In the circulation, bilirubin is tightly bound to albumin. The complex dissociates, and bilirubin enters the liver cell by a process of facilitated diffusion. A fraction of bilirubin derives from intrahepatic heme breakdown. Bilirubin inside the liver cells binds to cytosolic proteins (ligandin, Z protein), which prevents the efflux from the cells. The bilirubin bound to its protein carriers is practically insoluble in aqueous solution and thus not easily excreted. In the liver microsomes, bilirubin can be conjugated with glucuronic acid and to a slight extent also with glucose, xylose or sulfate. These conjugations seem to disrupt the multiple intramolecular hydrogen bonds responsible for the nonpolar character of bilirubin, hence facilitating the biliary excretion of the compound.

Fig. 2   *Conjugation of bilirubin*

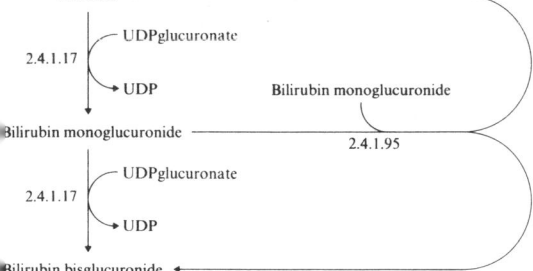

Enzymes involved:

2.4.1.17 Glucuronosyltransferase (UDPglucuronate–bilirubin glucuronosyltransferase)
2.4.1.95 Bilirubin-glucuronoside glucuronosyltransferase

Fig. 3   *Formation of bile pigments*

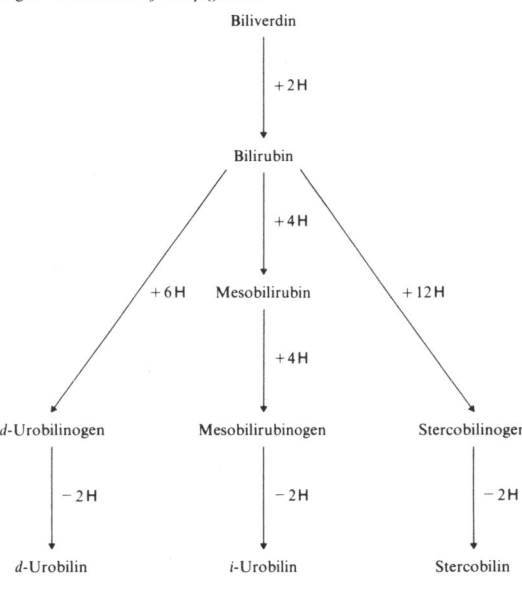

The main enzyme catalyzing the conjugation, glucuronosyltransferase (2.4.1.17), is an integral part of the microsomal membrane. Bilirubin bisglucuronide is formed by this enzyme in a 2-step mechanism via bilirubin monoglucuronide. A second enzyme catalyzes the dismutation of 2 mol bilirubin monoglucuronide to 1 mol bilirubin and 1 mol bilirubin bisglucuronide (Fig. 2). The excretion of the conjugates in the bile is thought to be an energy-dependent process. Bilirubin reaches the small intestine mainly in conjugated form and is not substantially reabsorbed. The conjugates are hydrolyzed by bacteria in the terminal ileum and in the colon, and bilirubin is then degraded by bacterial enzymes into a series of urobilinogen and related products (Fig. 3). These products are excreted with the feces or reabsorbed from the intestine and reexcreted in the bile.

Reviews

· MAINES, M. D., New developments in the regulation of heme metabolism and their implications, *CRC Crit. Rev. Toxicol.*, **12**, 241 (1984).
· IBRAHAM et al., Heme metabolism in erythroid and hepatic cells, *Progr. Hemat.*, **13**, 75 (1983).
· WOLKOFF et al., Hereditary jaundice and disorders of bilirubin metabolism, in STANBURY et al., *The Metabolic Basis of Inherited Disease*, 5th ed., McGraw-Hill, New York, 1983, page 1385.
· BERK et al., Disorders of bilirubin metabolism, in BONDY and ROSENBERG (Eds.), *Metabolic Control and Disease*, 8th ed., Saunders, Philadelphia, 1980, page 1009.
· KIKUCHI and YOSHIDA, Heme degradation by the microsomal heme oxygenase system, *Trends biochem. Sci.*, **5**, 323 (1980).
· BLANCKAERT et al., Mechanism of bilirubin diglucuronide formation in intact rats, *J. clin. Invest.*, **65**, 1332 (1980).
· LESTER and TROXLER, Recent advances in bile pigment metabolism, *Gastroenterology*, **56**, 143 (1969).

The nucleases responsible for the cleavage of nucleic acids occur in practically all tissues. They attack the phosphodiester linkage, either at the end of the chain, forming mononucleotides (with the aid of exonucleases), or within the chain, forming various oligonucleotides (with the aid of endonucleases) (see Figure and Table).

Restriction endonucleases. These enzymes are strain-specific endonucleases of bacteria. They enable prokaryotic organisms to recognize and destroy foreign DNA by splitting double-stranded DNA at a limited number of sites. In addition, the restriction endonucleases possess properties of a DNA methyltransferase in that they transfer the methyl group of S-adenosylmethionine to specific adenine and cytosine units in the DNA, so that the bacterial DNA itself is modified and thereby protected from its own restriction.

The restriction enzymes have been classified into the following 3 groups:

– Type I site-specific deoxyribonuclease (3.1.21.3) is a large group of enzymes which have an absolute requirement for ATP and S-adenosylmethionine. They recognize specific short DNA sequences and cleave at sites *remote* from the recognition site (at least 1000 base pairs away). These multifunctional proteins also catalyze methylation at host-specific sites. The endonucleolytic cleavage of DNA gives *random* double-stranded fragments with terminal 5′-phosphates. ATP is simultaneously hydrolyzed.

Reactions of the breakdown of nucleic acids

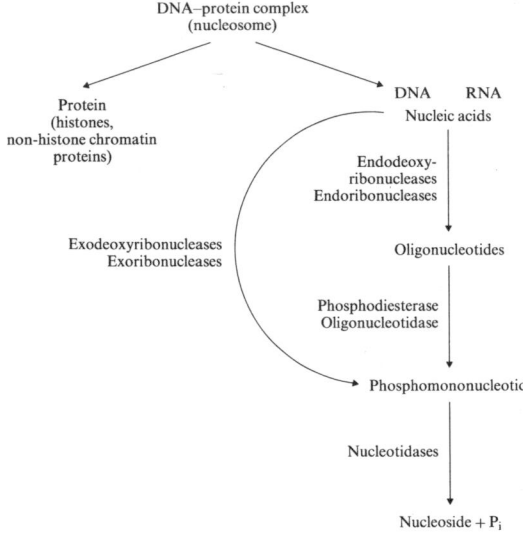

– Type II site-specific deoxyribonuclease (3.1.21.4) is a large group of enzymes which require only Mg^{2+}. They recognize specific short DNA sequences and cleave generally within the recognition site or 5 to 9 base pairs away. Site-specific methyltransferases (2.1.1.72 and 2.1.1.73) catalyze methylation at host-specific sites. The endonucleolytic cleavage of DNA gives *specific* double-stranded fragments with terminal 5′-phosphates.

– Type III site-specific deoxyribonuclease (3.1.21.5) is a group of enzymes which have an absolute requirement for ATP but do not hydrolyze it. S-Adenosylmethionine stimulates the reaction but is not absolutely needed. These enzymes recognize specific short DNA sequences and cleave a short distance away from the recognition site (24 to 26 base pairs away in 3′ direction). They exist as complexes with the methylating enzymes 2.1.1.72 and 2.1.1.73. The endonucleolytic cleavage of DNA gives *specific* double-stranded fragments with terminal 5′-phosphates.

On account of the site-specific cleavage, type II restriction endonucleases are extensively used in establishing the DNA structure (base-sequence determination) and in the synthesis of recombinant DNA (genetic engineering).

Some of the restriction endonucleases cleaving double-stranded DNA form staggered cuts, as for example the enzyme *Eco* RI:

$$\begin{array}{l} \text{\underline{5′}–G}\mid\text{A A T T C\underline{–3′}} \\ \text{—C T T A A}\mid\text{G—} \end{array}$$

The staggered cuts thus formed are also called 'sticky ends' because they recombine with complementary sequences of similarly cut DNA produced by the same enzyme: hydrogen bondings between the complementary bases are formed, and the ends are stabilized by a ligase. Other restriction endonucleases produce blunt-ended cuts, as for example *Sma* I:

$$\begin{array}{l} \text{\underline{5′}–C C C}\mid\text{G G G\underline{–3′}} \\ \text{—G G G}\mid\text{C C C—} \end{array}$$

For recombination with a differently cut DNA, a staggered end must be created by attaching a suitable synthetic polynucleotide, a process known as 'homopolymer tailing'.

At least 300 restriction endonucleases were known in 1984. Their nomenclature accords with the organism from which they are obtained (for example *Eco* RI from *E. coli*, *Sma* I from *Serratia marcescens*).

Reviews

· International Union of Biochemistry, *Enzyme Nomenclature*, Recommendations 1984, Academic Press, Orlando, Fla., 1984.
· YUAN, R., Structure and mechanism of multifunctional restriction endonucleases, *Ann. Rev. Biochem.*, **50**, 285 (1981).
· SMITH, H. O., Nucleotide sequence specificity of restriction endonucleases, *Science*, **205**, 455 (1979).
· ARBER, W., Restriktionsendonucleasen, *Angew. Chem.*, **90**, 79 (1978).
· NATHANS and SMITH, Restriction endonucleases in the analysis and restructuring of DNA molecules, *Ann. Rev. Biochem.*, **44**, 273 (1975).

Some important nucleases in mammals

Enzyme	EC number	Reaction
Exodeoxyribonuclease I .... (mammalian DNase III)	3.1.11.1	Exonucleolytic cleavage of single-stranded DNA in the 3′ to 5′ direction to yield 5′-phosphomononucleotides
Exodeoxyribonuclease (lambda-induced) (mammalian DNase IV)	3.1.11.3	Exonucleolytic cleavage of double-stranded DNA in the 5′ to 3′ direction to yield 5′-phosphomononucleotides
Spleen exonuclease	3.1.16.1	Exonucleolytic cleavage of single-stranded DNA and RNA in the 5′ to 3′ direction to yield 3′-phosphomononucleotides
Deoxyribonuclease I .... (DNase I)	3.1.21.1	Endonucleolytic cleavage of double-stranded DNA into 5′-phosphodinucleotide and 5′-phosphooligonucleotide end-products
Deoxyribonuclease II .... (DNase II)	3.1.22.1	Endonucleolytic cleavage of double-stranded DNA into 3′-phosphomononucleotide and 3′-phosphooligonucleotide end-products. Favored site of cleavage between the nucleosomes
Pancreatic ribonuclease .... (RNase I)	3.1.27.5	Endonucleolytic cleavage of RNA into 3′-phosphomononucleotides and 3′-phosphooligonucleotides ending in Cp or Up with 2′,3′-cyclic phosphate intermediates

Cleavage of purine and pyrimidine nucleotides (Fig. 1)

Hydrolytic cleavage of nucleotides takes place by means of 5'-nucleotidase (3.1.3.5), forming nucleosides and inorganic phosphate. In animals, nucleosides are split phosphorolytically into free bases and ribose 1-phosphate – purine nucleosides by purine-nucleoside phosphorylase (2.4.2.1) and pyrimidine nucleosides by pyrimidine-nucleoside phosphorylase (2.4.2.2).

In mammals, it seems that adenosine is hardly split by purine-nucleoside phosphorylase to form adenine; the latter compound derives rather from the breakdown of 5'-methylthioadenosine, which is a metabolite in the pathway of polyamine synthesis (see Fig. 5, page 160).

Nucleosidases (3.2.2) occur in microorganisms but have not been detected in higher animals.

Metabolism of purines

The degradation of AMP and GMP, as well as of the corresponding nucleosides and free bases, involves hydrolytic deamination and subsequent oxidation. In the case of GMP, the deamination is coupled with a reduction. These steps are represented in Figure 1.

The end-product of purine degradation is uric acid in man and other primates, and allantoin in other mammals, irrespective of the degradation pathway. Amphibians and fish convert allantoin to allantoic acid, urea and glyoxylic acid. Some lower species such as crustaceans – but also some intestinal bacteria – further degrade urea to ammonia and carbon dioxide.

Purine deaminases. Three types of enzyme are known – adenine deaminase (3.5.4.2), adenosine deaminase (3.5.4.4) and AMP deami-

Fig. 1 *Degradation of purines*

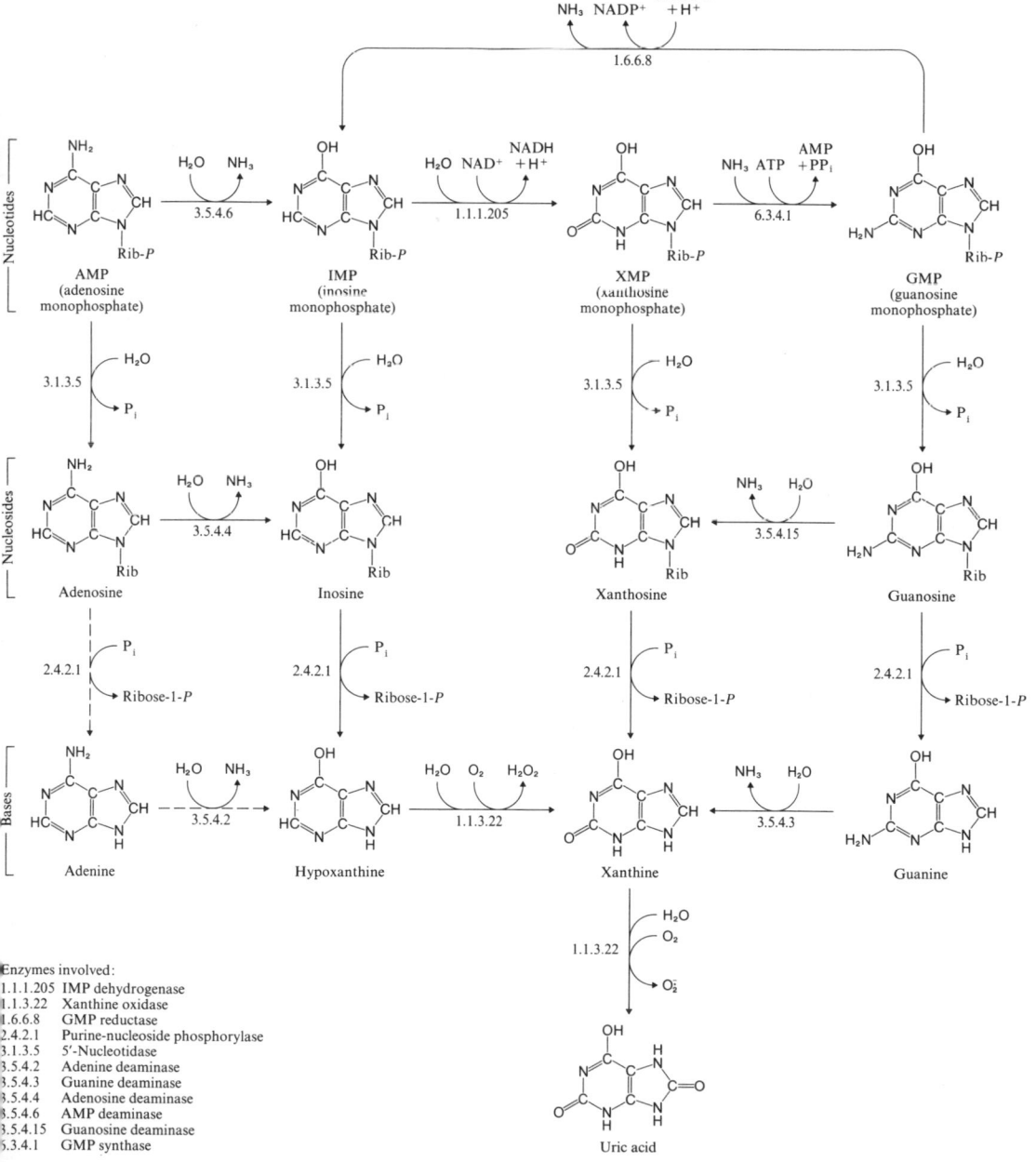

Enzymes involved:
1.1.1.205 IMP dehydrogenase
1.1.3.22 Xanthine oxidase
1.6.6.8 GMP reductase
2.4.2.1 Purine-nucleoside phosphorylase
3.1.3.5 5'-Nucleotidase
3.5.4.2 Adenine deaminase
3.5.4.3 Guanine deaminase
3.5.4.4 Adenosine deaminase
3.5.4.6 AMP deaminase
3.5.4.15 Guanosine deaminase
6.3.4.1 GMP synthase

Fig. 2 *Purine nucleotide cycle*

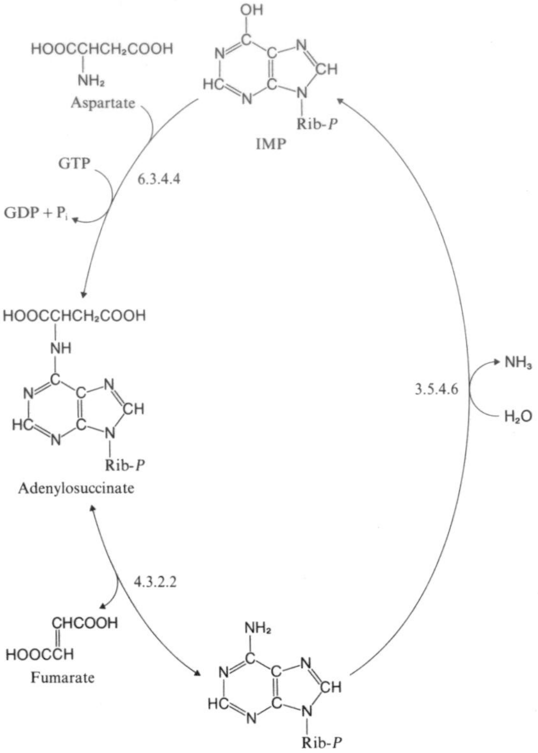

Enzymes involved:
3.5.4.6 AMP deaminase
4.3.2.2 Adenylosuccinate lyase
6.3.4.4 Adenylosuccinate synthase

Fig. 3 *Inhibition of xanthine oxidase by allopurinol and oxipurinol*

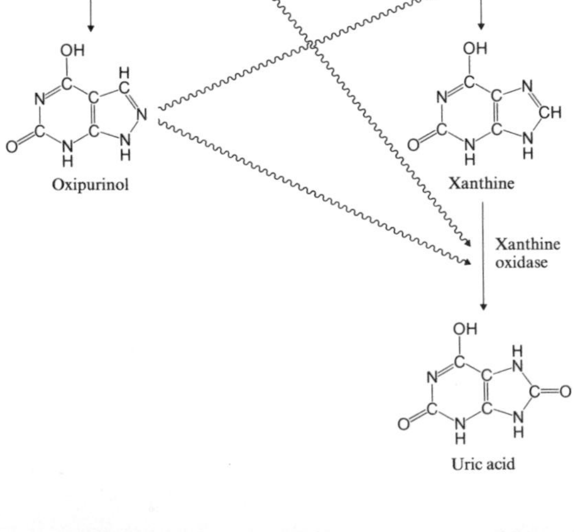

nase (3.5.4.6) – that hydrolyze adenine, adenosine and AMP, respectively, to yield ammonia and the corresponding derivative of hypoxanthine. Of these, the occurrence of adenine deaminase in mammals is uncertain, but adenosine deaminase occurs in most tissues of higher animals. Deamination by adenosine deaminase is also an important reaction of deoxyadenosine, yielding deoxyinosine. Deficiency of this enzyme leads to accumulation of dATP, which interferes with the immune system.

Deamination of AMP plays an important role in skeletal muscle function. AMP deaminase activity in skeletal muscle is several times higher than in any other tissue, including the heart muscle. The AMP deaminase reaction is one component of the purine nucleotide cycle in which IMP is reconverted to AMP in 2 steps (Fig. 2). During exercise, NH_3 production and IMP content of skeletal muscle increase in proportion to the work performed. Glycolysis may thereby be stimulated, and NH_3 may buffer the H^+ accumulated during ATP hydrolysis.

Another two specific deaminases – guanine deaminase (3.5.4.3) and guanosine deaminase (3.5.4.15) – hydrolyze guanine to xanthine or guanosine to xanthosine, thereby releasing ammonia. GMP, on the other hand, is not deaminated to XMP but rather, with the aid of reduced NADP, to IMP.

Purine oxidases. Purines can be oxidized as ribonucleotides or as free bases. The oxidation of IMP to XMP is an intermediate step of GMP synthesis (page 170), but it only plays a small part in purine degradation because the major portion is broken down via the oxidation of the free purine bases.

Xanthine oxidase (1.1.3.22) catalyzes the oxidation of hypoxanthine to xanthine and of xanthine to uric acid. The enzyme occurs in high activity only in the liver and the small intestine mucosa, but it is also found in milk. Xanthine oxidase is competitively inhibited by allopurinol and its oxidation product, oxipurinol. Administration of these compounds therefore impairs the formation of uric acid (Fig. 3).

Urate oxidase (1.7.3.3) oxidizes uric acid, with dioxygen as acceptor, to yield unidentified products which decompose to allantoin. The enzyme occurs in the liver and kidneys of some mammals, but not in man and primates.

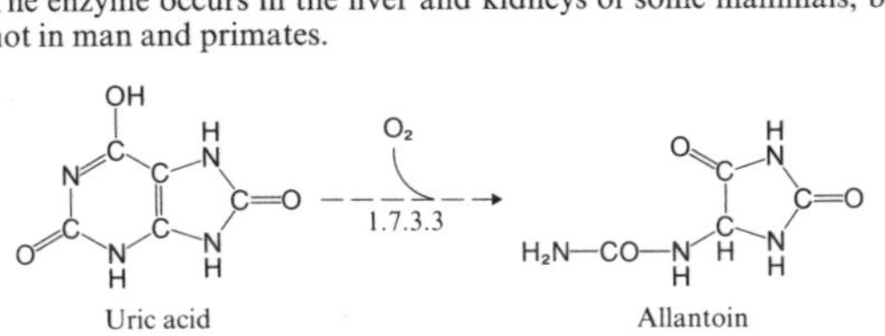

Uric acid   Allantoin

Reutilization of purines

Free purine bases are not exclusively broken down to uric acid; they may be reutilized for nucleotide synthesis ('salvage pathway'). In this case the purines react with 5-phosphoribose 1-diphosphate (*P*Rib-*PP*), the reactions being catalyzed by specific ribosyltransferases.

Adenine + *P*Rib-*PP* $\xrightarrow{2.4.2.7}$ AMP + PP$_i$

Hypoxanthine + *P*Rib-*PP* $\xrightarrow{2.4.2.8}$ IMP + PP$_i$

Guanine + *P*Rib-*PP* $\xrightarrow{2.4.2.8}$ GMP + PP$_i$

Enzymes involved:
2.4.2.7 Adenine phosphoribosyltransferase
2.4.2.8 Hypoxanthine phosphoribosyltransferase

This reaction is illustrated below, using adenine as an example.

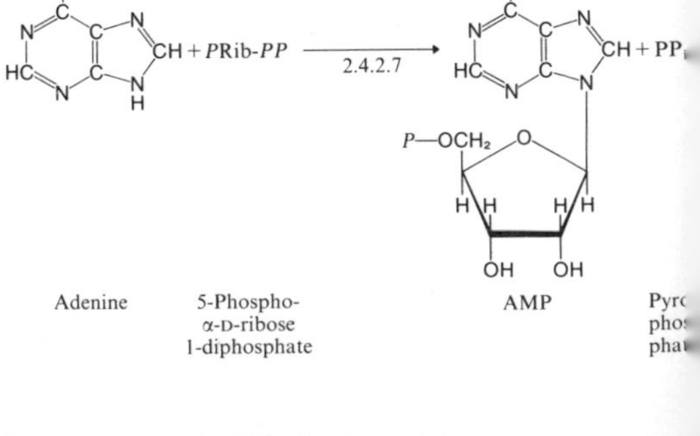

Adenine   5-Phospho-α-D-ribose 1-diphosphate   AMP   Pyrophosphate

In the case of adenine phosphoribosyltransferase deficiency, non-reutilized adenine is transformed by xanthine oxidase (1.1.3.22) to 2,8-dihydroxyadenine.

Adenine $\xrightarrow{1.1.3.22}$ 8-Hydroxyadenine $\xrightarrow{1.1.3.22}$ 2,8-Dihydroxyadenine

Metabolism of pyrimidines

The degradation of the pyrimidines cytosine, uracil and thymine (Fig. 4) is much more efficient than that of the purines since the pyrimidine ring can be broken down and the products completely metabolized. Cytosine is first converted to uracil by hydrolytic de-amination. Uracil and thymine (methyluracil) degradation follows identical pathways, resulting in the formation of malonate semialde-hyde and methylmalonate semialdehyde, respectively. Acetyl-CoA is then formed from malonate semialdehyde, and succinyl-CoA from methylmalonate semialdehyde. Acetyl-CoA and succinyl-CoA are both oxidized to CO_2 in the tricarboxylic acid cycle.

The free pyrimidine bases, however, are not always broken down but may be reutilized for nucleotide synthesis ('salvage pathway'):

Uracil + ribose 1-phosphate $\xrightarrow{2.4.2.3}$ Uridine + P_i

Uridine + ATP $\xrightarrow{2.7.1.48}$ UMP + ADP

Enzymes involved:
2.4.2.3 Uridine phosphorylase
2.7.1.48 Uridine kinase

Fig. 4 *Degradation of pyrimidines*

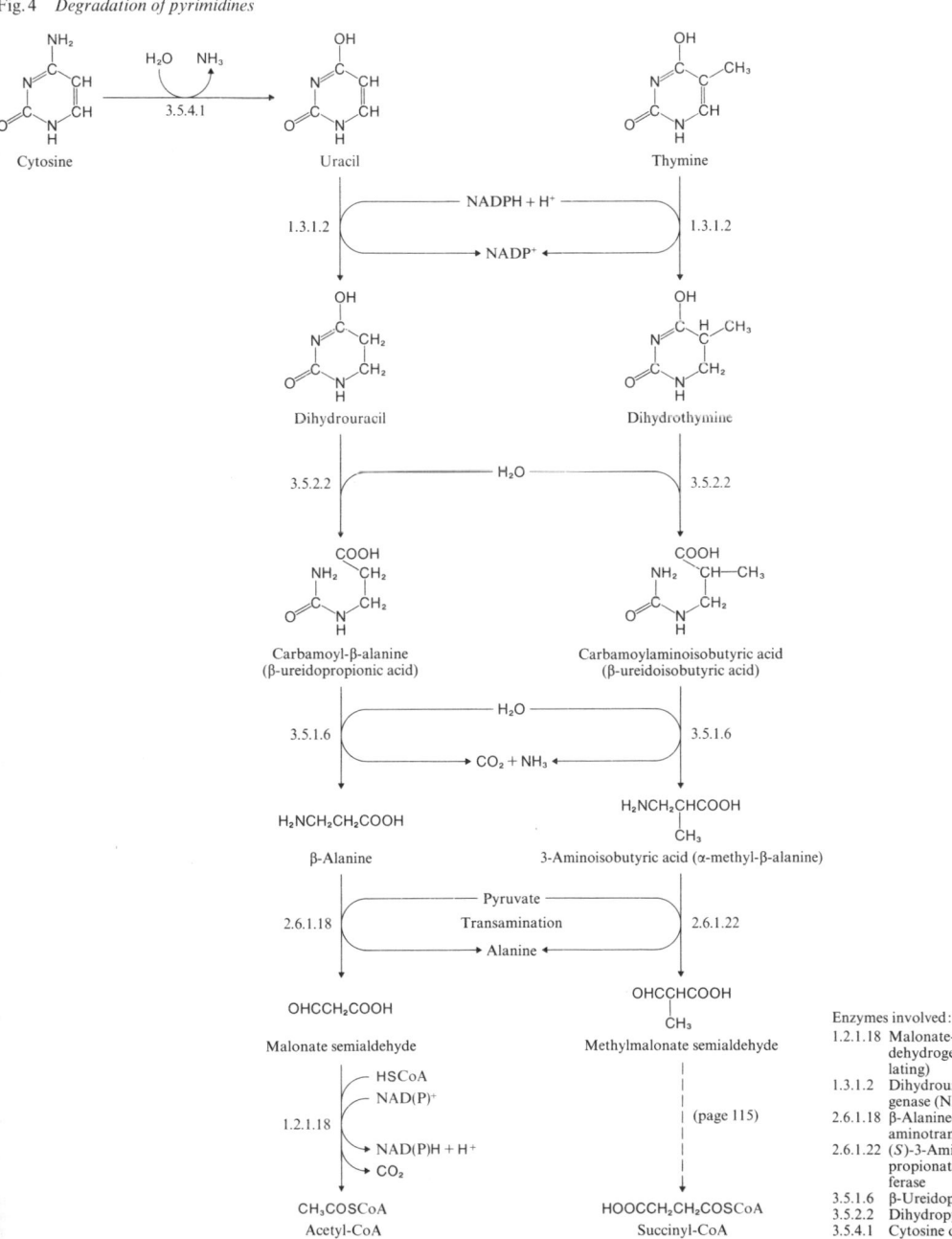

Enzymes involved:
1.2.1.18 Malonate-semialdehyde dehydrogenase (acety-lating)
1.3.1.2 Dihydrouracil dehydro-genase (NADP⁺)
2.6.1.18 β-Alanine–pyruvate aminotransferase
2.6.1.22 (S)-3-Amino-2-methyl-propionate aminotrans-ferase
3.5.1.6 β-Ureidopropionase
3.5.2.2 Dihydropyrimidinase
3.5.4.1 Cytosine deaminase

Reviews

· STANBURY et al., *The Metabolic Basis of Inherited Disease*, 5th ed., Part 7: Disorders of purine and pyrimidine metabolism, McGraw-Hill, New York, 1983, page 1041.
· KELLEY and WEINER (Eds.), *Uric Acid*, Springer, Berlin, 1978.
· Purine and pyrimidine metabolism, *Ciba Found. Symp.*, NS **48** (1977).

· HENDERSON and PATERSON, *Nucleotide Metabolism: An Introduction*, Academic Press, New York, 1973.
· MURRAY, A. W., The biological significance of purine salvage, *Ann. Rev. Biochem.*, **40**, 811 (1971).
· HARTMAN, S. C., Purines and pyrimidines, in GREENBERG, D. M. (Ed.), *Metabolic Pathways*, 3rd ed., Volume 4, Academic Press, New York, 1970, page 1.

Gluconeogenesis

In the pathway of gluconeogenesis there are 3 steps that differ from those in the pathway of glycolysis (page 95) as a result of their thermodynamic irreversibility. These steps are: the conversion of glucose 6-phosphate to glucose, of fructose 1,6-bisphosphate to fructose 6-phosphate, and of pyruvate to phospho*enol*pyruvate. In the pathway of gluconeogenesis, phospho*enol*pyruvate is formed by the following reactions:

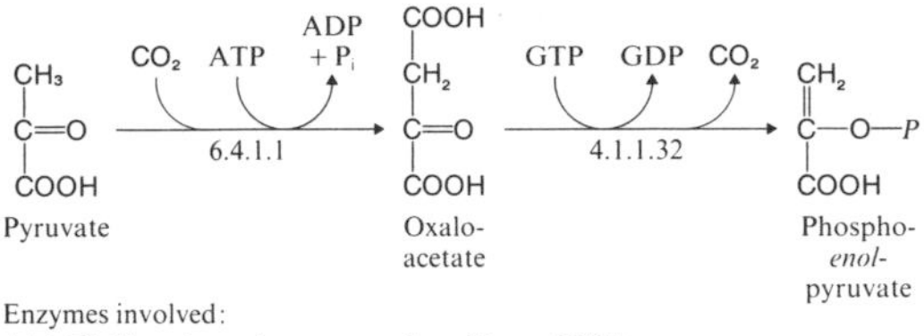

Pyruvate   Oxalo-   Phospho-
                  acetate   *enol*-
                                  pyruvate

Enzymes involved:
4.1.1.32 Phospho*enol*pyruvate carboxykinase (GTP)
6.4.1.1   Pyruvate carboxylase

Fructose-bisphosphatase (3.1.3.11) and glucose-6-phosphatase (3.1.3.9) catalyze the dephosphorylation steps, yielding ultimately glucose (page 199).

Besides pyruvate, lactate (via pyruvate), amino acids (alanine via pyruvate, branched-chain amino acids via the tricarboxylic acid cycle), glycerol (via glyceraldehyde phosphate), and fructose (via fructose 6-phosphate) are substrates for gluconeogenesis.

Gluconeogenesis occurs only in the liver and in the kidney; other organs do not possess the complete set of enzymes necessary for this pathway. Hepatic gluconeogenesis is highly regulated (page 198), partly due to compartmentalization of the reactions involving the cytosol, the mitochondria, and the endoplasmatic reticulum.

Fig. 1 *Formation of UDPglucuronate*

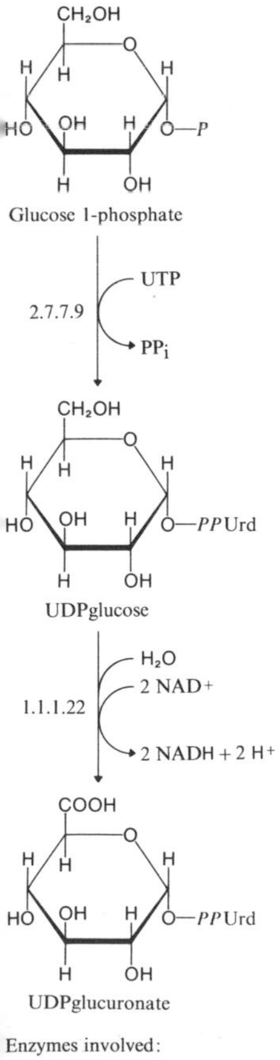

Glucose 1-phosphate

2.7.7.9

UTP
PP$_i$

UDPglucose

1.1.1.22

H$_2$O
2 NAD$^+$
2 NADH + 2 H$^+$

UDPglucuronate

Enzymes involved:
1.1.1.22 UDPglucose dehydrogenase
2.7.7.9   UTP–glucose-1-phosphate uridylyltransferase

Fructose 2,6-bisphosphate

This phosphorylated sugar is formed from fructose 6-phosphate and ATP by the action of 6-phosphofructo-2-kinase, an enzyme isolated from liver. This enzyme and the one responsible for the hydrolysis of fructose 2,6-bisphosphate – fructose-2,6-bisphosphatase – are thought to be subunits of a single protein. The reactions shown below are involved in the regulation of gluconeogenesis. In the fed state, fructose 2,6-bisphosphate is abundant in the liver, a signal that gluconeogenesis can be stopped.

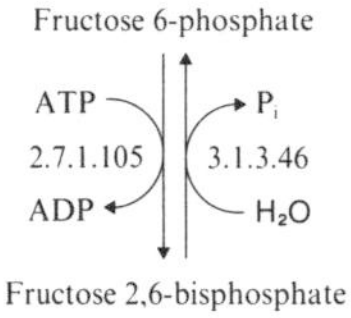

Fructose 6-phosphate

ATP   P$_i$
2.7.1.105   3.1.3.46
ADP   H$_2$O

Fructose 2,6-bisphosphate

Enzymes involved:
2.7.1.105 6-Phosphofructo-2-kinase
3.1.3.46   Fructose-2,6-bisphosphatase

5-Phosphoribose 1-diphosphate

This compound plays an important role in a whole series of biosyntheses, such as the de novo synthesis of purines (page 170), the reutilization of purines (page 128), the formation of orotidine 5'-phosphate (page 172), the formation of NAD$^+$ (page 170), and the synthesis of histidine (page 156). 5-Phosphoribose 1-diphosphate is formed from ribose 5-phosphate (see Fig. 1, page 169), which is either supplied by the pentose phosphate cycle or originates from the breakdown of nucleotides.

Fructose from sorbitol

Fructose – an energy source for the spermatozoa – is formed in the seminal vesicles by oxidation of the sugar alcohol sorbitol, which is produced by reduction of glucose.

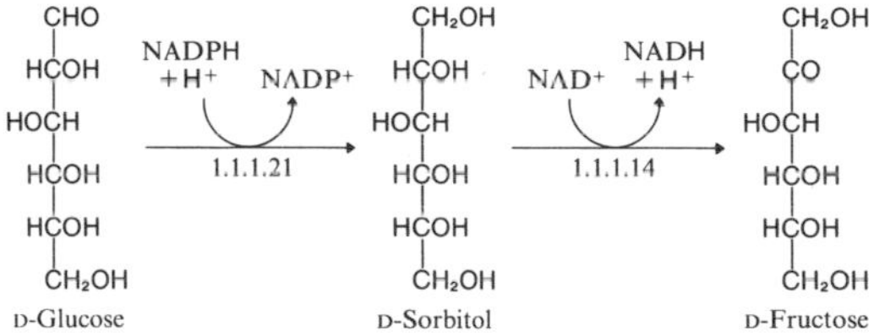

D-Glucose   D-Sorbitol   D-Fructose

Enzymes involved:
1.1.1.14 L-Iditol dehydrogenase
1.1.1.21 Aldehyde reductase

This reaction sequence also occurs in the lens of the eye and is thought to play a part in diabetic cataracts.

In a reaction analogous to that shown above, galactose is reduced to galactitol by the action of aldehyde reductase.

myo-Inositol

1L-*myo*-Inositol 1-phosphate is formed from glucose 6-phosphate by an NAD$^+$-dependent oxidation/reduction in accordance with the mechanism of an internal aldol condensation.

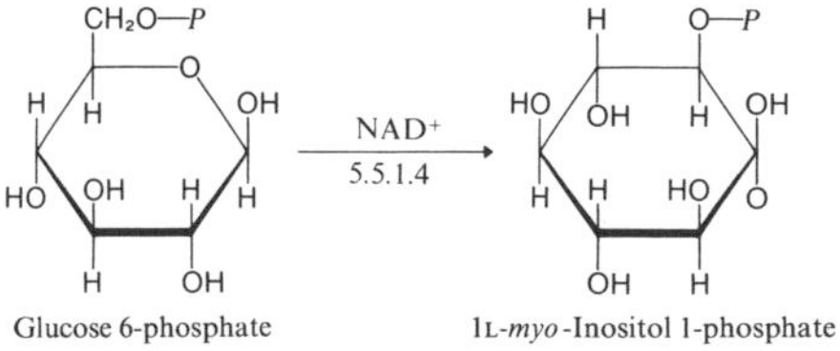

Glucose 6-phosphate   1L-*myo*-Inositol 1-phosphate

Enzyme involved:
5.5.1.4 *myo*-Inositol-1-phosphate synthase
         (glucose-6-phosphate cycloaldolase)

Orthophosphate is then split off by 1L-*myo*-inositol-1-phosphatase (3.1.3.25), a reaction which is a step in the phosphatidylinositol turnover cycle (page 138).

Uronic acids

Uronic acids react in the form of the UDP derivatives. UDPglucuronic acid is formed from glucose 1-phosphate in the sequence shown in Figure 1.

Fig. 2　*Formation of amino sugars*

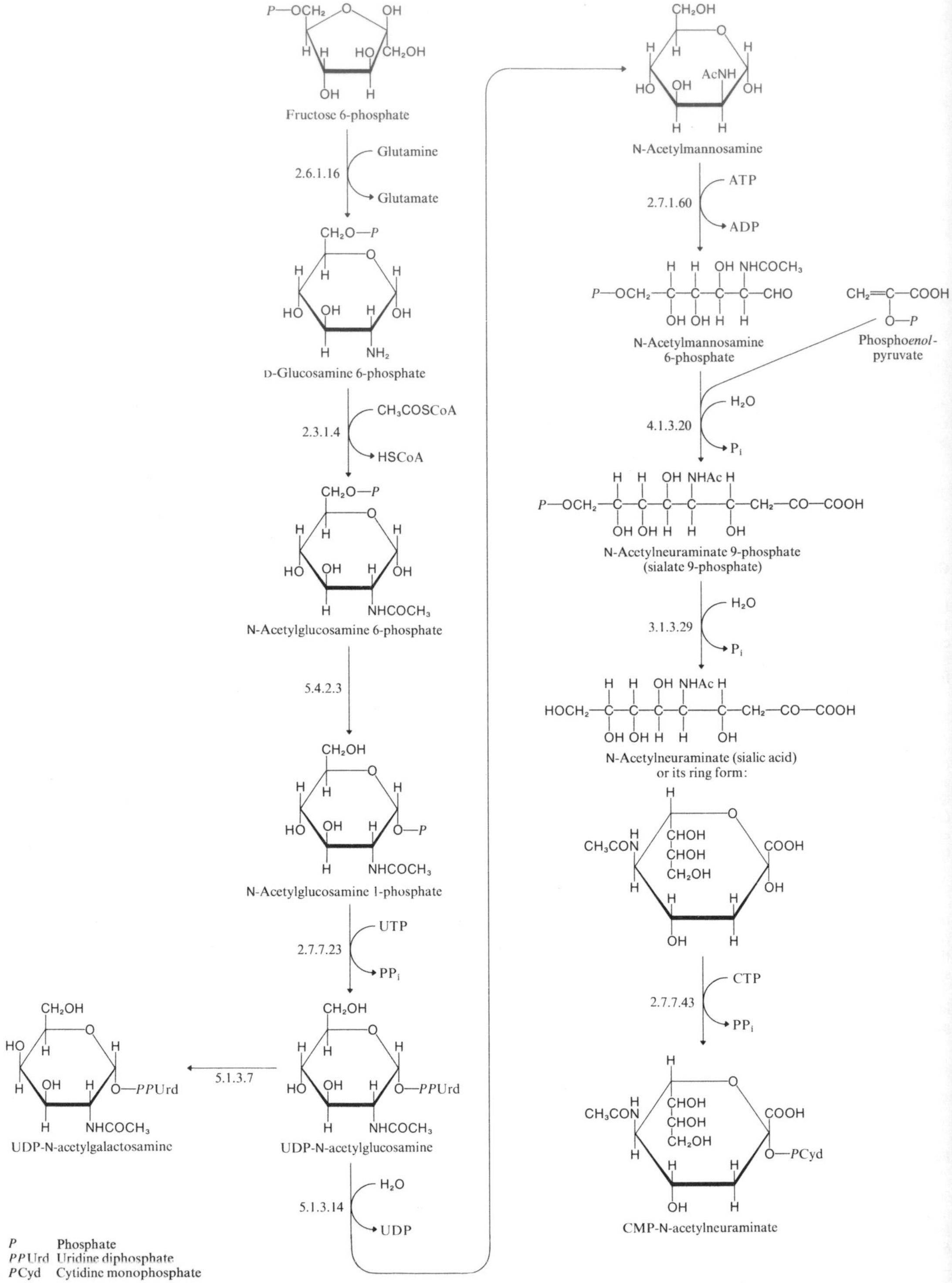

P　　　Phosphate
*PP*Urd　Uridine diphosphate
*P*Cyd　Cytidine monophosphate

Enzymes involved:

2.3.1.4　Glucosamine-phosphate acetyltransferase
2.6.1.16　Glutamine–fructose-6-phosphate amino-
　　　　transferase (isomerizing)

2.7.1.60　N-Acylmannosamine kinase
2.7.7.23　UDP-N-acetylglucosamine pyrophosphorylase
2.7.7.43　Acylneuraminate cytidylyltransferase
3.1.3.29　N-Acylneuraminate-9-phosphatase

4.1.3.20　N-Acylneuraminate-9-phosphate synthase
5.1.3.7　UDP-N-acetylglucosamine 4-epimerase
5.1.3.14　UDP-N-acetylglucosamine 2-epimerase
5.4.2.3　Phosphoacetylglucosamine mutase

UDPglucuronic acid can react with many substances containing a hydroxy or carboxy group, forming conjugates which are more easily excreted than the parent substance. The conjugation with bilirubin is described on page 125, that with xenobiotics on page 212. Glucuronic acid and iduronic acid are also constituents of glycosaminoglycans (page 23).

The synthesis of glucuronides from UDPglucuronic acid and an alcohol or a carboxylic acid proceeds as follows:

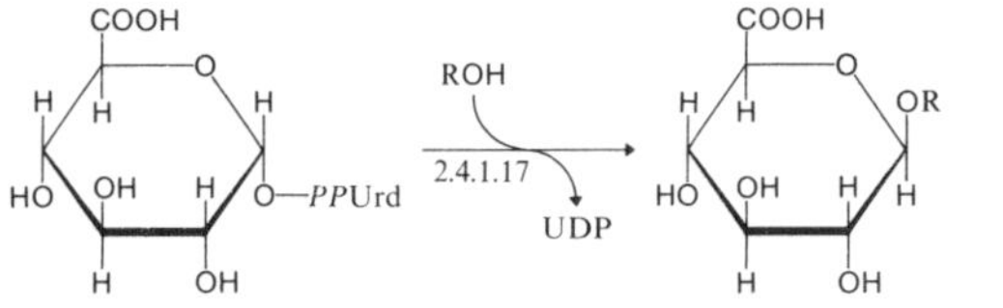

Enzyme involved:
2.4.1.17 Glucuronosyltransferase

The reversible conversion of UDPglucuronic acid to UDPiduronic acid is catalyzed by the UDPglucuronate 5'-epimerase (5.1.3.12):

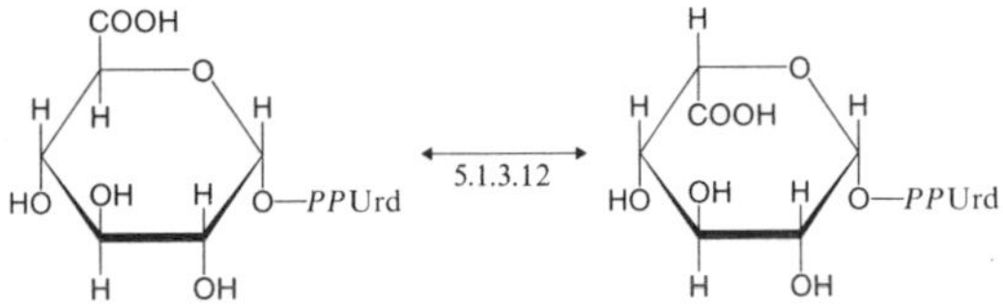

Glycogen

Glycogen (page 22) is synthesized in the liver and in muscle from UDPglucose, the precursor of which is glucose 1-phosphate (page 131). For glycogen formation, a starter molecule is required which consists of a chain of at least 4 glucose residues probably attached to a polypeptide. Elongation of the chain takes place according to the following general formula:

$$\text{UDPglucose} + (1,4\text{-}\alpha\text{-D-glucosyl})_n \xrightarrow[2.4.1.11]{} \text{UDP} + (1,4\text{-}\alpha\text{-D-glucosyl})_{n+1}$$

This reaction is catalyzed by glycogen synthase (2.4.1.11), whereas the branches of glycogen are formed by transfer of glucosyl chains containing 6 or 7 glucose residues from their 1,4-binding sites to the OH group at C-6 by the action of 1,4-α-glucan-branching enzyme (2.4.1.18). By the reaction shown above the branches can be further elongated. Glycogen formation and breakdown is highly regulated (page 199).

Amino sugars

N-Acetylated derivatives of glucosamine, mannosamine, galactosamine and neuraminic acid are constituents of many oligosaccharide chains. Incorporation takes place via the UDP derivatives or, in the case of the acylneuraminic acids, via the CMP derivatives. The syntheses of these compounds are illustrated in Figure 2.

N-Acetylneuraminic acid may be irreversibly oxidized to N-glycoloylneuraminic acid by the action of N-acetylneuraminate monooxygenase (1.14.99.18) (for formulae see page 14):

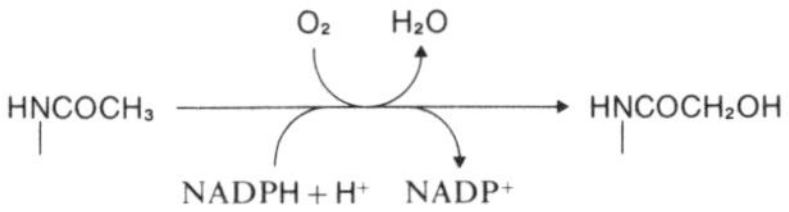

Fucose

L-Fucose is a constituent of ABH blood-group substances (page 30) and oligosaccharides of human milk (page 15). Incorporation takes place via GDP-L-fucose with the aid of various L-fucosyltransferases (2.4.1). The formation of GDP-L-fucose from D-fructose 6-phosphate is shown in Figure 3.

Fig. 3   *Formation of GDP-L-fucose*

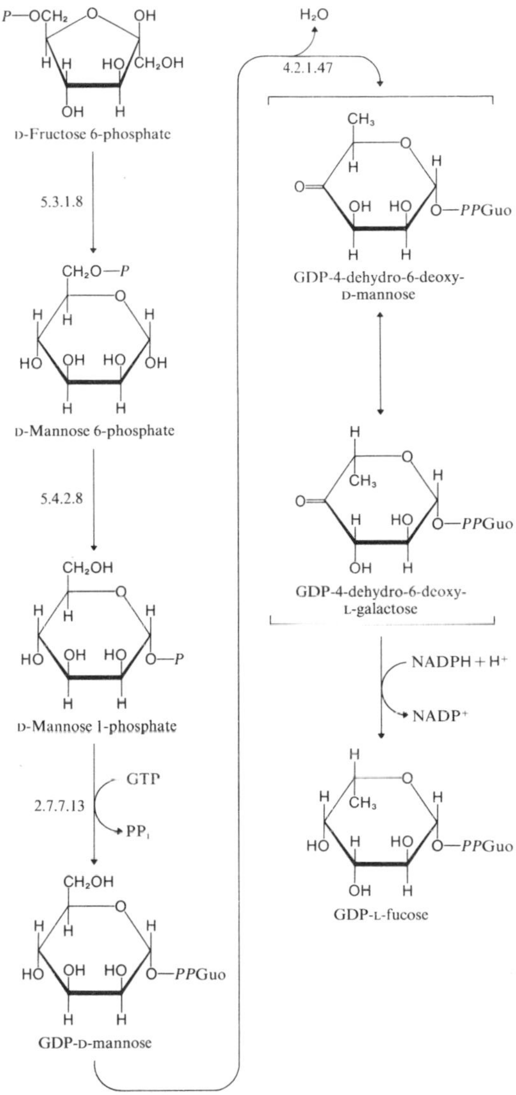

Enzymes involved:
2.7.7.13 Mannose-1-phosphate guanylyltransferase
4.2.1.47 GDPmannose 4,6-dehydratase
5.3.1.8   Mannose-6-phosphate isomerase
5.4.2.8   Phosphomannomutase

Reviews

· HERS and HUE, Gluconeogenesis and related aspects of glycolysis, *Ann. Rev. Biochem.*, **52**, 617 (1983).
· EISENBERG, F., Intermediates in the *myo*-inositol 1-phosphate synthase reaction, in WELLS and EISENBERG (Eds.), *Cyclitols and Phosphoinositides*, Academic Press, New York, 1978, page 269.

Fig. 1   *Pentose phosphate cycle*

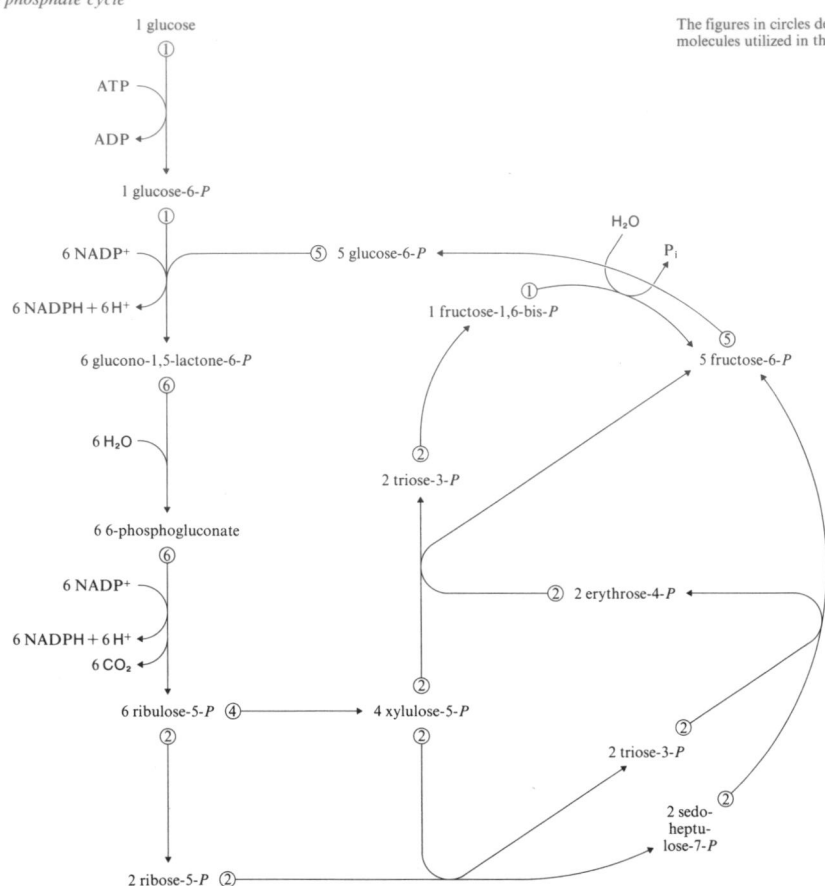

The figures in circles denote the number of molecules utilized in the different reactions.

When discussing the formation of biological energy in the form of ATP, it was stressed that the most efficient pathway was glycolysis (page 95), followed by the tricarboxylic acid cycle and the electron transfer system (pages 96–98). The provision of ATP, however, is inadequate for many biosynthetic reactions. Just as biological degradation often involves *oxidation* and the *production of energy*, biosynthesis often involves *reduction* and *utilization of energy*. Reducing power therefore has to be made available – usually in the form of reduced NADP. There is an important difference between reduced NAD and reduced NADP. The former is usually oxidized in the electron transfer system, with the formation of ATP, whereas the latter is utilized as a hydrogen or electron donor in reductive biosyntheses such as the formation of fatty acids.

One of the functions of the pentose phosphate pathway is to synthesize reduced NADP. Since the function of this pathway differs from that of the tricarboxylic acid cycle, the two cycles can coexist, though the relative importance of each may vary. For example, in some tissues, such as adipose tissue, the pentose phosphate cycle may predominate, whereas in other tissues, such as muscle, it may be virtually non-existent. Moreover, the enzymes involved in the pentose phosphate pathway are found in the cytosol and not in the mitochondria, as is the case with many of the enzymes involved in energy production. Besides producing reduced NADP, the pentose phosphate cycle is also essential as a source of ribose 5-phosphate, which is needed for the formation of 5-phosphoribose 1-diphosphate (*P*Rib-*PP*). An excess of ribose 5-phosphate is channeled into the glycolytic pathway, inasmuch as 2 molecules of fructose 6-phosphate and 1 molecule of glyceraldehyde 3-phosphate may be formed from 3 molecules of pentose phosphate.

Figure 1 shows a general outline of the pentose phosphate cycle, while details of the sequence of reactions are shown in Figure 2: 1 molecule of glucose is first phosphorylated, and the glucose 6-phosphate molecule thus formed is joined by another 5 molecules

from the cycle. The 6 molecules of glucose 6-phosphate then undergo oxidation to phosphogluconic acid, followed by oxidative decarboxylation to ribulose 5-phosphate. It is in these two oxidative stages that reduced NADP is produced. The rest of the cycle is concerned with the regeneration of the original 5 molecules of glucose 6-phosphate from 6 molecules of pentose phosphate, and in this regeneration, trioses, tetroses, pentoses and heptoses as well as hexoses are intermediates.

The pentose phosphate cycle described in the foregoing is characteristic of adipose (fat) tissue and is therefore also referred to as 'F type'. It has been suggested that another pathway – the 'L type' – takes place in the liver, the characteristics of this pathway being the conversion of ribose 5-phosphate to arabinose 5-phosphate with the aid of an epimerase and the conversion of arabinose 5-phosphate + glyceraldehyde 3-phosphate to octulose 1,8-bisphosphate by an aldolase-controlled reaction.

Reviews
· LANDAU and WOOD, The pentose cycle in animal tissues: evidence for the classical and against the 'L-type' pathway, *Trends biochem. Sci.*, **8**, 292 (1983).
· WILLIAMS, J. F., A critical examination of the evidence for the reactions of the pentose pathway in animal tissues, *Trends biochem. Sci.*, **5**, 315 (1980).
· HORECKER, B. L., Unravelling the pentose phosphate pathway, in KORNBERG et al. (Eds.), *Reflections on Biochemistry*, Pergamon, Oxford, 1976, page 65.

Fig. 2 *Reactions of the pentose phosphate cycle*

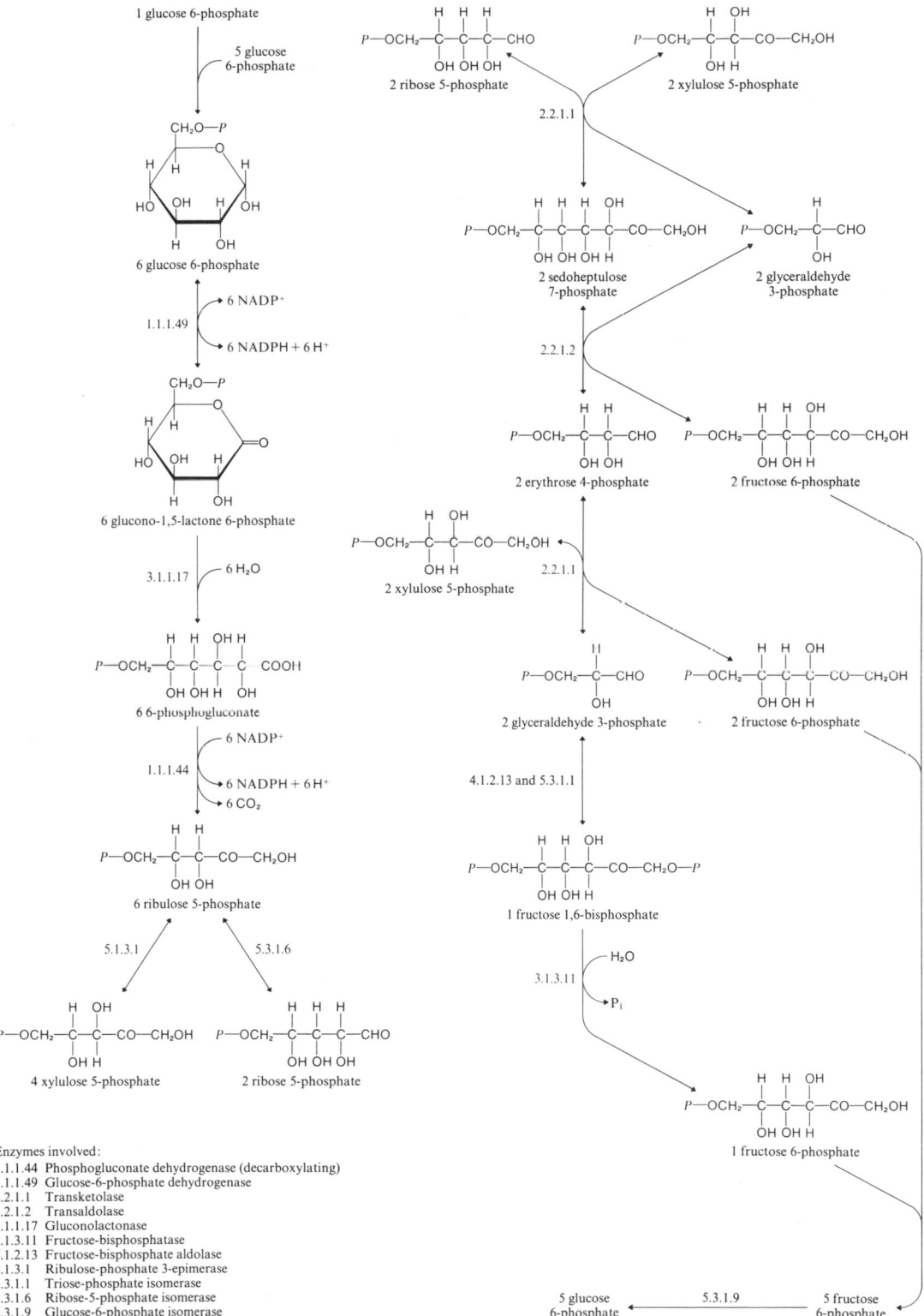

Enzymes involved:
1.1.1.44 Phosphogluconate dehydrogenase (decarboxylating)
1.1.1.49 Glucose-6-phosphate dehydrogenase
2.2.1.1   Transketolase
2.2.1.2   Transaldolase
3.1.1.17 Gluconolactonase
4.1.2.13 Fructose-bisphosphatase aldolase
5.1.3.1   Ribulose-phosphate 3-epimerase
5.3.1.1   Triose-phosphate isomerase
5.3.1.6   Ribose-5-phosphate isomerase
5.3.1.9   Glucose-6-phosphate isomerase

Formation of fatty acids

The amount of glycogen that can be stored by animals is limited, so that any excess of carbohydrate that is ingested is usually converted to fatty acids and hence to fat (triacylglycerol).

Usually, fatty acids consist of even-numbered carbon chains with 14 to 24 C atoms, those with 16 and 18 C atoms predominating. Fatty acids of animal origin are either saturated or more or less unsaturated, and are rarely hydroxylated or branched.

The synthesis of fatty acids differs from their degradation in several important respects:

1. Degradation of fatty acids (page 100) takes place in the mitochondria, whereas synthesis occurs in the soluble fraction of the cytoplasm, the cytosol.
2. Synthesis of fatty acids in animals is catalyzed by a multifunctional protein, the fatty-acid synthase (2.3.1.85), in contrast to degradation in which the enzymes are not associated.
3. The intermediates of synthesis are thioesters of acyl-carrier protein (ACP) and not of coenzyme A as in degradation.
4. The elongation and breakdown of the fatty-acid chains take place by the sequential addition or removal of C_2 units. In breakdown the C_2 unit is acetyl-CoA. In synthesis (which is an endergonic reaction) the C_2 donor is malonyl-CoA. This is, of course, a C_3 compound, but its reaction involves the release of CO_2 and with it some energy.
5. Biosyntheses of fatty acids, as already mentioned in the description of the pentose phosphate cycle (page 134), need reduced NADP as a reductant; in the oxidative processes of degradation, on the other hand, FAD and NAD are the coenzymes involved.

The synthesis of palmitic acid can be rendered stoichiometrically by the following equation:

$$\text{Acetyl-CoA} + 7 \text{ malonyl-CoA} \longrightarrow \text{Palmitate} + 7 CO_2 + 14 \text{ NADP}^+ + 14 \text{ NADPH} + 14 H^+ \qquad + 8 \text{ HSCoA} + 6 H_2O$$

Formation of the starting material in fatty-acid synthesis – acetyl-CoA – takes place *in* the mitochondria, whereas synthesis of the fatty acids is an extramitochondrial process. Pyruvate – formed during glycolysis – diffuses into the mitochondria, where it undergoes an oxidative decarboxylation to acetyl-CoA with the aid of the pyruvate dehydrogenase complex (page 96).

As the mitochondrial membrane is impervious to acetyl-CoA, various mechanisms of transfer of acetyl-CoA into the cytosol have to be considered.

1. Acetyl-CoA is deacylated in the mitochondria. The acetate thus formed can diffuse across the mitochondrial membrane into the cytosol, where acetyl-CoA is re-formed with the aid of acetate–CoA ligase (6.2.1.1).
2. Acetyl-CoA reacts with carnitine to yield acetylcarnitine, which can diffuse across the mitochondrial membrane into the cytosol and there be converted to acetyl-CoA again.
3. Acetyl-CoA is converted to citrate, which can diffuse across the mitochondrial membrane into the cytosol where it is broken down, with the release of acetyl-CoA.

The first two mechanisms seem to be of little importance; a detailed explanation of the reactions is therefore confined to the pathway via citrate.

In the mitochondria, citrate is formed from acetyl-CoA as follows:

Enzyme involved:
4.1.3.7 Citrate (*si*)-synthase

Extra-mitochondrial cleavage of citrate:

Enzyme involved:
4.1.3.8 ATP citrate (*pro-3 S*)-lyase

In this process not only acetyl-CoA but also oxaloacetate has been transferred from mitochondria to cytosol, which must therefore be returned to the mitochondria to perpetuate the cycle (Fig. 1). Oxaloacetate is therefore reduced to malate by malate dehydrogenase (1.1.1.37). The malate is then oxidatively decarboxylated to pyruvate in a reaction catalyzed by malate dehydrogenase (oxaloacetate-de-

Fig. 1   *Transfer of acetyl-CoA from mitochondria to cytosol by formation and breakdown of citrate*

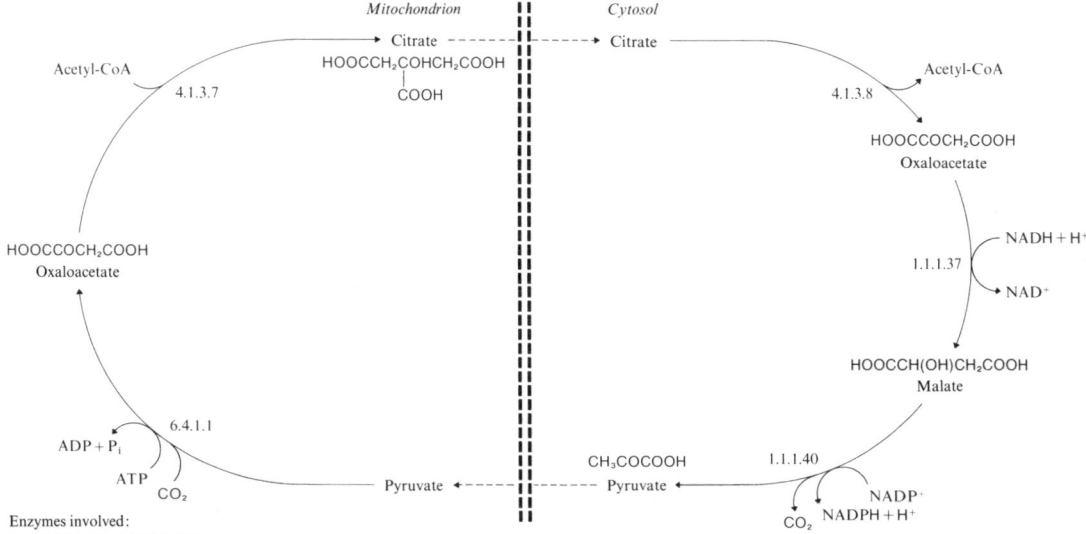

Enzymes involved:
1.1.1.37   Malate dehydrogenase
1.1.1.40   Malate dehydrogenase (oxaloacetate-decarboxylating) (NADP⁺)
4.1.3.7   Citrate (*si*)-synthase
4.1.3.8   ATP citrate (*pro-3 S*)-lyase
6.4.1.1   Pyruvate carboxylase

carboxylating) ($NADP^+$) (1.1.1.40). This reaction also provides reduced $NADP^+$ for synthetic purposes. The pyruvate readily passes through the membrane, and when it reaches the mitochondrial matrix it is carboxylated to oxaloacetate by the action of pyruvate carboxylase (6.4.1.1).

Formation of malonyl-CoA. In the first step of fatty-acid synthesis, malonyl-CoA is formed by carboxylation of acetyl-CoA in an irreversible reaction at the expense of ATP. This reaction is catalyzed by acetyl-CoA carboxylase (6.4.1.2), a biotinyl-protein. (For the mechanism of carboxylation see page 78.)

The formation of malonyl-CoA is the rate-limiting reaction in fatty-acid synthesis, the regulation of which is discussed on page 200.

Chain formation. In bacteria and in plants the individual steps of fatty-acid synthesis are catalyzed by the fatty-acid synthase complex, which readily dissociates into distinct components with specific catalytic activities (7 in *E. coli*), whereas multifunctional enzymes are involved in fatty-acid synthesis in yeast and animals. The fatty-acyl-CoA synthase (2.3.1.86) of yeast is a complex of 2 nonidentical polypeptide subunits which requires FMN as coenzyme and yields palmitoyl-CoA or stearoyl-CoA as the end-product. Animal fatty-acid synthase (2.3.1.85) consists of 2 identical subunits, has no requirement for FMN and yields palmitate or stearate as the end-pro-

Fig. 2a *Biosynthesis of long-chain fatty acids in the cytosol of animals*

CH3COSCoA
Acetyl-CoA
CO2
ATP+H2O
Biotin
6.4.1.2
ADP+Pi
HOOCCH2COSCoA
Malonyl-CoA
HS-ACP
Acyl-carrier protein
HSCoA
HS-ACP
HSCoA
CH3COS-ACP
Acetyl-ACP
HOOCCH2COS-ACP
Malonyl-ACP
CO2
CH3COCH2COS-ACP
Acetoacetyl-ACP
NADPH+H+
NADP+
CH3CH(OH)CH2COS-ACP
D-3-Hydroxybutyryl-ACP
H2O
CH3CH=CHCOS-ACP
Crotonyl-ACP
NADPH+H+
NADP+
CH3CH2CH2COS-ACP
Butyryl-ACP
2.3.1.85

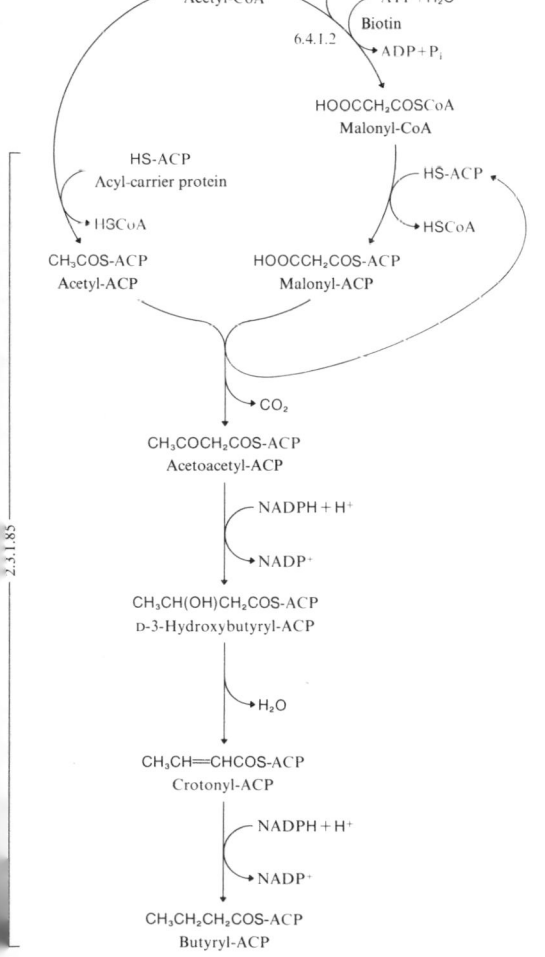

Enzymes involved:
2.3.1.85 Fatty-acid synthase
6.4.1.2 Acetyl-CoA carboxylase

Fig. 2b *Biosynthesis of long-chain fatty acids in the cytosol of animals: chain formation*

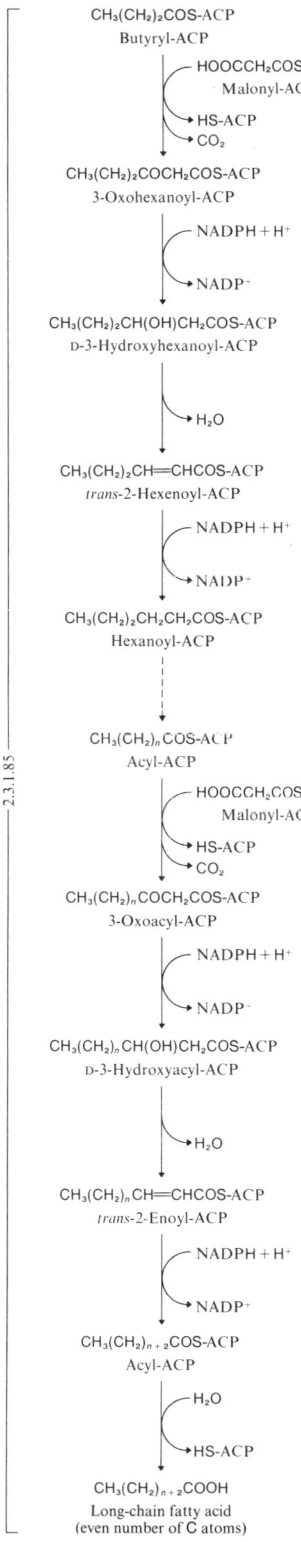

CH3(CH2)2COS-ACP
Butyryl-ACP
HOOCCH2COS-ACP
Malonyl-ACP
HS-ACP
CO2
CH3(CH2)2COCH2COS-ACP
3-Oxohexanoyl-ACP
NADPH+H+
NADP+
CH3(CH2)2CH(OH)CH2COS-ACP
D-3-Hydroxyhexanoyl-ACP
H2O
CH3(CH2)2CH=CHCOS-ACP
trans-2-Hexenoyl-ACP
NADPH+H+
NADP+
CH3(CH2)2CH2CH2COS-ACP
Hexanoyl-ACP
CH3(CH2)nCOS-ACP
Acyl-ACP
HOOCCH2COS-ACP
Malonyl-ACP
HS-ACP
CO2
CH3(CH2)nCOCH2COS-ACP
3-Oxoacyl-ACP
NADPH+H+
NADP+
CH3(CH2)nCH(OH)CH2COS-ACP
D-3-Hydroxyacyl-ACP
H2O
CH3(CH2)nCH=CHCOS-ACP
trans-2-Enoyl-ACP
NADPH+H+
NADP+
CH3(CH2)n+2COS-ACP
Acyl-ACP
H2O
HS-ACP
CH3(CH2)n+2COOH
Long-chain fatty acid
(even number of C atoms)
2.3.1.85

Fatty acids with an odd number of C atoms are formed by an initial condensation of propionyl-ACP with malonyl-ACP.

duct. The sites of catalytic activities of the multifunctional enzymes are a series of globular domains on the polypeptide chain.

The intermediates in long-chain fatty-acid synthesis stay attached to ACP, a coenzyme that binds the acyl intermediates as thioesters. ACP is a protein with a relative molecular mass of about 10000; prosthetic group is phosphopantetheine, whose phosphate is attached to the hydroxy group of a serine residue of the polypeptide chain. ACP and its phosphopantetheine arm constitutes a certain site of the fatty-acid synthase.

The component steps in the formation of butyryl-ACP can be seen from Figure 2a. Reduced NADP is required in mammals, but in bacteria, plants and yeast the synthesis also needs reduced NAD.

Butyryl-ACP then reacts with malonyl-ACP and yields 3-oxo-hexanoyl-ACP and thence hexanoyl-ACP. The addition of C_2 units is continued in the same way up to the formation of palmitoyl-ACP or stearoyl-ACP (a C_{16} or C_{18} chain). (Fig. 2b). The free fatty acid is then released from the acyl-ACP enzyme complex by hydrolysis. In the lactating mammary gland, fatty-acid synthesis ends with shorter-chain fatty acids (C_4 to C_{14}).

Chain elongation. In cytosol, the end-product formed by fatty-acid synthase is normally palmitic acid (C_{16}). Further elongation may be brought about by two other systems, one found in the *mitochondria* and the other in the *microsomes* (enclosed vesicles of endoplasmic reticulum). In the *mitochondria*, fatty acyl-CoA esters with chain length C_{12} to C_{16} are lengthened by successive addition of acetyl-CoA (not malonyl-ACP). This pathway is virtually the reverse of the β-oxidation pathway except that the double bond in position C-2 is reduced by NADPH and not by FADH$_2$. In the *microsomes*, malonyl-CoA is utilized as the source of C_2 units, but the fatty acids are elongated in the form of CoA esters, and not of ACP esters. Unsaturated fatty acids may also be elongated by both systems.

Formation of unsaturated fatty acids. The two most abundant unsaturated fatty acids are palmitoleic acid and oleic acid. Both are monoenoic acids and derive from palmitic acid and stearic acid,

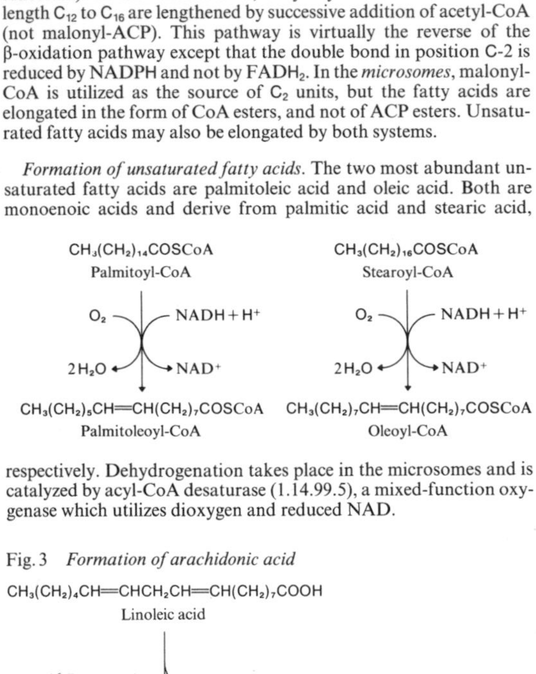

CH$_3$(CH$_2$)$_{14}$COSCoA   CH$_3$(CH$_2$)$_{16}$COSCoA
Palmitoyl-CoA   Stearoyl-CoA

O$_2$ ⤸ NADH+H$^+$ O$_2$ ⤸ NADH+H$^+$

2H$_2$O ⤹ NAD$^+$ 2H$_2$O ⤹ NAD$^+$

CH$_3$(CH$_2$)$_5$CH=CH(CH$_2$)$_7$COSCoA   CH$_3$(CH$_2$)$_7$CH=CH(CH$_2$)$_7$COSCoA
Palmitoleoyl-CoA   Oleoyl-CoA

respectively. Dehydrogenation takes place in the microsomes and is catalyzed by acyl-CoA desaturase (1.14.99.5), a mixed-function oxygenase which utilizes dioxygen and reduced NAD.

Fig. 3   *Formation of arachidonic acid*

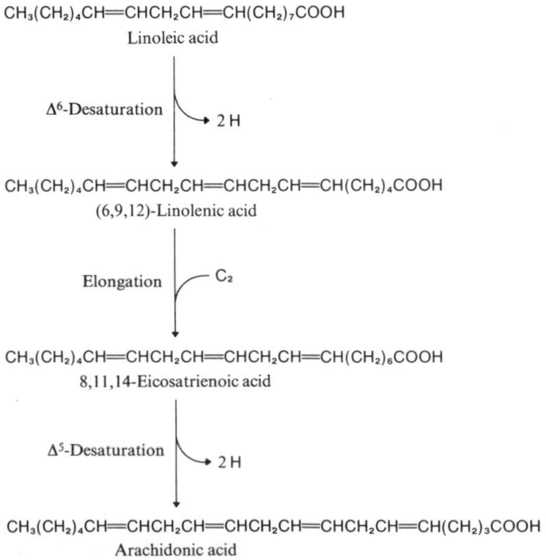

CH$_3$(CH$_2$)$_4$CH=CHCH$_2$CH=CH(CH$_2$)$_7$COOH
Linoleic acid

Δ^6-Desaturation ⟍ 2 H

CH$_3$(CH$_2$)$_4$CH=CHCH$_2$CH=CHCH$_2$CH=CH(CH$_2$)$_4$COOH
(6,9,12)-Linolenic acid

Elongation ⟍ C$_2$

CH$_3$(CH$_2$)$_4$CH=CHCH$_2$CH=CHCH$_2$CH=CH(CH$_2$)$_6$COOH
8,11,14-Eicosatrienoic acid

Δ^5-Desaturation ⟍ 2 H

CH$_3$(CH$_2$)$_4$CH=CHCH$_2$CH=CHCH$_2$CH=CHCH$_2$CH=CH(CH$_2$)$_3$COOH
Arachidonic acid

Polyunsaturated acids can be derived from the fatty-acid families given on page 25 by elongating the chain and/or by dehydrogenation. In mammals, double bonds cannot be introduced beyond the C-9 position. However, linoleic acid, with double bonds in the C-9 and C-12 positions, and linolenic acid, with double bonds in the C-9, C-12 and C-15 positions, are needed by the organism (especially during growth) and must therefore be supplied with the food. They are thus 'essential' fatty acids. Arachidonic acid, with double bonds in the C-5, C-8, C-11 and C-14 positions (Fig. 3), on the other hand, can be synthesized by animals if linoleic acid is available, and it is therefore not essential.

Formation of triacylglycerols and phospholipids (Fig. 5)

In the intestinal mucosa, triacylglycerols are synthesized from absorbed monoacylglycerols and fatty acids (page 99), whereas glycerol 3-phosphate is the starting material of triacylglycerol synthesis in the liver and in fat cells. The reactions take place mainly in the endoplasmic reticulum, but in part also in the mitochondria. 1,2-Diacylglycerol 3-phosphate (phosphatidic acid), which is also a starting material for the synthesis of phospholipids, is formed in two acylation steps. Diacylglycerol is first formed from 1,2-diacylglycerol 3-phosphate by release of phosphate and is then converted to triacylglycerol by an acyltransferase in the microsomes.

Phospholipids are formed either from 1,2-diacylglycerol 3-phosphate – with the aid of a cytidylyltransferase – or from diacylglycerol and activated ethanolamine or choline in the form of CDPethanolamine or CDPcholine, respectively. The latter two compounds are formed from ethanolamine phosphate or choline phosphate by the action of the corresponding cytidylyltransferases.

The synthesis of 1-phosphatidylinositol from CDPdiacylglycerol is a step in the phosphatidylinositol turnover cycle[1] (Fig. 4). The

Fig. 4   *Phosphatidylinositol turnover cycle*

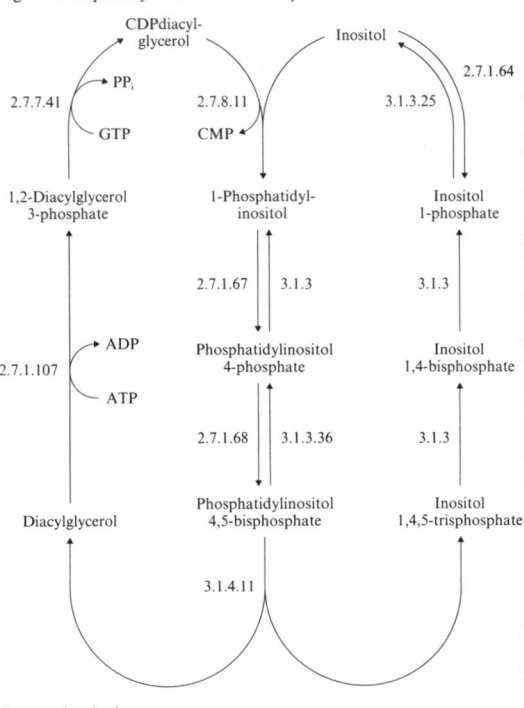

Enzymes involved:
2.7.1.64   *myo*-Inositol 1-kinase
2.7.1.67   1-Phosphatidylinositol kinase
2.7.1.68   1-Phosphatidylinositol-4-phosphate kinase
2.7.1.107 Diacylglycerol kinase
2.7.7.41   Phosphatidate cytidylyltransferase
2.7.8.11   CDPdiacylglycerol–inositol 3-phosphatidyltransferase
3.1.3   Inositol-1,4-bisphosphate 4-phosphatase
           Inositol-1,4,5-trisphosphate 5-phosphatase
           Phosphatidylinositol-4-phosphatase
3.1.3.25   1L-*myo*-Inositol-1-phosphatase
3.1.3.36   Phosphatidylinositol-bisphosphatase
3.1.4.11   1-Phosphatidylinositol-4,5-bisphosphate phosphodiesterase

Fig. 5 *Biosynthesis of triacylglycerol and phospholipids*

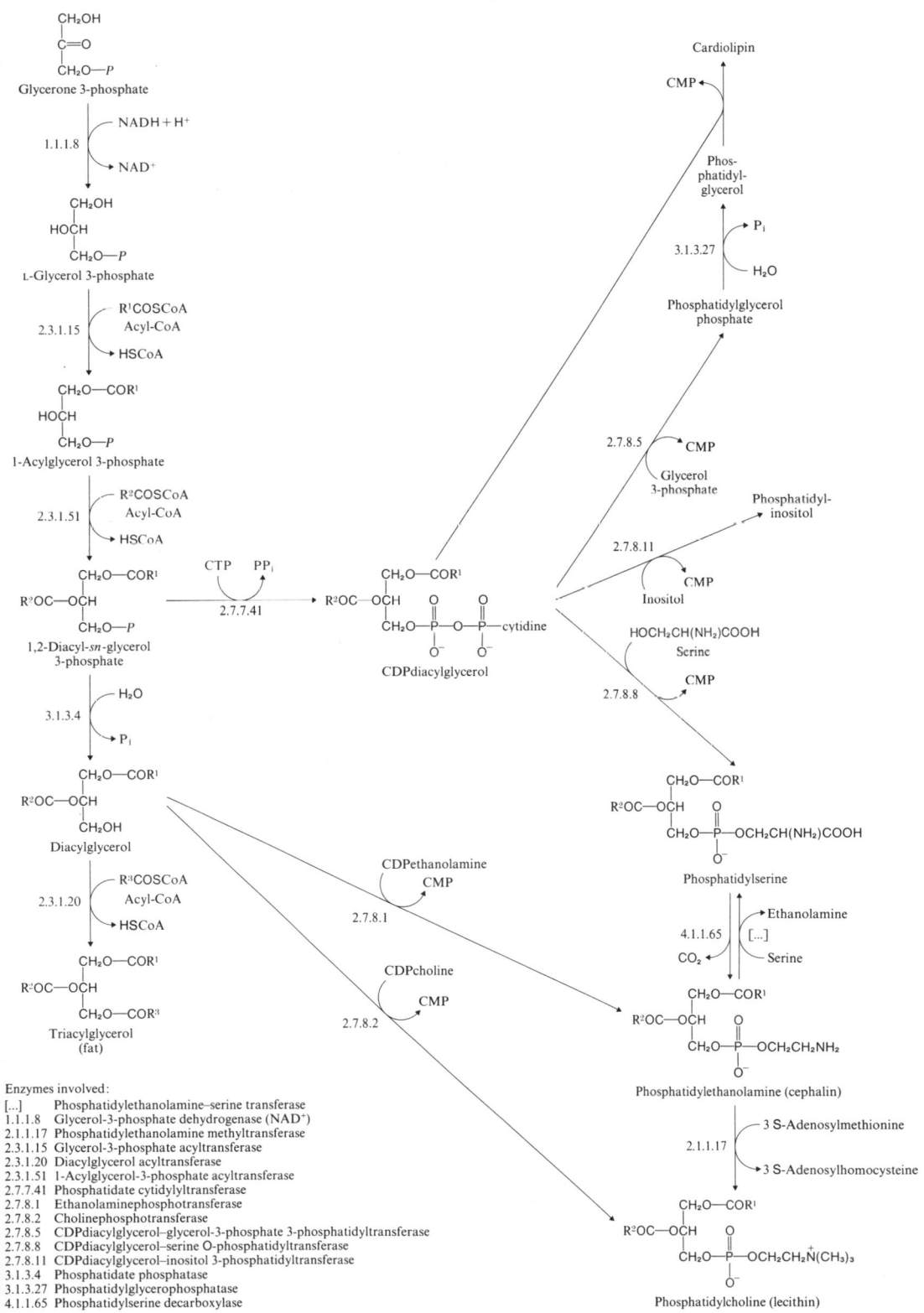

Enzymes involved:
[...]   Phosphatidylethanolamine–serine transferase
1.1.1.8   Glycerol-3-phosphate dehydrogenase (NAD⁺)
2.1.1.17 Phosphatidylethanolamine methyltransferase
2.3.1.15 Glycerol-3-phosphate acyltransferase
2.3.1.20 Diacylglycerol acyltransferase
2.3.1.51 1-Acylglycerol-3-phosphate acyltransferase
2.7.7.41 Phosphatidate cytidylyltransferase
2.7.8.1   Ethanolaminephosphotransferase
2.7.8.2   Cholinephosphotransferase
2.7.8.5   CDPdiacylglycerol–glycerol-3-phosphate 3-phosphatidyltransferase
2.7.8.8   CDPdiacylglycerol–serine O-phosphatidyltransferase
2.7.8.11 CDPdiacylglycerol–inositol 3-phosphatidyltransferase
3.1.3.4   Phosphatidate phosphatase
3.1.3.27 Phosphatidylglycerophosphatase
4.1.1.65 Phosphatidylserine decarboxylase

Fig. 6 *Biosynthesis of plasmalogen*

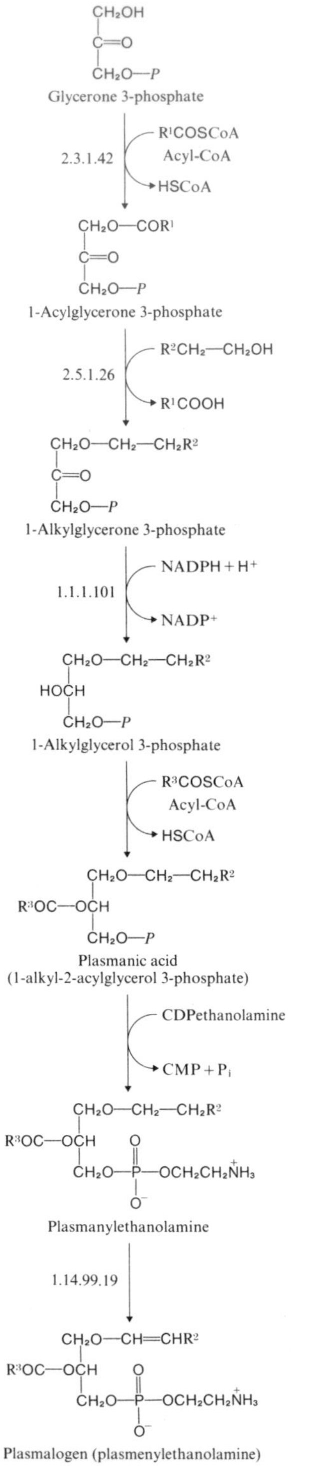

CH₂OH
|
C=O
|
CH₂O—P
Glycerone 3-phosphate

2.3.1.42 ⟶ R¹COSCoA Acyl-CoA ⟶ HSCoA

CH₂O—COR¹
|
C=O
|
CH₂O—P
1-Acylglycerone 3-phosphate

2.5.1.26 ⟶ R²CH₂—CH₂OH ⟶ R¹COOH

CH₂O—CH₂—CH₂R²
|
C=O
|
CH₂O—P
1-Alkylglycerone 3-phosphate

1.1.1.101 ⟶ NADPH + H⁺ ⟶ NADP⁺

CH₂O—CH₂—CH₂R²
|
HOCH
|
CH₂O—P
1-Alkylglycerol 3-phosphate

⟶ R³COSCoA Acyl-CoA ⟶ HSCoA

CH₂O—CH₂—CH₂R²
|
R³OC—OCH
|
CH₂O—P
Plasmanic acid
(1-alkyl-2-acylglycerol 3-phosphate)

⟶ CDPethanolamine ⟶ CMP + Pᵢ

CH₂O—CH₂—CH₂R²
|
R³OC—OCH   O
| ‖
CH₂O—P—OCH₂CH₂N⁺H₃
             |
             O⁻
Plasmanylethanolamine

1.14.99.19

CH₂O—CH=CHR²
|
R³OC—OCH   O
| ‖
CH₂O—P—OCH₂CH₂N⁺H₃
             |
             O⁻
Plasmalogen (plasmenylethanolamine)

Enzymes involved:
1.1.1.101   Acylglycerone-phosphate reductase
1.14.99.19 Plasmanylethanolamine desaturase
2.3.1.42   Glycerone-phosphate acyltransferase
2.5.1.26   Alkylglycerone-phosphate synthase

Fig. 7 *Biosynthesis of 4-sphingenin and ceramides*

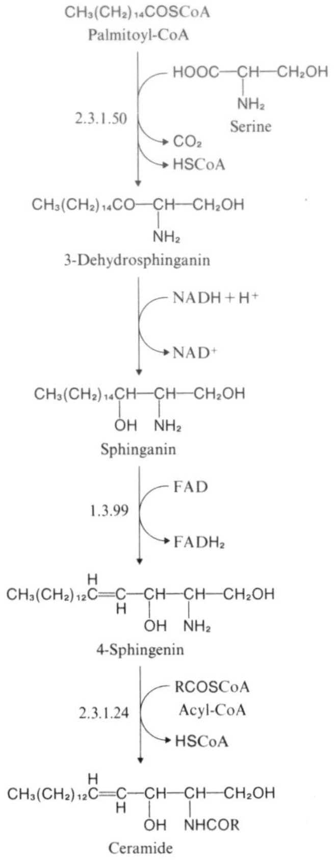

CH₃(CH₂)₁₄COSCoA
Palmitoyl-CoA

2.3.1.50 ⟶ HOOC—CH—CH₂OH
                  |
                  NH₂
                  Serine
⟶ CO₂
⟶ HSCoA

CH₃(CH₂)₁₄CO—CH—CH₂OH
                |
                NH₂
3-Dehydrosphinganin

⟶ NADH + H⁺ ⟶ NAD⁺

CH₃(CH₂)₁₄CH—CH—CH₂OH
           | |
           OH   NH₂
Sphinganin

1.3.99 ⟶ FAD ⟶ FADH₂

                  H
CH₃(CH₂)₁₂C=C—CH—CH—CH₂OH
           | | |
           H   OH NH₂
4-Sphingenin

2.3.1.24 ⟶ RCOSCoA Acyl-CoA ⟶ HSCoA

                  H
CH₃(CH₂)₁₂C=C—CH—CH—CH₂OH
           | | |
           H   OH NHCOR
Ceramide

Enzymes involved:
1.3.99   'Sphinganin Δ⁴-dehydrogenase'
2.3.1.24 Sphingosine acyltransferase
2.3.1.50 Serine palmitoyltransferase

Fig. 8 *Biosynthesis of gangliosides*

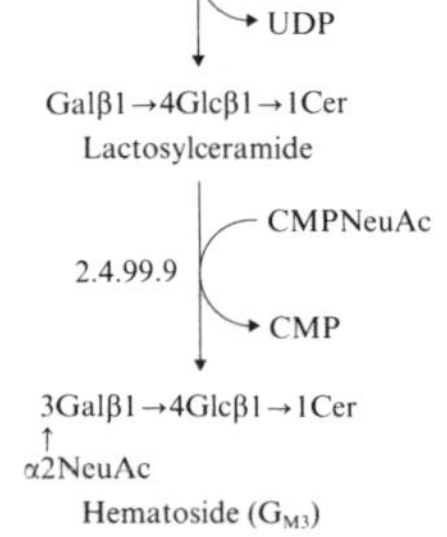

Ceramide

2.4.1.80 ⟶ UDPGlc ⟶ UDP

Glcβ1→1Cer

2.4.1 ⟶ UDPGal ⟶ UDP

Galβ1→4Glcβ1→1Cer
Lactosylceramide

2.4.99.9 ⟶ CMPNeuAc ⟶ CMP

3Galβ1→4Glcβ1→1Cer
   ↑
α2NeuAc
Hematoside (G_{M3})

Enzymes involved:
2.4.1   'UDPgalactose–glucosylceramide galactosyltransferase'
2.4.1.80 Ceramide glucosyltransferase
2.4.99.9 CMP-N-acetylneuraminate–lactosylceramide α-2,3-sialyltransferase

reactions of this cycle involve phosphorylation of the inositol part in positions 4 and 5 with the aid of ATP. The cycle takes place in the plasma membrane, but extracellular signals (e.g. acetylcholine) influence the breakdown of inositol phospholipids – particularly phosphatidylinositol 4,5-bisphosphate –, whereby Ca^{2+} is simultaneously released from intracellular stores[2].

The synthesis of plasmalogens (Fig. 6) starts with glycerone 3-phosphate (dihydroxyacetone phosphate), which is first acylated, and then the acyl group is exchanged for an alkyl group. As a last step, desaturation takes place to form the O-1-alk-1′-enyl chain.

Formation of sphingolipids

4-Sphingenin, the alcoholic component of the sphingolipids, is synthesized from palmitoyl-CoA and serine (Fig. 7). Ceramide (N-acylsphingosine) is then formed by acylation. Esterification of the hydroxy group of 4-sphingenin with choline phosphate leads to the sphingomyelins (for formula see page 30). Neutral (page 30) and acidic glycosphingolipids (gangliosides) result from the reaction of the hydroxy group of 4-sphingenin with activated carbohydrates (Fig. 8). Hematoside gives rise to the formation of disialogangliosides, by the addition of another N-acetylneuraminic residue on the NeuAc residue, as well as of various other gangliosides by elongation of the chain on the Gal residue (see Table 7, page 31). The sulfatation of sphingolipids takes place in the Golgi complex, catalyzed by galactosylceramide sulfotransferase (2.8.2.11). The sulfate group is transferred from adenosine 3′-phosphate 5′-phosphosulfate (PAPS) to the acceptor lipid[3].

References

Reviews:
· WAKIL et al., Fatty acid synthesis and its regulation, *Ann. Rev. Biochem.*, **52**, 537 (1983).
· BELL et al., Lipid topogenesis, *J. Lipid Res.*, **22**, 391 (1981).
· BELL and COLEMAN, Enzymes of glycerolipid synthesis in eukaryotes, *Ann. Rev. Biochem.*, **49**, 459 (1980).
· BLOCH and VANCE, Control mechanisms in the synthesis of saturated fatty acids, *Ann. Rev. Biochem.*, **46**, 263 (1977).
· KATIYAR and PORTER, Mechanism of fatty acid synthesis, *Life Sci.*, **20**, 737 (1977).
· FISHMAN and BRADY, Biosynthesis and function of gangliosides, *Science*, **194**, 906 (1976).
· VAN DEN BOSCH, H., Phosphoglyceride metabolism, *Ann. Rev. Biochem.*, **43**, 243 (1974).
· VOLPE and VAGELOS, Saturated fatty acid biosynthesis and its regulation, *Ann. Rev. Biochem.*, **42**, 21 (1973).
· LYNEN, F., The pathway from 'activated acetic acid' to the terpenes and fatty acids, in *Nobel Lectures: Physiology or Medicine 1963–1970*, Elsevier, Amsterdam, 1972, page 103.
· McMURRAY and MAGEE, Phospholipid metabolism, *Ann. Rev. Biochem.*, **41**, 129 (1972).
· WAKIL and BARNES, Fatty acid metabolism, *Comprehens. Biochem.*, **18S**, 57 (1971).
· STOFFEL, W., Sphingolipids, *Ann. Rev. Biochem.*, **40**, 57 (1971).

Special references:
[1] FISHER et al., Renewed interest in the polyphosphoinositides, *Trends biochem. Sci.*, **9**, 53 (1984).
[2] NISHIZUKA, Y., Turnover of inositol phospholipids and signal transduction, *Science*, **225**, 1365 (1984).
[3] FAROOQUI and HORROCKS, *Molec. cell. Biochem.*, **66**, 87 (1985).

Prostaglandins, leukotrienes and related compounds (page 27), generally designated 'eicosanoids', are oxidation products of specific polyunsaturated fatty acids, arachidonic acid being the most important. To undergo the various oxidation reactions these fatty acids must be in the free (nonesterified) form.

Arachidonic acid may be obtained directly from the diet or by desaturation and chain elongation of linoleic acid (page 138), but it is mainly released from phospholipids stored in cell membranes. A major precursor is phosphatidylinositol, which contains arachidonic acid in the C-2 position of the diacylglycerol moiety. A specific phospholipase C (1-phosphatidylinositol phosphodiesterase, 3.1.4.10) cleaves phosphatidylinositol to inositol 1-phosphate and 1,2-diacylglycerol, from which arachidonic acid is released by the action of 'diacylglycerol lipase'. Phosphatidylcholine and phosphatidylethanolamine may also contribute to the free arachidonic acid pool; the enzyme catalyzing the liberation of the fatty acid from these phospholipids is phospholipase A_2 (3.1.1.4).

In the *cyclooxygenase pathway* (Fig. 1), arachidonic acid is converted to cyclic endoperoxides (PGG_2, PGH_2). PGH_2 isomerizes to PGD_2 and PGE_2. $PGF_{2\alpha}$ is thought to be formed directly from PGG_2 as well as from PGE_2 by the action of prostaglandin-E_2 9-oxoreductase (1.1.1.189). PGH_2 may also be transformed to thromboxane A_2 and further to thromboxane B_2; in addition, it may give rise to the unstable prostacyclin (PGI_2), which is further converted to 6-oxo-$PGF_{1\alpha}$. Nonenzymatically, PGH_2 yields a C_{17} hydroxy acid together with malondialdehyde.

Fig. 1   *Metabolism of arachidonic acid: the cyclooxygenase pathway*

Enzymes involved:
-        Cyclooxygenase (prostaglandin synthase)
- 1.1.1.189 Prostaglandin-E_2 9-oxoreductase
- 5.3.99.2 Prostaglandin-H_2 D-isomerase
- 5.3.99.3 Prostaglandin-H_2 E-isomerase
- 5.3.99.4 Prostacyclin synthase
- 5.3.99.5 Thromboxane synthase

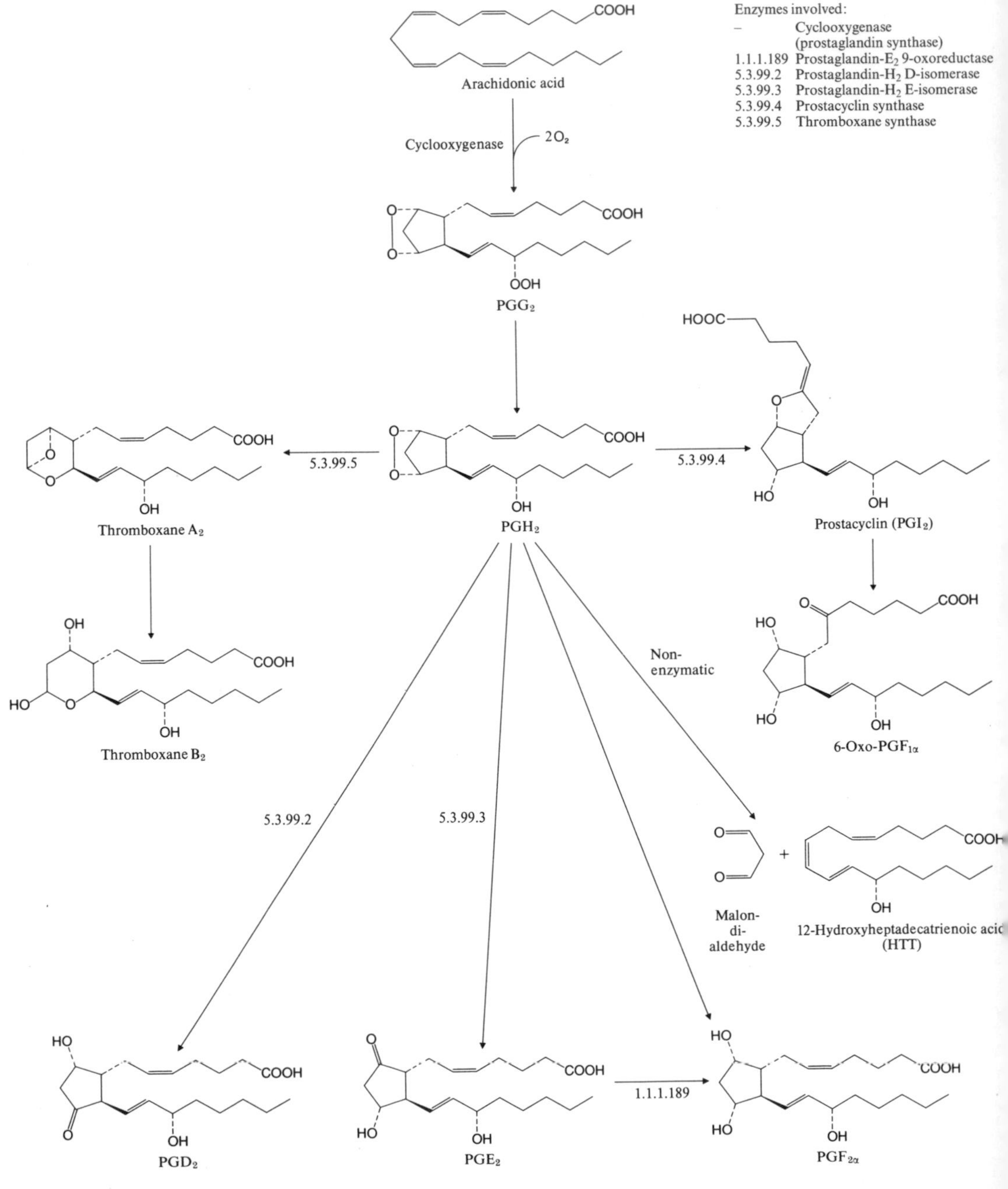

Fig. 2 *Metabolism of arachidonic acid: the lipoxygenase pathway*

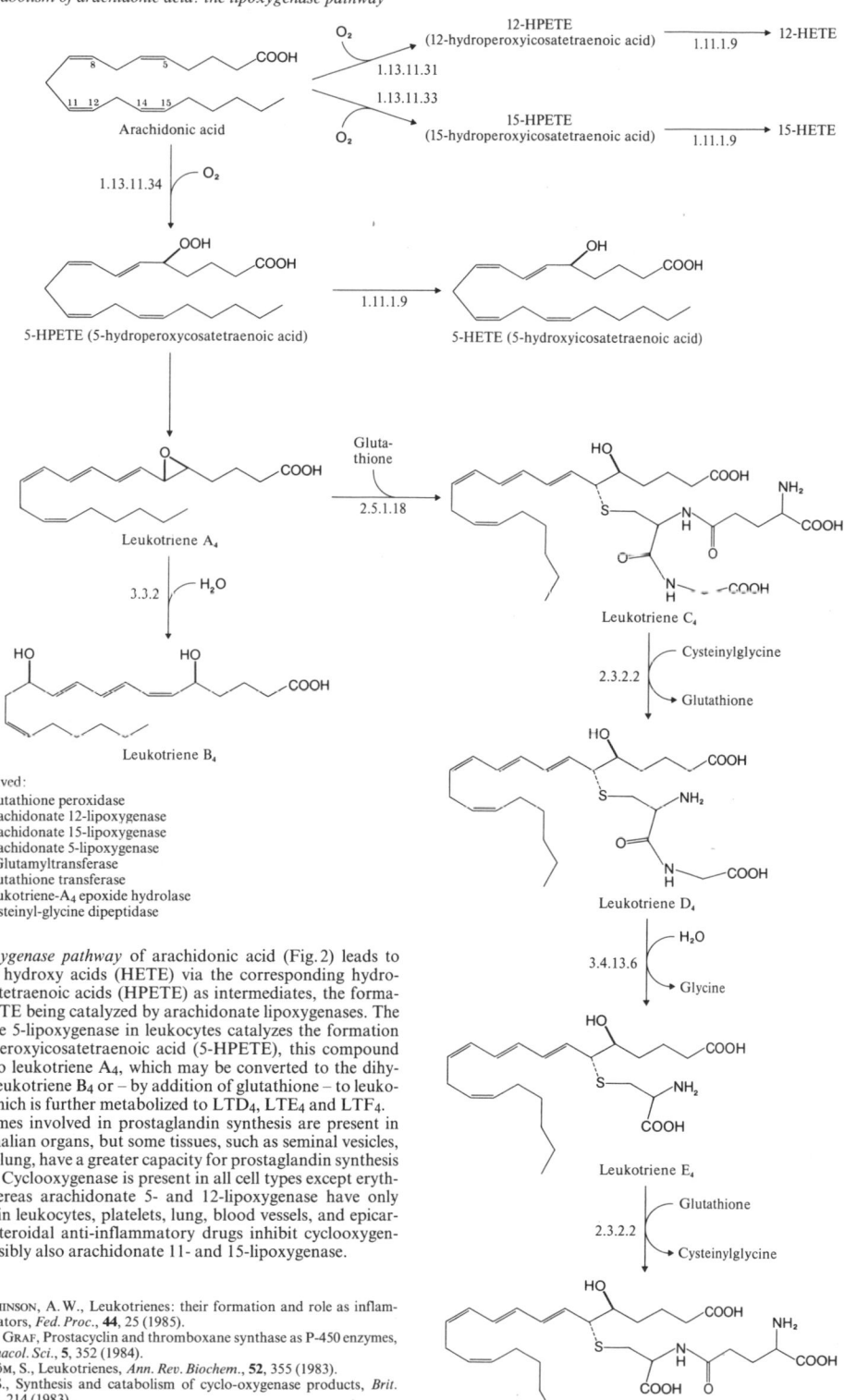

Enzymes involved:

1.11.1.9   Glutathione peroxidase
1.13.11.31 Arachidonate 12-lipoxygenase
1.13.11.33 Arachidonate 15-lipoxygenase
1.13.11.34 Arachidonate 5-lipoxygenase
2.3.2.2   γ-Glutamyltransferase
2.5.1.18   Glutathione transferase
3.3.2   Leukotriene-A$_4$ epoxide hydrolase
3.4.13.6   Cysteinyl-glycine dipeptidase

The *lipoxygenase pathway* of arachidonic acid (Fig. 2) leads to noncyclized hydroxy acids (HETE) via the corresponding hydroperoxyicosatetraenoic acids (HPETE) as intermediates, the formation of HPETE being catalyzed by arachidonate lipoxygenases. The arachidonate 5-lipoxygenase in leukocytes catalyzes the formation of 5-hydroperoxyicosatetraenoic acid (5-HPETE), this compound giving rise to leukotriene A$_4$, which may be converted to the dihydroxy acid leukotriene B$_4$ or – by addition of glutathione – to leukotriene C$_4$, which is further metabolized to LTD$_4$, LTE$_4$ and LTF$_4$.

The enzymes involved in prostaglandin synthesis are present in most mammalian organs, but some tissues, such as seminal vesicles, kidneys and lung, have a greater capacity for prostaglandin synthesis than others. Cyclooxygenase is present in all cell types except erythrocytes, whereas arachidonate 5- and 12-lipoxygenase have only been found in leukocytes, platelets, lung, blood vessels, and epicardium. Nonsteroidal anti-inflammatory drugs inhibit cyclooxygenase, and possibly also arachidonate 11- and 15-lipoxygenase.

Reviews

FORD-HUTCHINSON, A. W., Leukotrienes: their formation and role as inflammatory mediators, *Fed. Proc.*, **44**, 25 (1985).
ULLRICH and GRAF, Prostacyclin and thromboxane synthase as P-450 enzymes, *Trends pharmacol. Sci.*, **5**, 352 (1984).
HAMMARSTRÖM, S., Leukotrienes, *Ann. Rev. Biochem.*, **52**, 355 (1983).
BAKHLE, Y. S., Synthesis and catabolism of cyclo-oxygenase products, *Brit. med. Bull.*, **39**, 214 (1983).
TAYLOR and MORRIS, Lipoxygenase pathways, *Brit. med. Bull.*, **39**, 219 (1983).
MONCADA, S., Prostacyclin and arterial wall biology, *Arteriosclerosis*, **2**, 193 (1982).

The first steps in the formation of the polyisoprenoids – carotenes, ubiquinones (page 163), dolichols, squalene – are identical (Fig. 1), mevalonate, isopentenyl diphosphate and farnesyl diphosphate being important intermediates.

Formation of farnesyl diphosphate (Fig. 3). Acetyl-CoA is the starting material. The formation of 3-hydroxy-3-methylglutaryl-CoA from acetoacetyl-CoA takes place in the cytosol, while the pathway of ketone body synthesis (page 102) has the same reaction taking place in the mitochondria. The next – rate-limiting – step is catalyzed by a reductase localized in the endoplasmic reticulum. Phosphorylation of mevalonate and subsequent decarboxylation lead to the isoprenoid compound isopentenyl diphosphate. The latter is in equilibrium with dimethylallyl diphosphate, and condensation reactions lead to the formation of farnesyl diphosphate. The prenyltransferases involved specifically form double bonds in the *trans* configuration.

Formation of dolichyl phosphate (Fig. 2). Stepwise condensations of farnesyl diphosphate with several isopentenyl-diphosphate or dimethylallyl-diphosphate units and a final reduction give rise to dolichyl phosphate, a polyisoprenoid compound in which the majority of the double bonds are in the *cis* configuration. Dolichyl phosphate and dolichyl diphosphate, owing to their solubility in lipids, are able to pass through membranes. Dolichyl phosphate acts as the 'carrier lipid' in the assembly of diphosphate-linked oligosaccharides to protein, and it is also the acceptor of mannose and glucose from GDP-Man and UDPGlc, respectively. Mannosylphosphodolichol and glucosylphosphodolichol are the sugar donors in the synthesis of asparagine-linked oligosaccharides (page 182).

Formation of squalene, lanosterol and cholesterol (Fig. 3). In the presence of farnesyl-diphosphate farnesyltransferase (2.5.1.21), 2 molecules of farnesyl diphosphate condense to yield presqualene diphosphate. The polymeric form of the enzyme also catalyzes the reduction of presqualene diphosphate by NADPH to squalene, with the splitting off of pyrophosphate. The conversion of squalene to lanosterol takes place in 2 steps: epoxidation of squalene, catalyzed by a mixed-function oxidase – a reaction in which dioxygen is consumed –, followed by enzymatic cyclization of (S)-2,3-epoxysqualene to lanosterol.

The enzymatic conversion of lanosterol to cholesterol involves the following processes: reduction of the double bond in position 24, removal of 3 methyl groups (2 from C-4 and 1 from C-14), and shift of the double bond in the ring system from position 8 to position 5. The exact sequence in which these reactions occur is not known. The enzymes responsible are generally considered to be membrane-asso-

Fig. 1   *Formation of polyisoprenoids*

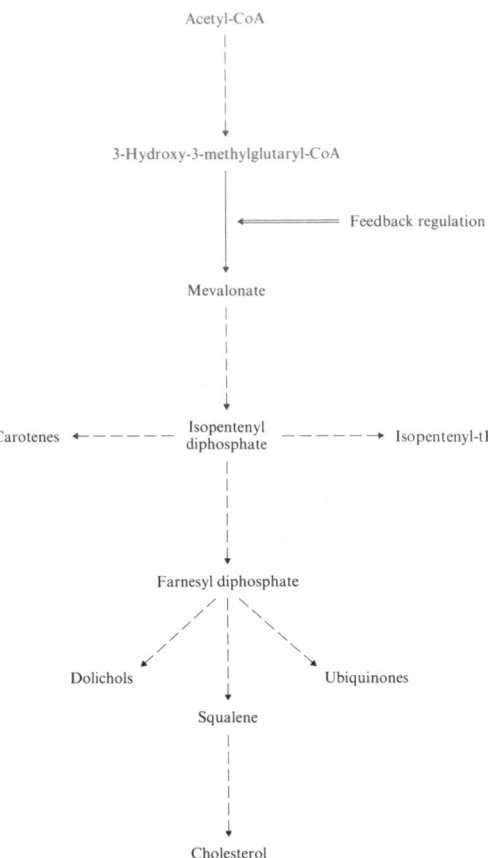

Fig. 2   *Biosynthesis of dolichyl phosphate*

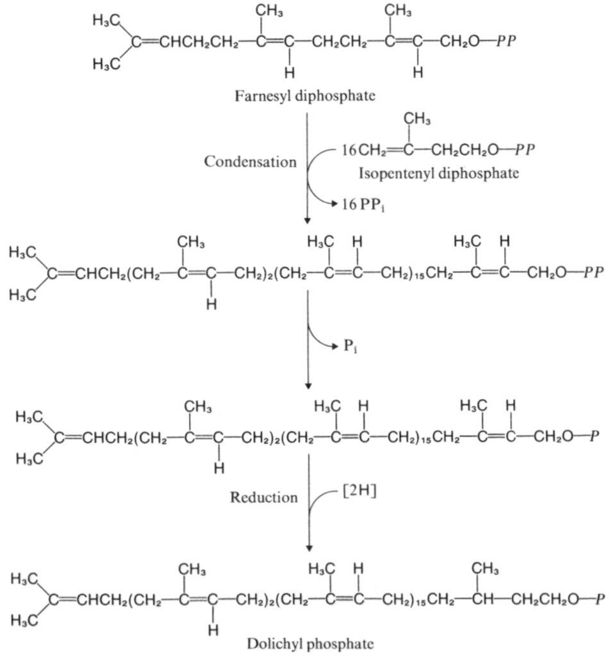

Fig. 3 *Biosynthesis of cholesterol*

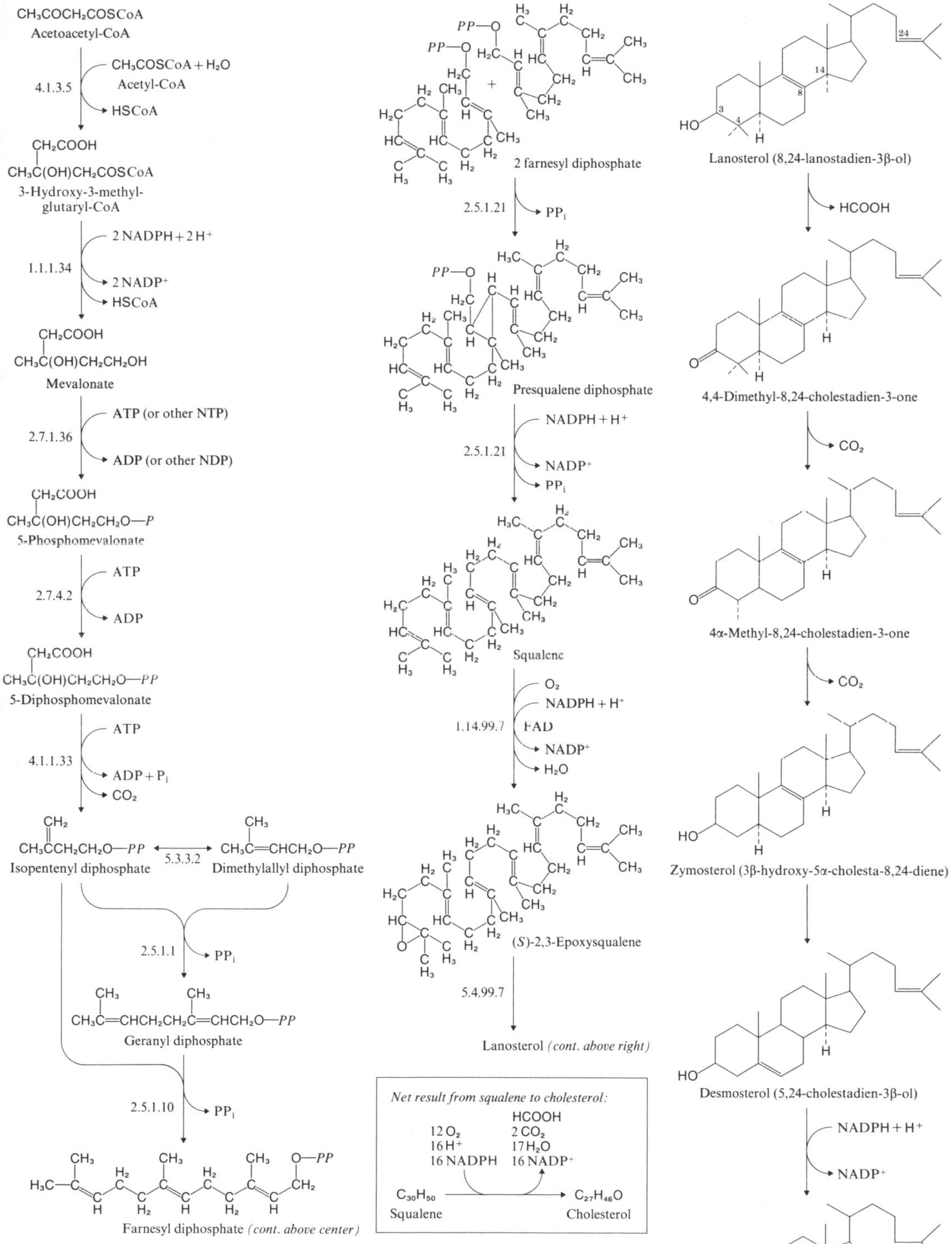

CH₃COCH₂COSCoA
Acetoacetyl-CoA

4.1.3.5
CH₃COSCoA + H₂O Acetyl-CoA
HSCoA

CH₂COOH
CH₃C(OH)CH₂COSCoA
3-Hydroxy-3-methyl-glutaryl-CoA

1.1.1.34
2 NADPH + 2 H⁺
2 NADP⁺
HSCoA

CH₂COOH
CH₃C(OH)CH₂CH₂OH
Mevalonate

2.7.1.36
ATP (or other NTP)
ADP (or other NDP)

CH₂COOH
CH₃C(OH)CH₂CH₂O—P
5-Phosphomevalonate

2.7.4.2
ATP
ADP

CH₂COOH
CH₃C(OH)CH₂CH₂O—PP
5-Diphosphomevalonate

4.1.1.33
ATP
ADP + Pᵢ
CO₂

CH₂
CH₃CCH₂CH₂O—PP
Isopentenyl diphosphate
5.3.3.2
CH₃
CH₃C=CHCH₂O—PP
Dimethylallyl diphosphate

2.5.1.1
PPᵢ

CH₃   CH₃
CH₃C=CHCH₂CH₂C=CHCH₂O—PP
Geranyl diphosphate

2.5.1.10
PPᵢ

CH₃   CH₃   CH₃   O—PP
H₃C—C═C—C—C═C—C—C═C—CH₂
    H H₂ H H₂ H
Farnesyl diphosphate *(cont. above center)*

2 farnesyl diphosphate

2.5.1.21
PPᵢ

Presqualene diphosphate

2.5.1.21
NADPH + H⁺
NADP⁺
PPᵢ

Squalene

1.14.99.7
O₂
NADPH + H⁺
FAD
NADP⁺
H₂O

(S)-2,3-Epoxysqualene

5.4.99.7

Lanosterol *(cont. above right)*

Net result from squalene to cholesterol:

	HCOOH
12 O₂	2 CO₂
16 H⁺	17 H₂O
16 NADPH	16 NADP⁺

C₃₀H₅₀ ⟶ C₂₇H₄₆O
Squalene   Cholesterol

Lanosterol (8,24-lanostadien-3β-ol)
HCOOH

4,4-Dimethyl-8,24-cholestadien-3-one
CO₂

4α-Methyl-8,24-cholestadien-3-one
CO₂

Zymosterol (3β-hydroxy-5α-cholesta-8,24-diene)

Desmosterol (5,24-cholestadien-3β-ol)
NADPH + H⁺
NADP⁺

Cholesterol (5-cholesten-3β-ol)

Enzymes involved:
1.1.1.34 Hydroxymethylglutaryl-CoA reductase (NADPH)
1.14.99.7 Squalene monooxygenase
2.5.1.1 Dimethylallyl*trans*transferase
2.5.1.10 Geranyl*trans*transferase
2.5.1.21 Farnesyl-diphosphate farnesyltransferase
2.7.1.36 Mevalonate kinase
2.7.4.2 Phosphomevalonate kinase
4.1.1.33 Diphosphomevalonate decarboxylase
4.1.3.5 Hydroxymethylglutaryl-CoA synthase
5.3.3.2 Isopentenyl-diphosphate Δ-isomerase
5.4.99.7 Lanosterol synthase

Fig. 4   *Formation of cholesterol esters*

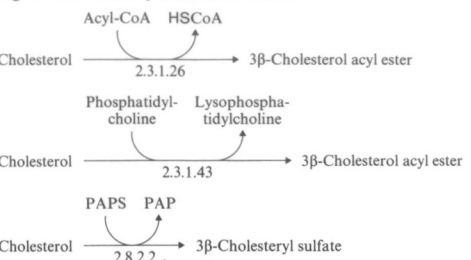

PAPS   Adenosine 3'-phosphate 5'-phosphosulfate
PAP   Adenosine 3',5'-bisphosphate

Enzymes involved:

2.3.1.26   Cholesterol acyltransferase
2.3.1.43   Phosphatidylcholine–sterol acyltransferase
2.8.2.2   Alcohol sulfotransferase

ciated and localized in the microsomal fraction. Several of the more than 20 individual steps seem to rely on specific sterol-carrier proteins (SCP). One possible biosynthetic pathway is shown in Figure 3.

Cholesterol can be synthesized in practically all vertebrate tissues, primarily in the liver, intestine, skin, adrenal cortex and gonads. In most animals the liver is the major site of synthesis, followed by the intestine and the skin. Cholesterol synthesis does not take place in erythrocytes and is reduced to extremely low rates in nerve and brain after myelination is completed. Cholesterol is a component of cell membranes and subcellular membrane structures and is of importance as a starting material for the formation of steroid hormones in the adrenal cortex and gonads (page 150) and bile acids (page 104).

Formation of cholesterol esters (Fig. 4). Within cells, cholesterol esters are generally formed with the aid of the microsomal cholesterol acyltransferase. Highest activity of this enzyme is found in the intestine, but it is also present in the liver and most other tissues.

In plasma, cholesterol accepted from peripheral cells by HDL particles receives the fatty-acid residues of phospholipids in the presence of phosphatidylcholine–sterol acyltransferase. The most important acyl-group donor is the C-2 position of phosphatidylcholine. By this reaction disc-like 'nascent' HDL change to spherical particles.

Sulfatation of cholesterol – with adenosine 3'-phosphate 5'-phosphosulfate as donor of the sulfate group (see also page 79) – takes place in the cytosol of many tissues, especially in the liver, adrenal cortex and gonads. Cholesteryl sulfate is a precursor of pregnenolone sulfate, as well as dehydroepiandrosterone sulfate and other steroid hormones (page 150).

Reviews

· RILLING, H. C., The mechanism of the condensation reactions of cholesterol biosynthesis, *Biochem. Soc. Trans.*, **13**, 997 (1985).
· GOAD, L. J., Cholesterol biosynthesis and metabolism, in MAKIN, H. L. (Ed.), *Biochemistry of Steroid Hormones*, 2nd ed., Blackwell, Oxford, 1984, page 20.
· NORUM et al., Transport of cholesterol, *Physiol. Rev.*, **63**, 1343 (1983).
· SCHROEPFER, G. J., Sterol biosynthesis, *Ann. Rev. Biochem.*, **51**, 555 (1982).
· SCHROEPFER, G. J., Sterol biosynthesis, *Ann. Rev. Biochem.*, **50**, 585 (1981).
· WALSH, C., *Enzymatic Reaction Mechanisms*, Freeman, San Francisco, 1979.
· NES and MCKEAN, *Biochemistry of Steroids and Other Isopentenoids*, University Park Press, Baltimore, 1977.
· BEYTIA and PORTER, Biochemistry of polyisoprenoid biosynthesis, *Ann. Rev. Biochem.*, **45**, 113 (1976).
· BLOCH, K., On the evolution of a biosynthetic pathway, in KORNBERG et al. (Ed.), *Reflections on Biochemistry*, Pergamon, Oxford, 1976, page 143.
· GATT and BARENHOLZ, Enzymes of complex lipid metabolism, *Ann. Rev. Biochem.*, **42**, 61 (1973).
· BLOCH, K., The biological synthesis of cholesterol, *Science*, **150**, 19 (1965).

Fig. 1   *Metabolism of retinol*

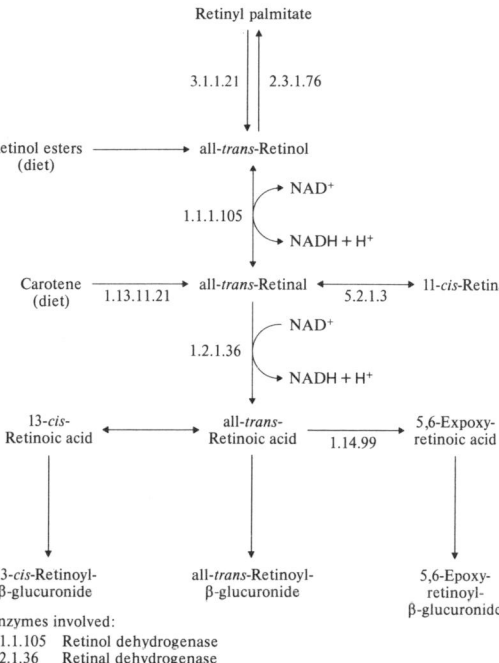

Enzymes involved:

1.1.1.105	Retinol dehydrogenase
1.2.1.36	Retinal dehydrogenase
1.13.11.21	β-Carotene 15,15′-dioxygenase
1.14.99	Retinoic-acid 5,6-epoxidase
2.3.1.76	Retinol fatty-acyltransferase
3.1.1.21	Retinyl-palmitate esterase
5.2.1.3	Retinal isomerase

Fig. 2   *Biochemistry of the visual process*

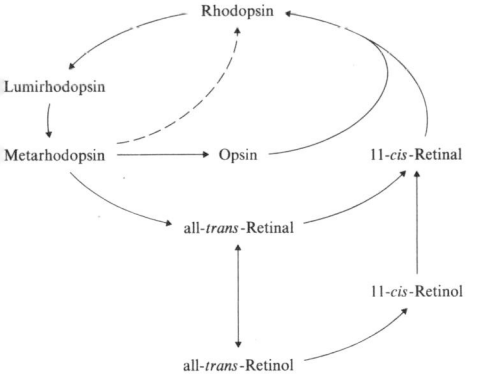

Sources of retinol in the diet are plant carotenoids (mainly β-carotene) and retinol esters deriving from animal tissues. Retinol esters are hydrolyzed in the lumen of the small intestine prior to absorption. The absorption of retinol and β-carotene into the cells of the intestinal mucosa requires the presence of lipids to form micelles. Vitamin E seems to be needed to guard against oxidative destruction. Inside the mucosal cells β-carotene is cleaved at the central double bond to retinal, which is then reduced to retinol (Fig. 1). Retinol is reesterified in the mucosal cells with long-chain, mainly saturated fatty acids. The retinol esters, together with some uncleaved β-carotene – in association with chylomicrons – are then transported in the lymph. Chylomicrons are metabolized in extrahepatic tissues, and the chylomicron remnants containing the retinol esters as well as some β-carotene are taken up by the liver, where conversion of β-carotene to retinol can also take place. Retinol esters in the liver are hydrolyzed and reesterified, mainly with palmitate. These esters are stored inside the liver bound to a lipoprotein complex which is also associated with the hydrolysis of the esters. Free retinol bound to retinol-binding protein and prealbumin is then transported in the bloodstream to the target organs. Mobilization and delivery of retinol are highly regulated.

Retinol is susceptible to several kinds of transformation (Fig. 1), but it is not possible to separate these reactions with regard to elimination or functional activation. A step quite likely of importance for both of these metabolic pathways is the oxidation of retinol to retinoic acid. This compound exerts full vitamin A activity for the maintenance of growth and a healthy epithelium, while it is inactive as regards maintenance of spermatogenesis and the visual process. The supposed intermediate in this conversion – retinal – has been found only in the eye. The further conversion of all-*trans*-retinoic acid may be seen from Figure 1. In addition, the ring can be attacked by oxidation in position 4, leading ultimately to retinotaurine, which may be the final excretion product of vitamin A.

Retinotaurine

Metabolites of retinol probably not involved in elimination of the vitamin comprise the functionally active phosphorylated derivatives, e.g. retinyl phosphate and mannosylretinyl phosphate (page 62).

The molecular mechanism of the function of retinal in night vision is well known (Fig. 2). all-*trans*-Retinal is isomerized to 11-*cis*-retinal, which combines with the visual pigment of the rods – the glycoprotein opsin – to form rhodopsin. By the influence of light, opsin and all-*trans*-retinal are re-formed from this complex via intermediate steps, and the cycle can then begin again. During these reactions the optic nerve is stimulated, in which process hydrolysis of cGMP and the release of Ca^{2+} are involved. 11-*cis*-Retinal is also the prosthetic group of three specific visual pigments of the cones which are responsible for color vision (red, green and blue).

Reviews

· WOLF, G., Multiple functions of vitamin A, *Physiol. Rev.*, **64**, 873 (1984).
· GOODMAN, D. S., Vitamin A metabolism, *Fed. Proc.*, **39**, 2716 (1980).
· DELUCA, H. F., Retinoic acid metabolism, *Fed. Proc.*, **38**, 2519 (1979).
· DELUCA, H. F., Function of the fat-soluble vitamins, *Amer. J. clin. Nutr.*, **28**, 339 (1975).

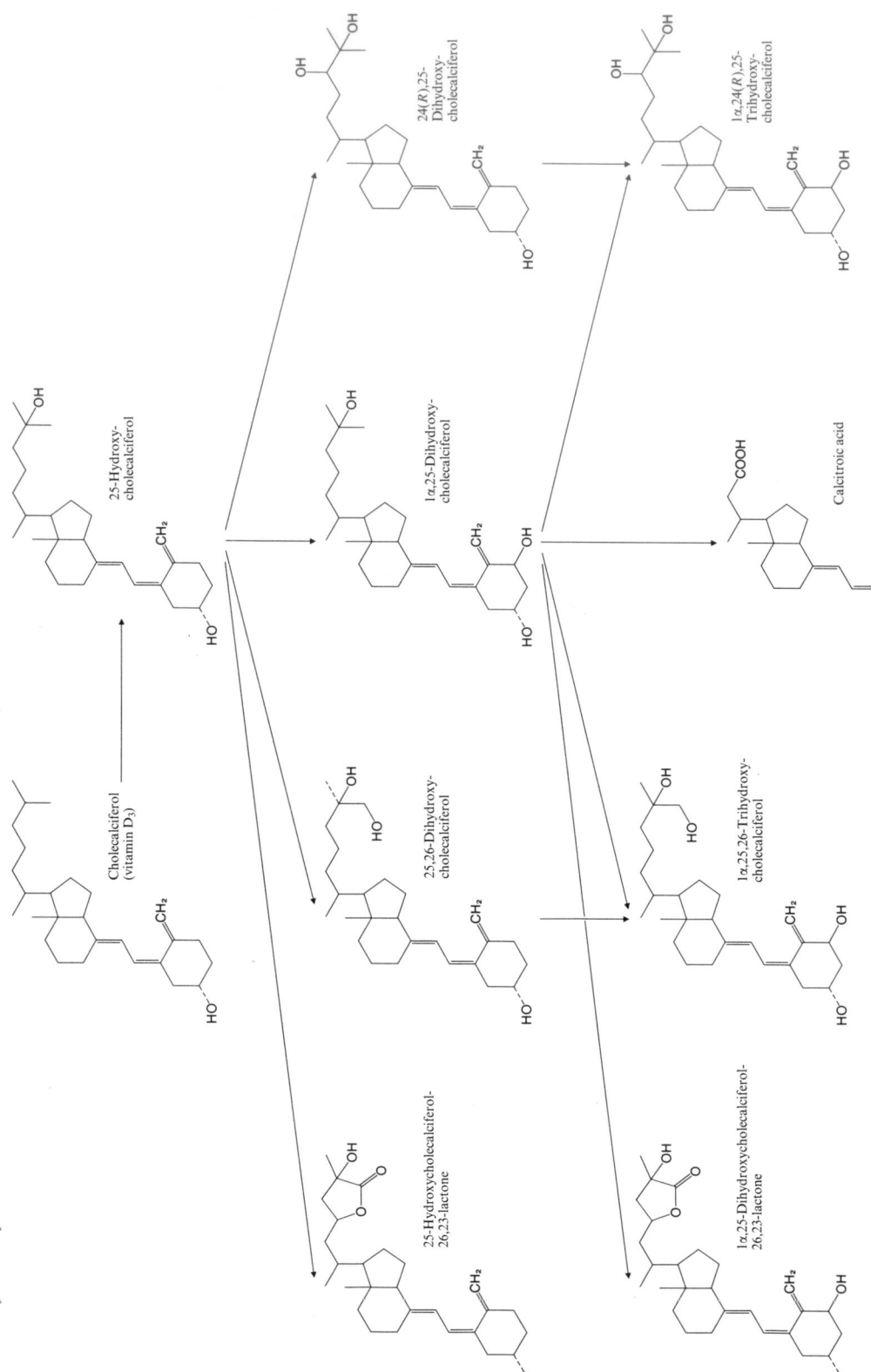

Metabolism of cholecalciferol

Most of present-day knowledge concerning vitamin D metabolism relates to cholecalciferol (vitamin D$_3$), a substance formed in the body; the metabolism of ergocalciferol (vitamin D$_2$), which is derived from the diet, seems to proceed along the same pathways. Physiologically the most important metabolites are the 1α,25-dihydroxylated derivatives, which exert their effects by mechanisms analogous to those of the steroid hormones.

Cholecalciferol (calciol)

The 7-dehydrocholesterol present in the epidermis is split by ultraviolet light to yield provitamin D$_3$. Cholecalciferol, which has the

7-Dehydrocholesterol

Precholecalciferol

Cholecalciferol (vitamin D$_3$)

thermally more stable cis-6,7 form, is formed from this compound by means of thermal energy.

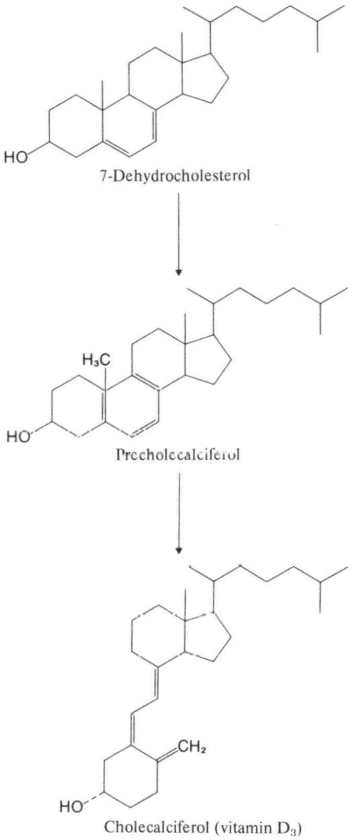

Products of cholecalciferol metabolism are discussed below (for the reactions see facing page).

25-Hydroxycholecalciferol (calcidiol)

Cholecalciferol in man is almost exclusively converted in the liver to the corresponding 25-hydroxy derivative. The enzyme responsible for this – calciol 25-monooxygenase – is localized in the endoplasmic reticulum as well as the mitochondria of the liver. The reaction requires NADPH and dioxygen and takes place via a system dependent on a heme–thiolate protein (P-450).

1α,25-Dihydroxycholecalciferol (calcitriol)

Hydroxylation in the 1α position takes place exclusively in the kidneys. The enzyme responsible, calcidiol 1-monooxygenase (1.14.13.13), is localized in the mitochondria of the renal tubuli. The reaction requires NADPH and dioxygen and takes place via a system dependent on a heme–thiolate protein (P-450) and ferredoxin.

24(R),25-Dihydroxycholecalciferol and 1α,24(R),25-trihydroxycholecalciferol

Hydroxylation at C-24 in the R position takes place in the kidneys, the intestine, the cartilage and possibly other tissues. The enzyme responsible is a mixed-function oxygenase, not further characterized, which apparently hydroxylates only 25-hydroxy metabolites and is localized in the mitochondria. The hydroxy group at C-24 may be reversibly oxidized to the oxo group.

Other metabolites

Several metabolites derive from oxidation at C-23 and/or C-26; the physiological meaning of these pathways is not clear.

The side chain of the hydroxylated metabolites can be oxidatively broken down, whereupon water-soluble acids such as calcitroic acid (1α-hydroxy-24,25,26,27-tetranorcholecalciferol-23-carboxylic acid) are formed, with release of CO$_2$.

Reviews

· KUMAR, R., Metabolism of 1,25 dihydroxyvitamin D$_3$, *Physiol. Rev.*, **64**, 478 (1984).
· DeLUCA and SCHNOES, Vitamin D: recent advances, *Ann. Rev. Biochem.*, **52**, 411 (1983).
· SCHNOES and DeLUCA, Recent progress in vitamin D metabolism and the chemistry of vitamin D metabolites, *Fed. Proc.*, **39**, 2723 (1980).
· DeLUCA and SCHNOES, Metabolism and mechanism of action of vitamin D, *Ann. Rev. Biochem.*, **45**, 631 (1976).

Fig. 1   *Interconnections between the principal pathways in the biosynthesis of the most important corticosteroids, androgens and estrogens*

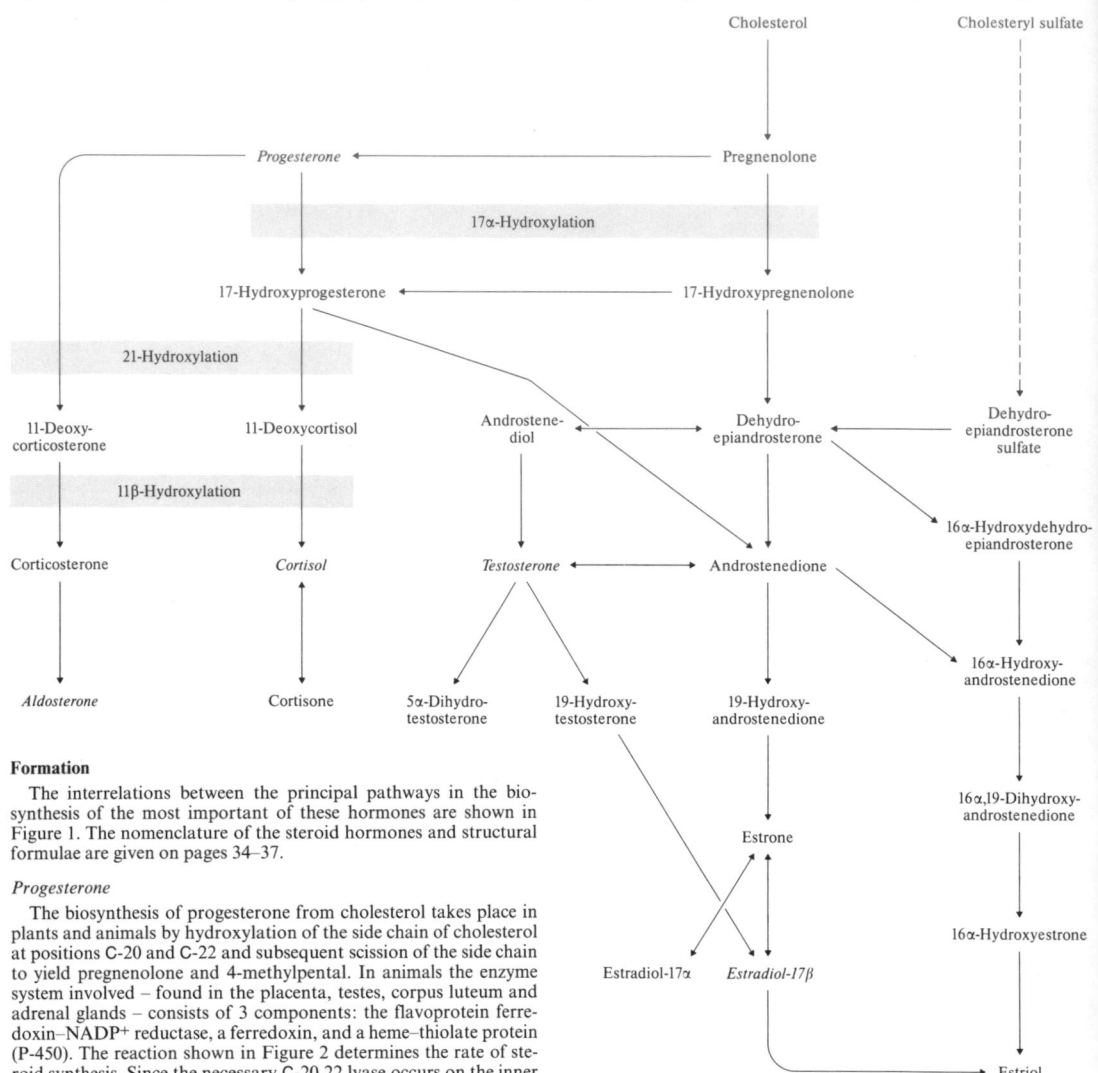

Formation

The interrelations between the principal pathways in the biosynthesis of the most important of these hormones are shown in Figure 1. The nomenclature of the steroid hormones and structural formulae are given on pages 34–37.

Progesterone

The biosynthesis of progesterone from cholesterol takes place in plants and animals by hydroxylation of the side chain of cholesterol at positions C-20 and C-22 and subsequent scission of the side chain to yield pregnenolone and 4-methylpental. In animals the enzyme system involved – found in the placenta, testes, corpus luteum and adrenal glands – consists of 3 components: the flavoprotein ferredoxin–NADP$^+$ reductase, a ferredoxin, and a heme–thiolate protein (P-450). The reaction shown in Figure 2 determines the rate of steroid synthesis. Since the necessary C-20,22 lyase occurs on the inner mitochondrial membrane, the transport of cholesterol to that site can be regarded as the actual limiting factor. The splitting off of the side chain is regulated extracellularly, either by gonadotropins or by ACTH – depending on the tissue – via a complex intracellular mechanism, with the assistance of phospholipids and cAMP-dependent phosphoproteins. In an additional NAD-dependent step pregnen-

olone is oxidized to progesterone by a 3β-hydroxy-Δ^5-steroid dehydrogenase (1.1.1.145) and a steroid Δ-isomerase (5.3.3.1). Which steroids are subsequently formed in which tissue depends on the relative content – or relative activity – of the various enzymes and on the supply of appropriate precursors. Thus corticosteroids are formed exclusively in the adrenal cortex – specific for steroid 11β-monooxygenase (1.14.15.4) –, and androgens and estrogens are formed mainly in the male or female gonads. Androgens, however,

* This chapter on 'Formation and Metabolism of Steroid Hormones' (pages 150–153) has been compiled in collaboration with R. NEHER, CH–4102 Binningen, Switzerland.

Fig. 2   *Cholesterol side-chain cleavage*

$$3\,NADPH + 3\,H^+ + 3\,O_2 \quad 3\,NADP^+ + 4\,H_2O$$

1.14.15.6

Cholesterol ⟶ 22(R)-Hydroxy-cholesterol ⟶ 20,22(R)-Dihydroxy-cholesterol ⟶ Pregnenolone   4-Methyl-pental

Enzyme involved:
1.14.15.6 Cholesterol monooxygenase (side-chain-cleaving)

are also found in the adrenals and ovary, and estrogens in the adrenals and testes, of course with wide quantitative variations depending on the species and functional state.

Corticosteroids

In mammals, the biosynthesis of corticosteroids from progesterone by means of a series of hydroxylases takes place principally in the zona fasciculata and the zona glomerulosa, following a definite sequence of reactions. If the pathway proceeds first via 17-hydroxyprogesterone (or 17-hydroxypregnenolone), subsequent hydroxylation in the 21 and 11β positions leads to 11-deoxycortisol or cortisol; the latter is in equilibrium with the 11-oxo analog cortisone. If 21-hydroxylation to 11-deoxycorticosterone takes place first, essentially only 11β-hydroxylation and 18-hydroxylation to corticosterone or aldosterone, respectively, are possible.

Steroid 17α-monooxygenase (1.14.99.9) and steroid 21-monooxygenase (1.14.99.10) are microsomal enzymes; steroid 11β-monooxygenase (1.14.15.4) and corticosterone 18-monooxygenase (1.14.15.5) are mitochondrial enzymes. Aldosterone is formed exclusively in the zona glomerulosa because it alone contains the enzyme system for the formation of an 18-oxo group. 21-Hydroxylation of progesterone to 11-deoxycorticosterone has also been observed in the kidneys[1].

Corticosterone, cortisol and aldosterone are major hormones secreted by the adrenal cortex. 11-Deoxycorticosterone is not normally secreted but serves as an intermediate. The relative amounts of corticoid hormone produced depend very much on the species. Cortisol predominates in man, apes and dogs, corticosterone in rats, mice and rabbits, while comparable amounts of both these hormones are produced in cattle and pigs. Aldosterone predominates in the bullfrog (*Rana catesbeiana*).

Androgens

The biosynthesis of androgens from pregnenolone or progesterone first requires 17α-hydroxylation of these C_{21} steroids, whose short side chain (C-20 and C-21) may then be split off by a C-17,20 lyase, with the formation of the C_{19} steroids dehydroepiandrosterone

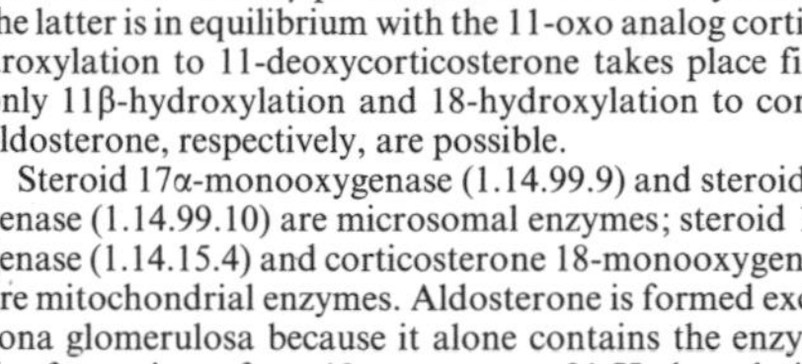

and androstenedione. In contrast to mitochondrial C-20,22 lyase, the C-17,20 lyase – a mixed-function monooxygenase containing P-450 – is located in the microsomal membrane, where it forms a complex with 3β-hydroxy-Δ5-steroid dehydrogenase (1.1.1.145), steroid 17α-monooxygenase (1.14.99.9) and 3(or 17)β-hydroxysteroid dehydrogenase (1.1.1.51).

Androstenedione is a key steroid that is mainly derived from dehydroepiandrosterone in the adrenals and from 17-hydroxyprogesterone in the gonads. Dehydroepiandrosterone sulfate also represents an important source. Androstenedione is converted to testosterone – with the aid of 3(or 17)β-hydroxysteroid dehydrogenase – by reversible reduction of the 17-oxo group to the 17β-hydroxy group; testosterone formation via androstenediol is also possible. A second powerful, yet distinct, androgen – 5α-dihydrotestosterone (Fig. 1) – is formed with the aid of cholestenone 5α-reductase (1.3.1.22) (5α-reductase) almost exclusively at the peripheral site of action.

Estrogens

Biosynthesis of the estrogens – mainly in the ovary and placenta, but also in the adrenals and testes – starts from the same C_{19} steroids as does androgen synthesis. Formation of the estrogens requires successive microsomal oxidation at C-19, which is ultimately split off as formaldehyde, and aromatization of ring A (Fig. 3). The 3-hydroxy group hereby acquires phenolic properties. The enzyme involved is a C-10,19 lyase; P-450 serves as terminal oxidase. Primarily estrone, estradiol-17β, estriol, 16α-hydroxyestrone and, in certain species, also estradiol-17α are formed.

The fetus and placenta are often regarded as a metabolic unit because they are mutually complementary in the biosynthesis of steroid hormones, especially estriol[2]. Because the fetus lacks 3β-hydroxy-Δ5-steroid dehydrogenase (1.1.1.145) it is dependent on the placenta for its supply of 3-oxo-4-ene steroids. On the other hand,

Fig. 3 *Aromatization of 19-oxotestosterone*

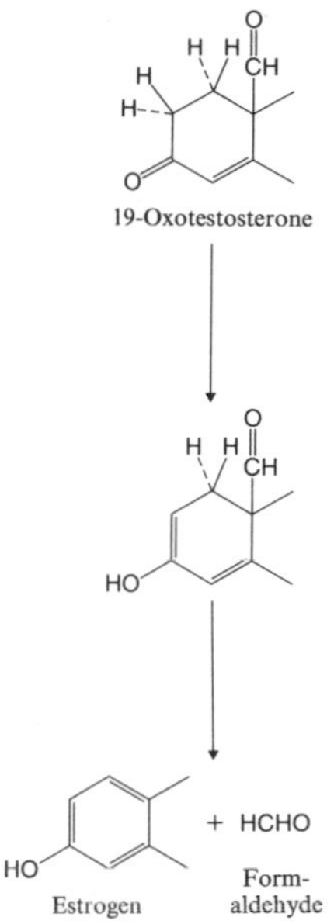

19-Oxotestosterone

HO

+ HCHO
Form-
aldehyde

Estrogen

the placenta shows no C-17,20-lyase activity, so that for estrogen synthesis in the placenta, C_{19} steroids have to be supplied by the fetus and mother. The principal pathway of estriol synthesis proceeds via the 16α-hydroxylation of dehydroepiandrosterone sulfate, of which only the fetal liver is capable, and not the placenta. The release of sulfate from 16α-hydroxydehydroepiandrosterone sulfate then takes place in the placenta with the aid of steryl-sulfatase (3.1.6.2), and the free compound is aromatized to 16α-hydroxyestrone and reduced to estriol.

Metabolism

Steroid hormones are not broken down completely; the ring system is retained. As already mentioned in the section on biosynthesis of androgens, the C_{19} steroids are formed from the C_{21} steroids by the splitting off of the short side chain (C-20 and C-21). Further reactions are the hydrogenation of the double bond in ring A, the introduction of hydroxy groups into various positions and the hydrogenation or dehydrogenation of oxygen functions, of which the hydrogenation of oxo groups is the most important. Hydroxy groups can form conjugates with glucose, glucuronic acid and/or sulfuric acid, by which means a special compartmentation or an easier excretion is made possible. The most important modifications of C_{21} and C_{19} steroids can be seen from Figures 4 and 5.

While the *reduction of steroids unsaturated in ring A* to the 5β form almost always renders them biologically inactive, the formation of the 5α form is not as a rule linked with the loss of biological activity, though probably with qualitative changes. For the reduction of C_{19} steroids to the 5β-androstanes, specific β-reductases accept exclusively 17-β-glucuronides, converting them to 17β-hydroxy-5β-androstane-17-β-D-glucuronide-3-one derivatives. On the other hand, 5α-reductase accepts only free, unconjugated C_{19} steroids. The saturation of ring A as a rule represents the rate-limiting step of metabolism. If it is brought about by reductases of eukaryotes, it is irreversible.

The *introduction of hydroxy groups* takes place with a P-450-dependent enzyme system that is located either in the mitochondria (11β-hydroxylase and 18-hydroxylase) or on the microsomes. The hydroxylase content is highest in the liver, where the activity and specificity of most hydroxylases are also differentiated according to sex.

Hydrogenation and dehydrogenation of oxygen functions. After the saturation of ring A, reduction of the 3-oxo group takes place by the action of 3α-hydroxysteroid dehydrogenase (1.1.1.50) or 3(or 17)β-hydroxysteroid dehydrogenase (1.1.1.51). These enzymes require NADPH or NADH as a cofactor and have no marked substrate

Fig. 4 *Important reactions of the C_{21} steroids*

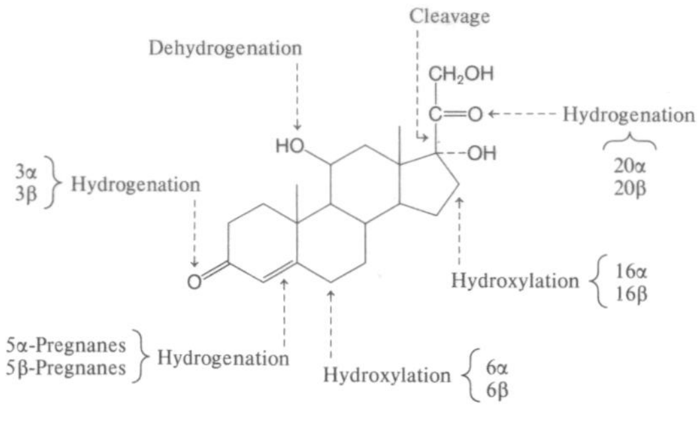

Fig. 5 *Important reactions of the C_{19} steroids*

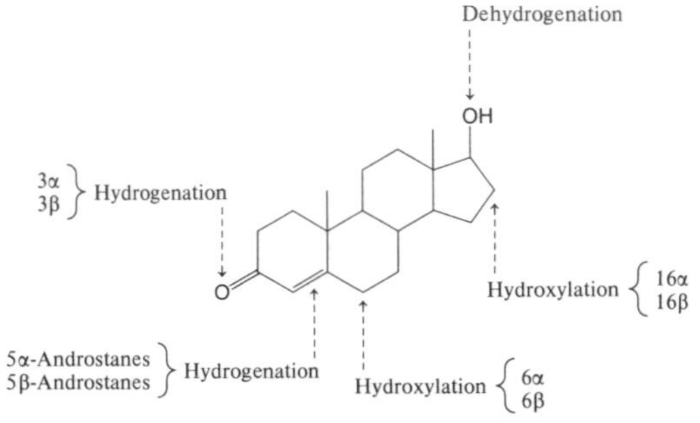

Fig. 6 *Forms of aldosterone*

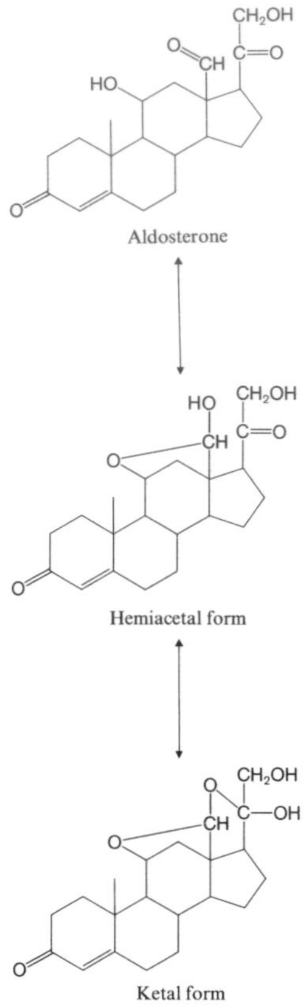

specificity. In man, 3α-hydroxysteroid dehydrogenase predominates.

Microsomal 11β-hydroxysteroid dehydrogenase (1.1.1.146) is responsible for the formation of 11β-hydroxypregnenes. The oxygen function at C-17 is converted either by testosterone 17β-dehydrogenase (NADP+) (1.1.1.64) or estradiol 17β-dehydrogenase (1.1.1.62). 20α-Hydroxysteroid dehydrogenase (included in 1.1.1.62) inactivates progesterone in the ovary.

The *corticosteroids* are metabolized and inactivated mainly in the liver, specifically by reduction of the double bond in ring A and of the oxo groups at C-3 and C-20. They are then excreted mostly as 3-glucuronides, and to a lesser extent as 21-sulfates, by the kidneys or also, in some species, via the bile.

Corticosterone

Corticosterone (compound B) and its 11-oxo analog (11-dehydrocorticosterone, compound A) are reduced by stages to 5β- and 5α-dihydro derivatives (5β-DH, 5α-DH) and then to the tetrahydro derivatives, primarily to 5β-THB, but also to 5β-THA and 5α-THB. The less effective reduction at the 20-oxo group can lead to 20α- or 20β-hydroxy derivatives at each stage.

Cortisol and cortisone

The metabolism of cortisol and cortisone as well as that of their precursors 17-hydroxyprogesterone and 11-deoxycortisol follow the same pattern as that of corticosterone metabolism. By the introduction of a 6β-hydroxy group into the cortisol molecule the compound is rendered easily water-soluble. 21-Deoxycortisone metabolites can be obtained from 21-deoxycortisone, a by-product of corticosteroid biosynthesis. Moreover, the tetrahydro derivatives formed in the adrenals themselves are mainly the 3β-hydroxy derivatives of 5α-pregnanes, in contrast to the 3α-hydroxy derivatives of the 5β-pregnanes of the liver. Oxidation of the hydroxy group in position C-21 of β-cortol or β-cortolone to the carboxy group leads to β-cortolic acid or β-cortolonic acid, respectively, both of which are excreted as conjugates in the urine[3].

In the steroids with a 17α-hydroxy group in the vicinity of a 20-hydroxy or 20-oxo group, another important breakdown reaction catalyzed by a C-17,20 lyase supervenes. This enzyme splits off the C_2 side chain, forming 17-oxosteroids (page 151). The C-17,20 lyase is found – together with 3(or 17)β-hydroxysteroid dehydrogenase (1.1.1.51), which can reversibly reduce the 17-oxo group – in the adrenals, gonads, placenta, liver and kidneys.

Aldosterone

In solution, aldosterone (Fig. 6) is in equilibrium with the tautomeric forms (hemiacetal and ketal), in which the 18-aldehyde group is largely protected[4]. Aldosterone, like the other corticosteroids, is reduced by stages to the dihydro and tetrahydro derivatives. The most important metabolite in the urine is 3α,5β-tetrahydroaldosterone with a glucuronide residue at C-3. In addition, the 18-β-D-glucuronide of the otherwise unchanged steroid is excreted in the urine. It is relatively resistant to β-glucuronidase (3.2.1.31) but can be readily cleaved at pH 1. Free aldosterone is present only in very small amounts in the urine, as is the case with the hexahydro derivative and its 21-deoxy derivative.

Androgens

The C_{19} steroids are metabolized chiefly in the liver, and partly in the prostate and skin, specifically by reduction in ring A at C-3 to dihydro and tetrahydro derivatives; this reduction and the reversible reduction of the 17-oxo group are described on the preceding page. Androsterone and 3α-hydroxy-5β-androstan-17-one are the principal metabolites. The metabolite pattern is certainly highly dependent on the species and partly also on sex and functional state and on whether free testosterone or testosterone 17-glucuronide is reduced. Thus male rats produce substantially more 5β metabolites than female animals. In man the ratio is approximately 1:1; myxedema patients, however, excrete up to 8 times more 5β metabolites than 5α metabolites. In C_{19} steroids with 11β-hydroxy or 11-oxo groups the ratio shifts in favor of the 5α metabolites. Similar differences are involved in the reduction of the 3-oxo group in the 4,5-dihydro metabolites 5α- or 5β-androstane-3,17-dione. In human tissue the 3-oxo group is reduced mainly to the 3α-hydroxy group. In rats the ratio between 3α and 3β reduction is sex-specific: 2.3–2.5 in the liver of male animals, 0.12–0.16 in the liver of female animals. 5α-Androstane-3α,17β-diol is relatively easily oxidized to yield 5α-dihydrotestosterone, which is an active androgen. The 17-oxo group is reduced mainly to the 17β-hydroxy group in man, to the 17α-hydroxy group in rabbits, and in rats the reduction is sex-dependent.

Among the relatively rare metabolites can be mentioned 6β-, 15β- and 16α-hydroxy derivatives, and also certain 16-dehydroandrostenes which have a musky odor.

The 3α-hydroxy C_{19} steroids are excreted in the urine mainly as 3-glucuronides, while the 3β-hydroxy compounds are esterified to 3-sulfates. Sulfate formation predominates in the androgen metabolism of infants and toddlers, glucuronide formation in that of adults.

In men, about two-thirds of the oxosteroids in the urine are metabolites of steroids of the adrenal cortex; the remainder are derived from the gonads. Also worth mentioning are the 3β-hydroxysteroids (chiefly from adrenal dehydroepiandrosterone), which constitute up to 20% of the 17-oxosteroids in the urine.

Progesterone

Progesterone is very rapidly metabolized mainly in the liver, specifically by reduction of the double bond in ring A and of the oxo groups at C-3 and C-20, with the formation of a series of 5β- and 5α-pregnane derivatives which are excreted as glucuronides mainly in the urine, the remainder via the bile and feces. The principal metabolite is 5β-pregnane-3α,20α-diol. The urine of pregnant women may contain up to 100 mg/d progesterone metabolites, especially 5β-pregnane-3α,20α-diol, 3α-hydroxy-5β-pregnan-20-one, 5β-pregnane-3β,20α-diol and 5α-pregnane-3α,20α-diol ('allopregnanediol'). Yet more 5β- and 5α-pregnane derivatives can be detected in small concentrations, including those with additional hydroxy groups in the α position at C-6 and C-16. These compounds are largely excreted as glucuronides or sulfates.

A special feature in the metabolism of progesterone is the selective reduction of the 20-oxo group in the ovaries and placenta, resulting in 20α- and 20β-hydroxy derivatives with weak gestagen activity. The equilibrium between progesterone and its 20α-hydroxy derivative is regulated by 20α-hydroxysteroid dehydrogenase (included in 1.1.1.62). This equilibrium undergoes a shift – in the ovary but also in the endometrium, to an extent depending on menstrual phase or stage of pregnancy – in favor of the reduced form and thus determines local gestagen activity.

Estrogens

The interrelations between estradiol, estrone and estriol can be seen from Figure 1 (page 150). Hydroxylations in positions 2, 15α and 16α take place in further conversions that lead to less active compounds. 15α-Hydroxyestriol is an important metabolite of the fetal liver. The estrogens cannot, however, be hydrogenated in ring A like other steroid hormones.

Conjugation with glucuronic acid or sulfate may take place at the C-3, C-16 and C-17 positions of the estrogens. Estrogen metabolites are present in the urine mainly as glucuronides, but also partly as double conjugates of sulfuric acid and glucuronic acid. Estriol 16-glucuronide is the principal metabolite during pregnancy.

References

Reviews:

- MAKIN, H.L. (Ed.), *Biochemistry of Steroid Hormones*, 2nd ed., Blackwell, Oxford, 1984.
- TRÄGER, L., *Steroidhormone*, Springer, Berlin, 1977.
- DORFMAN and UNGAR, *Metabolism of Steroid Hormones*, Academic Press, New York, 1965.

Special references:

[1] WINKEL et al., *Proc. nat. Acad. Sci. (Wash.)*, **77**, 7069 (1980).
[2] DICZFALUSY, E., *J. Endocr.*, **79**, 3P (1978).
[3] MONDER and BRADLOW, *Recent Progr. Hormone Res.*, **36**, 345 (1980).
[4] NEHER, R., *J. Endocr.*, **81**, 25P (1979).

Essential amino acids cannot be synthesized by man and must therefore be assimilated with the diet. They are formed by bacteria, yeasts and plants in complex processes.

Essential amino acids	Nonessential amino acids
Leucine	Alanine
Isoleucine	Aspartic acid
Valine	Glutamic acid
Methionine	Cysteine (if sufficient methionine is present)
Phenylalanine	Tyrosine (if sufficient phenylalanine is present)
Tryptophan	Proline
Threonine	Serine
Lysine	Glycine
Histidine	Histidine (for adults)
Arginine	Arginine (for adults)

Glutamic acid

This amino acid is of central importance in the metabolic pathways of amino groups, on the one hand as a starting material for the synthesis of various nitrogen-containing compounds, and on the other hand because of its involvement in transaminations. It can be formed either by transfer of the amino group from any other amino acid to 2-oxoglutarate or – the reverse of the reaction described on

COOH $\quad$ NAD(P)H $\quad$ COOH
| $\quad\quad$ + H$^+$ $\quad$ NAD(P)$^+$ $\quad$ |
CH$_2$ $\quad\quad\quad\quad\quad\quad\quad\quad$ CH$_2$
| $\quad\quad\quad\quad\quad\quad\quad\quad\quad$ |
CH$_2$ $\quad\quad\quad\quad\quad\quad\quad\quad$ CH$_2$
| $\quad\quad\quad\quad\quad\quad\quad\quad\quad$ |
CO $\quad\quad$ NH$_3$ $\quad$ H$_2$O $\quad$ CH(NH$_2$)
| $\quad\quad\quad\quad$ 1.4.1.2 $\quad\quad\quad$ |
COOH $\quad\quad\quad\quad\quad\quad\quad\quad$ COOH

2-Oxo-glutarate $\quad\quad\quad\quad\quad\quad$ L-Glutamic acid

Enzyme involved:
1.4.1.2 Glutamate dehydrogenase

page 110 – by reductive amination of 2-oxoglutarate. Glutamic acid is the only amino acid in animal tissues that can be synthesized directly from ammonia and the appropriate carbon skeleton (in the form of the 2-oxo acid). All other nonessential amino acids are formed from the corresponding 2-oxo acids by transamination with glutamic acid.

Glutamine

Glutamine is of importance for the transport of ammonia from peripheral tissue to the liver ('urea cycle', page 110), as a starting material in pyrimidine synthesis (page 172), and as NH$_2$ donor in purine synthesis (page 169) and in the formation of glucosamine

COOH $\quad\quad\quad\quad$ ADP $\quad$ CO(NH$_2$)
| $\quad$ NH$_3$ $\quad$ ATP $\quad$ + P$_i$ $\quad$ |
CH$_2$ $\quad\quad\quad\quad\quad\quad\quad\quad$ CH$_2$
| $\quad\quad\quad\quad\quad\quad\quad\quad\quad$ |
CH$_2$ $\quad\quad\quad\quad\quad\quad\quad\quad$ CH$_2$
| $\quad\quad$ 6.3.1.2 $\quad\quad\quad\quad$ |
CH(NH$_2$) $\quad\quad\quad\quad\quad\quad\quad$ CH(NH$_2$)
| $\quad\quad\quad\quad\quad\quad\quad\quad\quad$ |
COOH $\quad\quad\quad\quad\quad\quad\quad\quad$ COOH

L-Glutamic acid $\quad\quad\quad\quad\quad$ L-Glutamine

(page 132). It is formed by the amidation of glutamic acid with the aid of glutamate–ammonia ligase (6.3.1.2). The concentration of glutamine in blood is higher than that of any other amino acid.

Glutathione

Glutathione is formed intracellularly in 2 steps, catalyzed by glutamate–cysteine ligase (6.3.2.2) and glutathione synthase (6.3.2.3) (Fig. 1). Glutathione can be recycled to glutamate via 5-oxoproline. This breakdown of glutathione occurs by the action of a transpeptidase (2.3.2.2), which catalyzes the transfer of the γ-glutamyl moiety to acceptors – amino acids, certain dipeptides or glutathione itself. Glutathione occurs mainly intracellularly, but the major fraction of the transpeptidase is located on the external surface of the cell membranes, and glutathione must be transported through the cell membranes to react. γ-Glutamyl–amino acids formed are then transported into cells and are the substrates for the γ-glutamylcyclotransferase (2.3.2.4), which converts these compounds to the corre-

Fig. 1 *Biosynthesis of glutathione (γ-glutamyl cycle)*

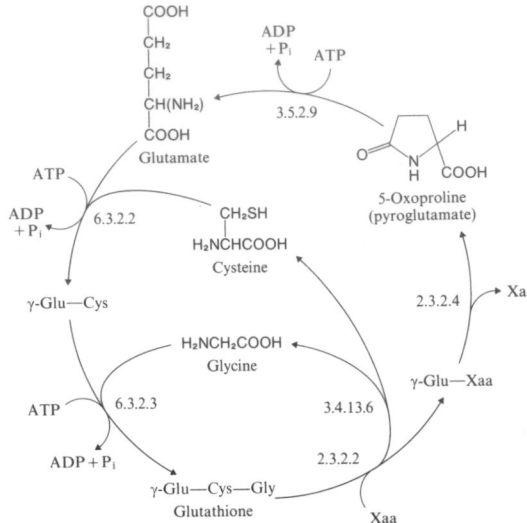

Xaa	Unspecified amino acid	Enzymes involved:
Glu	Glutamic acid	2.3.2.2 γ-Glutamyltransferase
Gly	Glycine	2.3.2.4 γ-Glutamylcyclotransferase
Cys	Cysteine	3.4.13.6 Cysteinyl-glycine dipeptidase
		3.5.2.9 5-Oxoprolinase (ATP-hydrolyzing)
		6.3.2.2 Glutamate–cysteine ligase
		6.3.2.3 Glutathione synthase

sponding amino acids and 5-oxoproline. The cleavage of 5-oxoproline to glutamate is ATP-dependent.

Intracellular glutathione is oxidized by the selenium-containing enzyme glutathione peroxidase (1.11.1.9), which catalyzes the reduction of H$_2$O$_2$ and other peroxides. Glutathione is also converted to oxidized glutathione (GSSG) by transhydrogenation, which involves thiol–disulfide exchanges.

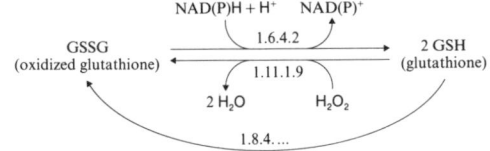

Enzymes involved:
1.6.4.2 Glutathione reductase [NAD(P)H]
1.8.4.1 Glutathione–homocystine transhydrogenase
1.8.4.2 Protein-disulfide reductase (glutathione)
1.8.4.4 Glutathione–cystine transhydrogenase
1.11.1.9 Glutathione peroxidase

Extracellular conversion of glutathione to oxidized glutathione has also been observed; this reaction requires O$_2$ and yields H$_2$O$_2$.

Oxidized glutathione can be reduced to glutathione by glutathione reductase (NAD[P]H) (1.6.4.2); the reaction is essentially irreversible and accounts for the very high GSH:GSSG ratios found in cells.

4-Aminobutyric acid

The neurotransmitter 4(γ)-aminobutyric acid is formed in the nervous system by the decarboxylation of glutamate. The reaction is catalyzed by glutamate decarboxylase (4.1.1.15), an enzyme that is localized in the gray matter, predominantly in the synaptosome fraction.

4-Carboxyglutamic acid

Vitamin K metabolism is necessary for the carboxylation of glutamic-acid residues in vitamin K-dependent proteins. Carboxylation requires vitamin K hydroquinone, dioxygen and carbon dioxide. 4-Carboxyglutamate synthesis is coupled with the oxidation of vitamin K hydroquinone to vitamin K 2,3-epoxide (page 77). The enzyme catalyzing the carboxylation – vitamin K-dependent 4-glutamyl carboxylase – is present in the microsomes of the liver, lung, kidney and some other tissues, but not in those of muscle.

Aspartic acid

Aspartic acid is formed by the transamination of oxaloacetate with the aid of aspartate aminotransferase (2.6.1.1). Asparagine, the acid amide corresponding to glutamine, is formed in a reaction that is analogous to glutamine formation: by amidation of aspartic acid with the aid of aspartate–ammonia ligase (ADP-forming) (6.3.1.4).

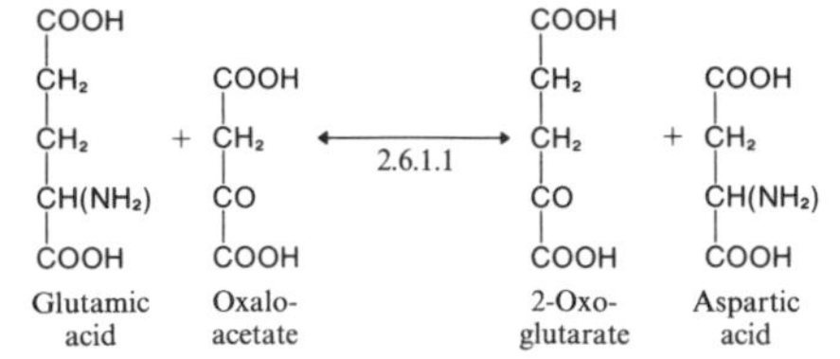

COOH		COOH		COOH		COOH
CH₂	COOH		CH₂	COOH		CH₂	COOH
CH₂ + CH₂		CH₂ + CH₂	
CH(NH₂) CO		CO CH(NH₂)	
COOH COOH		COOH COOH	
Glutamic Oxalo-		2-Oxo- Aspartic	
acid acetate		glutarate acid	

(2.6.1.1)

Alanine

COOH		COOH
CH₂		CH₂
CH₂ + CH₃		CH₂ + CH₃
CH(NH₂) CO		CO CH(NH₂)
COOH COOH		COOH COOH
Glutamic Pyruvate		2-Oxo- Alanine
acid		glutarate

(2.6.1.2)

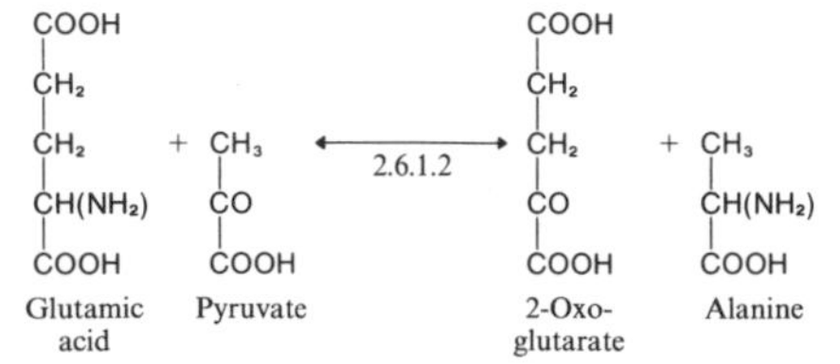

Alanine is formed by the transamination of pyruvate with the aid of alanine aminotransferase (2.6.1.2). The muscle plays an important part in alanine formation. The amino group is supplied primarily by branched-chain amino acids. The formation of glutamate is interposed because, for the amino groups of branched-chain amino acids, 2-oxoglutarate is a better acceptor than pyruvate. Alanine formation in the muscle is an additional means of bringing amino groups from the periphery into the liver.

Proline (Fig. 2)

Proline is formed from ornithine or glutamic acid via glutamate 5-semialdehyde, reversing the degradation pathway (page 121). The reduction of glutamic acid to glutamate 5-semialdehyde seems to proceed via a two-step reaction mechanism involving the unstable glutamate 5-phosphate. The enzymes catalyzing the conversion of glutamic acid to pyrroline-5-carboxylate have not yet been defined in animal cells. The enzyme catalyzing the final step of proline synthesis – pyrroline-5-carboxylate reductase – is of wide tissue distribution and is the only enzyme of proline metabolism in erythrocytes; therefore, proline synthesis in erythrocytes depends on the supply of 1-pyrroline-5-carboxylate from the plasma.

4-Hydroxyproline

The hydroxylation of proline to 4-hydroxyproline does not take place in the free amino acid but at proline residues of certain proteins (page 193). The preferred site of hydroxylation is the proline residue in the third position of the Gly—Pro—Pro triplet of procollagen. The reaction, catalyzed by procollagen-proline,2-oxoglutarate 4-dioxygenase (1.14.11.2), requires Fe²⁺ and ascorbate, in addition to 2-oxoglutarate and dioxygen.

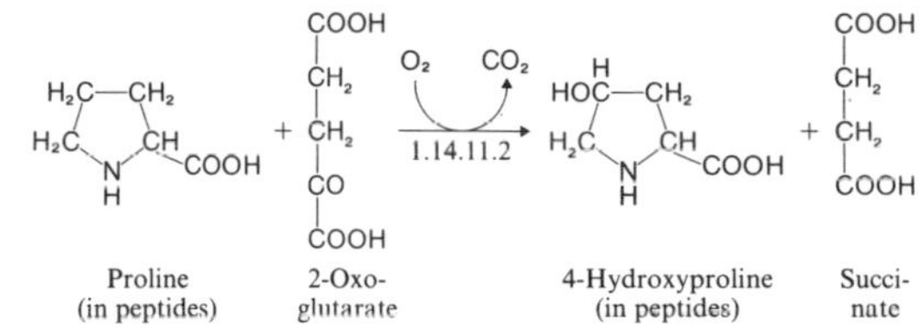

COOH			COOH
H₂C—CH₂	CH₂ O₂ CO₂ H	HOC—CH₂	CH₂
H₂C CH—COOH + CH₂	→ H₂C CH—COOH + CH₂
N CO	1.14.11.2 N COOH
H COOH	H
Proline 2-Oxo-	4-Hydroxyproline Succi-
(in peptides) glutarate	(in peptides) nate

During the reaction, Fe²⁺ is oxidized to Fe³⁺, which becomes bound to the active site of the enzyme, thus inactivating it. In the enzyme-regenerating reaction, enzyme-bound Fe³⁺ is reduced to Fe²⁺ by ascorbate.

Enzyme Fe³⁺ + ascorbate ⟶ Enzyme + Fe²⁺ + dehydroascorbate

By the same mechanism, proline residues can be hydroxylated to 3-hydroxyproline, and lysine to 5-hydroxylysine. The enzymes catalyzing these reactions are procollagen-proline,2-oxoglutarate 3-dioxygenase (1.14.11.7) and procollagen-lysine,2-oxoglutarate 5-dioxygenase (1.14.11.4).

Tyrosine (Fig. 3)

The aromatic ring of tyrosine cannot be synthesized by mammals and must be obtained from the diet in the form of phenylalanine.

The hydroxylation of phenylalanine to tyrosine involves a mixed-function oxygenase, phenylalanine 4-monooxygenase (1.14.16.1), an

Fig. 2 *Biosynthesis of proline*

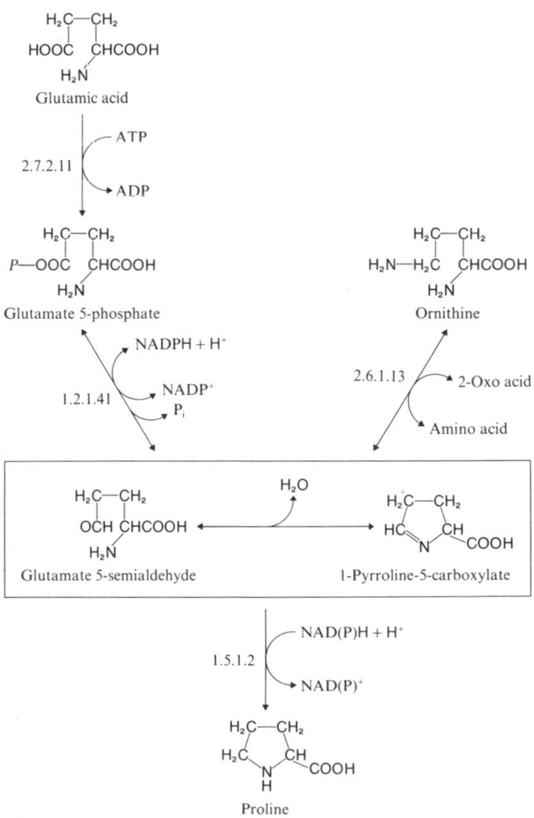

H₂C—CH₂
HOOC CHCOOH
H₂N
Glutamic acid

2.7.2.11 — ATP → ADP

H₂C—CH₂
P—OOC CHCOOH
H₂N
Glutamate 5-phosphate

1.2.1.41 — NADPH + H⁺ → NADP⁺ + Pᵢ

H₂C—CH₂
H₂N—H₂C CHCOOH
H₂N
Ornithine

2.6.1.13 — 2-Oxo acid → Amino acid

H₂C—CH₂
OCH CHCOOH
H₂N
Glutamate 5-semialdehyde

H₂O

H₂C—CH₂
HC CH—COOH
N
1-Pyrroline-5-carboxylate

1.5.1.2 — NAD(P)H + H⁺ → NAD(P)⁺

H₂C—CH₂
H₂C CH—COOH
N
H
Proline

Enzymes involved:
1.2.1.41 Glutamate-5-semialdehyde dehydrogenase
1.5.1.2 Pyrroline-5-carboxylate reductase
2.6.1.13 Ornithine–oxo-acid aminotransferase
2.7.2.11 Glutamate 5-kinase

Fig. 3 *Formation of tyrosine*

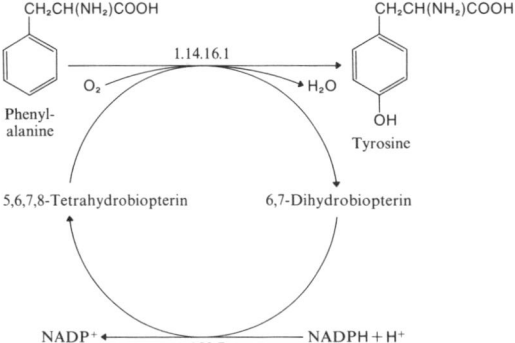

CH₂CH(NH₂)COOH

1.14.16.1

Phenyl-
alanine
O₂ → H₂O

CH₂CH(NH₂)COOH
OH
Tyrosine

5,6,7,8-Tetrahydrobiopterin   6,7-Dihydrobiopterin

NADP⁺ ← 1.6.99.7 ← NADPH + H⁺

Enzymes involved:
1.6.99.7 Dihydropteridine reductase
1.14.16.1 Phenylalanine 4-monooxygenase

Fig. 4 *Biosynthesis of serine and glycine*

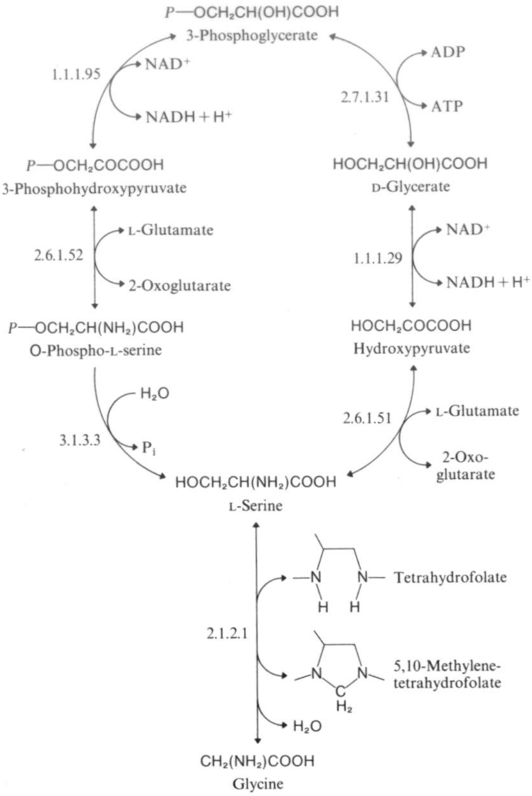

Enzymes involved:
1.1.1.29 Glycerate dehydrogenase
1.1.1.95 Phosphoglycerate dehydrogenase
2.1.2.1   Glycine hydroxymethyltransferase
2.6.1.51 Serine–pyruvate aminotransferase
2.6.1.52 Phosphoserine aminotransferase
2.7.1.31 Glycerate kinase
3.1.3.3   Phosphoserine phosphatase

Fig. 5 *Biosynthesis of histidine in bacteria*

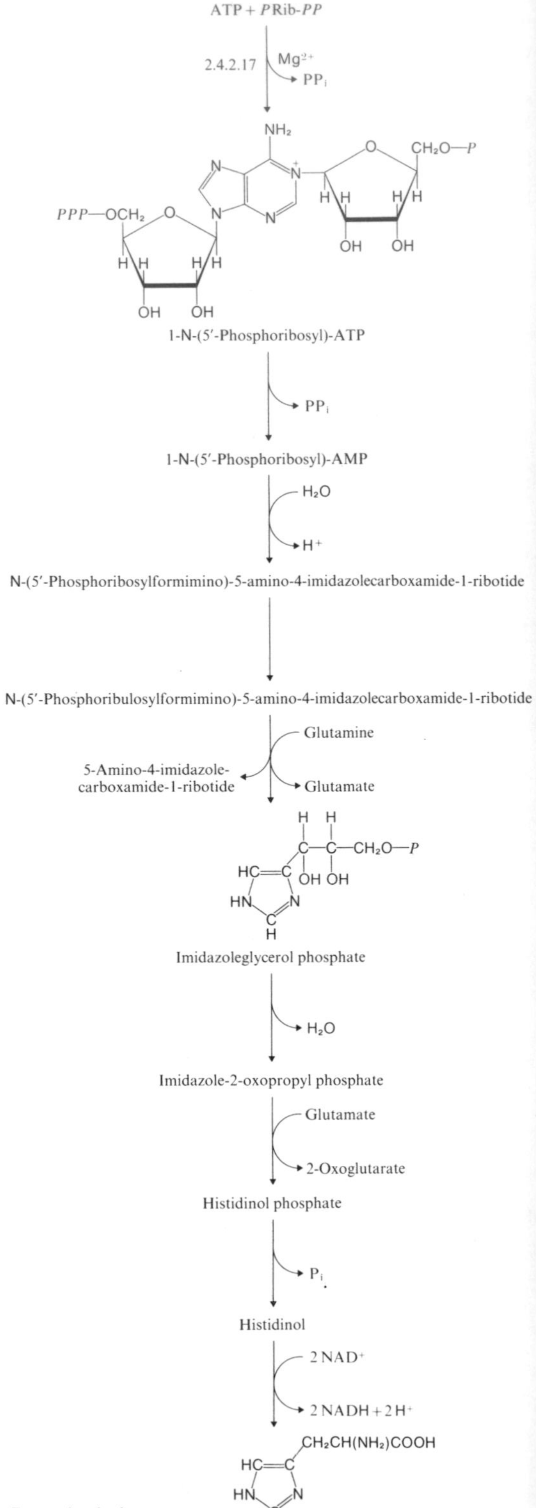

Enzyme involved:
2.4.2.17 ATP phospho-
          ribosyltransferase

iron protein found mainly in the liver microsomes. The reaction requires dioxygen and a reduced cofactor, 5,6,7,8-tetrahydrobiopterin. Regeneration of the cofactor, which takes place by reduction of the quinoid form of dihydrobiopterin with the aid of dihydropteridine reductase (1.6.99.7), is necessary for completion of the reaction.

Cysteine

Cysteine is formed in the reaction pathway described on page 122, given an adequate supply of methionine. Only the SH group of cysteine derives from methionine, the carbon skeleton coming from serine. Cystathionine γ-lyase (4.4.1.1), the enzyme responsible for the last step – cleavage of cystathionine – contains pyridoxal phosphate.

Serine and glycine (Fig. 4)

The carbon skeleton of both amino acids derives from 3-phosphoglycerate. There are two pathways represented in Figure 4: the one via 3-phosphohydroxypyruvate is the more important in mammals. Removal of the hydroxymethyl group from serine gives rise to 5,10-methylenetetrahydrofolate, an important constituent of the one-carbon unit pool.

Histidine (Fig. 5)

The adult human is the only mammalian species that does not have to depend on an alimentary intake of histidine. How histidine is synthesized by man is uncertain – possibly via the pathway detected in *E. coli* and *S. typhimurium*. In the first step (Fig. 5) an unusual reaction gives rise to 1-N-(5′-phosphoribosyl)-ATP, a compound that already contains all the C and N atoms of histidine with the exception of one N atom (the one supplied by glutamine). Possibly compounds with the imidazole ring are also reconverted to histidine in the animal organism.

Carnosine and homocarnosine

The formation of both dipeptides is probably catalyzed by the same enzyme, carnosine synthase (6.3.2.11), with cleavage of ATP to yield AMP and pyrophosphate.

Carnosine is formed in the brain and muscle and consists of β-alanine (3-aminopropionate, a degradation product of pyrimidines [page 129]) and histidine. Homocarnosine is formed in the brain and consists of 4-aminobutyrate and histidine.

Reviews

· MEISTER and ANDERSON, Glutathione, *Ann. Rev. Biochem.*, **52**, 711 (1983).
· KOVACEVIC and McGIVAN, Mitochondrial metabolism of glutamine and glutamate and its physiological significance, *Physiol. Rev.*, **63**, 547 (1983).
· ADAMS and FRANK, Metabolism of proline and the hydroxyprolines, *Ann. Rev. Biochem.*, **49**, 1005 (1980).
· UMBARGER, H. E., Amino acid biosynthesis and its regulation, *Ann. Rev. Biochem.*, **47**, 533 (1978).
· FELIG, P., Amino acid metabolism in man, *Ann. Rev. Biochem.*, **44**, 933 (1975).
· BENDER, D. A., *Amino Acid Metabolism*, Wiley, New York, 1975.
· TRUFFA-BACHI and COHEN, Amino acid metabolism, *Ann. Rev. Biochem.*, **42**, 113 (1973).
· MEISTER, A., *Biochemistry of the Amino Acids*, 2nd ed., Volumes 1 and 2, Academic Press, New York, 1965.

Creatine and creatine phosphate (Fig. 1)

Creatine is formed in the liver and pancreas from arginine, glycine and methionine. After formation it diffuses into the vascular system and is transported by the plasma and erythrocytes to the muscles where it is in equilibrium with creatine phosphate. Creatine phosphate contains a high-energy phosphate bond and is responsible for the energy transport in muscle fiber according to the so-called 'creatine phosphate shuttle'. The basis for the effectiveness of this shuttle is the functional compartmentation of the enzyme creatine kinase (Fig. 2).

Fig. 1   *Formation of creatine, creatine phosphate and creatinine*

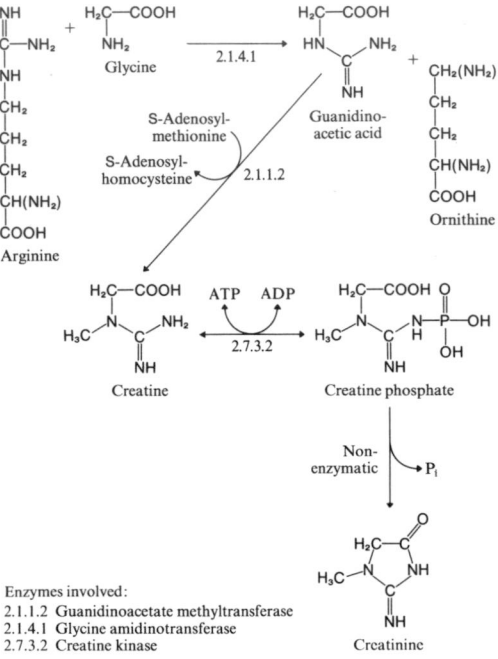

Enzymes involved:
2.1.1.2 Guanidinoacetate methyltransferase
2.1.4.1 Glycine amidinotransferase
2.7.3.2 Creatine kinase

Fig. 2   *Energy transport system of muscle ('creatine phosphate shuttle')*

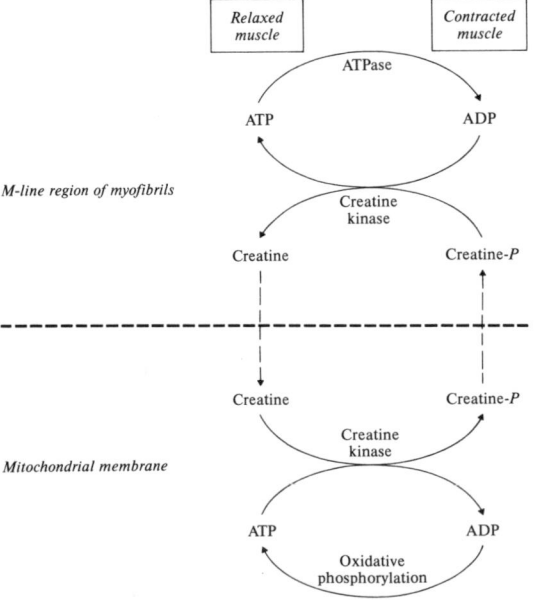

Fig. 3   *Biosynthesis of carnitine*

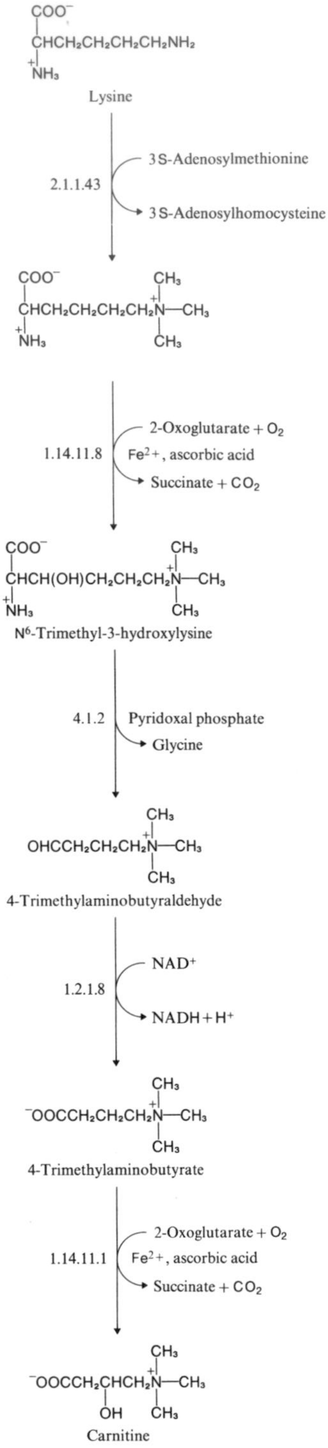

COO^-
$CHCH_2CH_2CH_2CH_2NH_2$
$\overset{+}{N}H_3$
Lysine

2.1.1.43
→ 3 S-Adenosylmethionine
→ 3 S-Adenosylhomocysteine

COO^- CH_3
$CHCH_2CH_2CH_2CH_2\overset{+}{N}{-}CH_3$
$\overset{+}{N}H_3$ CH_3

1.14.11.8
→ 2-Oxoglutarate + O_2
Fe^{2+}, ascorbic acid
→ Succinate + CO_2

COO^- CH_3
$CHCH(OH)CH_2CH_2CH_2\overset{+}{N}{-}CH_3$
$\overset{+}{N}H_3$ CH_3
N^6-Trimethyl-3-hydroxylysine

4.1.2
Pyridoxal phosphate
→ Glycine

CH_3
$OHCCH_2CH_2CH_2\overset{+}{N}{-}CH_3$
CH_3
4-Trimethylaminobutyraldehyde

1.2.1.8
→ NAD$^+$
→ NADH + H$^+$

CH_3
$^-OOCCH_2CH_2CH_2\overset{+}{N}{-}CH_3$
CH_3
4-Trimethylaminobutyrate

1.14.11.1
→ 2-Oxoglutarate + O_2
Fe^{2+}, ascorbic acid
→ Succinate + CO_2

CH_3
$^-OOCCH_2CHCH_2\overset{+}{N}{-}CH_3$
OH CH_3
Carnitine

Enzymes involved:
1.2.1.8   Betaine-aldehyde dehydrogenase
1.14.11.1   γ-Butyrobetaine,2-oxoglutarate dioxygenase
1.14.11.8   Trimethyllysine,2-oxoglutarate dioxygenase
2.1.1.43   Histone-lysine methyltransferase
4.1.2   Aldolase

Fig. 4   *Transfer of one-carbon units (one-carbon group cycle)*

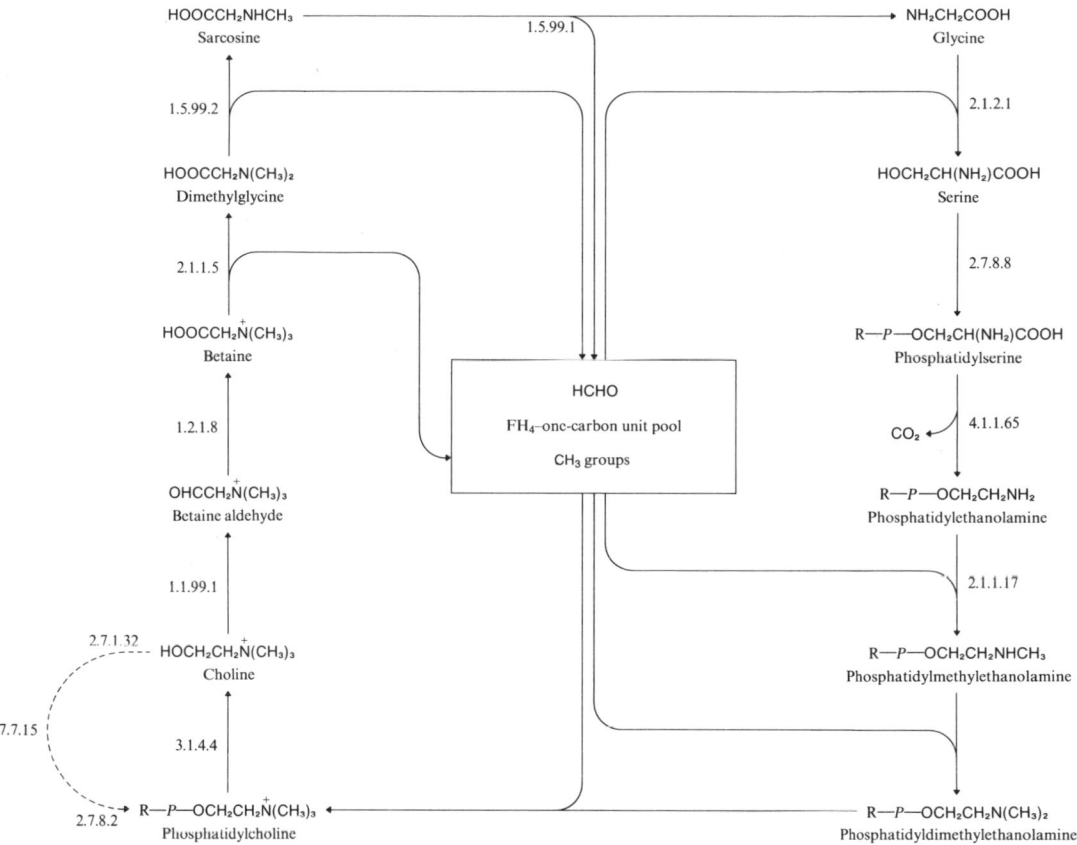

R: Diacylglycerol

Enzymes involved:

1.1.99.1 Choline dehydrogenase	2.1.1.5 Betaine-homocysteine methyltransferase	2.7.8.2 Cholinephosphotransferase
1.2.1.8 Betaine-aldehyde dehydrogenase	2.1.1.17 Phosphatidylethanolamine methyltransferase	2.7.8.8 CDPdiacylglycerol–serine O-phosphatidyltransferase
1.5.99.1 Sarcosine dehydrogenase	2.1.2.1 Glycine hydroxymethyltransferase	3.1.4.4 Phospholipase D
1.5.99.2 Dimethylglycine dehydrogenase	2.7.1.32 Choline kinase	4.1.1.65 Phosphatidylserine decarboxylase
	2.7.7.15 Choline-phosphate cytidylyltransferase	

Carnitine (Fig. 3)

In animals the synthesis begins with the methylation of lysine residues in proteins such as myosin, actin and histones. The further reactions take place after liberation of N^6-trimethyllysine by protein breakdown, presumably in the lysosomes. The enzymes for the first 3 reactions shown in Figure 3 are present in most tissues, whereas γ-butyrobetaine,2-oxoglutarate dioxygenase (1.14.11.1) occurs only in a few tissues (in man: liver, kidney and brain). The aldolase cleaving N^6-trimethyl-3-hydroxylysine may be identical to glycine hydroxymethyltransferase (2.1.2.1).

Choline (Fig. 4)

Choline can be formed endogenously via the methylation of phosphatidylethanolamine to phosphatidylcholine. If phosphatidylcholine and choline are lacking in the diet, these compounds will be synthesized at a rate determined by the size of the one-carbon unit pool. Choline is present in food primarily as phosphatidylcholine, which is hydrolyzed to glycerophosphorylcholine in the intestinal mucosa and further to choline in the liver. Choline can be regenerated after phosphorylation to phosphatidylcholine; a small portion, however, reaches the brain with the blood, where it is converted to acetylcholine by the action of choline acetyltransferase (2.3.1.6).

$$HOCH_2CH_2\overset{+}{N}(CH_3)_3 \xrightarrow[2.3.1.6]{\text{Acetyl-CoA \quad HSCoA}} CH_3\overset{O}{\overset{\|}{C}}OCH_2CH_2\overset{+}{N}(CH_3)_3$$

Choline → Acetylcholine

Polyamines (Fig. 5)

The polyamines putrescine, spermidine and spermine are formed from ornithine and S-adenosylmethionine. Ornithine is available only to the extent that it is formed from arginine in the urea cycle. The formation of S-adenosylmethionine depends – at least in the liver – on available methionine. The enzyme responsible for the decarboxylation of ornithine, ornithine decarboxylase (4.1.1.17), is dependent on pyridoxal phosphate and is present only in very small amounts in quiescent cells, but the activity can be increased many times over by exposure to trophic stimuli, e.g. hormones, growth factors, drugs. The turnover of this enzyme is much faster than that of any other mammalian enzyme known ($t_{1/2}$ 10–30 min).

Before S-adenosylmethionine can be used for the synthesis of spermidine and spermine, it must be converted to an 'active propylamine residue' by decarboxylation. The catalyzing enzyme, adenosylmethionine decarboxylase (4.1.1.50) does not seem to be dependent on pyridoxal phosphate but contains covalently bound pyruvate. 5'-Methylthioadenosine formed in the condensation reactions is converted to 5-methylthioribose 1-phosphate and adenine (page 127).

For animal cells a 'putrescine cycle' has been postulated involving, besides the synthesis of spermidine and spermine, the acetylation of these compounds to N^1-acetylspermidine and N^1-acetylspermine and the oxidation of these N^1-acetyl derivatives to putrescine or spermidine by splitting off acetylpropionaldehyde. The enzyme catalyzing the latter reaction, polyamine oxidase, appears to use FAD as cofactor.

Fig. 5 *Biosynthesis and metabolism of polyamines*

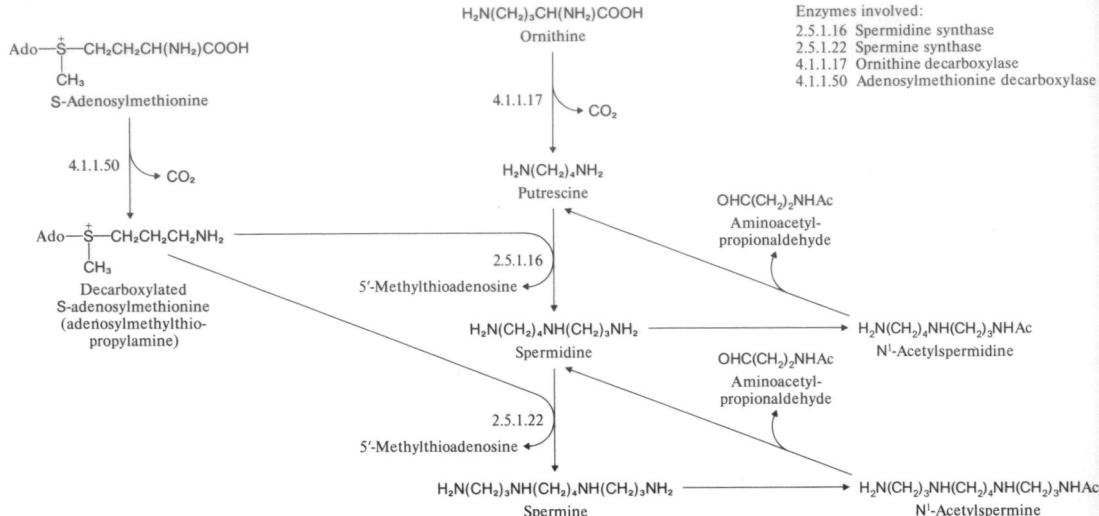

Enzymes involved:
2.5.1.16 Spermidine synthase
2.5.1.22 Spermine synthase
4.1.1.17 Ornithine decarboxylase
4.1.1.50 Adenosylmethionine decarboxylase

Reviews

· BESSMAN and GEIGER, Transport of energy in muscle: the phosphorylcreatine shuttle, *Science*, **211**, 448 (1981).
· BREMER, J., Carnitine – metabolism and functions, *Physiol. Rev.*, **63**, 1420 (1983).
· TABOR and TABOR, Polyamines, *Ann. Rev. Biochem.*, **53**, 749 (1984).
· PEGG and McCANN, Polyamine metabolism and function, *Amer. J. Physiol.*, **243**, C212 (1982).

Fig. 1　*Biosynthesis of serotonin and melatonin*

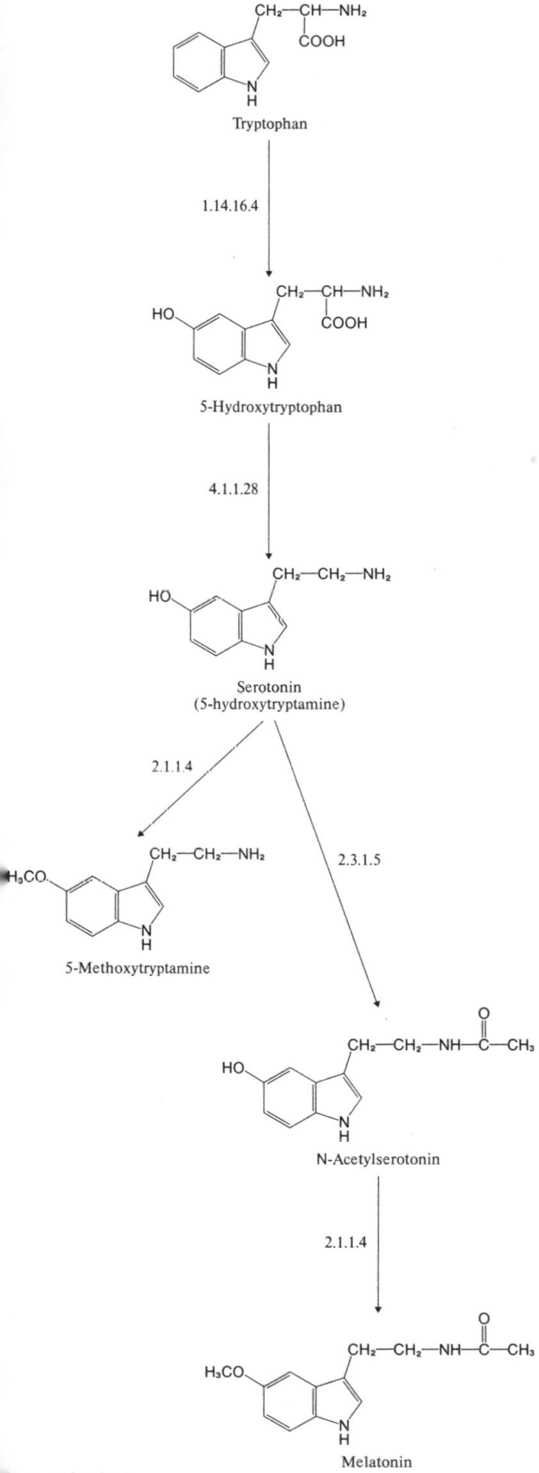

Tryptophan

1.14.16.4

5-Hydroxytryptophan

4.1.1.28

Serotonin
(5-hydroxytryptamine)

2.1.1.4

5-Methoxytryptamine

2.3.1.5

N-Acetylserotonin

2.1.1.4

Melatonin

Enzymes involved:
1.14.16.4　Tryptophan 5-monooxygenase
2.1.1.4　Acetylserotonin methyltransferase
2.3.1.5　Arylamine acetyltransferase
4.1.1.28　Aromatic-L-amino-acid decarboxylase

Fig. 2　*Biosynthesis of catecholamines*

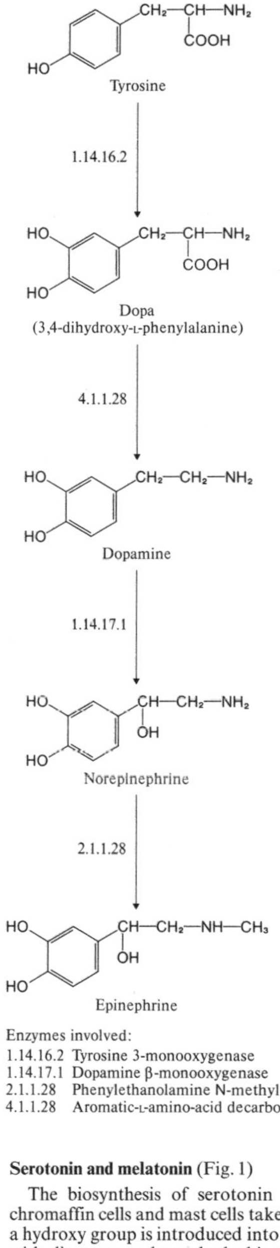

Tyrosine

1.14.16.2

Dopa
(3,4-dihydroxy-L-phenylalanine)

4.1.1.28

Dopamine

1.14.17.1

Norepinephrine

2.1.1.28

Epinephrine

Enzymes involved:
1.14.16.2　Tyrosine 3-monooxygenase
1.14.17.1　Dopamine β-monooxygenase
2.1.1.28　Phenylethanolamine N-methyltransferase
4.1.1.28　Aromatic-L-amino-acid decarboxylase

Serotonin and melatonin (Fig. 1)

The biosynthesis of serotonin in serotonergic nerves, entero-chromaffin cells and mast cells takes place in 2 steps: In the first step a hydroxy group is introduced into the aromatic ring of tryptophan, with dioxygen and tetrahydrobiopterin taking part. In the second step decarboxylation takes place, analogously to the formation of the catecholamines. 5-Methoxytryptamine and melatonin are formed in the pineal gland by methylation of the phenolic hydroxy group.

Catecholamines (Fig. 2)

The formation of catecholamines – starting from L-tyrosine – takes place in the chromaffin cells of the adrenal medulla and in the sympathetic neurons. The rate-limiting step of formation is the hydroxylation of tyrosine to dopa (3,4-dihydroxy-L-phenylalanine), a reaction requiring dioxygen and tetrahydrobiopterin. After decarboxylation of this compound, hydroxylation of the side chain takes place, with the participation of dioxygen and ascorbic acid. The noradrenalin thus formed is methylated to adrenalin mainly in the chromaffin cells of the adrenal medulla.

Fig. 3 *Biosynthesis of melanins*

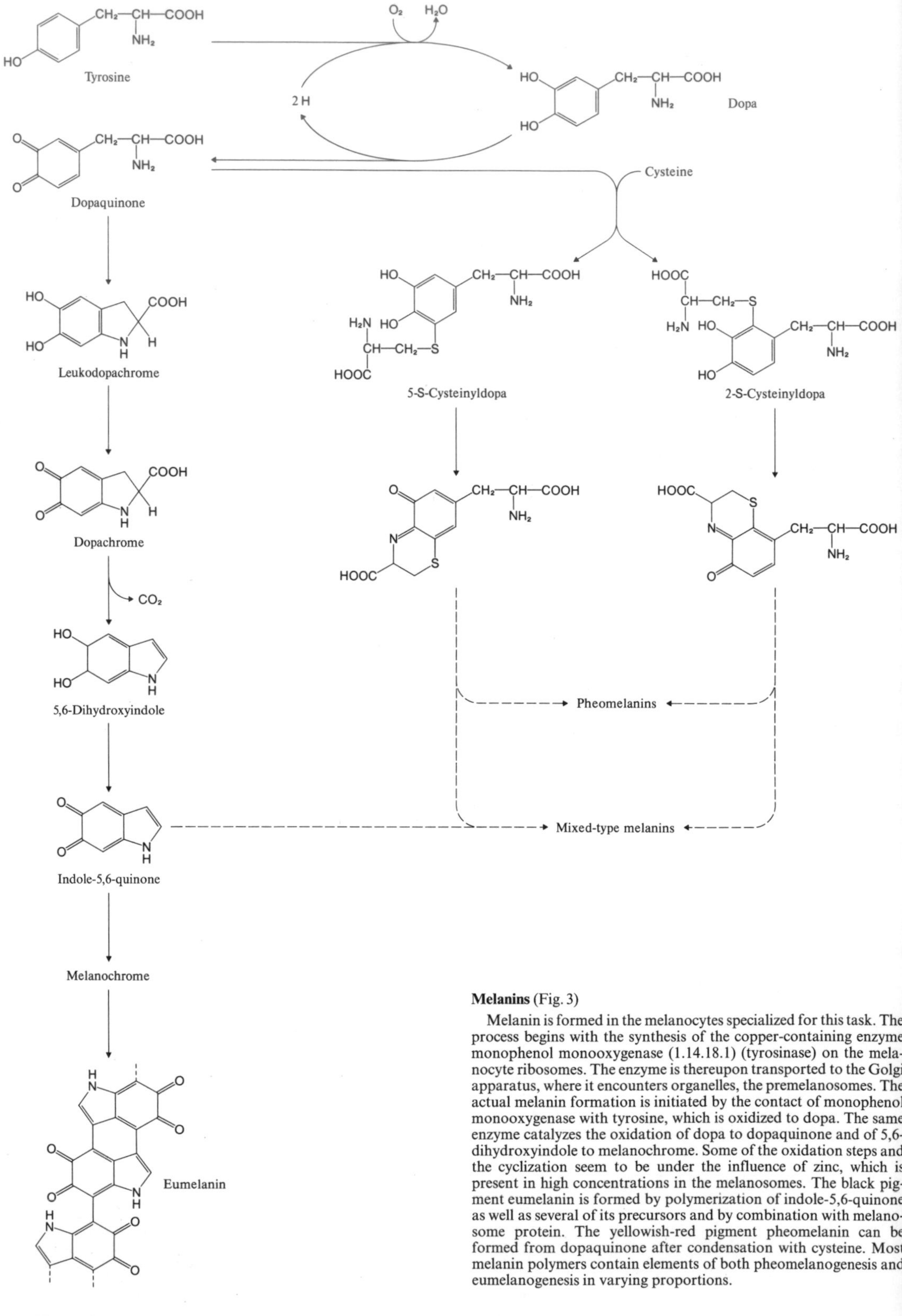

Melanins (Fig. 3)

Melanin is formed in the melanocytes specialized for this task. The process begins with the synthesis of the copper-containing enzyme monophenol monooxygenase (1.14.18.1) (tyrosinase) on the melanocyte ribosomes. The enzyme is thereupon transported to the Golgi apparatus, where it encounters organelles, the premelanosomes. The actual melanin formation is initiated by the contact of monophenol monooxygenase with tyrosine, which is oxidized to dopa. The same enzyme catalyzes the oxidation of dopa to dopaquinone and of 5,6-dihydroxyindole to melanochrome. Some of the oxidation steps and the cyclization seem to be under the influence of zinc, which is present in high concentrations in the melanosomes. The black pigment eumelanin is formed by polymerization of indole-5,6-quinone as well as several of its precursors and by combination with melanosome protein. The yellowish-red pigment pheomelanin can be formed from dopaquinone after condensation with cysteine. Most melanin polymers contain elements of both pheomelanogenesis and eumelanogenesis in varying proportions.

Fig. 4 *Initial reactions of ubiquinone biosynthesis*

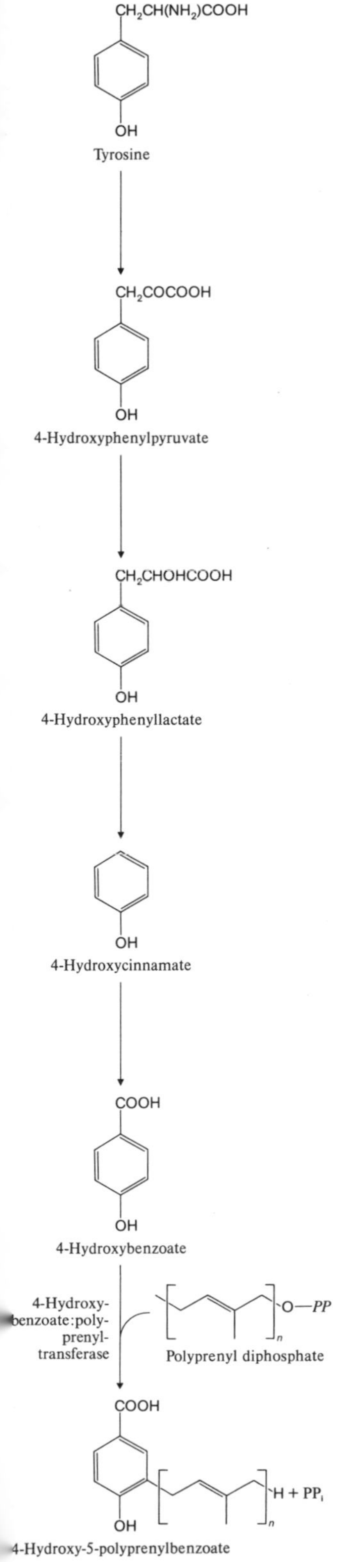

Fig. 5 *Pathway of biosynthesis from 4-hydroxy-5-polyprenylbenzoate to ubiquinone*

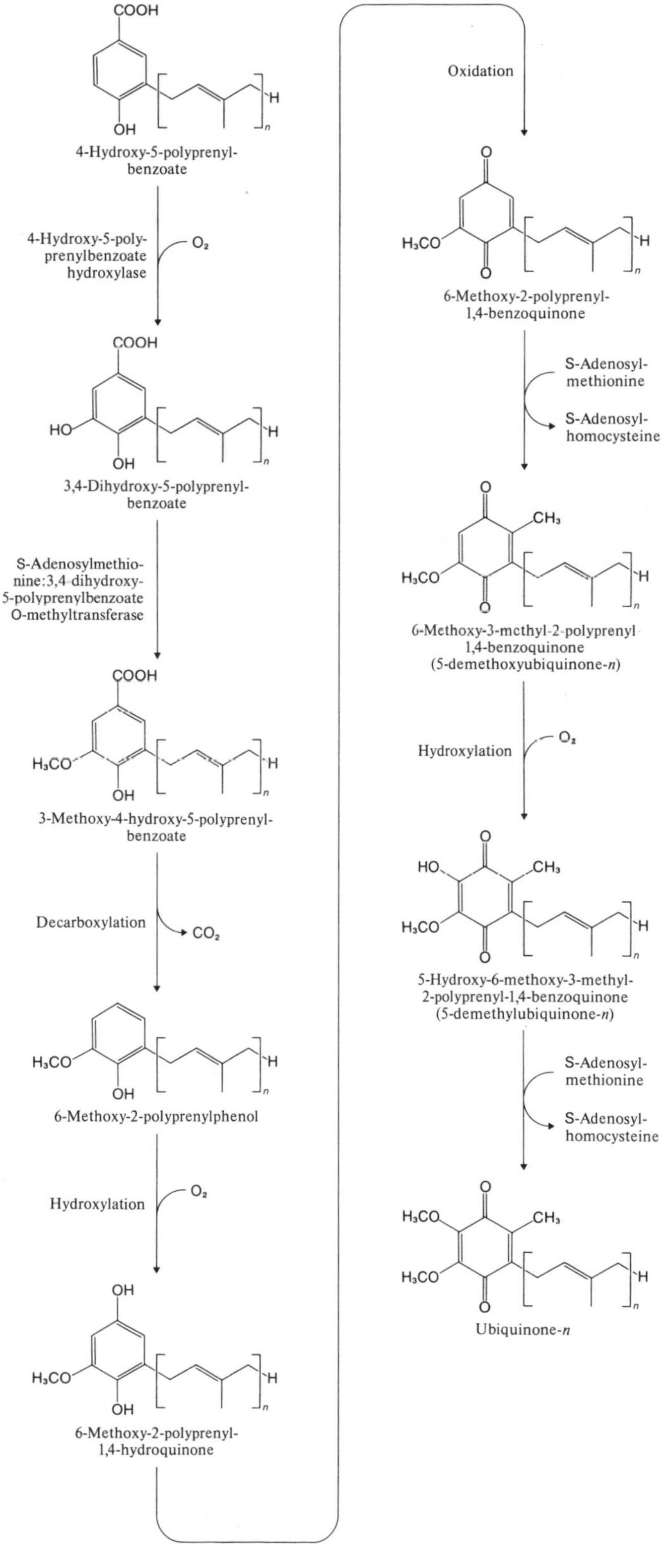

Fig. 4

CH₂CH(NH₂)COOH / OH — Tyrosine

↓

CH₂COCOOH / OH — 4-Hydroxyphenylpyruvate

↓

CH₂CHOHCOOH / OH — 4-Hydroxyphenyllactate

↓

OH — 4-Hydroxycinnamate

↓

COOH / OH — 4-Hydroxybenzoate

4-Hydroxy-benzoate:poly-prenyl-transferase

Polyprenyl diphosphate

↓ H + PP₁

4-Hydroxy-5-polyprenylbenzoate

Fig. 5

COOH / OH — 4-Hydroxy-5-polyprenyl-benzoate

4-Hydroxy-5-poly-prenylbenzoate hydroxylase — O₂

↓

COOH / HO, OH — 3,4-Dihydroxy-5-polyprenyl-benzoate

S-Adenosylmethio-nine:3,4-dihydroxy-5-polyprenylbenzoate O-methyltransferase

↓

COOH / H₃CO, OH — 3-Methoxy-4-hydroxy-5-polyprenyl-benzoate

Decarboxylation — CO₂

↓

H₃CO, OH — 6-Methoxy-2-polyprenylphenol

Hydroxylation — O₂

↓

OH / H₃CO, OH — 6-Methoxy-2-polyprenyl-1,4-hydroquinone

Oxidation

↓

6-Methoxy-2-polyprenyl-1,4-benzoquinone

S-Adenosylmethionine → S-Adenosylhomocysteine

↓

6-Methoxy-3-methyl-2-polyprenyl-1,4-benzoquinone (5-demethoxyubiquinone-*n*)

Hydroxylation — O₂

↓

5-Hydroxy-6-methoxy-3-methyl-2-polyprenyl-1,4-benzoquinone (5-demethylubiquinone-*n*)

S-Adenosylmethionine → S-Adenosylhomocysteine

↓

Ubiquinone-*n*

Fig. 6　*Iodination of peptide-linked tyrosine*

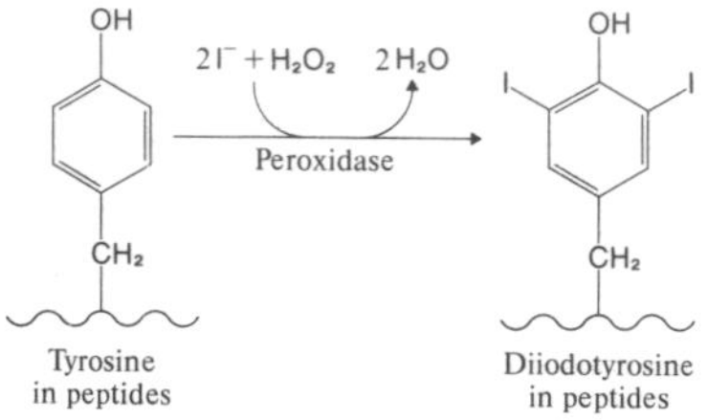

Fig. 7　*Formation of peptide-linked thyroxine by coupling of peptide-linked diiodotyrosine*

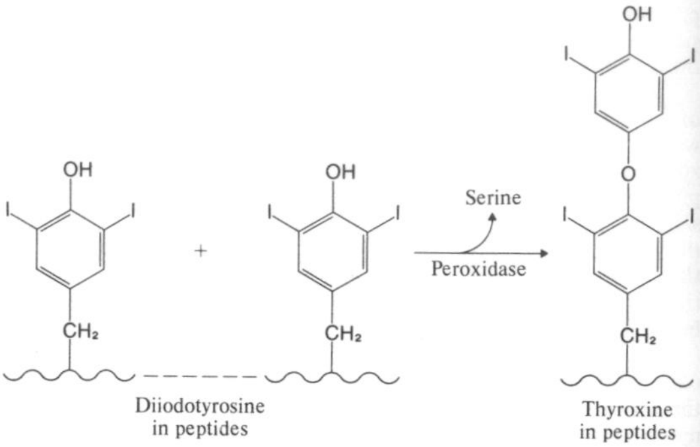

Fig. 8　*Metabolism of thyroxine*

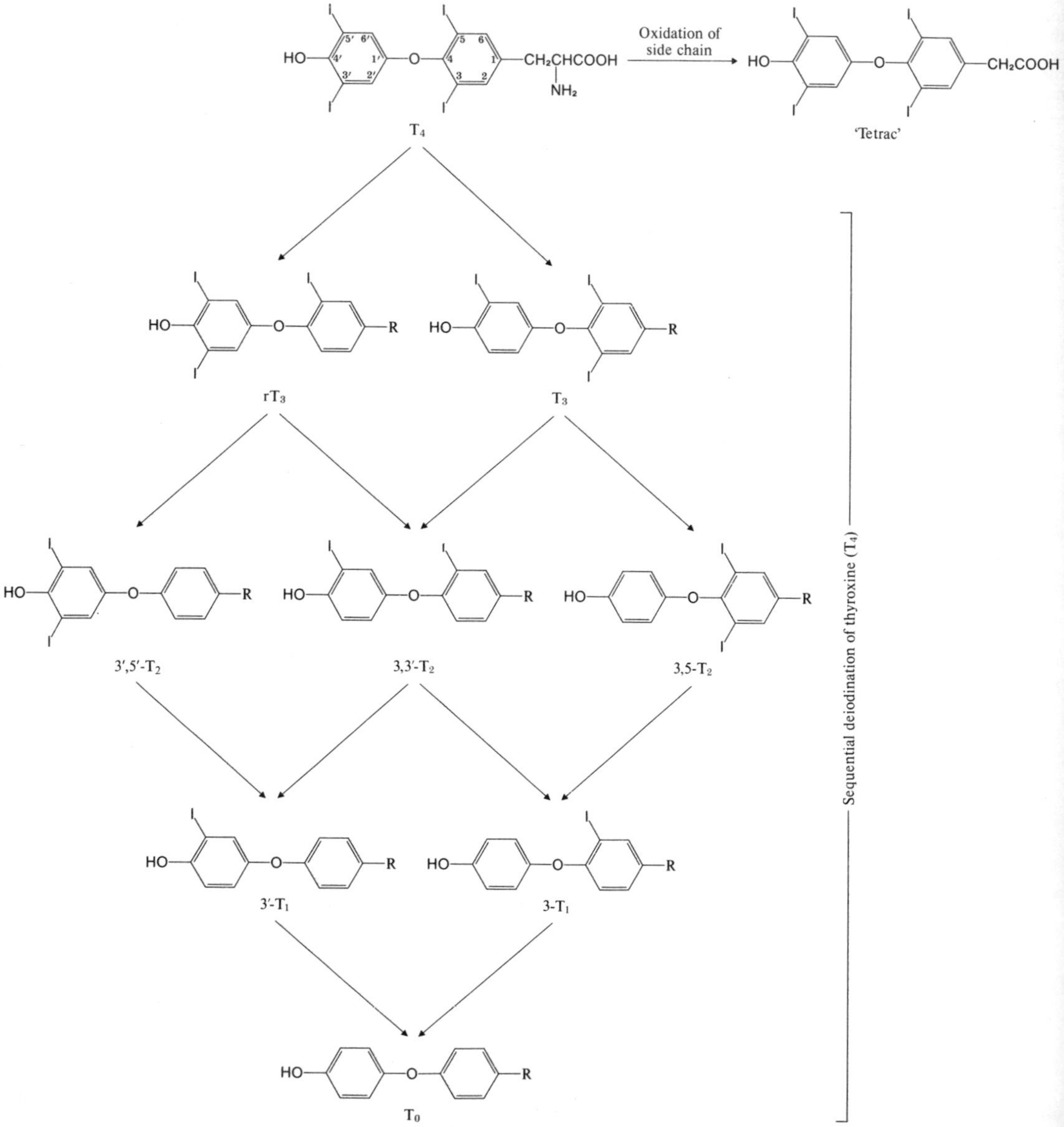

Ubiquinone

Ubiquinone is synthesized in the mitochondria from a variety of precursors. The aromatic ring derives from tyrosine, the isoprenyl side chain from mevalonate, the hydroxy groups from dioxygen, and the methyl groups from S-adenosylmethionine.

Tyrosine is first converted to 4-hydroxybenzoate by the sequence of reactions shown in Figure 4. The 4-hydroxybenzoate then reacts with polyprenyl diphosphate to form 4-hydroxy-5-polyprenylbenzoate, a reaction catalyzed by the enzyme 4-hydroxybenzoate: polyprenyl transferase. The polyprenyl diphosphate which provides the side chain is itself derived from isopentenyl diphosphate, the synthesis of which is described on page 144. These reactions take place in the cytosol, and the polyprenyl compound is then transported across the mitochondrial membrane prior to reacting with the 4-hydroxybenzoate.

In eukaryotes the biosynthesis of ubiquinone then proceeds according to the sequence shown in Figure 5. In prokaryotic organisms the sequence of the first 3 steps is decarboxylation, hydroxylation, methylation.

Formation and degradation of thyroid hormones

Iodination of the aromatic ring of peptide-linked tyrosine requires iodide, hydrogen peroxide and a peroxidase. The thyroid gland has the capability of sequestering iodide in an energy-consuming process. Iodination begins with the formation of mono- and diiodotyrosine within the protein thyroglobulin (Fig. 6). From these iodinated tyrosine residues, thyroxine (T_4) as well as small amounts of triiodothyronine (T_3) are formed within the protein with the aid of iodine and peroxidase by a coupling mechanism that is not fully understood (Fig. 7). By the action of a proteinase, the iodinated thyronines are then released in the thyroid gland. The main portion of the active hormone triiodothyronine and of the 'reverse' triiodothyronine (rT_3) is probably formed only in peripheral tissues by deiodination of thyroxine, a reaction that requires SH groups (reduced glutathione may be the endogenous cofactor):

$$T_4 + 2RSH \longrightarrow T_3 + RS{-}SR + H$$

Further breakdown by sequential deiodination proceeds in accordance with the scheme shown in Figure 8. In addition, tetraiodothyroacetic acid ('tetrac') is formed from thyroxine by oxidative deamination of the side chain.

Reviews

· BLASCHKO, H., Catecholamine biosynthesis, *Brit. med. Bull.*, **29**, 105 (1973).
· WITKOP et al., Albinism and other disorders of pigment metabolism, in STANBURY et al., *The Metabolic Basis of Inherited Disease*, 5th ed., McGraw-Hill, New York, 1983, page 301.
· OLSON and RUDNEY, Biosynthesis of ubiquinone, *Vitam. and Horm.*, **40**, 1 (1983).
· FRIEDEN, E., Iodine and the thyroid hormones, *Trends biochem. Sci.*, **6**, 50 (1981).
· NUNEZ and POMMIER, Formation of thyroid hormones, *Vitam. and Horm.*, **39**, 175 (1982).
· ENGLER and BURGER, The deiodination of the iodothyronines and of their derivatives in man, *Endocr. Rev.*, **5**, 151 (1984).

Fig. 1 *Biosynthesis of porphyrins*

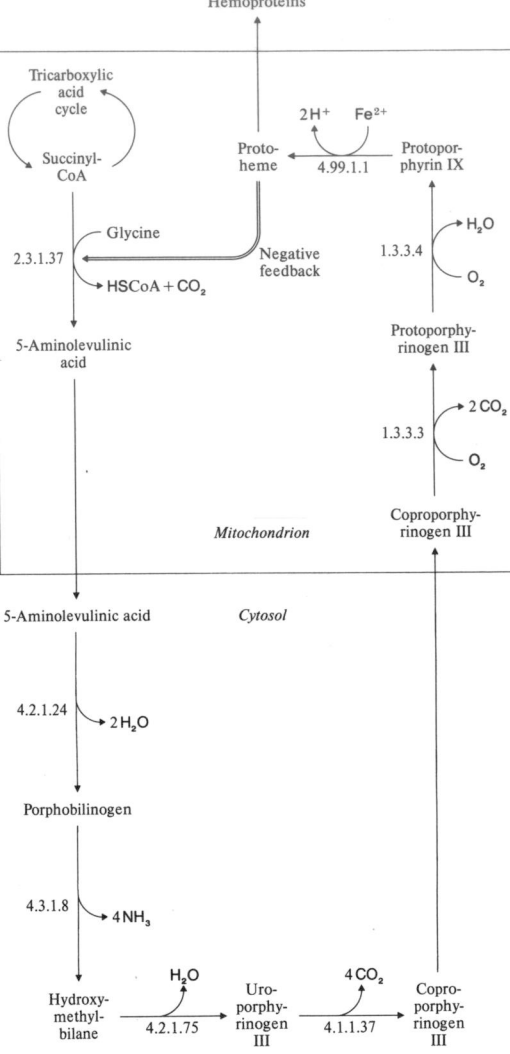

Enzymes involved:
1.3.3.3   Coproporphyrinogen oxidase
1.3.3.4   Protoporphyrinogen oxidase
2.3.1.37 5-Aminolevulinate synthase
4.1.1.37 Uroporphyrinogen decarboxylase
4.2.1.24 Porphobilinogen synthase
4.2.1.75 Uroporphyrinogen-III synthase
4.3.1.8   Porphobilinogen deaminase
4.99.1.1 Ferrochelatase

The synthesis of heme in mammalian cells involves cooperation between the mitochondrial and cytosolic compartments (Fig. 1).

In the first step – a mitochondrial process –, 5-aminolevulinate synthase (2.3.1.37) catalyzes the condensation of succinyl-CoA from the tricarboxylic acid cycle with glycine. Pyridoxal phosphate is required as cofactor, and the 5-aminolevulinate synthase is the rate-limiting enzyme in hepatic heme synthesis.

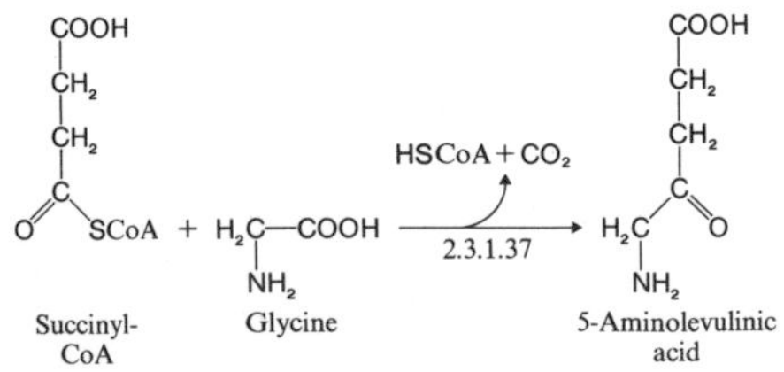

The 5-aminolevulinic acid thus formed passes into the cytosol, where 2 molecules condense to yield porphobilinogen in the following reaction sequence: the first molecule is covalently bound to porphobilinogen synthase (4.2.1.24) (5-aminolevulinate dehydratase) through the formation of a Schiff's base; then, with the second molecule of 5-aminolevulinic acid, porphobilinogen is formed by aldol condensation, ring formation and elimination of water (Fig. 2). The purified enzyme porphobilinogen synthase contains 2 cysteine residues and 1 zinc atom, which seems to protect the essential SH groups of the enzyme. Lead, on the other hand, is a potent inhibitor of the erythrocyte porphobilinogen synthase and presumably displaces Zn from the enzyme.

The next step consists of a sequential head-to-tail condensation of 4 porphobilinogen molecules, splitting off 4 NH_3 molecules and forming hydroxymethylbilane. The reaction is catalyzed by porphobilinogen deaminase (4.3.1.8) (pre-uroporphyrinogen synthase) which forms stable complexes with the intermediates. Hydroxymethylbilane cyclizes spontaneously to uroporphyrinogen I. In the formation of uroporphyrinogen III, however, the enzyme uroporphyrinogen-III synthase (4.2.1.75) (uroporphyrinogen-III cosynthase) is needed for the rearrangement of the finally added porphobilinogen ring (ring D) just prior to the closure of the macrocyclic ring (Fig. 3). The activity of uroporphyrinogen-III synthase is usually 10 times greater than that of porphobilinogen deaminase, thus ensuring the formation of the physiologically important isomer III.

Uroporphyrinogen III is then decarboxylated with the aid of uroporphyrinogen decarboxylase (4.1.1.37) to yield coproporphyrinogen III. The reaction consists of 4 sequential steps, in each of which 1 CO_2 molecule is lost, and gives rise to intermediates with 7, 6 and 5 carboxy groups (Fig. 3). Decarboxylation of the first acetyl group takes place fastest. At the porphyrin stage with 5 carboxy groups a secondary pathway probably begins, which leads to the isocoproporphyrinogen series.

The conversion of coproporphyrinogen III to protoporphyrinogen III takes place in the mitochondria and consists of a combined oxidation and decarboxylation of 2 propionyl residues with harderoporphyrinogen as an intermediate. The reaction is catalyzed by coproporphyrinogen oxidase (1.3.3.3) and requires dioxygen (Fig. 4).

Fig. 2 *Synthesis of porphobilinogen*

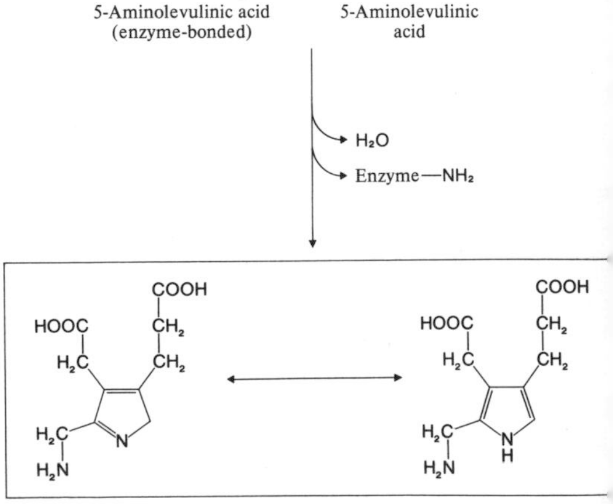

5-Aminolevulinic acid
(enzyme-bonded)

+

5-Aminolevulinic
acid

Porphobilinogen

Enzyme involved:
4.2.1.24 Porphobilinogen synthase

Fig. 3 *Synthesis of uroporphyrinogen III and coproporphyrinogen III*

Porphobilinogen
(4 molecules)

Hydroxymethylbilane

Uroporphyrinogen III

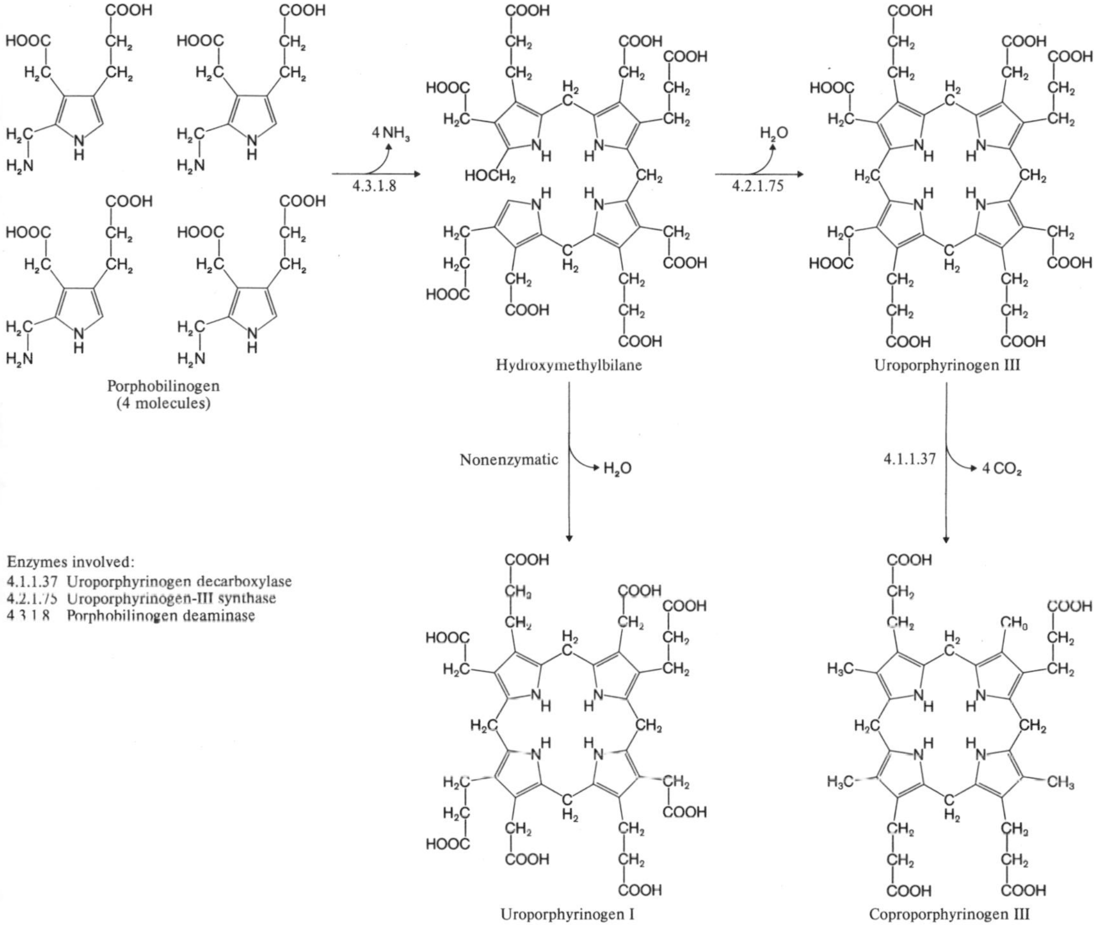

Enzymes involved:
4.1.1.37 Uroporphyrinogen decarboxylase
4.2.1.75 Uroporphyrinogen-III synthase
4.3.1.8 Porphobilinogen deaminase

Uroporphyrinogen I

Coproporphyrinogen III

Fig. 4 *Synthesis of protoporphyrinogen III*

Coproporphyrinogen III

Harderoporphyrinogen

Protoporphyrinogen III

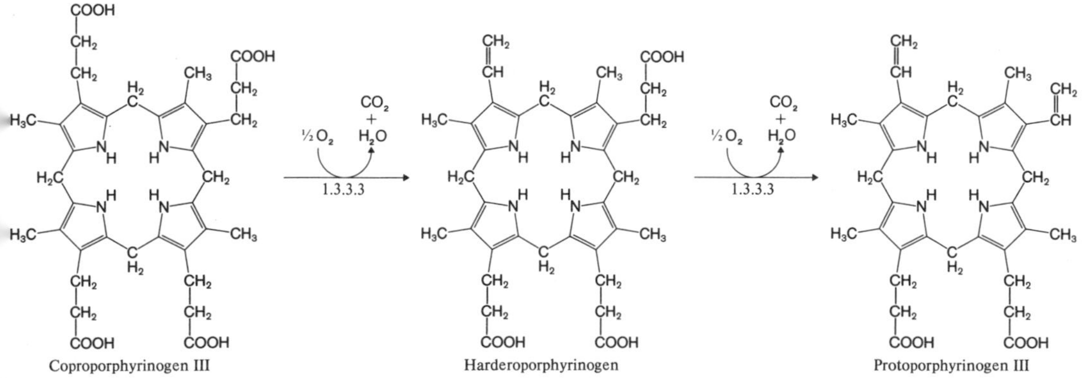

Enzyme involved:
1.3.3.3 Coproporphyrinogen oxidase

An enzyme specific for protoporphyrinogen III – protoporphyrinogen oxidase (1.3.3.4) – catalyzes the desaturation of this substrate by removing 6 H atoms from the porphyrinogen nucleus (Fig. 5). The reaction requires dioxygen.

The final step in heme biosynthesis is the incorporation of Fe^{2+} into protoporphyrin IX (for structure see next page) with the aid of ferrochelatase (4.99.1.1), which is associated with the inner membrane of the mitochondria. Lipids seem to be needed for the activity.

Porphyrin synthesis is regulated by a negative feedback mechanism (see Fig. 1) in that the synthesis of 5-aminolevulinate synthase (2.3.1.37) is inhibited at the post-transcriptional stage by protoheme (but not by hemoproteins).

Fig. 5   *Synthesis of protoporphyrin IX (protoporphyrin III)*

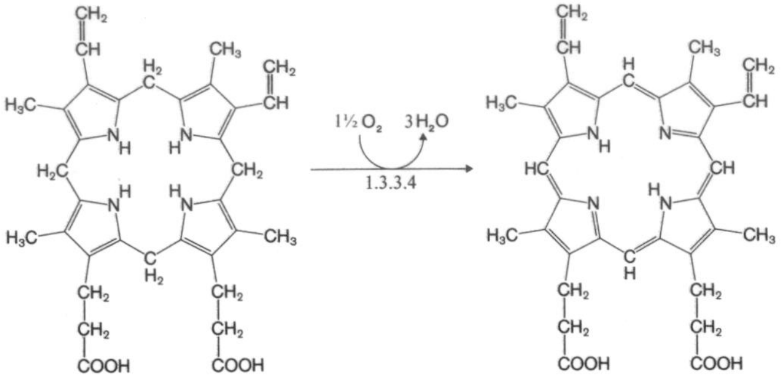

Enzyme involved:
1.3.3.4 Protoporphyrinogen
oxidase

Protoporphyrinogen III

Protoporphyrin IX (protoporphyrin III)

Reviews

· IBRAHAM et al., Heme metabolism in erythroid and hepatic cells, *Progr. Hemat.*, **13**, 75 (1984).
· KAPPAS et al., The porphyrias, in STANBURY et al., *The Metabolic Basis of Inherited Disease*, 5th ed., McGraw-Hill, New York, 1983, page 1301.

· MOORE, R. M., The biochemistry of the porphyrins, *Clin. Haemat.*, **9**, 227 (1980).
· BATTERSBY et al., Biosynthesis of the pigments of life: formation of the macrocycle, *Nature*, **285**, 17 (1980).

Fig. 1 *Biosynthesis of IMP (inosine monophosphate)*

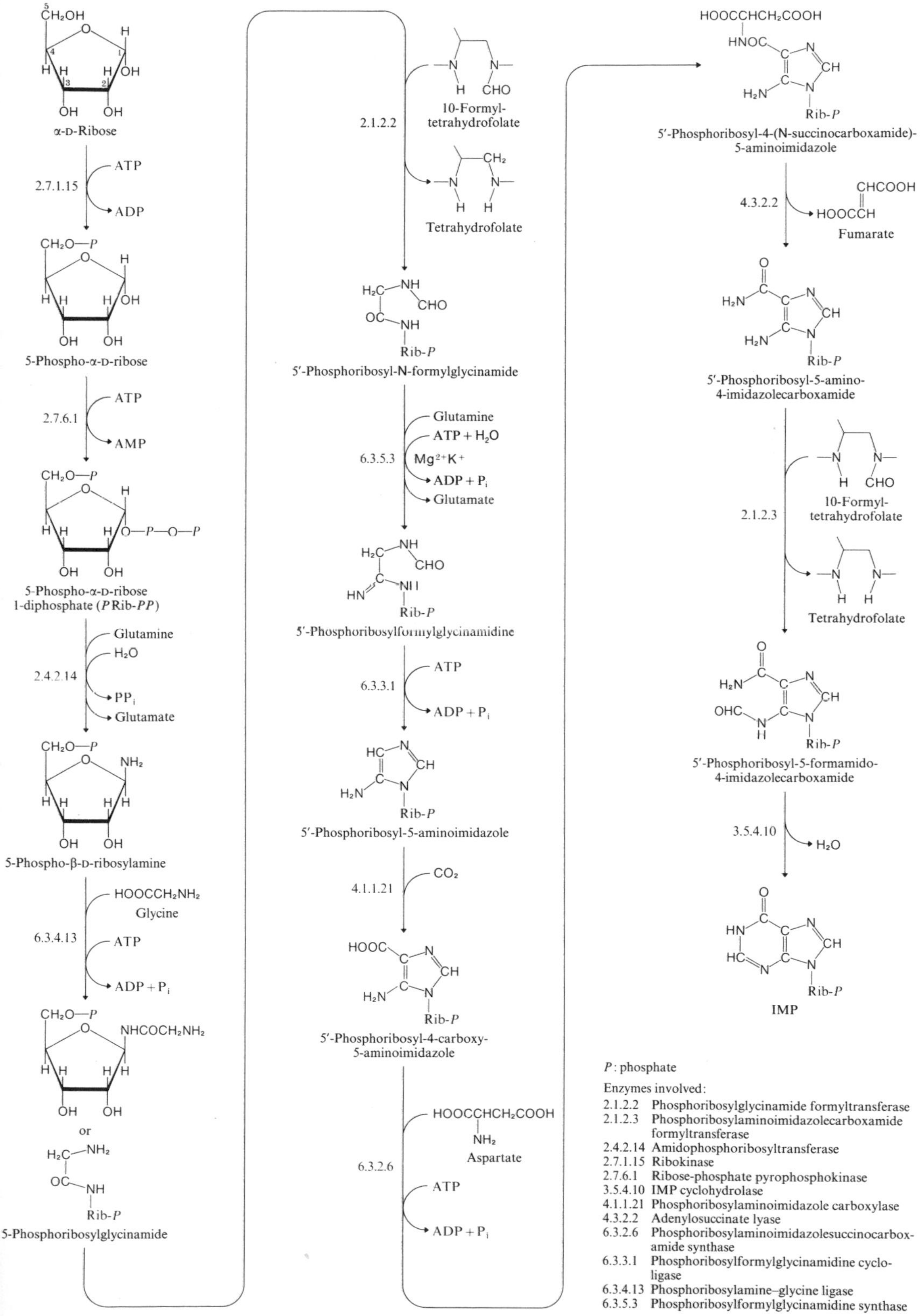

α-D-Ribose

2.7.1.15 — ATP → ADP

5-Phospho-α-D-ribose

2.7.6.1 — ATP → AMP

5-Phospho-α-D-ribose 1-diphosphate ($PRib$-PP)

2.4.2.14 — Glutamine, H_2O → PP_i, Glutamate

5-Phospho-β-D-ribosylamine

6.3.4.13 — $HOOCCH_2NH_2$ Glycine, ATP → $ADP + P_i$

5-Phosphoribosylglycinamide

2.1.2.2 — 10-Formyl-tetrahydrofolate → Tetrahydrofolate

5'-Phosphoribosyl-N-formylglycinamide

6.3.5.3 — Glutamine, $ATP + H_2O$, $Mg^{2+}K^+$ → $ADP + P_i$, Glutamate

5'-Phosphoribosylformylglycinamidine

6.3.3.1 — ATP → $ADP + P_i$

5'-Phosphoribosyl-5-aminoimidazole

4.1.1.21 — CO_2

5'-Phosphoribosyl-4-carboxy-5-aminoimidazole

6.3.2.6 — $HOOCCHCH_2COOH$ / NH_2 Aspartate, ATP → $ADP + P_i$

5'-Phosphoribosyl-4-(N-succinocarboxamide)-5-aminoimidazole

4.3.2.2 — CHCOOH / HOOCCH Fumarate

5'-Phosphoribosyl-5-amino-4-imidazolecarboxamide

2.1.2.3 — 10-Formyl-tetrahydrofolate → Tetrahydrofolate

5'-Phosphoribosyl-5-formamido-4-imidazolecarboxamide

3.5.4.10 — H_2O

IMP

P: phosphate

Enzymes involved:
2.1.2.2 Phosphoribosylglycinamide formyltransferase
2.1.2.3 Phosphoribosylaminoimidazolecarboxamide formyltransferase
2.4.2.14 Amidophosphoribosyltransferase
2.7.1.15 Ribokinase
2.7.6.1 Ribose-phosphate pyrophosphokinase
3.5.4.10 IMP cyclohydrolase
4.1.1.21 Phosphoribosylaminoimidazole carboxylase
4.3.2.2 Adenylosuccinate lyase
6.3.2.6 Phosphoribosylaminoimidazolesuccinocarbox-amide synthase
6.3.3.1 Phosphoribosylformylglycinamidine cyclo-ligase
6.3.4.13 Phosphoribosylamine–glycine ligase
6.3.5.3 Phosphoribosylformylglycinamidine synthase

Purine nucleotides

The synthesis of purine nucleotides begins at the ribose portion (Fig. 1). 5-Phosphoribose (ribose 5-phosphate) is activated to form 5-phosphoribose 1-diphosphate, onto which the purine ring is synthesized in 10 steps (the origin of the individual C and N atoms can be seen from Figure 2). The first of these steps – transfer of an amino group from glutamine to replace pyrophosphate – is irreversible and also includes an inversion of the glycoside configuration: 5-phosphoribose 1-diphosphate has an α configuration at the C-1 atom, whereas the naturally occurring nucleotides have a β configuration. Synthesis of the purine ring (Fig. 1) is highly energy-dependent and requires 6 molecules of ATP.

Since folic acid – in the form of 10-formyltetrahydrofolate – takes part in 2 steps of the purine-ring synthesis, folic-acid deficiency or the administration of a folic-acid antagonist such as the cytostatic methotrexate (bonding to dihydrofolate reductase) impairs the formation of purine nucleotides (see also page 173).

XMP and, in a further step, GMP are synthesized from IMP (Fig. 3). IMP is also the starting material for the synthesis of AMP via a condensation reaction with aspartate, driven forward by GTP hydrolysis (see Fig. 2, page 128).

Purine nucleotides can not only be formed de novo but may also be resynthesized from the free bases that result from the breakdown of purine nucleotides (page 128).

Conversion of the various nucleoside monophosphates (NMP) to the corresponding triphosphates (NTP) takes place in 2 steps, in each of which an energy-rich phosphate group is transferred:

$$NMP + ATP \xrightarrow[2.7.4.4]{} NDP + ADP$$

$$NDP + ATP \xrightarrow[2.7.4.6]{} NTP + ADP$$

Enzymes involved:
2.7.4.4 Nucleoside-phosphate kinase
2.7.4.6 Nucleoside-diphosphate kinase

Coenzymes containing adenine nucleotide

Nicotinamide adenine dinucleotide (NAD). Formation starts with nicotinate ribonucleotide (Fig. 4), which is either a metabolic product of tryptophan or is formed from nicotinic acid ingested with the food (by condensation with 5-phosphoribose 1-diphosphate). An AMP residue is transferred from ATP to the nicotinate ribonucleotide, and in the last step the carboxamide group is formed from the carboxy group of the nicotinic acid, with glutamine as the NH$_2$ donor.

Flavin adenine dinucleotide (FAD). This compound is formed from riboflavin via FMN (riboflavin 5'-phosphate) and 2 molecules of ATP in the following 2 steps:

$$Riboflavin + ATP \xrightarrow[2.7.1.26]{} FMN + ADP$$

$$FMN + ATP \xrightarrow[2.7.7.2]{} FAD + PP_i$$

Enzymes involved:
2.7.1.26 Riboflavin kinase
2.7.7.2 FMN adenylyltransferase

Fig. 2 *Origin of the carbon and nitrogen atoms in the purine nucleus*

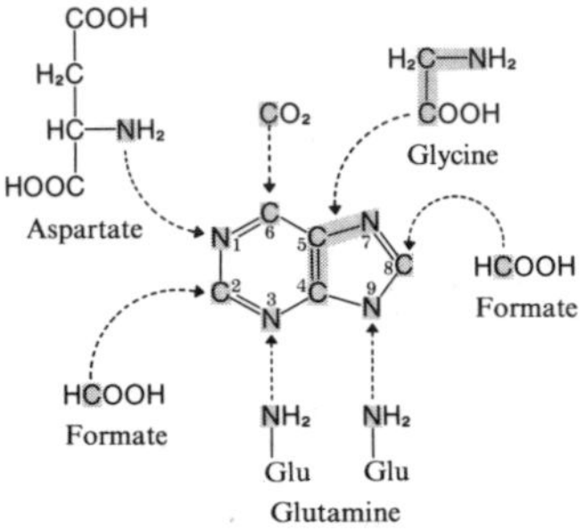

Fig. 3 *Biosynthesis of XMP (xanthosine monophosphate) and GMP (guanosine monophosphate)*

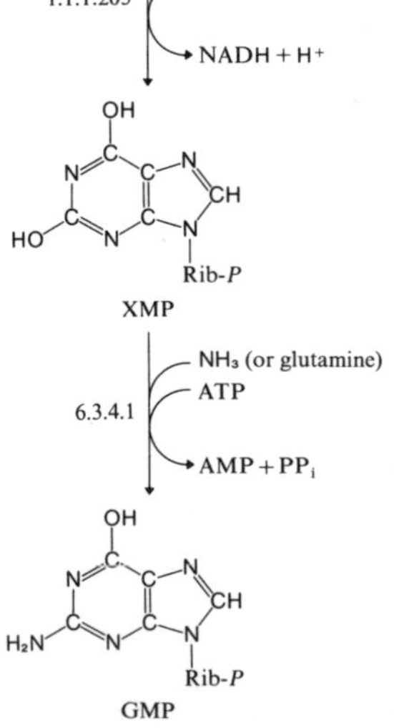

IMP

1.1.1.205

XMP

6.3.4.1

GMP

Enzymes involved:
1.1.1.205 IMP dehydrogenase
6.3.4.1 GMP synthase

Fig. 4 *Biosynthesis of NAD+*

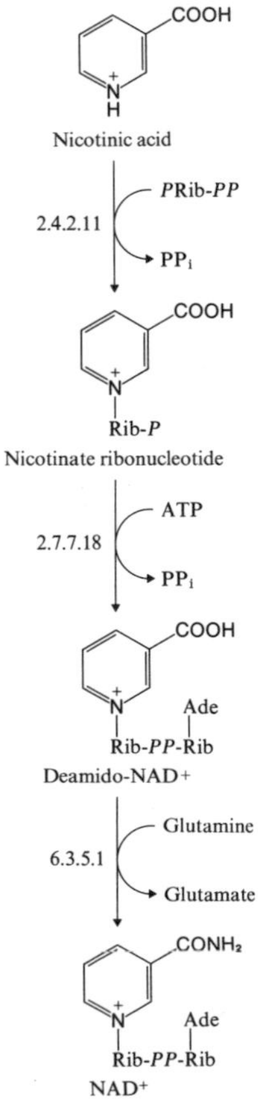

Nicotinic acid

2.4.2.11

Nicotinate ribonucleotide

2.7.7.18

Deamido-NAD+

6.3.5.1

NAD+

Enzymes involved:
2.4.2.11 Nicotinate phosphoribosyl-transferase
2.7.7.18 Nicotinate-nucleotide adenylyl-transferase
6.3.5.1 NAD+ synthase (glutamine-hydrolyzing)

Fig. 5 *Biosynthesis of coenzyme A*

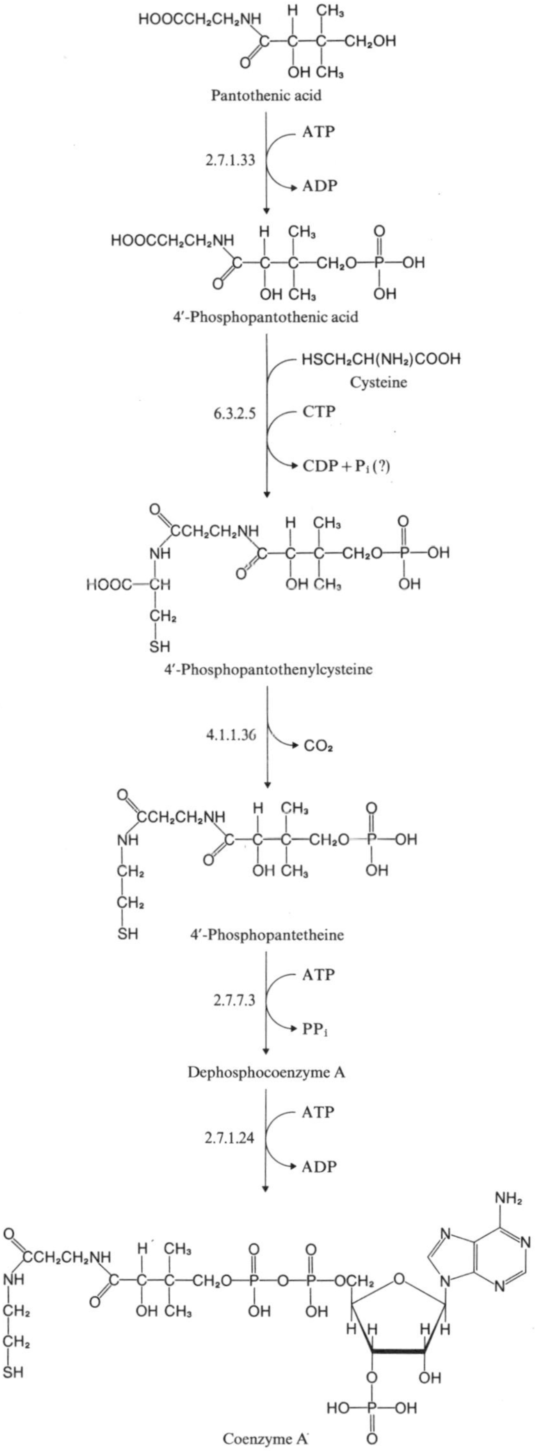

Pantothenic acid

2.7.1.33
− ATP
↘ ADP

4′-Phosphopantothenic acid

6.3.2.5
− HSCH₂CH(NH₂)COOH Cysteine
− CTP
↘ CDP + Pᵢ (?)

4′-Phosphopantothenylcysteine

4.1.1.36
↘ CO₂

4′-Phosphopantetheine

2.7.7.3
− ATP
↘ PPᵢ

Dephosphocoenzyme A

2.7.1.24
− ATP
↘ ADP

Coenzyme A

Enzymes involved:
2.7.1.24 Dephospho-CoA kinase
2.7.1.33 Pantothenate kinase
2.7.7.3 Pantetheine-phosphate adenylyltransferase
4.1.1.36 Phosphopantothenoylcysteine decarboxylase
6.3.2.5 Phosphopantothenate–cysteine ligase

Fig. 6 *Biosynthesis of 5,6,7,8-tetrahydrobiopterin*

GTP (guanosine triphosphate)

3.5.4.16
↘ HCOOH

Dihydroneopterin triphosphate

↘ Pᵢ + PPᵢ

5,6-Dihydrosepiapterin

1.1.1.153
− NADPH + H⁺
↘ NADP⁺

5,6,7,8-Tetrahydrobiopterin

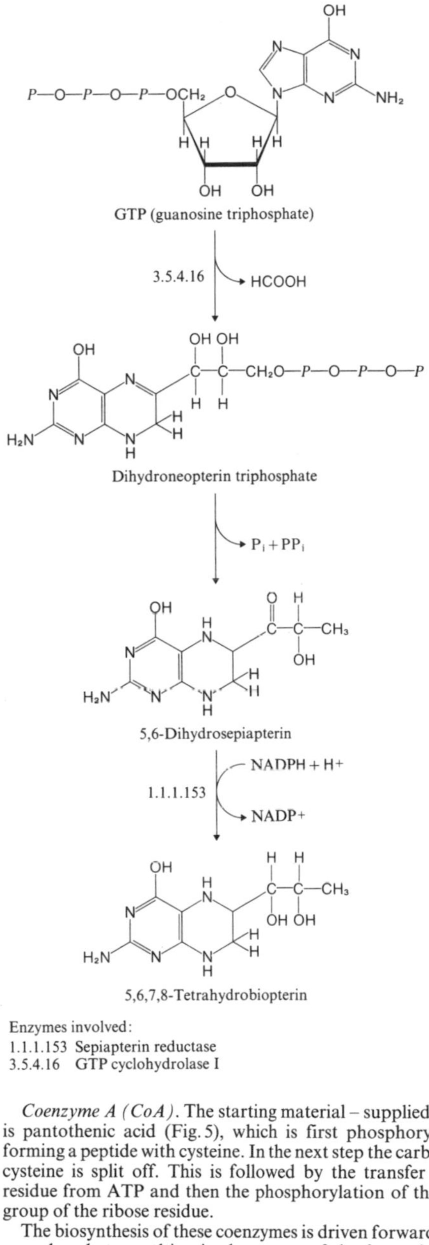

Enzymes involved:
1.1.1.153 Sepiapterin reductase
3.5.4.16 GTP cyclohydrolase I

Coenzyme A (CoA). The starting material – supplied by the diet – is pantothenic acid (Fig. 5), which is first phosphorylated before forming a peptide with cysteine. In the next step the carboxy group of cysteine is split off. This is followed by the transfer of an AMP residue from ATP and then the phosphorylation of the 3′-hydroxy group of the ribose residue.

The biosynthesis of these coenzymes is driven forward because the pyrophosphate resulting in the course of the formation process is rapidly hydrolyzed, making a reversal of the reactions practically impossible.

5,6,7,8-Tetrahydrobiopterin (Fig. 6). The starting material is GTP, which is converted to dihydroneopterin triphosphate with the aid of GTP cyclohydrolase I (3.5.4.16), one C atom being eliminated in the form of formate. The reaction involves hydrolysis of 2 C—N bonds and isomerization of the pentose unit; the recyclization may be nonenzymatic. From dihydroneopterin triphosphate, 5,6-dihydro-sepiapterin is formed by dephosphorylation and internal oxidation/reduction. 5,6-Dihydrosepiapterin is then reduced to 5,6,7,8-tetra-hydrobiopterin by the action of sepiapterin reductase (1.1.1.153) and reduced NADP.

Fig. 7 *Biosynthesis of pyrimidines and their nucleotides*

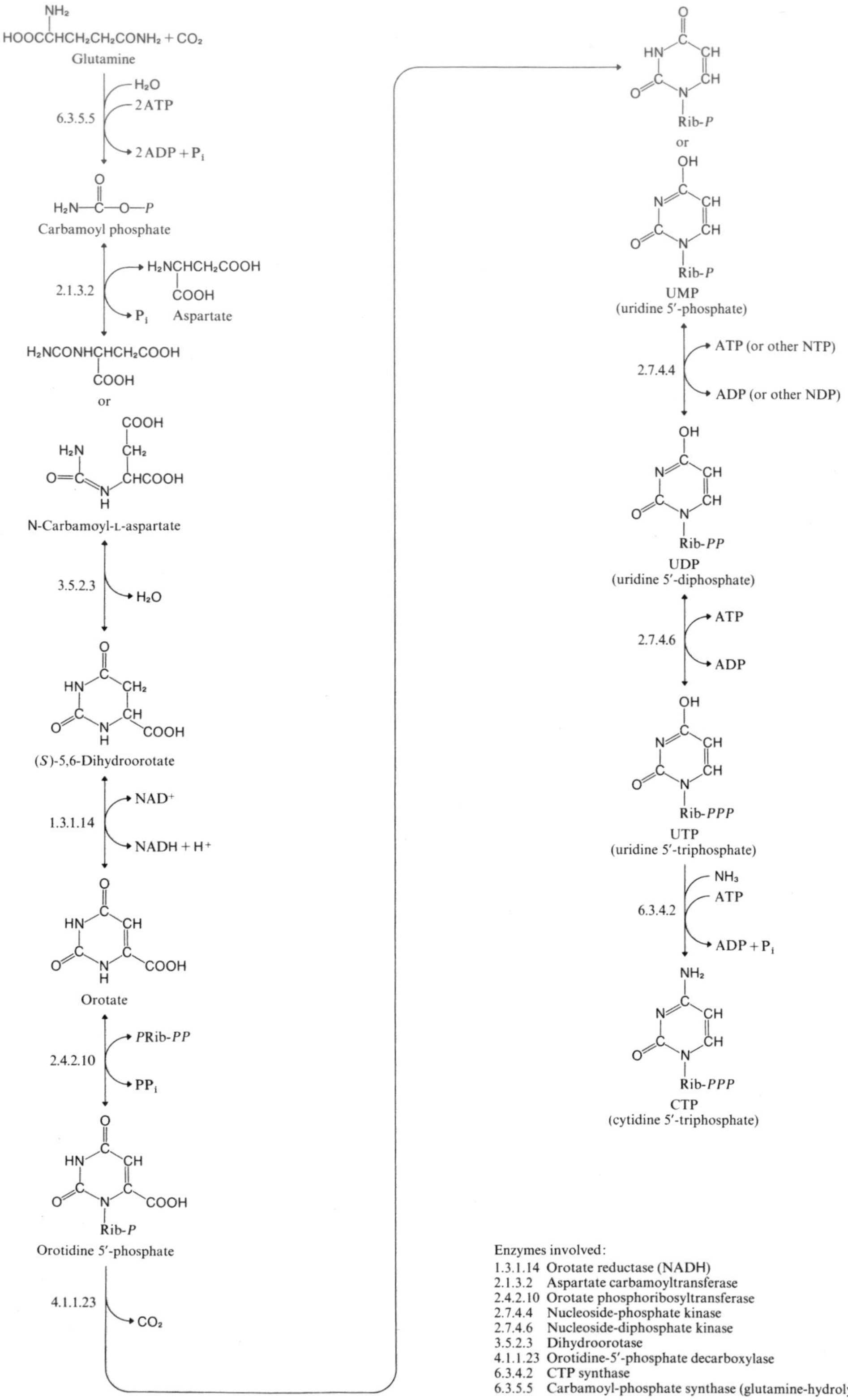

Enzymes involved:
1.3.1.14 Orotate reductase (NADH)
2.1.3.2 Aspartate carbamoyltransferase
2.4.2.10 Orotate phosphoribosyltransferase
2.7.4.4 Nucleoside-phosphate kinase
2.7.4.6 Nucleoside-diphosphate kinase
3.5.2.3 Dihydroorotase
4.1.1.23 Orotidine-5'-phosphate decarboxylase
6.3.4.2 CTP synthase
6.3.5.5 Carbamoyl-phosphate synthase (glutamine-hydrolyzing)

Fig. 8 *Biosynthesis of dCTP (deoxycytidine triphosphate)*

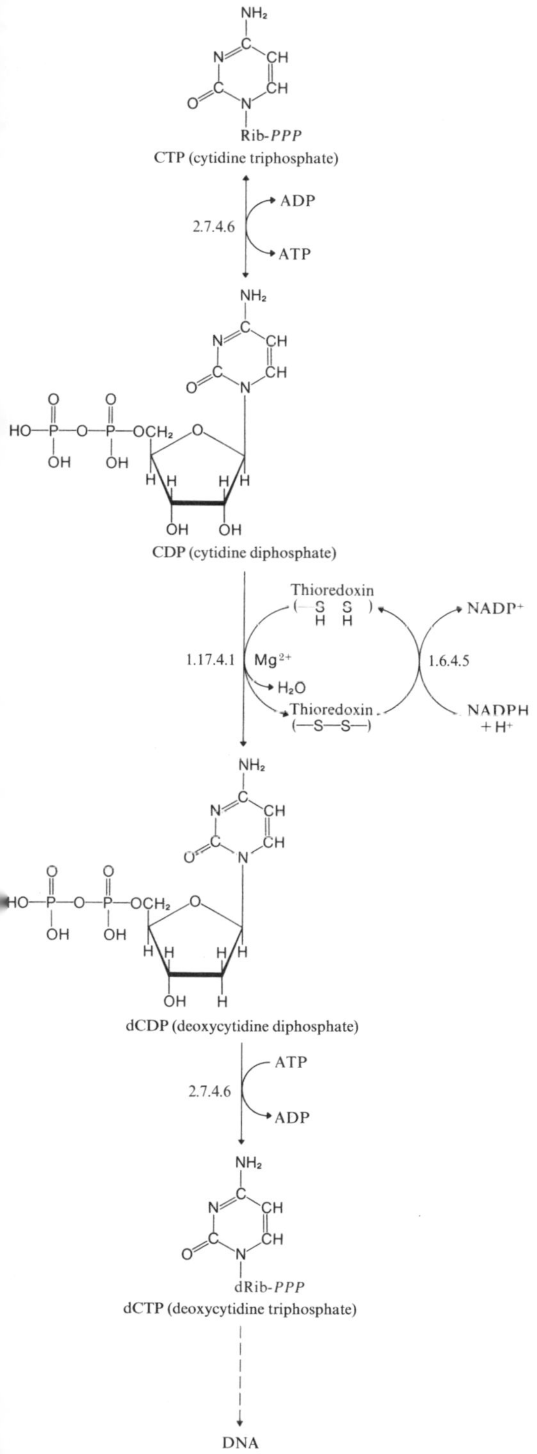

NH₂

Rib-*PPP*
CTP (cytidine triphosphate)

↑ → ADP

2.7.4.6

↓ → ATP

NH₂

$$HO-\overset{O}{\underset{OH}{P}}-O-\overset{O}{\underset{OH}{P}}-OCH_2$$

CDP (cytidine diphosphate)

Thioredoxin
(—S S—)
  H H
↖ ↘ → NADP⁺

1.17.4.1   Mg²⁺   1.6.4.5

↓ → H₂O

Thioredoxin·   NADPH
(—S—S—)   + H⁺

NH₂

$$HO-\overset{O}{\underset{OH}{P}}-O-\overset{O}{\underset{OH}{P}}-OCH_2$$

dCDP (deoxycytidine diphosphate)

↓ → ATP

2.7.4.6

↓ → ADP

NH₂

dRib-*PPP*
dCTP (deoxycytidine triphosphate)

↓

DNA

Rib: deoxyribose

Enzymes involved:
1.6.4.5   Thioredoxin reductase (NADPH)
1.17.4.1 Ribonucleoside-diphosphate reductase
2.7.4.6   Nucleoside-diphosphate kinase

Pyrimidine nucleotides (Fig. 7)

In contrast to the synthesis of the purine nucleotides, in the formation of pyrimidine nucleotides the pyrimidine ring is synthesized first, and only then is the phosphoribosyl residue introduced. The reaction of orotate and 5-phosphoribose 1-diphosphate (*P*Rib-*PP*) is irreversible inasmuch as the resultant pyrophosphate is immediately hydrolyzed in the cell.

In the first step of the pyrimidine synthesis, carbamoyl phosphate is formed. This reaction takes place in the cytosol and requires glutamine as a donor of the NH₂ group. In urea synthesis, on the other hand, carbamoyl phosphate is formed in the mitochondria with the aid of NH₃. In the case of a high NH₃ yield or an interruption of the urea cycle owing to enzyme defects, so much carbamoyl phosphate can be formed in the mitochondria that it diffuses into the cytosol and gives rise to an increased pyrimidine synthesis.

The rate-determining step of pyrimidine synthesis is probably the formation of carbamoyl phosphate; the enzyme required, carbamoyl-phosphate synthase (glutamine-hydrolyzing) (6.3.5.5), is inhibited by UTP in a negative feedback mechanism.

Synthesis of the pyrimidine ring requires 4 molecules of ATP. NADH, which can be utilized in the electron transfer system for the formation of 3 molecules of ATP (page 98), is formed in the reaction with orotate reductase (NADH) (1.3.1.14); this enzyme is bound to the surface of the inner mitochondrial membrane.

UMP is formed from orotate in a 2-step mechanism. In yeast the 2 enzymes involved – orotate phosphoribosyltransferase (2.4.2.10) and orotidine-5'-phosphate decarboxylase (4.1.1.23) – are individual proteins, whereas in animals the 2 enzyme characteristics are due to 2 catalytic centers on a single polypeptide.

UMP can not only be formed de novo, but may also be resynthesized from the uracil released in the breakdown of pyrimidine nucleotides (page 129). In the fetus, de novo synthesis seems to predominate; in adults, on the other hand, resynthesis is paramount.

Deoxyribonucleotides

Reduction of the OH group at C-2 of ribose takes place not on the free sugar but in the ribonucleotides, according to the following reaction:

$$NADPH + H^+ + \text{ribonucleotide} \xrightarrow{1.17.4} NADP^+ + \text{deoxyribonucleotide} + H_2O$$

The ribonucleoside-diphosphate reductase responsible for the reaction is poorly characterized in mammals. The reaction requires compounds with SH groups as hydrogen donors. In *E. coli* the SH groups are contained in the form of 2 cysteine residues in the polypeptide thioredoxin, which consists of 108 amino acids. The transfer of hydrogen from NADPH to thioredoxin takes place via FADH₂. Details are presented in Figure 8 – taking the synthesis of deoxycytidine diphosphate as an example – and on page 77. The formation of deoxyribonucleotides is carefully controlled to limit the amount to that which is required for DNA synthesis.

Thymidine nucleotides (Fig. 9)

The formation of dTMP from dUMP requires the introduction of a methyl group which is supplied by 5,10-methylenetetrahydrofolate. The reaction is irreversible and is catalyzed by the enzyme thymidylate synthase (2.1.1.45). 5,10-Methylenetetrahydrofolate is present only in the amount needed for catalysis and must be constantly regenerated for a continuous dTMP synthesis. For this purpose, dihydrofolate needs to be reduced to tetrahydrofolate with the aid of dihydrofolate reductase (1.5.1.3). Doses of folic-acid antagonists, such as methotrexate, inhibit this enzyme and hence also the formation of DNA, in which process cells with a highly accelerated metabolism are especially vulnerable. Another drug used as an antineoplastic agent, fluorouracil, is first converted in the body to the corresponding deoxyribonucleotide, which then reacts with 5,10-methylenetetrahydrofolate and thymidylate synthase to yield a ternary complex that suppresses the methylation of dUMP.

Fig. 9 *Biosynthesis of dTMP, dTDP and dTTP (thymidine mono-, di- and triphosphate)*

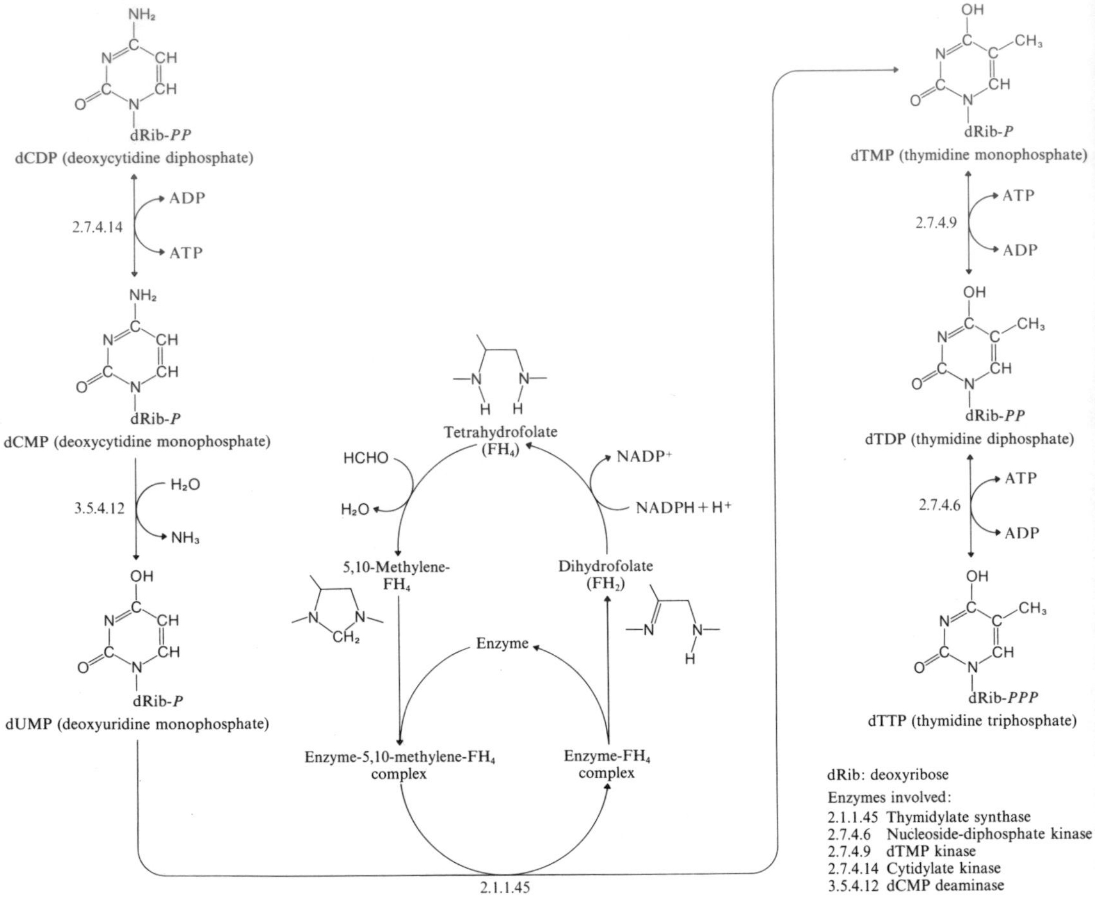

dCDP (deoxycytidine diphosphate)

2.7.4.14 ADP / ATP

dCMP (deoxycytidine monophosphate)

3.5.4.12 H$_2$O / NH$_3$

dUMP (deoxyuridine monophosphate)

Tetrahydrofolate (FH$_4$)

HCHO

H$_2$O

5,10-Methylene-FH$_4$

Enzyme

NADP$^+$

NADPH + H$^+$

Dihydrofolate (FH$_2$)

Enzyme-5,10-methylene-FH$_4$ complex

Enzyme-FH$_4$ complex

2.1.1.45

dTMP (thymidine monophosphate)

2.7.4.9 ATP / ADP

dTDP (thymidine diphosphate)

2.7.4.6 ATP / ADP

dTTP (thymidine triphosphate)

dRib: deoxyribose

Enzymes involved:
2.1.1.45 Thymidylate synthase
2.7.4.6 Nucleoside-diphosphate kinase
2.7.4.9 dTMP kinase
2.7.4.14 Cytidylate kinase
3.5.4.12 dCMP deaminase

Reviews

· STANBURY et al., *The Metabolic Basis of Inherited Disease*, 5th ed., Part 7: Disorders of purine and pyrimidine metabolism, McGraw-Hill, New York, 1983, page 1041.
· JONES, M. E., Pyrimidine nucleotide biosynthesis in animals: genes, enzymes and regulation of UMP biosynthesis, *Ann. Rev. Biochem.*, **49**, 253 (1980).
· KORNBERG, A., *DNA Replication*, Freeman, San Francisco, 1980, page 39.

· THELANDER and REICHARD, Reduction of ribonucleotides, *Ann. Rev. Biochem.*, **48**, 133 (1979).
· KELLEY and WEINER (Ed.), *Uric Acid*, Springer, Berlin, 1978.
· Purine and pyrimidine metabolism, *Ciba Found. Symp.*, NS **48** (1977).
· HEINTEL et al., Biosynthesis of tetrahydrobiopterin: possible involvement of tetrahydrobiopterin intermediates, *Neurochem. Int.*, **6**, 141 (1984).

Deoxyribonucleic acid (DNA)

DNA contains equal amounts of deoxyguanosine monophosphate and deoxycytidine monophosphate and also of deoxyadenosine monophosphate and thymidine monophosphate.

The DNA molecule consists of a pair of polynucleotide chains aligned in the form of a double helix. The alignment is such that bases in one chain are linked to bases in the other chain by hydrogen bonds, guanine being linked to cytosine and adenine to thymine.

Cytosine   Guanine

Thymine   Adenine

This association of purines with pyrimidines means that 4 combinations are possible, namely cytosine–guanine, guanine–cytosine, thymine–adenine and adenine–thymine (C–G, G–C, T–A and A–T). Thence arises a number of possible sequence variations, which increases with polymer size. The possible structural variations of a polynucleotide consisting of 300 mononucleotide units (or base pairs) can be estimated at about 4×10^{87}. The nucleic acids are thus capable of great specificity, and this specificity can be transferred to proteins during their synthesis.

The DNA polymer is arranged in the form of a double helix. This can best be visualized as a flexible ladder in which the rungs are base pairs and the flexible uprights sugar phosphates (strands with antiparallel 'polarity'). If a polymer consisting of 10 base pairs is fixed at one end and rotated 360° at the other end it results in the formation of a double helix (Fig. 1).

The Watson-Crick model of DNA (the B form) and the related A form of DNA are right-handed helices. Left-handed Z-DNA has been shown to exist in equilibrium with right-handed DNA. Z-DNA has about 12 base pairs per turn of the helix. Z-DNA is less stable than A and B conformations. Segments of polydeoxynucleotides in which purines and pyrimidines alternate are the most favored for forming Z-DNA.

Example:

```
A C A C A C A C
| | | | | | | |
T G T G T G T G
```

Fig. 1 *Schematic representation of the structure of right-handed DNA*

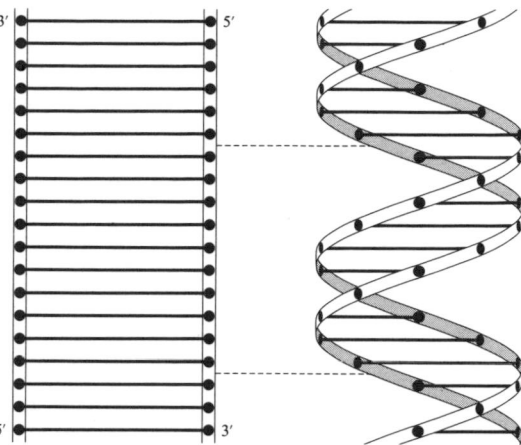

In eukaryotes, short segments of DNA exist as Z-DNA. It has been suggested that Z-DNA acts as a regulatory signal in transcription. Probably Z-DNA activity operates through specific interactions with Z-DNA-binding proteins.

The structure of DNA is ideal for the function for which DNA exists, namely to reproduce itself exactly (replication), and to make possible the synthesis of thousands of enzymes and other proteins upon which the metabolic activities of the organism depend. This structure is also very stable – a vital requirement for the survival and continued existence of any organism.

The ability of DNA to replicate exactly depends upon the strict pairing of adenine with thymine (A–T or T–A) and of guanine with cytosine (G–C or C–G). In the process of cell division there is a longitudinal cleavage of the chromosomal DNA. In the formation of new strands the original ones diverge, and each parent strand functions as a template for the formation of complementary strands (Fig. 2). The reaction is catalyzed by DNA-directed DNA polymerase (2.7.7.7), which has an absolute requirement for Mg^{2+} as well as for a primer – i.e. an oligonucleotide that is hydrogen-bonded to the template strand and whose terminal 3'-OH group is available for reaction. The enzyme is specific for the deoxyribonucleoside triphosphates dATP, dTTP, dGTP and dCTP.

$$n \text{ deoxynucleoside triphosphates} \xrightarrow{\ 2.7.7.7\ } DNA_n + n\, PP_i$$

The base composition of the enzymatically formed DNA is a complementary copy of that of the single-stranded template, regardless of the relative amounts of each deoxyribonucleoside triphosphate present in the reaction mixture. As the 2 strands of the DNA helix unwind and separate, the exposed purines and pyrimidines react with their complementary bases. Where the template contains adenine, the nucleotide inserted into the growing molecule will contain thymine, and vice versa. Similarly guanine reacts only with the cytosine in the template, and vice versa.

In the formation of new strands of DNA the DNA-directed DNA polymerase catalyzes the nucleophilic attack of the oxygen of the

Fig. 2 *Semiconservative replication of DNA*

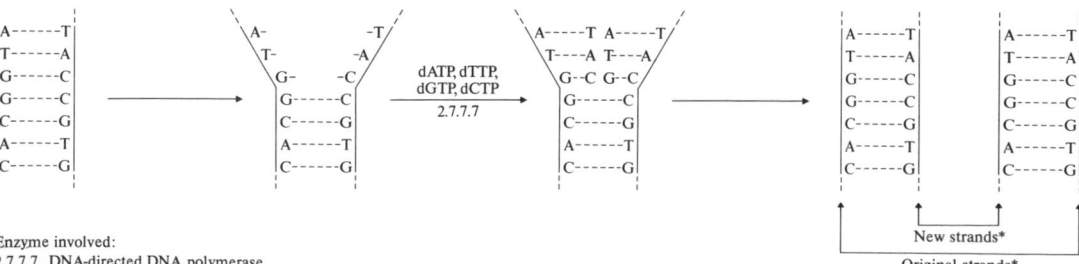

Enzyme involved:
2.7.7.7. DNA-directed DNA polymerase

New strands*

Original strands*

* A new double strand consists in each case of one strand with old material and one strand with newly synthesized material.

Fig. 3 *Condensation of a deoxyribonucleotide*

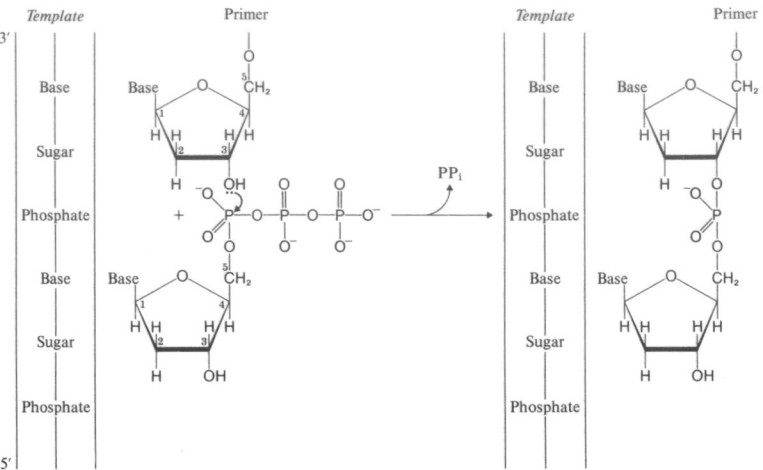

3'-OH group on the primer strand on the inside phosphate group in position 5' of the incoming deoxyribonucleotide. This reaction shows that the DNA strand can grow only from the 5' end to the 3' end (Fig. 3). The energy needed for this condensation is provided by hydrolysis of the pyrophosphate high-energy bond.

The elongation of DNA strands does not take place continuously, but fragments consisting of about 1000 nucleotides (Okazaki fragments) are formed at several sites on the template. The breaks between the Okazaki fragments are closed with the aid of polydeoxyribonucleotide synthase (DNA ligase) (Fig. 4). Upon closure of the breaks the 3'-OH group at the end of one fragment of a DNA strand condenses with the phosphate group at the 5' end of the other fragment. The energy for this reaction is provided by the hydrolysis of ATP (or of NAD).

Another significant aspect of DNA synthesis is the process of initiation, since it can be shown that DNA-directed DNA polymerase requires a starter molecule before it will act. It appears that, at the beginning of the replication, DNA-directed RNA polymerase (2.7.7.6) or specialized primases form a short sequence of RNA nucleotides, which can then function as a primer for the subsequent elongation of the DNA strand. This initial primer RNA is subsequently removed by hydrolysis.

DNA methylation. The DNA of prokaryotes contains N6-methyladenine and 5-methylcytosine, whereas that of eukaryotes contains only 5-methylcytosine. Methylation of the bases, catalyzed by DNA methyltransferases (2.1.1), is inheritable and takes place in the early post-replicative stage: only the newly synthesized strand becomes methylated. In eukaryotes, 5-methylcytosine occurs predominantly in the sequence CpG (p: phosphate residue). DNA methylation affects DNA–protein interactions, protects DNA against restriction endonucleases (page 126) and regulates gene expression in eukaryotes.

Supercoiled DNA, and DNA topoisomerases. The double helix of DNA can wind in space to form a new helix of higher order – the so-called 'supercoiled DNA'. Besides DNA with a linear axis, DNA may occur as a ring (for example in tumor viruses and in mitochondria), consisting either of a single strand or of 2 strands wound in a double helix. These rings can be arranged in different topological forms, depending on the kind of supercoiling. DNA topoisomerases

are involved in topological conversions. The type I enzyme (5.99.1.2) breaks and rejoins one strand at a time and catalyzes the crossing of one strand through another; the ATP-dependent type II enzyme (5.99.1.3) – also called 'DNA gyrase' – breaks and rejoins a pair of strands in concert and catalyzes the crossing of a double-stranded segment through a double-stranded break.

DNA repair. Ultraviolet radiation, chemicals, and other influences can lead to damage of the DNA structure; in most cases only one base is affected. The consequence may be cell death, a mutation, or even reproduction of the original structure because the cell has repair mechanisms at its disposal. Thus, for example, the dimer of thymine formed by UV radiation can be separated again into the individual bases with the aid of light and deoxyribodipyrimidine photo-lyase (light repair). In excision repair, other adjoining bases are also cut out along with the damaged base; the gaps thus formed in the DNA strand are filled up to the original state by DNA synthesis. Both these repair mechanisms operate flawlessly; however, in other mechanisms (recombinational repair, templateless synthesis in the case of rupture of the double strand) errors must be reckoned with.

Excision repair requires a temporary relaxation of the nucleosomal structure, so that repaired regions are more accessible to nucleases. Temporary change may involve poly(ADP-ribose) attachment on to histone H1.

Nucleosomes. The constituent material of the chromosomes is wholly or partly formed by the combination of DNA with protein (chromatin). 'Nucleosome' is the generally accepted term for the chromatin subunit. Basic proteins – the histones – are involved in the packaging of the enormous length of eukaryotic DNA into the different conformational states of chromosomes. An octamer of histones – the histone tetramer (H3,H4)$_2$ and 2 pairs of the dimer (H2A,H2B) – forms the core particle of the nucleosomes, around which the nucleic acid strands (146 base pairs) are wound. The nucleosomes are connected by linker DNA (20–80 base pairs); histone H1 is bound to linker DNA. The nucleosome strand will arrange itself into a series of loops. Nonenzymatic acidic proteins – 'nonhistone chromatin proteins' (NHCP) – are involved in the control of transcription in eukaryotes.

Fig. 4 *Closure of breaks in DNA*

```
|A------T|                          |A------T|              |A------T|
|G------C|   ATP      PP_i          |G------C|              |G------C|
|C------G|  [NAD]    [NMN]          |C------G|      AMP      |C------G|
|T------A|³'—OH                     |T------A|³'—OH          |T------A|
|T------A|₅'—P                      |T------A|₅'—P—P—Ado     |T------A|
|G------C|    6.5.1.1               |G------C|              |G------C|
|C------G|   [6.5.1.2]              |C------G|              |C------G|
|A------T|                          |A------T|              |A------T|
```

Enzymes involved (DNA ligases):
6.5.1.1 Polydeoxyribonucleotide synthase (ATP)
[6.5.1.2 Polydeoxyribonucleotide synthase (NAD+)]

Fig. 5 *Diagram of the removal of intron transcript in the transcription process in eukaryotes[1]*

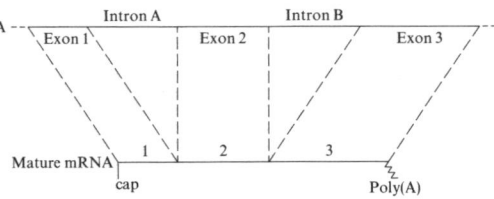

cap   7-Methylguanosine triphosphate
Poly(A) Polyadenylate

Fig. 6 *General structure of transfer RNA[4]*

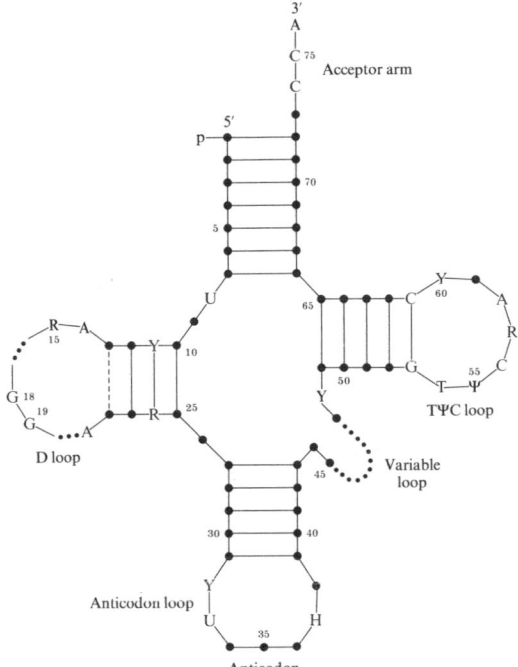

p. phosphate residue
Nonvariable nucleotides are indicated with the symbol of the nucleoside: A (adenosine), C (cytidine), G (guanosine), H (modified purine nucleoside), Ψ (pseudouridine), R (purine nucleoside), T (ribosylthymine), U (uridine), Y (pyrimidine nucleoside)

Ribonucleic acid (RNA)

There are 3 types of RNA, each with a specific function: messenger RNA (mRNA), transfer RNA (tRNA) and ribosomal RNA (rRNA).

All these forms of RNA are similar to DNA inasmuch as they consist of long sequences of nucleotides linked together by $3' \rightarrow 5'$ phosphodiester linkages. Contrary to DNA the constituent sugar is ribose, and the pyrimidine uracil replaces the methylated analog thymine. Although the RNA molecules are mainly single-stranded, to a certain degree there is base pairing as in DNA – due to additional folding or loop formation in the molecule –, in which adenine pairs with uracil and guanine with cytosine.

The chain length can vary from about 80 nucleotides in the case of tRNA up to many thousands in mRNA. The nucleotide sequence of RNA is determined by the complementary nucleotide sequence of DNA.

Although single stranded DNA will act as a template, double-stranded DNA is preferable, in which case, however, only one strand is 'copied'. This implies that the DNA remains fully conserved during RNA synthesis, instead of being split as in semiconservative DNA synthesis. Formation of RNA does not require a primer.

The formation of RNA from the appropriate ribonucleoside triphosphates takes place by the action of DNA-directed RNA polymerase (2.7.7.6); the enzyme requires a divalent metal ion, Mn^{2+} being more effective than Mg^{2+}. The enzyme is specific for the ribonucleotides ATP, GTP, UTP and CTP.

$$n \text{ nucleoside triphosphates} \xrightarrow{\;2.7.7.6\;} RNA_n + 4n \text{ PP}_i$$

The chief physiological function of this enzyme is probably the formation of *mRNA* for protein synthesis, i.e. to transcribe information contained in the DNA code into RNA (transcription). This involves the formation of relatively short RNA strands which correspond approximately to the structural genes in the DNA, and which will ultimately be responsible for the synthesis of a protein (enzyme) on a ribosome. mRNA therefore has to be continually formed, depending upon the enzyme requirement of the cell. In this way also RNA formation differs from that of DNA, which is discontinuously but completely replicated in each cell generation. The mRNA fraction of total cellular RNA is about 5%.

Mature mRNA in the cytoplasm of eukaryotes does not commonly contain the entire nucleotide sequence corresponding to the DNA; rather, the primary transcript (pre-mRNA) is processed in the nucleus by removal of 'nonsense' sequences – which correspond to the intron sequences of DNA –, and the sequences corresponding to the exons are united (RNA splicing) (Fig. 5). Splicing proceeds in 2 steps. The first involves the cleavage of the 5' site, whereupon the intron folds back to form a covalently bonded lariat structure. In the second step the first exon comes together with the second, the two are ligated and the lariat lost[2].

Almost all mRNA strands in the cytoplasm have a poly(A) tail at the 3' end. The function of the tail seems to be to protect mRNA from enzymatic breakdown in the cytoplasm. However, poly(A) is not required for mRNA to be translated. At the 5' end, methylated guanosine triphosphate (the 'cap') is added.

In the cytoplasm of eukaryotes, mRNA is complexed with proteins of unknown function, the size of the particles ('messenger ribonucleoproteins' or 'informosomes') depending on the size of their mRNA[3].

tRNA is formed by the synthesis of a precursor (~ 100 nucleotides) that is about 20% larger than the mature molecule. Nucleotides are removed at both the 5' and the 3' end by specific nucleases. Mature tRNA contains modified bases (see page 53) formed by the introduction of, for example, methyl or isopentenyl groups or by the conversion of uridine to pseudouridine. Dimeric and polymeric precursors are not found in eukaryotes.

The secondary structure of tRNA is of cloverleaf shape. Nucleotide sequences of a series of tRNA molecules have been determined. The general tRNA structure is shown in Figure 6. The importance of the anticodon loop is described on page 179. The TΨC loop is probably involved in the interaction between tRNA and ribosome.

In eukaryotes, the synthesis of *rRNA* takes place in the nucleolus. Mature rRNA species result from rRNA precursor molecules (45 S-pre-rRNA) comprising 18 S, 5.8 S and 28 S rRNA as well as spacer sequences. 15–45% of the precursor molecule is discarded during processing. The rRNA species are then methylated to varying degrees.

The replication of RNA viruses requires only the formation of new RNA. In a first step a complementary RNA strand is synthesized with the aid of RNA-directed RNA polymerase (2.7.7.48), and in a second step this strand serves as a template for the synthesis of viral RNA. In retroviruses (RNA tumor viruses), on the other hand, replication proceeds indirectly. During cell infection, single-stranded RNA is transcribed into double-stranded DNA (provirus, which is integrated into the host genome) by the action of RNA-directed DNA polymerase (2.7.7.49) (reverse transcriptase). This DNA serves as template for both viral mRNA and viral progeny RNA synthesis.

References

Reviews:
· KORNBERG, A:, DNA replication, *Trends biochem. Sci.*, **9**, 122 (1984).
· NOLLER, H. F., Structure of ribosomal RNA, *Ann. Rev. Biochem.*, **53**, 119 (1984).
· RICH et al., The chemistry and biology of left-handed Z-DNA, *Ann. Rev. Biochem.*, **53**, 791 (1984).
· FREIFELDER, D., *Molecular Biology*, Jones and Bartlett, Boston, 1983.
· DARNELL, J. E., The processing of RNA, *Sci. Amer.*, **249**, No. 4, 72 (1983).
· DICKERSON, R. E., The DNA helix and how it is read, *Sci. Amer.*, **249**, No. 6, 86 (1983).
· DOERFLER, W., DNA methylation and gene activity, *Ann. Rev. Biochem.*, **52**, 93 (1983).
· LINDAHL, T., DNA repair enzymes, *Ann. Rev. Biochem.*, **51**, 61 (1982).

· ZIMMERMAN, S.B., The three-dimensional structure of DNA, *Ann. Rev. Biochem.*, **51**, 395 (1982).
· WANG, J.C., DNA topoisomerases, *Sci. Amer.*, **247**, No. 1, 84 (1982).
· WEISBROD, S., Active chromatin, *Nature*, **297**, 289 (1982).
· SZEKELY, M., *From DNA to Protein*, Macmillan, London, 1980.
· OGAWA and OKAZAKI, Discontinuous DNA replication, *Ann. Rev. Biochem.*, **49**, 421 (1980).
· DePAMPHILIS and WASSARMAN, Replication of eukaryotic chromosomes: a close-up of the replication fork, *Ann. Rev. Biochem.*, **49**, 627 (1980).
· BAUER et al., Supercoiled DNA, *Sci. Amer.*, **243**, No. 1, 100 (1980).

· HANAWALT et al., DNA repair in bacteria and mammalian cells, *Ann. Rev. Biochem.*, **48**, 783 (1979).
· RICH and KIM, The three-dimensional structure of transfer RNA, *Sci. Amer.*, **238**, No. 1, 52 (1978).

Special references:
[1] CRICK, F., *Science*, **204**, 264 (1979).
[2] WEISSMANN, C., *Nature*, **311**, 103 (1984); LEWIN, R., *Science*, **228**, 977 (1985).
[3] SPIRIN and AJTKHOZHIN, *Trends biochem. Sci.*, **10**, 162 (1985).
[4] RICH and RAJBHANDARY, *Ann. Rev. Biochem.*, **45**, 805 (1976).

The genotype – the invariable genetic constitution – is given by the structure of the stored DNA. The phenotype – the outward aspect of the individual –, which comprises all the measurable or quantifiable properties, depends on the structure of the proteins (primarily enzymes). These are decisive for the synthesis and structure of all the additional organic substances necessary for building up the organism and for the organism's functioning and its reaction to the environment. The structure of a protein, i.e. the position of each individual amino acid within the hundreds or thousands of amino acids sequentially linked to form polypeptide chains, is determined by the information stored in the DNA. In other words, the nucleotide sequences of DNA – or of complementary RNA – determine the amino-acid sequences in proteins. The genetic code is concerned with the nature of this relationship.

Since 20 different amino acids occur as constituents of proteins and only 4 bases or their nucleotides are available in DNA, a 2-base code is inadequate because only 16 variations would be possible. A 3-base code is therefore required, which produces 4^3 (= 64) possible variations. Each of the trinucleotide sequences (triplets) is called a codon, and of the 64 possibilities of variation, 61 code for amino acids. It therefore follows that some amino acids must have more than one codon and 3 codons must fulfill other functions.

The genetic code, in which X stands for any of the 4 nucleosides A (adenosine), U (uridine), C (cytidine) or G (guanosine), is represented in Table 1.

This code is almost universal; that is, it holds true for all organisms. Exceptions to this standard code were, however, detected for mitochondrial mRNA (Table 2). In different genetic systems the same codon may therefore lead to different amino-acid sequences.

Although DNA is equipped with all the information that makes the formation of specific amino-acid sequences possible, it is not directly involved in protein synthesis. For this, 3 types of RNA are necessary – messenger RNA (mRNA), transfer RNA (tRNA) and ribosomal RNA (rRNA).

Messenger RNA. In the first step – transcription – the code message in DNA, i.e. the information encoded in the chromosome, is transmitted to mRNA, which carries the information across the nuclear membrane and through the cytoplasm to the site of protein synthesis – the ribosome. The reason for this is primarily to retain the integrity of the DNA molecule, upon which the whole genetic future of an organism depends. DNA is therefore a very stable molecule, whereas mRNA is short-lived and is broken down into its constituent nucleotides, which can then be used again.

Transfer RNA. tRNA is concerned with the selection of specific amino acids from the pool and with their transfer to the ribosome. Here the amino acids are marshalled in the correct sequence, as determined by the coding of the mRNA (translation). Since the formation of polypeptides involves condensation of amino acids, energy will be required. The amino acids must first be raised to a high group-transfer potential (activation) by reaction with ATP to form aminoacyladenylate and pyrophosphate:

$$\underset{\text{RCHCOOH} + \text{ATP}}{\overset{\text{NH}_2}{|}} \Longleftrightarrow \underset{\text{RCHCO}-\overset{\text{O}}{\underset{|}{\overset{||}{P}}}-\text{O}-\text{Ado} + \text{PP}_i}{\overset{\text{NH}_2}{|}}$$

The next step is the transfer of the aminoacyl group of the aminoacyl-AMP to a specific tRNA molecule to form aminoacyl-tRNA:

$$\underset{\substack{\text{RCHCO}-\overset{\text{O}}{\underset{|}{\overset{||}{P}}}-\text{O}-\text{Ado} + \text{tRNA}\\ \text{Aminoacyl-AMP}}}{\overset{\text{NH}_2}{|}} \Longleftrightarrow \underset{\substack{\text{RCHCO}-\text{tRNA} + \text{AMP}\\ \text{Aminoacyl-tRNA}}}{\overset{\text{NH}_2}{|}}$$

Additional energy for driving the reactions in the desired direction is supplied by hydrolysis of the pyrophosphate. The combined reactions can therefore be summarized in the following equation:

$$\text{Amino acid} + \text{ATP} + \text{tRNA} + \text{H}_2\text{O} \longrightarrow \substack{\text{Aminoacyl-tRNA}\\ + \text{AMP} + 2\,\text{P}_i}$$

Activation of the amino acids thus involves the hydrolysis of both the energy-rich bonds in ATP. Although the two stages occur separately, both reactions are associated with and catalyzed by the same enzyme, aminoacyl-tRNA ligase. These ligases are highly specific; a different one exists for each amino acid (6.1.1.1–6.1.1.22). Each of these enzymes has the ability to select its specific amino acid and bind

Table 1 *The genetic code: nucleotide sequences* of messenger RNA*

Amino acid	Codons	No. of codons
Alanine	GCX	4
Arginine	CGX AGA AGG	6
Asparagine	AAU AAC	2
Aspartic acid	GAU GAC	2
Cysteine	UGU UGC	2
Glutamic acid	GAA GAG	2
Glutamine	CAA CAG	2
Glycine	GGX	4
Histidine	CAU CAG	2
Isoleucine	AUU AUC AUA	3
Leucine	UUA UUG CUX	6
Lysine	AAA AUG$^\lozenge$	2
Methionine	AUG	1
Phenylalanine	UUU UUC	2
Proline	CCX	4
Serine	UCX AGU AGC	6
Threonine	ACX	4
Tryptophan	UGG	1
Tyrosine	UAU UAC	2
Valine	GUX$^\lozenge$	4
		61

* Nucleotides are denoted with the symbol of the nucleoside.
$^\lozenge$ AUG and GUG are initiation codons; the remaining 3 codons UAA, UAG and UGA ('nonsense' codons) are involved in termination.

Table 2 *Some deviations from the standard code in mitochondria*

DNA	3′ GTTCAGTATGATACT 5′
mRNA	5′ CAAGUCAUACUAUGA 3′
Cytoplasm: bacteria	—Gln—Val—Ile—Leu—termi-
Mitochondria:	nation
Yeast	—Gln—Val—Ile—Thr—Trp
Man	—Gln—Val—Met—Leu—Trp
Neurosporum	—Gln—Val—Ile—Leu—Trp

it in activated form to the correct tRNA. The tRNA molecules specific for each amino acid must also be able to recognize the mRNA codons which are appropriate to those amino acids.

The size of the tRNA molecule with an average of 80 nucleotides is small compared to other forms of RNA. Despite their specificity for both amino acids and mRNA codons, all tRNA molecules have two characteristics in common (page 177): 1. The nucleotide sequence at the end to which the amino acid is attached is CCA, the terminal base – adenine – being condensed with the amino acid. 2. Although about half the nucleotides are double-stranded to form double helices, several groups of nucleotides remain single-stranded; the most important one is the so-called *anticodon loop*, which is situated spatially remote from the aminoacyl end. An anticodon is a nucleotide triplet that is complementary to a codon. tRNA thus acts as a kind of adapter which carries a specific amino acid and, by virtue of its corresponding anticodon, can be inserted into the codon on a mRNA molecule which codes for this specific amino acid. In this way a sequence of codons on the mRNA is converted to a sequence of amino acids in a polypeptide chain or protein (or enzyme). An interesting feature of many anticodon triplets is the introduction of another nucleoside – inosine (deaminated guanosine). Inosine (I), like its related nucleoside G, pairs with C; however, this pairing is not specific. Inosine can pair with more than one base ('wobble hypothesis'), so that for example CAI – the anticodon for valine – can pair with either GUC or GUU. This makes possible the recognition of more than one codon by an anticodon assigned to a specific amino acid. For most amino acids there are 2 or more codons (Table 1).

Ribosomes. Ribosomes are structural units of cells in all organisms and consist essentially of RNA (rRNA) and protein in a mass ratio of about 2:1 in prokaryotes, or 1:1 in eukaryotes. In eukaryotes they are usually associated with the endoplasmic reticulum. They are the

Protein synthesis in prokaryotes (E. coli)

Initiation

The 30 S subunit is bound to an initiation factor IF3.

mRNA is bound to the 30 S subunit with the aid of the initiation factor IF3.

Formylmethionyl-tRNA (fMet-tRNA) is bound – with the aid of an additional initiation factor IF2 as well as GTP – in such a way that its anticodon (UAC) pairs with the initiation codon of mRNA (AUG). (These first 2 steps may take place in the reverse order.) Factor IF1 and GTP are likewise added to the 30 S subunit.

Factor IF3 separates from the complex, which makes possible the binding of the 50 S subunit to form a complete ribosome. Factors IF1 and IF2 also separate from the complex, as well as GTP, which is split into GDP and P_i. The alignment takes place in such a manner that fMet-tRNA is bound to the P site of the 50 S subunit.

Elongation

Binding. The second aminoacyl-tRNA is bound to the A site of the ribosome so that its anticodon (CUC) pairs with the next codon (GAG) on the mRNA. This binding needs GTP as well as the elongation factors EF-Tu and EF-Ts. The function of EF-Ts is to regenerate EF-Tu—GTP from EF-Tu—GDP:

$$\text{EF-Tu—GDP} + \text{GTP} \xrightarrow{\text{EF-Ts}} \text{EF-Tu—GTP} + \text{GDP}$$

Peptide formation. This requires peptidyltransferase (2.3.2.12), which is built into the 50 S subunit. The formylmethionyl fragment of formylmethionyl-tRNA is transferred to the amino group of the following aminoacyl-tRNA to form formylmethionylaminoacyl-tRNA, the nonacylated tRNA remaining at the P site. The transfer reaction does not require extra energy.

CHO   R²   CHO
| H| |
NH   :NCH   NH   R²
| H| | |
R¹CHCO   CO   R¹CHCONHCH
                     |
                     CO

U A C   C U C   U A C   C U C

Formyl-methionyl-tRNA   Aminoacyl-tRNA   tRNA   Dipeptidyl-tRNA (formylmethionyl-glutamyl-tRNA)

+ ... 2.3.2.12 ... OH + ...

In *translocation*, 3 rearrangements take place:
1. Free tRNA is released from the P site.
2. Dipeptidyl-tRNA moves from the A site to the P site.
3. mRNA shifts by a distance of 1 codon (3 nucleotides).

GTP is hydrolyzed during translocation, a reaction catalyzed by the ribosome-dependent GTPase activity of factor EF-G.

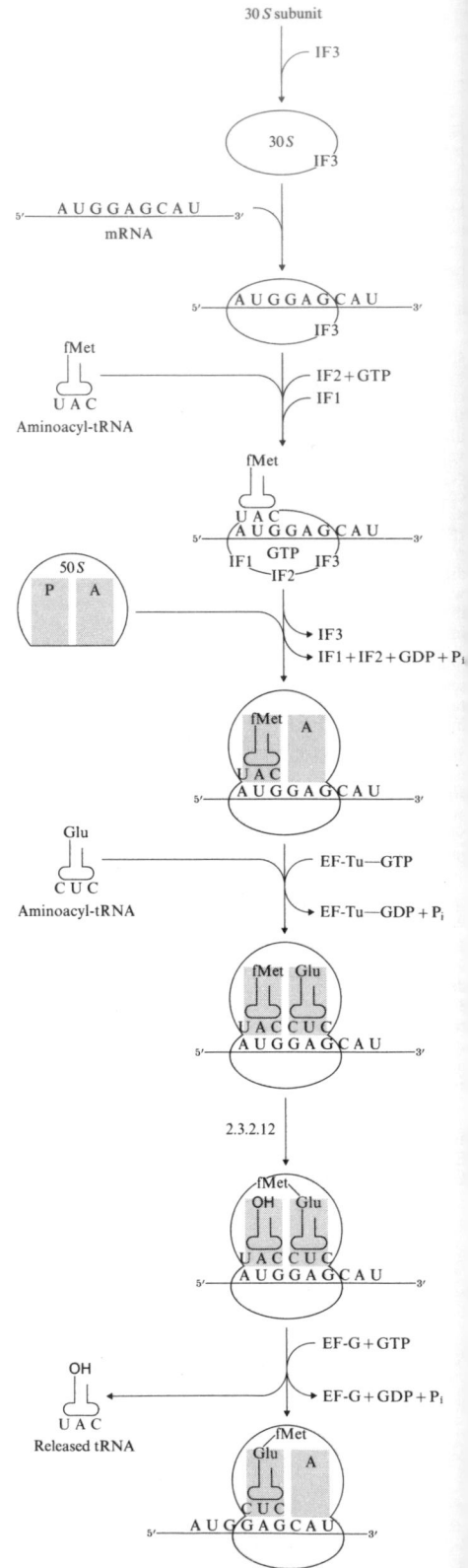

Table 3   *Structure of the ribosomes*

Prokaryotes (*E. coli*)		Eukaryotes (rat liver)	
70 *S* ($M_r = 2.6 \times 10^6$)		80 *S* ($M_r = 4.3 \times 10^6$)	
50 *S* subunit	30 *S* subunit	60 *S* subunit	40 *S* subunit
5 *S*-RNA + 23 *S*-RNA + 32 different proteins	16 *S*-RNA + 21 different proteins	5 *S*-RNA + 5.8 *S*-RNA + 28 *S*-RNA + 45–50 different proteins	18 *S*-RNA + 30 different proteins

site of protein synthesis and occur in all cells in which proteins are synthesized. They are characterized by their sedimentation coefficient (*S* values), which depends on the specific gravity and shape of the ribosomes. In eukaryotes, ribosomes have *S* values of 80 and are about twice as large as ribosomes in prokaryotes, which have *S* values of 70. Ribosomes consist of 2 parts, or subunits (Table 3), each of which has a specific function: the smaller subunit is concerned with the recognition of the initiation codon of mRNA as well as the interaction between codon and complementary anticodon of tRNA; the larger subunit is the site where amino acids condense to form polypeptide chains or proteins. The larger subunit possesses 2 areas or sites: the peptidyl-binding site (P site), to which the tRNA with a growing polypeptide chain is bound, and the aminoacyl-binding site (A site), which binds the next aminoacyl-tRNA molecule involved in the elongation process.

Initiation of protein synthesis. Since mRNA consists of a very long sequence of nucleotides that have to be read in triplets, it is important that the 'reading' should commence in the correct position. For instance, the sequence

···GAUCCGCAGCUGUCC···

could be read as

···GAU/CCG/CAG/CUG/UCC···

or as

···G/AUC/CGC/AGC/UGU···

or as

···GA/UCC/GCA/GCU/GU···

depending upon the nucleotide at which the 'reading' started. These 3 triplet sequences would result in the formation of very different polypeptides or proteins. To ensure the correct starting point, a specific tRNA with the anticodon UAC is responsible for the initiation of 'reading'; in prokaryotes it is formylmethionyl-tRNA, in eukaryotes methionyl-tRNA.

Elongation of the peptide. 'Elongation' involves the alignment of amino acids corresponding to the sequence of codons in the mRNA. Elongation occurs in 3 stages: *binding* of aminoacyl-tRNA, *peptide*

formation and *translocation.* In the illustration on the preceding page these steps are described as they occur in *E. coli*.

The completion of translocation results in a ribosome in which the P site is occupied by a dipeptidyl-tRNA; the A site is empty. Hence the A site can bind another aminoacyl-tRNA, the nature of which depends on the identity of the next nucleotide triplet on the mRNA. (In the illustration on page 180 this is CAU, the codon for histidine.) Another round of elongation then begins, resulting in the formation of a tripeptidyl-tRNA (formylmethionylglutamylhistidinyl-tRNA).

Termination of protein synthesis. Elongation of the polypeptide chain continues as described until a codon on the mRNA is reached that cannot react with any aminoacyl-tRNA. Such termination codons are UAA, UAG and UGA, which do not code for any amino acid (Table 1).

The termination of chain growth is followed by hydrolysis of the polypeptide chain from the tRNA that carries it, a reaction that requires a complex system of termination or release factors. In prokaryotes, 2 release factors are known (RF1, RF2); RF1 terminates at the codons UAA and UAG, RF2 at UAA and UGA.

After the release of the polypeptide chain from the ribosome the latter dissociates into the 2 subunits, and the whole process of initiation, elongation and termination begins again.

Protein synthesis in eukaryotes

The basic pattern of protein synthesis in eukaryotes, though similar to that in prokaryotes, is less well known than that in prokaryotes.

Initiation. Methionyl-tRNA responding to the codon AUG initiates protein synthesis. At least 5 initiation factors (eIF) and GTP are required for the binding of Met-tRNA to the initiation complex of the 40 *S* ribosomal subunit. Binding of Met-tRNA must occur *before* mRNA can bind. For the binding of mRNA, other initiation factors are needed, and ATP must be cleaved to form ADP and P$_i$. Binding of mRNA occurs at or near the 5'-cap terminus (see Fig. 5, page 177) and is mediated by a specific protein, the cap-binding factor. The AUG codon nearest the 5' terminus is always the initiating codon. More factors are needed for binding the 60 *S* subunit than for binding the prokaryotic 50 *S* subunit.

Elongation. Four elongation factors (eEF1$_\alpha$, eEF1$_\beta$, eEF1$_\gamma$, eEF2) are needed; in terms of function, the factors correspond roughly to those of *E. coli*.

Termination. Little is known about termination, though release factors have been isolated.

For the *regulation* of protein synthesis see page 197.

Reviews

· MOLDAVE, K., Eukaryotic protein synthesis, *Ann. Rev. Biochem.*, **54**, 1109 (1985).
· FREIFELDER, D., *Molecular Biology*, Jones and Bartlett, Boston, 1983, page 491.
· MAITRA et al., Initiation factors in protein synthesis, *Ann. Rev. Biochem.*, **51**, 869 (1982).
· LAKE, J. A., The ribosome, *Sci. Amer.*, **245**, No. 2, 56 (1981).
· SZEKELY, M., *From DNA to Protein*, Macmillan, London, 1980.
· WEISSBACH and PESTKA (Ed.), *Molecular Mechanisms of Protein Biosynthesis*, Academic Press, New York, 1977.
· HASELKORN and ROTHMAN-DENES, Protein synthesis, *Ann. Rev. Biochem.*, **42**, 397 (1973).
· LUCAS-LENARD and LIPMANN, Protein biosynthesis, *Ann. Rev. Biochem.*, **40**, 409 (1971).
· The mechanism of protein synthesis, *Cold Spr. Harb. Symp. quant. Biol.*, **34** (1969).
· CLARK and MARCKER, How proteins start, *Sci. Amer.*, **218** (1), 36 (1968).

Fig. 1 *Biosynthesis of the O-glycosidically bound carbohydrate units of glycoproteins in saliva*

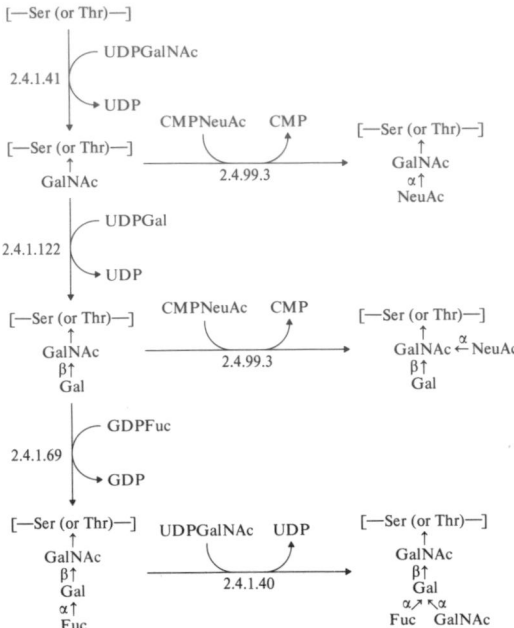

Enzymes involved:
2.4.1.40 Fucosylgalactose α-N-acetylgalactosaminyltransferase
2.4.1.41 Polypeptide N-acetylgalactosaminyltransferase
2.4.1.69 Galactoside 2-L-fucosyltransferase
2.4.1.122 Glycoprotein-N-acetylgalactosamine 3-β-galactosyltransferase
2.4.99.3 CMP-N-acetylneuraminate–α-N-acetylgalactosaminide α-2,6-sialyl-transferase

The starting materials in the formation of oligosaccharide chains in glycoproteins are activated sugars, namely GDP-α-D-mannose, UDP-α-D-glucose, UDP-β-D-xylose and UDP-α-D-N-acetylglucosamine.

Two pathways for adding carbohydrate residues to a polypeptide chain have been described. When the oligosaccharide chain is linked O-glycosidically to serine or threonine, or – as in collagen – to hydroxylysine, the carbohydrate residues are attached in a stepwise sequence. When the oligosaccharide chain is linked N-glycosidically to asparagine, the oligosaccharide chain is synthesized before attachment to the polypeptide chain.

The formation of oligosaccharide chains linked O-*glycosidically* to serine or threonine proceeds with the aid of various glycosyltransferases. The formation of glycoproteins (mucins) in the salivary glands and in the mucous glands of the gastrointestinal and urogenital tracts has been thoroughly investigated. In the first step, N-acetylgalactosamine is attached to threonine or serine residues of the peptide chain, and the carbohydrate portion of the glycosylated peptide is then lengthened by the addition of either a sialic-acid residue or a galactose residue. If sialic acid is incorporated before galactose, the synthesis of the oligosaccharide stops; if galactose is transferred before sialic acid, further chain elongation takes place. Some steps of that type are represented in Figure 1.

In the synthesis of N-*glycosidically* linked oligosaccharide chains, dolichyl diphosphate (Dol-*PP*) takes part as a 'carrier lipid'. The synthesis of oligosaccharides linked to dolichyl diphosphate begins with the formation of N-acetylglucosaminyldiphosphodolichol by means of UDP-N-acetylglucosamine–dolichyl-phosphate N-acetyl-glucosaminephosphotransferase (2.7.8.15). Another N-acetylglucosamine residue as well as 5 mannose residues are then attached. Further synthesis of the chain takes place by the attachment of mannosyl and glucosyl groups via their dolichyl-phosphate derivatives. The entire oligosaccharide thus formed is attached en bloc to specific asparagine residues of the nascent polypeptide chain on the ribosome by means of protein oligosaccharyltransferase (Fig. 2).

Shortly after transfer to the acceptor proteins the initially homogeneous precursor oligosaccharide chains begin to undergo a series of modifications that will eventually produce the diverse N-linked oligosaccharides of mature glycoproteins.

In the rough endoplasmatic reticulum the glucose residues are split off, and the remaining high-mannose glycoprotein is transferred to the Golgi complex, where the oligosaccharide chains are further processed by removal of mannose residues as well as attachment of N-acetylglucosamine, galactose, sialic-acid and fucose residues (Fig. 3). The glycoproteins transferred to the cell surface may be further modified, e.g. by sulfatation, as is the case with keratan sulfates.

Phosphorylation of the high-mannose glycoprotein may take place by attachment of GlcNAc-*P* via UDPGlcNAc. Thereafter, mannose residues and N-acetylglucosamine are split off (Fig. 3). The

Fig. 2 *Biosynthesis of lipid-bound oligosaccharides and N-glycosidic linking of the oligosaccharide to asparagine*

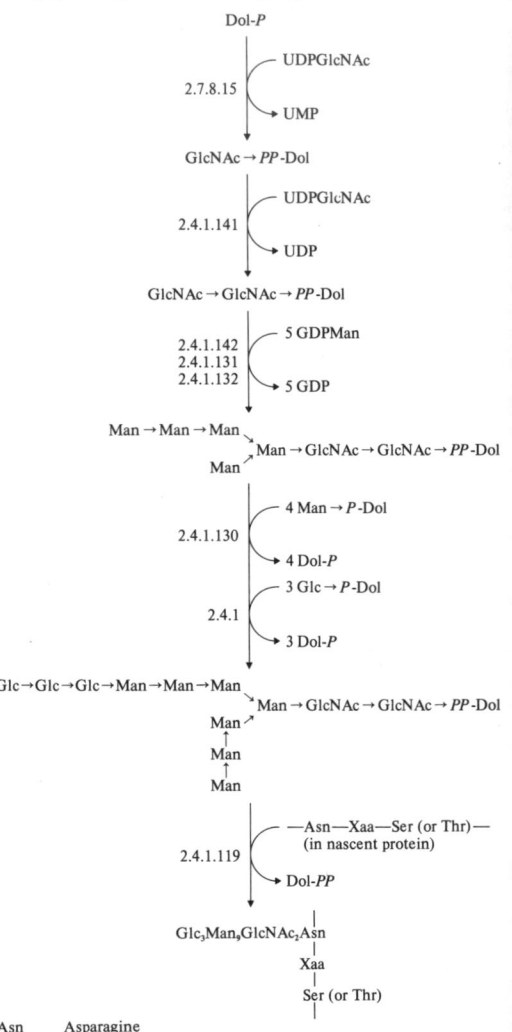

Asn   Asparagine
Ser   Serine
Xaa   Unspecified amino acid

Enzymes involved:
2.4.1.119 Dolichyl-diphosphooligosaccharide–protein glycotransferase
2.4.1   Dolichyl-phosphate-glucose–glycolipid α-glucosyltransferase
2.4.1.130 Dolichyl-phosphate-mannose–glycolipid α-mannosyltransferase
2.4.1.131 Glycolipid 2-α-mannosyltransferase
2.4.1.132 Glycolipid 3-α-mannosyltransferase
2.4.1.141 N-Acetylglucosaminyldiphosphodolichol N-acetylglucosaminyltransferase
2.4.1.142 Chitobiosyldiphosphodolichol α-mannosyltransferase
2.7.8.15 UDP-N-acetylglucosamine–dolichyl-phosphate N-acetylglucosamine phosphotransferase

Fig. 3 *Glc₃Man₉GlcNAc-processing*

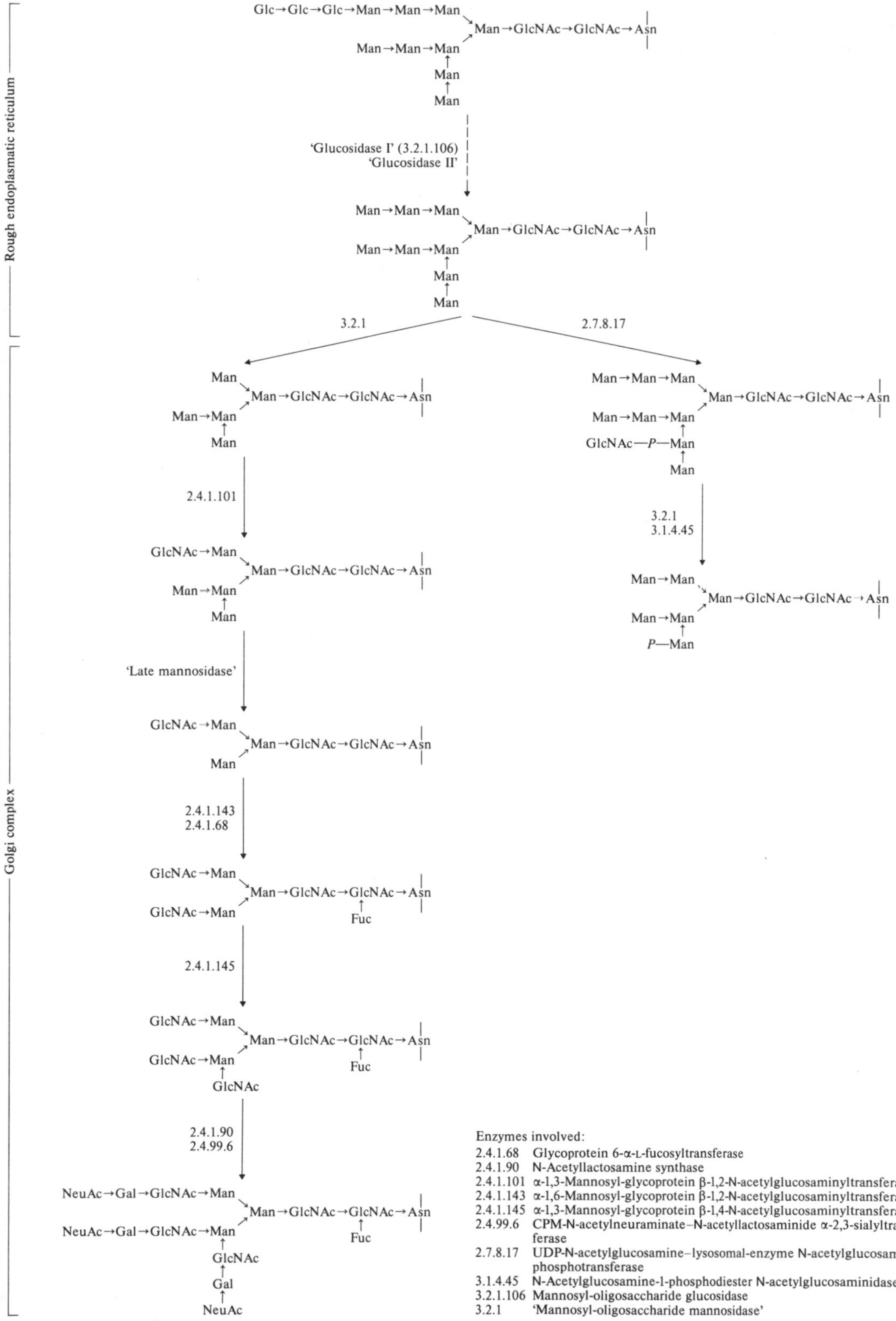

Enzymes involved:

resulting Man$_6$-phosphorylated glycoprotein is believed to function as a signal for correct subcellular routing of newly synthesized lysosomal enzymes; it is also recognized by cell-surface receptors that mediate endocytosis of extracellular enzymes.

In the formation of some glycoproteins with an N-glycosidic linkage, mannose residues seem to be transferred with the aid of retinyl phosphate instead of dolichyl phosphate.

Nonenzymatic glycation of proteins

With a sufficiently high carbohydrate concentration – physiologically only glucose comes into consideration – oxoamines can be formed on suitable amino groups of proteins with a slow turnover rate, as shown on the right. Thus, for example, the NH$_2$ group of the terminal amino acid (valine) in the β chain of hemoglobin A reacts with glucose to form hemoglobin A$_{Ic}$, and the 6-amino group of the lysine of various proteins in the erythrocyte membrane as well as of lens crystallin reacts with glucose to form the corresponding glucose derivatives.

Nonenzymatic glycation has also been reported for albumin and apolipoproteins.

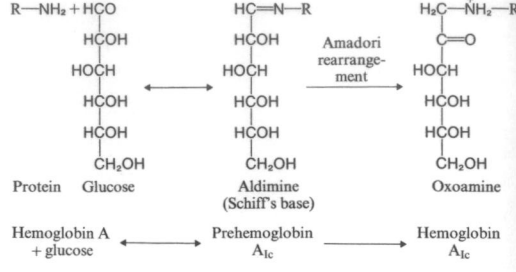

Protein Glucose

Hemoglobin A + glucose ⟷ Prehemoglobin A$_{Ic}$ ⟶ Hemoglobin A$_{Ic}$

Reviews

· DAUTRY-VARSAT and LODISH, The Golgi complex and the sorting of membrane and secreted proteins, *Trends Neurosci.*, **6**, 484 (1983).
· HUBBARD and IVATT, Synthesis and processing of asparagine-linked oligosaccharides, *Ann. Rev. Biochem.*, **50**, 555 (1981).
· LENNARZ, W.J. (Ed.), *The Biochemistry of Glycoproteins and Proteoglycans*, Plenum, New York, 1980.

Fig. 1 *Structure of linkage regions in proteoglycans*

$$\rightarrow 4\text{GlcUA}\beta1 \rightarrow 3\text{Gal}\beta1 \rightarrow 3\text{Gal}\beta1 \rightarrow 4\text{Xyl}\beta1 \rightarrow \text{Ser}$$

(Chondroitin sulfate, dermatan sulfate, heparan sulfate)

$$\rightarrow 3\text{Gal6SO}_4 1 \rightarrow 6\text{GalNAc}\alpha1 \rightarrow \text{Thr (or Ser)}$$
$$\uparrow$$
$$\text{Gal} \leftarrow \text{NeuAc}$$

(Keratan sulfate II)

$$(\text{Gal}\beta1 \rightarrow 4\text{GlcNAc6SO}_4)_m\beta1 \rightarrow 3(\text{Gal}\beta1 \rightarrow 4\text{GlcNAc})_2\beta1 \rightarrow 2\text{Man}\alpha1$$
$$(\text{Gal}\beta1 \rightarrow 4\text{GlcNAc6SO}_4)_n\beta1 \rightarrow 3(\text{Gal}\beta1 \rightarrow 4\text{GlcNAc})_2\beta1 \rightarrow 2\text{Man}\alpha1$$

$$\overset{3}{\underset{6}{}}\text{Man}\beta1 \rightarrow 4\text{GlcNAc}\beta1 \rightarrow 4\text{GlcNAc}\beta1 \rightarrow \text{Asn}$$
$$\overset{6}{\underset{\uparrow}{}}$$
$$\alpha1\,\text{Fuc}$$

(Keratan sulfate I)

Proteoglycans are important constituents of the extracellular space of vertebrate tissues. They consist of a protein portion and long, unbranched polysaccharide chains, the glycosaminoglycans. The seven thoroughly investigated glycosaminoglycans – hyaluronic acid, chondroitin 4-sulfate, chondroitin 6-sulfate, dermatan sulfate, keratan sulfate, heparan sulfate, and heparin – differ in the disaccharide units of which they are built. The disaccharide units of the four first-mentioned glycosaminoglycans consist of 1 uronic-acid residue and 1 hexosamine residue. The disaccharide in keratan sulfate contains D-galactose instead of a uronic acid. Present in the oligosaccharide subunits of heparan sulfate and heparin are not only D-glucosamine but also – in varying degrees of recurrence – D-glucuronic acid and L-iduronic acid. (For the structure of the disaccharide units of glycosaminoglycans see pages 23 and 24.)

Although hyaluronic acid and heparan sulfate or heparin do not seem to be bound to protein in the extracellular space, it is nevertheless assumed that the formation of all the polysaccharide chains of the glycosaminoglycans starts at a polypeptide core.

The linkage region between core protein and polysaccharide chain (Fig. 1) is either a neutral trisaccharide (Gal—Gal—Xyl) on the reducing end of the carbohydrate chain, in which case D-xylose is O-glycosidically linked to a serine residue of the polypeptide chain or an oligosaccharide group in which N-acetylhexosamine is O-glyco-sidically linked to threonine or serine (keratan sulfate II) or an oligosaccharide group in which N-acetylhexosamine is N-glycosidically linked to the amide group of asparagine (keratan sulfate I).

*This chapter on 'Proteoglycans' (pages 185–190) has been compiled in collaboration with B. Exer, CIBA-GEIGY Limited, Basle, Switzerland.

By virtue of the high content of carboxy groups (—COO$^-$), esterified sulfate groups (—O—SO$_3^-$) and also sulfamino groups (—NH—SO$_3^-$), the glycosaminoglycans are polyanions; the number of negative charges per disaccharide unit (see Table 12, page 24) is 1 (hyaluronic acid) or less (keratan sulfate) up to a maximum of 4 (heparin).

Occurrence

Hyaluronic acid is found in a wide variety of organs and tissues of the mammalian organism, such as synovial fluid, vitreous humor of the eye and connective tissue. It is present in an especially high concentration in embryonic tissue. In contrast to other glycosaminoglycans, hyaluronic acid is also synthesized by bacteria and is, for example, a constituent of the protoplast membrane of group A streptococci. Hyaluronic acid isolated from mammals contains less than 1% protein; the type of carbohydrate–protein linkage is unknown. In cartilage, hyaluronic acid forms aggregates with proteoglycans (Fig. 2).

Dermatan sulfate has been isolated from various tissues (skin, umbilical cord, intestinal mucosa, vascular wall, sclera, articular capsule, tendons, etc.). Although L-iduronic acid predominates as a constituent of the disaccharide unit, in some preparations D-glucuronic acid constitutes more than half of the uronic acids in the polysaccharide chain. Dermatan-sulfate proteoglycan is closely associated with collagen in the skin.

The *proteoglycans of the cartilage* (ribs, nose, trachea, joints) are those that have been most extensively studied. 90% of the cartilage

Fig. 2 *Aggregate of proteoglycans*

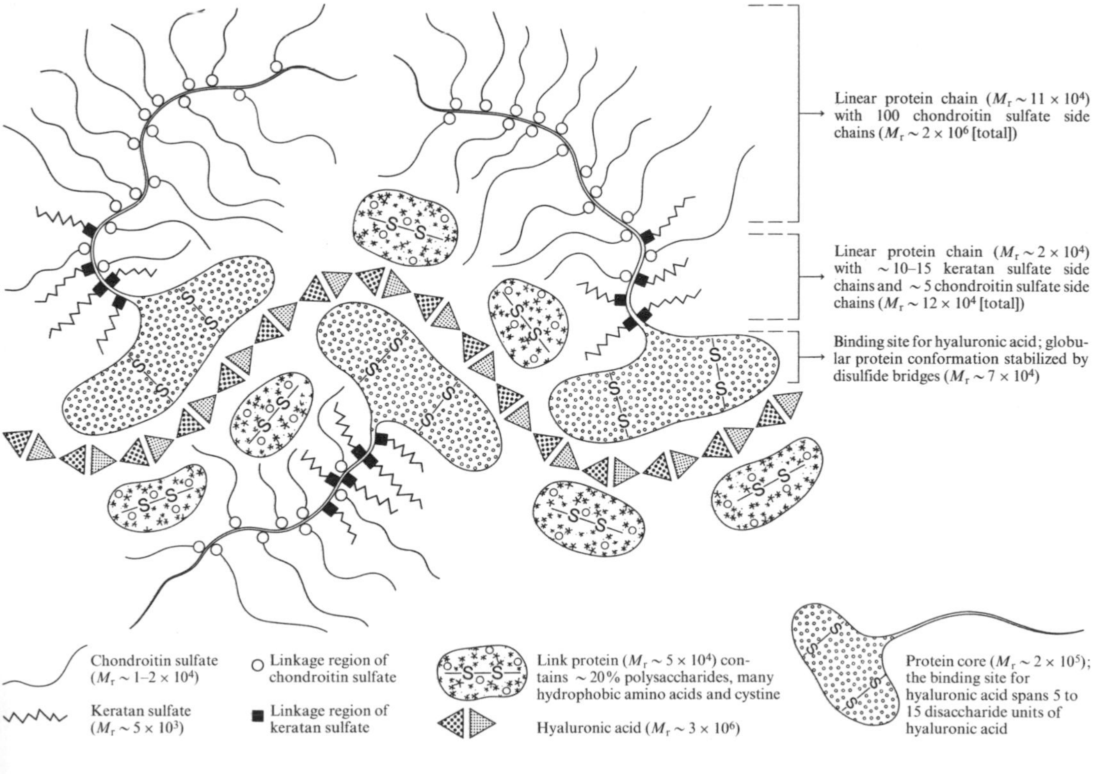

Linear protein chain ($M_r \sim 11 \times 10^4$) with 100 chondroitin sulfate side chains ($M_r \sim 2 \times 10^6$ [total])

Linear protein chain ($M_r \sim 2 \times 10^4$) with ~ 10–15 keratan sulfate side chains and ~ 5 chondroitin sulfate side chains ($M_r \sim 12 \times 10^4$ [total])

Binding site for hyaluronic acid; globular protein conformation stabilized by disulfide bridges ($M_r \sim 7 \times 10^4$)

Chondroitin sulfate ($M_r \sim 1$–2×10^4)

Keratan sulfate ($M_r \sim 5 \times 10^3$)

Linkage region of chondroitin sulfate

Linkage region of keratan sulfate

Link protein ($M_r \sim 5 \times 10^4$) contains $\sim 20\%$ polysaccharides, many hydrophobic amino acids and cystine

Hyaluronic acid ($M_r \sim 3 \times 10^6$)

Protein core ($M_r \sim 2 \times 10^5$); the binding site for hyaluronic acid spans 5 to 15 disaccharide units of hyaluronic acid

Composition of a cartilage proteoglycan molecule

Constituent	Number of chains	M_r	Portion of the total mass (%)	Number of charged groups
Protein	1 (?)	2×10^5 to 3×10^5	7–12	
Chondroitin sulfates	100	20000	80–85	$-SO_3^-$: 4500
Keratan sulfate	50	5500	7	$-COO^-$: 4200
Oligosaccharides ...	50	1200–2000	1–3	

Reference
HARDINGHAM, T., *Biochem. Soc. Trans.*, **9**, 489 (1981).

consists of extracellular matrix, which is composed of a dense network of type II collagen fibers and a highly concentrated solution of proteoglycan aggregates. The solids content of the extracellular component consists of 40–70% collagen and 10–30% proteoglycans.

The relative molecular mass (M_r) of a proteoglycan molecule extends from 0.5×10^6 to about 4×10^6. Many chondroitin-4-sulfate or chondroitin-6-sulfate chains, a smaller number of keratan-sulfate chains and many short-chain neutral oligosaccharides are bound to the protein core. The M_r values for polysaccharide chains in the above table are to be regarded merely as statistical means, owing to polydispersity.

20 to 250 proteoglycan molecules form an aggregate with hyaluronic acid, which is present in a chain length of 0.5–5.0 μm and which has a M_r of 2×10^5 to 2×10^6. 60–80% of the proteoglycan monomers are present in aggregate form. Binding to hyaluronic acid takes place at the globular end of the protein core ('hyaluronic-acid-binding site') and is stabilized by a so-called 'link protein', which occurs in 2 variants. The structure of an aggregate is schematically represented in Figure 2.

Juvenile cartilage contains more chondroitin 4-sulfate than chondroitin 6-sulfate. The ratio is reversed with age, practically no chondroitin 4-sulfate being found in nonagenarians[1]. The chain length also decreases with advancing age. The degree of sulfatation of the disaccharide unit is low in juvenile cartilage, and the proportion of sulfated disaccharide units increases with age, as does the ratio of the keratan-sulfate content to the chondroitin-sulfate content in cartilage. Because of increased proteolytic activity, degenerative changes result in a partial loss of the hyaluronate-binding region.

Aggregate formation in the *intervertebral discs* is less marked than in the cartilage. In the mature nucleus about 20–30% of the proteoglycan monomers are present as aggregate, as compared with about 60% in the annulus[2]. The intervertebral disc proteoglycans contain more keratan sulfate and protein, but less chondroitin sulfates than cartilage; the chondroitin-sulfate-rich region of the protein core is probably shorter.

Heparin consists of disaccharide units composed of a uronic acid and a derivative of D-glucosamine. Monosaccharide components (in the order of frequency of their occurrence) are 2-deoxy-2-sulfamino-α-D-glucose (disulfoglucosamine), α-L-iduronic acid 2-sulfate (2-sulfoiduronic acid), 2-acetamido-2-deoxy-α-D-glucose (N-acetylglucosamine), glucuronic acid 2-sulfate, β-D-glucuronic acid and α-L-iduronic acid.

Commercial heparin preparations from cattle lungs or hog intestinal mucosa are polydispers, consisting of about 20 to 40 different chains with a M_r ranging from 6000 to 30000. Native heparin in mast cells seems to be present in a form with a high molecular mass ($M_r \sim 10^6$) in which the carbohydrate chains are linked either to a protein core or to a polysaccharide skeleton. Some heparin preparations have a chain end of Gal—Gal—Xyl, a sequence that is characteristic for binding to the serine residue in peptides. Mast preparations from mast cells appear to have a protein core composed exclusively of serine and glycine in an equimolecular ratio.

Heparan sulfate has basically the same structure as heparin, but the degree of sulfatation is substantially less. Whereas heparin is stored in the granules of the mast cells, from which it can be released under the influence of certain stimuli, heparan sulfate in the form of

proteoglycan is a constituent of practically all cell surfaces. A preparation isolated from rat liver membranes and having a M_r of 80000, for example, consisted of a protein core to which 4 polysaccharide chains with an average M_r of 14000 were linked[3]. The amino-acid composition of the core protein is comparable to that of the other proteoglycans but not to that of the heparin preparation from mast cells.

Function

Hyaluronic acid as a linear macromolecule with a high molecular mass has a marked capacity for binding water. Aqueous solutions are of high viscosity – a property that makes them suitable as a lubricant, e.g. in synovial fluid.

In response to tension, both the skin and the aorta show viscoelastic properties, which may be attributable to the presence of hyaluronic acid (i.e. to its long entangled polysaccharide chains). The water-binding capacity and the resultant swelling pressure play a part in maintaining turgor in the vitreous humor of the eye.

Hyaluronic acid interacts with proteoglycans to form aggregates which are deposited in the collagen fiber network (Fig. 2), so that the mobility of proteoglycans in the tissue is restricted and they are less exposed to the attack of hydrolyzing enzymes.

The *sulfated proteoglycans* can bind up to 100 times their own mass of water. Since water distributes pressure uniformly, it is not surprising that the chondroitin-sulfate proteins are especially abundant in connective tissues which are exposed to high pressures (as for example joint cartilage and the nucleus pulposus). The chondroitin-sulfate content of individual zones of the joint cartilage reflects the corresponding pressure load. This correlation also holds true for skin; the skin of the heel contains more proteoglycans than the unstressed sole of the foot.

Another function of sulfated proteoglycans is that of a filter. Owing to the high degree of hydration, salts and other compounds of low molecular mass can diffuse through the proteoglycan gel, but proteins cannot. Hence sulfated proteoglycans also occur in basement membranes.

Both the sulfate groups and the carboxy groups of the proteoglycans are ionized at neutral pH. The polyanions are relatively immobile in cartilage and other connective-tissue systems and thus have the properties of a cation exchanger. The sodium ion concentration is therefore higher in the matrix than in the environment surrounding it.

Proteoglycan aggregates exert a regulating function in the calcification of cartilage in that they inhibit the crystallization of calcium phosphate.

Along with their property of increasing the pressure resistance of tissues by swelling and thus prestressing the collagen fibers, the proteoglycans containing dermatan sulfate or heparan sulfate in particular also interact strongly with fibrous proteins in the aorta, and probably also in the skin. This applies both to the collagen fibers (dermatan sulfate) and to the elastic fibers (proteoheparan sulfate). In mammals moulting periodically, an increase in heparan sulfate can always be detected in the skin during these moulting phases.

The glycosaminoglycans containing L-iduronic acid – dermatan sulfate, heparan sulfate and heparin – form insoluble complexes with low-density serum lipoproteins, a mechanism which may be involved in atherosclerotic plaque formation.

In aqueous solution the polysaccharide chain of *heparin* is highly negatively charged on account of the many sulfate groups. Owing to the mutual repulsion of these charged groups, the chain cannot coil up and cannot form cross-linkages. Conversely the chain forms very stable complexes with cations and above all with polycations – in the mast cells primarily complexes with chymosin. In the form of the heparin complex this neutral proteinase is inactive.

The effect of heparin upon blood coagulation is due to the fact that a part of the heparin molecule combines with the proteinase inhibitor antithrombin III, giving rise to a conformational change in the antithrombin molecule. This leads to an accelerated inactivation of the serum proteinases involved in blood coagulation. The antithrombin-binding region of the heparin molecule is contained within an octasaccharide sequence (Fig. 3)[4]. The anticoagulant property of heparin is neutralized by a platelet protein – the platelet factor 4. The C terminus of this protein is rich in cationic lysine and arginine residues which enter into electrostatic bonding with strongly anionic portions of the heparin molecule.

Fig. 3   *Structure of the antithrombin-binding octasaccharide*

IdoUAα1 → 4GlcNAc6SO$_4$α1 → 4GlcUAβ1 → 4GlcNSO$_3$(3SO$_4$,6SO$_4$)α1 → 4IdoUA2SO$_4$α1 → 4GlcNSO$_3$(6SO$_4$)α1 → 4IdoUA2SO$_4$α1 → 4GlcNSO$_3$(6SO$_4$)

Fig. 4 *Biosynthesis of proteochondroitin 4-sulfate*

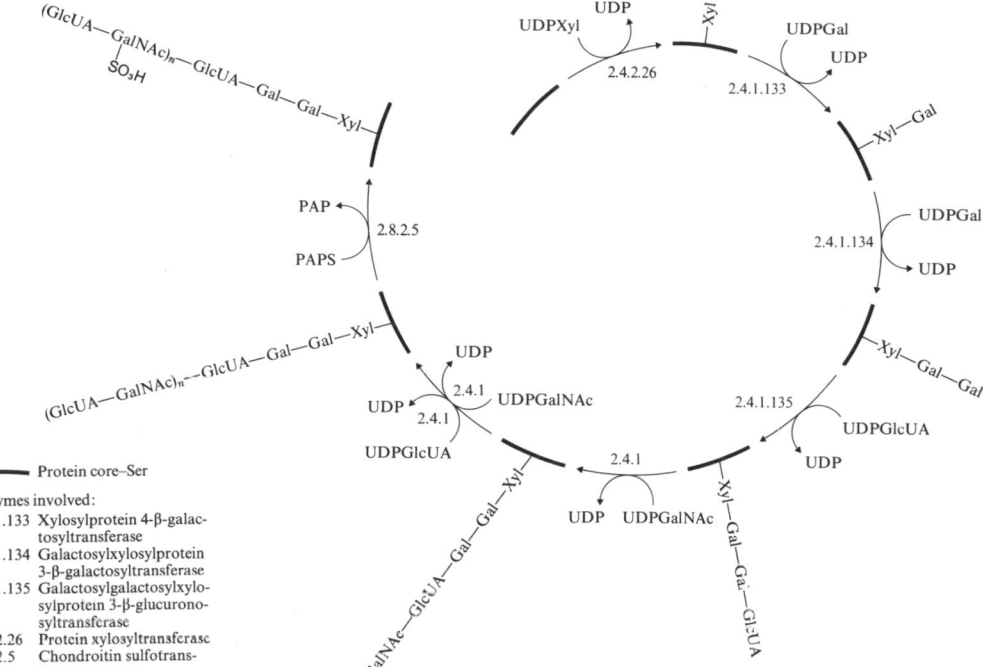

Enzymes involved:
2.4.1.133 Xylosylprotein 4-β-galac-
tosyltransferase
2.4.1.134 Galactosylxylosylprotein
3-β-galactosyltransferase
2.4.1.135 Galactosylgalactosylxylo-
sylprotein 3-β-glucurono-
syltransferase
2.4.2.26   Protein xylosyltransferase
2.8.2.5   Chondroitin sulfotransferase

Another enzyme that bonds with heparin is lipoprotein lipase (3.1.1.34). The binding region of heparin for this enzyme is not identical with the one for antithrombin III.

Biosynthesis

Complexes of polysaccharide or oligosaccharide chains and protein – be they glycoproteins or proteoglycans – seem to be synthesized according to the same mechanisms. The synthesis begins with the formation of the peptide chain of the protein core. In the cell-free protein-synthesizing system from cultures of limb buds of chicken embryos a protein with a M_r of 340 000 has been found, whereas the core protein from tissue-isolated proteoglycan has an M_r of only 210 000; this may be attributable to cleavage of the core-protein precursor. In the rough endoplasmic reticulum either monosaccharide residues are successively added to the core protein (O-glycosidically linked glycosaminoglycans) or a previously assembled oligosaccharide chain is attached to the core protein (N-glycosidically linked glycosaminoglycans).

The monosaccharide residues must first be activated by conversion to esters. Since these esters have an α-glycosidic linkage, but β-glycosidic linkages are present in most glycosaminoglycans, a steric inversion is necessary when adding appropriate monosaccharide residues.

An exception to the basic scheme of the synthesis consists in the fact that α-glycosidically linked α-L-iduronic acid in dermatan sulfate, heparin and heparan sulfate is formed only by subsequent isomerization within the chain from β-glycosidically linked D-glucuronic acid by means of a C-5 epimerase (heparosan-N-sulfate-glucuronate 5-epimerase, 5.1.3.17).

In the synthesis of O-glycosidically linked glycosaminoglycans, a monosaccharide unit of the linkage region is first attached to the protein. Thus xylose in the form of UDPxylose is transferred to the hydroxy group of serine, or acetylgalactosamine in the form of UDP-N-acetylgalactosamine is transferred to the hydroxy group of threonine or serine. The binding of the oligosaccharide chain via N-acetylglucosamine to asparagine in the core protein, as is to be found in keratan sulfate I, proceeds via the dolichyl-phosphate pathway. This pathway has been thoroughly studied in the formation of glycoproteins (page 182). The formation of chondroitin 4-sulfate is represented in Figure 4.

For sulfation the sulfate group must first be activated (see page 79). Sulfatation then takes place with the aid of sulfotransferases as follows:

$$\text{ROH} + \text{PAPS} \xrightarrow{\text{2.8.2.5}} \text{RO—SO}_3\text{H} + \text{adenosine 3',5'-bisphosphate}$$

or

$$\text{RNH}_2 + \text{PAPS} \xrightarrow{\text{2.8.2.12}} \text{RNH—SO}_3\text{H} + \text{adenosine 3',5'-bisphosphate}$$

Enzymes involved:
2.8.2.5   Chondroitin sulfotransferase
2.8.2.12 Heparitin sulfotransferase

A series of enzymes which are specific for the monosaccharide donor, the acceptor and the conformation of the linkage ('one enzyme – one linkage') are available for chain synthesis. Further chain growth can be blocked by the adding of N-acetylneuraminic acid or fucose or by the sulfatation of N-acetylgalactosamine in position 4.

Hyaluronic acid is synthesized mainly by fibroblasts and also to some extent by human chondrocytes. The first disaccharide unit is formed from UDPglucuronic acid and UDP-N-acetylglucosamine. The polysaccharide chain is formed by stepwise and alternating addition of UDPglucuronic acid and UDP-N-acetylglucosamine to the reducing end of the chain. At each step, the UDP moiety attached to the growing chain is released as the subsequent sugar nucleotide is added (Fig. 5). It is not yet known whether at some stage of its metabolism hyaluronic acid is covalently linked to protein.

Chondroitin sulfates. Several different glycosyltransferases are required for their formation (Fig. 4).

Keratane sulfates. The formation of keratan sulfate II proceeds like that of the chondroitin sulfates; the transfer of the galactose residues occurs with the aid of UDPgalactose:keratan galactosyltransferase. The synthesis of keratan sulfate I, which contains a N-glycosidical linkage, proceeds according to the scheme represented in Figure 2 on page 182.

Dermatan sulfate. The synthesis proceeds like that of the chondroitin sulfates. The C-5 epimerization of D-glucuronic acid to L-iduronic acid is closely connected with the sulfatation process, i.e. this epimerization occurs only after the formation of the galactosamine 4-sulfate.

Heparin and *heparan sulfate.* As regards the basic structure, the synthesis proceeds like that of the chondroitin sulfates. Additional steps are the N-deacetylation of N-acetylglucosamine residues and the N-sulfatation (Fig. 6), and the last step is indispensable for the C-5 epimerization of D-glucuronic acid to L-iduronic acid[5]. Since

Fig. 5 *Biosynthesis and breakdown of hyaluronic acid*

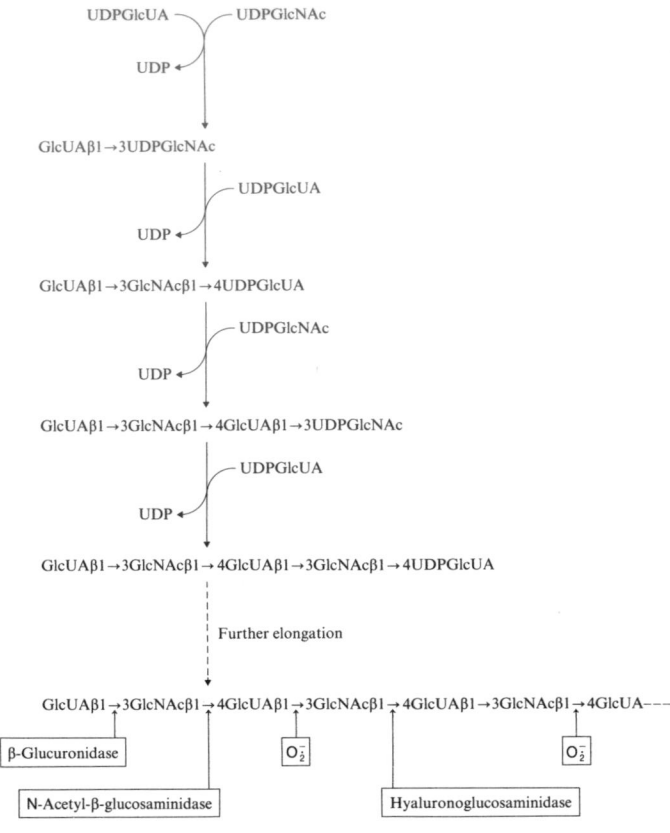

sulfotransferase has a greater affinity for the 2-amino group than for the 6-hydroxy group of glucosamine, O-sulfatation can take place only when the N-sulfatation of the entire chain has been completed. Additional sulfatation takes place in position 3 of the glucosamine residue. Neither the specificity of O-sulfotransferases nor the sequence of the O-sulfatation steps are known. If at the outset N-acetylglucosamine deacetylase (3.5.1.33) is only slightly active, polymers richer in glucuronic acid and with a low sulfate content are formed. In addition the supply of activated sulfate (PAPS) controls the degree of sulfatation.

Breakdown

The breakdown of proteoglycans involves on the one hand hydrolysis of the protein core by proteinases, and on the other hand cleavage of the polysaccharide chain by endoglycosidases or a breakdown of the chain by exoglycosidases progressively splitting off glycosyl groups from the nonreducing end. Other exoenzymes remove the sulfate groups.

In *hyaluronic acid* an endoglycosidase – hyaluronoglucosaminidase (3.2.1.35) (hyaluronidase) – splits the β-1,4 linkage between N-acetylglucosamine and D-glucuronic acid. After prolonged action of this testicular enzyme the tetrasaccharide

GlcUAβ1→3GlcNAcβ1→4GlcUAβ1→3GlcNAc

is formed as the principal product. The β-1,3 linkage between D-glucuronic acid and N-acetylglucosamine can be cleaved by the exoenzyme β-glucuronidase (3.2.1.31), and the β-1,4 linkage between N-acetylglucosamine and D-glucuronic acid by the exoenzyme N-acetyl-β-glucosaminidase (3.2.1.30), these enzymes working alternately. Complete breakdown of hyaluronic acid, however, does not seem to be necessary for its elimination, since various polysaccharides and oligosaccharides derived from hyaluronic acid are detectable in the urine. An enzyme from leeches, hyaluronate lyase (4.2.2.1), splits hyaluronic acid into oligosaccharides, forming a double bond at the site of cleavage in position 4 of D-glucuronic acid.

Superoxide ion radicals (O_2^-) are involved in the depolymerization of hyaluronic acid in inflammatory joint diseases. The reaction of O_2^- and H_2O_2 (hydrogen peroxide) – both of which are secreted from polymorphonuclear granulocytes during phagocytosis – leads to the formation of $OH \cdot$ (hydroxy radical) which probably brings about cleavage of the glycosidic linkage:

$$O_2^- + H_2O_2 \longrightarrow O_2 + OH^- + OH \cdot$$

The conversion of O_2^- by superoxide dismutase (1.15.1.1) prevents the depolymerization of hyaluronic acid:

$$2\,O_2^- + 2\,H^+ \longrightarrow O_2 + H_2O_2$$

The breakdown of *cartilage proteoglycans containing chondroitin sulfate* and *keratan sulfate* takes place stepwise. First the protein core is probably attacked, for which neutral proteinases, either tissue-specific ones or those from leukocytes – such as cathepsin G (3.4.21.20) and leukocyte elastase (3.4.21.37) – are held responsible.

The fragments thus formed can diffuse out of the matrix and are either excreted almost unchanged in the urine or phagocytized by cells (such as synovial cover cells or granulocytes) and then broken down intracellularly by lysosomal enzymes with an acid pH optimum. In this breakdown 3 classes of enzymes are involved: proteinases (for example certain cathepsins), sulfatases and glycosidases. Hyaluronoglucosaminidase (3.2.1.35) can depolymerize not only hyaluronic acid but also chondroitin sulfates. Exoglycosidases progressively attack the polysaccharide chain from the nonreducing end, this being a process in which terminal N-acetylneuraminic acid or fucose first has to be split off. If N-acetylgalactosamine 4-sulfate or N-acetylgalactosamine 6-sulfate is present terminally, the sulfate group must first be split off before the glycosidases can attack. The further breakdown is carried out by β-N-acetylhexosaminidase (3.2.1.52) alternating with β-glucuronidase (3.2.1.31) in the case of chondroitin sulfates, and with β-galactosidase (3.2.1.23) in the case of keratan sulfate. For the breakdown of chondroitin sulfate and keratan sulfate see also Figures 7a and b (page 190).

Fig. 6 *Modifications on the disaccharide units of heparin*

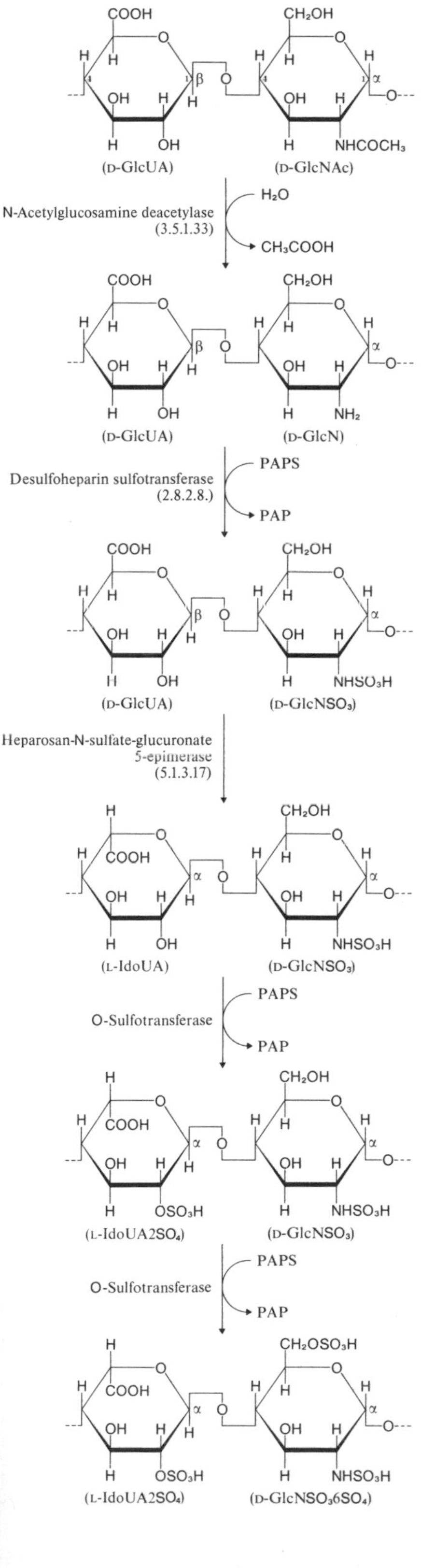

COOH CH₂OH

H H H H H

OH H H OH H O---

β O α

H OH H NHCOCH₃

(D-GlcUA) (D-GlcNAc)

N-Acetylglucosamine deacetylase (3.5.1.33)

H₂O

CH₃COOH

COOH CH₂OH

H H H H H

OH H H OH H O---

β O α

H OH H NH₂

(D-GlcUA) (D-GlcN)

Desulfoheparin sulfotransferase (2.8.2.8.)

PAPS

PAP

COOH CH₂OH

H H H H H

OH H H OH H O---

β O α

H OH H NHSO₃H

(D-GlcUA) (D-GlcNSO₃)

Heparosan-N-sulfate-glucuronate 5-epimerase (5.1.3.17)

H CH₂OH

H COOH H H H

OH H H OH H O---

α O α

H OH H NHSO₃H

(L-IdoUA) (D-GlcNSO₃)

PAPS

O-Sulfotransferase

PAP

H CH₂OH

H COOH H H H

OH H H OH H O---

α O α

H OSO₃H H NHSO₃H

(L-IdoUA2SO₄) (D-GlcNSO₃)

PAPS

O-Sulfotransferase

PAP

H CH₂OSO₃H

H COOH H H H

OH H H OH H O---

α O α

H OSO₃H H NHSO₃H

(L-IdoUA2SO₄) (D-GlcNSO₃6SO₄)

There is no specific enzyme available for hydrolysis of the linkage between serine and xylose. β-Glucosidase (3.2.1.21) can act as a β-xylosidase. Such a cleavage is evidently of little importance in mammals, because xylosylserine is present in fairly large amounts in the urine.

The turnover time of cartilage glycosaminoglycan sulfate, which is expressed by the formula

$$\frac{\text{Total glycosaminoglycan sulfate (mmol)}}{\text{Mean rate of sulfate incorporation (mmol/d)}}$$

corresponds to the time needed to synthesize the amount of glycosaminoglycans present in the tissue. For human adults the mean turnover time amounts to 600–1000 d and the half-life (turnover time × ln 2) to 400–700 d.

Heparin and *heparan sulfate* seem to be broken down not only by well-defined exoglycosidases but also by endoglycosidases. For example, heparin lyase (4.2.2.7) (heparinase) from rat liver splits heparin into fragments with a M_r of ∼ 4000, and an enzyme from platelets depolymerizes heparin and heparan sulfate at the surface of endothelial cells. Exoenzymes attack the nonreducing end of the polysaccharide chain; the sequence of action of these enzymes (Fig. 7d) depends on the structure of the chain. The sulfate group in iduronic acid 2-sulfate is split off by a specific enzyme, iduronate 2-sulfatase (3.1.6.13) ('Hunter corrective factor'). This enzyme and L-iduronidase (3.2.1.76) are also involved in the breakdown of *dermatan sulfate* (Fig. 7c). An additional enzyme – a specific 3-O-sulfatase – is involved in heparin degradation.

A special feature in the breakdown of heparan sulfate consists in the fact that after sulfate is split off from the N-sulfated glucosamine by heparan N-sulfatase – the 'Sanfilippo A factor' – a glucosamine residue with a free amino group is formed. No enzyme is available for splitting this residue from oligosaccharides, this is possible only after primary N-acetylation by means of glucosamine acetyltransferase (2.3.1.3).

References

Reviews:
· Workshop on proteoglycans, *Fed. Proc.*, **44**, 369 (1985).
· Höök et al., Cell-surface glycosaminoglycans, *Ann. Rev. Biochem.*, **53**, 847 (1984).
· Muir, H., Proteoglycans as organizers of the intercellular matrix, *Biochem. Soc. Trans.*, **11**, 613 (1983).
· Greiling et al., Pathobiochemie und Pathophysiologie des Bindegewebes, in Mathies, H. (Ed.), *Handbuch der inneren Medizin*, Volume 6/2A: Rheumatologie, 5th ed., Springer, Berlin, 1983, page 29.
· Berger et al., Structure, biosynthesis and functions of glycoprotein glycans, *Experientia (Basel)*, **38**, 1129 (1982).
· Kleesiek et al., Zur Pathobiochemie der Proteoglykane und des Hyaluronats bei der chronischen Polyarthritis, in Otte, P. (Ed.), *Gelenkdestruktion bei Polyarthritis*, Steinkopff, Darmstadt, 1982, page 57.
· Brandt, K. D., Glycosaminoglycans, in Kelley et al., *Textbook of Rheumatology*, Saunders, Philadelphia, 1981, page 239.
· Kresse et al., The mucopolysaccharidoses: biochemistry and clinical symptoms, *Klin. Wschr.*, **59**, 867 (1981).
· Roden, L., Structure and metabolism of connective tissue proteoglycans, in Lennarz, W. J. (Ed.), *The Biochemistry of Glycoproteins and Proteoglycans*, Plenum, New York, 1980, page 267.
· Jaques, L. B., Heparin: an old drug with a new paradigm, *Science*, **206**, 528 (1979).
· Comper and Laurent, Physiological function of connective tissue polysaccharides, *Physiol. Rev.*, **58**, 255 (1978).
· Lindahl and Höök, Glycosaminoglycans and their binding to biological macromolecules, *Ann. Rev. Biochem.*, **47**, 385 (1978).

Special references:
[1] Greiling et al., in Lang et al. (Ed.), *Aktuelle Probleme der Pathobiochemie*, Springer, Berlin, 1978, page 15.
[2] Urban and Maroudas, *Clin. rheum. Dis.*, **6**, 51 (1980).
[3] Oldberg et al., *J. biol. Chem.*, **254**, 8505 (1979).
[4] Rosenberg, R. D., *Fed. Proc.*, **44**, 404 (1985).
[5] Jacobsson et al., *J. biol. Chem.*, **259**, 1056 (1984).

Fig. 7 *Breakdown of glycosaminoglycans*

(a) Chondroitin sulfate

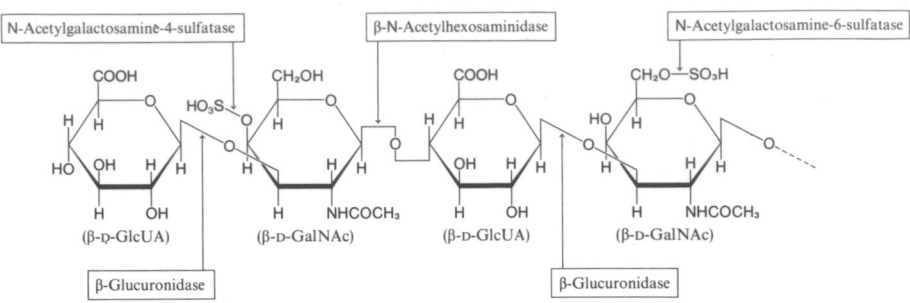

(b) Keratan sulfate

(c) Dermatan sulfate

(d) Heparan sulfate

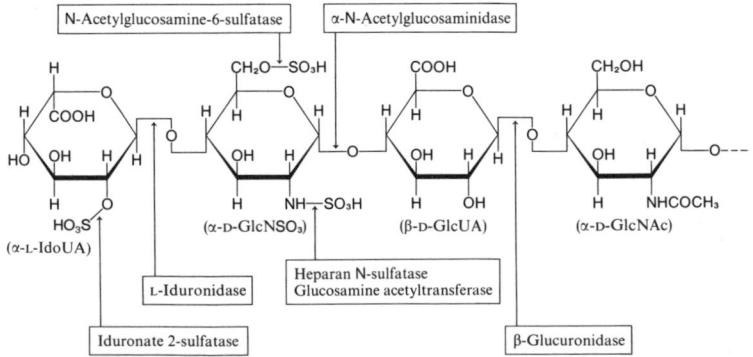

The connective tissues consist of cells and extracellular protein fibers with a largely amorphous ground substance that fills up the extracellular, interfibrillar space (Table 1). Collagen, elastin and reticulin are fibrillar components, the latter being chemically and structurally related to or identical with collagen. Reticulin may represent an embryonic form of collagen.

Table 1   *Extracellular components of connective tissues*

Group of components	Number of distinct molecules	Corresponding morphologic structure in tissues	Functions
Collagen	At least 10	Collagen fibrils Reticular network Basement membranes	Mechanical stability of tissues (especially tensile strength) Filtration Matrix for mineralization Induction of hemostasis
Elastin	1	Elastic fibers and membranes	Elasticity of tissues (vascular tissue, skin, interstitial connective tissue)
Glycoproteins	Probably numerous (laminin, fibronectin, chondronectin, osteonectin, etc.)	Fibrillar and amorphous components of the extracellular 'ground substance' Basement membranes Elastic fibers (microfibrillar protein)	Binding of water Binding and transport of minerals Filtration
Proteoglycans	–*	'Unstructured ground substance'	Cell–cell and cell–matrix interactions

* For structure see page 185 (number of core proteins unknown).   Reference   RAUTERBERG et al., *Klin. Wschr.*, 59, 767 (1981).

Table 2   *Structure and occurrence of collagen molecules*

Type	Chain composition	M_r	Length of triple helix (nm)	Main occurrence in tissue or organ	Morphologic equivalent	Ratio of hydroxylation Hyp/Pro	Ratio of hydroxylation Hyl/Lys	Further characteristics
I	$[\alpha1(I)]_2\alpha2(I)$	~ 300 000	300	Skin, bone, tendon, most connective tissues	Collagen fiber with cross-striated pattern	0.7	0.2	Only slight glycosylation of Hyl
I trimer . . .	$[\alpha1(I)]_3$	–	–	Skin, tendon, liver, tumors		0.8	0.2	
II	$[\alpha1(II)]_3$	~ 300 000	300	Hyaline cartilage, intervertebral disc, vitreous humor	Thin fibrils	0.8	1.9	Numerous Gal— and Glc—Gal— residues bound to Hyl
1α	–	–	–	Minor components of hyaline cartilage	–	0.9	2.0	
2α	–	–	–		–	0.8	2.7	
3α*	–	–	–		–	–	–	
III	$[\alpha1(III)]_3$	~ 300 000	300	Together with type I in vascular tissue, skin and interstitial connective tissue	Reticulin (?)	1.2	0.2	Minimal glycosylation of Hyl; intramolecular disulfide bonds
IV	$[\alpha1(IV)]_2\alpha2(IV)$	~ 600 000	400	Lens capsule, kidney, placenta, aorta	Basement membranes	2.1	4.4	Relatively rich in 3-Hyp; many Glc—Gal— residues; presence of disulfide bonds
V	$\alpha1(V)[\alpha2(V)]_2$	> 300 000	300	Placenta, skin, bone, tendon, cornea, etc.	Related to collagen types I and II	1.0	1.6	High glycosylation of Hyl
	$\alpha1(V)\alpha2(V)\alpha3(V)$	–	–	Placental villi, uterus		–	–	Slightly less glycosylation of Hyl in α3(V) chain
VI	$\alpha1(VI)\alpha2(VI)\alpha3(VI)$	~ 400 000	105	Placenta, uterus, vascular tissue, skin	Microfibrils	0.6	2.0	Large nontriple-helical domains; high proportion of cysteine, tyrosine, aspartic acid
VII	$(LC)_3$**	~ 500 000	450	Chorionamniotic membrane, skin, esophagus	–	–	–	–
VIII	–	–	–	–	–	–	–	Nondisulfide-bonded chains
IX (M) . . .	$\alpha1(IX)\alpha2(IX)\alpha3(IX)$	~ 300 000	–	Cartilage, vitreous humor, intervertebral disc	Associated with collagen type II	–	–	Interchain disulfide bonds
X (G)	$[\alpha1(X)]_3$	~ 150 000	148	Cartilage	–	–	–	–

* The 3α chain may represent an α1(II) chain, but differently glycosylated.
** LC: long chain.

◊ Alternative designations for the α chains:
C for α1(IV)   αA for α1(V)
D for α2(IV)   αB for α2(V)
                  αC for α3(V)

Fig. 1   Typical amino-acid sequence of collagen α chains

—Gly—Pro—Xaa—Gly—Pro—Hyp—Gly—Xaa—Hyp—Gly—Xaa—Hyl—Gly—Xaa—Yaa—

|←——0.87 nm——→|

Xaa stands for any amino acid other than glycine, and Yaa for any amino acid other than the adjacent Xaa or glycine.

Fig. 2
Structure of type I collagen molecules and their arrangement in fibrils

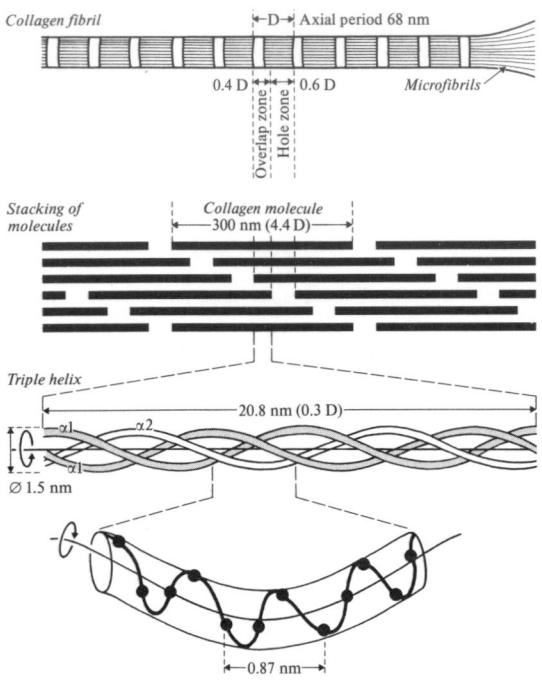

(From SAKAMOTO, S., in WEISS and JAYSON [Eds.], *Collagen in Health and Disease*, Churchill Livingstone, Edinburgh, 1982, page 362.)

Collagen

At least 10 different types of collagen have been identified, of which types I to VI are well characterized (Table 2).

Types I, II and III belong to the interstitial collagens. Type I predominates in most connective tissues (along with smaller amounts of type III); tendons and bones, on the other hand, contain almost exclusively type I collagen. Type II is present primarily in hyaline cartilage. Type IV collagen and laminin are characteristic components of the basement membranes. Type V collagen is a relatively minor component accounting for less than 10% of total collagen in any tissue; it possesses many properties characteristic of interstitial collagens. Type VI collagen can be isolated from the placenta, but occurs also in several other tissues.

Structure. The information on the chemical structure of collagen monomers is based on studies using the soluble portion of collagen of young animals. In the full-grown animal, collagen is present in cross-linked insoluble fibrils; high-angle X-ray diffraction patterns and scanning electron microscopy give information about its structure.

Type I, II and III collagen molecules ($M_r \sim 300000$) have the shape of rigid rods 300 nm long and only 1.5 nm thick. These collagen molecules consist of 3 identical polypeptide chains or of 3 polypeptide chains of which 2 are identical. Each chain is composed of about 1050 amino-acid residues ($M_r \sim 100000$); a typical amino-acid sequence is given in Figure 1. Each of the so-called α chains is coiled to a left-handed helix with a periodicity of 3 amino acids (0.87 nm). By repeated winding around a common axis, 3 α chains form a right-handed triple helix (Fig. 2). The triple helix is stabilized by hydrogen bonds between the 3 polypeptide chains.

Type IV collagen ($M_r \sim 600000$) has a multidomain structure composed of a major triple helix 330 nm in length which is flanked at the N terminus by a second triple-helical segment 60 nm in length (7 S fragment) and at the C terminus by a globular domain. The 2 triple-helical segments are separated by a larger nontriple-helical segment. Both terminal domains are the crucial sites in self-assembly, allowing the formation of a network-like structure which is stabilized by covalent cross-links ('chicken-wire' network).

Type V collagen resembles the interstitial collagens in the length of its triple helix and in the stability of the major helix to pepsin.

Type VI collagen is a protein with very large nontriple-helical domains; it is thought to be a dumbbell-shaped molecule with a rod-like segment separating 2 globular domains of different size.

Type VII collagen has also been referred to as 'long chain', since its triple-helical domain appears to be at least 1.5 times that of the interstitial collagens.

The amino-acid composition of the individual collagen α chains and of elastin is summarized in Table 3. The glycine portion is about one-third, and the imino-acid portion (proline and hydroxylated proline) is also high. In animals, up to 99% of the hydroxyprolines is found in the collagen. The basic unit of the collagen polypeptide chain has the structure —Gly—Xaa—Yaa—. The occurrence of glycine in every third position makes twisting to form the helix possible. 4-Hydroxyproline and 5-hydroxylysine are found only in position Yaa, 3-hydroxyproline, on the other hand, appearing only in position Xaa.

Collagens also contain carbohydrates. The content extends from 0.4% in skin collagen through about 4% in cartilaginous collagen to 12% in the collagen of the basement membrane. The carbohydrate residues (mainly glucose and galactose) are O-glycosidically linked to 5-hydroxylysine.

Procollagen. Tissues do not only contain the fully processed collagen molecule, but also partially processed and almost nonprocessed procollagen molecules. Procollagen I – similar structures have been proposed for type II and III procollagens – contains large peptide extensions at the N terminus and the C terminus of the triple helix. The N-terminal extension peptides (N-propeptides) ($M_r \sim 45000$) are composed of a short triple helix and a compact noncollagenous domain, 2 of the chains being stabilized by 5 intrachain disulfide bonds. The C-terminal extension peptides ($M_r \sim 100000$) have a globular shape and are connected by interchain disulfide bonds (Fig. 3).

Fig. 3   *Schematic representation of a procollagen molecule*

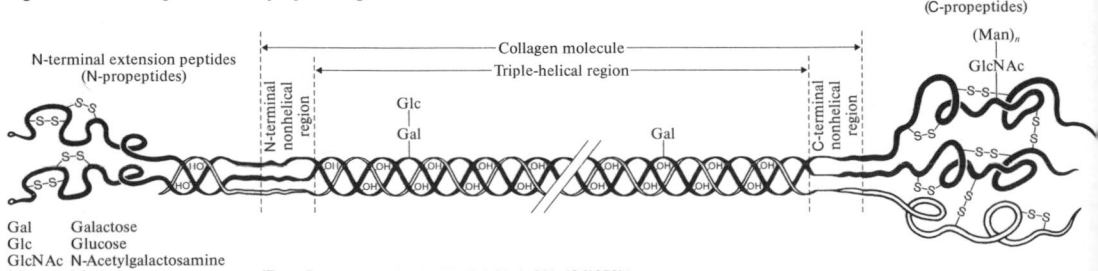

Gal   Galactose
Glc   Glucose
GlcNAc N-Acetylgalactosamine
Man   Mannose

(From PROCKOP et al., *New Engl. J. Med.*, **301**, 13 [1979].)

Table 3   Amino-acid composition of α chains of collagen and elastin in man (number of amino-acid residues per 1000 residues)

Amino acid	α1(I)	α2(I)	α1(II)	α1(III)	α1(IV)	α2(IV)	α1(V)	α2(V)		Elastin
3-Hydroxyproline	–	–	–	2.0	–	–	–	2.5	2.9	5	–
4-Hydroxyproline	111	101	92	99	125	134	122	109	109	114	11
Aspartic acid	35	46	48	42	42	50	52	51	50	44	12
Threonine	14	18	18	20	13	19	20	26	19	21	18
Serine	32	39	34	27	39	34	39	31	26	28	15
Glutamic acid	88	75	62	89	71	90	80	84	91	95	29
Proline	112	122	116	121	107	48	42	97	118	118	126
Glycine	328	321	315	333	350	350	337	319	322	321	283
Alanine	121	118	118	100	96	33	41	52	46	54	208
Valine	18	22	34	18	14	25	25	27	18	19	130
½ cystine	–	–	–	–	2	–	–	–	–	–	–
Methionine	7	5	3	9	8	14	14	11	8	8	–
Isoleucine	11	7	16	9	13	24	27	16	19	22	27
Leucine	24	21	32	26	22	52	58	35	39	37	63
Tyrosine	2	2	3	1	3	5.2	5.7	1.8	2.1	–	19
Phenylalanine	12	14	10	13	8	28	33	14	12	12	27
5-Hydroxylysine	9	3	6	14	5	59	50	24	35	35	–
Lysine	29	31	28	22	30	6.8	5.7	18	20	18	11
Histidine	3	4	12	2	6	8.7	7.9	11	7.5	6	3
Arginine	44	51	53	51	46	23	41	68	50	43	11
Isodesmosine*	–	–	–	–	–	–	–	–	–	–	3
Desmosine*	–	–	–	–	–	–	–	–	–	–	4
Origin:	Aorta[1]	Cranial bone[2]	Articular cartilage[3]	Dermis[3]	Glomerular basement membrane[4]		Fetal membranes (placenta)[3]		Aorta[1]	Aorta[5]

*Calculated as lysine equivalents.   **References**   [1] OOSHIMA, A., Science, 213, 666 (1981).   [2] KIRSCH et al., Europ. J. clin. Invest., 11, 39 (1981).   [3] BURGESON et al., Proc. nat. Acad. Sci. (Wash.), 73, 2579 (1976).   [4] TRÜEB et al., J. biol. Chem., 257, 5239 (1982).   [5] ABRAHAM et al., J. clin. Invest., 70, 1245 (1982).

Table 4   Sequence of events in interstitial collagen synthesis and fiber formation

Event	Requirement
Simultaneous translation of 3 pre-pro-α-chains	Ribosomes
Removal of 'signal' peptide at the N-terminal part of these chains	Specific proteinase
Hydroxylation of some proline and lysine residues (the hydroxylation is a prerequisite for the formation of the triple helix and takes place only in chains that are longer than [Gly—Xaa—Yaa]$_{50}$)	Procollagen-proline,2-oxoglutarate 4-dioxygenase (1.14.11.2), procollagen proline,2-oxoglutarate 3-dioxygenase (1.14.11.7), procollagen-lysine,2-oxoglutarate 5-dioxygenase (1.14.11.4), ascorbate, Fe^{2+}, 2-oxoglutarate, O$_2$
Glycosylation of hydroxylysine	Procollagen galactosyltransferase (2.4.1.50), procollagen glucosyltransferase (2.4.1.66), UDPgalactose, UDPglucose, Mn^{2+}
Formation of intrachain and interchain disulfide bonds in the extension peptides	Protein disulfide-isomerase (5.3.4.1)
Addition of a mannose-rich oligosaccharide to the C-terminal extension peptide	Dolichyl-diphosphoolioligosaccharide–protein glycotransferase (2.4.1.119)
Detachment of the chains from the ribosome	–
Association of the C-terminal extension peptides, the process being directed by the structure of these domains	–
Formation of triple helix	–
Secretion of procollagen from fibroblasts and splitting off of the N-terminal extension peptides	Procollagen N-proteinase (3.4.24.14) (cleaves Xaa—Gln bond in pro-α1 and pro-α2 chains)
Splitting off of the C-terminal extension peptides, which contain disulfide bonds, to form tropocollagen (does not occur if the collagen is insufficiently hydroxylated)	Procollagen C-proteinase (cleaves Ala—Asp bond)
Self-assembly of 5 tropocollagen molecules to form a microfibril (nucleation phase)	Spontaneous aggregation at 37°C, probably modulated by proteoglycans
Fibrillogenesis: (a) Linear growth of microfibril by addition of tropocollagen molecules (precipitation phase) (b) Lateral growth by association to produce collagen fiber	Spontaneous reaction at 37°C, perhaps modulated by proteoglycans
Inter- and intramolecular cross-links develop when microfibrils are formed and during and after fibrillogenesis	Protein-lysine 6-oxidase (1.4.3.13) (lysyl oxidase), Cu^{2+}
Linking of fibers to form collagen network	Perhaps by interaction with proteoglycans and glycoproteins

References   MUIR, I. H., in FREEMAN, M. A. (Ed.), Adult Articular Cartilage, 2nd ed., Pitman, Tunbridge Wells (Kent), 1979, page 145; KIVIRIKKO and MYLLYLÄ, in WEISS and JAYSON (Eds.), Collagen in Health and Disease, Churchill Livingstone, Edinburgh, 1982, page 101; KIVIRIKKO and MAJAMAA, Ciba Found. Symp., 114, 34 (1985).

Table 5   *Steps in degradation of collagen*

Process	Enzymes	Site of action
Breakdown of insoluble polymeric collagen fibrils (depolymerization)	Nonspecific proteinases, leukocyte elastase and limited action of collagenase	Extracellular, at neutral pH values
Cleavage of native collagen fibrils and monomers through the triple-helical portion into large fragments	Type-specific collagenases, leukocyte elastase	Extracellular and cell surface, at neutral pH values
Degradation of large collagen fragments after denaturation	'Gelatinases' and nonspecific tissue and plasma proteinases	Extracellular and cell surface
	Collagenolytic cathepsins	Intralysosomal after endocytosis
Final degradation of collagen-derived polypeptides to oligopeptides and amino acids	Tissue endopeptidase; exopeptidases	Extracellular fluids and intralysosomal

Reference   WERB, Z., in WEISS and JAYSON (Eds.), *Collagen in Health and Disease*, Churchill Livingstone, Edinburgh, 1982, page 121.

Formation. At least 10 genetically distinct types of collagen are known, for which a minimum of 18 genes must exist to code for their constituent α chains. Up to 1985, the gene structure has been determined for only a few collagen α chains. The complete structure of the chicken α2(I) gene has a size of 39 kilobases (kb), divided into 51 exons, but only a minimum of 5 kb is required to code for the 1500 amino acids of the pro-α2(I) chain. Therefore, extensive splicing of the primary transcript takes place to give mRNA of 5 kb. The genes for chicken type III collagen (~ 38 kb) and human type II collagen (~ 30 kb) are likewise large. The human α1(I) gene, however, has a size of only 18 kb; although it is also divided into 51 exons, its compressed structure is the result of smaller introns.

Biosynthesis of the pre-procollagen polypeptide chains initially follows the usual pathway of protein synthesis (page 179). The many co-translational and post-translational modifications characteristic of the interstitial collagens are shown in Table 4.

The newly formed collagen molecules tend to aggregate spontaneously to give long fibrils ('self-assembly') in which the molecules are aligned side-by-side in definite positions relative to one another, so that they overlap about one-quarter of their length (Fig. 2). Certain lysine and hydroxylysine residues in one molecule are thereby rendered close to those in an adjacent molecule. The copper-containing enzyme protein-lysine 6-oxidase (1.4.3.13) converts the 6-amino group of one lysine or 5-hydroxylysine residue to the corresponding aldehydes (allysine and hydroxyallysine). Two types of reaction that are probably nonenzymatic then lead to cross-links. In one type – which predominates in skin – an aldol condensation between 2 allysine residues takes place at the outset. Allysine aldol can react with 5-hydroxylysine and/or histidine to yield trifunctional and tetrafunctional condensates, such as dehydrohydroxymerodesmosine, aldolhistidine and histidinohydroxymerodesmosine. In the other type – which predominates in bone and cartilage – the hydroxyallysine reacts with the 6-amino group of lysine or 5-hydroxylysine, forming aldimines (Schiff's bases) such as dehydrolysinonorleucine, dehydrohydroxylysinonorleucine and dehydrohydroxylysinohydroxynorleucine. The aldimine compounds undergo Amadori rearrangement, whereupon stable oxoamines are formed. In mature fibrous collagen the prominent cross-linking residue is a trivalent amino acid based on a 3-hydroxypyridinium ring; the latter seems to derive from the oxoamine cross-links formed in the collagen of growing tissue.

Breakdown. Insoluble polymeric collagen fibrils are resistant to proteolytic attack. In adult organisms the turnover of intact collagen fibers is slow, although degradation of interstitial and basement membrane collagens is a fundamental process governing growth, development, morphogenesis, remodeling and repair. Collagen degradation may take place at extracellular sites, in the pericellular zone and in the vacuolar system within cells (Table 5).

Extracellular proteinases acting at neutral pH values are known to attack the nonhelical, cross-link-containing regions of collagen. In a later step these enzymes degrade collagenous polypeptide chains. The triple-helical domain of the collagen molecule is cleaved by the action of collagenases at neutral pH values (Fig. 4). These enzymes have a narrow specificity (Table 6), cleaving the triple helix only at one site and leaving fragments which are a quarter and three-quarters of the initial length. The fragments loose their helical structure (denaturation) and become more susceptible for further degradation.

Phagocytosis of collagen fibers takes place during rapid collagen breakdown (e.g. post partum involution of uterus). The collagen fibers found within cells in membrane-bound vesicles are broken down to fibrils by the action of specific and nonspecific collagenolytic enzymes; in lysosomes, cathepsins B, N, H and L may cleave

Table 6   *Collagen-type specificity of collagenolytic proteinases*

Enzyme	Collagen-type specificity
Vertebrate collagenase	I = III > II
	IV, V: no reaction
Granulocyte collagenase ...	I > III
Leukocyte elastase........	III, IV
	II > I; V: nonhelical peptides only
Mast-cell proteinase	IV > I
Tumor type IV collagenase .	IV
	I, II, III, V: no reaction
Macrophage type V collagenase	V
	I, III, IV: no reaction
Trypsin	III, IV, V
Collagenolytic cathepsins ..	I, II

Reference
WERB, Z., in WEISS and JAYSON (Eds.), *Collagen in Health and Disease*, Churchill Livingstone, Edinburgh, 1982, page 121.

Fig. 4   *Depolymerization of collagen fibrils and cleavage of the helical portion of the collagen molecule*

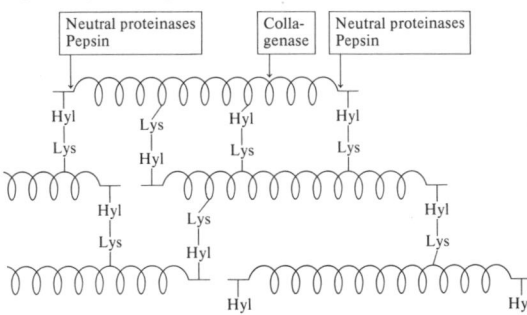

The terminal, nonhelical regions, which contain the cross-links, are hydrolyzed by neutral proteinases and pepsin, the triple-helical structures by collagenase. The joint action of the proteinases causes the collagen molecules to dissolve out of the fibril bonding. (From OTT and HAHN, in OTTE, P. [Ed.], *Gelenkdestruktion bei Polyarthritis*, Steinkopff, Darmstadt, 1982, page 52.)

collagen fibrils. Collagen degradation by lysosomal enzymes may be preceded by the action of extracellular proteinases and collagenase.

Elastin

The amorphous component of elastic fibers is referred to as 'elastin', which is characterized by an amino-acid composition of about 95 % nonpolar amino-acid residues and unique lysine-derived cross-links.

The fibrillar component of the fiber is chemically different from elastin in that it contains a high proportion of polar amino acids and a significant amount of disulfide bonds. The difficulty in characterizing elastin arises from the close association with the fibrillar component and also with collagen. Elastic fibers in the mammalian system are found in high concentrations in tissues that are subject to continual physical deformation, tension and marked fluctuations in pressure, e.g. the large blood vessels, skin and lung.

Elastin is richer in alanine than any other protein. As in collagen, the glycine portion of the amino acids is about one-third in elastin, and the proline portion is likewise similar to that in collagen (Table 3). The hydroxyproline content is low, however, and 5-hydroxy-lysine is largely absent; hence cross-links derive only from lysine residues. They are substantially more frequent than in collagen (1–2 per 1000 amino acids in collagen; up to 40 per 100 amino acids in mature elastin). Since Cu^{2+} is a cofactor of protein-lysine 6-oxidase, which is necessary for cross-linking, disturbances of elastin formation are a characteristic symptom of copper deficiency. In contrast to collagen and most other proteins, elastin contains no carbohydrate. The following amino-acid sequences recur frequently:

—Gly—Gly—Val—Pro—
—Pro—Gly—Val—Gly—Val—
—Pro—Gly—Val—Gly—Val—Ala—

Tropoelastin. The soluble precursor of elastin is a single polypeptide chain of about 800 amino-acid residues ($M_r \sim 70\,000$). Tropoelastin has a much higher lysine content than elastin because of direct conversion of lysine into the cross-links desmosine and isodesmosine in the process of elastin fiber formation. The lysine residues are present in an alanine-rich compact region. After initial oxidation of lysine to allysine, cross-linking is accomplished by forming pyridinium structures as found in desmosine and isodesmosine. One lysine and three allysine residues are embodied in each residue of desmosine and isodesmosine.

Desmosine

Isodesmosine

Laminin

Laminin is a glycoprotein that promotes the binding of epithelial cells to type IV collagen of basement membranes and links various macromolecules in the matrix. It is the first extracellular matrix protein to be formed during embryonic development and is present between cells in the 16-cell embryo (morula). Laminin is an abundant component of all basement membranes and is absent from other extracellular sites.

The structural model of laminin ($M_r \sim 950\,000$) is assumed to be an asymmetric cross, consisting of one long arm and three morphologically similar short arms linked by disulfide bonds. These arms are

Table 7   *Properties and biological activities of fibronectin*

Molecules known to interact with fibronectin
Heparin
Fibrinogen
Collagens I–V, C1q and acetylcholinesterase
Factor XIIIa (transglutaminase)
Fibronectin
Hyaluronic acid
Gangliosides G_{D1a}, G_{T1}
Actin
DNA
Polyamines
Biological activities
Mediates cell adhesion and spreading to plastic and collagen substrates
Reverses transformed phenotype
Mediates opsonization activity by macrophages
Agglutinates tanned erythrocytes
Promotes cell migration
Inhibits chondrogenic expression and myoblast fusion

Reference
KLEINMAN and WILKES, in WEISS and JAYSON (Eds.), *Collagen in Health and Disease*, Churchill Livingstone, Edinburgh, 1982, page 198.

rod-like segments which terminate in, and are interrupted by, at least 7 globular domains. Laminin contains distinct polypeptide chains whose M_r is about 220 000 and 440 000. Neither the precise arrangement of these chains in the molecule nor the biological function of the carbohydrates – which comprise 13% of laminin – is known.

Fibronectin

Fibronectin is a multifunctional glycoprotein occurring in both the soluble and the insoluble form. The soluble form is found in plasma and other body fluids; the insoluble form occurs in pericellular connective tissue matrix, around blood vessels, in basement membranes, on the abutting epithelial or endothelial cell surfaces, etc. Fibronectin is abundant in many developing tissues, but is often absent from the corresponding mature tissues. This temporary expression has led to the suggestion that fibronectin may have an organizing role in connective tissue formation. Fibronectin interacts with many macromolecules, as well as with cells, and has diverse biological activities (Table 7).

The insoluble form is only poorly characterized. Soluble fibronectin is an elongated molecule with globular domains composed of two very similar but nonidentical polypeptide chains (α and β), whose M_r is about 220 000 each. The disulfide bonds are located near the C terminus of the molecule. Fibronectins contain 4.5–9.5% carbohydrate. The oligosaccharide chains are linked to an arginine residue of the polypeptide via N-acetylglucosamine, but the interactions of fibronectin seem to be independent of carbohydrate. Each subunit of the soluble fibronectin contains one or two free —SH groups which may contribute to disulfide bonding of the molecule in the extracellular matrix beyond the dimeric state.

Reviews

· SEYER and KANG, Structural proteins: collagen, elastin, and fibronectin, in KELLEY et al., *Textbook of Rheumatology*, 2nd ed., Volume 1, Saunders, Philadelphia, 1985, page 211.
· Fibrosis, *Ciba Found. Symp.*, **114** (1985).
· MARTIN et al., The genetically distinct collagens, *Trends biochem. Sci.*, **10**, 285 (1985).
· HERBAGE et al., Study of collagen cross-links, *Front. Matrix Biol.*, **10**, 59 (1985).
· EYRE, D. R., Cross-linking in collagen and elastin, *Ann. Rev. Biochem.*, **53**, 717 (1984).
· TIMPL, R., Processed and non-processed forms of procollagens, *Biochem. Soc. Trans.*, **12**, 924 (1984).
· PROCKOP and KIVIRIKKO, Heritable diseases of collagen, *New Engl. J. Med.*, **311**, 376 (1984).
· YAMADA, K.M., Cell surface interactions with extracellular materials, *Ann. Rev. Biochem.*, **52**, 761 (1983).
· TIMPL et al., Laminin – a multifunctional protein of basement membranes, *Trends biochem. Sci.*, **8**, 207 (1983).
· VARTIO and VAHERI, Fibronectin: chains of domains with diversified functions, *Trends biochem. Sci.*, **8**, 442 (1983).
· FOSTER, J. A., Elastin structure and biosynthesis: an overview, *Meth. Enzymol.*, **82**, 559 (1982).

· MILLER, A., Molecular packing in collagen fibrils, *Trends biochem. Sci.*, **7**, 13 (1982).
· WEISS and JAYSON (Eds.), *Collagen in Health and Disease*, Churchill Livingstone, Edinburgh, 1982.
· SANDBERG et al., Elastin structure, biosynthesis, and relation to disease states, *New Engl. J. Med.*, **304**, 566 (1981).
· BORNSTEIN and BYERS, Disorders of collagen metabolism, in BONDY and ROSENBERG, *Metabolic Control and Disease*, 8th ed., Saunders, Philadelphia, 1980, page 1089.
· BORNSTEIN and SAGE, Structurally distinct collagen types, *Ann. Rev. Biochem.*, **49**, 957 (1980).

· ETHERINGTON, D. J., Proteinases in connective tissue breakdown, *Ciba Found. Symp.*, NS 75, 87 (1980).
· PROCKOP et al., The biosynthesis of collagen and its disorders, *New Engl. J. Med.*, **301**, 13 and 77 (1979).
· FESSLER and FESSLER, Biosynthesis of procollagen, *Ann. Rev. Biochem.*, **47**, 129 (1978).
· RAMACHANDRAN and REDDI (Eds.), *Biochemistry of Collagen*, Plenum, New York, 1976.
· GALLOP and PAZ, Posttranslational protein modifications, with special attention to collagen and elastin, *Physiol. Rev.*, **55**, 418 (1975).

Regulation by formation and structure of the enzyme		Regulation by function of the enzyme	
Activation	Inactivation	Activation	Inactivation
Enzyme induction (adaptation) *a* form ⟵ Covalent modulation ⟶ *b* form Type of isoenzyme Active form ⟵ Hydrolysis ⟶ Zymogen	Repression (of synthesis) Type of isoenzyme	Positive modulation Availability of the substrate Availability of cofactors	Negative modulation (inhibition by end-product) Unavailability of the substrate Unavailability of cofactors

Cellular metabolism is meaningful only if the reactions are adapted to the organism's needs; regulation mechanisms are therefore of major significance. Life is largely concerned with the synthesis of complex molecules from relatively small building units. These biosynthetic processes need energy and in most cases reducing power, so that the ratio between the concentrations of ATP and ADP (or AMP) and also the ratio between $NADH + H^+$ and NAD^+ or between $NADPH + H^+$ and $NADP^+$ have important regulatory functions. Very important control mechanisms also proceed via enzymes and may involve their synthesis, structure, breakdown or function (see table above).

A fundamental characteristic of metabolism is that anabolism and catabolism are largely independent of each other. Yet special regulating mechanisms exist for each procedure, for example in glycolysis and gluconeogenesis (page 198).

Control of enzyme synthesis (enzyme induction and repression)

A most important control mechanism consists in preventing the formation of enzymes until such time as they are required. A substance which inhibits enzyme formation is called a *repressor*; a substance that will stimulate the synthesis of an enzyme is called an *inducer* or *derepressor*. Repression and induction occur only with a minority of so-called *inducible* or *adaptive* enzymes, in contrast to *constitutive* enzymes which are more permanently required for general metabolism.

Enzyme induction can be illustrated by the example of β-galactosidase, which splits lactose into glucose and galactose. A bacterium such as *E. coli*, which has been grown in the presence of, say, glucose,

has no need to synthesize β-galactosidase. If, however, this organism is put into a medium in which lactose is the sole source of carbon, the survival of the organism depends on its ability to synthesize the lactose-splitting enzyme. After a short lag phase therefore this enzyme is synthesized. Clearly the organism must possess the genes which code for the enzyme when required.

Genes that code for enzymes are *structural* genes. In prokaryotes, genes for functionally related enzymes are organized into a structural and functional unit, the *operon*. In addition to the structural genes there are regions in the DNA, known as control regions, which are not transcribed but have an important regulatory function in enzyme synthesis. Figure 1 illustrates the regulation of the lac operon. Adjacent to the operon is another DNA sequence, the *operator*, which controls the whole operon. The *promotor*, which in part overlaps the operator, is the site of RNA polymerase interaction. The site where CAP (catabolic gene-activator protein) interacts with DNA is also part of the promotor. In conjunction with cAMP, the CAP interaction with the promotor facilitates the formation of the RNA polymerase–promotor complex. Thus CAP exercises a *positive* control of transcription. The *repressor* – which exercises a *negative* control – is itself a protein which is coded for by another gene, the repressor gene. In the absence of an *inducer* (in the case of the lac operon, the inducer is lactose) the repressor combines with the operator; no transcription takes place. In the presence of an inducer, on the other hand, the latter combines with the repressor in such a way that its affinity for the operator is destroyed. The operator then remains unbound, and transcription of the structural genes in the operon and synthesis of the corresponding enzymes can proceed.

Fig. 1 *Schematic representation of the regulation of the lac operon*

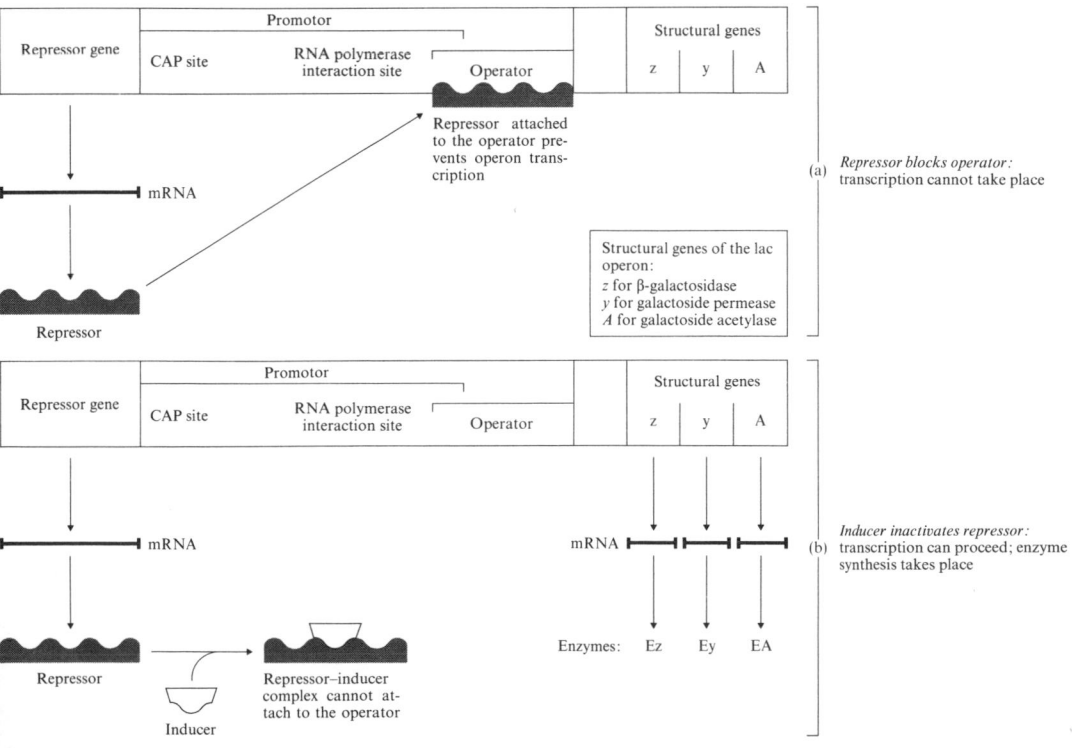

Covalent enzyme modification

Posttranslational modifications of individual amino acids in the peptide chain, such as phosphorylation, acetylation, etc. are of great importance for the regulation of metabolism. A prerequisite for the effectiveness of a modification is its reversibility, which requires a superimposed regulatory mechanism. The most important is the phosphorylation/dephosphorylation of enzymes, a process that has been most thoroughly investigated in glycogen metabolism. The corresponding reactions proceed as follows:

$$\text{Protein} + n\ \text{NTP} \xrightarrow[\text{Protein kinase}]{} \text{Protein-}P_n + n\ \text{NDP}$$

$$\text{Protein-}P_n + n\ H_2O \xrightarrow[\text{Phosphoprotein phosphatase}]{} \text{Protein} + n\ P_i$$

In general, NTP stands for ATP, but in at least one reaction it stands for GTP.

Isoenzymes

Some enzymes occur in several genetically determined variants that differ in structure and kinetic properties but catalyze the same reaction.

Lactate dehydrogenase, for example, exists in 5 forms. Its molecule is a tetramer whose subunits have a M_r of about 35000. The two different polypeptide chains are designated H and M. These can combine in every possible variation, namely H_4, H_3M, H_2M_2, HM_3, and M_4. These are the 5 isoenzymes that can be readily separated by electrophoresis. Their affinity for pyruvate and their reaction rates show considerable differences, H_4 having the least affinity for pyruvate, and M_4 the greatest; the others lie between. In examinations of various tissues for their lactate-dehydrogenase activity, significant differences are found with respect to the predominating isoenzyme. Thus the skeletal muscle is rich in M_4. The cardiac muscle is rich in H_4, which is strongly inhibited by pyruvate.

The reason for the existence of different isoenzymes in different tissues seems to depend on the functions of those tissues. Lactate dehydrogenase is the last enzyme in the anaerobic glycolytic pathway. Lactic acid itself is useless metabolically and is only produced in order to reoxidize the NADH which is formed in an earlier stage of glycolysis (page 94). Pyruvate is much more efficiently oxidized aerobically, but under anaerobic conditions its conversion to lactate at least makes possible the supply of some energy in the form of ATP. Skeletal muscle which has been exercised extensively may become anaerobic, and under these circumstances further ATP must be obtained anaerobically, even though this is inefficient. The skeletal muscle is therefore rich in the isoenzyme which most rapidly converts pyruvate to lactate. On the other hand, since it is undesirable for cardiac muscle to function anaerobically, the isoenzyme of this muscle is the one which is least able to reduce pyruvate and which is in fact inhibited by pyruvate. The cardiac muscle is thus almost forced to obtain its energy aerobically.

A different isoenzyme distribution in different tissues also seems to play a part in the metabolism of ketone bodies. Acetyl-CoA acetyltransferase exists in two differently charged forms. The A form is found only in liver and kidney, and its primary function is thought to be to catalyze the synthesis of acetoacetyl-CoA, thereby promoting ketogenesis (page 102). The B form preferentially catalyzes the reverse reaction, thereby stimulating the β-oxidation of fatty acids and the extrahepatic utilization of acetoacetate.

Activation of zymogens

Many digestive enzymes are synthesized in an inactive form (zymogens). This may be necessary to prevent breakdown of tissue – such as the intestine – which is not protected by mucus. When they are secreted into the gastrointestinal tract, part of the peptide sequence is split off by hydrolysis, which frees the active center of the protein, making it enzymatically effective (page 108). The size of the peptide split off varies considerably among the individual enzymes. For example, trypsinogen is converted to active trypsin by the action of enteropeptidase, which releases a hexapeptide. This type of enzyme activation is irreversible.

Negative and positive modulation of enzyme activity

In the reaction sequence

$$A \xrightarrow{\text{(ab)}} B \xrightarrow{\text{(bc)}} C \xrightarrow{\text{(cd)}} D - - - - \rightarrow P$$

the product P can inhibit (usually) or activate (rarely) the enzyme (ab), which catalyzes the first reaction. P is termed the 'modulator' or 'effector'. Enzymes that respond to such a modulation are the allosteric enzymes, which have 2 or more active sites – one for combining with the substrate, the other for combining with the modulator.

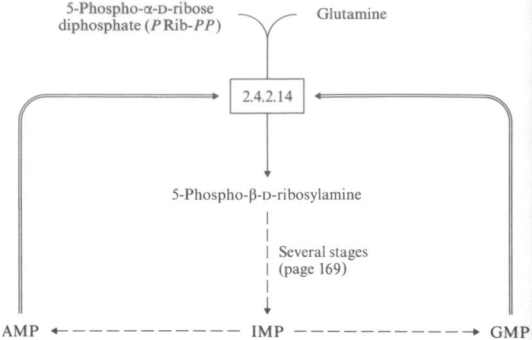

Enzyme involved:
2.4.2.14 Amidophosphoribosyltransferase

Negative modulation is an important control mechanism which prevents the excess formation of metabolic products. The reactions described above continue until the concentration of P has risen so high that the formation of B is suppressed, owing to inhibition of the enzyme (ab). The inhibition of amidophosphoribosyltransferase by the end-products of purine synthesis may be cited as an example of such a regulatory mechanism, which is also referred to as 'negative feedback' (Fig. 2).

Isocitrate dehydrogenase (NAD+), a key enzyme in the tricarboxylic acid cycle (page 96), is subject to a negative as well as positive modulation. It is activated by ADP, and inhibited by ATP and NADH. A control of energy production or energy utilization is thereby made possible. A large supply of ATP or NADH inhibits the further formation of these substances. If energy is needed, the concentration of ATP will be low and that of ADP high, so that isocitrate dehydrogenase (NAD+) will be stimulated with the ultimate production of more ATP.

The calcium messenger system of regulation

Ca^{2+} is a nearly universal messenger in animal cells. The Ca^{2+} in the cytosol is in exchange with the extracellular Ca^{2+} pool and with the mitochondrial and the plasma membrane–endoplasmic reticular pools. An increase in the amplitude of the Ca^{2+} message occurs either when a hormone or other extracellular messenger interacts with its plasma-membrane receptor or when a nerve impulse is transmitted to potential operated Ca^{2+} channels. An increase in the cytosol Ca^{2+} concentration may lead to the association of Ca^{2+} with the binding sites of calcium-binding proteins (e.g. calmodulin, troponin C). Ca^{2+} may also bind directly to enzymes that are activated by Ca^{2+}, for example mitochondrial glyceraldehyde-3-phosphate dehydrogenase and the phospholipid-dependent, Ca^{2+}-activated protein kinase (protein kinase C). In contrast, a change in the function of a Ca^{2+}-regulated enzyme can be induced by a change in the sensitivity of a Ca^{2+}-dependent reaction to activation by Ca^{2+}. Sensitivity modulation can be achieved in two ways: by an increase in the calmodulin concentration, or by a change in the structure (e.g. phosphorylation) of the enzyme to be activated, so that its association with Ca^{2+}-calmodulin is increased (positive modulation) or decreased (negative modulation).

Control mechanisms of anaerobic glycolysis and gluconeogenesis (Fig. 3)

Five steps are common to both processes in that they are reversible; that is, the same enzyme acts in the breakdown and the synthesis. The remaining steps are catalyzed by different enzymes for breakdown and for synthesis. The control mechanism for glycolysis and gluconeogenesis depends on these complementary enzymes. Since the function of these processes consists mainly in the production and storage of energy, the ratio between the concentrations of ATP and ADP (or AMP) in the environment is of importance in regulating them. The pathways are controlled in such a way as to promote glycolysis at low ATP concentration, and gluconeogenesis at high ATP concentration. Thus:

- *6-Phosphofructokinase* is allosterically inhibited by ATP. This inhibition can be relieved by high concentrations of AMP and inorganic phosphate.

Fig. 3 *Regulation of glucose breakdown and synthesis*

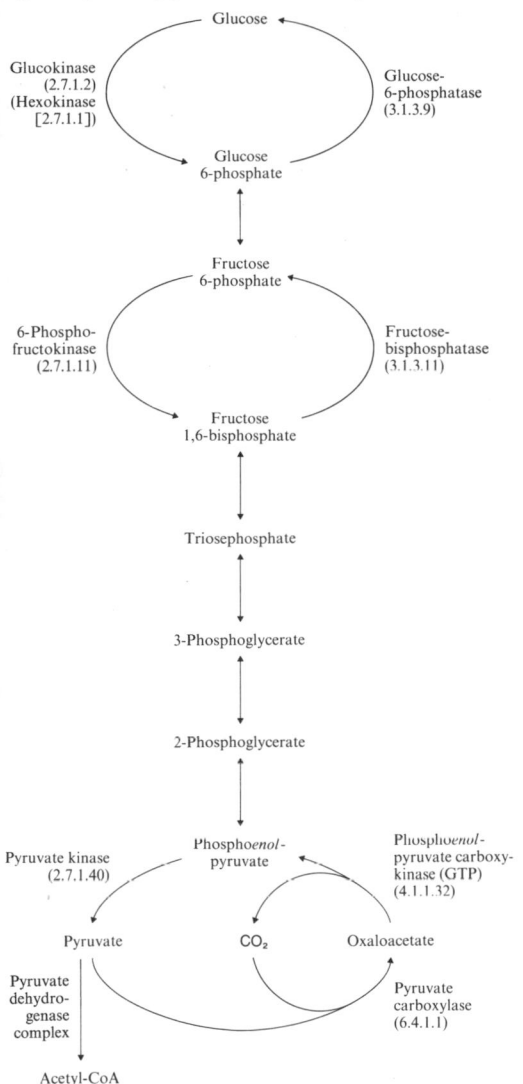

- *Fructose-bisphosphatase*, the enzyme catalyzing the reverse reaction, is activated by ATP and inhibited by AMP.
- *Pyruvate kinase* is inhibited by ATP and activated by fructose 1,6-bisphosphate.
- *Pyruvate carboxylase*, the enzyme involved in the reverse reaction, is inhibited by ADP.

A superior control mechanism consists in the involvement of the tricarboxylic acid cycle and the breakdown of fats:

- Citrate, like ATP, is an allosteric inhibitor for 6-phosphofructokinase; if there is no need for the tricarboxylic acid cycle pathway, glycolysis is slowed down.
- Acetyl-CoA is an obligatory activator for pyruvate carboxylase and thereby stimulates gluconeogenesis; that is, no formation of acetyl-CoA by glycolysis is necessary when enough is supplied by the breakdown of fats.

Breakdown and formation of glycogen

In most mammalian tissues glucose is stored as its polymer glycogen; the formation and breakdown of glycogen is therefore a vital feature of energy metabolism. In general, glycogen will be broken down when energy is needed, and it will be synthesized when energy is supplied from other sources, such as lipids.

Fig. 4 *Stimulation of the breakdown of glycogen*

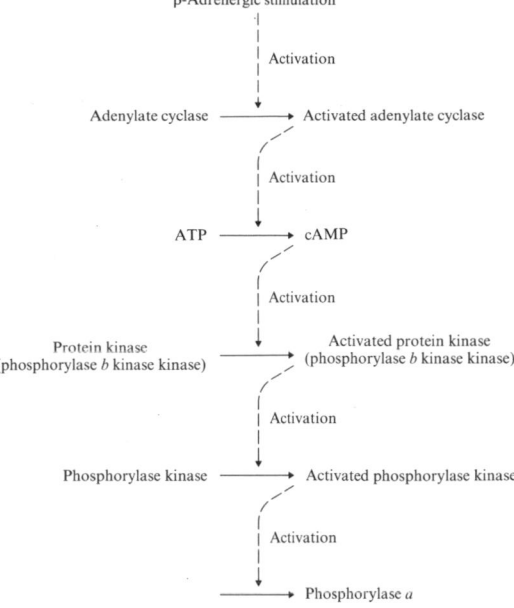

The *breakdown of glycogen into glucose* takes place as follows:

$$(1,4\text{-}\alpha\text{-}D\text{-Glucosyl})_n + \text{orthophosphate} \longrightarrow (1,4\text{-}\alpha\text{-}D\text{-Glucosyl})_{n-1} + \alpha\text{-}D\text{-glucose 1-phosphate}$$

This reaction is catalyzed by glycogen phosphorylase (2.4.1.1), which exists in 2 forms, a highly active one (*a*) and a less active one (*b*). The *b* form is active primarily in the presence of AMP. The *a* form consists of 4 subunits with a M_r of 125000, whereas form *b* is composed of only 2 of these subunits. Phosphorylase *a* contains a phosphoserine residue in each subunit. Catalyzed by phosphorylase kinase (2.7.1.38), the phosphorylation of form *b* takes place:

$$2 \text{ phosphorylase } b + 4 \text{ ATP} \longrightarrow 1 \text{ phosphorylase } a + 4 \text{ ADP}$$

The reverse reaction, however, is catalyzed by the enzyme phosphorylase phosphatase (3.1.3.17):

$$1 \text{ phosphorylase } a + 4 \text{ H}_2\text{O} \longrightarrow 2 \text{ phosphorylase } b + 4 \text{ P}_i$$

Phosphorylase kinase also exists in both a less active and an activated form, the formation of the latter being catalyzed by a protein kinase (2.7.1.37) (phosphorylase *b* kinase kinase):

$$\text{Phosphorylase kinase (less active)} + \text{ATP} \longrightarrow \text{Phosphorylase kinase (activated)} + \text{ADP}$$

The activity of the protein kinase is dependent on cAMP. The enzyme is a heterogeneous dimer consisting of a regulatory and a catalytic subunit. cAMP is bound to the regulatory subunit and thereby induces the release of the active catalytic subunit that brings about the phosphorylation of phosphorylase kinase.

The formation of cAMP takes place with the aid of adenylate cyclase (4.6.1.1), which is activated by epinephrine and other β-adrenergic stimulators (page 79). The cascade effect, which leads from the β-adrenergic stimulation to the activation of glycogen phosphorylase, is represented in Figure 4.

Phosphorylase kinase is a polymer of 4 subunits (αβγδ); the γ subunit is identical to calmodulin, which is activated by Ca^{2+}. Hormonal as well as electrical stimulation via a release of Ca^{2+} into the cytosol leads to the breakdown of glycogen, a process that is involved in the supply of energy for muscle contraction.

Formation of glycogen from glucose. The synthesis of glycogen from glucose – which must be available in the form of UDPglucose – is catalyzed by glycogen synthase (2.4.1.11). This enzyme shows a certain relationship with glycogen phosphorylase (2.4.1.1) inasmuch as both contain an identical amino-acid sequence that contains phosphorylated serine. Glycogen synthase contains 7 phosphorylated

Fig. 5   *Inhibition of the synthesis of glycogen*

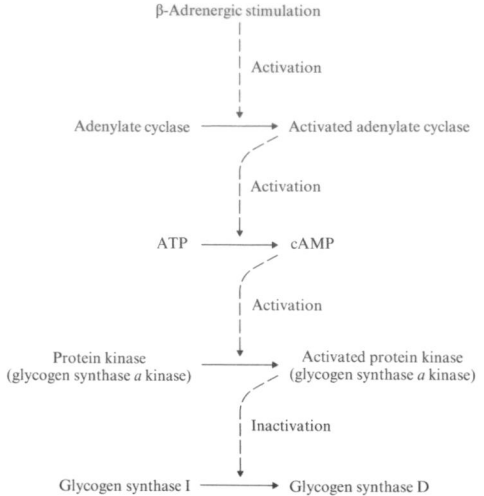

serine residues. Five different protein kinases take part in the phosphorylation:

$$\text{Glycogen synthase (I)} + 7\,\text{ATP} \dashrightarrow \text{Glycogen synthase (D)} + 7\,\text{ADP}$$

The phosphorylated D form (D for 'glucose-6-phosphate-dependent') is less active than the nonphosphorylated I form (I for 'independent'). β-Adrenergic stimulation thus has the net effect of bringing about an inhibition of glycogen formation (Fig. 5). The D form can, however, be allosterically activated by glucose 6-phosphate. Under stress with strong β-adrenergic stimulation the breakdown of glycogen to glucose 1-phosphate is pushed forward until enough glucose 6-phosphate is available to activate the D form and resume glycogen formation.

The action of insulin on glucose metabolism does not seem to proceed via a stimulation of cAMP or Ca^{2+} but via an as yet unidentified 'second messenger'. Insulin leads to an activation of glycogen synthase by lowering the degree of phosphorylation of the enzyme, resulting in an increased formation of glycogen.

Control mechanisms of triacylglycerol metabolism

Acetyl-CoA occupies a central role in the link between glucose metabolism and fat metabolism. With a normal diet, acetyl-CoA, which enters the tricarboxylic acid cycle and ultimately supplies energy in the form of ATP (page 96), is formed from glucose by glycolysis. Acetyl-CoA as part of the citrate molecule arrives in the cytosol from the mitochondria (page 136), where it is used in the synthesis of fatty acids. A small fraction of acetyl-CoA is utilized in the formation of cholesterol. The intermediate in cholesterol synthesis – 3-hydroxy-3-methylglutaryl-CoA – also results in the formation of ketone bodies from acetyl-CoA, a metabolic pathway that predominates when the glucose supply is limited.

The rate-limiting step in the synthesis of fatty acids from acetyl-CoA is the carboxylation of acetyl-CoA to malonyl-CoA, catalyzed

by the biotin-containing enzyme acetyl-CoA carboxylase (6.4.1.2) (page 137). The active form of the enzyme from animal tissues is a polymer ($M_r\,4 \times 10^6$ to 8×10^6) which can be dissociated into inactive monomers or dimers of the $M_r\,230\,000$ subunit. Each subunit is a multifunctional protein containing the functions of biotin carboxylase, biotin-carboxyl-carrier protein and transcarboxylase as well as of the regulatory allosteric site. Acetyl-CoA carboxylase provides the earliest point at which the control of de-novo synthesis of fatty acids can be exerted. Citrate and isocitrate activate the enzyme by promoting the aggregation of the subunits. Long-chain acyl-CoA, on the other hand, inhibits the enzyme as a result of its depolymerization. The stimulating action of glucagon and cAMP on fatty-acid synthesis can be explained by the fact that both substances lead to a decrease of the citrate concentration in the cytosol, whereas insulin lowers the cAMP concentration and thus indirectly promotes fatty-acid synthesis. With a diet rich in fats the synthesis of fatty acids and triacylglycerol is suppressed as a result of acetyl-CoA carboxylase inhibition by long-chain acyl-CoA.

Several additional mechanisms seem to contribute to the regulation of acetyl-CoA carboxylase, such as inactivation by phosphorylation of the enzyme protein and changes in the rate of synthesis and/or degradation of the enzyme protein.

Triacylglycerol breakdown in adipose tissues begins with the release of a fatty-acid residue catalyzed by the hormone-sensitive triacylglycerol lipase (page 100). The activation of this enzyme is due to phosphorylation which occurs by a mechanism similar to that shown for phosphorylase (Fig. 4). Epinephrine and glucagon, for example, stimulate the breakdown of triacylglycerol via β-adrenergic stimulation, followed by activation of adenylate cyclase and increased formation of cAMP. Insulin, on the other hand, seems to inhibit the release of fatty acids, owing to a lowered cAMP concentration. Besides β receptors, fat cells also contain α receptors; the stimulation of $α_1$ receptors (e.g. by clonidine) inhibits adenylate cyclase and results ultimately in the inhibition of lipolysis.

Reviews

· RASMUSSEN and BARRETT, Calcium messenger system: an integrated view, *Physiol. Rev.*, **64**, 938 (1984).
· WAKIL et al., Fatty acid synthesis and its regulation, *Ann. Rev. Biochem.*, **52**, 537 (1983).
· HERS and HUE, Gluconeogenesis and related aspects of glycolysis, *Ann. Rev. Biochem.*, **52**, 617 (1983).
· HARDIE, G., Fat and phosphorylation – the role of covalent enzyme modification in lipid synthesis, *Trends biochem. Sci.*, **6**, 75 (1981).
· ROSEN and KREBS (Eds.), *Protein Phosphorylation*, Cold Spring Harbor, New York, 1981.
· HEMS and WHITTON, Control of hepatic glycogenolysis, *Physiol. Rev.*, **60**, 1 (1980).
· McGARRY and FOSTER, Regulation of hepatic fatty acid oxidation and ketone body production, *Ann. Rev. Biochem.*, **49**, 395 (1980).
· CHOCK et al., Interconvertible enzyme cascades in cellular regulation, *Ann. Rev. Biochem.*, **48**, 923 (1979).
· KREBS and BEAVO, Phosphorylation–dephosphorylation of enzymes, *Ann. Rev. Biochem.*, **48**, 923 (1979).
· BLOCH and VANCE, Control mechanisms in the synthesis of saturated fatty acids, *Ann. Rev. Biochem.*, **46**, 263 (1977).
· HERS, H. G., The control of glycogen metabolism in the liver, *Ann. Rev. Biochem.*, **45**, 167 (1976).
· MANIATIS and PTASHNE, A DNA operator–repressor system, *Sci. Amer.*, **234**, 64 (1976).
· NEWSHOLME and START, *Regulation in Metabolism*, Wiley, London, 1973.
· MEHLMAN and HANSON (Eds.), *Energy Metabolism and the Regulation of Metabolic Processes in Mitochondria*, Academic Press, New York, 1972.
· LEESE, C. L., Enzymes and isoenzymes, in WOLSTENHOLME and KNIGHT (Eds.), *Homeostatic Regulators*, Churchill, London, 1969, page 144.

Table 1 *Differences between exotoxins and endotoxins*

	Exotoxins	Endotoxins
Parent organism..............................	Gram-positive and gram-negative	Gram-negative
Site of toxin	Within and outside parent organisms	Within parent organisms
Chemical structure...........................	Simple protein	Protein–lipopolysaccharide complex
Stability to heating (100 °C)	Labile	Stable
Effect of formaldehyde	Detoxified	Not detoxified
Neutralization by homologous antibodies	Complete	Partial
Biological effect	Individual according to toxin	Same for all toxins
Toxicity relative to strychnine	10^2–10^6	10^{-1}

Reference VAN HEYNINGEN, W. E., in BRAUDE et al., *Medical Microbiology and Infectious Diseases*, Saunders, Philadelphia, 1981, page 51.

The bacterial toxins can be divided into exotoxins and endotoxins (Table 1), depending on whether a direct secretion into the host milieu takes place or whether the microorganism must be partially or totally destroyed before the toxin is released.

Bacterial toxins may be classified according to their biological target: enterotoxins (that act on the intestinal tract to cause secretion), cytotoxins, neurotoxins, leukotoxins, dermonecrotic toxins, lymphocytosis-producing toxins, hemolytic toxins, histamine-sensitizing toxins. Some species of bacteria produce a series of toxins that differ in their effect. In the case of *Clostridium perfringens*, for example, its κ toxin is a collagenase that breaks down muscle tissue, whereas the α toxin – a phospholipase – has a necrotizing and hemolytic and therefore lethal effect; still another toxin has the properties of an enterotoxin.

Toxins act at very low concentrations and often help an invading bacterium to survive in the host organism. Thus many exotoxins are hydrolytic enzymes, such as phospholipase, elastase or hyaluronidase, that act in very different ways to break down tissue and thus enable the foreign organism to alter the host milieu, so that it can establish itself therein. Collagenase, for example, breaks down macromolecules of the host milieu into smaller, digestible fragments which the foreign organism may then use for nutritional purposes. These digestive enzymes act in much the same way as pepsin and trypsin and other enzymes in the mammalian intestine.

A further mechanism of action of bacterial toxins consists in their interference with the cAMP system, which is the connecting link in the effects exerted by various hormones on their respective target cells. The system comprises stimulatory and inhibitory receptors in the plasma membrane, the membrane-bound adenylate-cyclase complex, which is made up of the catalytic unit (C), and the stimulatory and inhibitory guanine-nucleotide-binding proteins (G_s, G_i), and the reactions leading to the formation of cAMP (Fig. 1). G_s is a heterodimer of M_r 45 000 and M_r 35 000 subunits, G_i a heterodimer of M_r 41 000 and M_r 35 000 subunits. The larger (α) subunit of each protein contains the high-affinity guanine-nucleotide-binding sites. When GTP is bound to these subunits, they interact with the catalytic unit. By activating the catalytic unit, Mg^{2+}–ATP is converted to cAMP. Since the G units also possess GTPase activity, GTP is hydrolyzed to GDP, and the G units dissociate from the catalytic unit, bringing back the adenylate-cyclase complex to its ground state.

The α subunit is susceptible to NAD-dependent ADP-ribosylation, which results in characteristic modifications of the function of the G_s and G_i proteins. Several toxins have the properties of NAD^+ ADP-ribosyltransferase.

A few bacterial toxins differing from the forementioned have adenylate-cyclase activity. After invading mammalian cells they are activated by calmodulin, which is not present in bacteria; this results in an extremely high cAMP production.

Exotoxins

Clostridium perfringens α *toxin*. This was the first toxin to be identified as an enzyme. It is phospholipase C (3.1.4.3) which hydrolyzes phosphatidylcholine or sphingomyelin, with the formation of diacylglycerol and either choline phosphate or ceramide (see page 99).

Diphtheria toxin. This toxin is synthesized as a single polypeptide chain and processed upon secretion to a protein of M_r 62 000. It contains 2 intra-chain disulfide bonds and is composed of 2 moieties: fragment A – the N-terminal peptide chain (M_r 22 000) – is responsible for the enzymatic activity of the toxin; fragment B – the C-terminal peptide (M_r 40 000) – is involved in attachment and entry of the toxin into target cells (Fig. 2). Fragment A has the properties of NAD^+ ADP-ribosyltransferase. It inhibits protein synthesis by inactivating the elongation factor EF-2 necessary for the translocation of aminoacyl-tRNA. This takes place by splitting off the nicotinamide portion of NAD and transferring the ADPribose moiety to EF-2:

$$NAD^+ + EF\text{-}2 \longrightarrow ADPRib\text{—}EF\text{-}2 + nicotinamide + H^+$$

Pseudomonas aeruginosa toxins. The organism produces a wide variety of extracellular proteins which may be involved in its pathogenicity. The thermolabile toxin A is secreted as an inactive single polypeptide chain (M_r 66 000) containing 4 intra-chain disulfide bonds. Enzymatic activation of the toxin is probably achieved by proteolytic cleavage. The action of the enzyme seems to be identical to that of diphtheria toxin, namely ADP-ribosylation of EF-2.

Cholera toxin. This enterotoxin (M_r 84 000) is composed of 2 subunits (Fig. 3). The A subunit, which is synthesized as a single polypeptide chain (M_r 29 000), but subsequently hydrolyzed to the fragments A_1 and A_2, is responsible for the enzymatic activity of the toxin. The B subunit contains 5 identical polypeptide chains (M_r 11 600) and accomplishes the binding of the toxin to susceptible tissues. The binding fraction has been shown to have a fairly specific affinity for the ganglioside G_{M1}, which is a structural component of membranes (Table 2). Binding is followed by the passage of the toxic fraction across the membrane and by interference with the adenylate-cyclase system.

Fig. 1 *Schematic representation of the cAMP system*

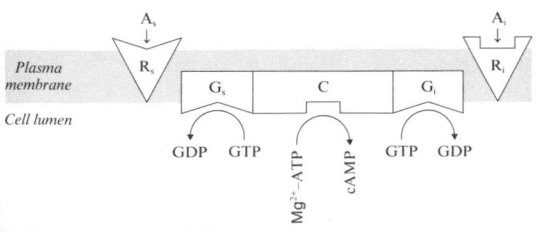

A_s, A_i Stimulatory agents, inhibitory agents
R_s, R_i Receptors for stimulatory and inhibitory agents
G_s, G_i Stimulatory and inhibitory guanine-nucleotide-binding regulatory protein
C Catalytic unit

Fig. 2 *Structure of the diphtheria toxin*

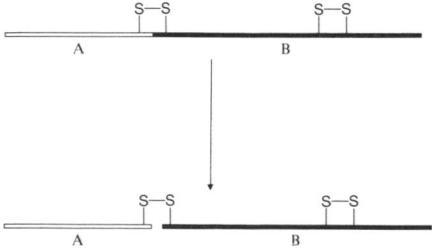

The polypeptide chain can be split by bacterial proteinases into the fragments A and B.

Table 2 *Biologically active polypeptides binding to ganglioside receptors*

Polypeptide	Receptor	Effect
Tetanus toxin..............................	$G_{D1b} > G_{T1} > G_{D1a} > G_{M1}$	Inhibition of synaptic transfer
Botulinum toxin...........................	Not identified (sensitive to sialidase?)	Inhibition of synaptic transfer
Cholera toxin.............................	G_{M1} only	Activation of adenylate cyclase
Escherichia coli toxin.....................	G_{M1} only	Activation of adenylate cyclase
Staphylococcus α toxin......................	G_{D1a}	Increased permeability of cell membrane
Vibrio parahaemolyticus toxin	G_{T1}	Unknown
Interferon................................	G_{M2}	Cell reactions to viruses

Reference VAN HEYNINGEN, W. E., in BRAUDE et al., *Medical Microbiology and Infectious Diseases*, Saunders, Philadelphia, 1981, page 51.

Fig. 3 *Structure of the cholera toxin*

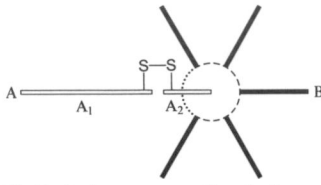

The B subunits are aggregated in a ring by noncovalent bonds. The A subunit is linked to and partially inserted in the B ring. The A subunit is usually interrupted between its 2 cysteine residues by a bacterial proteinase, giving rise to fragments A_1 and A_2. (From HOLMGREN, J., *Nature*, **292**, 413 [1981].)

Cholera toxin has the properties of NAD+ ADP-ribosyltransferase. The protein to which the ADPribosyl group is transferred is the stimulatory guanine-nucleotide-binding unit (G_s) of the system, thereby inhibiting the GTPase activity of this protein. As a result the adenylate-cyclase system is irreversibly stimulated, leading to the continuous formation of cAMP, one effect of which is the secretion of fluid from the intestinal tract.

Pertussis toxins. *Bordetella pertussis* is known to have at least 20 different effects on cells and organ systems, most of which can be assigned to a single protein, the islet-activating protein (IAP). The structure of this protein is similar to that of the cholera toxin; it consists of an A subunit which is responsible for the toxicity, and a B complex, a pentamer responsible for the binding to the tissues. The toxin has the property of NAD+ ADP-ribosyltransferase, but contrary to the cholera toxin it modifies the inhibitory guanine-nucleotide-binding unit (G_i) of the adenylate-cyclase system, thereby stabilizing G_i in its inactive state and resulting in a failure of G_i to inhibit cAMP formation.

A further toxin of *Bordetella pertussis* has adenylate-cyclase activity, its effects being exerted after invasion of cells and activation by calmodulin.

Anthrax toxin. The toxin of *Bacillus anthracis* is made up of 3 components: the protective antigen (PA), the lethal factor (LF), and the edema factor (EF). The latter, EF, has the property of an invasive adenylate cyclase, and as in the case of the pertussis toxin, calmodulin may be involved in activation.

Escherichia coli toxins. Some *Escherichia coli* strains produce a thermolabile toxin that is similar to or identical with the cholera toxin. The toxic part of the molecule with a M_r of about 24 000 acts

Table 3 *Polypeptide neurotoxins inhibiting transmitter release*

Source	Toxin	LD$_{50}$ (mouse) µg/g	M_r
Bacteria............	Botulinum toxin	2×10^{-6}	160 000
	Tetanus toxin	2×10^{-6}	160 000
Snakes.............	β-Bungarotoxin	0.025	20 500
	Crotoxin	0.05	22 000
	Notexin	0.025	13 600
	Taipoxin	0.002	46 000
'Black widow' (spider)	α-Latrotoxin	0.01	130 000

Reference HOWARD and GUNDERSEN, *Ann. Rev. Pharmacol.*, **20**, 307 (1980).

by stimulation of the adenylate cyclase in the intestinal mucosa. Similar or different *E. coli* strains can also form a thermostable toxin, which is probably a carbohydrate-containing peptide with a M_r of about 5000. The effect seems to be due to a stimulation of the guanylate cyclase in the intestinal mucosa.

Tetanus toxin (tetanospasmin). This is one of the most powerful toxins known (Table 3). It acts only on the nervous system, without causing morphologically discernible changes. Like the cholera toxin it is a dimeric protein ($M_r \sim 160000$) whose toxic effect is dependent on binding to specific gangliosides (Table 2). Only when this binding has been effective does the toxic part of the molecule react with the nerve cells so as to produce the characteristic muscular spasms.

Botulinum toxin. At least 8 immunologically different proteins (A, B, C_α, C_β, D, E, F, G) with similar relative molecular mass (M_r 135000–170000) and largely the same neurotoxicity can be distinguished in the toxins produced by *Clostridium botulinum*. Type A toxin – one of the most neurotoxic substances known – also has a hemagglutinating component. Acceptors for botulinum neurotoxin reside at motor nerve terminals and mediate its internalization. The neurotoxins irreversibly inhibit the release of acetylcholine from peripheral nerves.

Staphylococcal toxins. Several *membrane-damaging (cytolytic) toxins* produced by staphylococci are known: α toxin, β toxin, γ toxin, δ toxin and leucocidin. The γ toxin is not well characterized.

Staphylococcus β toxin damages susceptible membranes probably through altering membrane permeability, with consequent major disruption of cellular activity. It is particularly active against erythrocyte membranes and is therefore a hemolytic toxin. The toxin has the property of Mg^{2+}-requiring sphingomyelin phosphodiesterase (3.1.4.12), which splits sphingomyelin into ceramide and choline phosphate (see page 100).

Staphylococcus δ toxin likewise attacks cell membranes, but in a less specific manner than the β toxin. It is a complex protein with a high proportion of hydrophobic amino acids that seem to be able to penetrate, disrupt and produce lysis of some cell membranes. It also has the effect of stimulating the adenylate-cyclase system in a manner not unlike that shown by the cholera toxin.

Staphylococcus α toxin has a similar but obviously more specific effect than the δ toxin. It probably consists of a binding fragment, which reacts with specific membrane receptors, and a hydrophobic fragment, which penetrates and disrupts the integrity of the membrane. No enzymatic activity is definitely associated with this action.

Leucocidin. The activity of this cytolytic toxin is restricted to polymorphonuclear leukocytes and macrophages. It consists of 2 proteins without carbohydrate or lipid components. The toxin interferes with the membrane, resulting in the efflux of potassium ions.

Epidermolytic toxins (ET). Several toxins (also referred to as 'exfoliatin') produced mainly by phage-group II *Staphylococcus aureus* are responsible for exfoliative dermatitis. Proteins isolated with toxic activity have been designated ETA (M_r 30000) and ETB (M_r 29 500). The mechanism of action is unknown.

Staphylococcal enterotoxins are single-chain polypeptides with a M_r of about 26000–30000. Based on their immunological reactions, 8 individual enterotoxins have been identified (A, B, C_1, C_2, C_3, D, E, and F).

The *toxic-shock toxin* produced by some strains of *S. aureus* is a simple protein with M_r 24000 and an amino-acid composition similar to that of the staphylococcal enterotoxins. The toxin is a nonspecific T-cell mitogen.

Oxygen-sensitive toxins. These are a group of cytolytic toxins produced by a whole series of bacteria. The best known are *streptolysin O* and *Clostridium perfringens θ toxin*. Their characteristic sensitivity to oxygen is due to free SH groups, the integrity of which is indispensable for the toxic action and which are readily oxidizable by dioxygen. Another common characteristic is the reaction of the SH groups with cholesterol and other sterols. These toxins are thus especially effective in cholesterol-rich membranes, where they react with cholesterol after binding to the membrane and in this manner disrupt membrane function.

Endotoxins

The endotoxins of gram-negative bacteria are a constituent of the cell wall. They are lipopolysaccharides which consist of a core polysaccharide linked to lipid A and a polypeptide chain (0 antigen) (page 33). Macrophages, polymorphonuclear leukocytes, B lymphocytes, platelets and fibroblasts are classed among the cells that are sensitive to endotoxins, which have effects on practically all organs. They cause fever and activate the complement system as well as prostaglandin and interferon production.

Reviews

· Microbial toxins and diarrhoeal disease, *Ciba Found. Symp.*, **112** (1985).
· FOSTER et al., ADP-ribosylating microbial toxins, *CRC Crit. Rev. Microbiol.*, **11**, 273 (1985).
· HOMMA et al. (Eds.), *Bacterial Endotoxin: Chemical, Biological and Clinical Aspects*, Verlag Chemie, Weinheim, 1984.
· UI, M., Islet-activating protein, pertussis toxin, *Trends physiol. Sci.*, **5**, 277 (1984).
· KATHER and AKTORIES, cAMP-System und bakterielle Toxine, *Klin. Wschr.*, **61**, 1109 (1983).
· EASMON and ADLAM (Eds.), *Staphylococci and Staphylococcal Infections*, Volume 2, Academic Press, London, 1983.
· VAN HEYNINGEN, W. E., Bacterial exotoxins, in BRAUDE et al., *Medical Microbiology and Infectious Diseases*, Saunders, Philadelphia, 1981, page 51.
· BRAUDE, A. I., Bacterial endotoxins, in BRAUDE et al., *Medical Microbiology and Infectious Diseases*, Saunders, Philadelphia, 1981, page 63.
· LAI, C. Y., The chemistry and biology of cholera toxin, *CRC Crit. Rev. Biochem.*, **9**, 171 (1980/81).
· PAPPENHEIMER, A. M., Diphtheria toxin, *Ann. Rev. Biochem.*, **46**, 69 (1977).

Fig. 1   *Effect of antibiotics on the biosynthesis of the typical bacterial cell wall*

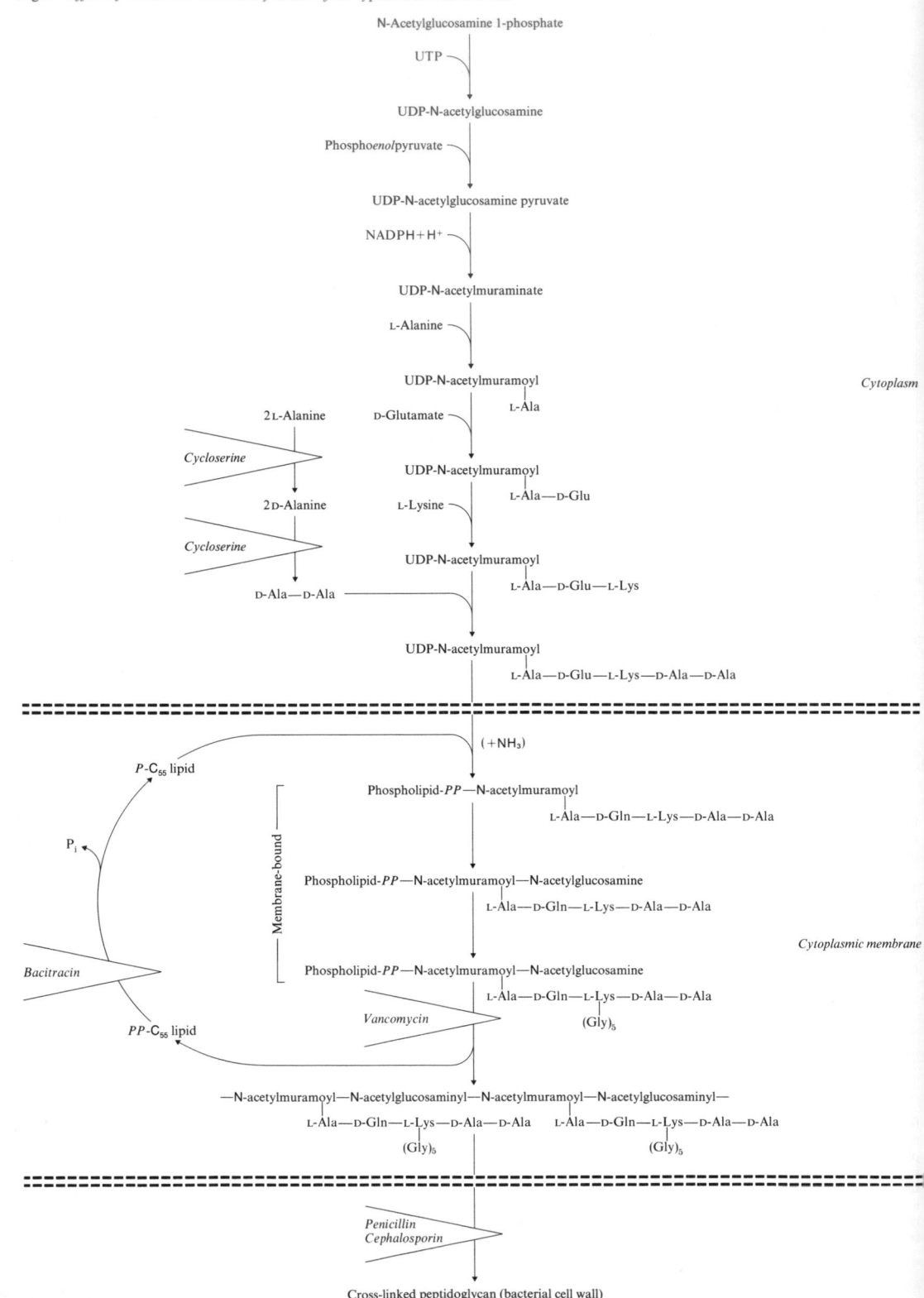

Antibiotics: mode of action and resulting defects

Resulting defect	Antibiotics	Mode of action
Defective cell-wall peptidoglycan	β-Lactams (penicillins, cephalosporins)	Bind to proteins (enzymes) of the bacterial cell wall. Prevent final cross-linkage of peptidoglycan chains
	Bacitracin, vancomycin.............	Prevent transport of carbohydrate pentapeptides from the site of synthesis (cytoplasmic membrane) to the bacterial cell wall
	Cycloserine......................	Prevents D-alanyl-D-alanine formation
Altered permeability of cytoplasmic membrane	Polymyxins......................	Disorganize lipoproteins of cell membranes
	Polyenes	React with sterols in fungal membranes
Impaired function of nucleic acid	Actinomycin D, bleomycins..........	Alter DNA structure. Prevent transcription and DNA replication
	Rifamycins, streptovaricins	Prevent transcription by inhibition of bacterial DNA-directed RNA polymerase
Impaired function of ribosomes.............	Aminoglycosides (streptomycin, etc.) ..	Bind to 30 S subunit of ribosomes, causing conformational changes which disturb P- and A-site functions
	Tetracyclines	Bind to 30 S and 40 S subunits of ribosomes. Prevent elongation of peptides
	Chloramphenicol..................	Binds to 50 S subunit of ribosomes. Inhibits peptidyltransferase and formation of peptide bonds
	Erythromycin, lincomycin, clindamycin	Bind to 50 S subunit of ribosomes. Prevent formation of peptide bonds (similar to mode of action of chloramphenicol)

'Antibiotics' may be defined as substances of microbial origin which in low concentration prevent the growth or existence of other microorganisms. Most antibiotics, however, act not only on the metabolic processes of prokaryotic cells but also on those of eukaryotic cells, so that only a few antibiotics can be used for combating infectious diseases. Many of the antibiotics used today are semisynthetic variants.

The antibiotics can be divided up into groups on the basis of their mode of action (see table above).

Antibiotics affecting the biosynthesis of bacterial cell-wall peptidoglycans

The biosynthesis of a typical peptidoglycan of the bacterial cell walls can be summarized as shown in Figure 1 (facing page).

The first stage – within the bacterial cytoplasm – involves the formation of UDP-N-acetylmuramoyl pentapeptide, the basic unit from which the peptidoglycans are built. The final step in this stage involves the condensation of a dipeptide of D-alanine with the carbohydrate-bound tripeptide*, whereupon the pentapeptide is formed. The formation of D-alanyl-D-alanine takes place in 2 steps. In the first step, D-alanine is formed from L-alanine by the action of alanine racemase (5.1.1.1), and in the second step the dipeptide is formed by D-alanine–D-alanine ligase (6.3.2.4). Both these reactions are inhibited by *cycloserine*, which is a structural analog of D-alanine. Generally cycloserine is too toxic for therapeutic use.

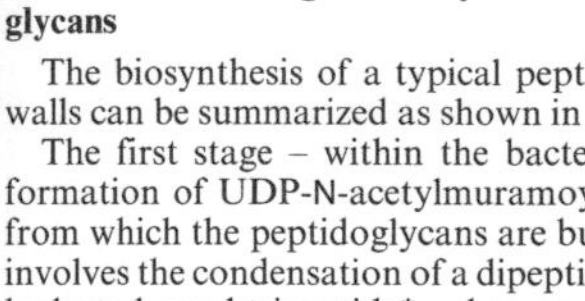

D-Alanine   Cycloserine

The second stage of peptidoglycan synthesis is concerned with the formation of a disaccharide pentapeptide by condensation of the monosaccharide pentapeptide with N-acetylglucosamine. This takes place within the cytoplasmic membrane. Since the compound must be transported to the outside of the membrane for subsequent assembly, the condensation takes place via a membrane-bound carrier lipid, undecaprenyl phosphate (C_{55} lipid), which is linked with the muramoyl pentapeptide via a pyrophosphate bridge. In another reaction a pentaglycine chain is added to the 6-amino group of

lysine. The disaccharide pentapeptide is then separated from the membrane-bound undecaprenyl diphosphate and condenses with the acceptor molecule of growing peptidoglycan. This reaction is inhibited by *vancomycin*, which has a high affinity for the terminal D-alanyl-D-alanine dipeptide of the disaccharide pentapeptide. In the absence of vancomycin the membrane-bound lipid undecaprenyl diphosphate separates and is then dephosphorylated to generate the original carrier lipid. The dephosphorylation is inhibited by *bacitracin*, which has a high affinity for the undecaprenyl diphosphate.

The final stage in the formation of peptidoglycan takes place outside the cytoplasmic membrane and involves the condensation of the disaccharide pentapeptide to form the polymerized peptidoglycan. In the case of *Staphylococcus aureus* (Fig. 2) the terminal glycine

Fig. 2   *Cross-linking of the peptidoglycan chain*

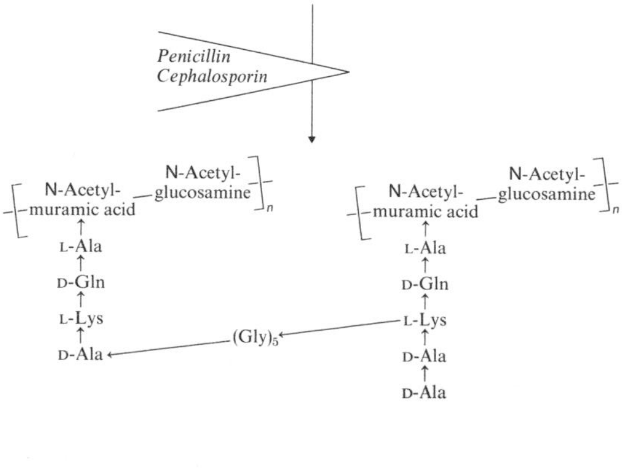

---

*The last amino acid in *Staphylococcus aureus* is L-lysine; in *Escherichia coli* it is 2,6-diaminopimelic acid.

of the pentaglycine side chain reacts with the penultimate D-alanyl residue of the adjoining pentaglycine side chain. This reaction requires energy which, in the absence of ATP at the site, is obtained by hydrolysis of the terminal D-alanine.

The cell walls of bacteria contain proteins (penicillin-binding protein, PBP) that covalently bind *penicillins* and *cephalosporins*. Some of these proteins display enzyme activity and are involved in cross-linking of the peptidoglycan chains. Penicillin inhibits transpeptidase activity, which catalyzes the cross-linking and the release of D-alanine. This inhibitory action may be due in part to the structural similarity of penicillin and the terminal D-alanyl-D-alanine groups of the peptidoglycan.

Penicillin　　　　　D-Alanyl-D-alanine group

In gram-negative bacteria, the mechanism by which β-lactams bonding to PBP interact with the synthesis of cell-wall peptidoglycans is but poorly understood.

Antibiotics affecting the permeability of cell membranes

Several classes of *polypeptide antibiotics* exert an antibacterial action by binding to the cytoplasmic membrane, with subsequent disturbance of its function. Their therapeutic application, however, is limited, since most organisms have a similar cell-wall structure. The mode of action of the therapeutically utilizable *polymyxins* is explained by their structure: the positively charged peptide ring – owing to the high proportion of 2,4-diaminobutyric acid (L-Dab) – interacts with the anionic phosphate groups of the membrane phos-

Polymyxin B₁

pholipids, displacing magnesium ions, which normally contribute to membrane stability. At the same time the fatty side chain is inserted into the hydrophobic inner region of the membrane. The polymyxins thus interfere with the normal organization of the membrane and alter its permeability characteristics.

The *polyene antibiotics* are large-ring lactones. Part of the ring is a hydrophobic region comprising a sequence of 4 to 7 conjugated double bonds. In another part of the ring the C atoms carry hydroxy groups, creating a hydrophilic area. The polyene antibiotics act exclusively on cells that have a sterol-containing membrane, such as yeast, fungi and animal cells; they have no effect on bacteria. *Nystatin* and *amphotericin B* are used therapeutically on the basis of their preferred interaction with ergosterol-containing membranes. The action of the compounds of this group is to increase the permeability of the fungal membrane.

Antibiotics affecting nucleic acid synthesis

Actinomycin D and the *bleomycins* are antibiotics that act on the DNA not only of bacterial but also of animal cells, so that a thera-

peutic use is limited to some forms of cancer. Actinomycin D binds to double-stranded DNA by intercalation into the narrow groove of the DNA helix, whereupon both the DNA-dependent synthesis of RNA and DNA replication (at higher concentrations) are inhibited. The bleomycins produce breaks in the single-stranded and double-stranded DNA and release DNA bases, thus preventing DNA replication and RNA synthesis.

The *rifamycins* as well as the related *streptovaricins* inhibit nucleic acid synthesis at the level of transcription, that is, the transfer of the information contained in the DNA to the mRNA, in bacteria. These antibiotics bind to the DNA-directed RNA polymerase (2.7.7.6) and thereby inhibit this enzyme in bacteria, whereas they neither bind to nor inhibit the mammalian enzyme.

Antibiotics affecting protein synthesis

Streptomycin and other aminoglycosides (such as *kanamycins*, *gentamicins* and *neomycins*) are bactericidal, producing a marked inhibition of protein synthesis before cell death. The main target of streptomycin is the 30 S subunit of the bacterial ribosomes, to which the antibiotic binds tightly. It shows no affinity for the 40 S subunit of eukaryotic ribosomes. Binding to ribosomes probably has various effects on protein synthesis: streptomycin, for example, inactivates the initiation complex, interferes with the binding of tRNA and distorts the mRNA codons, inducing misreadings of the genetic code and incorporation of a wrong amino acid into the growing peptide chain ('nonsense' polypeptide).

A similar mechanism of action seems to hold true for the other aminoglycosides, although their binding site is probably not identical with that of streptomycin.

The *tetracyclines* possess a wide range of antimicrobial activity not only against gram-positive and gram-negative bacteria, but also against mycoplasma species and rickettsiae. Protein synthesis is inhibited not only on the ribosomes of bacteria, but also – contrary to the action of aminoglycosides – on the ribosomes of eukaryotes. The tetracyclines seem to bind to the 30 S subunits of ribosomes (40 S subunits of ribosomes of eukaryotes), thereby preventing the access of aminoacyl-tRNA to the A site (page 180) on the mRNA–ribosome complex. This inhibits the addition of amino acids to the growing peptide chain.

Chloramphenicol is a substance of comparatively simple structure with a broad antibiotic spectrum similar to that of the tetracyclines, but its therapeutic potential is limited by its toxicity. It binds exclusively to the 50 S subunit of bacterial ribosomes and not to the 60 S subunit of eukaryotic ribosomes. A maximum of one molecule of chloramphenicol can be bound by each ribosome. The binding of chloramphenicol to the ribosome is reversible, so that the action is bacteriostatic rather than bactericidal. This bacteriostatic action is due to an inhibition of peptidyltransferase (2.3.2.12) and, thus, to prevention of peptide formation.

The biochemical mechanism underlying the toxic action of chloramphenicol on erythropoiesis is not known in detail. It may be connected with an effect on the mitochondrial ribosomes causing a disruption of the electron transfer system in bone marrow cells.

Erythromycin is an antibiotic of the macrolide group, which is characterized by a large lactone ring linked to sugar residues. Erythromycin acts bacteriostatically on gram-positive and some gram-negative bacteria. The mode of action seems to be similar to that of chloramphenicol. Erythromycin binds to the 50 S subunit of the ribosomes and probably acts by limiting the access of peptidyl-tRNA to the P site on the ribosome (page 180). The action of *lincomycin* and *clindamycin* seems to be due to a similar mechanism, but is restricted to gram-positive bacteria.

Reviews

· Braude, A.I., Mechanisms of action of antimicrobial drugs, in Braude et al., *Medical Microbiology and Infectious Diseases*, Saunders, Philadelphia, 1981 page 234.
· Franklin and Snow, *Biochemistry of Antimicrobial Action*, 3rd ed., Chapman and Hall, London, 1981.
· Eisenstein, B.I., Bacterial variation and antibiotic action, *Advanc. intern. Med.* **26**, 393 (1980).

The term 'xenobiotics' is used to describe foreign compounds which include drugs, pesticides, food additives and other chemicals used by man. The metabolism of foreign compounds in the living organism (biotransformation) usually proceeds in such a way that compounds with lowered toxicity are formed, which can easily be excreted. Therefore these reactions are classed as detoxication mechanisms[◊]. On the other hand, there are xenobiotics which are not detoxified but converted to compounds with increased toxicity[1-3].

The majority of xenobiotics are metabolized in the body by enzymes found mainly in the liver, but to some extent also in other tissues, such as kidney, intestine and lung. On the other hand, there are some compounds which are not metabolized and are excreted unchanged, whilst some change spontaneously into other substances without the intervention of enzymes. Therefore, xenobiotics can be divided broadly into 3 types, namely:

(1) Substances *metabolized by enzymes*.
(2) Substances *excreted unchanged*.
(3) Substances *undergoing spontaneous transformations* due to instability at physiological pH values or to reactivity towards certain physiological molecules.

Most xenobiotics belong to the first category, but some can undergo a combination of enzyme-catalyzed and spontaneous reactions. In the gut, some xenobiotics can be metabolized by the intestinal microflora[4,5].

The biphasic metabolism of xenobiotics

The reactions which xenobiotics undergo in the body are oxidations, reductions, hydrolyses and syntheses. These reactions usually occur in 2 phases[6,7], the oxidations, reductions and hydrolyses occurring in the first phase and the syntheses in the second. The synthetic reactions are referred to as conjugations. The reactions of the first phase can result in the conversion of (1) a biologically active compound to an inactive one, (2) a biologically inactive compound to an active one, and (3) a biologically active compound to another active compound. The reactions of the second phase, however, usually result in inactive excretory products. The phase I reactions introduce into the xenobiotic molecule OH, COOH, NH_2 and SH groups which enable the products of phase I to undergo the synthetic or conjugation reactions. This concept of xenobiotic metabolism can be represented as follows:

Xenobiotic

| Phase I enzymes | Activation or inactivation |

Oxidation, reduction and/or hydrolysis products

| Phase II enzymes | Inactivation |

Synthetic or conjugation products

If the compound contains any of the above-mentioned groups, it can undergo phase II reactions directly; this applies, for example, to phenol, which contains an OH group. Some compounds only undergo phase I reactions, as for example ethanol, which is mainly oxidized to CO_2.

In both phases the polarity of the compound is increased, and the products of phase II are usually strong organic acids or, occasionally, strong bases, which are readily excreted. The metabolism of the well-known antipyretic and analgesic drug phenacetin illustrates this point[8]. This drug is a neutral, lipid-soluble compound which is

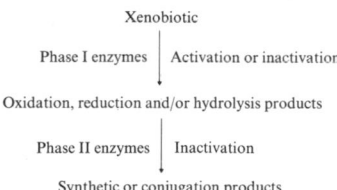

| Phenacetin (neutral) | p-Acetamido-phenol ($pK_a \sim 10$) | p-Acetamidophenyl-glucuronide ($pK_a \sim 3.5$) |
| | Ionization at pH 7.4: $\sim 0.25\%$ | Ionization at pH 7.4: 99.99% |

oxidatively de-ethylated in the first phase of its metabolism to the weak acid p-acetamidophenol, which has a pK_a of about 10. In the second phase, p-acetamidophenol is conjugated mainly with glucuronic acid[9] to give p-acetamidophenylglucuronide, a strong acid with a pK_a of about 3.5. At the pH value of the blood this glucuronide is virtually completely ionized, highly water-soluble and readily excreted by the kidney.

Drugs therefore appear to be metabolized in the body along pathways tending to lead to the formation of water-soluble, polar compounds which can be readily excreted. Both phenacetin and its phase I metabolite, p-acetamidophenol, are active drugs, but the activity of phenacetin is largely due to this metabolite known as paracetamol. The phase II metabolite, p-acetamidophenylglucuronide, is an inactive excretory product, and its formation terminates the activity of phenacetin.

Phase I reactions

The reactions of drugs, which can be classified as oxidations, reductions and hydrolyses, are catalyzed by enzymes occurring predominantly in the liver, although such metabolizing activity is also found in extrahepatic tissues such as the kidney and intestinal tissue and to a lesser extent in the lungs, adrenals and blood. The majority of these reactions are carried out by enzymes located in the endoplasmic reticulum of the hepatic cells[10]. On homogenization of the liver the endoplasmic reticulum is disrupted, forming small vesicles which can be separated from the homogenate by high-speed centrifugation to give the fraction of microsomes. Many of the reactions of drugs can be carried out in vitro with microsomes and suitable cofactors occurring in the cytosol, particularly reduced NADP.

The oxidative reactions carried out by microsomes have been extensively studied[10,14]; the oxidizing system involves an electron transfer chain. The 2 major protein components are the NADPH-oxidizing flavoprotein, NADPH–ferrihemoprotein reductase (1.6.2.4) – formerly called 'cytochrome P-450 reductase' – and a CO-binding heme-thiolate protein (P-450)[◊◊], the unspecific monooxygenase (1.14.14.1) – formerly referred to as 'cytochrome P-450'. Microsomal oxidation has a specific requirement for NADPH and dioxygen. The active site of P-450 seems to be in close proximity to the heme iron

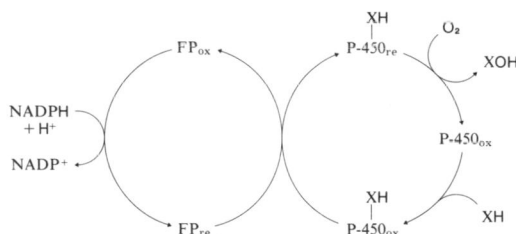

FP: flavoprotein containing FAD or FMN; XH: xenobiotic; XOH: oxidized xenobiotic; ox: oxidized; re: reduced

because it is the iron atom that binds dioxygen in forming a ternary iron–oxy–substrate complex prior to monooxygenation[13].

Reductive reactions are also well investigated[14]. The reduction of nitrogen-containing functional groups is mainly carried out by mitochondria, and the P-450 system is involved[15].

Oxidative reactions

The oxidative reactions carried out by liver microsomes are many and varied, and they include the following types: oxidation of aromatic rings, oxidation of alkyl chains, oxidative dealkylation, N-oxidation, S-oxidation, P-oxidation, replacement of S by O, epoxidation, oxidative deamination, and aromatization.

Oxidation of aromatic rings[16]. Aromatic rings are oxidized to produce phenols, and this reaction is usually referred to as 'aromatic hydroxylation', one of the most intensely studied of microsomal reactions. It occurs with carbocyclic and heterocyclic aromatic systems, and the main site of oxidation is usually, but not always, that of highest electron density; consequently the oxidation is orientated. It may occur at more than one site, so that more than one monophenol and some polyphenols may be produced. Aniline, for example,

---

*This chapter on 'Metabolism of Xenobiotics' (pages 207–216) has been compiled in collaboration with R. T. WILLIAMS, Metabolic Day Ward (Lab.), St Mary's Hospital, London.

[◊]Detoxication reactions are not restricted to foreign compounds. The formation of urea from the physiological metabolite ammonia (page 110) or the conjugation of bilirubin (page 125), for example, are also illustrations of this type of reaction.

[◊◊]P-450 refers collectively to multiple species of proteins which may differ in terms of their apoprotein moiety and substrate specificities but have similar spectral properties (the absorption maximum after binding of CO to the reduced form is 450 nm)[11]. It has been suggested that the number of P-450 proteins in an organism is at least 30 and most probably less than 200; some forms of P-450 proteins may be detected only after exposure to a xenobiotic[12].

gives rise to 2 monophenols and is hydroxylated in vivo in positions 2 and 4:

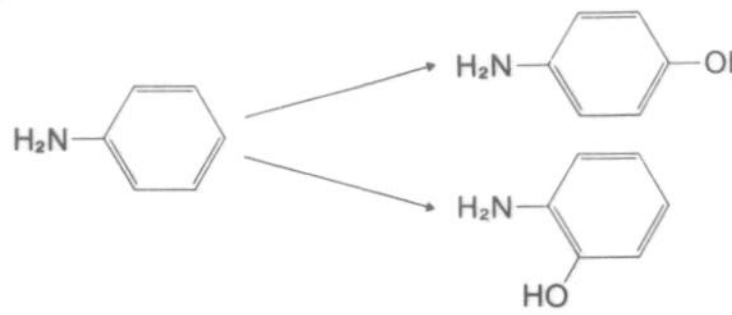

Benzene is hydroxylated mainly to phenol and to a lesser extent to the polyphenols catechol, quinol and hydroxyquinol.

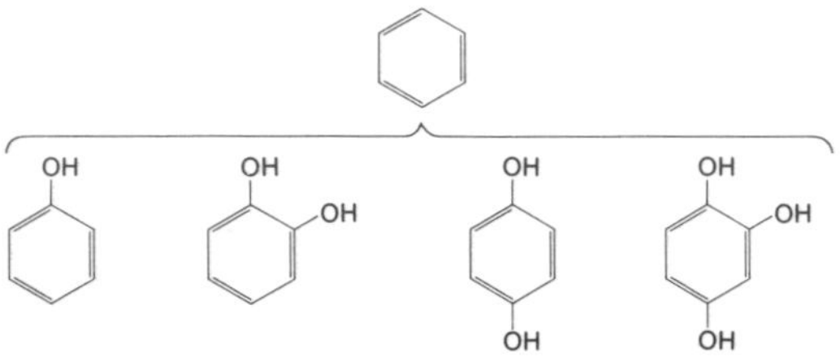

| Phenol | Catechol | Quinol | Hydroxyquinol |

Epoxidation is the primary step in aromatic hydroxylation.

Oxidation of alkyl chains. Compounds containing alkyl chains can be oxidized in the body, with the production of primary, secondary or tertiary alcohols, the nature of the alcohol produced depending upon the location of the oxidation in the alkyl chain and upon the nature of the alkyl group. Oxidation usually occurs at the ω or (ω − 1) carbon atom. If the attack occurs at the ω position of a chain, then further oxidation to a carboxylic acid can occur. These reactions can be summarized as follows (R, R′ and R″ are alkyl groups):

(1) ω-Oxidation:

$$R \cdot CH_2 \cdot CH_3 \longrightarrow R \cdot CH_2 \cdot CH_2OH \longrightarrow R \cdot CH_2 \cdot COOH$$

(2) (ω − 1)-Oxidation:

$$R \cdot CH_2 \cdot CH_3 \longrightarrow R \cdot CHOH \cdot CH_3$$

(3) Formation of a tertiary alcohol:

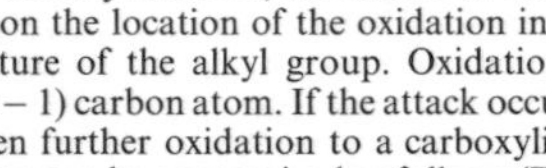

(4) Oxidation of compounds containing cycloalkane rings, the products in this case being secondary alcohols.

Examples of the above-mentioned reactions (Ⓑ is a barbiturate ring system*):

(1) *ω-Oxidation.* 5-Ethyl-5-hydroxyethylbarbituric acid is a minor metabolite of barbital.

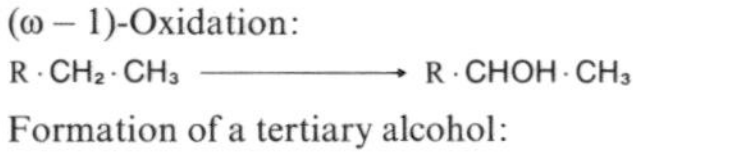

(2) *(ω − 1)-Oxidation.* 5-Ethyl-5-(1′-methyl-3′-hydroxybutyl)barbituric acid is a metabolite of pentobarbital.

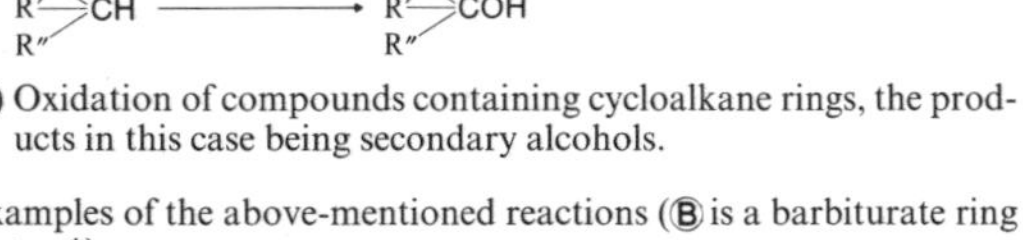

(3) *Tertiary alcohol formation.* 5-Ethyl-5-(3′-hydroxyisoamyl)barbituric acid is a metabolite of amobarbital.

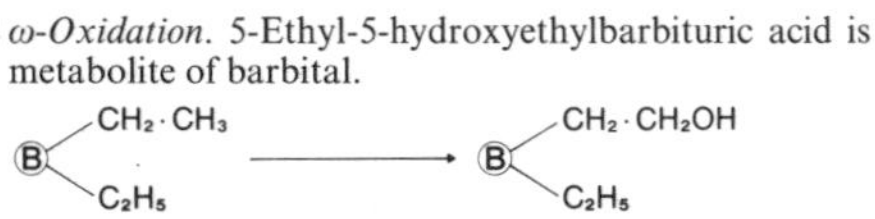

* Barbiturate ring:

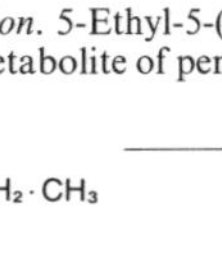

(4) *Cycloalkane oxidation.* Cyclohexanol is the main metabolite of cyclohexane.

Epoxidation[16, 17]. This reaction consists of the enzymatic addition of oxygen across a C=C double bond. It has been found to occur with aromatic compounds such as naphthalene and probably benzene, with certain organochlorine insecticides such as heptachlor and aldrin and with drugs such as carbamazepine and cyproheptadine. The reaction is carried out by liver microsomes in the presence of dioxygen and NADPH and maintained by the P-450 system. It ap-

pears to be the initial method of oxidative attack on an aromatic system, since the epoxide can give rise to a phenol by rearrangement, to a dihydrodiol by enzymatic addition of water, and to a glutathione conjugate by reaction with glutathione (GSH) and a suitable enzyme.

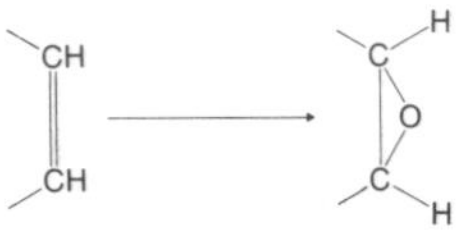

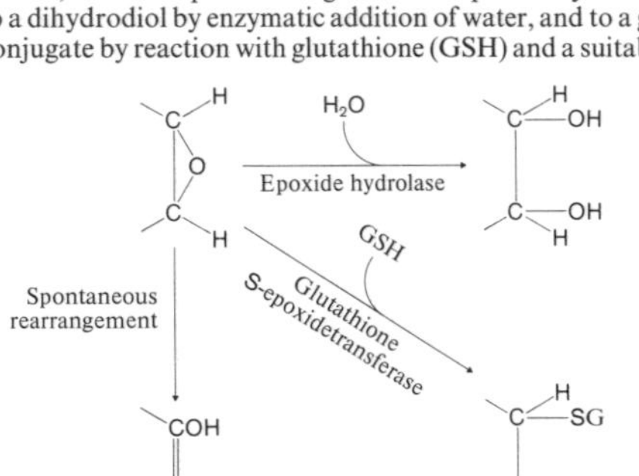

Oxidative dealkylation[16]. Alkyl groups, particularly methyl groups, can be oxidatively removed by liver microsomes when they are attached through oxygen (O-methyl), nitrogen (N-methyl) or sulfur (S-methyl). The reactions can be represented as follows:

$$ROCH_3 \longrightarrow ROCH_2OH \longrightarrow ROH + HCHO$$

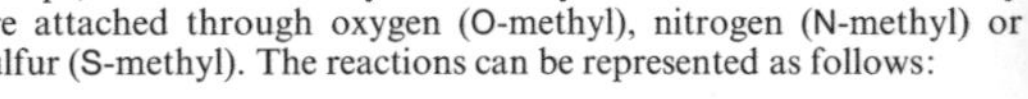

(R′: H or CH_3; R: alkyl group.) The initial step is apparently the oxidation of the CH_3 group to CH_2OH, which is then lost as formaldehyde and eventually oxidized to CO_2. Ethyl groups can be oxidized in a similar manner and released as acetaldehyde, which is then metabolized via acetate mainly to CO_2. Examples of these reactions are the O-*demethylation* of codeine (3-methylmorphine) to morphine, the N-*demethylation* of imipramine to demethylimipramine (desipramine) and the O-de-ethylation of phenacetin to p-acetamidophenol. S-*Demethylation* (—SCH_3 $\longrightarrow$ —SH) also occurs, possibly by a similar mechanism, an example being the demethylation of 6-methylthiopurine to 6-mercaptopurine.

Oxidative deamination[16, 22]. Amines such as amphetamine are deaminated in the body by an enzyme system which occurs in liver microsomes. The mechanism of this deamination is not yet clear, but it does require O_2 and NADPH. It has been suggested that the process involves either N-oxidation or aliphatic C-oxidation or both:

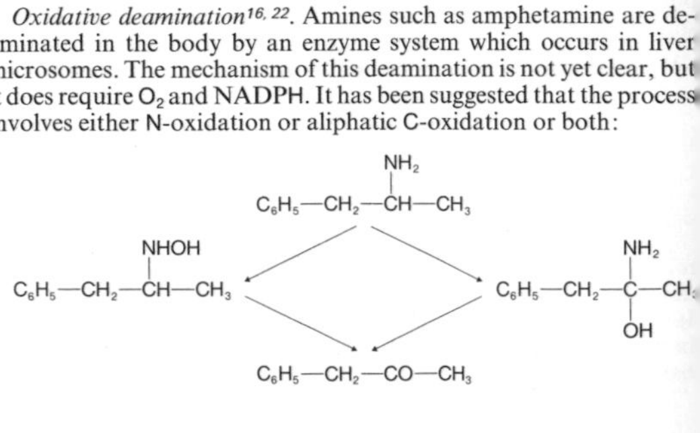

N-Oxidation[16,18,19]. Primary, secondary and tertiary amines are oxidized in the body, and these reactions can be carried out by liver microsomes. The primary and secondary amines give rise to hydroxylamines and the tertiary amines to amine oxides (R, R', and R" are usually alkyl groups, although one of them can be an aryl group):

(a) $RNH_2 \longrightarrow RNHOH$

(b)
$$\begin{array}{c} R \\ \diagdown \\ R' \end{array} NH \longrightarrow \begin{array}{c} R \\ \diagdown \\ R' \end{array} NOH$$

(c)
$$\begin{array}{c} R \\ R' \\ R'' \end{array} N \longrightarrow \begin{array}{c} R \\ R' \\ R'' \end{array} NO$$

The first reaction (a) occurs frequently with arylamines such as aniline, p-chloroaniline, p-phenetidine and carcinogenic amines (2-naphthylamine, 4-biphenylamine, 4-aminostilbene, etc.), and in the rabbit it is a major reaction of the aliphatic amine chlorphentermine. The second reaction (b) has been found with N-methylaniline and its ethyl and butyl homologs, and the third (c) with trimethylamine, chlorpromazine, N,N-dimethyltryptamine and guanethidine.

N-Hydroxylation has also been found to occur with urethane ($C_2H_5OCONH_2$) and the carcinogen N-fluorenylacetamide, an acetylated primary amine. Moreover, acetylhydrazine and isopropylhydrazine can be hydroxylated at the terminal N atom; these compounds spontaneously split off water, forming very reactive diazenes[20]. The oxidation of 2,4,6-trimethylacetophenone imine to give the corresponding oxime has been reported to occur in microsomes, and the oxidation of the amino group in chlorphentermine to a nitro group occurs to a small extent in the rabbit.

N-Fluorenylacetamide

2,4,6-Trimethyl-acetophenone imine

Chlorphentermine

Thus reactions (a) to (c) can be supplemented as follows:

(d) $ROCONH_2 \longrightarrow ROCONHOH$

(e) $Aryl{-}NHCO \cdot CH_3 \longrightarrow Aryl{-}N(OH)CO \cdot CH_3$

(f)
$$\begin{array}{c} \diagdown \\ / \end{array} C{=}NH \longrightarrow \begin{array}{c} \diagdown \\ / \end{array} C{=}NOH$$

(g)
$$\begin{array}{c} \diagdown \\ / \end{array} CNH_2 \longrightarrow \begin{array}{c} \diagdown \\ / \end{array} CNO_2$$

S-Oxidation[21]. This reaction consists of the microsomal oxidation of divalent sulfur – especially in a heterocyclic system – to the sulfoxide and sometimes to the sulfone:

$$\begin{array}{c} \diagdown \\ / \end{array} S \longrightarrow \begin{array}{c} \diagdown \\ / \end{array} SO \longrightarrow \begin{array}{c} \diagdown \\ / \end{array} SO_2$$

Examples are chlorpromazine and other phenothiazines, which are oxidized to the corresponding 5-oxides and in some cases to the sulfones. Sulfoxides, such as sulfinpyrazone, are also oxidized to sulfones.

P-Oxidation. The oxidation of trisubstituted phosphines to phosphine oxides has been reported to occur in vitro with rat liver microsomes. Example:

Diphenylmethyl-phosphine

Diphenylmethyl-phosphine oxide

Replacement of S by O[16]. This reaction is carried out by liver microsomes, involving the P-450 system. It is of considerable importance in the activity of some types of organophosphorus insecticides. It also occurs to some extent during the metabolism of certain thiobarbiturates which are partly converted to the corresponding oxybarbiturates. There are therefore at least two kinds of reactions

under this heading, namely the conversion of P=S to P=O and of C=S to C=O. For organophosphorus insecticides the reaction is

$$R'O{-}\underset{\underset{OR}{|}}{\overset{\overset{OR}{|}}{P}}{=}S \longrightarrow \left[R'O{-}\underset{\underset{OR}{|}}{\overset{\overset{OR}{|}}{P}}{=}S{\rightarrow}O \right] \longrightarrow R'O{-}\underset{\underset{OR}{|}}{\overset{\overset{OR}{|}}{P}}{=}O$$

with an unstable sulfoxide as an intermediate[21]. An example of this type of reaction is the conversion of 4-nitrophenyldiethyl thiophosphate (parathion) (C_2H_5 for R; $C_6H_4NO_2$ for R') to 4-nitrophenyldiethyl phosphate (paraoxon), which is an active metabolite.

A thiobarbiturate undergoing the reaction C=S $\longrightarrow$ C=O is thiopental, which is partly converted to pentobarbital in vivo [C_2H_5 for R; $CH(CH_3) \cdot (CH_2)_2 \cdot CH_3$ for R']:

Thiopental

Pentobarbital

Oxidative dehalogenation[16,23]. Dihalomethanes are oxidized to CO by liver microsomes in a reaction involving the P-450 system:

$$CH_2Br_2 \longrightarrow CO + 2 Br^-$$

In a similar reaction, halothane is converted to trifluoroacetic acid[24]:

$$F_3C \cdot CHClBr \longrightarrow F_3C \cdot COOH + Br^- + Cl^-$$

Aromatization. The conversion of a certain limited number of alicyclic compounds to aromatic compounds can be regarded as oxidations in the sense that hydrogen is being abstracted. Cyclohexanecarboxylic acid is converted to hippuric acid in animals, the reaction being carried out by liver mitochondria in the presence of glycine:

Cyclohexanecarboxylic acid

Hippuric acid

Quinic acid (1,3,4,5-tetrahydroxycyclohexanecarboxylic acid) is also converted to hippuric acid in man and Old World monkeys, but this conversion is carried out by the intestinal flora and is a complicated process which may involve oxidation, reduction and dehydration:

Quinic acid

Hippuric acid

Reductions

(a) *Reduction of nitro compounds*[15] to amines occurs in several steps:

$$RNO_2 \longrightarrow RNO \longrightarrow RNHOH \longrightarrow RNH_2$$

These take place partly in liver microsomes which contain an enzyme system ('nitroreductase') involving the P-450 system[16]. An example of this type of reaction is the reduction of aromatic nitro compounds such as chloramphenicol, nitrobenzene, 2,4,6-trinitrotoluene and 4-nitrobenzoic acid. Both 4-hydroxyamino-2,6-dinitrotoluene and 4-amino-2,6-dinitrotoluene have been shown to be urinary metabolites of trinitrotoluene:

Trinitrotoluene

4-Hydroxyamino-2,6-dinitrotoluene

4-Amino-2,6-dinitrotoluene

(b) *Reduction of azo compounds* to amines[15]. The following steps are involved in this reaction:

$$RN{=}NR' \longrightarrow RNHNHR' \longrightarrow RNH_2 + R'NH_2$$

The reduction of drugs such as prontosil and neoprontosil to sulfanilamide, which is responsible for the antibacterial activity of the parent drug, is an example of this type of reaction. Liver mitochondria contain an enzyme system ('azoreductase') which includes the P-450 system[16] and is responsible for the reduction of these drugs, but evidence shows that these azo drugs and azo dyes used for food-coloring can also be reduced by the intestinal flora.

Prontosil

Triaminobenzene   Sulfanilamide

(c) *Reduction of ketones* to secondary alcohols[25]. The reaction

$$R \cdot CO \cdot R' \longrightarrow R \cdot CHOH \cdot R'$$

may be catalyzed by NADH-dependent alcohol dehydrogenase (1.1.1.1) or by NADPH-dependent reductases. Ketones such as acetophenone, propiophenone and metyrapone (a microsomal monooxygenase inhibitor) are reduced in the body to the corresponding secondary alcohols methylphenylcarbinol, ethylphenylcarbinol, and 2-methyl-1,2-bis-(3-pyridyl)propan-1-ol, respectively. The reaction is usually stereospecific, but the reduction of acetophenone by rabbit kidney yields 76% of the (S)-enantiomer and 24% of the (R)-enantiomer.

$$C_6H_5 \cdot CO \cdot CH_3 \longrightarrow C_6H_5 \cdot CHOH \cdot CH_3$$

Acetophenone   (−)-Methylphenylcarbinol

Metyrapone   2-Methyl-1,2-bis-(3-pyridyl)propan-1-ol

(d) *Less frequent reductive reactions.* Examples:

– Some aldehydes are reduced to primary alcohols; a well-known case is the conversion of chloral hydrate to trichloroethanol:

$$R \cdot CHO \longrightarrow R \cdot CH_2OH$$

– Occasionally double bonds are reduced:

$$R \cdot CH{=}CH \cdot R' \longrightarrow R \cdot CH_2{-}CH_2 \cdot R'$$

– Pentavalent arsenicals are reduced to the trivalent form:

$$R \cdot AsO(OH)_2 \longrightarrow R \cdot AsO$$

– Compounds containing disulfide links are reduced to the corresponding mercapto derivatives:

$$RS \cdot SR' \longrightarrow RSH + R'SH$$

– Sulfoxides are reduced to divalent S:

– Amine oxides are reduced to tertiary amines in liver microsomes, with the participation of the P-450 system[16] (a substrate for this reaction is for example imipramine N-oxide):

– Aromatic dihydroxycarboxylic acids are dehydroxylated:

Several of these reductions can also be carried out by the intestinal flora; in the latter reaction dehydroxylation is carried out exclusively by the intestinal flora[4].

Hydrolyses

The hydrolysis of carboxylic esters, phosphoric esters – including thiophosphoric esters – and amides occur in the body, the products being alcohols, phenols, thiols, carboxylic acids, phosphoric acids and amines. The enzymes catalyzing these reactions may occur in all mammalian tissues; liver, gastrointestinal tract and plasma, however, have by far the highest share of the total hydrolytic capacity[26]. The participating enzymes – esterases, phosphatases, amidases – vary widely with tissue and with species and strain. Atropine, for example, is hydrolyzed by rabbit plasma, but not by human plasma. The reactions include the following examples:

(a) Hydrolysis of carboxylic esters:

$$R \cdot COOR' \xrightarrow{H_2O} R \cdot COOH + R'OH$$

(b) Hydrolysis of phosphoric esters:

$$(RO)_2PO \cdot OR' \xrightarrow{H_2O} (RO)_2PO \cdot OH + R'OH$$

(c) Hydrolysis of phosphorothioic esters:

$$(RO)_2PS \cdot OR' \xrightarrow{H_2O} (RO)_2PS \cdot OH + R'OH$$

(d) Hydrolysis of phosphorothiolic esters:

$$(RO)_2PO \cdot SR' \xrightarrow{H_2O} (RO)_2PO \cdot OH + R'SH$$

(e) Hydrolysis of amides:

$$R \cdot CONHR' \xrightarrow{H_2O} R \cdot COOH + R'NH_2$$

Hydrolysis comprises the addition of water and the cleavage of the molecule as shown above, but an important reaction in detoxication of epoxides involves the addition of water only to give diols by the action of microsomal epoxide hydrolase (3.3.2.3)[27].

Epoxide hydrolase

Phase II reactions or conjugations[28]

Foreign compounds containing suitable chemical groups such as OH, NH$_2$, SH and COOH, phase I metabolites of drugs and many natural metabolites of the body can undergo synthetic reactions called 'conjugations' which usually result in their detoxication. 'Conjugation' means the union or coupling of two substances in the body, and 'detoxication' implies that the toxicity of a compound has been reduced or abolished. The conjugation product is thus made up of two parts, one the foreign compound or its phase I metabolite and the other a compound provided by the organism and called a 'conjugating agent'. Conjugating agents arise mainly from the body's carbohydrate and protein sources. The phase I active metabolite of phenacetin, p-acetamidophenol (paracetamol), is converted in the body to p-acetamidophenylglucuronide. In this case the conjugating agent is glucuronic acid, which is provided by the body via glucose from its carbohydrate sources. The conjugation product, p-acetamidophenylglucuronide, is readily excreted and shows no pharmacological activity.

There are 10 major conjugation reactions, 9 of which occur in man (Table 1). Apart from these, there are several minor conjugation processes (Table 2).

Mechanism of conjugation

Conjugations are synthetic reactions and require a source of energy which is usually supplied by ATP. With the exception of mercapturic acid formation and cyanide detoxication these reactions are characterized by the formation of an activated nucleotide as an intermediate and a transferase which catalyzes the final step between the nucleotide and the conjugation product. The activated nucleotide, however, can be a derivative of either the conjugating agent or the foreign compound, so that there are 2 types of conjugation reaction which can be represented approximately as follows:

Type I:

Conjugating agent $\xrightarrow[\text{(ATP)}]{\text{Energy}}$ Intermediate containing conjugating agent $\xrightarrow[\text{Transferase}]{\text{Xenobiotic}}$ Conjugation product

Type II:

Xenobiotic $\xrightarrow[\text{(ATP)}]{\text{Energy}}$ Intermediate containing xenobiotic $\xrightarrow[\text{Transferase}]{\text{Conjugating agent}}$ Conjugation product

Table 1 *Conjugations*

Conjugation reaction	Conjugating agent	Nature of conjugation product*
Glucuronic acid conjugation	Glucuronic acid (from glucose)	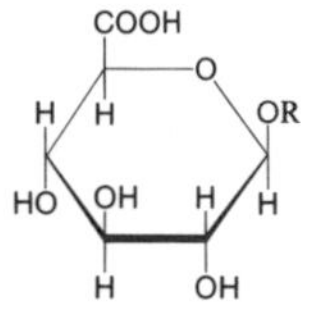 $COOH$ (structure of glucuronic acid ring with OR)
Glucose conjugation	Glucose..........................	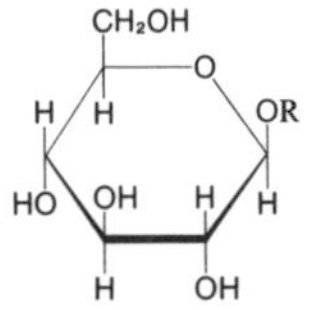 CH_2OH (structure of glucose ring with OR)
Hippuric acid synthesis...........................	Glycine	$R \cdot CO—NHCH_2 \cdot COOH$
Ornithuric acid synthesis	Ornithine	$R \cdot CO—NHCH_2 \cdot CH_2 \cdot CH_2$ $R \cdot CO——NH(COOH) \cdot CH_2$
Glutamine conjugation..........................	Glutamine	$R \cdot CO—NHCH(COOH) \cdot CH_2 \cdot CH_2 \cdot CONH_2$
Mercapturic acid synthesis	Cysteine (via glutathione); acetic acid	$R—SCH_2 \cdot CH(NHCOCH_3) \cdot COOH$
Sulfate ester synthesis	Sulfate	$R—OSO_3H$
Cyanide–thiocyanate detoxication	Sulfur (from thiosulfate)...........	$S—CN^-$
Methylation......................................	Methyl group (from methionine)....	$R—CH_3$
Acetylation.......................................	Acetic acid	$R—CO \cdot CH_3$

*R, RCO and CN are derived from the foreign compound (exogenous metabolite), the rest of the molecule is provided by the body (endogenous metabolite).

Table 2 *Uncommon conjugations*

Conjugating agent	Example of compound conjugating	Conjugation product (species)
Phosphate............	Phenol.............................	Monophenylphosphate (cat)
Taurine..............	Phenylacetic acid	Phenacetyltaurine (ferret, pigeon)
Serine	Xanthurenic acid .... (4,8-dihydroxyquinoline-2-carboxylic acid)	4,8-Diglucuronosidoquinoline-2-carbonylserine (rabbit)
Arginine	Benzoic acid........................	Benzoylarginine (arachnids)
Acetylglucosamine	Estradiol...........................	Estradiol-3-β-glucuronide-17α-β-N-acetylglucosaminide (rabbit)
Ribose	Allopurinol	7-Ribosylallopurinol (man)
Peptides	Quinaldic acid	Quinaldylglycyltaurine (cat)
Carnitine	Valproic acid	Valproylcarnitine (man)[50]

Defects in conjugation reactions can arise as a result of an inability to form the intermediate nucleotide or of faulty production of the transferase. Glucuronic acid and glucoside conjugations, sulfate ester synthesis, methylation and acetylation belong to type I, hippuric acid and ornithuric acid synthesis and glutamine conjugation belong to type II conjugations.

An example of type I conjugation is glucuronide synthesis, and of type II conjugation hippuric acid synthesis; the relevant steps in these reactions, with phenol and benzoic acid as examples of foreign compounds, are as follows:

Type I:

Glucose $\xrightarrow[\text{(ATP)}]{\text{Series of reactions}}$ UDPglucuronic acid $\xrightarrow[\substack{\text{Glucuronosyl-}\\\text{transferase}}]{\text{Phenol}}$ Phenylglucuronide

Type II:

Benzoic acid $\xrightarrow[\text{(ATP)}]{\text{Series of reactions}}$ Benzoyl-CoA $\xrightarrow[\substack{\text{Glycine benzoyl-}\\\text{transferase}}]{\text{Glycine}}$ Hippuric acid

The intermediate for various conjugation reactions is shown in Table 3.

The active intermediate in the cyanide detoxication, however, is not a nucleotide but thiosulfate, whose labile sulfur atom is transferred enzymatically to cyanide. This reaction, therefore, can be classified as a type I conjugation. Similarly, in mercapturic acid synthesis the intermediate is not a nucleotide but often an epoxide formed by microsomal oxidation, and the reaction can be classified as a type II conjugation (Table 3).

There also appears to be a difference in tissue distribution of type I and type II conjugations, apart from mercapturic acid synthesis and cyanide detoxication. Although the liver is the main organ for type I conjugations, these reactions may also occur in other tissues, such as the kidney, intestine, lung and in some cases in the spleen, brain, pancreas and blood. Type II conjugations seem to be confined to the liver and kidney.

Table 3 *Classification of phase II conjugation reactions*

Reaction	Intermediate	Transferring enzyme
Intermediate containing conjugating agent (type I)		
Glucuronide synthesis.............	UDPglucuronic acid	Glucuronosyltransferase (2.4.1.17)
Glucoside synthesis	UDPglucose......................	Glucosyltransferase (2.4.1)
Sulfate ester synthesis	Adenosine 3'-phosphate 5'-phosphosulfate (PAPS)	Sulfotransferase (2.8.2)
Methylation......................	S-Adenosylmethionine	Methyltransferase (2.1.1)
Acetylation.......................	Acetyl-CoA	Acetyltransferase (2.3.1)
Cyanide detoxication	Thiosulfate.............................	Thiosulfate sulfurtransferase (2.8.1.1)
Intermediate containing xenobiotic (type II)		
Glycine conjugation	Aroyl-CoA..........................	Glycine acyltransferase (2.3.1.13)
Glutamine conjugation.............	Arylacetyl-CoA	Not defined (glutamine acyltransferase?)
Ornithine conjugation.............	Aroyl-CoA.........................	Not defined (ornithine acyltransferase?)
Mercapturic acid synthesis..........	Epoxide* of xenobiotic......................	Glutathione transferase (2.5.1.18)

*Some compounds are sufficiently reactive to combine with glutathione without further change; others, such as hydrocarbons, require activation by oxidation to epoxides.

Types of conjugation reaction

Glucuronic acid conjugation[29]. This is the most widespread of the conjugation reactions and can occur with compounds containing all the commonly reactive groups, i.e. OH, COOH, NH_2 and SH. These compounds include alcohols, phenols, carboxylic acids (mainly aromatic), amines, amides, certain sulfonimides ($—SO_2NH—$), thiols and dithioic acids (CSSH). The donor of glucuronic acid is UDPglucuronic acid, and the reaction is catalyzed by glucuronosyltransferases (2.4.1.17). The products are β-D-glucuronides of the following general structure (where X is O, N, NH or S, or possibly C):

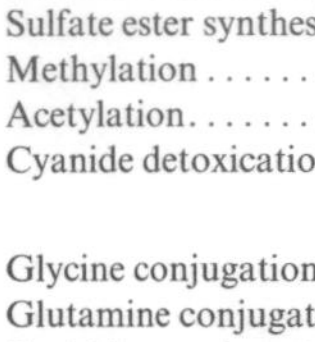

The C-β-glucuronides are resistant to hydrolysis by β-glucuronidase. Phenylbutazone and sulfinpyrazone, for example, are converted to C-β-glucuronides[30].

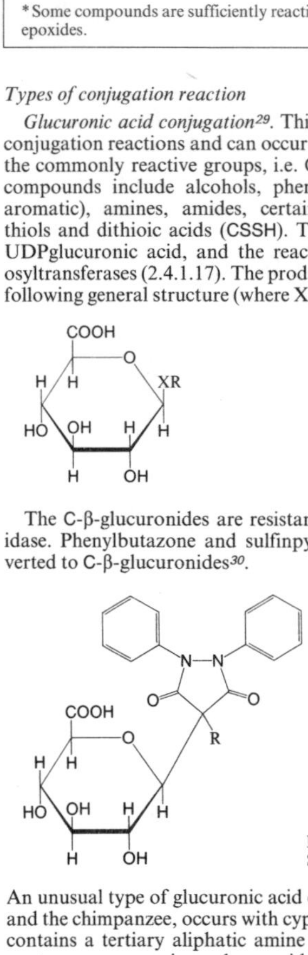

Phenylbutazone (R: $CH_2CH_2CH_2CH_3$)
Sulfinpyrazone (R: $CH_2CH_2SOC_6H_5$)

An unusual type of glucuronic acid conjugation, found only in man and the chimpanzee, occurs with cyproheptadine[31]. This compound contains a tertiary aliphatic amine group which is converted to a quaternary ammonium–glucuronide-like conjugate without loss of any of the nitrogen substituents.

Glucose conjugation[32]. This occurs almost exclusively in insects with compounds containing OH groups, the conjugates being β-glucosides of the following structure:

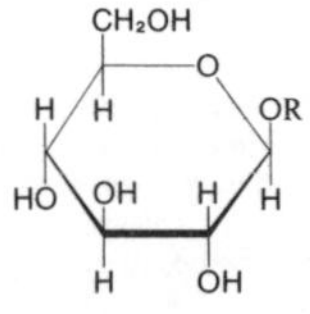

N-glucosylation of amobarbital[69] and phenobarbital[70] has been reported to occur in man.

Conjugation with amino acids. Depending on the species and availability of the amino acids, a series of amino acids form peptide linkages with xenobiotics[33]. This conjugation also takes place with endogenous substances, as, for example, with bile acids.

Aromatic acids are mainly conjugated with *glycine*, whereupon compounds of the general formula R · $CONHCH_2$ · COOH are formed. The simplest example is the conversion of benzoic acid to hippuric acid.

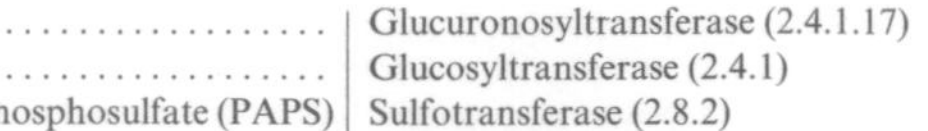

Benzoic acid → Hippuric acid

The reaction of *ornithine* instead of glycine with aromatic acids occurs in many birds and reptiles, but not in pigeons and wild doves, in which the conjugation takes place with glycine, as in mammals. An example is the formation of ornithuric acid (N^2,N^5-dibenzoylornithine) in chickens:

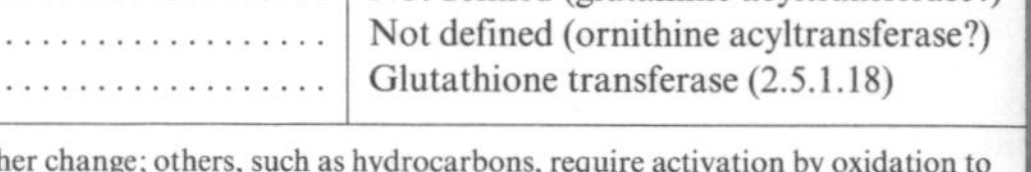

Benzoic acid → Ornithuric acid

Conjugation with *glutamine* is also peculiar to certain species and certain compounds; for example, the main metabolite of phenylacetic acid in man is phenacetylglutamine. It occurs in Old and New World monkeys, but not in species lower on the evolutionary scale[34]. Glutamine conjugation has been found to occur with certain arylacetic acids, such as phenylacetic acid, 3-indoleacetic acid, diphenylmethoxyacetic acid (a metabolite of diphenhydramine in the rhesus monkey) and 3,4-dihydroxy-5-methoxyphenylacetic acid (a metabolite of mescaline in man).

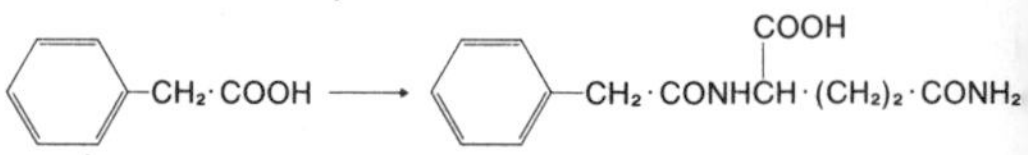

Phenylacetic acid → Phenylacetylglutamine

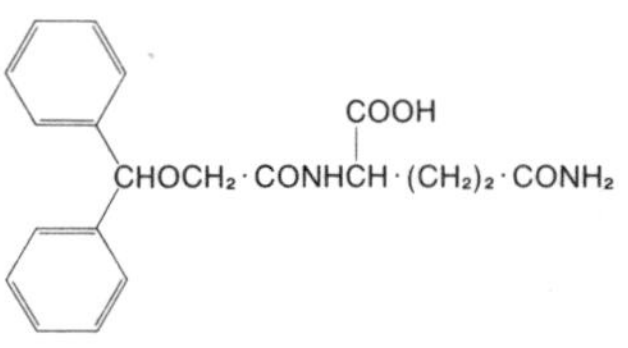

Diphenylmethoxyacetylglutamine

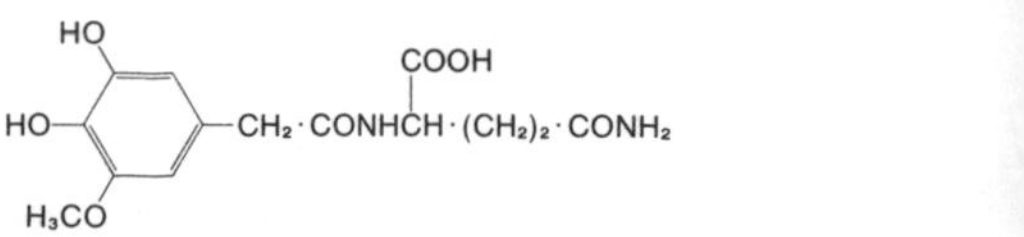

3,4-Dihydroxy-5-methoxyphenylacetylglutamine

Methotrexate, a folic acid analog, undergoes *polyglutamation* analogous to that of folic acid (page 84), resulting in the addition of 1 to 4 glutamyl groups[71].

Mercapturic acid synthesis[35]. Mercapturic acids are derivatives of N-acetylcysteine, the cysteine moiety being derived from glutathione:

$$R \cdot S \cdot CH_2 \cdot CH(NHCOCH_3) \cdot COOH$$

Mercapturic acid formation occurs with a wide variety of foreign compounds, which include aromatic hydrocarbons, arylamines, aryl, alkyl and aralkyl halides, nitroaryl and nitroalkyl compounds, certain phenols, esters, unsaturated carboxylic acids, epoxides, etc. In most cases, these compounds react with glutathione by the action of one of the many glutathione transferases (2.5.1.18)[36] to give a glutathione conjugate which is converted in a series of enzymatically controlled reactions to $R \cdot S \cdot CH_2 \cdot CH(NH_2) \cdot COOH$, a cysteine derivative. The final step involves the acetylation of this cysteine derivative to mercapturic acid with the aid of a N-acetyltransferase[37]. In some cases the compound – usually aromatic – is converted to an active intermediate, such as an epoxide, before glutathione conjugation:

R
↓
[Active metabolite]
↓
R—glutathione
↓
R—cysteinylglycine
↓
R—cysteine
↓
R — mercapturic acid
(R—acetylcysteine)

The cysteine derivative can also be excreted unchanged or else split at the S—C bond by means of a β-lyase, with the formation of a mercapto derivative[38].

$$R \cdot S \cdot CH_2 \cdot CH(NH_2) \cdot COOH \longrightarrow R \cdot SH + NH_3 + CH_3 \cdot CO \cdot COOH$$

The mercapto group can be methylated (see below), so that methylthio compounds can also be formed as an end-product of the mercapturic acid formation pathway[38]. Examples of this are the breakdown of bromazepam, carbamazepine and caffeine.

Dismutation reaction of organic nitrates. The breakdown of glyceryl trinitrate (nitroglycerin), isosorbide nitrate and similar compounds could occur via a conjugate of the mercapto group of glutathione (GSH) with the nitro group of organic nitrate esters[39]. In the net result the nitro group is reduced to nitrite, and GSH is oxidized to GSSG:

$$RO \cdot NO_2 + 2\,GSH \longrightarrow ROH + HNO_2 + GSSG$$

Sulfate ester synthesis[40]. Compounds bearing OH or NH_2 groups may form sulfate monoesters. The donor is adenosine 3'-phosphate 5'-phosphosulfate (PAPS). Several sulfotransferases (2.8.2.1 to 2.8.2.3) are involved in the reaction, which occurs

(a) mainly with phenols:

(b) with some aliphatic alcohols (i.e. ethanol, ascorbic acid):

$$C_2H_5OH + PAPS \xrightarrow{\text{Alcohol sulfotransferase}} C_2H_5OSO_3H + PAP$$

(c) with aromatic amines (i.e. 2-naphthylamine), which are converted to sulfamates:

The supply of PAPS depends on a sufficient supply of inorganic sulfate, which derives mainly from cysteine and methionine in the diet.

Cyanide detoxication[41]. The conjugation of cyanide to form thiocyanate is limited to the cyanide ion alone, i.e. $CN^- \longrightarrow SCN^-$.

The reaction is enzymatic, the donor of sulfur being thiosulfate and the enzyme thiosulfate sulfurtransferase (2.8.1.1):

$$CN^- + S \cdot SO_3^{2-} \xrightarrow{\text{Thiosulfate sulfurtransferase}} SCN^- + SO_3^{2-}$$

The reaction is widespread among species, and the conversion of cyanide to thiocyanate involves a 200-fold reduction in toxicity. Despite this, the process must be inefficient since cyanide is a highly toxic compound.

Methylation[42]. Compounds containing OH, SH and NH_2 or substituted NH_2 groups can be methylated in the body. The nitrogen atom in aromatic nitrogen heterocycles can also be methylated in vivo to give rise to a quaternary nitrogen cation. The methylation of free or substituted amino groups has been observed mainly with endogenous amines containing aliphatic groups. Methylation of aromatic amines may not occur. Examples of these methylations are the conversion of the primary amine, norepinephrine, to epinephrine, of the secondary amine, guanidinoacetic acid, to creatine, and of the tertiary amine, dimethylaminoethanol, to the quaternary base, choline. These reactions can be written in the general form:

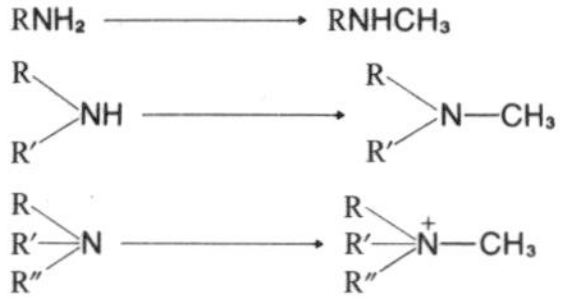

Methylation of heterocyclic nitrogen is a minor reaction of pyridine, quinoline and isoquinoline, which are converted to the corresponding N-methyl quaternary bases.

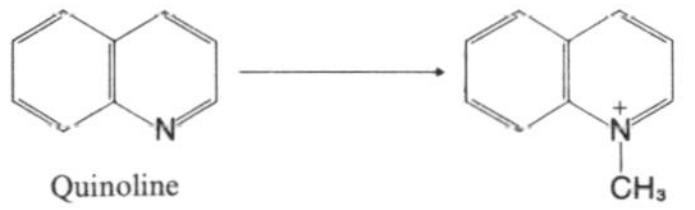

Quinoline CH_3

The hydroxy compounds which are methylated in vivo are usually phenols. However, the methylation of monophenols is relatively rare, examples being the conversion of N-acetylserotonin to melatonin (page 161) and of 4-hydroxy-3,5-diiodobenzoic acid to the corresponding 4-methoxy acid in man.

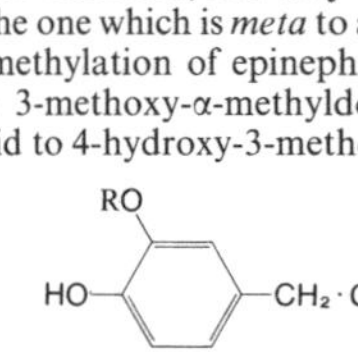

4-Hydroxy-3,5-diiodobenzoic acid (H for R)
4-Methoxy metabolite (CH₃ for R)

Methylation is more characteristic of polyphenols, provided at least 2 of the hydroxy groups are vicinal. O-Methylation is therefore a reaction of catechols, but only one hydroxy group is methylated – usually the one which is *meta* to a substituent. Well-known examples are the methylation of epinephrine to metanephrine, of α-methyldopa to 3-methoxy-α-methyldopa, and of 3,4-dihydroxyphenylacetic acid to 4-hydroxy-3-methoxyphenylacetic acid.

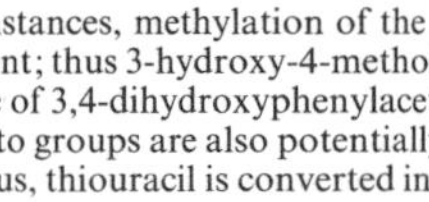

3,4-Dihydroxyphenylacetic acid (H for R)
4-Hydroxy-3-methoxyphenylacetic acid (CH₃ for R)

In some instances, methylation of the *p*-hydroxy group occurs to a minor extent; thus 3-hydroxy-4-methoxyphenylacetic acid is a minor metabolite of 3,4-dihydroxyphenylacetic acid.

Mercapto groups are also potentially capable of being methylated in vivo; thus, thiouracil is converted in vivo to S-methylthiouracil to a small extent:

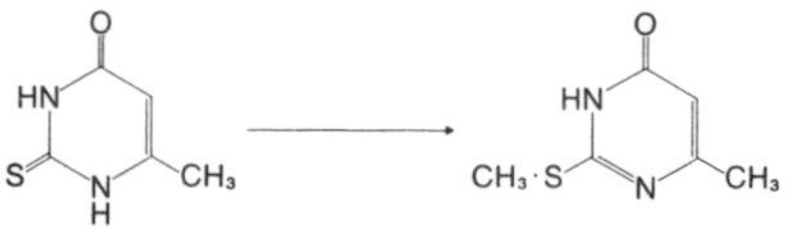

Thiouracil   S-Methylthiouracil

There is evidence that ethylmercaptan is also methylated in vivo since ethylmethyl sulfone is a metabolite of diethyldisulfide (R: C_2H_5).

RS·SR
Diethyl-
disulfide

$\downarrow$

RSH $\longrightarrow$ RS·CH₃ $\longrightarrow$ RSO·CH₃ $\longrightarrow$ RSO₂·CH₃

Ethyl-   Ethylmethyl-   Ethylmethyl-   Ethylmethyl-
mercaptan   sulfide   sulfoxide   sulfone

These methylations are catalyzed by specific methyltransferases which determine to which acceptor molecule the methyl group is transferred. Besides S-adenosylmethionine, which is an almost universal methyl donor, 5-methyltetrahydrofolic acid proved to be a donor in the N-methylation of dopamine in the rat brain[43] as well as in the O-methylation of serotonin to 5-methoxytryptamine in the brains of rats, rabbits and chickens[44].

Dopamine   Epinine

The fact that arsenic, selenium and tellurium can be methylated by microorganisms has been known for a long time[45]; the methylation mechanism, however, is only partly elucidated. Mercury can also be methylated by microorganisms, including human intestinal bacteria[46]; the methyl donor is very probably a methylcorrinoid such as methylcobalamin[47].

Acetylation[48]. Acetylation is mainly a reaction of NH_2 groups. The acetylation of OH and SH groups in specific compounds is known, but it is not a general reaction of such groups; the known instances of O- and S-acetylation are the conversion of choline to acetylcholine and of CoA to acetyl-CoA, respectively.

At least 5 types of NH_2 groups can be acetylated in vivo:

(a) Aliphatic amines (RNH_2; R for alkyl group). Examples are histamine and mescaline, which are partly converted to N-acetylhistamine and N-acetylmescaline, respectively, in the body.

N-Acetylhistamine   N-Acetylmescaline

(b) Certain amino acids [$-CH(NH_2)\cdot COOH$]. S-Phenylcysteine is acetylated in the body to give phenylmercapturic acid or N-acetyl-S-phenylcysteine. The guinea pig appears to be defective in this reaction.

S-Phenylcysteine   N-Acetyl-S-phenylcysteine

(c) Aromatic amines (aryl—NH_2). The best known example of this reaction is the conversion of sulfanilamide to N⁴-acetylsulfanilamide. Practically all sulfonamide drugs undergo acetylation in most animal species, but not in the dog.

Sulfanilamide   N⁴-Acetylsulfanilamide

(d) Sulfonamide ($-SO_2NH_2$). Sulfanilamide has been shown to be acetylated not only in position N⁴ but also, to a lesser extent, in position N¹ to form N¹-acetylsulfanilamide (sulfacetamide). This reaction also occurs in the dog.

Sulfanilamide   N¹-Acetylsulfanilamide

In a number of species including man, but not dog, sulfanilamide gives rise to three acetyl derivatives, namely N¹-monoacetyl-, N⁴-monoacetyl- and N¹,N⁴-diacetylsulfanilamide.

(e) Hydrazine and hydrazide (—$NHNH_2$, —$CONHNH_2$)[49]. Hydrazine is acetylated in the body to 1,2-diacetylhydrazine, and since monoacetylhydrazine is also converted to diacetylhydrazine in vivo, the monoacetyl derivative is probably formed first.

NH_2NH_2 $\longrightarrow$ $NH_2NHCO\cdot CH_3$ $\longrightarrow$ $CH_3\cdot CONHNHCO\cdot CH_3$

Hydrazine   Monoacetylhydrazine   Diacetylhydrazine

Hydrazides such as isoniazid are also acetylated. This reaction occurs in man and in rabbit, but not in the dog, which is thus unable to acetylate hydrazides or aromatic amines.

Isoniazid

Species variations in acetylation indicate that there are several acetyltransferases. In all these reactions the donor of the acetyl group is acetyl-CoA.

Other forms of biological acylation, namely formylation and succinylation, have been observed, but these are usually minor and rare reactions. 2-Formamido-1-naphthyl hydrogen sulfate has been detected as a minor metabolite of 2-naphthylamine and N-(p-chloro-α-methylphenacyl)succinamic acid as a metabolite of 4'-chloro-2-ethylaminopropiophenone in the urine of rats and dogs.

2-Naphthylamine   2-Formamido-1-naphthyl
                              hydrogen sulfate

4'-Chloro-2-ethylaminopropiophenone

N-(p-Chloro-α-methylphenacyl)succinamic acid

Uncommon conjugations[7]. In some species certain compounds undergo conjugations (see Table 2) which do not appear to be widespread like those listed in Table 1.

Compounds resistant to metabolism[51]

Most xenobiotics are metabolized in the body, but there are a number of compounds which are not metabolized and are eliminated from the body almost entirely unchanged, some rapidly and some slowly. These compounds include highly polar compounds which may be anions such as the sweetener saccharin (pK_a 1.9) and the drug cromoglycate (pK_a 1.7), or cations such as guanidine (pK_a 13.6) and morpholine (pK_a 8.36), highly halogenated compounds such as the fungicide hexachlorobenzene and the aerosol propellant gas trichlo-

Saccharin   Guanidine   Morpholine   Hexachloro-
                                         benzene

Cromoglycate

Ionox 312

rofluoromethane (Freon 11), highly volatile compounds whose contact with metabolizing tissue is very short, such as ethyl ether, and compounds which, if given by mouth, are not readily absorbed from the gastrointestinal tract, such as the antioxidant Ionox 312 [2,4,6-tri-(3′,5′-di-t-butyl-4′-hydroxybenzyl)phenol].

Spontaneous reactions[52]

Some compounds are known which, when they enter the body, undergo transformation without the intervention of enzymes. This occurs when they meet the appropriate conditions of pH values or molecules – e.g. macromolecules – with which they can react spontaneously. Phase I metabolites may also undergo spontaneous reactions, so that some compounds could be metabolized by an enzymatic reaction followed by a nonenzymatic one and vice versa.

Thalidomide is an example of a compound which undergoes hydrolysis spontaneously at physiological pH values to give 12 other compounds. In the body or in the test tube in aqueous solution, thalidomide breaks down at the substituted amide bonds and has a half-life of about 5 hours at pH 7.4. (Dotted lines in the formula indicate points of spontaneous hydrolysis.)

Thalidomide

Reactive compounds such as phosgene ($COCl_2$), ketene ($CH_2=CO$), methylbromide (CH_3Br), diazomethane (CH_2N_2), and ethylene oxide react nonenzymatically with tissues or compounds containing groups such as NH_2, OH, COOH, or SH and are toxic.

Ethylene oxide

Hydrazines and hydrazides such as phenylhydrazine and isonicotinylhydrazide (isoniazid) can react spontaneously with oxo acids such as pyruvic acid and with aldehydes such as pyridoxal.

Phase I metabolites which can undergo spontaneous reactions are of considerable importance, and some of them are regarded as active intermediates in the production of cancer and tissue damage (especially of liver[1], lung[53], kidney[54]). These metabolites include epoxides especially of aromatic hydrocarbons, hydroxylamines, nitrosamines and the oxygen metabolites (oxons) of organothiophosphorus insecticides (thions). These metabolites can react spontaneously with proteins and nucleic acids, which can thus be modified and produce deleterious consequences.

An aromatic hydrocarbon X could react as follows:

$$X \xrightarrow[\text{Microsomal enzyme system}]{} \text{X-epoxide} \xrightarrow{} \begin{array}{l}\text{Spontaneous reactions}\\ \text{with tissues}\end{array}$$

In the case of carbon tetrachloride the reactive intermediate may be the trichloromethyl radical.

$$CCl_4 \xrightarrow[\text{Microsomal enzyme system}]{} \cdot CCl_3 \xrightarrow{} \text{Spontaneous reactions}$$

For an organophosphorus insecticide such as parathion, an anticholinesterase, the reaction is as follows:

$$\text{Parathion} \xrightarrow[\text{Microsomal enzyme system}]{} \text{Paraoxon} \xrightarrow{} \begin{array}{l}\text{Spontaneous}\\ \text{phosphorylation}\\ \text{of cholinesterase}\end{array}$$

Factors which affect xenobiotic metabolism

Since the metabolism of most xenobiotics is carried out by enzymes, any factor which can influence the activity of these enzymes will in turn alter this metabolism in some way[55]. A number of factors have been identified, as shown in the following table.

Species[34, 60–62]	Sex[57, 67]
Genotype[63]	Stress
Age[56, 57, 61, 64]	Temperature
Chronic administration	Time of day
Other xenobiotics[65]	Intestinal flora[4, 5]
Route of administration[60]	Biliary excretion[68]
Diet, especially protein intake[11, 66]	Enterohepatic circulation
Disease	Season
	Altitude

Some of these factors, especially those in the first column of the table, are of considerable importance. The others may be important in certain situations. Some of the enzyme systems necessary for the metabolism of xenobiotics are not fully developed in the fetus and newborn[56, 57], which has to be taken into account when treating pregnant women and neonates[58]. Differences in biotransformation as a function of sex may be connected with an effect of the sex hormones[57]. Infections and inflammations may alter the metabolism of xenobiotics by interaction with the immune system[59].

References

[1] MITCHELL and JOLLOWS, *Gastroenterology*, **68**, 392 (1975); GILLETTE, J. R., *Ciba Found. Symp.*, NS **26**, 29 (1974); GILLETTE et al., *Ann. Rev. Pharmacol.*, **14**, 271 (1974).

[2] CUMMINGS and PROUGH, in CALDWELL and JAKOBY (Eds.), *Biological Basis of Detoxication*, Academic Press, New York, 1983, page 1.

[3] JEFCOATE, C. R., in CALDWELL and JAKOBY (Eds.), *Biological Basis of Detoxication*, Academic Press, New York, 1983, page 31.

[4] GOLDMAN et al., *Amer. J. clin. Nutr.*, **27**, 1348 (1974); SCHELINE, R. R., *Pharmacol. Rev.*, **25**, 451 (1973); WILLIAMS, R. T., *Toxicol. appl. Pharmacol.*, **23**, 769 (1972).

[5] GOLDMAN, P., in JAKOBY et al. (Eds.), *Metabolic Basis of Detoxication*, Academic Press, New York, 1982, page 323.

[6] WILLIAMS, R. T., *Detoxication Mechanisms*, 2nd ed., Chapman, London, 1959.

[7] WILLIAMS and MILLBURN, in BLASCHKO, II. K. (Ed.), *Physiological and Pharmacological Biochemistry*, Butterworth, London, 1975, page 211.

[8] SMITH and WILLIAMS, *Biochem. J.*, **44**, 239 (1949).

[9] SMITH and TIMBRELL, *Xenobiotica*, **4**, 489 (1974)

[10] GILLETTE, J. R., *Fortschr. Arzneimittelforsch.*, **6**, 11 (1963).

[11] ANDERSON et al., *Nutr. Rev.*, **40**, 161 (1982).

[12] NEBERT and GONZALEZ, *Trends pharmacol. Sci.*, **6**, 160 (1985).

[13] WOLF, C. R., in JAKOBY et al. (Eds.), *Metabolic Basis of Detoxication*, Academic Press, New York, 1982, page 5.

[14] GILLETTE et al., *Ann. Rev. Pharmacol.*, **12**, 57 (1972); GILLETTE, J. R., *Advanc. Pharmacol.*, **4**, 219 (1966).

[15] HEWICK, D. S., in JAKOBY et al. (Eds.), *Metabolic Basis of Detoxication*, Academic Press, New York, 1982, page 151.

[16] WISLOCKI et al., in JAKOBY, W. B. (Ed.), *Enzymatic Basis of Detoxication*, Volume 1, Academic Press, New York, 1980, page 136.

[17] JERINA and DALY, *Science*, **185**, 573 (1974).

[18] BRIDGES et al. (Eds.), *Biological Oxidation of Nitrogen in Organic Molecules*, Taylor, London, 1972.

[19] DAMANI, L. A., in JAKOBY et al. (Eds.), *Metabolic in Basis of Detoxication*, Academic Press, New York, 1982, page 127.

[20] NELSON et al., *Science*, **193**, 901 (1976).

[21] ZIEGLER, D. M., in JAKOBY et al. (Eds.), *Metabolic Basis of Detoxication*, Academic Press, New York, 1982, page 171.

[22] LINDEKE and CHO, in JAKOBY et al. (Eds.), *Metabolic Basis of Detoxication*, Academic Press, New York, 1982, page 105.

[23] ANDERS, M. W., in JAKOBY et al. (Eds.), *Metabolic Basis of Detoxication*, Academic Press, New York, 1982, page 29.

[24] WIERSMA et al., in CALDWELL and PAULSON (Eds.), *Foreign Compound Metabolism*, Taylor & Francis, London, 1984, page 53; ROSENBERG and AIRAKSINEN, *Toxicity of the Metabolites of Inhalation Anesthetics*, Fischer, Stuttgart, 1982.

[25] McMAHON, R. E., in JAKOBY et al. (Eds.), *Metabolic Basis of Detoxication*, Academic Press, New York, 1982, page 91.

[26] HEYMANN, E., in JAKOBY et al. (Eds.), *Metabolic Basis of Detoxication*, Academic Press, New York, 1982, page 229.

[27] OESCH, F., in JAKOBY, W. B. (Ed.), *Enzymatic Basis of Detoxication*, Volume 2, Academic Press, New York, 1980, page 277; LU and MIWA, *Ann. Rev. Pharmacol.*, **20**, 513 (1980).

[28] WILLIAMS, R. T., in BERNFELD, P. (Ed.), *Biogenesis of Natural Compounds*, 2nd ed., Pergamon, Oxford, 1967, page 589.

[29] KASPER and HENTON, in JAKOBY, W. B. (Ed.), *Enzymatic Basis of Detoxication*, Volume 2, Academic Press, New York, 1980, page 4; DUTTON and BURCHELL, *Progr. Drug Metab.*, **2**, 1 (1977).

[30] PEDERSEN et al., *Clin. Pharmacokinet.*, **7**, 42 (1982); RICHTER et al., *Helv. chim. Acta*, **58**, 2512 (1975).

31 CALDWELL, J., in JAKOBY et al. (Eds.), *Metabolic Basis of Detoxication*, Academic Press, New York, 1982, page 291.

32 SMITH, J. N., *Advanc. comp. Physiol. Biochem.*, **25**, 324 (1965).

33 KILLENBERG and WEBSTER, in JAKOBY, W. B. (Ed.), *Enzymatic Basis of Detoxication*, Volume 2, Academic Press, New York, 1980, page 141.

34 WILLIAMS, R. T., *Biochem. Soc. Trans.*, **2**, 359 (1974).

35 BOYLAND and CHASSEAUD, *Advanc. Enzymol.*, **32**, 173 (1969).

36 JAKOBY and HABIG, in JAKOBY, W. B. (Ed.), *Enzymatic Basis of Detoxication*, Volume 2, Academic Press, New York, 1980, page 63.

37 TATE, S. S., in JAKOBY, W. B. (Ed.), *Enzymatic Basis of Detoxication*, Volume 2, Academic Press, New York, 1980, page 95.

38 TATEISHI and SHIMIZU, in JAKOBY, W. B. (Ed.), *Enzymatic Basis of Detoxication*, Volume 2, Academic Press, New York, 1980, page 121.

39 NEEDLEMAN, P., *Ann. Rev. Pharmacol.*, **16**, 81 (1976).

40 JAKOBY et al., *Progr. Drug Metab.*, **8**, 11 (1984); JAKOBY et al. in JAKOBY, W. B. (Ed.), *Enzymatic Basis of Detoxication*, Volume 2, Academic Press, New York, 1980, page 199.

41 WESTLEY, J., in JAKOBY, W. B. (Ed.), *Enzymatic Basis of Detoxication*, Volume 2, Academic Press, New York, 1980, page 245.

42 BORCHARDT, R. T., in JAKOBY, W. B. (Ed.), *Enzymatic Basis of Detoxication*, Volume 2, Academic Press, New York, 1980, page 43; WEISIGER and JAKOBY, in JAKOBY, W. B. (Ed.), *Enzymatic Basis of Detoxication*, Volume 2, Academic Press, New York, 1980, page 131.

43 LADURON, P., in USDIN and SNYDER (Eds.), *Frontiers in Catecholamine Research*, Pergamon, New York, 1973, page 121.

44 BANERJEE and SNYDER, *Science*, **182**, 74 (1973).

45 JERNELÖV and MARTIN, *Ann. Rev. Microbiol.*, **29**, 61 (1975).

46 ROWLAND et al., *Experientia (Basel)*, **31**, 1064 (1975).

47 WOOD, J. M., *Science*, **183**, 1049 (1974).

48 WEBER and GLOWINSKI, in JAKOBY, W. B. (Ed.), *Enzymatic Basis of Detoxication*, Volume 2, Academic Press, New York, 1980, page 169.

49 JUCHAU and HORITA, *Drug Metab. Rev.*, **1**, 71 (1972).

50 MILLINGTON et al., *Clin. chim. Acta*, **145**, 69 (1985).

51 RENWICK, A. G., in CALDWELL and JAKOBY (Eds.), *Biological Basis of Detoxication*, Academic Press, New York, 1983, page 151.

52 TESTA, B., in CALDWELL and JAKOBY (Eds.), *Biological Basis of Detoxication*, Academic Press, New York, 1983, page 137; TESTA, B., *Drug Metab. Rev.*, **13**, 25 (1982).

53 MINCHIN and BOYD, *Ann. Rev. Pharmacol.*, **23**, 217 (1983).

54 RUSH et al., *CRC Crit. Rev. Toxicol.*, **13**, 99 (1984).

55 BRODIE and GILLETTE (Eds.), *Handbook of Experimental Pharmacology*, Volume XXVIII/2, Springer, Berlin, 1971; LA DU et al. (Eds.), *Fundamentals of Drug Metabolism and Drug Disposition*, Williams & Wilkins, Baltimore, 1971; HATHWAY, D. E., *Foreign Compound Metabolism in Mammals*, Volumes 1 and 2, The Chemical Society, London, 1970/72.

56 YAFFE and JUCHAU, *Ann. Rev. Pharmacol.*, **14**, 219 (1974); ERIKSSON and YAFFE, *Ann. Rev. Med.*, **24**, 29 (1973).

57 HENDERSON, P. T., *Europ. J. Drug Metab.*, **3**, 1 (1978).

58 NEIMS et al., *Ann. Rev. Pharmacol.*, **16**, 427 (1976); ARANDA et al., *J. Pediat.*, **85**, 534 (1974).

59 RENTON and PETERSON, in CALDWELL and PAULSON (Eds.), *Foreign Compound Metabolism*, Taylor & Francis, London, 1984, page 289.

60 TEORELL et al. (Eds.), *Pharmacology and Pharmacokinetics*, Plenum, New York, 1974.

61 DUNCAN et al. (Eds.), *Developmental and Genetic Aspects of Drug and Environmental Toxicity*, Proceedings of the European Society of Toxicology, Volume 16, Excerpta Medica, Amsterdam, 1975; VESTAL et al., *Clin. Pharmacol. Ther.*, **18**, 425 (1975).

62 CALDWELL, J., in JAKOBY, W. B. (Ed.), *Enzymatic Basis of Detoxication*, Volume 1, Academic Press, New York, 1980, page 85; LITTERST et al., *Drug Metab. Dispos.*, **3**, 259 (1975).

63 VESELL and PENNO, in CALDWELL and JAKOBY (Eds.), *Biological Basis of Detoxication*, Academic Press, New York, 1983, page 369; NEBERT, D. W., in JAKOBY, W. B. (Ed.), *Enzymatic Basis of Detoxication*, Volume 1, Academic Press, New York, 1980, page 25; VESELL, E. S., *Progr. med. Genet.*, **9**, 291 (1973).

64 KITANI, K., in CALDWELL and PAULSON (Eds.), *Foreign Compound Metabolism*, Taylor & Francis, London, 1984, page 275; GREENBLATT et al., *New Engl. J. Med.*, **306**, 1081 (1982); SALEM et al., *Age and Ageing*, **7**, 68 (1978); FARAH et al., *Brit. med. J.*, **2**, 155 (1977).

65 PARK and BRECKENRIDGE, *Clin. Pharmacokinet.*, **6**, 1 (1981); BRESNICK, E., in JAKOBY, W. B. (Ed.), *Enzymatic Basis of Detoxication*, Volume 1, Academic Press, New York, 1980, page 69; GRILLE et al., *Med. Klin.*, **74**, 55 (1979); PARKE, D. V., in PARKE, D. V. (Ed.), *Enzyme Induction*, Plenum, New York, 1975; CONNEY and BURNS, *Science*, **178**, 576 (1972).

66 ANDERSON and KAPPAS, in CALDWELL and PAULSON (Eds.), *Foreign Compound Metabolism*, Taylor & Francis, London, 1984, page 299; BOYD and CAMPBELL, in CALDWELL and JAKOBY (Eds.), *Biological Basis of Detoxication*, Academic Press, New York, 1983, page 287; CARR, C. J., *Ann. Rev. Pharmacol.*, **22**, 19 (1982); CONNEY et al., *Ciba Found. Symp.*, NS **76**, 147 (1980).

67 KATO and KAMATAKI, in CALDWELL and PAULSON (Eds.), *Foreign Compound Metabolism*, Taylor & Francis, London, 1984, page 269; KATO, R., *Drug Metab. Rev.*, **3**, 1 (1974).

68 LEVINE, W. G., *Ann. Rev. Pharmacol.*, **18**, 81 (1978); SMITH, R. L., *The Excretory Function of Bile. The Elimination of Drugs and Toxic Substances in Bile*, Chapman, London, 1973.

69 TANG et al., *Res. Commun. chem. Path. Pharmacol.*, **21**, 45 (1978).

70 TANG et al., *Drug Metab. Dispos.*, **7**, 315 (1979).

71 CHABNER et al., *J. clin. Invest.*, **76**, 907 (1985).

McKUSICK recorded, in 1982, 3368 human disorders inherited in a simple Mendelian fashion[1], i.e. caused in each case by a mutant gene. A gene consists of DNA – a chain of deoxyribonucleotides – and acts as a template for the biosynthesis of a chain of ribonucleotides – primary messenger RNA or 'heterogeneous nuclear RNA' – equal in length to the DNA chain and with the identity of each ribonucleotide determined by the identity of the deoxyribonucleotide at the corresponding position of the DNA chain[2,3]. This process is known as 'transcription' and proceeds from the 5' end ('upstream') of the DNA towards the 3' end ('downstream'). Parts of the heterogeneous nuclear RNA, the intervening sequences (introns), are deleted, and the remaining sequences (exons) are joined to form a shorter chain, the structure of which is determined by the coding sequences of the DNA chain, i.e. by the structural gene or cistron. This process is termed 'splicing'.

This shorter RNA chain undergoes further changes: a methylated guanyl nucleotide (the 'cap') is attached to the 5' end, which is methylated in the ribose moiety, and a polyadenylic-acid 'tail' [poly(A)] to the 3' end; it combines with a protein and leaves the nucleus as 'mature' messenger RNA (mRNA). In the cytoplasm, each molecule of mRNA acts as a template for the synthesis of a polypeptide chain. Each triplet of ribonucleotides codes for a specific amino acid; since the sequence of ribonucleotides in the mRNA is fixed by the sequence in the DNA, the structure of the polypeptide chain thus formed is also fixed. The process is known as 'translation'. The polypeptide chains are released from the ribosome and often undergo posttranslational changes such as folding, combination with similar or different polypeptides to form larger protein molecules, which combine with carbohydrates or carbohydrate-like molecules, with lipids, with metal ions or organometallic compounds, etc.

There are 4 types of deoxyribonucleotides in DNA differing only in the nature of the purine or pyrimidine base attached to the sugar-phosphate backbone (the 4 bases are adenine, guanine, cytosine and thymine), and there are 4 corresponding types of ribonucleotide in RNA. From 4 different deoxyribonucleotides, 64 possible different triplets can be formed, and 61 of these are known to correspond to 20 amino acids (the genetic code is degenerate, i.e. though each triplet codes for a specific amino acid, in most cases an amino acid is coded for by more than 1 triplet). The remaining 3 triplets are chain terminators; a chain terminator triplet in mRNA causes release of the polypeptide chain synthesized up to that point[◊].

One type of mutation of a gene consists in substitution of one base for another at some point on the DNA chain, i.e. substitution of one deoxyribonucleotide and, hence, of one triplet or codon, for another. If the base substitution occurs in a region of the gene which is normally translated, 1 of 3 possible consequences follows: (1) because the genetic code is degenerate, the new triplet may code for the same amino acid as before, (2) the new triplet may code for a different amino acid, or (3) the new triplet may be a chain terminator curtailing the length of the polypeptide coded for by the nonmutated gene. In case (1) there may be some effect on the rate of synthesis of the polypeptide, but the nature of the polypeptide is unchanged. In case (2) a variant polypeptide and, hence, variant protein(s), with a different amino-acid residue substituted at a specific site, are produced; the physical or chemical properties of the new protein sometimes leads to disease. In case (3), if the chain-terminator triplet is near the beginning of the chain, then no polypeptide or protein recognizably related to the wild type is produced; if near the end of the chain, then a protein of lower M_r is formed – in either case disease may result.

In some thalassemias, changes (especially deletions) in a noncoding part of the DNA chain greatly decrease the rate of synthesis of the mRNA corresponding to the adjacent coding sequences (i.e. the structural gene) and, hence, of the corresponding globin chain. The noncoding DNA appears to act as a controller gene. In other cases, changes in a noncoding part of the DNA have little or no effect, though they may act as useful genetic markers in prenatal diagnosis or in population genetics.

Another, possibly commoner, mechanism of mutation is unequal crossing-over, resulting in one or more amino-acid residues being inserted into or deleted from the polypeptide chain in cases where the unequal crossing-over is intracistronic (e.g. Hb Gun Hill, Hb CS, Hb Freiburg). Unequal crossing-over may involve the partial deletion and fusion of two neighboring cistrons causing the formation of a new polypeptide with an amino-acid sequence reflecting the beginning of one cistron and the end of the normally adjacent cistron (e.g. serum haptoglobin, Hb Lepore). A frameshift mutation can occur if the unequal crossing-over does not involve an integral number of deoxyribonucleotide triplets, i.e. the insertion or deletion of $3n + 1$ or $3n + 2$ nucleotides at some point in the DNA; all nucleotides downstream are thereby reorganized into new triplets, many coding for amino acids different from those in the wild-type polypeptide (e.g. Hb Wayne, Hb Cranston).

Failure to synthesize an enzyme can cause a complete or partial block of a metabolic pathway and usually leads to the accumulation of the intermediary metabolite that is normally the substrate of the missing enzyme. In some cases the accumulation of this metabolite leads to abnormal side reactions. In phenylketonuria, for example, absence of phenylalanine 4-monooxygenase leads to accumulation of phenylalanine, some of which is converted to phenylpyruvic acid, and this undergoes further changes to o-hydroxyphenylacetic acid, phenyllactic acid and phenylacetylglutamine.

In some cases the defective protein is not an enzyme in the narrower sense, i.e. a catalyst bringing about a chemical change, but a substance concerned with the active transport of a metabolite from one compartment of the body to another[4]. Examples are intestinal absorption and renal tubular reabsorption. In such cases the resulting disease or abnormality is not caused by a metabolic block, but by a disorder of transportation and the secondary effects of this disorder. In Hartnup disease, for example, tryptophan is poorly absorbed from the intestine and is in consequence acted on by bacteria in the colon to produce abnormal indolic compounds that are absorbed. In this disease there is also a renal tubular defect leading to aminoaciduria.

These defects in the synthesis of an enzyme or transport mechanism are genetically determined and are referred to as 'inborn errors of metabolism'[5]. According to McKUSICK, an enzyme deficiency had been demonstrated in over 200 of the 650 certain recessive (autosomal and X-linked) disorders up to 1982[1].

Some defects consisting of single enzyme failures can be acquired, like the action of a heavy metal poison on proximal renal tubular transport of amino acids and of hexachlorobenzene on porphyrin metabolism or the production of alkaptonuria in experimental animals by administration of α,α'-dipyridyl. Such acquired defects are often temporary.

Some gene mutations lead to the formation of an abnormal structural protein rather than the absence of an enzyme. The clearest examples are the hemoglobinopathies, where the structure of many of the abnormal proteins has been completely elucidated. In the thalassemias there is a relative failure to synthesize hemoglobin rather than production of an abnormal hemoglobin. Thalassemia is thought to be often caused by the mutation of 'controller' or 'tap' genes, and abnormal hemoglobins by the mutation of 'structural' genes. Inborn errors of metabolism may resemble either type of hemoglobinopathy: mutation of the relevant structural gene would produce in place of the normal enzyme a protein lacking catalytic properties, whereas a 'silent gene' mutation would produce neither the enzyme nor an abnormal protein.

The physiological and clinical effect of a mutation leading to an amino-acid substitution in an enzyme depends on the location of the amino acid in the polypeptide chain. A substitution near the active site of the enzyme may affect its affinity for substrate or coenzyme (i.e. the K_m value), its affinity for the reaction product or for competitive inhibitors, its turnover rate (i.e. V_{max}) or more than one of these. Alternatively, the stability of a prosthetic group may be altered by such an amino-acid substitution. On the other hand, an amino-acid substitution in a part of the polypeptide which is far from the active site when the enzyme molecule has assumed its tertiary or quaternary shape may have little or no effect on the enzymatic properties unless tertiary folding or combination with other polypeptide chains is affected. Substitutions of the first type, affecting the K_m value, the V_{max} value or the stability of an enzyme, account for many of the inborn errors of metabolism so far described. However, it is becoming clear that many enzymes exist in multiple forms (differing in the identity of a single amino acid), all with the same or very similar enzymatic properties leading to no discernible disease or disability and often occurring at relatively high frequency in a population. If the substituted amino acid differs in charge from the original (e.g. glutamic acid substituted for valine or lysine or vice versa, lysine substituted for asparagine or vice versa) the altered enzyme molecule will differ from the original in its electrophoretic mobility. About one-third of all amino-acid substitutions lead to electrophoretically detectable variant proteins. Taking only 8 blood enzymes, the frequency of electrophoretic variations is so high that there is no

---

*The chapters on 'Inborn Errors of Metabolism' (pages 217–288) have been compiled in collaboration with L.I. WOOLF, University of British Columbia, Vancouver (Canada).

◊ For more details see the chapters on 'Synthesis of Nucleic Acids' (page 175), 'Protein Synthesis' (page 179), and 'Regulation of Metabolism' (page 197).

more than a 0.005 probability that two individuals chosen at random will have the same forms of all 8 enzymes. These variants result from virtually neutral mutations and reflect biochemical individuality.

The clinical effects of the inborn errors of metabolism vary from lethality in utero or in early postnatal life to complete harmlessness and, in some cases, depend on interaction with the environment[6]. For example, phenylketonuria leads to neurologic disease and mental retardation unless the environment is modified to provide an abnormal dietary amino-acid balance with relatively very little phenylalanine. Man, together with the other higher primates and a few other species, lacks L-gulonolactone oxidase, the enzyme converting L-gulono-1,4-lactone to the precursor of ascorbic acid. So long as man's diet contains adequate amounts of ascorbic acid this universal enzyme defect does not lead to disease, but with inadequate diets scurvy develops.

The mechanism by which an enzyme deficiency develops in an inborn error of metabolism may be more complex than, for instance, an amino-acid substitution in the enzyme – a problem of enzyme regulation may be involved[7]. For example, many peptide hormones act on receptors in the membrane of target cells to activate adenylate cyclase, which generates cAMP, and this in turn leads to a chain of activation or deactivation of different enzymes in the cell. A mutation may cause an amino-acid substitution in the protein of the receptor, altering its affinity for the hormone, or may prevent the receptor protein from being synthesized either at all or in sufficient quantity, thus leading to partial or complete inactivity of an enzyme normally so activated. An example is provided by the X-linked form of nephrogenic diabetes insipidus, in which the epithelial cells of the collecting ducts lack the receptor for antidiuretic hormone, so that a chain of events that normally bring about the reabsorption of water is not activated. A different regulatory mechanism, acting over a period of hours rather than minutes or seconds, involves repression or de-repression of a gene in response to the interaction of a hormone or other molecule with a receptor on the target cell, leading to suppression or induction of the enzyme for which the gene is coded. An example is provided by familial hypercholesterolemia, in which a genetically determined defect of plasma-membrane receptors for β-lipoprotein leads to inadequate repression of the gene coding for the enzyme hydroxymethylglutaryl-CoA reductase (NADPH) (i.e. loss of feedback control) and hence excessive biosynthesis of cholesterol[8]. Related to this group is the condition of complete androgen insensitivity, in which a specific cytoplasmic binding protein is either absent or inactive owing to a mutation of the gene coding for this protein, with which dihydrotestosterone has to combine before it can enter the nucleus and there cause its characteristic pattern of gene repressions and de-repressions. The transient tyrosyluria[9] of some neonates (particularly premature infants) is another related phenomenon; except in those cases that respond to ascorbic acid, this tyrosyluria is caused by a delay, lasting days to months, in the de-repression of a gene, possibly the gene coding for 4-hydroxyphenylpyruvate dioxygenase.

Regulation of the activity of an enzyme can also be brought about in other ways. For example, glycogenosis type VIII is caused by inactivity of phosphorylase b, but it can be shown that the primary defect is the loss of the kinase that normally converts phosphorylase b from the inactive to the active form, i.e. in this inborn error of metabolism the substrate of the deficient enzyme is itself an enzyme. In the Lesch-Nyhan syndrome, the activity of amidophosphoribosyltransferase is many times higher than normal; the defect lies in a lack of hypoxanthine phosphoribosyltransferase, which normally synthesizes guanosine monophosphate and inosine monophosphate, the feedback inhibitors of amidophosphoribosyltransferase.

The investigation of many inborn errors of metabolism has been greatly facilitated by studying the enzymatic activities of fibroblasts grown in tissue culture and, to a lesser extent, of leukocytes[10]. Fibroblasts and leukocytes contain a remarkable range of enzymes; only where the relevant enzyme is confined to a particular tissue – e.g. phenylalanine 4-monooxygenase in the liver – does this technique fail. The technique can be used in studying both homozygotes and heterozygotes and permits metabolic experiments which would be unethical in vivo.

Treatment

New ways of treating inborn errors of metabolism are being explored[11-13]. Dietary restriction of the toxic substrate of the deficient enzyme, i.e. modification of the environment, is still the most widely used (e.g. low-phenylalanine diet in phenylketonuria, low-galactose diet in galactosemia). In cases where the mutation has resulted in the enzyme having reduced affinity for a vitamin-related cofactor, massive doses of the vitamin sometimes increase the enzyme activity (vitamin dependency). Where a lysosomal enzyme is deficient, intravenous injection of the enzyme results in its uptake into some cells by pinocytosis, the injected enzyme entering the lysosomes with partial correction of the biochemical error and, sometimes, clinical improvement. Enzymes covalently linked to serum albumin or protected by lipid envelopes in 'liposomes' have been injected. Kidney transplants in Fabry's disease, made necessary by renal failure, are reported to metabolize ceramide trihexoside, leading to a lowering of blood levels and clinical remission, though this has been disputed. Infusion of leukocytes and transplantation of fibroblasts have been reported to have favorable clinical and biochemical effects in Hunter's syndrome and some other mucopolysaccharidoses. Liver transplants in some cases of galactosemia, familial hypercholesterolemia and Wilson's disease have been life-saving. Recently also bone-marrow transplantations have been successful in the treatment of a number of heritable diseases.

Procedures have now been developed for inserting functional genes into the bone marrow of mice[14]. An effective delivery system uses retroviral-based vectors – obtained by gene technology methods – to transfer a gene into murine bone-marrow culture. The genetically altered bone marrow is then implanted into the recipient animals. Prime candidates for the replacement of a defective or absent enzyme in human bone marrow are those deficient in hypoxanthine phosphoribosyltransferase (page 257), purine-nucleoside phosphorylase (page 261) or adenosine deaminase (page 261). At present (1985), however, such attempts for enzyme replacement are still in an experimental stage[15].

Identification of the primary defect does not necessarily lead to a rational or effective treatment. For example, therapy is virtually nonexistent for any of the various lipidoses involving neurological deterioration, though most can be diagnosed prenatally by amniocentesis. If the primary defect is unknown the position may be even worse, e.g. in cystic fibrosis[16] (the commonest lethal genetic disease in Europeans or people of European descent), where complications can often be prevented with antibiotics, pancreatic enzymes and physiotherapy, but we do not know a more fundamental therapy. The same is true for Duchenne muscular dystrophy (the commonest X-linked lethal disease)[17].

References

[1] McKusick, V. A., Mendelian Inheritance in Man, 6th ed., Johns Hopkins University Press, Baltimore, 1983.
[2] Lewin, B. H., Gene Expression, Volume 2: The eucaryotic chromosomes, 2nd ed., Wiley, Toronto, 1980.
[3] Axel et al. (Eds.), Eucaryotic Gene Regulation, Academic Press, New York, 1979.
[4] Segal, S., New Engl. J. Med., 294, 1044 (1976).
[5] Garrod, A. E., Lancet, 2, 1, 73, 142 and 214 (1908).
[6] Rosenberg, L. E., in Bondy and Rosenberg, Metabolic Control and Disease, 8th ed., Saunders, Philadelphia, 1980, page 73.
[7] Galton et al., Clin. Sci., 53, 197 (1977).
[8] Brown and Goldstein, Progr. med. Genet., NS 1, 109 (1976).
[9] Bloxam et al., Biochem. J., 77, 320 (1960).
[10] Harkness and Cockburn (Eds.), The Cultured Cell and Inherited Metabolic Disease, MTP, Lancaster, 1977.
[11] Raine, D. N. (Ed.), The Treatment of Inherited Metabolic Disease, MTP, Lancaster, 1975.
[12] Hobbs, J. R., Lancet, 2, 735 (1981).
[13] Pyeritz, R. E., Nature, 312, 405 (1984).
[14] Anderson, W. F., Science, 226, 401 (1984).
[15] Culliton, B. J., Science, 227, 493 (1985).
[16] Hodson, M. E., Postgrad. med. J., 60, 225 (1984); Di Sant'Agnese and Davis, New Engl. J. Med., 295, 481, 534 and 597 (1976); Bowman and Mangos, New Engl. J. Med., 294, 937 (1976).
[17] Gardner-Medwin, D., Brit. med. Bull., 36, 109 (1980); Moser, H., Praxis, 66, 814 (1977); Hutton and Thompson, Canad. med. Ass. J., 115, 749 (1976).

Many inborn errors of metabolism are, at present, untreatable and have an inexorable course, leading to death in utero or in childhood or to very severe handicap (e.g. Tay-Sachs disease, Hurler's syndrome, homozygous α-thalassemia, and Lesch-Nyhan syndrome), and genetic counseling is of outstanding importance[1-4].

Some of these diseases can be diagnosed prenatally by the examination of amniotic fluid. Amniocentesis is usually carried out for the prenatal diagnosis of neural tube defects — by determination of α-fetoprotein in the amniotic fluid[3, 5] — or for the detection of chromosomal aberrations[3, 6] where the mother is in a high-risk group because of her age, a previous affected child, etc. Amniotic fluid is obtained at or after the 16th week of pregnancy, and presents a negligible hazard to mother or fetus at this time provided the amniocentesis is carried out under ultrasonography; earlier reports of a slight but statistically significant increase in fetal deaths after amniocentesis refer to older techniques[7]. However, more information is needed on a possible relation to fetal morbidity. The cells in the amniotic fluid are of fetal origin and resemble fibroblasts in their complement of enzymes. Thus it is possible to culture these cells in vitro and to determine whether, for instance, a certain enzyme is active[4, 8-10]. In one or two conditions, e.g. methylmalonic aciduria, analysis of the supernatant obtained following the centrifugation of amniotic fluid enables a diagnosis to be established; in all other cases, however, the use of cells is necessary. The number of viable cells obtained on amniocentesis is so small that, in general, they must be grown in tissue culture to provide enough of the relevant enzyme to exclude the diagnosis. Originally 4 to 6 weeks were needed for growing the cells, but with the development of more sensitive enzyme assay methods and, in consequence, the ability to use fewer cells, incubation for 1 to 3 weeks is often sufficient[8]. Altogether over 135 inborn errors of metabolism are or can be tested for at various centers (Tables 1 and 2). No center can be expert in prenatal screening for more than a very few of these rare conditions, and it is necessary for the various centers to collaborate. The procedure is expensive and is used almost exclusively in families at risk, e.g. where a previous child has been affected or where the mother's mother is known or suspected to carry a harmful X-linked recessive gene. This is in contrast to prenatal screening for the much commoner anencephaly and spina bifida, which are tested for on a large scale using maternal blood, a technique which is both easier and less expensive than amniocentesis.

More recently biopsy specimens of chorionic villi have been examined in the same way as amniocytes[1, 19, 42, 46]. Chorionic villi are of fetal origin, and a specimen can be obtained much earlier in pregnancy than is the case with amniotic fluid. The hazards involved have not yet been fully evaluated.

Table 1   *Inborn errors of metabolism detected prenatally using cultured amniocytes[4, 8-10, 12, 43]*

Condition	N^*	Condition	N^*
Amino-acid metabolism		Sanfilippo's syndrome B (mucopolysaccharidosis III B)	10^4
Phenylketonuria	1–10	Morquio-Brailsford syndrome	–
Maple syrup urine disease (severe infantile)	10^4	(mucopolysaccharidosis IV A)	
Propionic acidemia	–	Maroteaux Lamy syndrome A	10^3–10^4
Methylmalonic acidemia, vitamin B_{12}-nonresponsive	–	(mucopolysaccharidosis VI A)	
Citrullinemia	6×10^5	Maroteaux-Lamy syndrome B	10^3–10^4
Argininosuccinic acidemia	10^5–10^6	(mucopolysaccharidosis VI B)	
Glutaric aciduria type I	–	Sly's syndrome (mucopolysaccharidosis VII)	1–100
Cystinosis	10^4	Mannosidosis	1–100
Homocystinuria	–	Fucosidosis	1–10
		Sialidosis (mucolipidosis I)	10–100
Metabolism of connective tissue			
Osteogenesis imperfecta type II	1–10	*Metabolism of mucolipids and sphingolipids*	
		Mucolipidosis II (I-cell disease)	10–100
Metabolism of carbohydrates		Mucolipidosis III	10–100
Glycogenosis type II	1–100	Mucolipidosis IV	–
Glycogenosis type III	–	Generalized gangliosidosis	1–10
Glycogenosis type IV	–	Juvenile G_{M1} gangliosidosis	–
Galactosemia	10^5	G_{M1} gangliosidosis with sialidosis	10–100
Isolated pyruvate carboxylase deficiency[13]	–	Tay-Sachs disease	100–300
Pyruvate dehydrogenase deficiency	–	Sandhoff's disease	1–10
		Metachromatic leukodystrophy (late infantile form)	10^3–10^4
Vitamin metabolism		Metachromatic leukodystrophy (juvenile form)	100–1000
5,10-Methylenetetrahydrofolate reductase ($FADH_2$) deficiency[14]	–	Gaucher's disease	1–10
Methylmalonic acidemia, vitamin B_{12}-responsive	–	Krabbe's disease	2×10^4
		Fabry's disease◊	1–100
Purine metabolism		Farber's disease	–
Lesch-Nyhan syndrome◊	1–100	Niemann-Pick disease type A	2×10^4 to 4×10^4
Immune disorders			
Severe combined immunodeficiency	10–10^3	*Metabolism of lipoproteins, cholesterol and fatty acids*	
Ataxia telangiectasia	10–100	Familial hypercholesterolemia	10^5
		Wolman's disease	10^3
Porphyrin metabolism		Adrenoleukodystrophy	–
Congenital erythropoietic porphyria	–	Zellweger's syndrome[15]	–
Acute intermittent porphyria	–		
		Trace metal disorders	
Metabolism of glycosaminoglycans and oligosaccharides		Menkes' disease◊	2×10^5
Hurler's syndrome (mucopolysaccharidosis I_H)	1–100		
Scheie's syndrome (mucopolysaccharidosis I_S)	1–100	*Other disorders*	
Hurler-Scheie 'compound'	1–100	Lysosomal acid phosphatase deficiency	–
(mucopolysaccharidosis $I_{H/S}$)		Xeroderma pigmentosum	1–100
Hunter's syndrome (mucopolysaccharidosis II A)◊	–	Cockayne's syndrome[16]	3×10^5
Sanfilippo's syndrome A	–	Methemoglobinemia type II	–
(mucopolysaccharidosis III A)		(cytochrome-b_5 reductase deficiency)	

*Number of cells required for diagnosis; ultramicro techniques are now available for certain conditions.

◊X-linked recessive condition (karyotype of amniocyte informative).

Table 2
Inborn errors of metabolism for which prenatal detection is possible or potentially possible using amniocytes, amniotic fluid, chorionic villi, fetal blood or tissue[4, 8–10, 12, 43]

Amino-acid metabolism
Malignant hyperphenylalaninemia
Tyrosinemia type I
Histidinemia
Saccharopinuria
Maple syrup urine disease (intermittent variant)
Isovaleric acidemia
Hypervalinemia
Hyperammonemia type II
Nonketotic hyperglycinemia
Sulfituria

Metabolism of connective tissue
Procollagen-lysine,2-oxoglutarate 5-dioxygenase deficiency
Hypophosphatasia[45]

Metabolism of carbohydrates
Glycogenosis type VIII
Galactosuria
Pyruvate decarboxylase deficiency
Glucose-6-phosphate isomerase deficiency (nonspherocytic hemolytic anemia)
Glucose-6-phosphate dehydrogenase deficiency

Vitamin metabolism
Cobalamin metabolic defects
5-Methyltetrahydrofolate–homocysteine methyltransferase deficiency
Leigh's subacute necrotizing encephalomyelopathy

Pyrimidine metabolism
Orotic aciduria

Immune disorders
Chronic granulomatous disease
C3 deficiency
Chediak-Higashi syndrome
Wiscott-Aldrich syndrome
Purine-nucleoside phosphorylase deficiency

Metabolism of glycosaminoglycans and oligosaccharides
Hunter's syndrome (mucopolysaccharidosis II B)
Aspartylglycosaminuria

Metabolism of mucolipids and sphingolipids
Juvenile G_{M2} gangliosidosis
G_{M3} sphingolipodystrophy
Niemann-Pick disease type B

Metabolism of cholesterol and related compounds
Cholesterol-ester storage disease
Phytanic-acid storage disease

Steroid metabolism
Congenital adrenal hyperplasia (21-hydroxylase deficiency)
Testicular feminization[18]

Bleeding disorders[11]
Hemophilia A
Hemophilia B
von Willebrand's disease
Thrombocytopenia

Other disorders
Glutaric aciduria type II[17]
Acatalasemia
Protein C deficiency[37]
α_1-Antitrypsin deficiency
Pituitary dysgenesis

These disorders are in addition to those listed in Table 1.

Most hemoglobinopathies can be diagnosed prenatally by direct analysis of the DNA of the amniocytes or chorionic villi[20–23]; the method is available for α-thalassemias, some β-thalassemias, sickle-cell anemia and other hemoglobinopathies involving a known amino-acid substitution[44]. Purified mRNA for the α-globin chain provides a template for the synthesis – by the use of reverse transcriptase (RNA-directed DNA polymerase) – of DNA, which is identical in structure to the coding portions of the α-globin gene and known as cDNA (globin complementary DNA)[24]. This cDNA, produced in vitro and rendered highly radioactive after cloning, is hybridized with the fractions produced by digesting the DNA of the amniocytes with a specific restriction endonuclease that yields fragments, each containing 3000 to 5000 nucleotide residues, which are separated by gel electrophoresis. Different restriction endonucleases split the DNA chain at different points to give fragments differing in relative molecular mass and mobility. The cDNA probe hybridizes with the DNA of the α-globin gene and, in its absence (i.e. if the fetus is homozygous for α-thalassemia), does not attach itself to any other DNA fragment, allowing a conclusive prenatal diagnosis. This is an example of RFLP (restriction fragment length polymorphism)[41, 44]. A similar cDNA corresponding to the exons of the β-globin gene has been prepared[20]; it is specific for β-globin and δ-globin genes (the two are very similar, differing in only 10 amino-acid residues out of 146). This cDNA can be used to detect δβ-thalassemia, HPFH (hereditary persistence of fetal hemoglobin), Hb Lepore and some varieties of β⁰- and β⁺-thalassemia. β-Globin cDNA can also be used for prenatal diagnosis of sickle-cell anemia by analysis with one of several restriction enzymes that cleave DNA at the codon corresponding to amino-acid No. 6 of the β-globin chain of HbA, but do not cleave DNA corresponding to HbS at this position[25, 39]. Other tests for HbS, etc. use synthetic oligonucleotide probes, instead of cDNA, and amplification of DNA target sequences[39, 40].

The technique for direct investigation of the gene has been used in the prenatal diagnosis of phenylketonuria[26], osteogenesis imperfecta[27] and other conditions[44].

Huntington's disease (Huntington's chorea) is an autosomal dominant condition with a prevalence of between 4 and 8 per 100 000 (more in some groups). The nature of the primary biochemical defect is unknown. The disease, which leads to mental deterioration secondary to the destruction of certain cells in the brain, usually strikes in adults when their reproductive life is over, so that there is no reduction in gene frequency. Affected families are well aware that they carry the gene, but up to recently no test was available for detecting the heterozygote before he or she had passed the gene onto the next generation. By gene-mapping of restriction fragment length polymorphisms a marker fragment (G8) closely linked to the Huntington disease locus has been found recently, making prenatal and postnatal diagnosis possible[28].

Duchenne muscular dystrophy is both the commonest and the most severe of the muscular dystrophies, causing death in childhood or adolescence. The disease is transmitted as an X-linked recessive character, but nothing is known of the primary biochemical defect. The gene has been localized to the p21 region of the X chromosome because some female Duchenne patients have X-autosome translocation[29, 30]. By using suitable DNA probes carrier detection and prenatal diagnosis has been feasible[31]. The gene for cystic fibrosis has been localized to the q21.3–q22.1 region of chromosome 7, and prenatal diagnosis should soon be available[38].

For some conditions occurring in certain families, testing the amniotic fluid for a substance not related to the condition is useful diagnostically where the gene determining the presence of the substance tested for is closely linked to the gene causing the disease. An example is provided by myotonic dystrophy[32], a disease which usually strikes in early adult life and which is transmitted as an autosomal dominant character. The gene for myotonic dystrophy, *Dm* (on chromosome 19), is closely linked to the 'secretor' locus which determines whether blood-group substances A, B and H are secreted into the saliva and other secretions, including amniotic fluid (a fetal secretion). The 2 alleles at the locus are designated *Se* (secretor) and *se* (nonsecretor); the character 'secretor' is dominant to 'nonsecretor'. Where family studies reveal that the parent carrying the *Dm* gene has the genotype *Se/se* (i.e., is heterozygous), that the *Dm* gene is linked to *se*, and that the unaffected parent is a nonsecretor (genotype *se/se*), then it is possible to determine prenatally with near certainty whether the fetus has inherited the *Dm* gene and will eventually develop the disease. If, in the case considered, the amniotic fluid contains A, B or H substance, there is a 92% probability that the fetus will be unaffected; if A, B and H substances are absent, there is a 92% probability that the fetus carries the *Dm* gene. The figure 92% (rather than 100%) arises because the linkage between the *Dm* gene and the secretor locus permits a recombination frequency of 0.078. A similar prenatal diagnosis would be possible if, in the hypothetical family considered above, the *Dm* gene were linked to *Se* rather than *se*, the *presence* of A, B or H substance in amniotic fluid indicating the possession of the *Dm* gene in this case. If the unaffected parent has the secretor genotype *Se*/*se*, this complicates prenatal diagnosis but does not necessarily rule it out[32]. Prenatal diagnosis becomes impossible if the affected parent is homozygous for *Se* or *se* or if the unaffected parent is homozygous for *Se*/*Se*.

Linkage between the *HLA* genes and the gene causing adrenal hyperplasia (21-hydroxylase deficiency) permits, in some families, the prenatal diagnosis of this disease by HLA-typing the amniotic cells in a way analogous to the prenatal detection of myotonic dystrophy. Rapid progress is being made in the drawing of human chromosome linkage maps[33], and many more such examples of the use of linkage in prenatal diagnosis will undoubtedly soon appear.

In X-linked recessive conditions where the mother is known to be a carrier, it is useful to karyotype the amniocytes grown in tissue culture. If the fetus is female (XX), one can safely exclude the disease, though in some cases the carrier status of the fetus can be determined by enzyme assay. If the fetus is male (XY), and the disease is one for which there is no reliable prenatal biochemical test using amniotic fluid, one can only predict a 50% probability that the infant will be affected, unless a RFLP test is available.

It is possible to examine fetal blood for the diagnosis of conditions in which amniotic fluid and amniocytes show no abnormality, but the procedure is not without risk to the fetus. One method is to obtain blood from a fetal vessel in the placenta, close to the point of insertion of the umbilical cord[22,34]. This is done using a fetoscope, and there is an associated mortality of the fetus of 5–10%. Alternatively, ultrasound is used to locate the placenta, and blood is withdrawn (placentesis), usually a mixture of maternal and fetal blood, which requires either selective hemolysis of maternal cells or determination of the relative numbers of maternal and fetal cells by determination of cell size. Fetal blood is useful for the prenatal diagnosis of some varieties of thalassemia[35], of some other hemoglobinopathies[35] and of bleeding disorders[11,22], as well as protein C deficiency[37].

Maternal blood serum is useful for prenatal diagnosis in a very few conditions, e.g. anencephaly, spina bifida and rhesus incompatibility. A fetus with a neural tube defect causes the α-fetoprotein content of the maternal blood to rise between 15 and 20 weeks' gestation (maximum at 17 weeks). There are a few other conditions (e.g. congenital nephrotic syndrome, absent anterior abdominal wall, and fetal death) which cause a similar rise in the α-fetoprotein concentration in both amniotic fluid and maternal blood, but the incidence of these is rare by comparison with anencephaly or spina bifida. The test, using maternal blood serum, is by far the easiest and cheapest method of prenatal screening for a serious disease, is suitable for employment in an entire population and is widely available (e.g. in Great Britain)[36]. The sensitivity and specificity of the test at the optimum stage of pregnancy are fair; about 5% of mothers of affected infants give a false negative result, and about 5% of the cases where the infant is normal give a false positive test result. Because of this, a positive result is regarded as an indication for further investigation by ultrasonography and amniocentesis rather than as an indication for terminating pregnancy. In the case of rhesus incompatibility, a high or rising titer of incomplete antibodies (Coombs' test) in the maternal blood indicates rhesus incompatibility and the danger of fetal death or hemolytic disease of the newborn.

References

[1] MUELLER, R. F., in MACLEOD and SIKORA (Eds.), *Molecular Biology and Human Disease*, Blackwell, Oxford, 1984, page 131; BRAMBATI et al. (Eds.), *Chorionic Villus Sampling*, Dekker, New York, 1986.

[2] FERGUSON-SMITH, M. A. (Ed.), *Brit. med. Bull.*, **39**, No. 4 (1983).

[3] BROCK, D. J., *Early Diagnosis of Fetal Defects*, Churchill Livingstone, Edinburgh, 1982.

[4] MILUNSKY, A. (Ed.), *Genetic Disorders and the Fetus: Diagnosis, Prevention and Treatment*, Plenum, New York, 1979; MILUNSKY, A. (Ed.), *The Prevention of Genetic Disease and Mental Retardation*, Saunders, Philadelphia, 1975.

[5] BROCK, D. J., *Brit. med. Bull.*, **39**, 373 (1983); BROCK, D. J., *Progr. med. Genet.*, NS **2**, 1 (1977).

[6] FERGUSON-SMITH, M. A., *Brit. med. Bull.*, **39**, 355 (1983).

[7] Working Party on Amniocentesis, *Brit. J. Obstet. Gynaec.*, **85**, Suppl. 2 (1978); NICHD National Registry for Amniocentesis Study Group, *J. Amer. med. Ass.*, **236**, 1471 (1976); SIMPSON et al., *Canad. med. Ass. J.*, **115**, 739 (1976).

[8] GALJAARD, H., *Genetic Metabolic Diseases: Early Diagnosis and Prenatal Analysis*, Elsevier, Amsterdam, 1980; HECHT and CADIEN, in WALD, N. J. (Ed.), *Antenatal and Neonatal Screening*, Oxford University Press, Oxford, 1984, page 128.

[9] KABACK, M. M., *Pediat. Ann.*, **10**, No. 2, 22 (1981); THOMPSON, J. N., *Pediat. Ann.*, **7**, No. 6, 25 (1978).

[10] PATRICK, A. D., *Brit. med. Bull.*, **39**, 378 (1983).

[11] MIBASHAN and MILLAR, *Brit. med. Bull.*, **39**, 392 (1983); MIBASHAN et al., *Lancet*, **1**, 1309 (1979).

[12] LINCH and LEVINSKY, *Brit. med. Bull.*, **39**, 399 (1983).

[13] MARSAC et al., *Clin. chim. Acta*, **119**, 121 (1982).

[14] CHRISTENSEN and BRANDT, *New Engl. J. Med.*, **313**, 50 (1985).

[15] BJÖRKHEM et al., *Lancet*, **1**, 1234 (1984); SCHUTGENS et al., *Lancet*, **2**, 1339 (1984); SCHUTGENS et al., *Prenat. Diagn.*, **5**, 337 (1985).

[16] LEHMANN et al., *Lancet*, **1**, 486 (1985).

[17] MITCHELL et al., *Lancet*, **1**, 1099 (1983); BOUÉ et al., *Lancet*, **1**, 846 (1984).

[18] STEPHENS, J. D., *Lancet*, **2**, 1038 (1984).

[19] RODECK and MORSMAN, *Brit. med. Bull.*, **39**, 338 (1983); HOGGE et al., *Prenat. Diagn.*, **5**, 393 (1985); JACKSON, L. G., *Hosp. Pract.*, **20**, 39 (1985).

[20] BANK et al., *Science*, **207**, 486 (1980).

[21] ORKIN, S. H., *Blood*, **63**, 249 (1984).

[22] ALTER, B. P., *Blood*, **64**, 329 (1984); ANTSAKLIS et al., in FILKINS and RUSSO (Eds.), *Human Prenatal Diagnosis*, Dekker, New York, 1985, page 109.

[23] KAZAZIAN, H. H., *Clin. Chem.*, **31**, 1509 (1985).

[24] KAN et al., *New Engl. J. Med.*, **295**, 1165 (1976).

[25] CHANG and KAN, *Lancet*, **2**, 1127 (1981).

[26] LEDLEY et al., *Trends Genet.*, **1**, 309 (1985); WOO et al., *Nature*, **306**, 151 (1983).

[27] POPE et al., *Brit. med. J.*, **288**, 431 (1984).

[28] CONNEALLY, P. M., *Amer. J. hum. Genet.*, **36**, 506 (1984).

[29] WORTON et al., *Science*, **224**, 1447 (1984).

[30] KEDES, L. H., *Trends Genet.*, **1**, 205 (1985).

[31] BAKKER et al., *Lancet*, **1**, 655 (1985).

[32] SCHROTT et al., *Clin. Genet.*, **4**, 38 (1973); TSIPOURAS et al., *Amer. J. hum. Genet.*, **36**, 1172 (1984).

[33] Human Gene Mapping 8, *Cytogenet. Cell Genet.*, **40**, Nos. 1–4 (1985).

[34] RODECK and NICOLAIDES, *Brit. med. Bull.*, **39**, 332 (1983); MAHONEY, M. J., *Pediat. Ann.*, **10**, No. 2, 94 (1981).

[35] JENSEN et al., *Europ. J. Pediat.*, **127**, 197 (1978); KAN et al., *New Engl. J. Med.*, **294**, 1039 (1976); KAN et al., *New Engl. J. Med.*, **292**, 1096 (1975).

[36] BROCK et al., *Lancet*, **1**, 1281 (1979); U. K. collaborative study on alpha-fetoprotein in relation to neural-tube defects, *Lancet*, **1**, 1323 (1977).

[37] MIBASHAN et al., *New Engl. J. Med.*, **313**, 1607 (1985).

[38] SCAMBLER et al., *Lancet*, **2**, 1241 (1985); KNOWLTON et al., *Nature*, **318**, 380 (1985); WHITE et al., *Nature*, **318**, 382 (1985); WAINWRIGHT et al., *Nature*, **318**, 384 (1985).

[39] LOUKOPOULOS, D., *Hemoglobin*, **9**, 435 (1985).

[40] SAIKI et al., *Science*, **230**, 1350 (1985); MARX, J. L., *Science*, **230**, 1365 (1985).

[41] FERRARI et al., in BRAMBATI et al. (Eds.), *Chorionic Villus Sampling*, Dekker, New York, 1986, page 191; OLD, J. M., in BRAMBATI et al. (Eds.), *Chorionic Villus Sampling*, Dekker, New York, 1986, page 165; McCORMACK, M. K., in FILKINS and RUSSO (Eds.), *Human Prenatal Diagnosis*, Dekker, New York, 1985, page 139.

[42] GATTI et al., *Prenat. Diagn.*, **5**, 329 (1985); STOUT et al., *Prenat. Diagn.*, **5**, 183 (1985); LILFORD, R. J., *Arch. Dis. Childh.*, **60**, 897 (1985).

[43] DESNICK et al., in FILKINS and RUSSO (Eds.), *Human Prenatal Diagnosis*, Dekker, New York, 1985, page 59.

[44] BURLINGHAM, B. T., in FILKINS and RUSSO (Eds.), *Human Prenatal Diagnosis*, Dekker, New York, 1985, page 363; NUSSBAUM et al., *Amer. J. hum. Genet.*, **38**, 149 (1986).

[45] WARREN et al., *Lancet*, **2**, 856 (1985).

[46] MAXWELL et al., *Lancet*, **1**, 123 (1986); NICOLAIDES et al., *Lancet*, **1**, 543 (1986); JACKSON et al., *Lancet*, **1**, 674 (1986).

A wealth of reviews deals with molecular biological as well as clinical aspects of normal and abnormal hemoglobins[1-11].

The types of hemoglobin found in normal erythrocytes of adults are summarized in Table 1. HbA_{Ia1}, HbA_{Ia2}, HbA_{Ib} and HbA_{Ic} are compounds of HbA with a carbohydrate component – glucose in HbA_{Ic}. HbF, quantitatively the most important hemoglobin of the fetus, is normally contained only in the so-called F cells, which constitute 0.2–5% of the total erythrocytes in adults. HbF_I is an acetylated form of HbF.

Table 1
Types of hemoglobin present in normal erythrocytes of adults

$HbA \sim 97\%$		HbA_2 $\sim 2.5\%$	$HbF < 1.0\%$	
$HbA_0 \sim 90\%$	HbA_{Ia} 1.6% HbA_{Ib} 0.8% HbA_{Ic} 4%		$HbF_0 < 0.9\%$	$HbF_I < 0.1\%$

Every hemoglobin is composed of 2 pairs of different polypeptide chains and 4 heme groups. The hemoglobins $\alpha_2^A\beta_2^A$ (HbA), $\alpha_2^A\gamma_2^F$ (HbF) and $\alpha_2^A\delta_2^{A2}$ (HbA$_2$) are formed by the combination of 2 α chains with 2 β chains, 2 γ chains or 2 δ chains.

The amino-acid sequence of these 4 polypeptide chains is shown in Table 2. The synthesis of the α chain is coded by 2 genes per haploid chromosome or 4 genes per diploid cell; 1 gene each per haploid chromosome is responsible for the synthesis of the β and δ chains. The synthesis of the γ chain is controlled by 2 genes per haploid chromosome. The γ chain is present in all persons in 2 forms: one with glycine at position 136 ($^G\gamma$ chain), coded for by the gene $^G\gamma$, and the other with alanine at position 136 ($^A\gamma$ chain), coded for by the nonallelic gene $^A\gamma$, which is adjacent to $^G\gamma$. The ratio of the glycine-containing chain to the alanine-containing chain in newborn infants is 7:3; after about the 6th month of life it is 2:3. The structural origin of the α-globin gene cluster (on the short arm of chromosome 16) and of the β-globin gene cluster (on the short arm of chromosome 11) is known in detail (Fig. 1).

If the structure of one or more deoxyribonucleotide triplets (i.e. codons), in the translated portion of DNA forming the gene, is altered (a mutation), a polypeptide chain may be formed which differs from the normal chain in its amino-acid sequence. The combination of a normal pair of polypeptide chains with an abnormal pair, e.g. $\alpha_2^A\beta_2^S$, yields an abnormal hemoglobin, in this case HbS.

The abnormal hemoglobins – 538 different ones have been reported up to June 1985[12] – are identified by a letter, the geographic origin or both, for example HbS, HbChesapeake, HbG$_{Philadelphia}$. If one knows which polypeptide chain is altered, the chain combination can be given, as has already been shown above for HbS. The complete amino-acid sequence of most of the abnormal hemoglobins is known. Determination of the structure takes place essentially as follows: the chains are split at lysine and arginine residues by hydrolysis of hemoglobin or of the individual polypeptide chains with trypsin. The oligopeptides thus formed can be separated by electrophoretic and chromatographic methods to yield a two-dimensional peptide pattern, the so-called 'fingerprint'. Peptides that are not found in the 'fingerprint' of normal hemoglobin are isolated and their structure determined. If the structure of an abnormal hemoglobin is completely known, the position and type of the change in the chain are cited, for example $\alpha_2^A\beta_2^{6Val}$ for HbS, $\alpha_2^{92Leu}\beta_2^A$ for Hb Chesapeake.

Most of the abnormal hemoglobins so far described show a change in either the α or β chain; for technical reasons only 39 such

Fig. 1 *The human globin gene clusters*

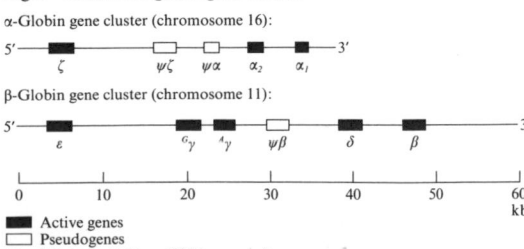

α-Globin gene cluster (chromosome 16):

β-Globin gene cluster (chromosome 11):

■ Active genes
□ Pseudogenes
kb Kilobases (1 kb = 1000 base pairs)

Fig. 2 *Tertiary structure of a single globin polypeptide chain[13]*

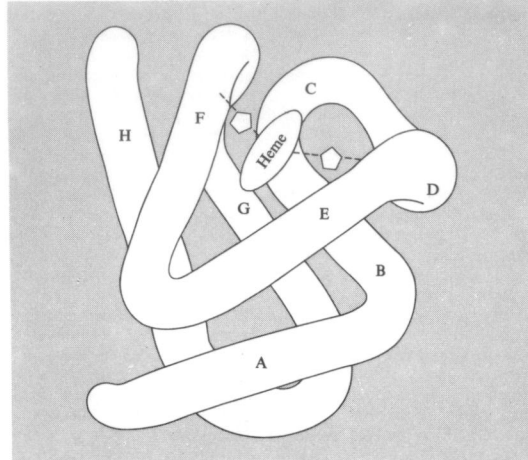

The helix segments labeled A to H are relatively linear. Folding takes place between the helices. The heme group is suspended in a crevice between the E helix and the F helix.

mutations affecting the γ and 15 the δ chain have as yet been found. Base substitution in the DNA can result in a chain-termination mutation; for example in Hb McKees Rocks, codon 145 in the β-chain mRNA, normally UAU coding for tyrosine, has probably changed to UAA, which is a chain-termination or nonsense mutation, resulting in shortened β chains. A similar but more extensive nonsense mutation near the 5′ end of the gene results in no recognizable β chain being formed, manifested clinically as thalassemia. In Hb Constant Spring (HbCS), the α-chain mRNA termination codon 142, normally UAA, has changed to CAA coding for glutamine, resulting in an α chain 31 amino-acid residues longer than normal. Hb Icaria and Hb Koya Dora have similarly elongated α chains resulting from different base substitutions in codon 142.

In addition to single amino-acid substitution, resulting from replacement of one purine or pyrimidine base by another in the relevant deoxyribonucleotide triplet, unequal crossing-over at meiosis can result in the insertion or deletion from the polypeptide chain of one or more (up to 5) amino-acid residues. Such nonhomologous crossing-over can delete variable lengths of the δ and β genes, as well as the nontranslated DNA between them, resulting in a fused $\delta\beta$ gene coding for a hybrid $\delta\beta$ chain (i.e. N-terminal derived from δ and C-terminal from β) which, with normal α chains, forms Hb Lepore (several variants are known depending on the positions of crossing-over). A similar but more extensive deletion leads to Hb Kenya, in which the non-α chains are hybrid $\gamma\beta$ chains. Unequal crossing-over can also lead to 'anti-Lepore' hemoglobins with the non-α chain having the N-terminal portion derived from a β chain and the C-terminal portion derived from a δ chain, with different crossover points and deleted portions in the $\delta\beta$ gene, for example Hb Miyada, HbP$_{Congo}$, and HbP$_{Nilotic}$.

Frameshift mutations result from unequal crossing-over in which the number of deoxyribonucleotide residues deleted from or inserted into DNA is not an exact multiple of 3. In Hb Wayne, for example, the α-chain amino-acid sequence up to No. 139 is normal, but is followed by an abnormal sequence of 8 amino acids. Deletion of a single nucleotide has disrupted all subsequent codon triplets, which rearrange themselves to form new triplets coding for amino acids differing from the original. Hb Cranston and Hb Tak are frame-shift mutations affecting the β chain; the amino-acid sequences are normal up to No. 145 and No. 147, respectively. Frame-shift mutations can be recognized only if they occur near the 3′ end of the gene.

Whether and in what manner changes in the polypeptide chain cause clinical symptoms depends on how the function of the hemoglobin is interfered with. In accordance with present knowledge of its tertiary structure and folding of the polypeptide chains (Fig. 2), the abnormal hemoglobins can be divided into several groups, depending on the type of impairment of function (Table 3).

In HbS only valine is substituted for glutamic acid in the β-6 position at the molecular surface; the resulting hemoglobin in the deoxygenated state forms aggregates in the shape of long rigid fibers

Table 2   *Primary and secondary structure of the hemoglobin polypeptide chains*[13]

Helix	Posi-tion	α	β	γ	δ	Posi-tion	Helix	Posi-tion	α	β	γ	δ	Posi-tion	Helix	Posi-tion	α	β	γ	δ	Posi-tion
NA1	1	Val	Val	Gly	Val	1	E1	52	Ser	Asn	Asn	Asn	57	GH1	113	Leu	Phe	Phe	Phe	118
NA2	2	Leu	His	His	His	2	E2	53	Ala	Pro	Pro	Pro	58	GH2	114	Pro	Gly	Gly	Gly	119
NA3			Leu	Phe	Leu	3	E3	54	Gln	Lys	Lys	Lys	59	GH3	115	Ala	Lys	Lys	Lys	120
							E4	55	Val	Val	Val	Val	60	GH4	116	Glu	Glu	Glu	Glu	121
A1	3	Ser	Thr	Thr	Thr	4	E5	56	Lys	Lys	Lys	Lys	61	GH5	117	Phe	Phe	Phe	Phe	122
A2	4	Pro	Pro	Glu	Pro	5	E6	57	Gly	Ala	Ala	Ala	62							
A3	5	Ala	Glu	Glu	Glu	6	E7	58	His	His	His	His	63	H1	118	Thr	Thr	Thr	Thr	123
A4	6	Asp	Glu	Asp	Glu	7	E8	59	Gly	Gly	Gly	Gly	64	H2	119	Pro	Pro	Pro	Pro	124
A5	7	Lys	Lys	Lys	Lys	8	E9	60	Lys	Lys	Lys	Lys	65	H3	120	Ala	Pro	Glu	Gln	125
A6	8	Thr	Ser	Ala	Thr	9	E10	61	Lys	Lys	Lys	Lys	66	H4	121	Val	Val	Val	Met	126
A7	9	Asn	Ala	Thr	Ala	10	E11	62	Val	Val	Val	Val	67	H5	122	His	Gln	Gln	Gln	127
A8	10	Val	Val	Ile	Val	11	E12	63	Ala	Leu	Leu	Leu	68	H6	123	Ala	Ala	Ala	Ala	128
A9	11	Lys	Thr	Thr	Asn	12	E13	64	Asp	Gly	Thr	Gly	69	H7	124	Ser	Ala	Ser	Ala	129
A10	12	Ala	Ala	Ser	Ala	13	E14	65	Ala	Ala	Ser	Ala	70	H8	125	Leu	Tyr	Trp	Tyr	130
A11	13	Ala	Leu	Leu	Leu	14	E15	66	Leu	Phe	Leu	Phe	71	H9	126	Asp	Gln	Gln	Gln	131
A12	14	Trp	Trp	Trp	Trp	15	E16	67	Thr	Ser	Gly	Ser	72	H10	127	Lys	Lys	Lys	Lys	132
A13	15	Gly	Gly	Gly	Gly	16	E17	68	Asn	Asp	Asp	Asp	73	H11	128	Phe	Val	Met	Val	133
A14	16	Lys	Lys	Lys	Lys	17	E18	69	Ala	Gly	Ala	Gly	74	H12	129	Leu	Val	Val	Val	134
A15	17	Val	Val	Val	Val	18	E19	70	Val	Leu	Ile	Leu	75	H13	130	Ala	Ala	Thr	Ala	135
A16	18	Gly					E20	71	Ala	Ala	Lys	Ala	76	H14	131	Ser	Gly	Gly*	Gly	136
														H15	132	Val	Val	Val	Val	137
AB1	19	Ala					EF1	72	His	His	His	His	77	H16	133	Ser	Ala	Ala	Ala	138
							EF2	73	Val	Leu	Leu	Leu	78	H17	134	Thr	Asn	Ser	Asn	139
B1	20	His	Asn	Asn	Asn	19	EF3	74	Asp	Asp	Asp	Asp	79	H18	135	Val	Ala	Ala	Ala	140
B2	21	Ala	Val	Val	Val	20	EF4	75	Asp	Asn	Asp	Asn	80	H19	136	Leu	Leu	Leu	Leu	141
B3	22	Gly	Asp	Glu	Asp	21	EF5	76	Met	Leu	Leu	Leu	81	H20	137	Thr	Ala	Ser	Ala	142
B4	23	Glu	Glu	Asp	Ala	22	EF6	77	Pro	Lys	Lys	Lys	82	H21	138	Ser	His	Ser	His	143
B5	24	Tyr	Val	Ala	Val	23	EF7	78	Asn	Gly	Gly	Gly	83							
B6	25	Gly	Gly	Gly	Gly	24	EF8	79	Ala	Thr	Thr	Thr	84	HC1	139	Lys	Lys	Arg	Lys	144
B7	26	Ala	Gly	Gly	Gly	25								HC2	140	Tyr	Tyr	Tyr	Tyr	145
B8	27	Glu	Glu	Glu	Glu	26	F1	80	Leu	Phe	Phe	Phe	85	HC3	141	Arg	His	His	His	146
B9	28	Ala	Ala	Thr	Ala	27	F2	81	Ser	Ala	Ala	Ser	86							
B10	29	Leu	Leu	Leu	Leu	28	F3	82	Ala	Thr	Gln	Gln	87							
B11	30	Glu	Gly	Gly	Gly	29	F4	83	Leu	Leu	Leu	Leu	88							
B12	31	Arg	Arg	Arg	Arg	30	F5	84	Ser	Ser	Ser	Ser	89							
B13	32	Met	Leu	Leu	Leu	31	F6	85	Asp	Glu	Glu	Glu	90							
B14	33	Phe	Leu	Leu	Leu	32	F7	86	Leu	Leu	Leu	Leu	91							
B15	34	Leu	Val	Val	Val	33	F8	87	His	His	His	His	92							
B16	35	Ser	Val	Val	Val	34	F9	88	Ala	Cys	Cys	Cys	93							
							FG1	89	His	Asp	Asp	Asp	94							
C1	36	Phe	Tyr	Tyr	Tyr	35	FG2	90	Lys	Lys	Lys	Lys	95							
C2	37	Pro	Pro	Pro	Pro	36	FG3	91	Leu	Leu	Leu	Leu	96							
C3	38	Thr	Trp	Trp	Trp	37	FG4	92	Arg	His	His	His	97							
C4	39	Thr	Thr	Thr	Thr	38	FG5	93	Val	Val	Val	Val	98							
C5	40	Lys	Gln	Gln	Gln	39														
C6	41	Thr	Arg	Arg	Arg	40	G1	94	Asp	Asp	Asp	Asp	99							
C7	42	Tyr	Phe	Phe	Phe	41	G2	95	Pro	Pro	Pro	Pro	100							
							G3	96	Val	Glu	Glu	Glu	101							
CD1	43	Phe	Phe	Phe	Phe	42	G4	97	Asn	Asn	Asn	Asn	102							
CD2	44	Pro	Glu	Asp	Glu	43	G5	98	Phe	Phe	Phe	Phe	103							
CD3	45	His	Ser	Ser	Ser	44	G6	99	Lys	Arg	Lys	Arg	104							
CD4	46	Phe	Phe	Phe	Phe	45	G7	100	Leu	Leu	Leu	Leu	105							
CD5	47	Asp	Gly	Gly	Gly	46	G8	101	Leu	Leu	Leu	Leu	106							
CD6	48	Leu	Asp	Asn	Asp	47	G9	102	Ser	Gly	Gly	Gly	107							
CD7	49	Ser	Leu	Leu	Leu	48	G10	103	His	Asn	Asn	Asn	108							
CD8			Ser	Ser	Ser	49	G11	104	Cys	Val	Val	Val	109							
							G12	105	Leu	Leu	Leu	Leu	110							
D1	50	His	Thr	Ser	Ser	50	G13	106	Leu	Val	Val	Val	111							
D2	51	Gly	Pro	Ala	Pro	51	G14	107	Val	Cys	Thr	Cys	112							
D3			Asp	Ser	Asp	52	G15	108	Thr	Val	Val	Val	113							
D4			Ala	Ala	Ala	53	G16	109	Leu	Leu	Leu	Leu	114							
D5			Val	Ile	Val	54	G17	110	Ala	Ala	Ala	Ala	115							
D6			Met	Met	Met	55	G18	111	Ala	His	Ile	Arg	116							
D7			Gly	Gly	Gly	56	G19	112	His	His	His	Asn	117							

* Another form of the normal γ chain contains alanine instead of glycine in position 136.

Table 3 *Functional classification of abnormal hemoglobins*[14]

Functional abnormality	Usual site of substitution	Clinical manifestation	Example
None..........................	Molecular surface	None	Hb G$_{Philadelphia}$ ($\alpha^{68Asn \to Lys}$)
Aggregation with reduced solubility	Molecular surface	Hemolytic anemia (homozygotes)	Hb S ($\beta^{6Glu \to Val}$)
Instability with reduced solubility ..	Internal nonpolar amino acids, heme pocket region, etc.	Hemolytic anemia (heterozygotes)	Hb Köln ($\beta^{98Val \to Met}$)
Methemoglobinemia.............	Proximal (F8) or distal (E7) histidine	Cyanosis	Hb M group
Increased oxygen affinity	$\alpha_1\beta_2$ contact or β-C-terminal amino acids	Erythrocytosis	Hb Chesapeake ($\alpha^{92Arg \to Leu}$)
Decreased oxygen affinity.........	Near heme and $\alpha_1\beta_2$ contact	Cyanosis	Hb Kansas ($\beta^{102Asn \to Thr}$)

Table 4 *Sickle-cell anemias and related anemias*

Disease or abnormal hemoglobin	Hemoglobins present		Clinical manifestation	Original geographical distribution
Sickle-cell anemia	$\alpha_2^A\beta_2^{6Val}$ (Hb S)	77–87%	Infarctions and hemolytic anemia	Central and West Africa, India, South Arabia, Mediterranean countries
	$\alpha_2^A\delta_2^A$ (Hb A$_2$)	2.5%		
	$\alpha_2^A\gamma_2^F$ (Hb F)	10–20%		
Sickle-cell trait (heterozygotes for sickle-cell anemia)	$\alpha_2^A\beta_2^A$ (Hb A$_1$)	56–76%	Generally symptomless; sickle-cell crises in anoxia	See above
	$\alpha_2^A\beta_2^{6Val}$ (Hb S)	20–40%		
Hb C disease	$\alpha_2^A\beta_2^{6Lys}$	88%	Mild hemolytic anemia, splenomegaly	For example northern Ghana
	$\alpha_2^A\delta_2^A$	9%		
	$\alpha_2^A\gamma_2^F$	2%		
Hb SC disease (heterozygotes for Hb S and Hb C)	$\alpha_2^A\beta_2^{6Val}$	52.5%	Severe hemolytic anemia	Parts of Ghana and neighboring countries
	$\alpha_2^A\beta_2^{6Lys}$	43.5%		
	$\alpha_2^A\gamma_2^F$	3.5%		
Hb E disease	$\alpha_2^A\beta_2^{26Lys}$		Relatively mild anemia	Thailand and Southeast Asia

which deform the erythrocytes into the characteristic sickle cells. This and similar hemoglobinopathies are summarized in Table 4.

Other substitutions – for example in the interior of the hemoglobin molecule – lead to denaturation, since bonds that hold the three-dimensional structure of the molecule together are weakened. These unstable hemoglobins – 111 are known – can be the cause of chronic hemolytic processes which are characterized by intraerythrocytic inclusions (Heinz bodies). Most carriers of unstable hemoglobins show only a slight hemolysis which, however, is intensified during crises, as, for example, is the case with Hb Zurich after intake of sulfonamides. The presence of some other unstable hemoglobins leads to a very severe hemolysis which cannot be controlled even by splenectomy. Another group of these hemoglobins can be detected only by hemolysis in vitro, while the carriers are symptom-free. An amino-acid substitution can render a variant hemoglobin susceptible to posttranslational changes; for example Hb Providence has, at β chain 82, lysine replaced by asparagine. The asparagine residue is posttranslationally deaminated to aspartic acid, and both forms of abnormal hemoglobin are present in the blood.

Hemoglobinopathies of the M group are caused by the fact that the abnormal methemoglobin cannot be reduced to the corresponding hemoglobin. In 4 of the Hb M forms (Hb M$_{Boston}$, Hb M$_{Iwate}$, Hb M$_{Saskatoon}$, Hb M$_{Hyde Park}$), tyrosine is substituted for histidine in the heme pocket of the globin chain; the phenolic group of tyrosine forms covalent bonds with heme iron, thus stabilizing iron in the oxidized form. The substitution in Hb M$_{Milwaukee-1}$ ($\beta^{67Val \to Glu}$) also involves the heme pocket, the carboxylic group of glutamic acid forming a bond with iron. Other forms of Hb M (for example Hb Freiburg) are classed with the unstable hemoglobins. Hb M$_{Iwate}$ is the most important hemoglobinopathy in Japan. These hemoglobinopathies have been described only in heterozygotes (the homozygote would probably be nonviable), i.e. this type of methemoglobinemia is inherited as an autosomal dominant character; cyanosis is usually the sole clinical symptom.

In a considerable number of stable hemoglobin variants the oxygen affinity is increased. In many of the 78 variants so far described, the resultant oxygen deprivation of the tissues is sufficient to cause erythrocytosis. As for the hemoglobins M, all affected individuals are heterozygotes for the relevant gene; the great majority are en-

tirely asymptomatic. Of the unstable hemoglobin variants investigated, 45 have increased oxygen affinity, whereas 22 stable hemoglobin variants have low oxygen affinity with no clinical manifestations (apart from cyanosis in 2 of them [Hb Kansas and Hb Beth Israel]). Low oxygen affinity is shown by 19 unstable hemoglobins, as is the case with Hb M$_{Boston}$, Hb M$_{Iwate}$ and Hb M$_{Milwaukee-1}$. Ready dissociation into αβ dimers or separate chains occurs in 10 hemoglobin variants, with increased oxygen affinity and/or instability in 7 of them.

The thalassemias (Table 5) are a heterogeneous group of genetically determined anemias in which the formation of α chains, β chains, or δ chains is greatly decreased or entirely absent. The α, β or δ chains are normal in structure, if one disregards Hb Constant Spring or similar hemoglobins and Hb Lepore.

Without the synthesis of α chains no Hb A, Hb A$_2$ and Hb F can be formed. In the α-thalassemias, abnormal hemoglobins with 4 β chains (Hb H), 4 γ chains (Hb Bart's) and probably also one with 4 δ chains are formed, due to the excess of β, γ and δ chains. Traces of Hb Portland can be detected in homozygotes for α-thalassemia (the embryonic hemoglobin Hb Portland $\zeta_2\gamma_2$ contains the α-like ζ chain).

In the β-thalassemias, excess α chains are formed and combine with the cell membrane, leading to lysis of the erythrocyte precursors; this is a major factor in causing the characteristic anemia of the β-thalassemias.

The classification of the thalassemias in Table 5 is based on the number and localization of the genes responsible for the formation of the polypeptide chains (Fig. 1). At present, 14 genetic determinants of α-thalassemia are known: 5 in which both α_2 and α_1 genes on chromosome 16 have been deleted (α^0), 2 in which there is deletion of only the α_2 gene (or partial deletion of both α_2 and α_1 genes leaving a single functional fused gene) (α^+), 3 nondeletion types (α^+) and 4 α-chain termination variants. Thus there are 90 theoretically possible α-thalassemia genotypes, including heterozygotes and double heterozygotes, of which 19 have been recognized. In the β-thalassemias there is often a point mutation or small deletion in a non-translated part of the DNA, for example in an intron which thereby inhibits, partially or completely, the splicing necessary to produce mature mRNA, or upstream of the 5' end, thereby probably chang

Table 5 *Clinical aspects of some thalassemias*[15]

Condition	Parental genotypes	α mRNA or β mRNA	Gene defect	Hemoglobin pattern	Clinical manifestation
Homozygous α-thalassemia (α-chain thalassemia 1; α⁰-thalassemia)	--/αα --/αα	Absent	All 4 α genes deleted	$\alpha_2^A\beta_2^A$: 0 $\alpha_2^A\gamma_2^F$: 0 $\alpha_2^A\delta_2^A$: 0 γ_4^F (Hb Bart's): 80–90% β_4^A (Hb H): ~10–20% Hb Portland: trace	Hydrops fetalis; death mostly in utero, between the 34th and 40th weeks of pregnancy, or directly following birth
Hb H disease (α-thalassemia 1–α-thalassemia 2; α⁺-thalassemia)	(a) --/αα -α/αα	Marked deficiency	3 of the 4 α genes deleted	$\alpha_2^A\beta_2^A$: 65–90% β_4^A (Hb H): 5–30% γ_4^F (Hb Bart's): 25% in cord blood	Moderate to severe anemia (thalassemia intermedia)
	(b) --/αα αCS/αα	Marked deficiency	2 of the 4 α genes deleted; 1 α gene replaced by Hb CS gene	Hb CS: 2–3%	Moderate to severe anemia (thalassemia intermedia)
Heterozygous α-thalassemia ('α-thal trait'; heterozygosity for α-chain thalassemia 1)	--/αα αα/αα or -α/αα -α/αα	Presumed deficiency	2 of the 4 α genes deleted	γ_4^F (Hb Bart's): 5–10% in cord blood	Mild anemia (especially mild in the African variant)
Silent carrier (heterozygosity for α-chain thalassemia 2)	-α/αα αα/αα	Presumed slight deficiency	1 of the 4 α genes deleted	γ_4^F (Hb Bart's): 1–2% in cord blood	Symptomless
Heterozygous Hb Constant Spring carrier	αCS/αα αα/αα	Unstable	1 α gene replaced by Hb CS gene	Hb CS: ~1%	Symptomless
Homozygous β⁺-thalassemia	β⁺/β β⁺/β	Marked deficiency	β genes present, but splicing or promoter defect	$\alpha_2^A\beta_2^A$: reduced $\alpha_2^A\gamma_2^F$: 20–30% $\alpha_2^A\delta_2^A$: variable	Mild to severe anemia (mostly Cooley's anemia)
Homozygous β⁰-thalassemia	β⁰/β β⁰/β	Absent	β genes present, but in some splicing or promoter defect; in others β gene 'amber' mutation or partial deletion	$\alpha_2^A\beta_2^A$: 0 $\alpha_2^A\gamma_2^F$: ≥95% $\alpha_2^A\delta_2^A$: variable	Severe anemia (Cooley)
Homozygous (δβ)⁰-thalassemia (F-thalassemia)	(δβ)⁰/δβ (δβ)⁰/δβ	δ and β mRNA absent	Deletion of β and δ genes; in some types $^A\gamma$ gene also deleted	$\alpha_2^A\beta_2^A$: 0 $\alpha_2^A\gamma_2^F$: 100% $\alpha_2^A\delta_2^A$: 0	Usually mild to moderate anemia
Homozygous Hb Lepore disease	Hb Lepore/β Hb Lepore/β	β-Like mRNA present in reduced amount	Normal β and δ genes deleted; δβ fusion genes present	$\alpha_2^A\beta_2^A$: 0 $\alpha_2^A\gamma_2^F$: 75% $\alpha_2^A\delta_2^A$: 0 Hb Lepore: 25%	Severe anemia (Cooley)
Heterozygous β⁺-thalassemia	β⁺/β Normal	Deficient	β genes present, but transcription or mRNA processing defective	$\alpha_2^A\beta_2^A$: reduced $\alpha_2^A\gamma_2^F$: slightly increased $\alpha_2^A\delta_2^A$: increased	Variable manifestation of anemia (thalassemia minor)
Heterozygous β⁰-thalassemia	β⁰/β Normal	Deficient	One active β gene present	$\alpha_2^A\beta_2^A$: reduced $\alpha_2^A\gamma_2^F$: slightly increased $\alpha_2^A\delta_2^A$: increased	Variable manifestation of anemia (thalassemia minor)
Heterozygous (δβ)⁰-thalassemia	(δβ)⁰/δβ Normal	Presumed deficiency of δ and β mRNA	1 of the 2 β genes and 1 of the 2 δ genes deleted	$\alpha_2^A\beta_2^A$: reduced $\alpha_2^A\gamma_2^F$: 5–20% $\alpha_2^A\delta_2^A$: reduced	Variable manifestation of anemia (thalassemia minor)
Heterozygous Hb Lepore disease	Hb Lepore/β Normal	β-Like mRNA present	1 of the 2 normal β and δ genes replaced by δβ fusion gene	$\alpha_2^A\beta_2^A$: reduced $\alpha_2^A\gamma_2^F$: increased $\alpha_2^A\delta_2^A$: reduced Hb Lepore: 5–15%	Variable manifestation of anemia (thalassemia minor)

Table 6 *Hereditary persistence of Hb F[16]*

	Characteristics of γ globin	δβ genes	HbF (fraction of total hemoglobin)	
			Heterozygotes	Homozygotes
Pancellular forms				
African	$^G\gamma/^A\gamma$ usually ⅔	Mostly absent	25–30%	100%
African	$^G\gamma$	Active	15–20%	Not described
Greek	$^A\gamma$	Active	10–20%	Not described
Hb Kenya	$^G\gamma$	$^A\gamma$–β fusion, δ portion absent	6–7%	Not described
Heterocellular forms				
Chinese (may be pancellular)	Mainly $^A\gamma$	Active	10–14%	Not described
British	Mainly $^A\gamma$	Active	6–12%	20%
Seattle	$^G\gamma/^A\gamma = $ ⅔	Active	3–8%	Not described
Georgia	$^A\gamma$	Active	4–7%	Not described
Swiss	?	Active	1–3%	Not described

ing a transcription promoter. In one type of Afro-Asian β⁰-thalassemia, the 3rd coding sequence (exon) of the β gene has been deleted together with neighboring nontranslated nucleotides. It has been reported that, in Ferrara-type β⁰-thalassemia, normal β-chain mRNA is produced, but the reticulocytes contain a protein which inhibits translation of the β-chain mRNA; this work requires confirmation. In 2 other forms of β⁰-thalassemia, base changes produce chain-terminating codons near the 5′ end of the β gene.

Hb Constant Spring to some extent resembles the α-thalassemias insofar as an α chain with an abnormal (lengthened) sequence is indeed formed, but the gene product is formed in greatly reduced amounts. Because the Hb Lepore gene, a product of fusion of the δ and β genes, replaces the normal δ and β genes, it behaves like a δβ-thalassemia mutation with greatly reduced formation of the chain that replaces the normal β and δ chains. Several different fused δβ genes are known; the different gene products, when combined with α chains and heme, are all termed 'Hb Lepore'.

The hereditary persistence of Hb F (HPFH) is closely connected with the δβ-thalassemias, since the formation of δ and β chains is partially or completely suppressed. This defect is compensated for by increased synthesis of $^G\gamma$ and/or $^A\gamma$ chains. All the erythrocytes are affected in the pancellular forms; in the heterocellular forms, only the F cells, which are either increased in number or richer in Hb F, are affected. At least 7 forms can be distinguished (Table 6). In the African pancellular $^G\gamma^A\gamma$ form there is deletion of the δ–β region of chromosome 11 (several variants are known, differing in the length of DNA deletion). In contrast, no major deletions have been found in the British, Greek or Chinese variants of $^A\gamma$ heterocellular HPFH or in the African pancellular $^G\gamma$ (β+) variant. These hemoglobinopathies usually are clinically harmless; this holds true for most cases of homozygosity, for all cases of heterozygosity and for double heterozygosity in conjunction with Hb C or Hb S.

Despite the relative rarity of most abnormal hemoglobins, the genes for thalassemia, Hb S, Hb C and Hb E are very widely distributed in some areas of the world or in certain populations[17]. Some of these genes, however, are lethal factors; homozygotes for thalassemia or Hb S often die in childhood, hence a continuous reduction of the genes concerned takes place. The Hb S gene is found almost exclusively in regions with endemic malignant malaria or in descendants of previous inhabitants of such regions. During childhood, heterozygotes for the Hb S gene are more resistant to malaria than normal homozygotes ('heterozygote advantage'); the thereby increased survival rate of the heterozygotes balances out the losses in homozygotes due to sickle-cell anemia. This can lead to a 'stable polymorphic population' with a sickle-cell gene frequency of up to 20%. The sickle-cell problem is not limited to persons of African ancestry[18]; indeed, it has been suggested that the gene has arisen several times in the course of evolution, as in Indians for example[19]. The increased proportion of Hb F in thalassemia also seems to bestow a certain protection against malaria. The uneven geographic distribution of the Hb C and Hb E genes can probably be explained by a similar relationship with a disease.

It has been suggested that there are over 200 million carriers for hemoglobinopathies in the world and that between 200000 and 300000 severely affected homozygotes or compound heterozygotes are born each year[20]. The most important of these conditions are α- and β-thalassemia and sickle-cell anemia. Since symptomatic treatment of these disorders is unsatisfactory, much effort has gone into evaluating prenatal diagnostic techniques[21–23] (page 219).

References

[1] BUNN et al., *Human Hemoglobins*, Saunders, Philadelphia, 1977.

[2] CAUGHEY, W. S. (Ed.), *Biochemical and Clinical Aspects of Hemoglobin Abnormalities*, Academic Press, New York, 1978.

[3] BANK, A., *Progr. Hemat.*, **12**, 25 (1981); BANK et al., *Science*, **207**, 486 (1980).

[4] SCHNEIDER et al., Human hemoglobins and hemoglobinopathies: a review to 1981, *Tex. Rep. Biol. Med.*, **40** (1980/1).

[5] WEATHERALL, D. J. (Ed.), *The Thalassemias*, Churchill Livingstone, Edinburgh, 1983; WEATHERALL and CLEGG, *The Thalassaemia Syndromes*, 3rd ed., Mosby, St. Louis, 1981.

[6] ORKIN and NATHAN, *Advanc. hum. Genet.*, **11**, 233 (1981).

[7] ORKIN et al., *Progr. Hemat.*, **13**, 49 (1983).

[8] SPRITZ and FORGET, *Amer. J. hum. Genet.*, **35**, 333 (1983).

[9] KAN, Y. W., in STANBURY et al., *The Metabolic Basis of Inherited Disease*, 5th ed., McGraw-Hill, New York, 1983, page 1711.

[10] WINSLOW and ANDERSON, in STANBURY et al., *The Metabolic Basis of Inherited Disease*, 5th ed., McGraw-Hill, New York, 1983, page 1666.

[11] NIENHUIS et al., *Blood*, **63**, 738 (1984).

[12] International Hemoglobin Information Center, *Hemoglobin*, **9**, 229 (1985).

[13] WINTROBE et al., *Clinical Hematology*, 8th ed., Lea & Febiger, Philadelphia, 1981, page 75.

[14] WINTROBE et al., *Clinical Hematology*, 8th ed., Lea & Febiger, Philadelphia, 1981, page 803.

[15] ORKIN and NATHAN, *New Engl. J. Med.*, **295**, 710 (1976).

[16] NIENHUIS and BENZ, *New Engl. J. Med.*, **297**, 1430 (1977).

[17] BOWMAN, J. E. (Ed.), *Distribution and Evolution of Hemoglobin and Globin Loci*, Elsevier, New York, 1983.

[18] ROTH, E., *J. Amer. med. Ass.*, **253**, 2259 (1985).

[19] KAN and DOZY, *Science*, **209**, 388 (1980); KAN and DOZY, *Lancet*, **2**, 910 (1978).

[20] World Health Organization Working Group, *Bull. Wld Hlth Org.*, **60**, 643 (1982).

[21] MODELL, B., *Brit. med. Bull.*, **39**, 386 (1983).

[22] WEATHERALL, D. J., *Brit. med. J.*, **288**, 1321 (1984).

[23] ORKIN, S. H., *Blood*, **63**, 249 (1984).

Inborn errors of renal and intestinal transport are dealt with in a series of reviews[1-6].

In active transport processes across biological membranes (transport of a substrate against a concentration gradient) a substance, after making contact with the cell membrane, is reversibly bound to the latter and then transported through the membrane by a saturable carrier which, like an enzyme, obeys Michaelis-Menten kinetics. Both the binding site and the carrier are probably proteins and can therefore be subject to genetic changes. Active transport presupposes the availability of energy – in which case the energy-supplying system may also be altered by a genetic defect.

The brush border (i.e. luminal membrane) of the epithelial cells lining the proximal renal tubule has different carriers specific for, among others: (a) glucose (also transports galactose), (b) glycine, proline and hydroxyproline, (c) a group of 13 monoamino-monocarboxylic acids, (d) lysine, arginine and ornithine, (e) another one for lysine, arginine and ornithine that also transports cystine, (f) one for cystine alone, (g) glutamic and aspartic acids, (h) methionine, (i) inorganic phosphate, and (j) bicarbonate ions. Similar carriers exist in the brush border of the jejunal mucosa and, in both organs, serve to transport their specific substrates from the lumen into the epithelial cells, where each transported substance is released and enters the circulation through the action of a, generally different, specific carrier protein in the basal–lateral (i.e. antiluminal) membrane. Genetically determined transport defects are known in the proximal renal tubule, loop of Henle, distal renal tubule, jejunum, ileum, hepatocyte, mitochondrion and lysosome.

The brush border of the proximal renal tubule also actively secretes certain substances (e.g. diodone, 4-aminohippurate, and other organic acids) from the blood into the lumen of the tubule, often against a concentration gradient. Several (perhaps all) of the substances actively absorbed are also actively secreted, the observed net absorption representing a balance between the two processes. The traces of serum albumin and smaller protein molecules which appear in the glomerular filtrate are normally reabsorbed by pinocytosis in the proximal renal tubule.

In Hartnup disease[7] the carrier for 13 monoamino-monocarboxylic acids (alanine, serine, threonine, asparagine, glutamine, valine, leucine, isoleucine, phenylalanine, tyrosine, tryptophan, histidine and citrulline) is defective or absent from the brush border of the proximal renal tubule. Of the two recognized types, in one the jejunal mucosa has a similar defect of absorption, causing large amounts of these amino acids to enter the colon, where they undergo bacterial degradation. Indole, indoleacrylic acid, indoleacetic acid and indolelactic acid, produced in this way from tryptophan, are absorbed and, after conjugation in the case of indole and indoleacetic acid, excreted in large amounts in the urine. The absorbed indole inhibits tryptophan 2,3-dioxygenase (1.13.11.11) and hence decreases the endogenous formation of nicotinamide.

In 'blue diaper syndrome'[8] only the absorption of tryptophan from the intestine is abnormal.

In the case of extensive or complete omission of the specific mechanism for the reabsorption of proline, hydroxyproline and glycine all three amino acids are excreted in increased amounts in the urine (iminoglycinuria); partial omission, which occurs in some of the heterozygotes, leads only to glycinuria[9].

In cystinuria there is a defect of the transport system for the reabsorption of arginine, lysine, ornithine and cystine in the proximal tubule[10]. In the usual form of cystinuria all 4 amino acids are excreted in increased amounts in the urine by homozygotes; in 2 of the 3 known types of cystinuria, the heterozygotes excrete increased amounts of lysine and cystine. There is also a different condition, isolated cystinuria[11], in which only cystine is excreted and in which presumably the low-affinity, high-capacity transport system for cystine alone is involved[10]. The transport system in the intestine, together with the transport system in the renal tubule, is genetically regulated; the enteral absorption of arginine, lysine and ornithine is impaired in some cystinurics, and bacterial metabolites of these amino acids are found in the urine in small amounts. In lysinuric protein intolerance[12] the carrier for lysine, ornithine and arginine in the basal–lateral membrane of the jejunum and the proximal tubule and in the plasma membrane of the hepatocyte is defective, resulting in impairment of the urea cycle; the highest reported prevalence of the disease is in Finland.

In dicarboxylic aminoaciduria[13] the amounts of glutamic and aspartic acids excreted exceed the amounts in the glomerular filtrate, i.e. there is (net) active secretion of these substances in the nephron. In methionine malabsorption[14] there is a defect of absorption of methionine from the jejunum and defective reabsorption of methionine in the proximal renal tubule.

Additional specific defects involve the transport of glucose and/or galactose, phosphate and bicarbonate. In glucose–galactose malabsorption[15] there is a defect of the Na^+-dependent transport system for both sugars in the small intestine. The defect in the intestinal mucosa is combined with a renal defect of glucose reabsorption. In renal glucosuria[17] there is a defect of the glucose transport system in the proximal tubule, in which either the tubular transport maximum for glucose is lowered (type A) or there is no clear maximum, some glucose appearing in the urine at any blood glucose concentration, i.e. exaggerated splay (type B). A family with both renal glucosuria and glycinuria has been described[16].

In familial X-linked hypophosphatemia[18, 19] the reabsorption of phosphate in the proximal tubule is restricted, accompanied by a relative deficiency of calcitriol production[20]. Hereditary hypouratemia has been reported in a few families and several isolated patients (mostly adults)[21]. The effects of probenecid and pyrazinamide administration on urate clearance suggest the existence of at least 2 types of renal abnormalities: defective presecretory tubular urate reabsorption and defective total pre- and postsecretory tubular urate reabsorption.

In the case of primary renal acidosis 2 main forms are to be distinguished[22]: in type I the defect is in the distal tubule (a disturbance of the mechanism that maintains the hydrogen ion gradient between the plasma and the tubular fluid), whereas in type II the reabsorption of bicarbonate in the proximal tubule is impaired. Type I is subdivided into several subtypes (e.g. San Francisco, 'Atlanta', iRTA-1, cRTA-1, etc.)[23]. A girl with proximal renal bicarbonate wasting had a massive active secretion of bicarbonate into the upper small intestine[24]. Type III is characterized by the involvement of both the proximal and distal tubules and is also regarded as a type I form with renal bicarbonate wasting[19]. Type IV renal tubular acidoses involve the distal tubule, but are distinguished from type I forms by the presence of hyperkalemia[18, 19, 25]; the genetically determined form of type IV is pseudohypoaldosteronism type II. Another type of hereditary distal renal tubular acidosis is transient, vanishing spontaneously after 2 to 5 years; it is probably a mild form of pseudohypoaldosteronism with little or no loss of sodium.

In addition to the above single transport defects, there exist multiple defects of renal tubular transport. Some cases of the Fanconi syndrome are genetically transmitted (idiopathic or primary Fanconi syndrome)[1-3, 23, 26, 27]; this syndrome is characterized by a nonselective loss of reabsorptive capacity for all substances normally reabsorbed in the proximal renal tubule, the extent of this loss and the consequent clinical effects varying from case to case. The oculocerebrorenal syndrome (Lowe-Terrey-MacLachlan syndrome)[28] shows considerable similarity to the Fanconi syndrome, though there are differences in the amino-acid pattern, and other organs as well as the renal tubule are involved. There may also be a defect in the intracellular synthesis of glycosaminoglycans and collagen[29].

Several metabolic errors cause a generalized impairment of the proximal renal tubular function. In these conditions, toxic metabolites accumulate: cystine in cystinosis (page 238), galactose 1-phosphate in galactosemia (page 248), maleylacetoacetate and fumarylacetoacetate (giving rise to succinylacetoacetate and succinylacetone) in hereditary tyrosinemia type I (page 233), fructose 1-phosphate in fructose intolerance (page 248), copper in Wilson's disease (page 287), glycogen in one form of type I glycogenosis (hepatorenal glycogenosis, page 246)[40].

Renal tubular reabsorption of some substances is under hormonal control; abnormal tubular response to these hormones will affect renal function. In nephrogenic diabetes insipidus[30] the collecting duct does not respond to vasopressin. In Albright's hereditary osteodystrophy[31] (phenotypically characteristic cases of pseudohypoparathyroidism and pseudo-pseudohypoparathyroidism), the phosphate-reabsorbing mechanism of the renal tubule does not respond to parathyroid hormone. The basic defect of type I pseudohypoparathyroidism is a deficiency in stimulatory guanine-nucleotide-binding regulatory protein (G_s) of the cAMP system (page 201)[32].

In pseudohypoaldosteronism (salt-losing syndrome of infancy)[23, 33] 2 types are usually differentiated, and in a few cases of type I a deficiency of aldosterone receptors has been detected[37]; furthermore, Na^+/K^+-transporting ATPase in both the proximal and the distal tubule may be absent. In Liddle's syndrome[39] (pseudohyperaldosteronism) there is probably a different defect of the Na^+/K^+-transporting ATPase making it hyperactive. Bartter's syndrome of familial renal hypoelectrolytemia[34] has been suggested to be caused by impaired reabsorption of chloride from the ascending limb of the loop of Henle; a hormone controlling the active reabsorption of chloride at this site may be involved. Besides the classical Bartter's syndrome several similar conditions exist, some involving the prox-

Table 1   *Inborn errors of transport mechanisms*

Condition	Site of defect	Biochemical findings	Clinical features	Treatment	Inheritance	Ref.
Hartnup disease (at least 2 types)	Renal tubules (and intestinal wall in one type)	Increased urinary excretion of 13 neutral amino acids; in some cases diminished intestinal absorption of tryptophan increases urinary excretion of indole derivatives	Cerebellar ataxia, photosensitive dermatitis; often symptomless	Nicotinamide	Autosomal recessive	7
Iminoglycinuria (at least 4 types)	Renal tubules (and jejunum in type I)	Increased excretion of proline, hydroxyproline and glycine in the urine; in heterozygotes of types III and IV, increased glycine excretion only	Probably benign; in some cases mental retardation, convulsions or deafness (probably coincidental)	None known	Autosomal recessive	9
Cystinuria (classical; at least 3 types)	Renal tubules (and intestinal wall in types I and II)	Increased excretion of cystine, lysine, arginine and ornithine in the urine	Cystine calculi in the urinary tract; often symptomless	High fluid intake, alkalinization, penicillamine	Autosomal recessive	10
Lysinuric protein intolerance (2 types)	Type I: renal tubules and intestinal wall; Type II: renal tubules, intestinal wall and liver	Increased excretion of lysine, arginine and ornithine in the urine	Growth retardation; osteoporosis Type II: hyperammonemia, diarrhea and vomiting after protein intake	Citrulline and N-acetyllysine	Autosomal recessive	12
Dicarboxyaminoaciduria	Renal tubules	High excretion of glutamic and aspartic acids in the urine (50 to 250 times the normal)	1 case with hypoglucosemia and mental retardation; 1 case without symptoms	Small doses of L-glutamine throughout the day	Not known	13
Methionine malabsorption	Intestinal wall (and renal tubules)	2-Hydroxybutyric acid in urine and feces, and 2-aminobutyric acid in feces after administration of methionine	Mental retardation; convulsions; hypotonia; white hair; sometimes diarrhea; characteristic body odor	Methionine-poor diet	Probably autosomal recessive	14
Glucose-galactose malabsorption	Intestinal wall and renal tubules	Glucose, galactose and products of bacterial fermentation in the feces; hyperglucosuria	Diarrhea, dehydration; sometimes fatal	Fructose as the only sugar	Autosomal recessive	15
Renal glucosuria (renal glucodiabetes)	Renal tubules	Hyperglucosuria; lowered transport maximum (Tm) for glucose in type A; increased splay of the glucose reabsorption curve in type B	Benign	None known	Autosomal dominant	17
Familial hypophosphatemia (phosphaturia; phosphate diabetes)	Renal tubules (and possibly intestinal wall in some cases)	Hypophosphatemia associated with hyperphosphaturia	Vitamin D-resistant rickets; disproportional dwarfism; often extraskeletal calcification; sometimes symptomless	Phosphate plus calcitriol	X-linked with expression in most hemizygotes and in some heterozygotes	18, 19
Hypouratemia	Renal tubules	Marked hypouratemia; mild hyperuricosuria; some cases with hypercalciuria	Kidney stones in some cases	None known	Autosomal recessive	21
Renal tubular acidosis type I (many subtypes)	Distal renal tubules (H⁺ exchange for Na⁺ disturbed)	Hypercalciuria; urinary pH value never below 6.0 even after administration of NH_4Cl; loss of calcium and phosphate in the feces; hypokalemia in adults	Hyperchloridemic acidosis; nephrocalcinosis and/or nephrolithiasis; rickets or osteomalacia and osteoporosis; thirst, polyuria, polydipsia; sometimes symptomless, especially in males	Alkalies, chloride-poor diet	Irregular dominant (X-dependent expressivity)	22, 23
Renal tubular acidosis type II (proximal tubular acidosis; bicarbonate loss)	Proximal renal tubules	Disturbed reabsorption of bicarbonate (low transport maximum or sharp drop of the reabsorption curve); urinary pH value dropping below 5.6 after administration of NH_4Cl	Involves the male sex exclusively; growth retardation; infrequently osteoporosis in adults	Alkalies	X-linked recessive	22, 23

Disorder	Defect/site	Biochemical findings	Clinical features	Treatment	Inheritance	Ref.
Idiopathic (primary) Fanconi syndrome (de Toni-Debré-Fanconi syndrome; adult Fanconi syndrome; Luder-Sheldon syndrome)	Renal tubules	Loss of glucose, phosphate, amino acids, protein and bicarbonate in the urine	Sometimes benign; severe phosphate loss leads to vitamin D-resistant rickets and dwarfism in children, to osteomalacia in adults; acidosis frequent	Alkalies, phosphate infusions, vitamin D or dihydrotachysterol	Autosomal dominant, autosomal recessive	2, 27
Oculocerebrorenal syndrome (Lowe-Terrey-MacLachlan syndrome)	Renal tubules, intestinal wall	Loss of amino acids and protein – in some cases also glucose – in the urine	Stunted growth; mental retardation; muscle hypotonia; cataracts; microphthalmia; acidosis frequent; rickets in some cases	Alkalies, vitamin D	X-linked recessive	28
Nephrogenic diabetes insipidus	Collecting duct (adenylate cyclase is not activated by vasopressin)	Large amounts of urine of low relative density	Dehydration; feeble-mindedness; death in childhood in about 5–10%	High fluid intake; diet low in NaCl and nitrogen; thiazide diuretics	X-linked recessive	30
Albright's hereditary osteodystrophy (pseudohypoparathyroidism and pseudo-pseudohypoparathyroidism types I and II)	Proximal and distal renal tubules (in type I, adenylate cyclase is not activated by parathyroid hormone; in type II, cAMP is formed, but does not activate the tubular mechanism)	Hypocalcemia and hyperphosphatemia (both sometimes normal); phosphate excretion unchanged by administering parathyroid hormone	Short stature, round face; in some cases short metacarpal and metatarsal bones; mental retardation; seizures (in ~60%); tetany; cataracts; soft tissue calcification (especially basal ganglia); sometimes normal	Vitamin D or, better, calcitriol	Probably X-linked dominant (may be autosomal dominant with sex-modified expression); autosomal dominant in some families	31
Pseudohypoaldosteronism type I	Deficiency of type I receptors in aldosterone target tissues	Renal salt wasting; hyponatremia; hyperkalemia; unresponsiveness to aldosterone	Acidosis; sometimes hypotension; usually recovery in later childhood	NaCl (up to 60 mmol/d) and $NaHCO_3$ in the first few years of life	Probably autosomal dominant or autosomal recessive	23, 37
Pseudohypoaldosteronism type II	High Cl^- reabsorption in distal tubule	Hyperchloridemia; hyperkalemia; unresponsiveness to aldosterone	Acidosis; growth retardation; hypertension	Restriction of NaCl intake; thiazide diuretics or furosemide	Not known	23
Liddle's syndrome (pseudohyperaldosteronism)	Na^+/K^+-transporting ATPase (of proximal tubule?) hyperactive and independent of mineralocorticoids	Urinary K^+ wasting and hypokalemia (as low as 2.4 mmol/L); low plasma and urinary aldosterone levels; urinary amino acids, glucose, protein all normal	Alkalosis; marked hypertension (up to 200/130 mmHg at 17 years of age)	KCl, triamterene; low sodium diet	Probably dominant (X-linked or autosomal)	39
Bartter's syndrome (familial renal hypoelectrolytemia)	Inactivity of Cl^--reabsorbing mechanism of ascending limb of loop of Henle; secondary hypertrophy of juxtaglomerular apparatus	Urinary NaCl wasting; hypochloridemia. hyponatremia, hypokalemia; often hypomagnesemia; elevated levels of renin, angiotensin II and aldosterone in plasma; high urinary excretion of prostaglandins (especially PGE_2)	Mild alkalosis; normotensive; failure to thrive; short stature; vomiting and anorexia; attacks of muscular weakness; polyuria; tendency to dehydration; may be fatal	KCl (up to 200 mmol/d); if necessary, $MgCl_2$ and NaCl; spironolactone, amiloride or triamterene; possibly indomethacin or ibuprofen	Autosomal recessive	34
Chloride diarrhea (congenital alkalosis with diarrhea)	Cl^-/HCO_3^- exchange in mucosa of ileum and colon	Watery acid stools with high chloride concentration	Metabolic alkalosis; dehydration; in some neonates also metabolic acidosis	NaCl and KCl	Autosomal recessive	35

imal or distal convoluted tubule and/or increased systemic production of prostaglandins[38].

Apart from these renal ion transport defects there exist specific intestinal ion absorption defects. Congenital chloride diarrhea[35] results from defective active transport and absorption of chloride ions from the distal ileum and colon. In 2 girls a defective Na^+/H^+ exchange in the mucosa of the small intestine has been detected, referred to as 'congenital sodium diarrhea'[36], which is characterized by severe metabolic acidosis and high sodium content of the feces.

References

[1] WOOLF, L. I., *Renal Tubular Dysfunction*, Thomas, Springfield, 1966.

[2] WOOLF, L. I., in CHURG et al. (Eds.), *Kidney Disease: Present Status*, Williams & Wilkins, Baltimore, 1979, page 218.

[3] CHURG et al., *Renal Disease: Developmental and Hereditary Diseases*, Igaku-Shoin, Tokyo (in press).

[4] SCRIVER et al., *Kidney Int.*, 9, 149 (1976).

[5] BELTON and TOOTHILL (Eds.), *Transport and Inherited Disease*, MTP Press, Lancaster, 1981.

[6] BUCKALEW and MOORE, *Renal Tubular Dysfunction*, Medical Examination Publ., New Hyde Park, N. Y., 1980.

[7] JEPSON, J. B., in STANBURY et al. (Eds.), *The Metabolic Basis of Inherited Disease*, 4th ed., McGraw-Hill, New York, 1978, page 1563.

[8] DRUMMOND et al., *Amer. J. Med.*, 37, 928 (1964).

[9] SCRIVER, C. R., in STANBURY et al., *The Metabolic Basis of Inherited Disease*, 5th ed., McGraw-Hill, New York, 1983, page 1792.

[10] SEGAL and THIER, in STANBURY et al., *The Metabolic Basis of Inherited Disease*, 5th ed., McGraw-Hill, New York, 1983, page 1774.

[11] BRODEHL et al., *Mschr. Kinderheilk.*, 115, 317 (1967).

[12] CARPENTER et al., *New Engl. J. Med.*, 312, 290 (1985); RAJANTIE et al., *Lancet*, 1, 1219 (1980).

[13] MELANÇON et al., *J. Pediat.*, 91, 422 (1977); TEIJEMA et al., *Metabolism*, 23, 115 (1974).

[14] HOOFT et al., *Helv. paediat. Acta*, 23, 334 (1968).

[15] GRAY, G. M., in STANBURY et al., *The Metabolic Basis of Inherited Disease*, 5th ed., McGraw-Hill, New York, 1983, page 1729.

[16] KÄSER et al., *J. Pediat.*, 61, 386 (1962).

[17] KRANE, S. M., in STANBURY et al. (Eds.), *The Metabolic Basis of Inherited Disease*, 4th ed., McGraw-Hill, New York, 1978, page 1607.

[18] RASMUSSEN and ANAST, in STANBURY et al., *The Metabolic Basis of Inherited Disease*, 5th ed., McGraw-Hill, New York, 1983, page 1743.

[19] CHAN and ALON, *Nephron*, 40, 257 (1985); POLISSON et al., *New Engl. J. Med.*, 313, 1 (1985).

[20] CHAN et al., *J. Pediat.*, 106, 533 (1985); HARRELL et al., *J. clin. Invest.*, 75, 1858 (1985).

[21] TAKEDA et al., *J. Pediat.*, 107, 71 (1985); SMETANA and BAR-KHAYIM, *Arch. intern. Med.*, 145, 1200 (1985); SPERLING, O., in *Third International Symposium on Inborn Errors of Metabolism in Humans*, Munich, 1984, Abstracts, Karger, Basle, 1984, page 64; TOFUKU et al., *Nephron*, 30, 39 (1982).

[22] McSHERRY, E., *Kidney Int.*, 20, 799 (1981); BATTLE and ARRUDA, *Miner. Electrolyte Metab.*, 5, 83 (1981).

[23] MORRIS and SEBASTIAN, in STANBURY et al., *The Metabolic Basis of Inherited Disease*, 5th ed., McGraw-Hill, New York, 1983, page 1808.

[24] SCHOENEMAN et al., *Pediat. Res.*, 8, 735 (1974).

[25] LICHT et al., *Quart. J. Med.*, 54, 161 (1985).

[26] LEE et al., *Medicine (Baltimore)*, 51, 107 (1972).

[27] ROTH et al., *Kidney Int.*, 20, 705 (1981).

[28] MATIN and SYLVESTER, *J. ment. Defic. Res.*, 24, 1 (1980).

[29] YOKOI and TANIGUCHI, *J. Lab. clin. Med.*, 100, 461 (1982); PALMIERI et al., *J. inherited metab. Dis.*, 8, 187 (1985).

[30] CULPEPPER et al., in STANBURY et al., *The Metabolic Basis of Inherited Disease*, 5th ed., McGraw-Hill, New York, 1983, page 1867.

[31] DREZNER and NEELON, in STANBURY et al., *The Metabolic Basis of Inherited Disease*, 5th ed., McGraw-Hill, 1983, page 1508; FITCH, N., *Amer. J. med. Genet.*, 11, 11 (1982); AVIOLI, L. V., *Progr. biochem. Pharmacol.*, 17, 199 (1980).

[32] VAN DOP and BOURNE, *Ann. Rev. Med.*, 34, 259 (1983).

[33] KLAUS, D., *Klin. Wschr.*, 62, 747 (1984); DILLON et al., *Arch. Dis. Childh.*, 55, 427 (1980).

[34] DÜSING et al., *Klin. Wschr.*, 61, 311 (1983); BARTTER and RODRIGUEZ, *Ergebn. inn. Med. Kinderheilk.*, 50, 79 (1982); WESTENFELDER and KURTZMAN, *Miner. Electrolyte Metab.*, 5, 135 (1981); GILL, J. R., *Ann. Rev. Med.*, 31, 405 (1980).

[35] HOLMBERG and PERHEENTUPA, *Ergebn. inn. Med. Kinderheilk.*, 49, 137 (1982).

[36] BOOTH et al., *Lancet*, 1, 1066 (1985); HOLMBERG and PERHEENTUPA, *J. Pediat.*, 106, 56 (1985).

[37] ARMANINI et al., *New Engl. J. Med.*, 313, 1178 (1985).

[38] BROUHARD, B. H., *J. Pediat.*, 107, 738 (1985).

[39] LIDDLE et al., in BAULIEU and ROBEL (Eds.), *Aldosterone*, Blackwell, Oxford, 1964, page 352.

[40] GARTY et al., *J. Pediat.*, 85, 821 (1974); BRIVET et al., *Pediat. Res.*, 17, 157 (1983).

At least 60 different clinical pictures are due to an inheritable disorder in the metabolism of one or several amino acids[1-4] – variant subtypes, disorders of amino-acid transport (page 227) and of collagen metabolism (page 241) not included.

Aspartylglucosaminuria is listed among the oligosaccharidoses (page 272), 3-aminoisobutyric aciduria among the inborn errors of pyrimidine metabolism (page 258). Some disorders of amino-acid metabolism manifest themselves as acidosis or aciduria in connection with the formation of nitrogen-free organic acids as metabolites of an amino acid. Although lactacidoses are related to alanine metabolism, they are discussed in the chapter on 'Inborn Errors –

Carbohydrate Metabolism' (page 245). Glutaric aciduria type II is dealt with in the chapter on 'Inborn Errors – Enzymes Coded on Mitochondrial DNA' (page 256) since the electron transfer system in the mitochondria of the acyl-CoA-dehydrogenase system is involved.

Almost all the genetically determined disorders of amino-acid metabolism are inherited as autosomal recessive traits; the known exceptions are ornithine carbamoyltransferase deficiency (X-linked recessive) and hawkinsinuria (autosomal or X-linked dominant). Many of them are linked with diminished survival capacity, i.e. with very severe illness. Some almost always lead to death; others run a benign course. In some of these metabolic disorders there are genetic

Table 1   *Incidences of several aminoacidopathies in different populations*

Condition	Geographic area or ethnic group	Approximate incidence per 10^6 live births	Reference	Remarks
Classical phenylketonuria.......	North America	72	7	Variation in incidence reflects real and major differences in gene frequency in different populations
	Eastern Ireland	187	7	
	Poland...............	129	7	
	Western Austria........	53	7	
	Eastern Austria........	115	7	
	Czechoslovakia	151	7	
	Switzerland...........	60	7	
	Western Scotland.......	~ 190	8	
	South-East England	55–72	7	
	Ashkenazi Jews	< 5	7	
	Yemeni Jews...........	≥ 190	9	
	Japan	9	10, 11	
	Finland...............	< 14	7	
Hyperphenylalaninemic variant..	All areas .... (except Japan and Finland)	20–76	7	Relatively minor variation between different populations
Malignant hyperphenylalaninemia	Panethnic	1–3	12	Of 50 cases discussed in 1984, 27 had 'dihydro-biopterin synthetase' deficiency, 22 dihydropteridine reductase deficiency and 1 GTP cyclohydrolase I deficiency[20]
Histidinemia..................	North America..........	51	7	May be panethnic. Possibly benign and pathogenic forms
	North London	79	7	
	Australia..............	60	7	
	New Zealand	73	7	
	Japan	120	11	
Albinism.....................	USA: Caucasians	53	13	Combined figures for tyrosinase-negative and tyrosinase-positive forms. Some genetic isolates have very high gene frequencies
	USA: Afro-Americans ...	100	13	
	Northern Ireland	131	14	
	Nigeria	200	15	
	Nigeria: Ibo	909	13	
	San Blas, Panama: Cuna .	~ 7000	13	
Cystinuria...................	Sweden	385	16	Apparent variation may reflect difficulties in diagnosis
	North America..........	~ 400	17	
	North America..........	63–71	7	
	Australia..............	197	7	
Tyrosinemia type I	Province of Quebec......	68	40	May be panethnic with high frequencies in some genetic isolates
	Czechoslovakia	23	7	
	All other areas	> 1 to 7.5	7	
Maple syrup urine disease.......	Panethnic	2–5	7, 11	–
Homocystinuria...............	Panethnic	0.6–5	7, 11	–
Methylmalonic aciduria	Massachusetts	21	18	–
Sarcosinemia	Massachusetts	3	19	–

subgroups that respond to pharmacological vitamin doses; in some cases a mutation seems to cause the formation of an enzyme with a decreased affinity for its coenzyme. Most of the inherited disorders of amino-acid metabolism occur very rarely; only single cases of some of them are known. Phenylketonuria and histidinemia are relatively frequent (Table 1). Hypothyroidism affects 1 in 4000 newborn infants, but only very few of the cases can be attributed to an inherited disorder of thyroxine synthesis[5]. A relatively high incidence of an inherited disorder of amino-acid metabolism within a circumscribed population may indicate a selection advantage for heterozygotes – as, for example, sickle-cell anemia protects against malaria (page 226). In the case of phenylketonuria, which occurs in approximately 1 in 5500 live births in Ireland and Western Scotland – at a gene frequency of 0.014 – the incidence of spontaneous abortion is far below the norm in the female heterozygotes, which can be interpreted as a selection advantage[6].

If an enzyme in the metabolic sequence is absent, the substrate of the enzyme accumulates and may undergo degradation by alternative pathways. The amino acid – or one or more of its metabolites – often accumulates in the plasma. If a renal threshold exists for such a substance it appears in the urine only when the concentration in the plasma exceeds this threshold. Phenylketonuria, histidinemia and citrullinemia, for example, are classed among these disorders; they are best identified by examining serum or plasma. For other substances, such as, for example, cystathionine and methylmalonic acid, no renal threshold exists; the corresponding metabolic disorders can be detected by urinalysis. In tyrosinase-negative oculocutaneous albinism there is no accumulation of an amino acid or a metabolite. In this disorder monophenol monooxygenase (tyrosinase) is absent from the melanocytes, but in nervous tissue and adrenal medulla tyrosine is oxidized to 3,4-dihydroxy-L-phenylalanine with the aid of tyrosine 3-monooxygenase (tyrosine 3-hydroxylase).

Table 2 *Inborn errors of amino-acid metabolism*

Condition	Defective enzyme or deficiency	Biochemical findings	Clinical features	Treatment	Reference
		Disorders of the metabolism of aromatic amino acids			
Classical phenylketonuria	Phenylalanine 4-monooxygenase (phenylalanine 4-hydroxylase) (complete or almost complete loss of activity)	Elevated phenylalanine level in blood (over 1.2 mmol/L after the first week of life) and in CSF; excretion of phenylpyruvic acid, phenylalanine, N-acetylphenylalanine, 2-hydroxyphenylacetic acid, phenylacetylglutamine as well as phenyllactic acid in the urine	Mental deficiency (progressive deterioration), seizures (in about 25%) and EEG abnormalities (in 90–95%) during the first years of life; rarely epilepsy in adult life; in addition extrapyramidal motor disorders, behavioral disorders, eczema	Diet low in phenylalanine (begin treatment as early as possible)	21–29
Atypical phenylketonuria	Phenylalanine 4-monooxygenase (phenylalanine 4-hydroxylase) (partial loss of activity or structural variant)	Phenylalanine level in blood 0.2–1.2 mmol/L after early childhood	Normal to slightly impaired intelligence	Diet low in protein if needed; in some cases also diet low in phenylalanine in early childhood	22–24, 28
Tetrahydrobiopterin deficiency (nonclassical phenylketonuria; malignant hyperphenylalaninemia)	(a) Dihydropteridine reductase (b) 'Dihydrobiopterin synthetase' (c) GTP cyclohydrolase I	As in classical phenylketonuria; in addition impaired formation of dopamine, norepinephrine and serotonin	As in classical phenylketonuria; in addition neurological disorders, in some cases connected with lack of catecholamines or serotonin; early death if untreated	Diet low in phenylalanine, supplemented with either dopa, carbidopa and 5-hydroxytryptophan, or tetrahydrobiopterin	26–31
Hyperphenylalaninemia with defective transamination	Phenylalanine aminotransferase (?)	With protein-rich diet in early childhood, phenylalanine level in blood up to 1.2 mmol/L and more; no excretion of phenylpyruvic acid and related metabolites in the urine	Probably benign	Diet low in protein	22, 24, 32
Alkaptonuria	Homogentisate 1,2-dioxygenase (homogentisate oxygenase)	Urinary excretion of 2,5-dihydroxyphenylacetic acid (homogentisic acid) (urine turns dark brown in air)	Ochronosis, arthritis, cardiopathy in later life	None known	21, 33, 34
Hereditary tyrosinemia type II (Richner-Hanhart syndrome; possibly several variants)	Cytosol form of tyrosine aminotransferase in the Oregon variant (possibly other enzymes in other variants)	Elevated tyrosine level in blood and CSF; increased excretion of tyrosine as well as 4-hydroxyphenylpyruvic, 4-hydroxyphenyllactic and 4-hydroxyphenylacetic acids in the urine	Photophobia; sometimes corneal ulceration; blisters and hyperkeratosis on palms and soles of feet; slight or moderate mental retardation; no hepatorenal dysfunction	Diet low in phenylalanine and tyrosine	35–37

Table 2   *Inborn errors of amino-acid metabolism (continued)*

Condition	Defective enzyme or deficiency	Biochemical findings	Clinical features	Treatment	Reference
Hereditary tyrosinemia type I (tyrosinosis; inborn hepatorenal dysfunction; several variants)	Fumarylacetoacetase (possibly other enzymes in other variants)	Succinylacetone in blood and urine; elevated tyrosine and, often, methionine levels in blood; increased excretion of tyrosine, of 4-hydroxyphenylpyruvic, 4-hydroxyphenyllactic and 4-hydroxyphenylacetic acids, as well as – by inhibition of porphobilinogen synthase – of 5-aminolevulinic acid, in the urine; generalized aminoaciduria, glucosuria and proteinuria; hypokalemia	Rapidly progressing liver enlargement in the first months of life; hypoprothrombinemia; jaundice; death in early childhood or survival with cirrhosis and hepatorenal dysfunction; often malignant hepatoma; vitamin D-resistant rickets; acidosis	No effective treatment known (restriction of intake of tyrosine and phenylalanine?). Liver transplantation[42]; blood transfusion or bone-marrow transplantation (?)[43]	36–41
Hawkinsinuria	Rearrangement of 4-hydroxyphenylpyruvic acid to homogentisic acid	Excretion of (2-cystein-S-yl-1,4-dihydroxycyclohex-5-en-1-yl)-acetic acid (hawkinsin) in the urine; mild hypertyrosinemia	Failure to thrive; acidosis. Inheritance autosomal dominant	Diet low in protein (breast milk); supplements of ascorbic acid	44
Tyrosinase-negative albinism	Monophenol monooxygenase (tyrosinase)	Lifelong total absence of melanin in skin, hair and eyes including the retina	Photophobia; nystagmus; often practically blind; intense sensitivity to sunlight with tendency to hyperkeratosis and carcinomata of the skin; heterozygotes normal except for transparent iris	None known	13
Tyrosinase-positive albinism (several variants)	Not known; in one variant a deficiency in the transport of tyrosine is probably present	Partial absence of melanin; white or light blond hair, which gradually darkens to blond or red; blue iris sometimes darkens to brown	Less severe than in the tyrosinase-negative form; heterozygotes normal; a variant, Hermansky-Pudlak syndrome, in addition shows hemorrhagic diathesis and an accumulation of ceroid-like material in the RES	None known	13, 100
Hypothyroidism (many variants)	(a) Iodide transport (b) Organification ('thyroid peroxidase' and other components) (c) Coupling of iodotyrosines (?) (d) Synthesis and secretion of thyroglobulin (e) Deiodination of iodotyrosines ('thyroid FMN deiodinase')	Plasma thyroxine level lowered	Goiter, cretinism, skeletal anomalies	Thyroid hormone substitution as soon as possible after birth; if symptoms have already developed, hormone substitution in carefully controlled doses	45
Disorders of histidine metabolism					
Histidinemia	Histidine ammonia-lyase (histidase)	Elevated levels of histidine in blood and CSF; increased excretion of histidine as well as imidazolepyruvic, imidazolelactic and imidazoleacetic acids in the urine	Often benign; sometimes abnormal EEG; rarely mental retardation	Diet low in histidine if necessary	46, 47
Formiminoglutamic aciduria (several variants [?])	Glutamate formiminotransferase; folic acid metabolism in a variant (page 251)	Increased excretion of formiminoglutamic acid in the urine	Rather benign; in some cases abnormal EEG and hematological changes	Folic acid (?)	48

Table 2   *Inborn errors of amino-acid metabolism (continued)*

Condition	Defective enzyme or deficiency	Biochemical findings	Clinical features	Treatment	Reference
Disorders of tryptophan metabolism					
Tryptophanuria	Tryptophan 2,3-dioxygenase (tryptophan pyrrolase) or arylformamidase (formylase)	Elevated levels of tryptophan in blood and urine; variable spectrum of tryptophan metabolites in the urine	Different degrees of mental retardation; dwarfism, cerebellar ataxis and photosensitivity in some cases	None known (nicotinamide?)	49
Xanthurenic aciduria	Kynureninase	Increased excretion of xanthurenic acid, kynurenine and 3-hydroxykynurenine, especially after ingestion of tryptophan	In some cases symptomless, in others mental retardation. Of 18 known patients 15 are female. Possibly inherited as dominant character	Pyridoxine	50
Hydroxykynureninuria	Kynureninase	Increased excretion of xanthurenic acid, 3-hydroxykynurenine and kynurenine in the urine	Slight mental retardation, transitory hepatosplenomegaly, nicotinamide deficiency (1 case)	No effective treatment known (nicotinamide supplement)	51
Disorders of lysine metabolism					
Hyperlysinemia (persistent)	Saccharopine dehydrogenase (NADP+, L-lysine-forming) (lysine-2-oxoglutarate reductase) and saccharopine dehydrogenase (NAD+, L-glutamate-forming)	Plasma lysine level 0.2–1.5 mmol/L; increased excretion of lysine, N$^\varepsilon$-acetyllysine, homocitrulline and homoarginine in the urine	Usually symptomless; in some cases physical and mental retardation, neurological collapse	Diet low in lysine	52, 53
Saccharopinuria (possibly a variant of hyperlysinemia)	Saccharopine dehydrogenase (NAD+, L-glutamate-forming)	Excretion of saccharopine in the urine; lysine and citrulline levels in the blood 4 to 5 times the normal	Slight mental retardation, dwarfism, abnormal EEG	Diet low in lysine	52, 53
Hyperpipecolic acidemia (non-Zellweger type; Zellweger's syndrome, see page 282)	Not known	Pipecolic acid content of blood, tissues and urine 3 to 6 times the normal	By 7 months marked mental and physical retardation; craniofacial dysmorphism; hypotonia. Pupils react sluggishly to light; retinopathy. Hearing impairment; seizures; micronodular cirrhosis. Some hepatocytes vacuolated; hepatic nodules present in some patients. Astrocytes in gray matter swollen and vacuolated with non-lipid storage material. Rarely survival > 3½ years. Peroxisomes present; no renal cysts; no storage of iron	Diet low in protein (efficacy?)	54
2-Aminoadipic aciduria	Not known	Excretion of 2-aminoadipic acid in the urine; 2-aminoadipate level in plasma elevated	Varying degrees of mental retardation	Not described	55
2-Oxoadipic aciduria	Oxidative decarboxylation of 2-oxoadipic acid	Excretion of large quantities of 2-aminoadipic and 2-oxoadipic acids; 2-aminoadipate level in plasma elevated, especially after administration of lysine	Psychomotor and mental retardation to a varying extent	Not described	56
Glutaric aciduria type I	Glutaryl-CoA dehydrogenase	Excretion of glutaric, 3-hydroxyglutaric and glutaconic acids in the urine	Motor retardation, speech disturbance; acidosis in some cases	None known	57, 58

Table 2   *Inborn errors of amino-acid metabolism (continued)*

Condition	Defective enzyme or deficiency	Biochemical findings	Clinical features	Treatment	Reference
		Disorders of the metabolism of branched-chain amino acids			
Hypervalinemia	Valine aminotransferase	Hypervalinemia without ketoaciduria	Mental retardation (1 case)	Diet low in valine	59
Maple syrup urine disease (leucinosis; several variants)	Branched-chain-oxo-acid dehydrogenase (BCOADH) complex responsible for the oxidative decarboxylation of 2-oxoisohexanoic, 2-oxo-3-methyl-valeric and 2-oxoisovaleric acids (residual activity in the intermittent variant)	Increased concentration of leucine, isoleucine, valine and the corresponding oxo acids in plasma and CSF; increased excretion of these amino and oxo acids in the urine	Cerebral degeneration, acidosis, ketosis; usually early death; episodes of ketoacidosis and coma in the intermittent variant	Diet low in leucine, isoleucine and valine as early as possible in the first week of life; peritoneal dialysis in crises; large doses of thiamin used in one very rare variant; high-energy diet	59, 60, 63
Isovaleric acidemia	Isovaleryl-CoA dehydrogenase	Concentration in the plasma and excretion in the urine of isovaleric acid markedly increased in crises (sweaty-foot syndrome); increased excretion of isovalerylglycine and isovalerylcarnitine, and in some cases 3-hydroxyisovaleric acid, in the urine	Ketoacidotic crises with lethargy or fatal coma, especially in the postnatal period; slight mental retardation in survivors	Diet low in leucine; peritoneal dialysis in crises; glycine and/or carnitine doses to increase excretion of conjugates with isovaleric acid	57, 59, 61
3-Hydroxyisobutyryl-CoA hydrolase deficiency	3-Hydroxyisobutyryl-CoA hydrolase	Cysteine and cysteamine conjugates of methylacrylic acid in tissues	Multiple malformations, failure to thrive, death at 3 months (1 case)	None known	62
3-Methylcrotonyl-glycinuria	Methylcrotonoyl-CoA carboxylase	Excretion of 3-methylcrotonylglycine and 3-hydroxyisovaleric acid in the urine	Variable; hypotonia and atrophy of muscles; acidosis in early childhood	Diet low in leucine; biotin-responsive cases seem to be due to multiple carboxylase deficiency (page 251)	59
3-Methyl-3-hydroxy-glutaric acidemia	Hydroxymethylglutaryl-CoA lyase	Urinary excretion of 3-methylglutaconic, 3-methyl-3-hydroxyglutaric, 3-hydroxyisovaleric and 3-methylglutaric acids	Acidosis; life-threatening hypoglucosemia in infancy in some cases	Diet low in leucine	59, 64
2-Methyl-3-hydroxy-butyric aciduria (one form of 'ketotic hyperglycinemia')	Acetyl-CoA acyltransferase (3-keto-thiolase)	Hyperglycinemia; urinary excretion of 2-methyl-3-hydroxybutyric and 2-methylacetoacetic acids, in some cases also of butanone, hexanone and tiglic acid	As in propionic acidemia	Diet low in isoleucine	59, 65
Methylmalonic acidemia (one form of 'ketotic hyperglycinemia')	(a) Apoenzyme of methylmalonyl-CoA mutase *mut⁰*: undetectable activity *mut⁻*: 2–75% activity	Large amounts of methylmalonic acid in the urine; methylmalonic acidemia, hyperglycinemia and hyperammonemia; also butanone and hexanone in the urine	Ketoacidosis (frequently in the first days of life); coma and death in infancy in about 50% of the cases (almost all with mut^0); survivors: muscular hypotonia, developmental disturbances, neutropenia, thrombocytopenia, abnormal EEG	Diet low in leucine, isoleucine, valine, threonine and methionine; administration of carnitine (vitamin B₁₂-responsive cases are dealt with in the chapter on 'Inborn Errors — Metabolism and Transport of Vitamins' [page 252])	66, 69
	(b) Methylmalonyl-CoA epimerase (?)	Large amounts of methylmalonic acid in the urine; methylmalonic acidemia, hyperammonemia; liver homogenate metabolizes (R)-methylmalonyl-CoA, but not the (S) isomer	Ketoacidosis, coma, death in early childhood (1 case)	Diet low in leucine, isoleucine, valine, threonine and methionine	70

Table 2   *Inborn errors of amino-acid metabolism (continued)*

Condition	Defective enzyme or deficiency	Biochemical findings	Clinical features	Treatment	Reference
Propionic acidemia (one form of 'ketotic hyperglycinemia'; several variants)	Propionyl-CoA carboxylase	Hyperglycinemia, hyperpropionatemia, odd-numbered fatty acids in the blood; hyperglycinuria; excretion of 3-hydroxypropionic, methylcitric and tiglic acids as well as of butanone and short-chain acylcarnitines in the urine	Severe ketoacidosis and coma in the first days of life; survivors: IQ below 50, convulsions, EEG disturbances, spasticity, episodes of lethargy and vomiting, neutropenia and thrombopenia	Diet low in leucine, isoleucine, valine, threonine and methionine; administration of carnitine; trial of large biotin supplements (biotin-responsive cases may be due to multiple carboxylase deficiency [page 251])	66–68
		*Disorders of the urea cycle*			
N-Acetylglutamate synthetase deficiency	N-Acetylglutamate synthetase	Hyperammonemia; generalized hyperaminoacidemia	Vomiting, apathy (1 case)	Sodium benzoate during episodes of hyperammonemia; carbamoylglutamate, arginine	71
Hyperammonemia type I (carbamoylphosphate synthase deficiency)	Mitochondrial carbamoyl-phosphate synthase (ammonia)	Extreme hyperammonemia; glutamine level in plasma and CSF elevated; mild hyperglycinemia; excretion of urea at the lower limit of the norm	Vomiting, apathy and flaccidity after protein intake; in some cases excessive irritability; coma and death usually in the postnatal period	Diet low in protein with addition of arginine; supplements of sodium benzoate, sodium phenylacetate and carbamoyl glutamate	72–75
Hyperammonemia type II (ornithine carbamoyltransferase deficiency)	Ornithine carbamoyltransferase (ornithine transcarbamylase)	Hyperammonemia; glutamine level in plasma and CSF elevated; excretion of urea at the lower limit of the norm; excretion of orotic acid in the urine increased; uracil and uridine in the urine	X-linked. Boys die in the postnatal period (enzyme activity in the liver 0 to 0.2% of the norm), but some cases of late onset are known. In some of the girls (enzyme activity in the liver 5–10% of the norm) mental retardation, abnormal EEG, atrophy of the brain, hepatomegaly; onset of symptoms at an age of 2 weeks to 9 years. In some cases mild symptoms in mothers	Diet low in protein with addition of arginine; supplements of sodium benzoate and sodium phenylacetate in episodes of hyperammonemia	72–75
Citrullinemia (argininosuccinate synthase deficiency; several variants)	Argininosuccinate synthase	Citrulline level in plasma 10 to 100 times the normal; usually hyperammonemia; excretion of citrulline and orotic acid in the urine elevated	Mental retardation, epilepsy, vomiting; in the newborn usually lethal; late-onset type occurs mainly in Japan	Diet low in protein with addition of arginine; supplements of sodium benzoate in episodes of hyperammonemia	72–75
Argininosuccinic aciduria (argininosuccinate lyase deficiency)	Argininosuccinate lyase	Excretion of argininosuccinic acid in the urine; ammonia level in blood and CSF elevated	Mental retardation, convulsions, hair anomalies; in the newborn usually lethal	Diet low in protein with addition of arginine; supplements of sodium benzoate (?)	72–75
Hyperargininemia (arginase deficiency)	Arginase	Arginine level in plasma, CSF and urine elevated; variable hyperammonemia; urinary amino-acid pattern somewhat similar to that in cystinuria; increased urinary excretion of orotic acid and monosubstituted guanidine	Convulsions from early infancy; abnormal EEG, spastic diplegia, mental retardation; sometimes hepatomegaly	Diet low in protein (?); supplements of sodium benzoate (?)	72–75
Hyperornithinemia type I (gyrate atrophy of the retina)	Ornithine–oxo-acid aminotransferase	Ornithine level in plasma, CSF and urine elevated	Progressive loss of vision, leading to blindness usually by the 4th decade	Restriction of arginine intake; large doses of pyridoxine; administration of creatine, lysine and/or 2-aminoisobutyric acid (?)	76
Hyperornithinemia type II (HHH syndrome)	Unknown (defective ornithine transport into mitochondria [?])	Hyperornithinemia, hyperammonemia, homocitrullinemia, homocitrullinuria	Episodes of lethargy and coma; mental retardation	Diet low in protein (with addition of arginine or ornithine [?])	76

Table 2   *Inborn errors of amino-acid metabolism (continued)*

Condition	Defective enzyme or deficiency	Biochemical findings	Clinical features	Treatment	Reference
Disorders in glycine, serine and proline metabolism					
Nonketotic hyperglycinemia	Glycine-cleaving system (glycine dehydrogenase[decarboxylating] and aminomethyltransferase)	Glycine level in CSF (up to 30 times the normal) and in serum elevated; large amounts of glycine in the urine	Apathy, spasticity, convulsions, abnormal EEG, hypsarrhythmia; developmental disturbances, often severe mental retardation	Diet low in serine and glycine; supplements of sodium benzoate; in the newborn, exchange transfusion; strychnine; diazepam (all of doubtful efficacy)	77, 78
D-*Glyceric acidemia* (several variants [?])	Not known	D-Glyceric acid in plasma and urine; in some cases hyperglycinemia	Acidosis (1 case) or motor and mental retardation (1 case)	Treatment of acidosis, otherwise none known	79
Oxalosis type I (primary hyperoxaluria type I; glycolic aciduria)	2-Hydroxy-3-oxoadipate synthase (not verified[101])	High excretion of oxalic acid and glycolic acid in the urine; deposition of calcium oxalate crystals in many body tissues	Nephrocalcinosis, urolithiasis, progressive renal insufficiency; death before the age of 20 in over 80%	Pyridoxine up to 1 g/d effective in some cases	80
Oxalosis type II (primary hyperoxaluria type II; L-glyceric aciduria)	Glycerate dehydrogenase	High excretion of oxalic acid and L-glyceric acid in the urine	Nephrocalcinosis, urolithiasis, milder than in type I	No effective treatment is known	80
Hypersarcosinemia (several variants)	Sarcosine dehydrogenase	Hypersarcosinemia, hypersarcosinuria	Probably benign; some cases with mental retardation	None known	81
Ethanolaminosis	Ethanolamine kinase	Increased ethanolamine excretion in the urine; accumulation of ethanolamine in the heart, skeletal muscles and hepatocytes	Cardiomegaly, cerebral dysfunction, developmental disorders; early death	None known	82
Hyperprolinemia type I	Proline dehydrogenase (proline oxidase)	Serum proline level 0.5 to 2.6 mmol/L; increased excretion of proline, hydroxyproline and glycine in the urine	Probably benign; mental retardation in some cases; an association with nephropathy and deafness may be coincidental	Diet low in proline	83
Hyperprolinemia type II	1-Pyrroline-5-carboxylate dehydrogenase	Serum proline level 0.5 to 3.7 mmol/L; pyrroline-5-carboxylate level 10 to 20 times the normal; increased excretion of pyrroline-5-carboxylate, proline, hydroxyproline and glycine in the urine	Mostly mental retardation and convulsions	Diet low in proline (only partially effective)	83, 84
Hydroxyprolinemia	Hydroxyproline dehydrogenase (hydroxyproline oxidase)	Serum hydroxyproline 30 to 50 times the normal; increased excretion of hydroxyproline in the urine	Probably benign; mental retardation is probably coincidental	None known	83
Disorders in the γ-glutamyl cycle					
5-Oxoprolinuria (pyroglutamic aciduria)	Glutathione synthase	Plasma 5-oxoproline level up to 4.5 mmol/L; 5-oxoproline excretion in the urine up to 270 mmol/d; concentrations of some of the free amino acids in erythrocytes up to 100 times the normal, that of glutathione very low	Acidosis (occasionally life-threatening crises); spasticity, ataxia, movement tremor (intention tremor), mental retardation, seizures; hemolytic anemia in early infancy; asymptomatic in some cases	Alkalies; buthionine sulfoximine (?); vitamin E (?)	85
Erythrocyte glutathione synthetase deficiency	Glutathione synthase active but unstable; only erythrocytes affected	Low glutathione levels in erythrocytes; no 5-oxoprolinuria	Well compensated hemolytic anemia	None necessary	85, 86

Table 2   *Inborn errors of amino-acid metabolism (continued)*

Condition	Defective enzyme or deficiency	Biochemical findings	Clinical features	Treatment	Reference
5-Oxoprolinase deficiency	5-Oxoprolinase (ATP-hydrolyzing)	5-Oxoproline concentration in plasma about 9 times the normal; 5-oxoproline excretion in the urine up to 71 mmol/d	Possibly benign (enterocolitis and urolithiasis in 2 cases, mild mental retardation in 1 case)	None described	85, 87
γ-Glutamylcysteine synthetase deficiency	Glutamate–cysteine ligase (γ-glutamylcysteine synthetase)	Very low glutathione levels in the erythrocytes; generalized aminoaciduria	Hemolytic anemia (often mild); in 3rd or 4th decade: spinocerebellar degeneration, peripheral neuropathy, myopathy, behavioral abnormalities	None described	85
Glutathionuria	γ-Glutamyltransferase (glutamyl transpeptidase)	Increased glutathione concentration in the plasma; glutathione excretion in the urine up to 1000 times the normal	Mental retardation (2 cases)	None described	85
Disorders in the metabolism of sulfur-containing amino acids					
Cystinosis	Defective transport out of lysosomes	Deposition of cystine in the reticuloendothelial system; increased excretion of amino acids, glucose, phosphate and protein in the urine; impaired concentration of urine	Dwarfism, photophobia, renal acidosis, vitamin D-resistant rickets; death before puberty (in type I); slow progressive renal deficiency in juvenile form (in type II); 'benign' (nonrenal) variant with corneal lesions in adults (in type III)	Palliative: potassium salts, alkalies, vitamin D Diet low in cystine and methionine; administration of cysteamine or phosphocysteamine; kidney transplantation	88, 89
Hypermethioninemia	Methionine adenosyltransferase	Plasma methionine level 10 to 20 times the normal; increased excretion of methionine and 2-oxo-4-(methylthio)butyric acid in the urine	Benign (?); growth retardation in some cases	Diet low in methionine	90, 91
Homocysteinemia (homocystinuria; several variants [?])	Cystathionine β-synthase	Homocysteine (up to 2 mmol/L), in the plasma; homocystine and homocysteine-cysteine disulfide in the urine; hypermethioninemia in early childhood	Tall stature and arachnodactyly; lens dislocation, retinal defects; malar flush, life-threatening arterial and venous thromboses; varying degrees of mental retardation	Diet low in methionine and high in cystine. A genetic subgroup (about 50% of cases) responds to pyridoxine; betaine for nonresponders (?)	91, 92
Cystathioninuria	Cystathionine γ-lyase (γ-cystathionase)	Elevated cystathionine level in plasma and tissues; increased cystathionine excretion in the urine, especially after methionine administration	Probably benign; in some cases mental retardation (chance association?)	A genetic subgroup responds to pyridoxine	91
3-Mercaptolactatecysteine disulfiduria	3-Mercaptopyruvate sulfurtransferase (absent in erythrocytes)	Increased excretion of 3-mercaptolactate-cysteine disulfide, 3-mercaptolactate and mercaptoacetate in the urine	Mental retardation in some cases (chance association?)	None known	93, 94
Sulfituria (sulfite oxidase deficiency)	Sulfite dehydrogenase (sulfite oxidase)	Urine contains sulfite, thiosulfate, S-sulfocysteine, but only little sulfate (for cases with xanthinuria see page 257)	Severe brain damage, lens dislocation, mental deficiency; death in postnatal period possible	Diet low in sulfur-containing amino acids	95

Table 2   *Inborn errors of amino-acid metabolism (continued)*

Condition	Defective enzyme or deficiency	Biochemical findings	Clinical features	Treatment	Reference
Disorders of β-alanine, 4-aminobutyric acid, carnosine and homocarnosine metabolism					
Hyper-β-alaninemia	β-Alanine aminotransferase (may be identical with 4-aminobutyrate aminotransferase)	High levels of β-alanine and 4-aminobutyric acid in blood, CSF, urine and tissues; elevated excretion of taurine and 3-aminoisobutyric acid in the urine; high levels of carnosine in brain and muscle	Lethargic from birth, uncontrollable seizures from 6 weeks, extreme somnolence, growth retardation, death at 4 months, small brain (1 case)	None known (high pyridoxine dosage [?])	96
GABA transaminase deficiency (4-aminobutyrate aminotransferase deficiency)	4-Aminobutyrate aminotransferase	Levels of 4-aminobutyric acid, homocarnosine and β-alanine in CSF 3 to 6 times the normal	Profound psychomotor retardation; high-pitched cry; gigantism; leukodystrophy	None known	97
4-Hydroxybutyric aciduria	Succinate-semialdehyde dehydrogenase	4-Hydroxy- and 3,4-dihydroxybutyric acids and succinate semialdehyde in urine, blood and CSF	Marked hypotonia; ataxia; mental retardation; seizures in some cases	None known	98
Homocarnosinosis	Homocarnosinase (absent in brain)	Homocarnosine level in CSF 20 to 30 times the normal; in frontal cortex 4 times the normal; excretion of carnosine in the urine 20 to 35 times the normal	Variable (4 cases in 1 family): no neurological symptoms (1 case) at 69 years; progressive spastic paraplegia (onset at 6–29 years); mental retardation; retinopathy and atrophy of cortical gyri (3 cases)	None known	96, 99
Carnosinuria	Aminoacylhistidine dipeptidase (carnosinase) (depressed activity in scrum)	High urinary carnosine excretion on a meat-free diet; serum carnosine level variable; no urinary Nπ-methylhistidine after feeding anserine	Variable: in some cases myoclonic seizures and psychomotor retardation in the first year, death or survival with spasticity and severe mental retardation, demyelination, neuron loss, muscle cell changes; others apparently normal; one patient normal until meat added to diet at 14 months	Avoidance of meat (?); enzyme infusion (?)	93

References

[1] SCRIVER and ROSENBERG, *Amino Acid Metabolism and Its Disorders*, Saunders, Philadelphia, 1973.

[2] WELLNER and MEISTER, *Ann. Rev. Biochem.*, **50**, 911 (1981).

[3] NYHAN, W.L., *Abnormalities of Amino Acid Metabolism in Clinical Medicine*, Appleton, Norwalk, Conn., 1984; NYHAN, W.L. (Ed.), *Heritable Disorders of Amino Acid Metabolism; Patterns of Clinical Expression and Genetic Variation*, Wiley, New York, 1974.

[4] STANBURY et al., *The Metabolic Basis of Inherited Disease*, 5th ed., Part 3, McGraw-Hill, New York, 1983, page 229.

[5] FISHER, D.A., *J. Pediat.*, **102**, 653 (1983).

[6] WOOLF et al., *Ann. hum. Genet.*, **38**, 461 (1975); WOOLF, L.I., *Amer. J. hum. Genet.*, in press (1986).

[7] Review article, *Hum. Genet.*, **30**, 273 (1975).

[8] LINDSAY, G., in HAMILTON and HUDSON (Eds.), *Errors of Phenylalanine, Thyroxine and Testosterone Metabolism*, Livingstone, Edinburgh, 1970, page 8.

[9] COHEN et al., *Pediatrics*, **32**, 1069 (1963).

[10] TANAKA et al., *Jap. J. hum. Genet.*, **6**, 65 (1961).

[11] TADA et al., *Europ. J. Pediat.*, **142**, 204 (1984).

[12] DANKS et al., *Pediat. Res.*, **13**, 1150 (1979).

[13] WITKOP et al., in STANBURY et al., *The Metabolic Basis of Inherited Disease*, 5th ed., McGraw-Hill, New York, 1983, page 301.

[14] FROGATT, P., *Ann. hum. Genet.*, **24**, 213 (1960).

[15] BARNICOT, N.A., *Ann. Eugen. (Lond.)*, **17**, 38 (1952).

[16] BOSTROM and TOTTIE, *Acta paediat. (Uppsala)*, **48**, 345 (1959).

[17] LEWIS, H.B., *Ann. intern. Med.*, **6**, 183 (1932).

[18] COULOMBE et al., *Pediatrics*, **67**, 26 (1981).

[19] LEVY et al., *Pediatrics*, **74**, 509 (1984).

[20] DHONDT, J.L., *J. Pediat.*, **104**, 501 (1984).

[21] WOOLF, L.I., *Advanc. clin. Chem.*, **6**, 97 (1963).

[22] KOCH et al., in NYHAN, W.L. (Ed.), *Heritable Disorders of Amino Acid Metabolism: Patterns of Clinical Expression and Genetic Variation*, Wiley, New York, 1974, page 109; RAMPINI, S., *Schweiz. med. Wschr.*, **103**, 537 (1973).

[23] LYMAN, F.L. (Ed.), *Phenylketonuria*, Thomas, Springfield, 1963.

[24] BICKEL et al. (Eds.), *Phenylketonuria and Some Other Inborn Errors of Amino Acid Metabolism*, Thieme, Stuttgart, 1971.

[25] KNOX, W.E., in STANBURY et al. (Eds.), *The Metabolic Basis of Inherited Disease*, 3rd ed., McGraw-Hill, New York, 1972, page 266.

[26] TOURIAN and SIDBURY, in STANBURY et al., *The Metabolic Basis of Inherited Disease*, 5th ed., McGraw-Hill, New York, 1983, page 270.

[27] SCRIVER and CLOW, *New Engl. J. Med.*, **303**, 1336 and 1394 (1980).

[28] KAUFMAN, S., *Advanc. hum. Genet.*, **13**, 217 (1983).

[29] GÜTTLER, F., *Acta paediat. scand.*, **73**, 705 (1984).

[30] MATALON, R., *J. Pediat.*, **104**, 579 (1984); MCINNES et al., *J. clin. Invest.*, **73**, 458 (1984).

[31] DHONDT et al., *J. Pediat.*, **106**, 954 (1985); NIEDERWIESER et al., *Europ. J. Pediat.*, **141**, 208 (1984).

[32] BLAU et al., *Clin. chim. Acta*, **132**, 43 (1983).

[33] MCKUSICK, V.A., *Heritable Disorders of Connective Tissue*, 4th ed., Mosby, St. Louis, 1972, page 455.

[34] LA DU, B.N., in STANBURY et al. (Eds.), *The Metabolic Basis of Inherited Disease*, 4th ed., McGraw-Hill, New York, 1978, page 268.

[35] GOLDSMITH, L.A., *Arch. intern. Med.*, **145**, 1697 (1985); MEDES, G., in GJESSING, L.R. (Ed.), *Symposium on Tyrosinosis*, Universitetsforlaget, Oslo, 1966, page 13.

[36] BUIST et al., in NYHAN, W.L. (Ed.), *Heritable Disorders of Amino Acid Metabolism: Patterns of Clinical Expression and Genetic Variation*, Wiley, New York, 1974, page 160; GOODWIN, B.L., *Tyrosine Catabolism*, Oxford University Press, Oxford, 1972; WOOLF, L.I., in GJESSING, L.R. (Ed.), *Symposium on Tyrosinosis*, Universitetsforlaget, Oslo, 1966, pages 24, 82 and 129.

[37] GOLDSMITH, L. A., in STANBURY et al., *The Metabolic Basis of Inherited Disease*, 5th ed., McGraw-Hill, New York, 1983, page 287.

[38] SCRIVER et al., *Canad. med. Ass. J.*, **97**, 1045 (1967); WOOLF, L. I., *Proc. roy. Soc. Med.*, **59**, 814 (1966).

[39] GJESSING, L. R. (Ed.), *Symposium on Tyrosinosis*, Universitetsforlaget, Oslo, 1966; WOOLF, L. I., *Renal Tubular Dysfunction*, Thomas, Springfield, 1966, page 171.

[40] GRENIER et al., *Clin. chim. Acta*, **123**, 93 (1982).

[41] BERGER et al., *Clin. chim. Acta*, **134**, 129 (1983); KVITTINGEN et al., *Clin. chim. Acta*, **115**, 311 (1981).

[42] STARZL et al., *J. Pediat.*, **106**, 604 (1985).

[43] HOLME et al., *Lancet*, **1**, 527 (1985).

[44] WILCKEN et al., *New Engl. J. Med.*, **305**, 865 (1981); NIEDERWIESER et al., *Clin. chim. Acta*, **76**, 345 (1977).

[45] STANBURY and DUMONT, in STANBURY et al., *The Metabolic Basis of Inherited Disease*, 5th ed., McGraw-Hill, New York, 1983, page 231; LEVER et al., *Endocrine Rev.*, **4**, 213 (1983).

[46] LA DU, B. N., in STANBURY et al. (Eds.), *The Metabolic Basis of Inherited Disease*, 4th ed., McGraw-Hill, New York, 1978, page 317.

[47] TADA et al., *J. Pediat.*, **101**, 562 (1982); KURODA et al., *J. Pediat.*, **97**, 269 (1980).

[48] ROWE, P. B., in STANBURY et al., *The Metabolic Basis of Inherited Disease*, 5th ed., McGraw-Hill, New York, 1983, page 498.

[49] SNEDDEN et al., *Clin. chim. Acta*, **131**, 247 (1983); WONG et al., *Pediat. Res.*, **10**, 725 (1976); TADA et al., *Tohoku J. exp. Med.*, **80**, 118 (1963).

[50] TADA et al., *Tohoku J. exp. Med.*, **95**, 107 (1968).

[51] KOMROWER and WESTAL, *Amer. J. Dis. Child.*, **113**, 77 (1967); KOMROWER et al., *Arch. Dis. Childh.*, **39**, 250 (1964).

[52] GHADIMI H., in STANBURY et al. (Eds.), *The Metabolic Basis of Inherited Disease*, 4th ed., McGraw-Hill, New York, 1978, page 387.

[53] CEDERBAUM et al., *J. Pediat.*, **95**, 234 (1979); DANCIS et al., *Amer. J. hum. Genet.*, **31**, 290 (1979).

[54] CHALLA et al., *J. Neuropath. exp. Neurol.*, **42**, 627 (1983); BURTON et al., *J. Pediat.*, **99**, 729 (1981).

[55] FISCHER et al., *Hum. Genet.*, **24**, 265 (1974); LORMANS and LOWENTHAL, *Clin. chim. Acta*, **57**, 97 (1974); BREMER et al., *Pediat. Res.*, **8**, 904 (1967).

[56] PRZYREMBEL et al., *Clin. chim. Acta*, **58**, 257 (1975); WILSON et al., *Pediat. Res.*, **9**, 522 (1975).

[57] GREGERSEN, N., *Scand. J. clin. Lab. Invest.*, **45**, suppl. 174 (1985).

[58] HYMAN and TANAKA, *J. clin. Invest.*, **73**, 778 (1984).

[59] TANAKA and ROSENBERG, in STANBURY et al., *The Metabolic Basis of Inherited Disease*, 5th ed., McGraw-Hill, New York, 1983, page 440.

[60] DANNER et al., *J. clin. Invest.*, **75**, 858 (1985); DIGEORGE et al., *New Engl. J. Med.*, **307**, 1492 (1982).

[61] ROE et al., *J. clin. Invest.*, **74**, 2290 (1984).

[62] BROWN et al., *Pediatrics*, **70**, 532 (1982).

[63] SNYDERMAN et al., *Pediat. Res.*, **18**, 851 (1984).

[64] HAGBERG et al., *Clin. chim. Acta*, **134**, 59 (1983); GIBSON et al., *Clin. chim. Acta*, **126**, 171 (1982).

[65] MIDDLETON and BARTLETT, *Clin. chim. Acta*, **128**, 291 (1983).

[66] WOLFF et al., *Lancet*, **1**, 289 (1986); ROSENBERG, L. E., in STANBURY et al., *The Metabolic Basis of Inherited Disease*, 5th ed., McGraw-Hill, New York, 1983, page 474.

[67] WOLF et al., *J. Pediat.*, **99**, 835 (1981); BERGSTRØM et al., *Scand. J. clin. Lab. Invest.*, **41**, 117 (1981).

[68] DI DONATO et al., *Clin. chim. Acta*, **139**, 13 (1984); ROE and BOHAN, *Lancet*, **1**, 1411 (1982).

[69] MATSUI et al., *New Engl. J. Med.*, **308**, 857 (1983).

[70] KANG et al., *Pediat. Res.*, **6**, 875 (1972).

[71] BACHMANN et al., *New Engl. J. Med.*, **304**, 543 (1981).

[72] SHIH, V. E., in STANBURY et al. (Eds.), *The Metabolic Basis of Inherited Disease*, 4th ed., McGraw-Hill, New York, 1978, page 362.

[73] WALSER, M., in STANBURY et al., *The Metabolic Basis of Inherited Disease*, 5th ed., McGraw-Hill, New York, 1983, page 402.

[74] LOWENTHAL et al. (Eds.), *Urea Cycle Diseases*, Plenum, New York, 1982; Symposium, *Pediatrics*, **68**, 271 and 446 (1981).

[75] BRUSILOW, S. W., *J. clin. Invest.*, **74**, 2144 (1984); BRUSILOW et al., *New Engl. J. Med.*, **310**, 1630 (1984); BATSHAW et al., *New Engl. J. Med.*, **306**, 1387 (1982).

[76] METOKI and HOMMES, *J. inherited metab. Dis.*, **7**, 9 (1984); VALLE and SIMELL, in STANBURY et al., *The Metabolic Basis of Inherited Disease*, 5th ed., McGraw-Hill, New York, 1983, page 382; TADA et al., *J. inherited metab. Dis.*, **6**, Suppl. 2, 105 (1983).

[77] NYHAN, W. L., in STANBURY et al., *The Metabolic Basis of Inherited Disease*, 5th ed., McGraw-Hill, New York, 1983, page 561.

[78] MATALON et al., *Pediatrics*, **71**, 581 (1983); HIRAGA et al., *J. clin. Invest.*, **68**, 525 (1981).

[79] BRANDT et al., *Acta paediat. scand.*, **65**, 17 (1976); WADMAN et al., *Clin. chim. Acta*, **71**, 477 (1976); BRANDT et al., *Brit. med. J.*, **4**, 344 (1974).

[80] WILLIAMS and SMITH, in STANBURY et al., *The Metabolic Basis of Inherited Disease*, 5th ed., McGraw-Hill, New York, 1983, page 204.

[81] GERRITSEN and WAISMAN, in STANBURY et al. (Eds.), *The Metabolic Basis of Inherited Disease*, 4th ed., McGraw-Hill, New York, 1978, page 514.

[82] VIETOR et al., *Europ. J. Pediat.*, **126**, 61 (1977).

[83] SCRIVER et al., in STANBURY et al., *The Metabolic Basis of Inherited Disease*, 5th ed., McGraw-Hill, New York, 1983, page 360.

[84] FLEMING et al., *Metabolism*, **33**, 739 (1984).

[85] MEISTER, A., in STANBURY et al., *The Metabolic Basis of Inherited Disease*, 5th ed., McGraw-Hill, New York, 1983, page 348.

[86] BEUTLER et al., *J. clin. Invest.*, **77**, 38 (1986).

[87] LARSSON et al., *Acta paediat. scand.*, **70**, 301 (1981).

[88] SCHNEIDER and SCHULMAN, in STANBURY et al., *The Metabolic Basis of Inherited Disease*, 5th ed., McGraw-Hill, New York, 1983, page 1844.

[89] SCHNEIDER, J. A., *New Engl. J. Med.*, **313**, 1473 (1985); GAHL et al., *Science*, **217**, 1263 (1982).

[90] GAULL et al., *J. Pediat.*, **98**, 734 (1981).

[91] MUDD and LEVY, in STANBURY et al., *The Metabolic Basis of Inherited Disease*, 5th ed., McGraw-Hill, New York, 1983, page 522.

[92] WILCKEN et al., *New Engl. J. Med.*, **309**, 448 (1983); PRZYREMBEL, H., *Ergebn. inn. Med. Kinderheilk.*, **49**, 77 (1982); SMOLIN et al., *J. Pediat.*, **99**, 467 (1981).

[93] CRAWHALL, J. C., in STANBURY et al. (Eds.), *The Metabolic Basis of Inherited Disease*, 4th ed., McGraw-Hill, New York, 1978, page 504.

[94] HANNESTAD et al., *Biochem. Med.*, **26**, 106 (1981).

[95] JOHNSON and RAJAGOPALAN, *Ciba Found. Symp.*, NS 72, 119 (1980); SHIH et al., *New Engl. J. Med.*, **297**, 1022 (1977).

[96] SCRIVER et al., in STANBURY et al., *The Metabolic Basis of Inherited Disease*, 5th ed., McGraw-Hill, New York, 1983, page 570.

[97] JAEKEN et al., *Neuropediatrics*, **15**, 165 (1984).

[98] RATING et al., *J. inherited metab. Dis.*, **7**, Suppl. 1, 90 (1984); DIVRY et al., *Clin. chim. Acta*, **129**, 303 (1983); GIBSON et al., *Clin. chim. Acta*, **133**, 33 (1983).

[99] LENNEY et al., *Clin. chim. Acta*, **132**, 157 (1983); LUNDE et al., *J. Neurochem.*, **38**, 242 (1982).

[100] DEPINHO and KAPLAN, *Medicine (Baltimore)*, **64**, 192 (1985).

[101] DANPURE et al., *Clin. Sci.*, **70**, 417 (1986).

Various heritable disorders of connective tissues are due to or associated with inborn defects of enzymes concerned in collagen synthesis and/or specific gene mutations that alter the structure of the procollagen molecule[1-9] (information on the biosynthesis and structure of collagen is given on pages 191–196).

The Ehlers-Danlos syndromes are a group of diseases usually divided into 11 types, though many of these can be subdivided and many patients cannot be assigned to one or other of the recognized types. Type X has features consistent with type II[10], but it has been suggested that a defect in glycosylation of fibronectin occurs in this disorder[7]. In Table 1, Ehlers-Danlos syndromes I to XI are listed

together with two other forms[11]. 'Cutis laxa' is the name given to a group of diseases that, strictly speaking, involve a defect of elastin rather than collagen metabolism, but it seems appropriate to include cutis laxa in Table 1. The X-linked form of cutis laxa is identical with Ehlers-Danlos syndrome IX.

Osteogenesis imperfecta is usually divided into 4 types, but, again, these can be subdivided (Table 2).

Some forms of osteogenesis imperfecta help to explain why heterozygotes are severely affected in some autosomal dominant conditions[1]. A common group of mutations consists of an insertion or deletion of repetitive exon DNA sequences leading to the synthesis of

Table 1   *Ehlers-Danlos syndromes*

Type	Inheritance	Biochemical defect	Clinical features
I (gravis)	Autosomal dominant	Unknown	Soft, velvety skin; marked hyperextensibility and fragility of skin; easy bruising; 'cigarette paper' scars; joint hypermobility; hernias; often prematurity associated with premature rupture of fetal membranes
II (mitis)	Autosomal dominant	Unknown; in 1 family, C-terminal deletion in α1(I) chains	As in type I, but less severe
III (benign, hypermobile)	Autosomal dominant	Unknown	Marked generalized joint hypermobility; dislocations common; skin soft; other changes minimal; tendency to osteoarthrosis in middle age
IV (arterial, ecchymotic; acrogeria; at least 5 forms)			
IV A	Autosomal dominant	Deficient synthesis of type III collagen due to defective transcription/translation of *pro-α(III)* gene; some type III collagen is synthesized	Thin, semitransparent, fragile skin; extreme bruisability; arterial rupture, aortic dissection or bowel perforation as common causes of death; extreme friability of vessel walls, etc.; characteristic, 'prematurely aged' appearance of face and hands; uterine rupture near term in pregnancy; life expectancy 30 to 50 years
IV B	Autosomal recessive	As in type IV A, but no type III collagen is synthesized	As in type IV A; life expectancy 15–30 years
IV C	Autosomal dominant	Pro-α1(III) chains synthesized at nearly normal rate, but failure to secrete procollagen type III into extracellular space (heterosaccharide modification defect?)	As in type IV A; dermal fibroblasts show massive engorgement with type III procollagen
IV D	Autosomal recessive	Unknown; normal amounts of procollagen type III synthesized and secreted by cultured fibroblasts	As in type IV A
IV E	Autosomal dominant	Normal amounts of procollagen type III synthesized and secreted, but half the pro-α1(III) chains have an insertion of about 20 amino acids leading to rapid degradation	As in type IV A
V	X-linked recessive	Unknown; most have normal protein-lysine 6-oxidase (an early report of deficient 'lysyl oxidase' may refer to a variant of type IX)	Resembles type II; extreme skin hyperextensibility; only males affected
VI (hydroxylysine deficient; at least 3 forms)	Autosomal recessive	Procollagen-lysine,2-oxoglutarate 5-dioxygenase (lysine hydroxylase) deficiency in many, normal in some cases; altered cross-link formation; lysine hydroxylation normal in bone and cartilage collagens	Blindness: microcornea, glaucoma, retinal detachment, severe scleral fragility; marked kyphoscoliosis; hyperextensible, fragile skin and 'cigarette paper' scars; deafness
VII (arthrochalasis multiplex congenita; 2 forms)			
VII A	Autosomal recessive	Deficiency of proteinase cleaving N-terminal extension peptide from pro-α2(I) chain	Joint hypermobility; multiple dislocations; floppy infants; soft and velvety skin, but not particularly fragile; may involve bruisability and wound-healing problems
VII B	Autosomal dominant	Amino-acid substitution at the N-terminal cleavage site of pro-α2(I) chain decreases conversion of procollagen to type I collagen	Joint hypermobility; multiple dislocations; floppy infants; soft but nonfragile skin

Table 1   *Ehlers-Danlos syndromes (continued)*

Type	Inheritance	Biochemical defect	Clinical features
VIII........... (periodontitis)	Autosomal dominant	Unknown	Marked skin fragility; scarring; generalized severe periodontitis
IX................. (occipital horn; cutis laxa, X-linked)	X-linked recessive	Copper metabolism; protein-lysine 6-oxidase deficiency; defective cross-linking of collagen and elastin	Only males affected; skeletal and urogenital tract abnormalities, especially bladder diverticula; bilateral inguinal hernias; 'cigarette paper' scars (sometimes minimal); mild mental retardation in some cases; hypermobility of some joints; varicose veins
Beasley-Cohen type........ (mental retardation)	Probably autosomal recessive	Unknown	Hyperextensible joints; bilateral inguinal hernias (in males); mental retardation; impaired hearing; moderately hyperelastic skin; slow healing of wounds; prominent ears; narrow face (midface deficiency)
X.................. (fibronectin)	Autosomal recessive	Fibronectin present, but does not act normally	Hyperextensible joints and skin; easy bruising; 'cigarette paper' scars; asymptomatic mitral valve prolapse; platelet–collagen interaction reduced unless fibronectin added, but no bleeding diathesis
XI................. (familial joint laxity)	Autosomal dominant	Unknown	Hypermobility of joints; recurrent dislocation of shoulder, hip, patella
–..................	Unknown	Unknown	Marked joint hypermobility; velvety, hyperextensible skin; severe progressive para-acinar emphysema; seizures; cerebral heterotopias with peculiar vascularization; aneurysms of Valsalva's sinus; death, aged 30 years, of myocardial infarction
Cutis laxa (several types) (a).................	Autosomal dominant	Abnormality of elastin; primary defect unknown	Skin is not hyperextensible but hangs loosely in folds, as though too large for the body, giving aged appearance
(b).................	Autosomal recessive	As in autosomal dominant form	As for autosomal dominant form, but also aortic dilation, pulmonary artery stenosis and progressive emphysema
(c).................	X-linked recessive	See type IX	See type IX

a longer or shorter pro-α1(I) polypeptide than normal but with normal end-sequences[12, 13]. The polypeptide chain thus synthesized combines with a normal pro-α1(I) chain, coded on the normal allele, and a pro-α2(I) chain forming disulfide bonds at the extension peptides of the resulting trimer. The trimer is, however, unable to twist into the normal triple-helical configuration and undergoes rapid intracellular degradation. If the normal allele produces half of the total pro-α1(I) chains and at least half of these are rendered ineffective by combining with mutant pro-α1(I), then the fibroblast produces not more than 25% of the normal amount of type I collagen. This has been termed 'protein suicide'[13]. A similar explanation may apply to some other autosomal dominant conditions.

Marfan's syndrome, a generalized disorder of connective tissue, too, seems to be heterogeneous, at least 4 types being recognized: (a) asthenic and (b) non-asthenic syndrome, (c) contractural arachnodactyly and (d) Marfanoid hypermobility syndrome. Marfan's syndrome is a dominantly inherited condition characterized by excessive length of the long bones, arachnodactyly, kyphoscoliosis, loose and hyperextensible joints. There is usually ectopia lentis, sometimes with retinal detachment. Vascular walls are weak and aortic aneurysms are common. The type I collagen in the aorta, for instance, is abnormally soluble. In some patients an insertion into or partial duplication of the α2(I) gene leads to collagen that will not readily form cross-links, presumably because the molecules in the fibrils are out of register, the mutant α2(I) peptide containing about 20 additional amino-acid residues. Some patients have a decreased elastin content in the aorta.

Homocysteinemia and Menkes' disease are considered on pages 238 and 287, respectively; in both conditions there are defects in collagen[7] – in homocysteinemia, homocysteine binds reversibly to aldehyde groups formed by protein-lysine 6-oxidase (lysyl oxidase), hindering cross-linking, whereas in Menkes' disease lack of copper decreases the activity of protein-lysine 6-oxidase. Several defects of collagen synthesis or breakdown have been reported in the group of diseases known as 'epidermolysis bullosa'[7]; it is not clear how these findings can be related to other features.

A high proportion of patients with congenital berry aneurysms of the circle of Willi have a deficiency of type III collagen. Such aneurysms are a frequent cause of strokes and are responsible, e.g., for 4000 deaths per year in the UK[14].

Iminodipeptiduria[15], inherited as an autosomal recessive character, is caused by the absence of proline dipeptidase (prolidase). Large amounts of dipeptides, most containing proline – and the rest hydroxyproline – at the C terminus, are excreted in the urine, these peptides being mainly derived from the catabolism of collagen. Proline concentration in the blood is at the lower limit of normal, and collagen synthesis may be hindered or the excess iminodipeptides present may cause hypercatabolism of type I collagen. Patients present with multiple chronic infections (sinusitis, otitis media, bacterial and viral skin infections, etc.) resulting from a disturbance of complement component C1q, (hepato)splenomegaly and dermatitis since early infancy. The skin is thick with lymphedema and, in some cases, shows multiple scars, fragility, and/or ulcerations. Some patients have lax joints. The disease resembles lathyrism. All have unusual facies and mild to severe physical and mental retardation. Administration of ascorbic acid in high dosage is reported to help in some cases.

Hypophosphatasia[16–19] is characterized by bone disease of severity varying with the age of onset, absent or very low levels of alkaline phosphatase in serum and all tissues, and urinary excretion of large amounts of O-phosphoethanolamine and inorganic pyrophosphate (Table 3). These two substances are also present in plasma in abnormally high concentration. Leukocytes of heterozygotes for the autosomal recessive forms of hypophosphatasia have approximately half the normal alkaline phosphatase activity. In some juvenile cases the sclerae are blue. Sometimes the serum alkaline phosphatase activity is apparently normal by the usual tests, but the enzyme present has a decreased affinity for phosphoethanolamine ('pseudohypophospha-

Table 2 *Osteogenesis imperfecta*

Type	Inheritance	Biochemical defect	Clinical features
I A	Autosomal dominant	Defective $\alpha 1(I)$ gene; pro-$\alpha 1(I)$ chain and collagen production half of normal	Bone fragility, particularly in childhood; blue sclerae; hearing loss in ~20%; Wormian bones in skull sutures; vertebrae biconcave
I B	Autosomal dominant	–	As in I A, but accompanied by dentinogenesis imperfecta
I C . . . . (type V)	Autosomal dominant	Amount of collagen normal, but half of the $\alpha 2(I)$ chains are abnormal	As in I A, but of greater severity; short stature and deformity
II . . . . (lethal perinatal disorder; probably heterogeneous)	Autosomal recessive or sporadic	Decreased secretion of type I procollagen; type I collagen formed is of abnormal structure; several variants: deletions or insertions in $\alpha 1(I)$ or $\alpha 2(I)$ genes; substitution of cysteine for glycine in $\alpha 1(I)$ chain	Intrauterine growth retardation; broad, crumpled femurs and beaded ribs; dark blue sclerae; perinatal death
III . . . . (severe; progressive deforming; probably heterogeneous)	Autosomal recessive	In some cases, delayed secretion of type I procollagen which contains excessive mannose residues in the C-terminal peptide, in others no $\alpha 2(I)$ chain synthesis	Fractures at birth; progressive limb deformation and kyphoscoliosis; normal sclerae and hearing; dwarfing
IV A	Autosomal dominant	Defective $\alpha 2$ gene; ratio of $\alpha 1(I)/\alpha 2(I)$ chains increased; homozygotes have only $[\alpha 1(I)]_3$	Similar to type III, severity variable; white sclerae
IV B	Autosomal dominant		As in type IV A, but also dentinogenesis imperfecta
—	Unknown	Abnormally low levels of 5-hydroxylysine in collagens of bone and cartilage	Multiple intrauterine fractures, severe bending of long bones and poor ossification of the skull

Table 3 *Other inherited metabolic disorders of bone*

Condition	Inheritance	Defective enzyme or system	Biochemical findings	Clinical features	Reference
Hypophosphatasia (a) Prenatal, congenital and infantile forms	Autosomal recessive	Alkaline phosphatase activity absent from plasma and tissues	High plasma and urinary O-phosphoethanolamine and pyrophosphate levels; hypercalcemia	Defective mineralization of skeleton; sometimes death in utero; in other cases severe rickets and poor ossification from birth, usually fatal by 18 months. Treatment by plasma infusions (?)	16–18
(b) Childhood form	Autosomal recessive	As in perinatal form	As in perinatal form	Severe vitamin D-resistant rickets; craniostenosis; blue sclerae; premature loss of teeth	16, 17
(c) Adult form	Often autosomal recessive, others possibly sporadic or autosomal dominant	Alkaline phosphatase activity usually low, in some cases apparently present in plasma (sometimes intermittently), but not acting on normal substrates	As in perinatal form	Age at onset varies from late childhood to 6th decade; usually osteomalacia of varying onset, severity and rate of progression; spontaneous fractures; premature loss of teeth; often a history of rickets	16, 17, 19
Osteopetrosis (a) Malignant form	Autosomal recessive	Osteoclasts do not mature or resorb bone	Organic and mineral components of bone do not turn over at normal rate	From birth, bones usually brittle or chalky and soft, sometimes very hard; often bone-marrow space reduced: pancytopenia; frequent spontaneous fractures; optic atrophy common; usually death in 1st decade. Bone-marrow transplantation curative	1, 20, 21
(b) Benign form	Autosomal dominant	Osteoclast function defective	As in malignant form	Fractures; osteomyelitis, especially of the mandible; skeletal radiopacity; life expectancy reduced	1
(c) With carbonate dehydratase II deficiency	Autosomal recessive	Osteoclast function defective; renal tubular function defective (?)	As in malignant form; no detectable activity of carbonate dehydratase II in erythrocytes	Heterogeneous; spontaneous fractures; mental retardation; cerebral calcification; proximal and distal renal tubular acidosis; failure to thrive or short stature	22

tasia'). Rare individuals excrete large amounts of O-phosphoethanol-amine without any other clinical or biochemical feature of hypophosphatasia. Normally osteoblasts secrete extracellular vesicles containing alkaline phosphatase which hydrolyzes inorganic pyrophosphate and organic phosphates such as O-phosphoethanol-amine. The resulting inorganic phosphate reacts with calcium to form apatite crystals within the vesicle, leading to mineralization of bone. In individuals with hypophosphatasia this process is defective. Other forms of vitamin D-resistant rickets are described in the chapters on 'Inborn Errors – Renal and Intestinal Transport' (pages 227–230) and 'Inborn Errors – Metabolism and Transport of Vitamins' (pages 251–254).

Osteopetrosis[1, 20, 21] ('marble bones', Albers-Schönberg disease) occurs in a severe, often fatal, autosomal recessive form, in a relatively benign autosomal dominant type and in a form associated with carbonate dehydratase II deficiency[22]. Similar diseases are known in animals and are associated with high levels of calcitonin. The disease is apparently caused by lack of active osteoclasts – cells derived from the bone marrow or spleen that resorb bone. Bone-marrow transplantation is curative where it can be employed[20]. Calcitriol (1α,25-dihydroxycholecalciferol) stimulates osteoclast maturation and, in 1 patient, produced biochemical and histological evidence of remission of the disease[21].

Many other inborn errors of bone are described by McKusick[1]. Bone remodeling, i.e. resorption of old bone by osteoclasts and formation of new bone by osteoblasts, is stimulated by parathyroid hormone (PTH) acting with 1α,25-dihydroxyvitamin D. PTH also controls plasma calcium and phosphate concentrations by stimulating net renal tubular reabsorption of calcium and excretion of phosphate. PTH stimulates the kidney to form 1α,25-dihydroxyvitamin D, and this, in turn, increases calcium flux across the basolateral membrane of the intestinal mucosal cell, thus participating in calcium homeostasis. Hypoparathyroidism, idiopathic or surgical, leads to hypocalcemia and skeletal disease.

Pseudohypoparathyroidism and pseudo-pseudohypoparathyroidism (page 227) are inborn errors of renal tubular transport showing close similarities to hypoparathyroidism.

References

[1] McKusick, V. A., *Mendelian Inheritance in Man*, 6th ed., Johns Hopkins University Press, Baltimore, 1983; McKusick, V. A., *Heritable Disorders of Connective Tissue*, 4th ed., Mosby, St. Louis, 1972.

[2] Byers et al., *Hum. Path.*, 13, 89 (1982); Bornstein and Byers, in Bondy and Rosenberg, *Metabolic Control and Disease*, 8th ed., Saunders, Philadelphia, 1980, page 1089.

[3] Hollister et al., *Advanc. hum. Genet.*, 12, 1 (1982); Hollister, D. W., *Pediat. Clin. N. Amer.*, 25, 575 (1978).

[4] Kirsch, E., *Enzyme (Basel)*, 27, 239 (1982); Ihme et al., *Europ. J. clin. Invest.*, 13, 357 (1983).

[5] Pinnell and Murad, in Stanbury et al., *The Metabolic Basis of Inherited Disease*, 5th ed., McGraw-Hill, New York, 1983, page 1425.

[6] Francis and Duskin, *Trends biochem. Sci.*, 8, 231 (1983); Smith and Francis, *Recent Advanc. Endocr. Metab.*, 2, 211 (1982); Byers et al., *Coll. relat. Res.*, 1, 475 (1981); Byers et al., *Hum. Genet.*, 47, 141 (1979).

[7] Pyeritz et al., *Amer. J. med. Genet.*, 19, 607 (1984); Pyeritz, R. E., *Progr. med. Genet.*, NS 5, 191 (1983).

[8] Prockop, D. J., *J. clin. Invest.*, 75, 783 (1985); Prockop and Kivirikko, *New Engl. J. Med.*, 311, 376 (1984); Peltonen et al., *Biochemistry*, 22, 6156 (1983).

[9] Cheah, K. S., *Biochem. J.*, 229, 287 (1985).

[10] Hammerschmidt et al., *J. Amer. med. Ass.*, 248, 2487 (1982); Arneson et al., *J. Amer. med. Ass.*, 244, 144 (1980).

[11] Cupo et al., *Amer. J. Med.*, 71, 1051 (1981).

[12] Shapiro and Rowe, *Ann. intern. Med.*, 99, 700 (1983).

[13] Prockop, D. J., *Amer. J. hum. Genet.*, 36, 499 (1984).

[14] Pope et al., *J. roy. Soc. Med.*, 76, 1050 (1983).

[15] Myara et al., *Life Sci.*, 34, 1985 (1984); Der Kaloustian et al., *Dermatologica (Basel)*, 164, 293 (1982).

[16] Rasmussen, H., in Stanbury et al., *The Metabolic Basis of Inherited Disease*, 5th ed., McGraw-Hill, New York, 1983, page 1497.

[17] Fallon et al., *Medicine (Baltimore)*, 63, 12 (1984).

[18] Whyte et al., *J. Pediat.*, 108, 82 (1986); Albeggiani and Cataldo, *Helv. paediat. Acta*, 37, 49 (1982).

[19] Eberle et al., *Klin. Wschr.*, 62, 371 (1984); Whyte et al., *Amer. J. Med.*, 72, 631 (1982); Weinstein and Whyte, *Arch. intern. Med.*, 141, 727 (1981).

[20] Coccia, P. F., *New Engl. J. Med.*, 310, 456 (1984); Sieff et al., *Lancet*, 1, 437 (1983); Sorrell et al., *Amer. J. Med.*, 70, 1280 (1981); Coccia et al., *New Engl. J. Med.*, 302, 701 (1980).

[21] Key et al., *New Engl. J. Med.*, 310, 409 (1984).

[22] Sly et al., *New Engl. J. Med.*, 313, 139 (1985); Maren, T. H., *New Engl. J. Med.*, 313, 179 (1985).

Glycogen metabolism

The glycogenoses are the result of either the synthesis of a glycogen with an abnormal structure, a defect in the breakdown of glycogen stored in the tissues, or the failure of glycogen synthesis. Originally 4 clinical pictures of the glycogenoses were differentiated and CORI and designated by the numbers I to IV. Today over 11 types are known, and various numbering systems have been used to designate them (the numbering system given in Table 1 is that of HUG[2]). Some types have been subdivided into subtypes, e.g. 6 subtypes of type III glycogenosis (III A to III F)[1]. Because of the different use of numbers by different authors, on the one hand, and the proliferation of 'subtypes', on the other, some workers prefer to abandon all numbering systems and name each condition according to the enzyme deficiency. Of type I glycogen storage disease 3 variants have been differentiated. All are characterized by a much diminished or absent function of glucose-6-phosphatase. It has been suggested[3] that type Ia glycogenosis results from the congenital absence of the catalytic unit of this enzyme. With types Ib and Ic the catalytic unit remains intact, but the microsomal membrane transport function specific for glucose-6-phosphatase is absent in type Ib, and aberrant function of a second transporter specific for orthophosphate, inorganic pyrophosphate and carbamoyl phosphate is involved in the type Ic condition. The distinctions between these types are related to the degree of detergent-dependence of the several glucose-6-phosphatase activities. Additional cases with the classic symptoms of type I glycogen storage disease have been grouped under the terms 'pseudo-type I glycogenosis' and 'type I *bis*glycogenosis'[4]. In type XI all enzyme activities measured are normal[2,50]. Furthermore, no enzyme deficiency was found in 7 male members of one family with glycogen storage disease inherited in an X-linked recessive pattern[46].

Type 0 glycogenosis is also referred to as 'aglycogenosis' because little or no glycogen synthesis takes place in the liver, while glycogen synthesis in muscle is normal; opinions differ as to the nature of the primary defect in aglycogenosis[1,2,5].

Another classification of the glycogenoses relates to the organ most affected. If the liver is primarily involved (glycogen content up to 20 g in 100 g compared to a normal content of 1–5 g in 100 g), such symptoms as hepatomegaly, hypoglucosemia, acidosis and growth disturbance are most prominent. If the skeletal muscles are primarily involved (glycogen content up to 15 g in 100 g compared to a normal content of 0.2–1.5 g in 100 g), the symptoms are muscle spasms and easy fatigability. If the heart is involved – primarily in a subtype of Pompe's disease – (glycogen content up to 10 g in 100 g compared to a normal content of 0.2–1.5 g in 100 g), cardiomegaly is found in early childhood, leading in most cases to heart failure.

The glycogenoses are relatively rare; the incidence of all the glycogen storage diseases combined is about 1:40000[6]. Mild glycogenoses are probably the most frequent. Types I and II are highly lethal forms of glycogenosis, with a frequency at birth of about 1:200000 each[6]. In glucose-6-phosphatase deficiency (type I glycogenosis) the enzyme activity is almost always below 5–10% of normal; prenatal diagnosis is possible by fetal liver biopsy at 21 weeks' gestation. In some cases – usually recognized only in adult life – the enzyme deficiency may be partial[7]. α-1,4-Glucosidase deficiency (type II glycogenosis) is a lysosomal storage disease, and treatment can only consist in a replacement of the enzyme[8]. Type IIa glycogenosis – a fatal disease of infancy – has been diagnosed prenatally by electron microscopy of uncultured amniotic fluid cells[9]. Treatment of the myopathy in type V glycogenosis is unsatisfactory; an adequate amino-acid supply as fuel for the muscle, supplied by a protein-rich diet, results in an improvement of muscle function[10]. Occasionally in the selfsame patient or within the same family two enzyme deficiencies can occur, perhaps by secondary inhibition of one enzyme, for example glucose-6-phosphatase deficiency *and* amylo-1,6-glucosidase deficiency, or glucose-6-phosphatase deficiency *and* glucose-6-phosphate dehydrogenase deficiency. This means that, as a matter of principle, all the enzymes involved in glycogen metabolism ought to be determined for the diagnosis.

Mono- and disaccharide metabolism

In all the defects of mono-, di- and oligosaccharide metabolism listed in Table 2, apart from hereditary sensitivity to leucine, autosomal recessive inheritance is certain or probable. One series of these defects is caused by the absence or inactivity, in the 'brush border' of the intestinal mucosa, of enzymes that break down lactose, sucrose or limit dextrin[11,12]. The deficiency of β-galactosidase (lactase) seems to be due to a depression or absence of the lactase protein, accounted for by a repression of the regulatory mechanism controlling the structural gene function; the absence of sucrose α-glucosidase (sucrase) could be due to a nonsense mutation of the structural gene or the complete repression of the regulatory mechanism[12]. The consequences of these enzyme defects are osmotic diarrhea and flatus. However, most cases of intolerance to carbohydrates are secondary – to mucosal damage for instance.

Alactasia is a rare, congenital, often fatal, inherited disorder[13]. Late-onset lactase deficiency, however, is the normal state in adult mammals and most adult humans; notable exceptions (people with so-called 'lactase persistence', which is inherited as an autosomal dominant character[14,15]) are groups of north European origin, groups from the west and northwest of the Indian subcontinent, and certain groups of pastoral tradition in Arabian countries and Africa. Among all other groups tested around the world, including Bantus, Thais, Chinese, Greenland Eskimos and Australian Aborigines, adult hypolactasia prevails[16] (see also page 298). A sucrose–limit dextrin malabsorption is frequently found in Eskimos[17] (sucrase and oligo-1,6-glucosidase [isomaltase] form a single hybrid molecule with 2 nonidentical subunits). The form of infantile lactose intolerance with lactosuria does not seem to be due to an enzyme deficiency in the intestinal mucosa[13].

UDPglucose–hexose-1-phosphate uridylyltransferase (galactose-1-phosphate uridyltransferase) occurs in several variants. In the classical form of galactosemia as well as in the Negro and Rennes variants, enzyme activity is about 7% of normal or less, and the conversion of galactose to glucose is blocked. The accumulated galactose 1-phosphate has a toxic effect due to inhibition of phosphoglucomutase and other enzymes. In the Duarte variant – with 50% enzyme activity – there are no galactosemic symptoms. Galactosemia is rare; a worldwide frequency of 1:62000 has been calculated[20]. Deficiency of UDPglucose 4-epimerase may be as common as classical galactosemia[21]; clinically it varies from the asymptomatic[21] to the life-threatening[22]. Galactokinase deficiency is rarer; in Austria a frequency of 1:168000 has been found[20]. Double heterozygosity for Duarte variant and transferase deficiency galactosemia, on the other hand, is quite frequent; an incidence of 1:3750 has been reported from Switzerland[23].

The enzyme deficient in hereditary fructose intolerance is the cytosolic isoenzyme B of fructose-bisphosphate aldolase (aldolase B), which is almost exclusively expressed in liver, kidney and intestine. The defect seems to be due to the synthesis of a functionally and structurally modified enzyme protein that results from a restricted mutation[27]. The accumulated fructose 1-phosphate probably inhibits phosphorylase *a* and, hence, glycogenolysis, with severe hypoglucosemia as a consequence. The true incidence of fructose intolerance is not known; it has been estimated to be 1:20000 in Switzerland[25]. As regards fructose-bisphosphatase deficiency, 38 cases from 25 families had been reported up to 1983[25], while its incidence is unknown. Since essential fructosuria is benign, there are no available data on its frequency.

The congenital lactacidoses form a heterogeneous group of inborn errors which are mainly concerned with gluconeogenesis and the electron transfer system. Hyperlactatemia has been found to occur in the following enzyme deficiencies:

Glucose-6-phosphatase (Table 1)
Fructose-bisphosphatase (Table 2)
Phospho*enol*pyruvate carboxykinase (Table 2)
Pyruvate carboxylase (Table 2)
Pyruvate dehydrogenase (Table 2)
Multiple carboxylase (page 251)
Thiamin pyrophosphokinase
NADH dehydrogenase (ubiquinone)
Succinate dehydrogenase (ubiquinone)
Ubiquinol–cytochrome-*c* reductase } (Table 2, page 256)
Cytochrome-*c* oxidase
H+-transporting ATP synthase
Acyl-CoA dehydrogenase

The complexity of the enzymes involved in pyruvate metabolism makes it difficult to diagnose these disorders, and the symptoms vary from case to case[29–31]. Up to 1985, 15 cases of isolated pyruvate carboxylase deficiency had been reported[36]. The isolated defect is debilitating and incurable, but when expressed together with methylcrotonoyl-CoA carboxylase and propionyl-CoA carboxylase deficiency, it is curable by the administration of biotin (page 251). The pyruvate dehydrogenase complex is made up of a sequence of 3 catalytic enzymes: pyruvate decarboxylase, dihydrolipoamide acetyltransferase and dihydrolipoamide dehydrogenase; a specific kinase inactivates the decarboxylase, and the phosphate group introduced by the kinase may be removed by a specific phosphatase. Deficiency of the kinase has not yet been described, whereas deficiencies of all the other enzymes have been observed[29]. Up to 1983, more than 50 cases of deficiency of the pyruvate dehydrogenase complex had been reported[32]. Depending on the type of defect, a well-considered diet may lead to some improvement[32, 37].

Erythrocyte enzymopathies

Hereditary defects are known for 11 of the 13 glycolytic enzymes[38, 39] (5 rather well described defects are listed in Table 3). Most of the defects are accompanied by nonspherocytic hemolytic anemia, moderate splenomegaly and, in some cases, jaundice that is manifested within the first 24 hours after birth. It is assumed that all these defects cause a reduction of the ATP content and hence a shortening of the life span of the erythrocytes, even though no reliable relationship exists between the degree of loss of activity of an enzyme and the changes in concentration of the metabolites as well as the extent of the clinical disorder[38, 39].

With the exception of pyruvate kinase deficiency, defects of glycolytic enzymes are rare. The number of known homozygotes with pyruvate kinase deficiency is above 300, the incidence being about 1 in 40000 births[39]. Pyruvate kinase deficiency is a heterogeneous molecular disorder with many enzyme variants, several of which show a decreased affinity for the substrate. Homozygotes (or, more often, double heterozygotes) for the defect have an enzyme activity of 5–20% of normal. The symptomatology extends from fully compensated nonspherocytic hemolytic anemia to severe hemolysis, needing repeated transfusions and splenectomy. The manifestations of nonspherocytic hemolytic anemia can appear between earliest infancy and adulthood and usually become milder with time. Increased pyruvate kinase activity has been found in the few cases of 'high ATP syndrome', which is characterized by an increased ATP content of the erythrocytes and polycythemia; the condition seems to be inherited as an autosomal dominant trait[40]. Only 3 cases of hemolytic anemia due to fructose-bisphosphate aldolase deficiency had been reported up to 1985[48]; genetic heterogeneity has been suggested[38]. There are conflicting reports on bisphosphoglycerate mutase deficiency; while in 2 cases severe hemolytic anemia was found[38], the case in which the enzyme defect has been best characterized shows no hemolysis and no clinical abnormality apart from increased oxygen affinity of the hemoglobin and a modest erythrocytosis[41]. A defect of another glycolytic enzyme – 6-phosphofructokinase – causes type VII glycogenosis with muscle involvement and can lead to nonspherocytic hemolytic anemia (Table 1); 24 cases had been reported up to 1985[48]. A case of phosphoglycerate kinase deficiency displayed episodes of rhabdomyolysis, but no signs of hemolysis[42].

Glycolysis is of importance for the production not only of the energy-rich ATP, but also of NADH, which is necessary for the reduction of methemoglobin and is made available by the glyceraldehyde-3-phosphate dehydrogenase reaction. Lack of a specific NADH-dependent methemoglobin reductase (cytochrome-b_5 reductase) leads to methemoglobinemia[43]. Several types of this defect have been reported[49].

About 5–10% of glucose 6-phosphate is broken down not in the course of glycolysis but via the pentose phosphate cycle (page 134)[44], in which the glucose-6-phosphate dehydrogenase (G-6-PD) reaction provides NADPH necessary for the reduction of oxidized glutathione. Both a deficiency of G-6-PD and a deficiency of enzymes of the γ-glutamyl cycle (page 154) can cause nonspherocytic hemolytic anemia. G-6-PD deficiency is one of the most common inherited disorders, with a gene frequency of 11% among black Americans and over 100 million people affected worldwide[45]. G-6-PD deficiency occurs most frequently in people from Africa, the Mediterranean area, the Near East and Middle East, Southeast Asia, China and Australasia, and in their descendants, but occasional cases occur also in Northern Europe, for instance. Over 150 variants of G-6-PD had been described by 1985[48], but some of these may be identical[44]. One variant leads to increased enzyme activity, 14 variants lead to normal activity and the remainder to a moderate or severe loss of enzyme activity. Of this last group, about one-third cause nonspherocytic hemolytic anemia in males (hemizygotes), even in the absence of a drug, etc.; about one-third (mild G-6-PD deficiency, enzyme activity 10–60% of normal) have no ill effects except under stress, e.g. after exposure to certain drugs, such as primaquine or sulfonamides, or to chemicals such as aniline derivatives or naphthalene, or following an infection or in diabetes mellitus; males with the remaining variants (severe G-6-PD deficiency, favism, enzyme activity below 10% of normal) are asymptomatic in adult life, but hemolytic crises are induced by a broader group of drugs and chemicals, fava beans (*Vicia faba*) or their pollen, infections, etc., and neonatal icterus occurs in G-6-PD deficient infants of several Mediterranean and oriental populations. The gene coding for G-6-PD is on the X chromosome. Heterozygotes are generally unaffected or mildly affected; however, apart from X-chromosome inactivation (Lyonization), the gene frequency in some populations is high enough for there to be an appreciable number of female homozygotes who are at least as severely affected as male hemizygotes for the relevant allele. The normal G-6-PD molecule has 495 amino-acid residues; it has been found that some variants have a single amino-acid substitution, the resulting molecule displaying lower stability, lower enzyme activity, increased susceptibility to inhibitors or a lower rate of biosynthesis.

Hemolytic anemia, moreover, may be associated with glutathione synthase deficiency (page 237) and deficiency of some enzymes of purine and pyrimidine metabolism (page 258).

Table 1   *Inborn errors of glycogen metabolism[1, 2]*

Condition	Type of glycogenosis	Biochemical findings	Clinical features Treatment	Inheritance
Glucose-6-phosphatase deficiency (von Gierke's glycogen storage disease; hepatorenal glycogenosis)	Ia Ib Ic (see page 245)	Accumulation of normal glycogen in liver and kidney; hyperuratemia	Hepatomegaly; hypoglucosemia (sometimes asymptomatic) and lactacidosis; retardation of growth and bone age, etc.; bleeding tendency; tendency to develop gout, nephropathy and hepatoma in adult life. Frequent meals to avoid hypoglucosemia (if needed, glucose intragastrically during the night); portacaval shunt	Autosomal recessive
α-1,4-Glucosidase (pH 4.0) deficiency (acid maltase deficiency; generalized glycogenosis; Pompe's disease)	IIa	Accumulation of normal glycogen in lysosomes of all organs	Cardiomegaly with death in the first year of life, or muscle hypotonia and neurological symptoms with death in the 2nd year of life; practically no survivors. Experiments on treatment with α-glucosidase (α-1,4-glucosidase)	Autosomal recessive
	IIb	Accumulation of normal glycogen in lysosomes of the muscles	Muscle weakness with onset in early childhood; death in adolescence	Autosomal recessive
	IIc	Little or no glycogen accumulation	Onset of muscle weakness in the 3rd to 5th decade of life	Autosomal recessive
Amylo-1,6-glucosidase (debrancher) deficiency (limit dextrinosis; Forbe's disease; Cori's disease)	III A to III F	Accumulation of abnormal, highly branched, short-chain glycogen in liver and, in some subtypes, in skeletal and heart muscle	Hepatomegaly in childhood; symptoms of hypoglucosemia; usually far less severe than von Gierke's disease; no growth retardation. Treatment, if necessary, as for von Gierke's disease	Autosomal recessive

Table 1   *Inborn errors of glycogen metabolism[1,2] (continued)*

Condition	Type of glycogenosis	Biochemical findings	Clinical features Treatment	Inheritance
Deficiency of 1,4-α-glucan-branching enzyme (Andersen's disease; amylopectinosis)	IV	Generalized low to normal levels of abnormally structured glycogen with long chains and few branch points	Hepatosplenomegaly; cirrhosis of the liver; neurologic dysfunction; death in the first 3 years of life	Autosomal recessive
Muscle phosphorylase deficiency (McArdle's syndrome)	V	Moderate accumulation of normal glycogen in skeletal muscle; lowered blood lactate and pyruvate levels in physical activity	Generalized myasthenia and, after exercise, myalgia which become progressively worse; myoglobinuria and kidney failure in later stages. Avoid heavy muscular work	Autosomal recessive
Liver phosphorylase deficiency (Hers' disease)	VI	Lowered activity of total liver phosphorylase (phosphorylase-activating system intact); accumulation of normal glycogen in liver	Asymptomatic hepatomegaly and slight growth retardation	–
Muscle phosphofructokinase deficiency (Tarui's disease)	VII	6-Phosphofructokinase activity in muscle absent or considerably reduced, in erythrocytes about 50% of normal; accumulation of normal glycogen, as well as glucose 6-phosphate and fructose 6-phosphate, in muscle; low level of muscle fructose 1,6-bisphosphate	Generalized myasthenia and myalgia after exercise; occasionally myoglobinuria; shortened life span of erythrocytes; reticulocytosis	Autosomal recessive
Inactive liver phosphorylase (Hug)	VIII	Liver phosphorylase is in the inactive form, but the phosphorylase-activating system is intact. The cause of the defect is unknown. Accumulation of glycogen in the α form in liver and central nervous system	Hepatomegaly; progressive degeneration of the central nervous system; death in childhood	–
Liver phosphorylase kinase deficiency (Hug)	IXa, IXb	Failure to activate phosphorylase in liver and leukocytes; accumulation of normal glycogen in liver	Marked hepatomegaly; no splenomegaly; no hypoglucosemia or acidosis; good prognosis	IXa: autosomal recessive IXb: X-linked recessive
Deficiency of cAMP-dependent protein kinase (Hug) (phosphorylase *b* kinase kinase deficiency)	X	Accumulation of normal glycogen in liver and muscle	Hepatomegaly; at 6 years mild myalgia; prognosis probably good	–
–	XI	Glycogen deposited in liver (and sometimes kidney), not in muscle; tendency for acidosis; no rise in blood glucose after i.v. glucagon; aminoaciduria (generalized), glucosuria, phosphaturia, hyperlipidemia; no enzyme defect identified; abnormal galactose metabolism	Marked hepatomegaly; Fanconi syndrome stunted growth; vitamin D-resistant rickets. High doses of vitamin D and oral phosphates cure the rickets	–
Phosphoglucomutase deficiency (Thomson)	–	Accumulation of normal glycogen in muscle	Similar to type V	–
Aglycogenosis (glycogen synthase deficiency)	0	Enzyme defect in the liver, but not in blood cells or muscle; no synthesis of glycogen in the liver	Symptoms of hypoglucosemia and hyperketonemia when food is unavailable; hyperglucosemia after administering carbohydrates	–

Table 2   *Inherited disorders of mono- and disaccharide metabolism*

Condition	Defective enzyme	Biochemical findings	Clinical features	Treatment	Reference
Alactasia	β-Galactosidase (lactase) of the intestinal mucosa (lifelong)	Failure of lactose hydrolysis to occur in the small intestine	Diarrhea, failure to gain body mass (manifested in infancy); life-threatening at times	Avoidance of lactose	[11–13]
Primary, late-onset lactase deficiency	β-Galactosidase (lactase) of the intestinal mucosa	Failure of lactose hydrolysis to occur in the small intestine; onset at age 1–5 years	Symptomless or colic attacks, flatulence, diarrhea	Avoidance of lactose	[11–13, 15]

Table 2   *Inherited disorders of mono- and disaccharide metabolism (continued)*

Condition	Defective enzyme	Biochemical findings	Clinical features	Treatment	Reference
Primary sucrase–isomaltase deficiency (sucrase–limit dextrinase deficiency)	Sucrose α-glucosidase (sucrase) and oligo-1,6-glucosidase (isomaltase, limit dextrinase) of the intestinal mucosa	Sucrose and 1,6-α-dextrin are not hydrolyzed in the intestine	Diarrhea after intake of sucrose, less severe after starch (manifestation from the first months of life onwards)	Avoidance of sucrose; diet low in starch	11, 12, 15
Galactosuria (galactose diabetes)	Galactokinase	Galactosuria, galactitoluria	Cataracts; possibly neurologic disease; possibly pseudotumor cerebri	Galactose-free diet from the first days of life	18, 19
Galactosemia	UDPglucose–hexose-1-phosphate uridylyltransferase (galactose-1-phosphate uridyltransferase)	Concentration of galactose and galactose 1-phosphate in tissues and body fluids increased	Failure to thrive; vomiting and diarrhea; sometimes hemolytic crises, severe liver damage, cataracts, mental deficiency, renal tubular dysfunction; often early death	Galactose-free diet	18, 19
UDPglucose-4-epimerase deficiency	UDPglucose 4-epimerase (UDPgalactose 4-epimerase)	Normal activity of the enzyme in the liver and in fibroblast cultures; activity absent (intermediate in heterozygotes) in erythrocytes and leukocytes	Benign	Regular consumption of milk	18, 19
Pentosuria	L-Xylulose reductase (NADP-specific xylitol oxidoreductase)	10–25 mmol/d L-xylulose in the urine	Benign	None needed	24
Fructose intolerance	Isoenzyme B of fructose-bisphosphate aldolase (aldolase B)	Fructosemia, fructosuria and hypoglucosemia after intake or infusion of fructose; intracellular accumulation of fructose 1-phosphate; hyperuratemia	Symptoms of hypoglucosemia, often severe; hepatomegaly; renal tubular dysfunction; intraocular bleeding	Avoidance of fructose, fructose-containing sugars, sorbitol and fruit	25, 26
Fructosuria	Ketohexokinase	Fructosemia and fructosuria after intake of fructose	Benign (no symptoms of hypoglucosemia after intake of fructose)	None needed	25, 26
Fructose-bisphosphatase deficiency	Fructose-bisphosphatase (hexosediphosphatase)	Lactacidosis; gluconeogenesis severely impaired; fasting hypoglucosemia	Symptoms of acidosis and hypoglucosemia	Carbohydrate-rich diet with the exclusion of fructose, fructose-containing sugars and sorbitol	25, 26
Hereditary leucine-sensitive hypoglucosemia	–	Hypoglucosemia, intensified by leucine or protein intake, due to release of insulin	Symptoms of hypoglucosemia; mental deficiency of varying degrees; sometimes symptomless	Protein only with carbohydrate supplements	28
Phosphoenolpyruvate carboxykinase deficiency	Phosphoenolpyruvate carboxykinase (GTP)	Hypoglucosemia, possibly mild hyperlactatemia and hyperalaninemia; deposition of fat in liver and kidneys	Symptoms of hypoglucosemia	None known	29
Isolated pyruvate carboxylase deficiency	Pyruvate carboxylase	Increased levels of lactate, pyruvate, 3-hydroxybutyrate and alanine in blood; increased urinary excretion of lactate and alanine; in some cases fasting hypoglucosemia	Age of onset of symptoms varies considerably; symptoms of acidosis, in some cases of progressive neurodegenerative disturbance (Leigh's subacute necrotizing encephalopathy); retarded development, seizures, ataxia, muscular hypotonia; death in infancy or early childhood	None known	29, 32, 33
Pyruvate dehydrogenase deficiency	Pyruvate dehydrogenase complex or one of its components	Similar to those in pyruvate carboxylase deficiency; when combined with 2-oxoglutarate dehydrogenase deficiency, increased urinary excretion of 2-oxoglutarate	Similar to those in pyruvate carboxylase deficiency, but neurological symptoms predominate	Some respond to a fat-rich diet, some to thiamin. In a case of dihydrolipoamide dehydrogenase deficiency, oral lipoic acid was of help[35]	29, 32, 34

Table 3 *Nonspherocytic hemolytic anemia due to erythrocyte enzymopathies*

Defective enzyme	Biochemical findings	Clinical features	Treatment	Frequency Inheritance	Reference
Hexokinase	Reduction of enzyme activity in erythrocytes and reticulocytes to 24–60% of normal	Hemolytic anemia, reticulocytosis; other cases with familial panmyelopathy of the Fanconi type	Splenectomy (moderate effectiveness)	14 cases up to 1985 Autosomal recessive	38, 39, 47, 48
Glucose-6-phosphate isomerase	Reduction of enzyme activity in erythrocytes to 15–25% of normal; enzyme deficiency also in leukocytes and platelets	Generally hemolytic anemia; some cases with neonatal jaundice	Splenectomy (moderate effectiveness)	45 cases up to 1985 Autosomal recessive	38, 39, 48
Triose-phosphate isomerase	Reduction of enzyme activity in erythrocytes to 10% of normal; enzyme deficiency also in leukocytes and muscle tissue; intracellular accumulation of glycerone 3-phosphate (dihydroxyacetone phosphate)	Jaundice within the first 24 hours of life, severe hemolytic anemia; in most cases death within the first 5 years of life due to ventricular fibrillation or heart failure; progressive neurologic deterioration, progressive spasticity; neuromuscular disorders; dementia	Splenectomy (?)	15 cases up to 1983 Autosomal recessive	38, 39, 48
Phosphoglycerate kinase	Reduction of enzyme activity in erythrocytes to 5 to 30% of normal; enzyme defect also in the leukocytes; single amino-acid substitution in the polypeptide chain has been documented in 4 variants	♂: severe hemolytic anemia with crises; reticulocytosis; slight mental retardation ♀: normal, with the exception of a few cases of mild chronic hemolytic anemia	♂: splenectomy; blood transfusions in crises ♀: none needed	11 cases up to 1983 X-linked recessive	38, 39, 48
Pyruvate kinase (several variants)	Homozygotes have 5 to 20% of the normal enzyme activity in the erythrocytes, and heterozygotes about 50%	Hemolytic anemia varying from severe neonatal forms to freedom from symptoms in adults depending on alleles; cases of death rare, except in one severe form; reticulocytosis; moderate splenomegaly	Blood transfusion if necessary; splenectomy	Over 300 cases up to 1985 Autosomal recessive	38, 39, 48
Glucose-6-phosphate dehydrogenase (many variants)	Moderate to severe loss of enzyme activity in many variants of the enzyme; reduced glutathione content mainly in older erythrocytes; NADP/NADPH ratio increased; increased formation of methemoglobin	♂: some variants with severe hemolytic crises as a reaction to certain substances and to fava beans (*Vicia faba*), neonatal jaundice, otherwise normal; other variants show chronic nonspherocytic hemolytic anemia, mostly mild ♀ (heterozygotes): mostly normal or mild hemolysis with varying reaction to certain substances	Avoidance of any substance that can trigger hemolysis in glucose-6-phosphate dehydrogenase deficiency, as well as all contact with fava beans (including pollen)	See text X-linked recessive	44, 48

References

[1] HOWELL and WILLIAMS, in STANBURY et al., *The Metabolic Basis of Inherited Disease*, 5th ed., McGraw-Hill, New York, 1983, page 141; BURMAN et al. (Eds.), *Inherited Disorders of Carbohydrate Metabolism*, section 6: Glycogen storage diseases, MTP Press, Lancaster, 1980, page 287.

[2] HUG, G., in BURMAN et al. (Eds.), *Inherited Disorders of Carbohydrate Metabolism*, MTP Press, Lancaster, 1980, page 327.

[3] NORDLIE and SUKALSKI, *Trends biochem. Sci.*, **11**, 85 (1986).

[4] HUE, L., *Advanc. Enzymol.*, **52**, 249 (1981).

[5] AYNSLEY-GREEN, A., in RANDLE et al. (Eds.), *Carbohydrate Metabolism and Its Disorders*, Volume 3, Academic Press, London, 1981, page 139.

[6] HUIJING, F., *Physiol. Rev.*, **55**, 609 (1975).

[7] STAMM and WEBB, *Arch. intern. Med.*, **135**, 1107 (1975).

[8] POZNANSKY and SINGH, in CRAWFORD et al. (Eds.), *Advances in the Treatment of Inborn Errors of Metabolism*, Wiley, Chichester, 1982, page 161; TYRRELL et al., *Brit. med. J.*, **2**, 88 (1976).

[9] HUG et al., *New Engl. J. Med.*, **310**, 1018 (1984).

[10] SLONIM and GOANS, *New Engl. J. Med.*, **312**, 355 (1985); LAYZER, R. B., *New Engl. J. Med.*, **312**, 370 (1985).

[11] HARRIES and MULLER, in BURMAN et al. (Eds.), *Inherited Disorders of Carbohydrate Metabolism*, MTP Press, Lancaster, 1980, page 21; McNEISH and HARRAN, in BURMAN et al. (Eds.), *Inherited Disorders of Carbohydrate Metabolism*, MTP Press, Lancaster, 1980, page 39.

[12] GRAY, G. M., in STANBURY et al., *The Metabolic Basis of Inherited Disease*, 5th ed., McGraw-Hill, New York, 1983, page 1729.

[13] HOLZEL, A., in SCHWIEGK, H. (Ed.), *Handbuch der inneren Medizin*, 5th ed., Volume 7, Part 1, Springer, Berlin, 1974, page 121.

[14] DAHLQVIST, A., *Postgrad. med. J.*, **53**, Suppl. 2, 57 (1977).

[15] SEMENZA, G., in RANDLE et al. (Eds.), *Carbohydrate Metabolism and Its Disorders*, Volume 3, Academic Press, London, 1981, page 425; KOLDOVSKÝ, O., in RANDLE et al. (Eds.), *Carbohydrate Metabolism and Its Disorders*, Volume 3, Academic Press, London, 1981, page 481.

[16] BRAND et al., *Amer. J. clin. Nutr.*, **37**, 449 (1983).

[17] McNAIR et al., *Brit. med. J.*, **2**, 19 (1972).

[18] SEGAL, S., in STANBURY et al., *The Metabolic Basis of Inherited Disease*, 5th ed., McGraw-Hill, New York, 1983, page 167; KALCKAR et al., in GAULL, G. E. (Ed.), *Biology of Brain Dysfunction*, Volume 1, Plenum, New York, 1973, page 31; HSIA, D. Y. (Ed.), *Galactosemia*, Thomas, Springfield, 1969; WOOLF, L. I., *Advanc. clin. Chem.*, **5**, 1 (1962).

[19] BURMAN et al. (Eds.), *Inherited Disorders of Carbohydrate Metabolism*, section 3: Disorders of galactose metabolism, MTP Press, Lancaster, 1980, page 59.

[20] LEVY and HAMMERSEN, *J. Pediat.*, **92**, 871 (1978).

[21] GITZELMANN and HANSEN, in BURMAN et al. (Eds.), *Inherited Disorders of Carbohydrate Metabolism*, MTP Press, Lancaster, 1980, page 61.

[22] HENDERSON et al., *J. inherited metab. Dis.*, **6**, 17 (1983).

[23] SCHWARZ et al., *J. Pediat.*, **100**, 704 (1982).

24 HIATT, H. H., in STANBURY et al. (Eds.), *The Metabolic Basis of Inherited Disease*, 4th ed., McGraw-Hill, New York, 1978, page 110.

25 GITZELMANN et al., in STANBURY et al., *The Metabolic Basis of Inherited Disease*, 5th ed., McGraw-Hill, New York, 1983, page 118.

26 BURMAN et al. (Eds.), *Inherited Disorders of Carbohydrate Metabolism*, section 4: Disorders of fructose metabolism, MTP Press, Lancaster, 1980, page 161.

27 COX et al., *J. clin. Invest.*, **72**, 201 (1983).

28 PAYNE and WOOLF, *Mod. Probl. Pädiat.*, **4**, 369 (1959).

29 LEONARD, J. V., *Ciba Found. Symp.*, **87**, 340 (1982).

30 BURMAN et al. (Eds.), *Inherited Disorders of Carbohydrate Metabolism*, section 5: Disorders of pyruvate metabolism, MTP Press, Lancaster, 1980, page 207.

31 ROBINSON, B. H., *Biochem. Soc. Trans.*, **11**, 623 (1983); ROBINSON, B. H., *Trends biochem. Sci.*, **7**, 151 (1982).

32 BLASS, J. P., in STANBURY et al., *The Metabolic Basis of Inherited Disease*, 5th ed., McGraw-Hill, New York, 1983, page 193.

33 HOMMES et al., in BURMAN et al. (Eds.), *Inherited Disorders of Carbohydrate Metabolism*, MTP Press, Lancaster, 1980, page 269.

34 BLASS, J. P., in BURMAN et al. (Eds.), *Inherited Disorders of Carbohydrate Metabolism*, MTP Press, Lancaster, 1980, page 239.

35 MATALON et al., *J. Pediat.*, **104**, 65 (1984).

36 GRAVEL and ROBINSON, *Ann. N. Y. Acad. Sci.*, **447**, 225 (1985).

37 KUHARA et al., *Clin. chim. Acta*, **133**, 133 (1983).

38 MIWA, S., *Amer. J. Hemat.*, **14**, 381 (1983).

39 VALENTINE et al., in STANBURY et al., *The Metabolic Basis of Inherited Disease*, 5th ed., McGraw-Hill, New York, 1983, page 1606.

40 STAAL et al., *J. clin. Invest.*, **74**, 231 (1984); MAX-AUDIT et al., *Blood*, **56**, 902 (1980).

41 ROSA et al., *J. clin. Invest.*, **62**, 907 (1978).

42 ROSA et al., *Blood*, **60**, 84 (1982).

43 SCHWARTZ et al., in STANBURY et al., *The Metabolic Basis of Inherited Disease*, 5th ed., McGraw-Hill, New York, 1983, page 1654.

44 BEUTLER, E., in STANBURY et al., *The Metabolic Basis of Inherited Disease*, 5th ed., McGraw-Hill, New York, 1983, page 1629.

45 WINTROBE et al., *Clinical Hematology*, 8th ed., Lea & Febiger, Philadelphia, 1981, page 786.

46 KEATING et al., *Amer. J. Dis. Child.*, **139**, 609 (1985).

47 MAGNANI et al., *Brit. J. Haemat.*, **61**, 41 (1985).

48 VALENTINE et al., *Ann. intern. Med.*, **103**, 245 (1985).

49 TANISHIMA et al., *Blood*, **66**, 1288 (1985).

50 GARTY et al., *J. Pediat.*, **85**, 821 (1974); BRIVET et al., *Pediat. Res.*, **17**, 157 (1983).

A defect in the transport mechanism (for example impaired enteral absorption), a defect in the conversion of the vitamin to the cofactor or to the active form, or a disrupted binding of the cofactor to the apoenzyme can produce biochemical and clinical symptoms similar to those of a vitamin deficiency disease[1,2]. Transport defects and disorders in vitamin metabolism are compiled in the following Table.

Multiple carboxylase deficiency is an example of how a disrupted vitamin metabolism — in this case, biotin metabolism — can influence the activity of several enzymes (the isolated deficiencies of the components are dealt with in the appropriate chapters: propionyl-CoA carboxylase [page 236], methylcrotonoyl-CoA carboxylase [page 235] and pyruvate carboxylase [page 248]). A rapid differential diagnosis of the various carboxylase deficiencies is desirable, so that suitable therapy can be started before irreversible damage develops[3]. One of the defects in biotin metabolism — biotinidase deficiency — shows a frequency which makes it worthwile to have it detected by neonatal screening (20:1 000 000 in Virginia, USA)[4].

About half the cases of L-methylmalonic acidemia are due to a defect in cobalamin metabolism (mutant classes cbl B, cbl A, cbl C or cbl D)[5]; the non-vitamin-B$_{12}$-responsive variants (mut^0, mut$^-$) are dealt with in the chapter on 'Inborn Errors — Metabolism of Amino Acids' (page 235).

These metabolic disorders are to be differentiated from those defects which also respond to large doses of vitamins and which are due to a structural alteration of the apoenzyme, so that the coenzyme is bound inadequately (vitamin dependency). Classed among these are the thiamin-dependent variant of maple syrup urine disease (page 235), the pyridoxine-dependent variant of cystathioninuria (page 238) and the pyridoxine-dependent xanthurenic aciduria (page 234) discussed in the chapter on 'Inborn Errors — Metabolism of Amino Acids'. Transketolase can also appear in a mutant form that binds thiamin only weakly; if the thiamin content of the diet is inadequate, the clinical picture of Wernicke's encephalopathy can appear under stress, for example in the case of excessive consumption of ethanol[2,6]. Thiamin given in large doses to patients with Leigh's subacute necrotizing encephalomyelopathy may produce remission in some cases, but the biochemical connection is obscure; whether the inhibition of thiamin pyrophosphokinase by a substance found in blood and urine is responsible remains uncertain[7]. A few cases with thiamin-dependent megaloblastic anemia have also been reported, but it is difficult to implicate thiamin in DNA synthesis[2,8].

Another form of vitamin dependency consists in the by-passing of a metabolic defect through the activation of a different metabolic pathway by high vitamin dosage. Some cases of type 1 oxalosis respond to high doses of pyridoxine; the vitamin seems to stimulate the transamination of glyoxylate[9].

Inherited disorders of vitamin metabolism and vitamin transport

Vitamin	Defective enzyme or impaired mechanism	Biochemical findings	Clinical features Treatment	Inheritance	Reference
Biotin	Biotin–carboxylase ligase(s)(holocarboxylase synthetase[s]) — the enzyme(s) that covalently link(s) biotin to the apocarboxylase(s)	Activity of carboxylases in leukocytes and fibroblasts deficient, but normalized by biotin; normal serum and urine biotin levels; hyperammonemia; excessive accumulation and urinary excretion of lactate, 3-hydroxypropionate, methylcitrate, 3-hydroxyisovalerate and 3-methylcrotonoylglycine	Neonatal vomiting, lethargy, hypotonia, seizures, occasionally dermatitis; acidosis Most cases respond to biotin (10 to 40 mg/d); prenatal treatment[35]	Autosomal recessive	10, 34
	Biotinidase — the enzyme that cleaves biocytin, resulting in recycling of biotin	Activity of carboxylases in cultured fibroblasts normal; low serum and urine biotin levels; hyperammonemia and organic aciduria (see above) in several cases	Usually late onset (2–14 months), sometimes earlier; seizures, ataxia, skin rash, alopecia, conjunctivitis; deficiency of immune system; acidosis Responds to biotin (10–20 mg/d)	Autosomal recessive	11
Folic acid	Folate transport in small intestine and at blood–brain barrier	Folate concentration in erythrocytes and serum lowered	Onset of recurrent megaloblastic anemia in early childhood; mental retardation, severe convulsions and EEG disorders; in some cases also diarrhea, stomatitis, anorexia, vulvovaginitis Responds to 10–40 mg/d folic acid orally or to physiological amounts parenterally	–	2, 12, 13
	5,10-Methylenetetrahydrofolate reductase (FADH$_2$)	Homocysteinemia, homocystinuria; hypomethioninemia (activity of cystathionine β-synthase normal); folate concentration in erythrocytes and serum lowered in some cases	Variable clinical picture; in some cases death in early or late childhood; psychiatric symptoms, neurological abnormalities; vascular thrombosis; mental retardation	Autosomal recessive (?)	2, 12, 13, 14
	Dihydrofolate reductase	Serum folate level elevated (only a few cases known)	Congenital megaloblastic anemia Responds to parenteral doses of 5-formyltetrahydrofolic acid (100 µg/d), but not to folic acid	Autosomal recessive (?)	2, 12, 13, 15
	5-Methyltetrahydrofolate–homocysteine methyltransferase (?)	Folate concentration in erythrocytes and serum elevated	Megaloblastic anemia in early childhood; mental retardation; dilation of the cerebral ventricles, hypsarrhythmia	–	12, 13
	Glutamate formiminotransferase (2 types, one probably lacking formiminotetrahydrofolate cyclodeaminase as well)	In some cases (lacking formiminotetrahydrofolate cyclodeaminase) serum folate concentration 5 to 12 times the normal, others normal; excretion of formiminoglutamate increased, especially after oral administration of histidine	Often benign; in those lacking formiminotetrahydrofolate cyclodeaminase, severe physical and mental retardation with atrophy of the cerebral cortex and hemosiderin depots in the liver; hematological status normal in most cases	–	2, 12, 13

Inherited disorders of vitamin metabolism and vitamin transport (continued)

Vitamin	Defective enzyme or impaired mechanism	Biochemical findings	Clinical features Treatment	Inheritance	Reference
Cobalamin (vitamin B_{12})	Intrinsic factor (IF) (a) Congenital deficiency of IF	Serum vitamin B_{12} level lowered; methylmalonic aciduria, homocystinuria	Megaloblastic anemia; neurological disturbances Responds to 1–5 µg/d vitamin B_{12} parenterally	–	16
	(b) Abnormal IF	As in deficiency of IF	As in deficiency of IF	–	16
	Attachment of vitamin B_{12}–IF complex to receptors in the ileum and transport through the wall of ileum (selective vitamin B_{12} malabsorption)	As in deficiency of IF	As in deficiency of IF; proteinuria in some cases	Autosomal recessive	17
	Transcobalamin II (TC II) in plasma (a) Deficiency of TC II	Normal serum vitamin B_{12} level (low level in 1 atypical case)	Megaloblastic anemia; possibly malabsorption and antibody deficiency syndrome Responds to 150–1000 µg/d vitamin B_{12} parenterally	Autosomal recessive	18, 20
	(b) Abnormal TC II does not bind cobalamin	Normal serum vitamin B_{12} level	Megaloblastic anemia; progressive mental retardation and severe neuropathy Responds to 450–1000 µg/d hydroxocobalamin parenterally	Autosomal recessive	19
	(c) Abnormal TC II binds to cobalamin, but not to cellular receptors	Markedly elevated serum B_{12} level; normal methylation of homocysteine; normal metabolism of methylmalonic acid	Intermittent severe megaloblastic anemia Responds to high doses of hydroxocobalamin parenterally	Autosomal recessive (?)	33
	R binder (including transcobalamin I)	Serum vitamin B_{12} level lowered	Benign (?)	–	21
	Vitamin B_{12} coenzyme metabolism (a) Cob(II)alamin reductase (mutant class *cbl A*)	Deficiency of adenosylcobalamin; normal serum vitamin B_{12} level; methylmalonic acidemia, methylmalonic aciduria; hyperglycinemia, hyperglycinuria; higher ketones in the urine	Anemia unusual; neutropenia and thrombocytopenia; metabolic ketoacidosis, delayed onset in infancy, in contrast to *mut⁰* cases (page 235); good long-term prognosis Responds to parenteral administration of vitamin B_{12} or adenosylcobalamin (500–1000 µg/d); prenatal treatment (?)[23]	Autosomal recessive	5, 22
	(b) Cob(I)alamin adenosyltransferase (mutant class *cbl B*)	As for mutant class *cbl A*	Anemia in some cases, otherwise similar to mutant class *cbl A* Less than half the cases respond to vitamin B_{12} supplements	Autosomal recessive	5, 22
	(c) Aquacobalamin reductase (?) (mutant classes *cbl C* and *cbl D*)	Deficiency of adenosylcobalamin and methylcobalamin; normal serum vitamin B_{12} level; homocysteinemia, homocystinuria, hypomethioninemia, cystathioninemia, methylmalonic acidemia, hyperammonemia, hyperglycinemia	Megaloblastic anemia (not reported in *cbl D* cases); developmental retardation, dementia; psychosis; unsteady gait; myelopathy; neonatal onset in many *cbl C* cases; some cases asymptomatic Improvement with high doses of hydroxocobalamin	–	20, 24
	(d) Reduction of cob(III)alamin bound to 5-methyltetrahydrofolate–homocysteine methyltransferase (?) (mutant class *cbl E*)	Deficiency of intracellular methylcobalamin, but normal adenosylcobalamin; homocystinuria, but no L-methylmalonic aciduria	Megaloblastic anemia; severe developmental retardation (1 case) Responds to hydroxocobalamin, but not to cyanocobalamin; prenatal treatment (?)[26]	–	25
Riboflavin	Synthesis or transport of FAD (?); attachment of FAD to ETF or ETF dehydrogenase (?) (see also glutaric aciduria type II [page 256])	Multiple acyl-CoA dehydrogenase deficiency; C_6 to C_{10} dicarboxylic aciduria; free carnitine concentration in plasma low	Attacks resembling Reye's syndrome in some cases; others normal except when pregnant (decreased fetal movement; offspring die in infancy); lipid myopathy in some cases Responds to riboflavin (20–300 mg/d)	–	27
	Respiratory chain at the level of NADH dehydrogenase (ubiquinone) (see also 'Inborn Errors — Enzymes Coded on Mitochondrial DNA' [page 255])	Hyperlactatemia	Progressive exercise intolerance with severe metabolic acidosis at low work loads Responds to riboflavin (100 mg/d)	–	28

Inherited disorders of vitamin metabolism and vitamin transport (continued)

Vitamin	Defective enzyme or impaired mechanism	Biochemical findings	Clinical features Treatment	Inheritance	Reference
Vitamin E	Transport through wall of small intestine (?) (selective vitamin E malabsorption)	No detectable vitamin E in serum (1 case)	Ataxia, areflexia; loss of proprioception Improvement with high doses of α-tocopherol	Autosomal recessive (?)	29
Vitamin D	Calcidiol 1-monooxygenase(25-hydroxycholecalciferol 1-hydroxylase) (vitamin D-dependent rickets type I)	Failure of the transformation of 25-hydroxycholecalciferol into 1α,25-dihydroxycholecalciferol in the kidneys, with an impairment of intestinal calcium absorption as a consequence; low 1α,25-dihydroxycholecalciferol level in plasma	Prader's hereditary pseudodeficiency rickets; hypocalcemia; lowered *Tmp*; aminoaciduria and tooth enamel defects in some cases; weak muscle tone; tetany (occasional) Responds to 1α-hydroxycholecalciferol and 1α,25-dihydroxycholecalciferol	Autosomal recessive	30
	Abnormality of osteoblast receptors for 1α,25-dihydroxycholecalciferol or of its nuclear transfer (vitamin D-dependent rickets types IIa and IIb)	High 1α,25-dihydroxycholecalciferol level in plasma	Type IIa: As type I, but also alopecia totalis Some patients respond to 1α-hydroxycholecalciferol, but none to 1α,25-dihydroxycholecalciferol; more resistant than type I to other D vitamins	Autosomal recessive	30, 31
			Type IIb: As type I; no alopecia Responds to large doses of 25-hydroxycholecalciferol, but poorly to 1α,25-dihydroxycholecalciferol; less resistant than type IIa to other D vitamins	Autosomal recessive (?)	30, 31
	Control of 1α,25-dihydroxyvitamin D synthesis (?) (absorptive hypercalciuria)	Intestinal hyperabsorption of calcium; hypercalciuria, but normal serum calcium level	Urolithiasis in adults; hematuria without detectable calculi in children Low calcium diet and high fluid intake	Autosomal dominant (?)	32

Cobalamin involvement in succinyl-CoA formation and in methylation of homocysteine

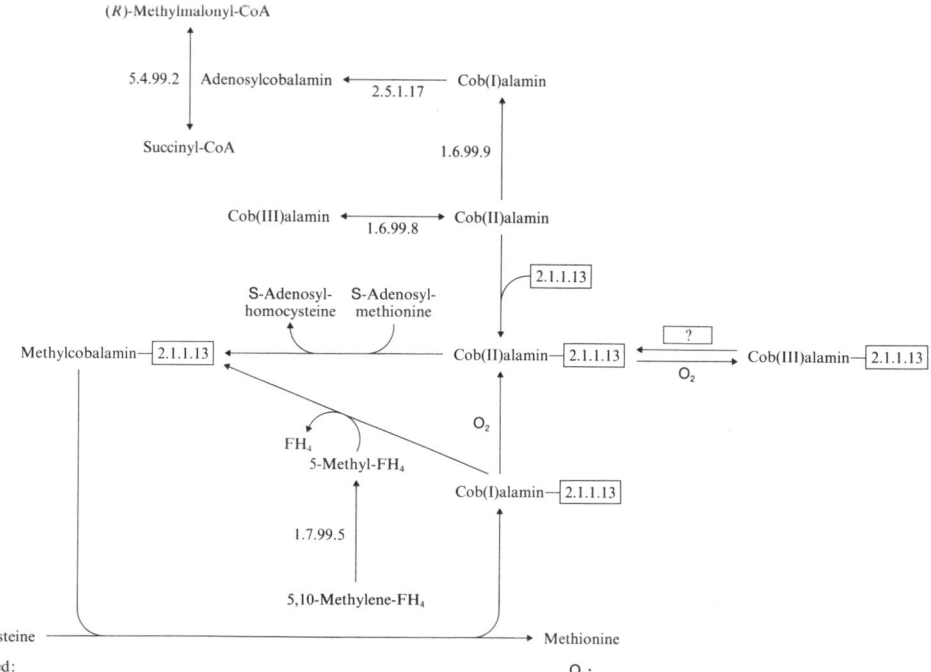

Enzymes involved:
1.6.99.8 Aquacobalamin reductase (deficient in mutant classes *cbl C* and *cbl D*)
1.6.99.9 Cob(II)alamin reductase (deficient in mutant class *cbl A*)
1.7.99.5 5,10-Methylenetetrahydrofolate reductase (FADH₂)
2.1.1.13 5-Methyltetrahydrofolate–homocysteine methyltransferase (methionine synthase)
2.5.1.17 Cob(I)alamin adenosyltransferase
5.4.99.2 Methylmalonyl-CoA mutase (deficient in mutant classes *mut⁰* and *mut⁻*)
  ?   Cob(III)alamin—2.1.1.13 reductase (?) (deficient in mutant class *cbl E*)

O₂:
Spontaneous oxidation of
  cob(I)alamin—2.1.1.13 to cob(II)alamin—2.1.1.13 and of
  cob(II)alamin—2.1.1.13 to cob(III)alamin—2.1.1.13

References

[1] ROSENBERG, L. E., *Advanc. hum. Genet.*, **6**, 1 (1976).

[2] BARTLETT, K., *Advanc. clin. Chem.*, **23**, 141 (1983).

[3] SUORMALA et al., *Clin. chim. Acta*, **145**, 151 (1985).

[4] WOLF et al., *New Engl. J. Med.*, **313**, 16 (1985); NYHAN, W. L., *New Engl. J. Med.*, **313**, 43 (1985).

[5] MATSUI et al., *New Engl. J. Med.*, **308**, 857 (1983).

[6] BLASS and GIBSON, *New Engl. J. Med.*, **297**, 1367 (1977).

[7] DAVIS and ICKE, *Advanc. clin. Chem.*, **23**, 93 (1983); COOPER and PINCUS, in HOMMES and VAN DEN BERG (Eds.), *Inborn Errors of Metabolism*, Academic Press, London, 1973, page 119.

[8] MANDEL et al., *New Engl. J. Med.*, **311**, 836 (1984); Editorial, *Nutr. Rev.*, **38**, 374 (1980).

[9] YENDT and COHANIM, *New Engl. J. Med.*, **312**, 953 (1985); WILL and BIJVOET, *Metabolism*, **28**, 542 (1979).

[10] SWEETMAN et al., *Ann. N. Y. Acad. Sci.*, **447**, 288 (1985); WOLF and FELDMAN, *Amer. J. hum. Genet.*, **34**, 699 (1982); GHNEIM and BARTLETT, *Lancet*, **1**, 1187 (1982).

[11] WOLF et al., *Ann. N. Y. Acad. Sci.*, **447**, 252 (1985); BAUMGARTNER et al., *Ann. N. Y. Acad. Sci.*, **447**, 272 (1985); WOLF et al., *New Engl. J. Med.*, **308**, 161 (1983); WOLF et al., *Clin. chim. Acta*, **131**, 273 (1983); WOLF et al., *J. Pediat.*, **103**, 233 (1983).

[12] ERBE, R. W., *Advanc. hum. Genet.*, **9**, 293 (1979); ERBE, R. W., *New Engl. J. Med.*, **293**, 753 and 807 (1975).

[13] ROWE, P. B., in STANBURY et al., *The Metabolic Basis of Inherited Disease*, 5th ed., McGraw-Hill, New York, 1983, page 498.

[14] PRZYREMBEL, H., *Ergebn. inn. Med. Kinderheilk.*, **49**, 77 (1982).

[15] Editorial, *Nutr. Rev.*, **43**, 309 (1985).

[16] KAPADIA and DONALDSON, *Ann. Rev. Med.*, **36**, 93 (1985); YANG et al., *J. clin. Invest.*, **76**, 2057 (1985).

[17] BROCH et al., *Acta paediat. scand.*, **73**, 248 (1984); SEETHARAM and ALPERS, *Nutr. Rev.*, **43**, 97 (1985).

[18] CARMEL and RAVINDRANATH, *Blood*, **63**, 598 (1984); SACHER et al., *Helv. paediat. Acta*, **38**, 549 (1983); BURMAN et al., *Brit. J. Haemat.*, **43**, 27 (1979); HITZIG et al., *J. Pediat.*, **85**, 622 (1974); HAKAMI et al., *New Engl. J. Med.*, **285**, 1163 (1971).

[19] HOFFBRAND et al., *New Engl. J. Med.*, **310**, 789 (1984); SELIGMAN et al., *New Engl. J. Med.*, **303**, 1209 (1980); THOMAS et al., *J. Neurol. Neurosurg. Psychiat.*, **45**, 74 (1982).

[20] MATTHEWS and LINNELL, *Europ. J. Pediat.*, **138**, 6 (1982).

[21] CARMEL, R., *J. Amer. med. Ass.*, **250**, 1886 (1983); CARMEL and HERBERT, *Blood*, **33**, 1 (1969).

[22] ROSENBERG, L. E., in STANBURY et al. (Eds.), *The Metabolic Basis of Inherited Disease*, 4th ed., McGraw-Hill, New York, 1978, page 411.

[23] AMPOLA et al., *New Engl. J. Med.*, **293**, 313 (1975).

[24] SHINNAR and SINGER, *New Engl. J. Med.*, **311**, 451 (1984).

[25] SHUH et al., *New Engl. J. Med.*, **310**, 686 (1984); ROSENBLATT et al., *J. clin. Invest.*, **74**, 2149 (1984).

[26] ROSENBLATT et al., *Lancet*, **1**, 1127 (1985).

[27] GREGERSEN et al., *Pediat. Res.*, **16**, 861 (1982); CARROLL et al., *Neurology (N. Y.)*, **31**, 1557 (1981).

[28] ARTS et al., *Lancet*, **2**, 581 (1983).

[29] HARDING et al., *New Engl. J. Med.*, **313**, 32 (1985).

[30] RASMUSSEN and ANAST, in STANBURY et al., *The Metabolic Basis of Inherited Disease*, 5th ed., McGraw-Hill, New York, 1983, page 1743.

[31] PIKE et al., *Science*, **224**, 879 (1984); LIBERMAN et al., *J. clin. Endocr.*, **57**, 958 (1983).

[32] HYMES and WARSHAW, *Amer. J. Dis. Child.*, **139**, 621 (1985); BROADUS et al., *New Engl. J. Med.*, **311**, 73 (1984); MÉHES and SZELID, *Europ. J. Pediat.*, **133**, 239 (1980).

[33] HAURANI et al., *J. clin. Invest.*, **64**, 1253 (1979).

[34] SHERWOOD et al., *J. Pediat.*, **101**, 546 (1982).

[35] ROTH, K. S., *Ann. N. Y. Acad. Sci.*, **447**, 263 (1985).

Mitochondrial DNA (mtDNA) differs from nuclear DNA and is organized into structural genes coding for 13 polypeptides (in man)[1-3]. Mitochondria also contain complete systems for protein synthesis, including mRNA, ribosomes and tRNA. Of the 300–400 different proteins contained in the mitochondrion, the vast majority are coded on nuclear genes and synthesized in the extramitochondrial cytoplasm before entering the mitochondrion; however, 4 mitochondrial enzyme complexes in man have been shown to contain polypeptides coded on mitochondrial genes and synthesized in the mitochondrion (Table 1), and others will undoubtedly be added. Mutation of a mitochondrial gene could lead to dysfunction of the relevant enzyme and, hence, to an inborn error of metabolism (Table 2).

Inheritance of a mitochondrial mutation does not obey Mendelian laws: in the fertilized ovum all, or almost all, of the mitochondria are of maternal origin, the spermatozoon contributing none or a negligible number. As the zygote divides and eventually forms an adult individual, the mitochondria reproduce by binary fission. Hence there is cytoplasmic – as opposed to nuclear – inheritance, with maternal transmission of mutations in the mitochondrial DNA and of consequent inborn errors of metabolism. Most affected individuals will have mixed populations of normal and mutated mitochondria within their cells and, therefore, a partial enzyme deficiency, the extent of which will vary from individual to individual and, perhaps, from tissue to tissue.

Mutations of mtDNA can be divided into mit^- point mutations or small deletions affecting a single polypeptide chain, syn^- point mutations or small deletions affecting protein synthesis and, hence, all such polypeptide chains, and ρ^- large deletions affecting protein synthesis, respiration and oxidative phosphorylation[1]. Since mitochondrial enzyme complexes such as cytochrome-c oxidase contain additional polypeptides coded on nuclear genes (Table 1), mutation of one of these nuclear genes could lead to partial or complete inactivation of the enzyme complex, resulting in a phenocopy of the mitochondrial mutation, but inherited in Mendelian fashion. In addition, nuclear genes profoundly affect the expression of mitochondrial genes, e.g. nuclear mutations are known which turn off the synthesis of single mitochondrial gene products. Quite separate, of course, are the many inborn errors of metabolism involving mitochondrial enzymes or transport proteins coded exclusively on nuclear genes.

Perhaps the most important function of mitochondria is the utilization of dioxygen, through the various enzyme complexes of the electron transfer system (see Figure), to oxidize fatty acids, amino acids and carbohydrates. Tissues such as red muscle fibers, which depend on such oxidation for ATP and energy generation, will be more severely affected by a defect in the electron transfer system than, e.g., white muscle fibers, which depend on glycolysis. A defect of a single enzyme complex of the electron transfer system may present with different clinical manifestations; on the other hand, defects of different enzyme complexes of the chain may be clinically indistinguishable (Table 2). Two defects of flavoprotein components of the electron transfer system are listed under 'riboflavin' in the chapter on 'Inborn Errors – Metabolism and Transport of Vitamins' (page 252).

References

[1] TZAGOLOFF, A., *Mitochondria*, Plenum, New York, 1982.
[2] CLAYTON, D.A., *Ann. Rev. Biochem.*, **53**, 573 (1984); GRIVELL, L.A., *Sci. Amer.*, **248**, No. 3, 60 (1983); HATEFI, Y., *Ann. Rev. Biochem.*, **54**, 1015 (1985); CHOMYN et al., *Nature*, **314**, 592 (1985).
[3] MERRIL and HARRINGTON, *Trends Genet.*, **1**, 140 (1985).
[4] MOREADITH et al., *J. clin. Invest.*, **74**, 685 (1984).
[5] NIKOSKELAINEN et al., *Acta neurol. scand.*, **69**, Suppl. 98, 172 (1984); CAGIANUT et al., *Lancet*, **2**, 981 (1981).
[6] EGGER and WILSON, *New Engl. J. Med.*, **309**, 142 (1983).
[7] EGGER et al., *Arch. Dis. Childh.*, **56**, 741 (1981); SHAPIRA et al., *Israel J. med. Sci.*, **13**, 161 (1977).
[8] CLARK et al., *J. inherited metab. Dis.*, **7**, Suppl. 1, 62 (1984); CLARK et al., *Biochem. Soc. Trans.*, **11**, 626 (1983); MORGAN-HUGHES, J. A., *Rec. Advanc. clin. Neurol.*, **3**, 1 (1982); MORGAN-HUGHES et al., *Brain*, **105**, 553 (1982).
[9] SENGERS et al., *Europ. J. Pediat.*, **141**, 192 (1984).
[10] GREGERSEN, N., *Scand. J. clin. Lab. Invest.*, **45**, Suppl. 174 (1985).
[11] FRERMAN and GOODMAN, *Proc. nat. Acad. Sci. (Wash.)*, **82**, 4517 (1985); NIEDERWIESER et al., *Helv. paediat. Acta*, **38**, 9 (1983).
[12] TANAKA and ROSENBERG, in STANBURY et al., *The Metabolic Basis of Inherited Disease*, 5th ed., McGraw-Hill, New York, 1983, page 461.
[13] GOODMAN and FRERMAN, *J. inherited metab. Dis.*, **7**, Suppl. 1, 33 (1984); GOODMAN et al., *J. Pediat.*, **102**, 411 (1983); LEHNERT et al., *Europ. J. Pediat.*, **139**, 56 (1982); SWEETMAN et al., *J. Pediat.*, **96**, 1020 (1980).
[14] DUSHEIKO et al., *New Engl. J. Med.*, **301**, 1405 (1979).
[15] MANTAGOS et al., *J. clin. Invest.*, **64**, 1580 (1979).
[16] SCHOLTE et al., *Biochem. Soc. Trans.*, **13**, 643 (1985).
[17] DIMAURO et al., *Biochem. Soc. Trans.*, **13**, 651 (1985).

Table 1   *Polypeptide chains and prosthetic groups of enzymes in the mitochondrial membrane*[1,2]

Complex	Recommended name	EC number	Polypeptide chains Total number	Polypeptide chains mtDNA-coded	Prosthetic groups
I	NADH dehydrogenase (ubiquinone)	1.6.5.3	25	6	FMN, Fe–S clusters
II	Succinate dehydrogenase (ubiquinone)	1.3.5.1	4–5	–	FAD, Fe–S clusters, b_{560} heme
III	Ubiquinol–cytochrome-c reductase	1.10.2.2	9–10	1	Hemes b_{562}, b_{564} and c_1, 2 Fe–2 S cluster
IV	Cytochrome-c oxidase	1.9.3.1	8	3	Hemes aa_3, Cu_a, Cu_{a_3}
V	H^+-transporting ATP synthase	3.6.1.34	12–14	2	Adenine nucleotides, Mg^{2+}

Enzyme complexes involved in the electron transfer system of the mitochondrial membrane[4]

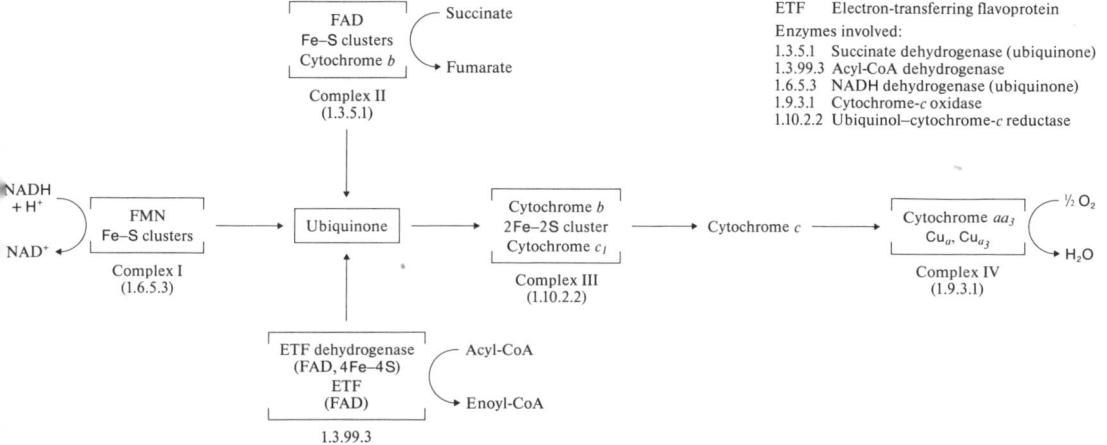

Table 2   *Inborn errors of metabolism involving mitochondrial enzymes*

Condition	Defective enzyme or enzyme complex	Biochemical findings	Morphological and clinical features	Inheritance	Reference
Leber's optic atrophy	Thiosulfate sulfurtransferase (rhodanese)	Blood cyanocobalamin levels high	Retinal atrophy and blindness on exposure to traces of cyanide (e.g. tobacco smoke, cider)	Cytoplasmic inheritance	*5, 6*
Mitochondrial (encephalo)myopathy *Oculocraniosomatic neuromuscular disease* *Kearns-Sayre syndrome* *'Ophthalmoplegia plus'*	NADH dehydrogenase (ubiquinone) (complex I); Fe–S cluster of this complex in 1 case or succinate dehydrogenase (ubiquinone) (complex II) or ubiquinol–cytochrome-*c* reductase (complex III) or H$^+$-transporting ATP synthase (complex V) in different cases	Hyperlactatemia and hyperpyruvatemia (only after glucose load in some cases)	Abnormal, large mitochondria, often with paracrystalline inclusions, particularly in type 1 muscle fibers, producing 'raggedred' fibers; sometimes lipid myopathy resembling carnitine deficiency. Very variable symptoms: in some cases poor fetal movements, floppy infants and/or muscular weakness in childhood and/or adult life; in some cases progressive cerebral and cerebellar degeneration (with or without myopathy), psychomotor retardation, ataxia; sometimes optic atrophy, myoclonus, hemiparesis, coma, respiratory failure in infancy, childhood or adolescence, usually leading to death; in some cases sudden onset in adult life of confusion, agitation, paranoid ideation, rigidity or muscular weakness and ataxia, with or without mild myopathy, optic atrophy, myoclonus, deafness	Cytoplasmic inheritance in many families, probably autosomal dominant in others	*4, 6–9, 16*
Leigh's subacute necrotizing encephalopathy (some cases)	Cytochrome-*c* oxidase (complex IV)				*9, 17*
Infantile mitochondrial myopathy with Fanconi syndrome	Cytochrome-*c* oxidase (complex IV)	Marked hyperlactatemia with raised lactate/pyruvate ratio; raised 3-hydroxybutyrate/acetoacetate ratio	Abnormal mitochondria and muscle fibers, as for deficiencies of complex I, II, III or V; profound neonatal hypotonia; cardiac and skeletal myopathy; generalized renal tubular dysfunction; death before 8 months; spontaneous recovery in 1 case ('benign' form)	Cytoplasmic inheritance in many families, probably autosomal recessive in others	*9, 17*
Multiple acyl-CoA dehydrogenation deficiency (a) Neonatal glutaric aciduria type II	Electron transfer system of the acyl-CoA dehydrogenase system: electron-transferring flavoprotein (ETF) or ETF dehydrogenase (an iron–sulfur flavoprotein)	Urinary excretion of free and conjugated glutaric, lactic, isobutyric, isovaleric, adipic, 2-methylbutyric, ethylmalonic, *n*-hexanoic and other mono- and dicarboxylic acids; hyperlactatemia; marked hypoglucosemia	Neonatal acidosis, but no ketosis; odor of 'sweaty feet' in some cases; neonatal death	Autosomal recessive; X-linked recessive in some cases (?)	*10–13*
(b) Neonatal glutaric aciduria type II with multiple congenital malformations	ETF dehydrogenase	As above	Large, polycystic kidneys at birth; face dysmorphic (Potter type); neonatal hypotonia; death within 5 days of birth	Autosomal recessive; X-linked recessive in some cases (?)	*13*
(c) Adult glutaric aciduria type II	ETF or ETF dehydrogenase (partial deficiency)	As above (?)	1 family described. Infrequent, recurrent, severe hypoglucosemic episodes; hepatomegaly; bouts of muscular weakness	Probably autosomal recessive	*10, 14*
(d) Ethylmalonic-adipic aciduria (glutaric aciduria type II B)	As above	As above, but predominant urinary excretion of ethylmalonic acid, adipic acid and *n*-hexanoylglycine	1 family described. Adult: hepatomegaly; fatty infiltration of the liver; infrequent, recurrent, severe hypoglucosemic episodes; lethargy. Neonatal death in 1 case	Autosomal recessive	*10, 15*

Gout ranks among the most widespread metabolic disorders. Primary gout is an inherited disorder leading to either overproduction of purines or a defect in renal uric-acid clearance or both. Several enzyme defects are known to be associated with excessive purine synthesis and hence with increased uric-acid formation[1,2]: e.g. hypoxanthine phosphoribosyltransferase deficiency, superactivity of ribose-phosphate pyrophosphokinase, AMP deaminase deficiency, glucose-6-phosphatase deficiency (page 246), fructose-bisphosphate aldolase deficiency (page 248) and increased glutathione reductase (NAD[P]H). The complete or partial hypoxanthine phosphoribosyltransferase defect produces a variable clinical picture, and there is evidence that many mutations at the *HPRT* locus are structural gene mutations which result in a catalytically defective or unstable enzyme protein. In four such proteins with residual enzyme activity, a single amino-acid exchange was revealed (HPRT$_{Toronto}$, HPRT$_{London}$, HPRT$_{Munich}$, HPRT$_{Kinston}$)[3,4]; ~10% of mutations resulting in the Lesch-Nyhan syndrome are characterized by deletion of gene fragments of various length[5].

Structural mutations resulting in superactive ribose-phosphate pyrophosphokinase (phosphoribosylpyrophosphate synthetase) had been found in 4 families up to 1984; none of the mutations seems to be exactly like any other[4].

Several reports deal with the association of gout and increased catalytic activity of a series of glutathione reductase (NAD[P]H) variants in erythrocytes[2].

Nephrolithiasis can occur as a consequence of two other disorders of purine metabolism due to enzyme defects. Thus xanthine stones are found in some cases of xanthine oxidase deficiency. When adenine phosphoribosyltransferase is completely absent the forma-

tion of 2,8-dihydroxyadenine stones, which are easily confused with uric-acid stones, occurs; in *partial* deficiency of this enzyme, on the other hand, characteristic symptoms are absent (40 cases in 15 families were known up to 1984)[4].

Succinyladenosine and 5'-phosphoribosyl-4-(N-succinocarboxamide)-5-aminoimidazole were found in cerebrospinal fluid, plasma and urine of 3 children with severe psychomotor retardation and autism[20]; a defect of adenylosuccinate lyase may be involved.

Disorders of pyrimidine metabolism are very rare. Of the 9 known homozygotes of hereditary orotic aciduria, 8 had a double enzyme defect (orotidine 5'-phosphate decarboxylase *and* orotate phosphoribosyltransferase), whereas in 1 homozygote a single enzyme (orotidine 5'-phosphate decarboxylase) was deficient at first, the double enzyme defect appearing only later. Heterozygotes are more common (about 1:600) than one would expect from this small number of homozygotes – many homozygotes may die in utero. An increased formation of orotic acid is also found in ornithine carbamoyltransferase deficiency (page 236).

3-Aminoisobutyric acid, a breakdown product of thymine, is excreted in large amounts in the urine with marked tissue breakdown and correspondingly increased DNA turnover, as for example in leukemia; nevertheless, increased excretion can also occur in healthy subjects with the appropriate gene. This type of 3-aminoisobutyric aciduria is found in 0–9% of Whites, 0–7% of Indians (India), 17–32% of Blacks, 42–46% of Mongoloids and more than 80% of Micronesians[13].

Some disorders of purine and pyrimidine metabolism in erythrocytes have detrimental effects on the cell. With more than 35 cases known, the deficiency of pyrimidine-specific 5'-nucleotidase is the

Inherited disorders of purine and pyrimidine metabolism

Condition	Defective enzyme or impaired mechanism	Biochemical findings	Clinical features	Frequency Inheritance	Reference
Primary gout (3 types)	Type I: excessive formation of uric acid from precursors or decreased excretion by the kidneys or both (variant form of AMP deaminase in liver resists control by inhibitor in some patients) Type II: partial deficiency of hypoxanthine phosphoribosyltransferase Type III: increased activity of ribose-phosphate pyrophosphokinase	Hyperuratemia, frequently hyperuricuria	Gouty arthritis, initially acute attacks with deposition of urate in the tissues in the later chronic stage; pathological changes in the kidneys due to urate stones ('gouty kidney'); 80% of cases symptomless (about 20% of type II cases show moderate mental retardation, occasionally with choreoathetosis, spasticity or ataxia)	Hyperuratemia in 1 to 2%, clinical gout in 0.2–0.4% of the population Type I: probably polygenic (may be autosomal dominant with variable and sex-limited expressivity) Type II (1–3% of all cases of clinical gout): X-linked Type III (rare): X-linked	1–4
Familial hyperuricemic nephropathy	Unknown (rate of purine synthesis normal)	Hyperuratemia	Gout; hypertension; renal failure in early adult life	Rare Autosomal dominant	6
Lesch-Nyhan syndrome	Hypoxanthine phosphoribosyltransferase; increased purine synthesis due to failure to inhibit amidophosphoribosyltransferase	Plasma urate mostly above 0.6 mmol/L; synthesis of uric acid 10 to 20 times the normal; urinary excretion of uric acid markedly increased	Exclusively in boys; delayed development of motor function; choreoathetosis, spasticity, convulsions (in ~50% of the cases); behavioral disorders, tendencies to self-mutilation, aggressiveness; emaciation; sometimes megaloblastic anemia; renal colic; death in late childhood or early adolescence	X-linked recessive	1, 3, 7
Dihydroxyadeninuria	Absence of adenine phosphoribosyltransferase (heterozygotes have 25% of normal activity)	Adenine, 8-hydroxyadenine and 2,8-dihydroxyadenine in the urine	2,8-Dihydroxyadenine stones in the urinary passages; renal failure in about half of the cases	27 cases up to 1986 Autosomal recessive	4, 8, 23
Xanthinuria (2 types)	Type I: xanthine oxidase deficiency Type II: molybdenum malabsorption (resulting in deficiency of xanthine oxidase, sulfite oxidase and aldehyde oxidase)	High xanthine excretion in the urine; marked hypouratemia	Type I: xanthine stones in urinary passages Type II: mental retardation; seizures; cerebral atrophy; dislocated lenses	Type I: ~1:45000 (?) Type II: 6 cases up to 1983 Autosomal recessive	1, 9, 10

Inherited disorders of purine and pyrimidine metabolism (continued)

Condition	Defective enzyme or impaired mechanism	Biochemical findings	Clinical features	Frequency Inheritance	Reference
Orotic aciduria	Orotate phosphoribosyltransferase (orotidine-5'-phosphate pyrophosphorylase) and/or orotidine-5'-phosphate decarboxylase absent	Large amounts of orotic acid in the urine; rapid reduction of orotic-acid synthesis by oral uridine	Severe megaloblastic anemia that responds only to oral uridine (150 mg kg^{-1} d^{-1}); slight mental retardation, improvement by oral uridine; orotic acid in the form of colorless, needle-like crystals in the urine; immunodeficiency syndrome in some cases	9 cases up to 1983 Autosomal recessive	1, 11
3-Aminoisobutyric aciduria	(S)-3-Amino-2-methylpropionate aminotransferase (β-aminoisobutyrate aminotransferase) (?); low activity in leukocytes	Large amounts of 3-aminoisobutyric acid in the urine	Benign	0 to over 80%, depending on the ethnic group Autosomal recessive	12, 13
Nonspherocytic hemolytic anemia	Deficiency of adenylate kinase	Activity of the enzyme in the erythrocytes 1 to 13% of normal	Chronic hemolytic anemia	Few cases Autosomal recessive (?)	14
	Deficiency of Na$^+$/K$^+$-transporting ATPase	No enzyme activity in the erythrocytes in some cases	Hemolytic anemia	Few cases Autosomal dominant (?)	15
	Deficiency of pyrimidine-specific 5'-nucleotidase	Accumulation of pyrimidine nucleotides in the erythrocytes; secondary decrease in activity of ribose-phosphate pyrophosphokinase	Hemolytic anemia; mental retardation (?)	Relatively many cases with wide geographic distribution Autosomal recessive	16, 17
Myoadenylate deaminase deficiency	AMP deaminase of muscle	Enzyme in muscle < 5% of normal; low ratio of ammonia:lactate release during hypoxic exercise	Post-exercise myalgia and rapid fatigue; mild or moderate muscle atrophy in some cases	At least 40 cases Probably autosomal recessive	18
Uraciluria	Unknown	Urinary excretion of uracil 7 times the normal; hyperammonemia in some cases	Physical and mental retardation; hypotonia; extensive neurological damage	Few cases	19
Thymine–uraciluria	Dihydrouracil dehydrogenase (NADP$^+$)	High levels of thymine and uracil in plasma and CSF; urinary excretion of thymine, uracil and 5-hydroxymethyluracil very high	Seizures; autistic behavior	Few cases	19

fourth commonest cause of nonspherocytic hemolytic anemia due to an enzyme defect – after deficiencies in glucose-6-phosphate dehydrogenase, pyruvate kinase and glucose-6-phosphate isomerase (page 249)[17].

Defective DNA repair[21, 22]. UV radiation, X radiation, carcinogens, etc. may modify DNA and alter its coding properties and normal function in replication or transcription. For it to be repaired, DNA damage must be recognized by proteins which can bring about a sequence of biochemical reactions leading to elimination of damaged bases (or nucleotides) and the restoration of the DNA structure.

Several diseases – especially the various forms of xeroderma pigmentosum – seem to be connected with a defect in the excision repair of damaged DNA, resulting in hypersensitivity to various forms of radiation and mutagenic agents.

Xeroderma pigmentosum groups A to G are due to a deficiency in gene products that are required for the initial step of excision, whereas the 'variant' form is connected with deficiency of a gene product that permits accurate semiconservative replication past damaged sites in the DNA. Xeroderma pigmentosum – inherited as an autosomal recessive trait – is a skin disease in which homozygotes show a marked tendency to develop skin cancer after exposure to sunlight; in North America the frequency is about 1:125 000.

Other inherited disorders related to defective DNA repair are: ataxia telangiectasia (Louis-Bar syndrome) (page 261), Cockayne's syndrome, Fanconi's anemia and Bloom's syndrome.

References

[1] SEEGMILLER, J. E., in BONDY and ROSENBERG, *Metabolic Control and Disease*, 8th ed., Saunders, Philadelphia, 1980, page 777.
[2] WYNGAARDEN and KELLEY, in STANBURY et al., *The Metabolic Basis of Inherited Disease*, 5th ed., McGraw-Hill, New York, 1983, page 1043.
[3] WILSON et al., *New Engl. J. Med.*, **309**, 900 (1983); PAGE et al., *J. inherited metab. Dis.*, **4**, 203 (1981).
[4] GUTENSOHN, W., *Klin. Wschr.*, **62**, 953 (1984).
[5] YANG et al., *Nature*, **310**, 412 (1984).
[6] DERMOT et al., in *Third International Symposium on Inborn Errors of Metabolism in Humans*, Munich, 1984, Abstracts, Karger, Basle, 1984, page 54.
[7] KELLEY and WYNGAARDEN, in STANBURY et al., *The Metabolic Basis of Inherited Disease*, 5th ed., McGraw-Hill, New York, 1983, page 1115.
[8] SIMMONDS and VAN ACKER, in STANBURY et al., *The Metabolic Basis of Inherited Disease*, 5th ed., McGraw-Hill, New York, 1983, page 1144.
[9] HOLMES and WYNGAARDEN, in STANBURY et al., *The Metabolic Basis of Inherited Disease*, 5th ed., McGraw-Hill, New York, 1983, page 1192.
[10] WADMAN et al., *J. inherited metab. Dis.*, **6**, Suppl. 1, 78 (1983); MUNNICH et al., *J. inherited metab. Dis.*, **6**, Suppl. 2, 95 (1983).
[11] KELLEY, W. N., in STANBURY et al., *The Metabolic Basis of Inherited Disease*, 5th ed., McGraw-Hill, New York, 1983, page 1202; GIROT et al., *New Engl. J. Med.*, **308**, 700 (1983).

[12] ROSENBERG and SCRIVER, in BONDY and ROSENBERG, *Metabolic Control and Disease*, 8th ed., Saunders, Philadelphia, 1980, page 583.

[13] EVERED et al., *Biochem. Soc. Trans.*, **13**, 705 (1985); EVERED and BARLEY, *Clin. chim. Acta*, **84**, 339 (1978).

[14] BOIVIN et al., *Presse méd.*, **79**, 215 (1971).

[15] HANEL and COHN, *Scand. J. Haemat.*, **9**, 28 (1972).

[16] VALENTINE and PAGLIA, *Blood*, **64**, 583 (1984); PAGLIA and VALENTINE, *Curr. Top. Hemat.*, **3**, 75 (1980).

[17] HANSEN et al., *Scand. J. Haemat.*, **31**, 122 (1983).

[18] FISHBEIN, W. N., *Advanc. exp. Med. Biol.*, **165A**, 77 (1984); SABINA et al., *J. clin. Invest.*, **73**, 720 (1984); GOEBEL et al., *Klin. Wschr.*, **64**, 342 (1986); PONGRATZ, D. E., *Klin. Wschr.*, **64**, Suppl. V, 96 (1986).

[19] WADMAN et al., *Advanc. exp. Med. Biol.*, **165A**, 109 (1984); BERGER et al., *Clin. chim. Acta*, **141**, 227 (1984); BAKKEREN et al., *Clin. chim. Acta*, **140**, 247 (1984).

[20] JAEKEN and VAN DEN BERGHE, *Lancet*, **2**, 1058 (1984).

[21] HANAWALT et al., *Ann. Rev. Biochem.*, **48**, 783 (1979); POLANI, P. E., *Ciba Found. Symp.*, NS **66**, 81 (1979).

[22] CLEAVER, J. E., in STANBURY et al., *The Metabolic Basis of Inherited Disease*, 5th ed., McGraw-Hill, New York, 1983, page 1227.

[23] SIMMONDS, H. A., *Klin. Wschr.*, **64**, Suppl. V, 96 (1986).

Inborn errors of specific immunity and phagocytosis are dealt with in a series of reviews[1-6].

Humoral and cell-mediated immunity

The body's ability to resist infection by viruses, bacteria and fungi depends on 3 varieties of leukocytes: T lymphocytes, B lymphocytes and phagocytes. All three derive from a single type of stem cell in the bone marrow. The stem cells divide and differentiate into macrophage precursors and lymphocyte precursors. The lymphocyte precursors migrate to the thymus and probably to lymphoid tissue associated with the intestine, where they mature into T lymphocytes and B lymphocytes, respectively. The T lymphocytes fall into several subsets: helper cells (T_H), suppressor cells (T_S) and cytotoxic cells (T_C) are the most important.

When an antigen meets a T lymphocyte, a surface receptor specific for the antigen is formed, and the lymphocyte enlarges to become a lymphoblast which divides exponentially, resulting in a clone of T lymphocytes capable of reacting with the antigen. Differentiation within the B-cell lineage occurs in 2 stages. In the first, which is antigen-independent, expression of the immunoglobin genes is activated. Different cells select different heavy-chain and light-chain variable region genes, so that a tremendous clonal diversity is initiated[40]. Membrane expression of the immunoglobulin molecules results in the production of a clonally diverse population of sIg^+ B cells. Following an encounter with the appropriate antigen, B cells may be activated to divide and to differentiate into plasma cells that excrete antibody molecules of the same specificity as those expressed on the B-cell surface. The secreted antibodies, chiefly IgM, IgD and IgG, are then able to combine with the inducing antigen, to neutralize it and aid in its elimination. The helper T lymphocytes are necessary for the triggering of B lymphocytes to produce antibody. Certain macrophages play an essential part in this process, combining with the antigen and presenting it in proper form to the T_H cell, which then interacts with the B cell.

In addition to humoral (i.e. antibody-mediated) immunity, which can destroy invading viruses, microorganisms and toxins only while they are in the blood or extracellular fluid, there is cell-mediated immunity in which the T lymphocytes act directly to kill invading viruses, bacteria and fungi, particularly within the cells of the body. Certain T lymphocytes kill and cause rejection of foreign grafts and, probably, some emerging tumor cells. Some T cells also secrete lymphokines, small protein molecules that not only produce inflammation and other features of delayed hypersensitivity, but also stimulate phagocytosis by macrophages. The T_S cells suppress both the production of lymphokines by T cells and the production of antibodies by B cells, tending to prevent autoimmune reactions to proteins to which the T_S cells have been previously exposed. These reactions of T lymphocytes to invading viruses, bacteria or fungi (but not to foreign grafts, etc.) in general depend on previous exposure to the antigen with consequent formation of a specific clone of T cells (memory cells).

Severe combined immunodeficiency (SCID) results from malfunction of both T cells and B cells. Several clinically similar forms of the disease exist, transmitted either as a Mendelian autosomal recessive or X-linked recessive character, the two being equally frequent. The patient lacks both humoral and cell-mediated immunity and, in consequence, generally succumbs at an early age to a viral, bacterial or fungal infection with an organism of low virulence which, in normal infants, produces minor and transient disease. The disorders are listed in Table 1.

About one-half of the patients with the autosomal recessive form of SCID are thought to have a deficiency of adenosine deaminase (ADA)[3]. Structural changes in the ADA protein, rather than regulatory mutations, may be responsible for most of the cases[30].

Deficiency or low activity of purine-nucleoside phosphorylase (PNP) is rarer (less than 15 cases reported up to 1985[29]) and results in human immunodeficiency disease which varies in severity from one family to another, with decreased numbers of T cells in all families, decreased numbers of B cells in many families, and a relatively mild antibody deficiency and decreased cell-mediated immunity. In different families the structural gene coding for PNP has undergone different mutations, producing mutant PNP with low affinity for its substrate, with low thermal stability or with altered charge.

ADA is a 'purine salvage enzyme' generating inosine from adenosine. It is present in high concentration in lymphoid tissue and rises following antigenic stimulation, the production of plasma cells, etc. In the absence of ADA, adenosine and deoxyadenosine accumulate, and the latter is successively phosphorylated by kinases to yield dATP which also accumulates and is a potent inhibitor of ribonucleotide reductase. In consequence, formation of other deoxy-

ribonucleotides, particularly dCMP, is inhibited, preventing formation of DNA and, therefore, cell replication.

In ADA deficiency, accumulation of dATP can be demonstrated in many tissues, e.g. a 50-fold rise in concentration in erythrocytes; because of the relative activities of the enzymes involved in different tissues, however, the accumulation of dATP is most marked in lymphoid tissue and adequately explains the lack of T cells and B cells in this disease.

PNP, another 'purine salvage enzyme', converts guanosine, deoxyguanosine, inosine and deoxyinosine to the purine base and to (deoxy)ribose 1-phosphate. In the absence of normal PNP, deoxyguanosine accumulates and, through the action of a deoxyribonucleoside kinase, dGTP is formed, which inhibits ribonucleotide reductase and, hence, DNA formation and cell replication. B cells contain 4 to 10 times as much 5'-nucleotidase as T cells and only one-third as much deoxyribonucleoside kinase, hence B cells form dGTP more slowly than T cells, and degradation of accumulating dGTP is much faster than in T cells. This explains why, in PNP deficiency, B cells are less susceptible than T cells.

An alternative mechanism for the pathogenetic effect of ADA may be the impairment of methylation reactions. In methylation reactions where S-adenosylmethionine serves as the methyl-group donor, S-adenosylhomocysteine (SAH) is formed besides the methylated product. Normally, S-adenosylhomocysteine is hydrolyzed by adenosylhomocysteinase (SAH hydrolase) to yield adenosine and homocysteine, but these reaction products must be metabolized simultaneously, so that the reaction can go on. In ADA deficiency, adenosine is not removed, and S-adenosylhomocysteine – a potent feedback inhibitor of methylation reactions – will accumulate. As mentioned before, in ADA deficiency deoxyadenosine accumulates, and this substance is an irreversible inactivator of SAH hydrolase. Low activity of SAH hydrolase has been demonstrated in the erythrocytes of some patients with ADA deficiency[9]. S-Adenosylhomocysteine, by inhibiting methylation reactions, inhibits cell differentiation and hence normal cell replication.

Deficiency of the principal transport protein for vitamin B_{12} in blood – transcobalamin II – leads to megaloblastic anemia of early onset in infancy (page 252). If the deficiency remains untreated, hypogammaglobulinemia also develops. The B cells are quantitatively normal, but terminal B-cell differentiation appears to require vitamin B_{12}. A vitamin B_{12} coenzyme – methylcobalamin – functions as a cofactor for 5-methyltetrahydrofolate–homocysteine methyltransferase, which forms methionine from homocysteine and 5-methyltetrahydrofolate. When homocysteine is not metabolized, its precursor, S-adenosylhomocysteine, will accumulate and inhibit methylation reactions as discussed under ADA deficiency.

Cases of agammaglobulinemia and hypogammaglobulinemia are known in which cell-mediated immunity is normal but there is a deficiency in antibody production[4,7]. Classical agammaglobulinemia (first described by BRUTON) is inherited as an X-linked recessive character. Affected boys usually have no circulating B cells or plasma cells, less than 1 g/L IgG in serum and no detectable IgA, IgM, IgE or IgD. They are usually well for the first 9 months, then gradually become unduly susceptible to infection by bacteria such as staphylococci, streptococci, pneumococci and Haemophilus influenzae, with frequent recurrences. Their reactions to some viral infections are normal, they are not particularly susceptible to fungal infection, but they do not form antibodies after typhoid vaccination, diphtheria immunization, etc. Many develop a disease of the joints resembling rheumatoid arthritis, and some develop a syndrome resembling dermatomyositis, sometimes with CNS involvement. A few patients have circulating B cells and, in at least some of these, antibodies are formed within the cell, but the heavy chain of the immunoglobulins is not glycosylated and the antibodies are not released into the circulation.

Several partial or selective hypogammaglobulinemias are known, e.g. with absent IgA and IgG but normal or elevated circulating IgM, with absent IgA but normal IgG and IgM or with absent IgG, IgG_2 and/or IgG_3. Some of these are inherited, others acquired. The patient may suffer from nontropical sprue, recurrent pyogenic infections or thrombocytopenia. Furthermore, 1 case of absent IgA lacked immunoglobulin κ chains (an amino-acid substitution on each nascent κ chain prevented formation of an essential disulfide bond) and a few cases showing reduced formation of κ chains have been reported[41].

Patients with SCID require complete isolation in a germ-free environment for survival. The best treatment, other than with antibiotics, etc., is by transplant of bone marrow or fetal tissue[4,5,8]. The recipient usually does not reject the graft, lacking the immune mechanism for doing so (this may not be completely true for PNP deficiency), but even with extremely close HLA-matching, some degree

Table 1   *Inborn errors of specific immunity*

Condition	Inheritance	Defective enzyme or system	Biochemical and biological features	Clinical features and treatment	Reference
Severe combined immunodeficiency (SCID)					1–6
(a) Reticular dysgenesia	Autosomal recessive	Unknown	Total absence of T cells, B cells and phagocytes	Patients succumb in early infancy to overwhelming infection (often by 'commensal' or other organisms of low virulence), unless isolated in a sterile environment. Transplant of bone marrow, fetal liver or fetal thymus is the only effective treatment	
(b) 'Swiss type'	Autosomal recessive	Unknown	Total absence of T cells and B cells		
(c) Adenosine deaminase deficiency	Autosomal recessive	Adenosine deaminase (ADA)	Accumulation of deoxyadenosine and dATP; inhibition of ribonucleotide reductase and adenosylhomocysteinase; T cells absent, B cells reduced or absent		
(d)	X-linked recessive	Unknown	T cells absent or very low, B cells reduced or absent	As above, but patients may survive into second year of life (only boys are affected)	
(e) Purinenucleoside phosphorylase deficiency	Autosomal recessive	Purine-nucleoside phosphorylase (PNP)	Accumulation of dGTP; inhibition of ribonucleotide reductase; decreased numbers of T cells and, often, B cells	Variable from family to family; patients may succumb to overwhelming infection, otherwise recurrent severe pyogenic infections; erythrocyte aplasia; death in infancy less common than in ADA deficiency	
Agammaglobulinemia					
(a) 'Classical' or Bruton type	X-linked recessive	Translocation of the V_H region of the Ig gene (?)	No B cells in blood; immunoglobulins almost completely absent from blood	Normal resistance to viruses, fungi and tuberculosis, but incapable of opsonizing pyogenic bacteria; recurrent sinusitis, bronchitis, otitis, etc. from infancy; autoimmune disease common. Monthly (or more frequent) i.m. γ-globulin is the most effective treatment	1, 4, 6, 7, 31
(b) Atypical	Autosomal recessive (?)	Glycosyltransferase (?)	No circulating immunoglobulins, but B-cell precursors contain nonglycosylated IgM		
Hypogammaglobulinemia (several types)	Various: autosomal recessive, X-linked, autosomal dominant and unknown	Unknown	Decreased amounts of one or more Ig proteins in blood; often decreased numbers of plasma cells	Resembles Bruton type, but generally more benign	1, 4, 6, 7
Ataxia telangiectasia	Autosomal recessive	DNA repair enzyme	Decreased numbers of T cells and plasma cells; reduced IgA and IgE	Progressive cerebellar ataxia; telangiectasia; malignancies in 8–10%; immunodeficiency and recurrent respiratory tract infections	1, 2, 6, 7
Wiskott-Aldrich syndrome	X-linked recessive	Unknown	Progressive decrease in numbers of T cells and B cells; monocyte function abnormal; reduced IgM, increased IgA and IgE; inability to make antibodies to polysaccharide antigens; unable to form isohemagglutinins	Thrombocytopenia; eczema; recurrent infections. Transplant of bone marrow has been life-saving	1, 2, 6, 7
T4 epitope deficiency	Autosomal dominant; detected in Blacks only	Unknown	Deficiency of T4 epitope of helper/inducer T-cell subset	Lymphadenopathy, alopecia, arthritis, rash	27
X-linked lymphoproliferative syndrome	X-linked recessive	Unknown	Normal cellular and humoral immunity before Epstein-Barr virus infection; after infection, global immune defects with abnormal function of T cells and natural killer cells; growth regulation of B cells defective in fatal infections; hypogammaglobulinemia	Fatal course of mononucleosis in 70% of affected males; in those who survive, recurrent infections	28

of graft-versus-host disease often develops. The success rate for transplants of bone marrow, fetal liver or fetal thymus for SCID has been rising markedly, some centers claiming over 90% success. Favorable measures include: a nonreactive mixed lymphocyte culture and closely matched HLA and blood groups in donor and recipient, a sterile environment for the recipient both before and for a time after transplantation with, if necessary, bowel sterilization, prophylaxis against *Pneumocystis carinii*, treatment of the recipient with cyclosporine and, sometimes, cyclophosphamide, high-dose steroids, methotrexate and/or whole-body radiation after infusion of bone-marrow cells, and pretreatment in vitro of the donor marrow with antithymocyte globulin. Fetal cells do not yet possess the immune mechanism causing graft-versus-host disease; fetal liver and thymus cell infusions have been successfully used to treat SCID.

Attempts to by-pass the metabolic block in ADA deficiency and PNP deficiency by administering deoxycytidine are moderately successful in vitro, but have so far proved impracticable in vivo. Enzyme replacement, by repeated infusions of irradiated normal erythro-

Fig. 1   *Reactions leading to peroxidative killing in phagocytes*

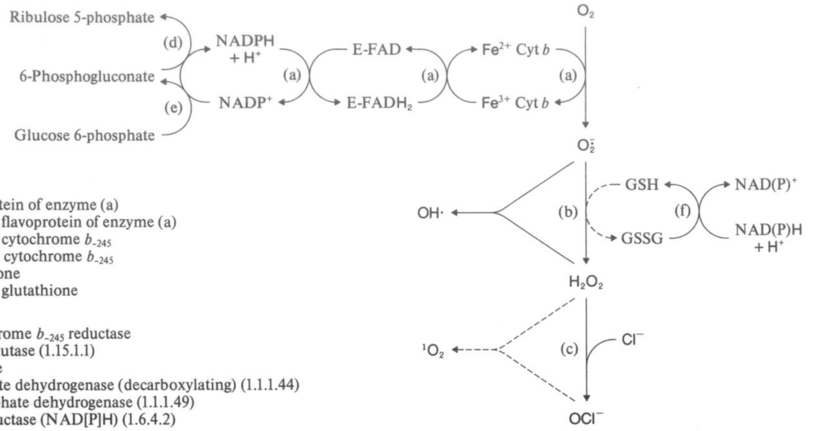

Ribulose 5-phosphate

6-Phosphogluconate

Glucose 6-phosphate

(d) NADPH + H⁺
(e) NADP⁺

E-FAD
E-FADH₂

Fe²⁺ Cyt *b*
Fe³⁺ Cyt *b*

O₂
O₂⁻

OH· (b) GSH / GSSG

(f) NAD(P)⁺ / NAD(P)H + H⁺

H₂O₂

¹O₂ (c) Cl⁻

OCl⁻

E-FAD   Flavoprotein of enzyme (a)
E-FADH₂   Reduced flavoprotein of enzyme (a)
Fe²⁺ Cyt *b* Reduced cytochrome *b*₋₂₄₅
Fe³⁺ Cyt *b* Oxidized cytochrome *b*₋₂₄₅
GSH   Glutathione
GSSG   Reduced glutathione

Enzymes involved:
(a) NADPH–cytochrome *b*₋₂₄₅ reductase
(b) Superoxide dismutase (1.15.1.1)
(c) Myeloperoxidase
(d) Phosphogluconate dehydrogenase (decarboxylating) (1.1.1.44)
(e) Glucose-6-phosphate dehydrogenase (1.1.1.49)
(f) Glutathione reductase (NAD[P]H) (1.6.4.2)

cytes, has given fairly good results in patients with some residual T-cell and B-cell functions[5]. Patients with agammaglobulinemia and hypogammaglobulinemia usually respond well to periodic injections of γ-globulin.

In acrodermatitis enteropathica (page 287) there is reduction in all T- and B-cell functions with particular susceptibility to viral and fungal infections[24].

Phagocytosis[1, 2, 14, 18, 21–23]

Polymorphonuclear neutrophil leukocytes (PMN), monocytes and eosinophils ingest and kill microorganisms. PMN are attracted to the microorganisms by chemotaxis, which requires opsonization of bacteria (by specific antibodies, complement, etc.), formation of lymphokines by T cells, release of bacterial products, etc. Actual movement of the PMN and ingestion of the bacteria involves actin microfilaments, myosin, tubulin, etc. The opsonized bacterium or other particle becomes attached to the plasma surface of the PMN, which invaginates – carrying the bacterium, etc. – into the body of the cell; then the invagination is pinched off to form a vacuole which fuses with azurophil and specific granules to form a 'phagosome'.

Fig. 2   *Detoxication of superoxide ions and hydrogen peroxide in the polymorphonuclear neutrophil leukocyte*

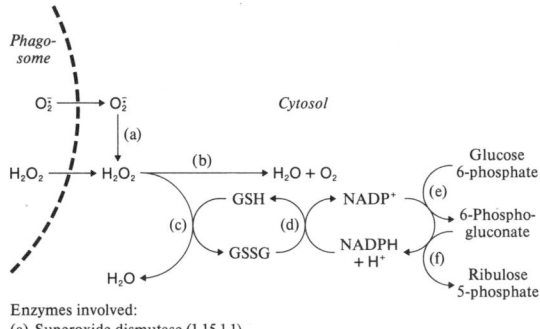

Enzymes involved:
(a) Superoxide dismutase (1.15.1.1)
(b) Catalase (1.11.1.6)
(c) Glutathione peroxidase (1.11.1.9)
(d) Glutathione reductase (NAD[P]H) (1.6.4.2)
(e) Glucose-6-phosphate dehydrogenase (1.1.1.49)
(f) Phosphogluconate dehydrogenase (decarboxylating) (1.1.1.44)

Fig. 3   *Biosynthesis of glutathione (see also page 154)*

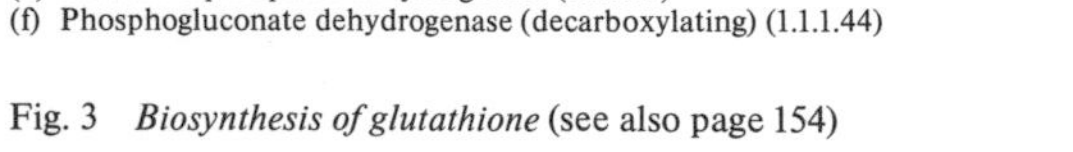

Enzymes involved:
6.3.2.2 Glutamate–cysteine ligase
6.3.2.3 Glutathione synthase

Once ingested, the bacteria are killed by release of H_2O_2 (hydrogen peroxide) into the phagocytic vacuole or phagosome. Phagocytosis by PMN is accompanied by a 'respiratory burst', a 30-fold increase in O_2 (dioxygen) consumption by the PMN. The probable mechanism is as follows: 'NADPH oxidase' in the plasma membrane is activated in the lining of the phagocytic vacuole to produce $NADP^+$ and O_2^- (superoxide ion, a free radical ion) from NADPH and O_2 by an electron transfer chain (Fig. 1). The oxygen molecule reacts first with cytochrome b_{-245} (a specific cytochrome with a redox potential of $-245\,mV$, sometimes referred to as cytochrome b_{559} to indicate the absorption maximum), and this is reduced by a flavoprotein (NADPH–cytochrome b_{-245} reductase) which in turn is reduced by NADPH[32, 33, 35]. Protein kinase C plays a vital role in activating the system, perhaps by phosphorylating the flavoprotein[33]. Superoxide dismutase acts on O_2^- to yield H_2O_2 and O_2. O_2^- can also be reduced to H_2O_2 by the —SH groups of glutathione or proteins: the activity of this system relative to superoxide dismutase is unknown. H_2O_2 is released into the phagocytic vacuole where some of it reacts nonenzymatically with O_2^- to produce OH· (hydroxy radical). H_2O_2 and Cl^- (chloride ion) react, in the presence of myeloperoxidase, to form OCl^- (hypochlorite ion), which may be a major bactericidal agent in the phagocytic vacuole, though H_2O_2, O_2^-, OH· and $^1O_2$ (singlet oxygen) are also bactericidal[42]. $^1O_2$ formation occurs in a reaction of OCl^- and H_2O_2. NADPH is regenerated via glucose 6-phosphate and the pentose phosphate pathway (page 134).

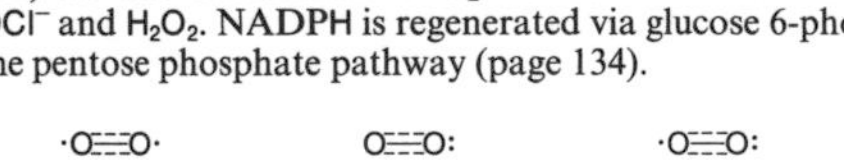

·O≡≡O·   O≡≡O: ·O≡≡O:
Triplet O₂   Singlet O₂   Superoxide ion
(ground state)   (O₂⁻)

— Sigma bond   · Unpaired electron
═ π bond   : Paired electrons

If the H_2O_2, O_2^-, etc. formed in the vacuole were to leak back into the cytoplasm, they would be cytotoxic. The PMN cytosol contains superoxide dismutase, catalase and reduced glutathione together with glutathione peroxidase and an active system for regenerating reduced glutathione and for its de-novo synthesis (page 154). These enzymes protect the PMN from the contents of the phagocytic vacuole, as shown in Figure 2, though the relative importance of catalase and of glutathione, together with glutathione peroxidase, in destroying H_2O_2 is disputed.

Although the major killing mode is believed to be peroxidative, the phagosome also contains substances, mainly derived from the azurophil and specific granules, which are bactericidal. These include lysozyme, lactoferrin (which can form H_2O_2 and OH· by a route different from that shown in Figure 1 and also chelates iron, which may be necessary for bacterial metabolism), cationic proteins and acid (pH 5.0).

Absence or inactivity of any of the enzymes shown in Figures 1–3 may be associated with defective phagocytic function and a tendency to repeated infection[43]. These conditions, among others, are listed in Table 2. Opsonization of a bacterium requires antibody and various components of complement. Defects of movement of the PMN (random and in response to a chemotactic stimulus) and defects of endocytosis are also listed in Table 2.

Table 2   *Inborn errors of metabolism affecting phagocytic function*

Condition	Inheritance	Defective enzyme or system	Biochemical and biological features	Clinical features	Reference
Complement deficiency					1, 2, 10–14
(a) C3 deficiency	Autosomal recessive	Factor C3 absent from plasma (< 0.01% of normal)	Failure to opsonize bacteria, endotoxin particles, etc.; total hemolytic complement activity markedly depressed	Numerous episodes of pyogenic infection, including pneumonia, septicemia, otitis media and meningitis	
(b) Factor I deficiency	Autosomal recessive	Factor I (C3b inactivator)	As above; increased catabolism of C3; plasma level of C3 < 5% of normal	As above; lifelong history of severe infections by *S. pneumoniae*, *H. influenzae*, β-hemolytic streptococci, etc.	
(c) C5 deficiency	Unknown	Factor C5 quantitatively normal, but qualitatively abnormal	Faulty generation of chemotactic and opsonic activity; phagocytosis of yeast particles diminished	Generalized seborrheic dermatitis; intractable severe diarrhea; recurrent *Candida albicans* infections; marked wasting; an autosomal recessive form with no C5 in blood may be associated with systemic lupus erythematosus	
(d) C6 deficiency	Autosomal recessive	Factor C6	–	Recurrent systemic gonococcal and meningococcal infections	
(e) C7 deficiency	Autosomal recessive	Factor C7	–	As above	
(f) C8 deficiency	Autosomal recessive	Factor C8	–	As above	
Decreased neutrophil mobility and ingestion					1, 2, 15
(a) Actin dysfunction	Autosomal recessive	Actin	Defective polymerization of PMN actin; slow mobility of leukocytes; impaired ingestion of opsonized bacteria, etc.; heterozygotes show defective leukocyte mobility	Recurrent gram-positive and gram-negative bacterial infections without pus	
(b) 'Lazy' leukocyte syndrome	Unknown	Unknown	Impaired random migration and chemotaxis of PMN; poor migration of PMN out of bone-marrow pool; normal ingestion and killing	Neutropenia; recurrent bacterial infections; dermatitis; periodontitis; otitis	1, 2, 14, 16
(c) Chediak-Higashi syndrome	Autosomal recessive	Organelle membrane; microtubule assembly (?)	Defective PMN mobility and chemotaxis, but normal ingestion; delayed killing of ingested bacteria; giant cytoplasmic granules (lysosomes) in PMN, monocytes, lymphocytes and other cells; high cAMP content of PMN; high O₂ consumption by 'resting' PMN	Light skin, photophobia and silvery hair; recurrent bacterial and viral infections; neutropenia; unexplained episodes of fever; peripheral neuropathy; in accelerated phase, lymphohistiocytic proliferation in liver, spleen and bone marrow, leading to pancytopenia, increased susceptibility to bacterial and viral infection and death. Large doses of ascorbic acid correct the PMN functions	1, 2, 14, 17, 18
(d) Hyper-IgE syndromes (at least 5 variants)	Unknown	Unknown	Elevated serum concentration of IgE; faulty chemotaxis of PMN and/or monocytes; eosinophilia in some variants	Type I: recurrent cutaneous, pulmonary and joint abscesses; chronic dermatitis Type II: mucocutaneous candidiasis, lifelong history of pyogenic infections Type III: chronic atopic dermatitis; recurrent abscesses of scalp, buttocks, thighs and trunk; suppurative lymphadenitis; cellulitis; marked pruritus Type IV: 'Job's syndrome'; recurrent 'cold' abscesses growing *S. aureus*; atopic-like eczema Type V: recurrent skin infections; craniosynostosis and other bone abnormalities	1, 2, 18, 19
(e) Schwachman's disease	Autosomal recessive	Unknown	Neutropenia; low PMN mobility	Frequent respiratory tract (and other) infections; pancreatic insufficiency; bone and endocrine abnormalities	1, 18
(f) 'Neutrophil paralysis'	Autosomal recessive (?) (also several acquired variants)	Absence of an antagonist to an inhibitor of leukotaxis normally present in serum	Defective chemotaxis	Recurrent staphylococcal, *Klebsiella* and/or *E. coli* lung and skin infections; also seen in severe shock, alcoholism, burns, rheumatoid arthritis, diabetes and chronic infections	20

Table 2 *Inborn errors of metabolism affecting phagocytic function (continued)*

Condition	Inheritance	Defective enzyme or system	Biochemical and biological features	Clinical features	Reference
Chronic granu-lomatous disease (CGD)					1, 2, 14, 18, 21–23, 32–38
(a)	X-linked recessive	Cytochrome b_{-245}		Catalase-positive bacteria are not killed; formation of granulomata in lymph glands, etc.; chronic or recurrent lymphadenitis, respiratory disease, etc.; usually death in childhood unless maintained on intracellular antibiotics; mainly boys affected; (b) less severe than (a)	
(b)	Autosomal recessive	Flavoprotein or protein kinase C	Failure to produce O_2^- or H_2O_2 in the phagosome		
(c)	?	Low-affinity NADPH oxidase			
CGD with gluta-thione peroxidase deficiency	Autosomal recessive	Glutathione peroxidase	Failure to destroy H_2O_2	As above; girls and boys affected	39
CGD with glu-cose-6-phosphate dehydrogenase deficiency	X-linked recessive	Glucose-6-phosphate dehydrogenase (G-6-PD) < 5% of normal	Reduced supply of NADPH necessary for the formation of O_2^- and H_2O_2	Some degree of CGD; only boys with the most severe European type of G-6-PD deficiency are affected	1, 2, 21–23
CGD with gluta-thione reductase deficiency	Autosomal recessive	Glutathione reductase (NAD[P]H)	H_2O_2 production initially normal, but ceases after 5 minutes (at 25% of normal level), probably due to cell damage by H_2O_2	Most patients have normal resistance to infection, but some show a certain degree of CGD; phagocytes do not kill catalase-positive bacteria in vitro if large numbers of bacteria are ingested	2, 22, 23
5-Oxoprolinuria (pyroglutam-ic aciduria) (1 case)	Autosomal recessive	Glutathione synthase; microtubule assembly	Very low glutathione level in all cells; excretion of 5-oxoproline	Killing capacity of phagocytes reduced	22, 23
Myeloperoxi-dase deficiency	Autosomal recessive (can also be acquired)	Myeloperoxidase	H_2O_2 in phagosome not converted to hypochlorite	Usually benign; delayed killing of *S. aureus*, *E. coli* and *Candida albicans*, for instance, after ingestion; generalized pustular psoriasis	1, 2, 18, 21–23

In contrast to the failures of chemotaxis and ingestion of bacteria, in some conditions bacteria and other opsonized particles are ingested normally, but the bacteria may not be killed. The commonest cause of X-linked chronic granulomatous disease (CGD) is absence of cytochrome b_{-245}, the gene for which is on the short arm of the X-chromosome; the apoprotein, though present, does not combine with heme, probably as the result of an amino-acid substitution. In other cases of X-linked CGD, cytochrome b_{-245} is present but is not reduced during phagocytosis, possibly because of a different amino-acid substitution. Most patients with the autosomal recessive form of CGD lack either the flavoprotein which normally reduces cytochrome b_{-245}, or protein kinase C[35], though a few lack cytochrome b_{-245} because of some unidentified genetic defect[34]. These molecular defects all prevent formation of O_2^- and, hence, H_2O_2; organisms which generate H_2O_2 (e.g. *Streptococcus faecalis*) are killed normally, but others (e.g. *Staphylococcus aureus*) that possess catalase and/or do not produce H_2O_2 survive. Persistence of the bacteria in the phagocyte results in granuloma formation, particularly in the lymph nodes, lungs, bone marrow and liver. This may lead to local sepsis with, typically, chronic or recurrent osteitis or liver abscesses. An eczema-like skin rash is often present, and some patients have mainly dermatologic symptoms. The term 'Job's syndrome' has been applied to 2 girls suffering from CGD with recurrent *S. aureus* infections leading to 'cold' (i.e. noninflamed) abscesses, etc.[25]. Later the patients were found to have high IgE levels and defective chemotaxis[26].

References

[1] WHO Scientific Group on Primary Immunodeficiency Diseases, *Clin. Immunol. Immunopath.*, **28**, 450 (1983); WHO Scientific Group on Immunodeficiency, *Wld Hlth Org. techn. Rep. Ser.*, No. 630 (1978); HILL, H. R., *Progr. clin. Path.*, **8**, 205 (1981).
[2] GÜTTLER et al. (Eds.), *Inborn Errors of Immunity and Phagocytosis*, MTP Press, Lancaster, 1979.
[3] Enzyme defects and immune dysfunction, *Ciba Found. Symp.*, NS **68** (1979); TRITSCH, G. L. (Ed.), *Ann. N. Y. Acad. Sci.*, **451** (1985).
[4] ROSEN, F. S., in STANBURY et al., *The Metabolic Basis of Inherited Disease*, 5th ed., McGraw-Hill, New York, 1983, page 1921.
[5] KREDICH and HERSHFIELD, in STANBURY et al., *The Metabolic Basis of Inherited Disease*, 5th ed., McGraw-Hill, New York, 1983, page 1157.
[6] ROSEN et al., *New Engl. J. Med.*, **311**, 235 and 300 (1984).
[7] SCHIMKE and KIRKPATRICK, *Mod. Trends hum. Genet.*, **1**, 68 (1970).
[8] O'REILLY et al., *Semin. Hemat.*, **21**, 188 (1984); NIETHAMMER, D., *Blut*, **42**, 137 (1981).
[9] HERSHFIELD et al., *J. clin. Invest.*, **63**, 807 (1979).
[10] SCHIFFERLI and PETERS, *Lancet*, **2**, 957 (1983); AGNELLO, V., *Medicine (Baltimore)*, **57**, 1 (1978).
[11] GLASS et al., in STANBURY et al., *The Metabolic Basis of Inherited Disease*, 5th ed., McGraw-Hill, New York, 1983, page 1934.
[12] MCLEAN and WINKELSTEIN, *J. Pediat.*, **105**, 179 (1984).
[13] LACHMANN and HOBART, *Trends Genet.*, **1**, 145 (1985).
[14] BAEHNER, R. L., *J. Pediat.*, **84**, 317 (1974).
[15] BOXER et al., *New Engl. J. Med.*, **291**, 1093 (1974).
[16] MILLER et al., *Lancet*, **1**, 665 (1971).
[17] WITKOP et al., in STANBURY et al., *The Metabolic Basis of Inherited Disease*, 5th ed., McGraw-Hill, New York, 1983, page 301; CLARK and KIMBALL, *J. clin. Invest.*, **50**, 2645 (1971).
[18] BAEHNER, R. L., *Pediat. Clin. N. Amer.*, **27**, 377 (1980).
[19] HILL and QUIE, in BELLANTI and DAYTON (Eds.), *The Phagocytic Cell in Host Resistance*, Raven, New York, 1975, page 249.
[20] SMITH et al., *J. Lab. clin. Med.*, **79**, 878 (1972); WARD and SCHLEGEL, *Lancet*, **2**, 344 (1969).
[21] BABIOR, B. M., *New Engl. J. Med.*, **298**, 659 and 721 (1978).
[22] SEGER, R., *Ergebn. inn. Med. Kinderheilk.*, **51**, 29 (1984).
[23] BABIOR and CROWLEY, in STANBURY et al., *The Metabolic Basis of Inherited Disease*, 5th ed., McGraw-Hill, New York, 1983, page 1956.
[24] OLESKE et al., *Cutis*, **21**, 297 (1978).
[25] DAVIS et al., *Lancet*, **1**, 1013 (1966).
[26] HILL et al., *Lancet*, **2**, 617 (1974).
[27] STOHL et al., *New Engl. J. Med.*, **312**, 1671 (1985).
[28] SULLIVAN et al., *J. clin. Invest.*, **71**, 1765 (1983).
[29] EDWARDS, N. L., *Med. Clin. N. Amer.*, **69**, 505 (1985).
[30] BONTHRON et al., *J. clin. Invest.*, **76**, 894 (1985).

[31] LEDERMAN and WINKELSTEIN, *Medicine (Baltimore)*, **64**, 145 (1985).

[32] SEGAL et al., *New Engl. J. Med.*, **308**, 245 (1985).

[33] SEGAL, A. W., *Lancet*, **1**, 1378 (1985).

[34] WEENING et al., *J. clin. Invest.*, **75**, 915 (1985).

[35] GABIG and LEFKER, *J. clin. Invest.*, **73**, 701 (1984).

[36] WEENING et al., *J. Pediat.*, **107**, 102 (1985).

[37] GALLIN and FAUCI (Eds.), *Chronic Granulomatous Disease*, Raven, New York, 1983.

[38] LEW et al., *New Engl. J. Med.*, **305**, 1329 (1981).

[39] MATSUDA et al., *J. Pediat.*, **88**, 581 (1976); HOLMES et al., *New Engl. J. Med.*, **283**, 217 (1970).

[40] HONJO and HABU, *Ann. Rev. Biochem.*, **54**, 803 (1985); LEDER, P., *Sci. Amer.*, **246**, No. 5, 102 (1982).

[41] ZEGERS et al., *New Engl. J. Med.*, **294**, 1026 (1976); STAVNEZER-NORDGREN et al., *Science*, **230**, 458 (1985).

[42] KLEBANOFF and ROSEN, *Ciba Found. Symp.*, NS **65**, 263 (1979).

[43] ROOS and WEENING, *Ciba Found. Symp.*, NS **65**, 225 (1979).

Porphyrin synthesis, as shown on page 166, starts with succinyl-CoA, an intermediate of the tricarboxylic acid cycle, and glycine to yield 5-aminolevulinic acid. With the exception of this first step in the heme synthesis pathway, an inherited defect has been described[1-7] for each of the enzymes involved (see Figure). Low 5-aminolevulinate synthase activity, however, has been reported in a case with congenital sideroblastic anemia[8]. Since heme is not only a constituent of hemoglobin and myoglobin, but also of various irreplaceable enzymes, a complete failure of heme synthesis can be assumed to be incompatible with life. No viable homozygotes are to be expected in the disorders inherited as autosomal dominant traits unless there is some residual activity of the corresponding enzyme; however, a few homozygous cases of variegate porphyria[9], of porphyria cutanea tarda (PCT; hepatoerythropoietic porphyria [HEP] is a more severe form of PCT[10]), of hereditary coproporphyria[11] and of a variant of coproporphyria known as 'harderoporphyria'[12] have been observed.

The porphyrias are classified as either erythropoietic or hepatic in type, depending on whether the failure of the heme synthesis pathway is located primarily in the erythroid cells or in the liver. The two most important clinical features in these diseases are neurological manifestations and cutaneous photosensitivity.

Porphyrias

Condition	Defective enzyme, impaired mechanism	Biochemical findings	Clinical features	Treatment	Frequency Inheritance
Congenital erythropoietic porphyria (Günther's disease)	Uroporphyrinogen-III synthase (activity in erythrocytes greatly reduced)	Content or excretion of uroporphyrin I and coproporphyrin I in tissues, plasma, urine and feces increased	Often early death; marked photosensitivity, eruptions that heal up with scarring after the action of light; erythrodontia, hemolytic anemia	Protection from UV light (sun); β-carotene orally (?); splenectomy; blood transfusions (long-term therapy)[17]; hematin i.v. (?)	~ 100 cases known Autosomal recessive
Acute intermittent porphyria (AIP) (pyrroloporphyria; 'Swedish' hepatic porphyria)	Porphobilinogen deaminase (activity in liver and erythrocytes about half of normal); excessive formation of 5-aminolevulinate and porphobilinogen as a result of impaired feedback inhibition of 5-aminolevulinate synthase	High excretion of porphobilinogen and 5-aminolevulinate in the urine; activity of liver 5-aminolevulinate synthase increased up to 8 times the normal	Onset after puberty; often flare-ups; abdominal colic; neuroses and psychoses; peripheral neuritis, paralyses, generalized demyelination; high mortality; no photosensitivity Asymptomatic in ~ 90%	Hematin i.v.; high carbohydrate intake; avoidance of initiating substances (see also text on page 268)	Frequency 0.015–0.1% Autosomal dominant
Variegate porphyria (VP) (porphyria variegata; protocoproporphyria; 'South African' hepatic porphyria)	Protoporphyrinogen oxidase; ferrochelatase activity may be reduced; excessive porphyrin formation as a result of impaired feedback inhibition of 5-aminolevulinate synthase	Fecal protoporphyrin and coproporphyrin constantly increased; fecal X-porphyrin fraction elevated; greatly increased excretion of porphobilinogen, 5-aminolevulinate, protoporphyrin and coproporphyrin in the urine during acute attacks; high activity of 5-aminolevulinate synthase in the liver	As in acute intermittent porphyria; moreover often moderate or mild photodermatoses	As in acute intermittent porphyria	Frequency 0.4% in white South Africans, rare in other populations Autosomal dominant
Porphyria cutanea tarda (PCT) (severe form: hepatoerythropoietic porphyria [HEP])	Uroporphyrinogen decarboxylase (instability of enzyme)	Increased excretion of uroporphyrin and porphyrins with 7 carboxy groups as well as coproporphyrin and isocoproporphyrin in the feces	Photodermatoses; hepatic siderosis	Phlebotomy	Autosomal dominant (acquired in some cases)
Hereditary coproporphyria (HCP)	Coproporphyrinogen oxidase	Large amounts of coproporphyrin III in urine and feces; greatly increased activity of liver 5-aminolevulinate synthase; high porphyrin content in the liver; in one variant, harderoporphyrin in the feces	Often symptomless; otherwise as in acute intermittent porphyria, but milder; photosensitivity nevertheless possible	As in acute intermittent porphyria	Autosomal dominant
Erythropoietic protoporphyria	Ferrochelatase (heme synthetase) (activity in bone marrow and liver greatly reduced)	Content or excretion of protoporphyrin in erythrocytes, normoblasts and feces greatly increased	Relatively mild photodermatoses; erythema and pruritus; mild edema; cholelithiasis in most cases; liver failure in some cases	Protection from UV light (sun); β-carotene orally	Autosomal dominant
Acute porphyria with porphobilinogen synthase deficiency	Porphobilinogen synthase (5-aminolevulinate dehydratase) (activity in erythrocytes ~ 1% of normal)	High excretion of 5-aminolevulinate and coproporphyrin III in the urine; normal porphyrin excretion in the feces	Neuropathic symptoms resembling those in acute intermittent porphyria	–	Autosomal recessive (?)

Heme synthesis

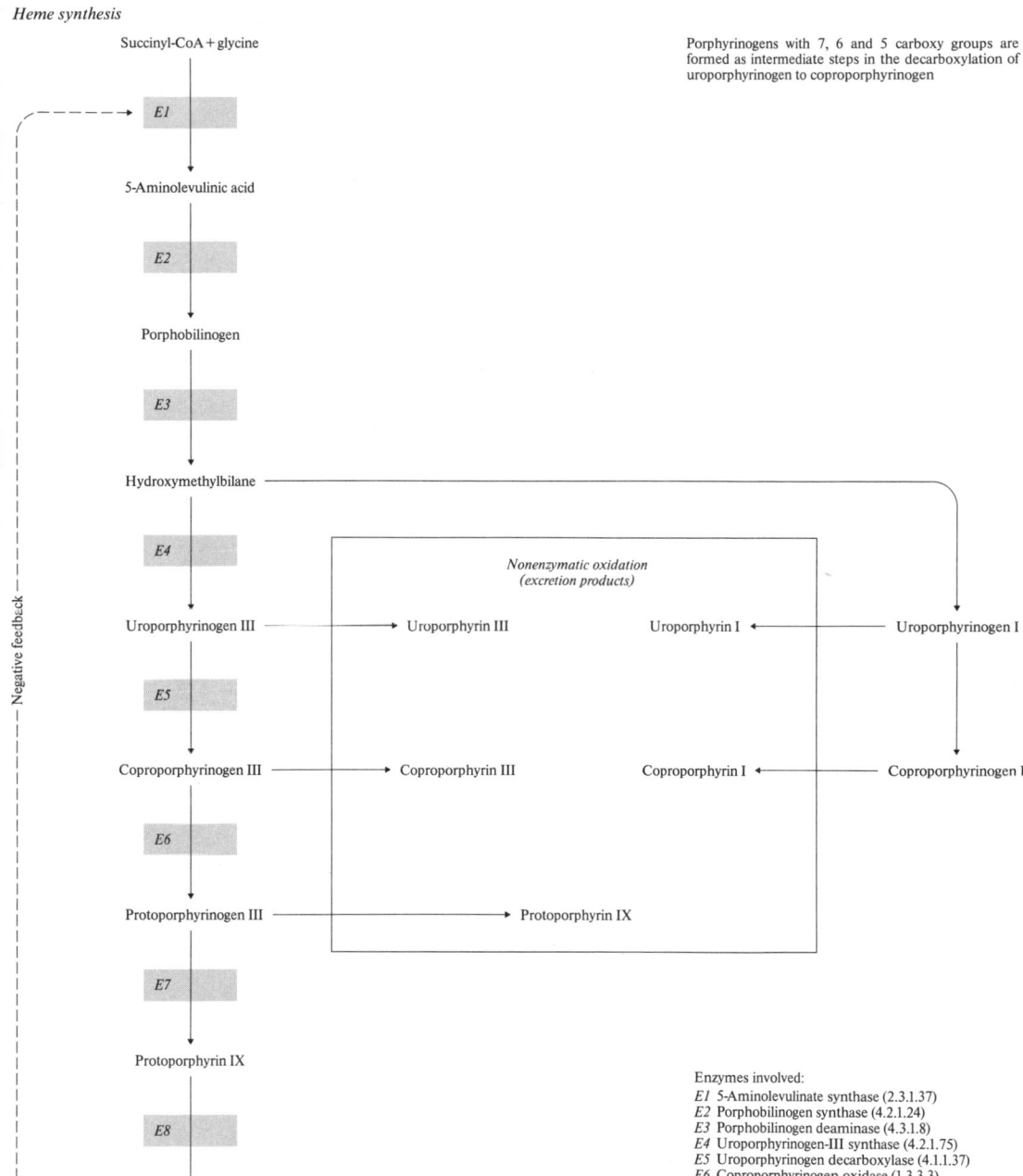

Porphyrinogens with 7, 6 and 5 carboxy groups are formed as intermediate steps in the decarboxylation of uroporphyrinogen to coproporphyrinogen

Enzymes involved:
E1 5-Aminolevulinate synthase (2.3.1.37)
E2 Porphobilinogen synthase (4.2.1.24)
E3 Porphobilinogen deaminase (4.3.1.8)
E4 Uroporphyrinogen-III synthase (4.2.1.75)
E5 Uroporphyrinogen decarboxylase (4.1.1.37)
E6 Coproporphyrinogen oxidase (1.3.3.3)
E7 Protoporphyrinogen oxidase (1.3.3.4)
E8 Ferrochelatase (4.99.1.1)

Acute intermittent porphyria (AIP), hereditary coproporphyria (HCP) and variegate porphyria (VP) have many clinical features in common and also ask for the same therapeutic approaches. AIP shows considerable genetic heterogeneity[13]; it seems to be the most common of the inherited porphyrias, occurring most frequently in Scandinavia, Britain and Ireland, but about 90% of the subjects who inherit porphobilinogen deaminase deficiency remain clinically latent and may be at risk only if exposed to harmful factors. Most patients with clinical expression also have a reduced activity of 3-oxo-5α-steroid Δ[4]-dehydrogenase in the liver. VP can present with neurovisceral symptoms, cutaneous photosensitivity or both. The disease is particularly common in the Dutch-speaking community of South Africa, and all of some 10 000 identified cases could be traced back to a single couple of Dutch immigrants who married in Cape Town in 1688[5,7]. The fecal X-porphyrin fraction is increased to a greater extent than in other porphyrias. In VP this fraction consists mainly of a group of porphyrin–peptide conjugates, and in PCT it consists of heptacarboxylate porphyrin. HCP appears to be much less common than AIP; most cases have been reported from Britain, Europe and North America. A few cases of acute porphyria may be due to a deficiency of porphobilinogen synthase. In a large kindred, apparent coexistence of AIP and VP has been reported ('Chester porphyria')[15], as has coexistence of VP and PCT[16].

PCT may be divided into 3 types: (1) sporadic cases in which family members show no evidence of the disease, (2) familial cases in which there is evidence of autosomal dominant inheritance, and (3)

cases resulting from exposure to halogenated aromatic hydrocarbons (e.g. hexachlorobenzene, polychlorinated biphenyls). In familial cases the activity of uroporphyrinogen decarboxylase in liver and erythrocytes is about half of normal. In PCT patients the risk of primary hepatocellular carcinoma is markedly increased.

The one biochemical feature common to all the porphyrias is more or less increased activity of 5-aminolevulinate synthase. As a consequence of this greater activity more substrate is delivered to the subsequent enzymes. Control of 5-aminolevulinate synthase has been shown to be mediated by protoheme concentration at both the transcriptional and translational cellular level by a negative feedback mechanism. In addition, the formation of 5-aminolevulinate synthase is stimulated by C_{19} and C_{21} steroids with a 5β-H configuration, so that a decrease in 3-oxo-5α-steroid Δ^4-dehydrogenase activity relative to 3-oxo-5β-steroid Δ^4-dehydrogenase activity also leads to an induction of 5-aminolevulinate synthase.

Lead poisoning has several symptoms in common with some of the porphyrias. Lead tends to concentrate particularly in erythroid cells where it inhibits porphobilinogen synthase and ferrochelatase. As in AIP, etc., activity of 5-aminolevulinate synthase is increased as is the urinary excretion of 5-aminolevulinate. Elevated erythrocyte protoporphyrin is a feature common to both erythrohepatic protoporphyria and lead poisoning. The erythrocyte protoporphyrin is present in free form in protoporphyria, but as a chelate with zinc in lead poisoning. Urinary coproporphyrin excretion is also increased in lead poisoning, suggesting that lead may inhibit coproporphyrinogen oxidase.

Avoidance of factors which precipitate an acute attack must be the main measure in dealing with patients or persons who may have the genetic trait. Heterozygotes in families of known carriers have to be identified in time by an appropriate biochemical test. Of the many factors known to precipitate acute attacks, drugs are the best investigated and include barbiturates, sulfonamides, sulfonylurea, pyrazinamide, griseofulvin, glutethimide, meprobamate and methyldopa. An extended list is given by KAPPAS et al.[1] and by MOORE and DISLER[14]. Other precipitating factors include ethanol, hormonal fluctuations, fasting, psychological stress and infection. Specific therapy for acute attacks consists of the use of carbohydrates, hematin and possibly β-blockers. A high carbohydrate diet reduces the overproduction of porphyrins and their precursors. The same effect is obtained by giving hematin, which is thought to enter the mitochondria and repress 5-aminolevulinate synthase activity.

References

[1] KAPPAS et al., in STANBURY et al., *The Metabolic Basis of Inherited Disease*, 5th ed., McGraw-Hill, New York, 1983, page 1301.

[2] IBRAHAM et al., *Progr. Hemat.*, **13**, 75 (1983).

[3] GOLDBERG and MOORE (Eds.), *Clin. Haemat.*, **9**, No. 2 (1980).

[4] TSCHUDY and LAMON, in BONDY and ROSENBERG, *Metabolic Control and Disease*, 8th ed., Saunders, Philadelphia, 1980, page 939.

[5] DEAN, G., *The Porphyrias*, 2nd ed., Pitman, London, 1971.

[6] DISLER et al., *Int. J. Derm.*, **23**, 2 (1984); EUBANKS et al., *Int. J. Derm.*, **22**, 337 (1983).

[7] Editorial, *Scand. J. clin. Lab. Invest.*, **45**, 291 (1985).

[8] BUCHANAN et al., *Blood*, **55**, 109 (1980).

[9] KORDA et al., *Lancet*, **1**, 851 (1984).

[10] DE VERNEUIL et al., *J. clin. Invest.*, **77**, 431 (1986); ELDER et al., *Lancet*, **1**, 916 (1981).

[11] GRANDCHAMP et al., *Lancet*, **2**, 1348 (1977).

[12] NORDMANN et al., *J. clin. Invest.*, **72**, 1139 (1983); DOSS et al., *Lancet*, **1**, 292 (1984).

[13] DESNICK et al., *J. clin. Invest.*, **76**, 865 (1985); GOLDBERG, A., *Brit. med. J.*, **291**, 499 (1985); MUSTAJOKI and DESNICK, *Brit. med. J.*, **291**, 505 (1985).

[14] MOORE and DISLER, *Advanc. Drug React.*, **2**, 149 (1983).

[15] QADIRI et al., *Brit. med. J.*, **292**, 455 (1986); McCOLL et al., *Lancet*, **2**, 796 (1985).

[16] DAY et al., *New Engl. J. Med.*, **307**, 36 (1982).

[17] POMELLI et al., *New Engl. J. Med.*, **314**, 1029 (1986).

Defects of bilirubin metabolism[1-3] may occur at any point during hepatic bilirubin transport: i.e. uptake from the circulation, intracellular binding, conjugation, biliary excretion.

A conjugation defect is present in the Crigler-Najjar syndrome. In type I, UDPglucuronate–bilirubin glucuronosyltransferase (now included with glucuronosyltransferase [2.4.1.17]) is completely absent, and treatment designed to reduce the unconjugated serum bilirubin level is often ineffective or impractical. Treatment may become available with enzyme replacement therapy. In type II a residual activity of the enzyme seems to be present, and therapy with microsomal enzyme inducers (e.g. phenobarbital) may ameliorate the hyperbilirubinemia. The conjugated bilirubin in bile in this condition is mainly bilirubin monoglucuronide. In type I Crigler-Najjar syndrome the activity of bilirubin-glucuronoside glucuronosyltransferase (page 125) is normal.

Gilbert's syndrome, characterized by mild, predominantly unconjugated hyperbilirubinemia – found in 2–5% of the population – is the most common form of conjugation defect[4]. The pathogenesis of the defect is not known. Reduction of hepatic bilirubin uptake as well as reduced activity of UDPglucuronate–bilirubin glucurono-syltransferase and bilirubin-glucuronoside glucuronosyltransferase may be involved. The serum bilirubin level fluctuates for reasons unknown. A 48-hour fast exaggerates the unconjugated hyperbilirubinemia. Type II Crigler-Najjar syndrome may be a more pronounced expression of Gilbert's syndrome.

The pathogenesis of the hereditary forms of chronic conjugated hyperbilirubinemia is only poorly understood. Dubin-Johnson syndrome and Rotor's syndrome are characterized by a diminished capacity to transport conjugated bilirubin into bile. In Dubin-Johnson syndrome this may well be due to a defect in porphyrin metabolism, resulting in a high proportion of coproporphyrin I in urine. In Rotor's syndrome the high urinary coproporphyrin excretion is most likely caused by reduced biliary excretion of coproporphyrins.

References

[1] WOLKOFF et al., in STANBURY et al., *The Metabolic Basis of Inherited Disease*, 5th ed., McGraw-Hill, New York, 1983, page 1385.
[2] BERK et al., in BONDY and ROSENBERG, *Metabolic Control and Disease*, 8th ed., Saunders, Philadelphia, 1980, page 1009.
[3] WHITMER et al., *Progr. Clin. biol. Res.*, **152**, 29 (1984).
[4] FEVERY, J., *Europ. J. clin. Invest.*, **11**, 417 (1981).

Hyperbilirubinemias

Condition	Defective enzyme, impaired mechanism	Biochemical findings	Clinical features	Treatment	Frequency Inheritance
Gilbert's syndrome (constitutional hepatic dysfunction)	Defect of bilirubin transport from blood to liver (?); activity of UDPglucuronate–bilirubin glucuronosyltransferase in the liver lowered	Serum bilirubin level normal to 60 mg/L (of which at most 10% is conjugated bilirubin); lowered proportion of bilirubin bisglucuronide in bile	Probably benign; intermittent jaundice	In pronounced jaundice phenobarbital	Probably autosomal dominant with incomplete penetrance
Crigler-Najjar syndrome type I	Complete lack of UDP-glucuronate–bilirubin glucuronosyltransferase in the liver	Serum bilirubin level 150 to 500 mg/L (no conjugated bilirubin)	Severe jaundice, almost invariably kernicterus; death usually in first 15 months of life	Exchange transfusion; phototherapy	About 70 cases described Autosomal recessive
Crigler-Najjar syndrome type II	Residual activity of UDP-glucuronate–bilirubin glucuronosyltransferase in the liver	Serum bilirubin level 40 to 230 mg/L (subnormal proportion of conjugated bilirubin); lowered proportion of bilirubin bisglucuronide in bile	Probably benign; kernicterus rare	Enzyme inducers	Probably autosomal dominant with incomplete penetrance
Dubin-Johnson syndrome	Defective excretion of conjugated bilirubin from the liver into the bile	Serum bilirubin level normal to 250 mg/L (about 60% of it conjugated); urinary excretion of coproporphyrin I increased, and of coproporphyrin III decreased; abnormal pigment in cells of the liver parenchyma	Benign; hepatosplenomegaly in rare cases	None	Uncommon, but frequent in Persian Jews Autosomal recessive
Rotor's syndrome (chronic familial nonhemolytic jaundice)	Defective excretion of conjugated bilirubin from the liver into the bile (?)	Serum bilirubin level from normal to 235 mg/L (mainly in conjugated form); urinary excretion of coproporhyrins I and III extremely high	Benign	None	Very rare Probably autosomal recessive
Recurrent intrahepatic cholestasis	Defective excretion of conjugated bilirubin from the liver into the bile (?)	Serum bilirubin (mainly in conjugated form) increased during cholestatic episodes	Benign; recurrent attacks of cholestasis; steatorrhoe	None; replacement of fat-soluble vitamins	Mode of inheritance unknown

Hypothetical pathway of asparagine-linked oligosaccharide degradation in lysosomes[3]

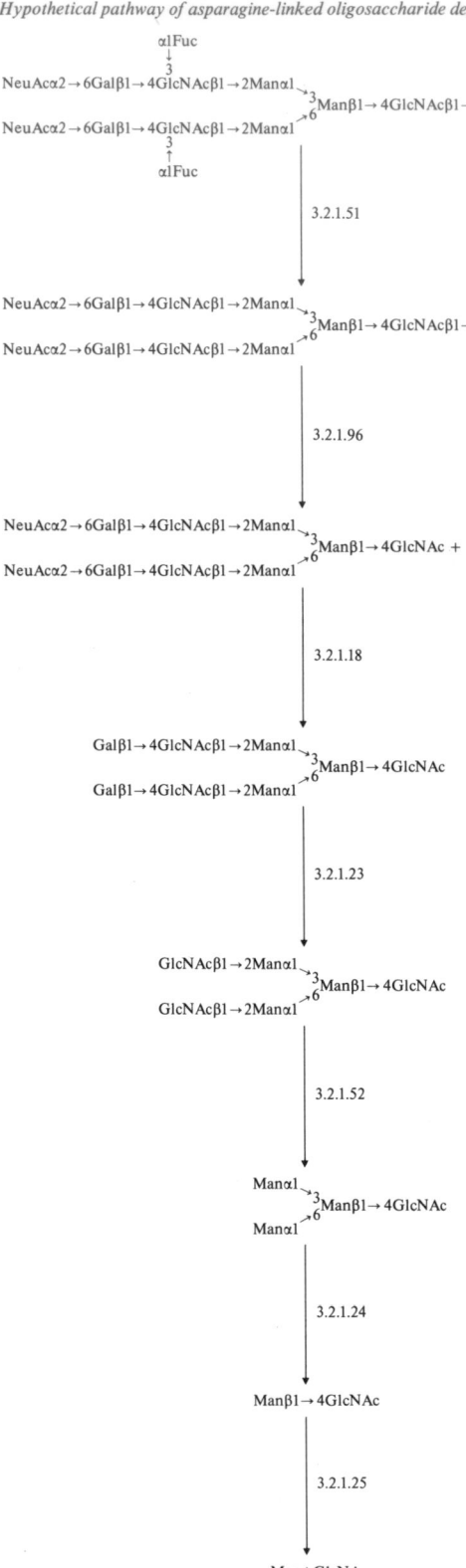

EC number	Enzyme	Associated disease
3.2.1.18	(Glycoprotein) sialidase	Sialidosis
3.2.1.23	β-Galactosidase	Mucopolysaccharidosis IV B; G_{M1} gangliosidosis
3.2.1.24	α-Mannosidase	Mannosidosis
3.2.1.25	β-Mannosidase	No human disease
3.2.1.51	α-L-Fucosidase	Fucosidosis
3.2.1.52	β-N-Acetylhexosaminidase	Sandhoff's disease
3.2.1.96	Mannosyl-glycoprotein endo-β-N-acetylglucosaminidase	No human disease
3.5.1.26	N^4-(β-N-Acetylglucosaminyl)-L-asparaginase	Aspartylglycosaminuria

Diseases known as 'mucopolysaccharidoses', 'oligosaccharidoses', 'sphingolipidoses' and 'mucolipidoses' are characterized by the accumulation of complex macromolecules (glycosaminoglycans, oligosaccharides, sphingolipids and related substances) in the lysosomes, resulting from a defective synthesis of specific hydrolases – enzymes active at an acid pH value which are responsible for the catabolism of these substances –, from a defect in the targeting of these enzymes to the lysosomes, from reduced stability of these enzymes within the lysosomes, or from absence of a lysosomal activating protein[1-3].

Lysosomal storage diseases described elsewhere in this volume are ethanolaminosis (page 237), cystinosis (page 238), glycogenosis type II (page 246), Wolman's disease (page 280) and cholesterol-ester storage disease (page 280).

Almost all of the disorders can be diagnosed by enzyme activity assays in serum, plasma, peripheral blood leukocytes or cultured skin fibroblasts[5]. Prenatal diagnosis for most of these disorders is possible by culturing amniotic fluid sediment or by using chorionic villi (page 219). Screening for mucopolysaccharidoses and oligosaccharidoses in the neonatal period is also possible by examination of the urine for a specific excretion pattern according to the storage products involved[6].

The *mucopolysaccharidoses* are listed in Table 1. The underlying enzyme defects are well characterized, but clinical and biochemical heterogeneity has been observed in all mucopolysaccharidoses[7].

Scheie's syndrome, previously cited as type V, is now classed with type I because L-iduronidase activity is lacking as in Hurler's syndrome, though the latter is caused by a mutant enzyme showing a high K_m for its substrate and in Scheie's syndrome the mutant enzyme has normal K_m, but low V_{max}[8].

Type VII was first described in 1973. Up to 1985 only 19 cases had been reported[9], but because of the extreme clinical variability seen in β-glucuronidase deficiency, this disorder seems to be underdiagnosed.

(Continued on page 273)

Table 1 *Mucopolysaccharidoses*

Disease	Classification	Defective enzyme	Accumulated compounds or compounds excreted in the urine	Mental retardation or mental deterioration	Clouding of the cornea	Facies	Skeletal involvement	Heart involvement
Hurler (gargoylism)	I_H	L-Iduronidase	Dermatan sulfate, heparan sulfate	Severe and progressive	Present	Characteristic (see text on page 273)	Characteristic (see text on page 273)	Almost always
Scheie	I_S	L-Iduronidase	Dermatan sulfate, heparan sulfate	None	Present	Similar to I_H	Less severe than in $I_{H/S}$	In some of the cases
Hurler-Scheie 'compound'	$I_{H/S}$	L-Iduronidase	Dermatan sulfate, heparan sulfate	None or mild	Present	Similar to I_H	Less severe than in I_H	In some of the cases
Hunter	II A	Iduronate 2-sulfatase	Dermatan sulfate, heparan sulfate	Less marked than in I_H	None	Similar to I_H	As in I_H	Rare
	II B	Iduronate 2-sulfatase	Dermatan sulfate, heparan sulfate	None	None	Similar to I_H	Less severe than in I_H	Rare
Sanfilippo A	III A	Heparan N-sulfatase (heparan-sulfate sulfamidase)	Heparan sulfate	Onset in early childhood with rapid progression	None	Less pronounced than in I_H	Slight	None
Sanfilippo B	III B	α-N-Acetylglucosaminidase	Heparan sulfate, glycosphingolipids (probably secondary)	As in III A	None	Less pronounced than in I_H	Slight	None
Sanfilippo C	III C	Glucosamine acetyltransferase	Heparan sulfate	As in III A	None	Less pronounced than in I_H	Slight	None
Sanfilippo D	III D	N-Acetylglucosamine-6-sulfatase	Heparan sulfate	As in III A	None	Less pronounced than in I_H	Hypoplastic odontoid process; mild osteochondrodystrophy	None
Morquio-Brailsford (probably several variants)	IV A	N-Acetylgalactosamine-6-sulfatase	Keratan sulfate/chondroitin sulfate peptide (in some of the cases)	None	In some of the cases	Different from I_H	Pronounced stunting of growth; severe distinctive bone changes in ribs, sternum, hands, feet and vertebrae (odontoid peg absent or severely hypoplastic); thin enamel	Rare; possibly a consequence of skeletal anomalies
	IV B	β-Galactosidase (high K_m for keratan sulfate, etc.; normal K_m for gangliosides[53,54])	Keratan sulfate	None	Present	Normal	Mild bone changes; odontoid peg hypoplastic; normal enamel	As in IV A
Maroteaux-Lamy	VI A	N-Acetylgalactosamine-4-sulfatase (arylsulfatase B)	Dermatan sulfate	None	Severe	Less pronounced than in I_H	Severe; similar to I_H, but no vertebral deformation	In some of the cases
	VI B	As in VIA	Dermatan sulfate	None	Moderately severe	Less pronounced than in I_H	Moderately severe	In some of the cases
	VI C	As in VIA	Dermatan sulfate	None	Mild	Less pronounced than in I_H	Mild	In some of the cases
Sly (probably several variants)	VII	β-Glucuronidase	Chondroitin 4-sulfate, chondroitin 6-sulfate; dermatan sulfate and/or heparan sulfate in some cases	None to severe	In some of the cases	In some cases resembles I_H; in others milder or normal	Pronounced in most cases	None

Table 2   *Oligosaccharidoses*

Condition	Defective enzyme	Accumulated compounds or compounds excreted in the urine	Mental retardation or mental deterioration	Clouding of the cornea, eye changes	Facies	Skeletal involvement	Involvement of other organs
Aspartylglycosaminuria	N⁴-(β-N-Acetylglucosaminyl)-l-asparaginase (aspartylglucosylaminase)	2-Acetamido-1-aspartamido-1,2-dideoxyglucose and other glycoasasparagines	Deterioration in childhood; behavioral abnormalities	Cataracts	Similar to Hurler's syndrome (see Table 1)	Very mild dysostosis multiplex; wedge-shaped vertebral bodies; thickened skull	Transient hepatosplenomegaly in some cases; mitral insufficiency in some cases
Mannosidosis (at least 2 types)	α-Mannosidase	Mannose-rich, glucosamine-containing oligosaccharides	Type I: early and rapidly progressive. Type II: in late childhood or adolescence	Present; also cataracts	Similar to Hurler's syndrome (see Table 1)	Similar to Hurler's syndrome; initially acceleration, then cessation of growth; milder in type II than in type I	Type I: hepatosplenomegaly. Type II: hearing loss; moderate hepatosplenomegaly
Fucosidosis (at least 2 types)	α-L-Fucosidase	Fucose-containing glycoproteins, sphingolipids and glycosaminoglycans (elevated Na⁺ and Cl⁻ concentrations in sweat in type I, normal concentrations in type II)	Severe progressive cerebral degeneration, rapidly advancing in type I, slowly advancing in type II	None	Different from Hurler's syndrome (see Table 1)	Similar to Hurler's syndrome	Hepatosplenomegaly (type I: cardiomegaly)
Sialidosis (mucolipidosis I; several types)	(Glycoprotein) sialidase (neuraminidase); activity of several lysosomal enzymes in the liver increased in some cases	Sialyloligosaccharides	Type I: none. Type IIa (juvenile): mild; adult onset. Type IIb (infantile): retarded. Type IIc (congenital): retarded (Types I and IIa: myoclonus; painful neuropathy; in some cases nystagmus, ataxia, grand mal seizures)	A cherry-red spot in the vicinity of the macula in type I, eventually blindness; similarly in some type II cases	Type I: normal. Type IIa: mild coarsening. Types IIb and IIc: as in Hurler's syndrome (see Table 1)	Type I: normal. Type IIa: moderate. Types IIb and IIc: severe	Hepatosplenomegaly in type IIc (and in some IIb cases); renal involvement in some IIb and IIc cases; hydrops fetalis in some IIc cases
Sialic-acid storage disorder (type I: Salla disease; type II: severe variant)	Unknown (lysosomal membrane transport defect?)	Free sialic acid in urine (type I: 0.05–0.1 g/d; type II: 0.2–1.2 g/d) and lysosomes	Severe, early, progressive; impaired motor function and ataxia; progressive neurologic deterioration and early death in type II	None in most cases; aneurysms of conjunctival capillaries in 1 severe case	Moderate coarsening; characteristic; fair complexion and hair in type II	Curved tibiae, thick calvarium; rickets, growth retardation in type II	Hepatosplenomegaly in type II
Sialuria (1 case)	Failure of regulation of UDP-N-acetylglucosamine 2-epimerase (?)	Free sialic acid (and other monosaccharides) in urine (5–7 g/d) and liver	Pronounced psychomotor retardation; severe and prolonged epileptic crises	None	Dysmorphic	Rickets; growth retardation; occult spina bifida; vertebral and thoracic anomalies	Hepatomegaly; vacuolated hepatocytes with swollen mitochondria
Mild variant (1 case)	Unknown	Free sialic acid in the urine (0.5 g/d)	Mild retardation, grand mal seizures	None	Normal	Slight; scoliosis and lordosis	None

Table 3 *Mucolipidoses*

Condition	Defective enzyme	Stored compounds	Site	Clinical features	Age at first manifestation	Refer-ence
Mucolipidosis II (I-cell disease)	UDP-N-acetylglucosamine–lysosomal-enzyme precursor N-acetylglucosaminephos-photransferase	Glycosamino-glycans, glyco-lipids	Characteristic stain-able inclusions in liv-ing fibroblasts, hepa-tocytes and Schwann cells	Similar to Hurler's syn-drome (Table 1); gingival hyperplasia; mild clouding of the cornea; often hepato-splenomegaly; death in childhood	Neonatal or early infan-cy	3, 15, 23
Mucolipidosis III (pseudo-Hurler polydystrophy)	UDP-N-acetylglucosamine–lysosomal enzyme precursor N-acetylglucosaminephos-photransferase	Glycosamino-glycans (?), glycolipids (?)	Acidic, stainable ma-terial in fibroblast cultures; vacuoles in bone-marrow cells	Stiff joints; similar to mu-colipidosis II, but milder course; resembles mucopo-lysaccharidosis VIB; sur-vival into adulthood	2–5 years	3, 15, 23
Mucolipidosis IV	(Ganglioside) sialidase spe-cific for gangliosides	Gangliosides; glycolipids, li-pofuscin, lyso-bisphospha-tidic acid	Lysosomes of many tissues	Clouding of the cornea; de-mentia; no skeletal change or hepatomegaly	Early child-hood	24

The mucopolysaccharidosis in which N-acetylglucosamine-6-sulfatase activity – not N-acetylgalactosamine-6-sulfatase – is absent is now classified as Sanfilippo D[10].

Some isolated cases of mucopolysaccharidoses cannot be classified at present. The Dyggve-Melchior-Clausen syndrome corresponds in phenotype to the Morquio Brailsford syndrome, but it differs from the latter by the presence of mental retardation and in the type of urinary glycosaminoglycans; the biochemical defect is still unknown[11].

Hurler's syndrome (gargoylism) has been known the longest. Its phenotype is characteristic: large, heavy-set skull, depressed bridge of the nose, hypertrichosis, projecting forehead, short neck, over-sized tongue, thick puffy lips, hypertrophy of the gums and widely spaced teeth. The skin is thickened and hairy, the cornea clouded in most cases. Along with the coronary valves the heart muscle and coronary vessels are often also affected, so that death (in most cases before the 20th year of life) almost always occurs due to heart failure. The abdomen is bloated as a result of hepatosplenomegaly. The skeletal anomalies are also characteristic: dwarfism and kyphosis, hyperostotic, deformed skull, ribs flattened and bent outwards, and short, heavy tubular bones. The upper lumbar vertebrae have a wedge-shaped deformity and show a spur toward the front at the lower end ('fishhook' or 'beak'). The fingers, especially the 4th and 5th, are affected by joint contractions due to changes in the tendons. Mental retardation is severe and progressive. Acidic glycosamino-glycans (heparan sulfate, dermatan sulfate) are stored in many tissues, as well as in leukocyte and fibroblast cultures, in the form of intracellular granules, and shorter-chain forms appear in increased amounts in the urine.

The other diseases more or less resemble Hurler's syndrome. All except Hunter's syndrome are inherited as autosomal recessive traits. Hunter's syndrome is inherited as an X-linked recessive trait and, with few exceptions, affects only male individuals.

When fibroblasts of patients with different mucopolysaccharidoses, for example Hurler's and Hunter's syndrome, are cultivated together, no storage of acidic glycosaminoglycans takes place. Each cell type secretes an enzyme into the culture medium which overcomes the enzyme defect of the other cell type. This finding is the basis for an attempt at treatment by enzyme substitution[7, 12, 13], as with plasma transfusion, leukocyte transfusion, bone-marrow transplants, and, in Hunter's syndrome, with skin transplants.

Oligosaccharidoses (Table 2) and *mucolipidoses* (Table 3) are genetic defects in glycoprotein metabolism. The former are due to defects in glycoprotein oligosaccharide degradation[14], the latter to defects in glycoprotein biosynthesis[3, 15]. A hypothetical scheme depicting lysosomal degradation of asparagine-linked oligosaccharide chains of a glycoprotein is shown in the Figure on page 270.

Aspartylglycosaminuria may be a defect not only of glycoprotein metabolism, but also of proteoglycan metabolism[16]; the connective-tissue abnormalities may result from disturbed metabolism of copper and zinc[52]. The disorder is prevalent among Finnish people; at least 138 cases have been reported from Finland and 14 from other countries up to 1983[3].

As regards mannosidosis, considerable phenotypic diversity has been found, and at least 70 cases have been reported up to 1983[3]. The most abundant compound excreted in the urine is a trisaccharide of the following structure:

$$Man\alpha1 \rightarrow 3Man\beta1 \rightarrow 4GlcNAc$$

The initial event in the hydrolytic cleavage of glycoproteins is most likely the removal of fucose from the oligosaccharide chain. Two general phenotypes of a defect of the enzyme responsible, α-fucosi-dase, have been identified[3]: on the one hand, patients who appear normal at birth, but develop clinical symptoms at the age of 5 to 8 months, followed by early death (infantile type); on the other hand, onset of symptoms after 1–2 years and normal mental development in patients surviving into adulthood (adult type). Up to 1983, about 60 cases of fucosidosis had been reported; many of them are of Italian ancestry[3].

Sialidosis – formerly known as 'mucolipidosis I' – occurs in 2 main types[3, 17]. Type I begins at about 8–15 years of age, and survival into adulthood is common. Type II is heterogeneous, and at least 3 sub-types can be identified, based on onset and severity of clinical features; the congenital form (6 cases have been reported up to 1983) is the most severe, and death usually occurs within the first months of life.

In addition to sialidosis, 4 different disorders of sialic-acid metabolism, characterized by an increased excretion of free N-acetyl-neuraminic acid in the urine (with lysosomal storage of free N-acetyl-neuraminic acid in 2 of them), have been described[22], whereas in sialidosis the excretion of this carbohydrate is normal. One variant of sialic-acid storage disorder – also known as 'Salla disease' – occurs almost exclusively in Finland (49 cases up to 1984[18]; in addition, 1 case in Italy[19]). Only a few cases of the more severe second variant have been described up to 1984[20]. The first report of a case of sialuria – observed in France – was published in 1968[21]; a novel type of sialuria, characterized by a milder clinical course, has recently been seen in Finland[22].

Mucolipidoses II and III (Table 3) are due to defects in glycopro-tein processing. Posttranslational modification of lysosomal acid hydrolases differs from that of other glycoproteins (page 182) by the attachment of an α-N-acetylglucosamine 1-phosphate moiety to position 6 of some mannose residues in the $Man_9GlcNAc_2$ inter-mediate (see page 183). This step is blocked in mucolipidoses II and III, which affects binding to a lysosomal membrane receptor and results in a defect in targeting the hydrolases to the lysosomes[3]. Both disorders show a high degree of genetic heterogeneity[23]. Mucolipi-dosis IV is not a defect of glycoprotein synthesis, but is closely related to the gangliosidoses[24].

The disorders of glycoprotein metabolism, as well as mucolipi-dosis IV, are transmitted as autosomal recessive traits[3].

A glycoproteinosis characterized by the storage of glutamylribose-5-phosphate in kidneys and brain has been described in a boy[4]; glutamylribose-5-phosphate is the linkage group in poly-ADP ribo-sylation of histones. This condition appears to be transmitted as an X-linked recessive trait.

The lysosomal enzyme defects of almost all the *sphingolipidoses* (Table 4) have long been known[25-32], though new forms continue to be discovered. Improved methods of investigation have led to a more correct classification of the defects. Thus the defect previously re-

(Continued on page 277)

Table 4   Sphingolipidoses (for structure of some of the stored lipids see Table 5)

Condition	Defective enzyme	Stored lipid	Site	Clinical features	Age at first manifestation	Reference
Generalized gangliosidosis (G_{M1} gangliosidosis type I; neurovisceral lipidosis; pseudo-Hurler syndrome; 'maladie de Landing')	β-Galactosidases A₁, A₂ and A₃ (activity 1% of normal or less)	G_{M1} and G_{A1}	G_{M1} and G_{A1} in neurons; small amounts of G_{M1} and a keratan-sulfate-like glycosaminoglycan in spleen, liver, kidneys (epithelial cells of the glomeruli), bone marrow, etc.	Progressive cerebral and cerebellar degeneration; severe retardation; bone deformities, coarse facial features (similar to Hurler's syndrome); cherry-red spot in the macular region in ~50% of the cases, but in most cases no clouding of the cornea; hepatosplenomegaly from about 6 months on; rapid deterioration after the 1st year of life; convulsions, decerebrate rigidity after the 16th month; death at about the age of 2 years	Birth or earliest childhood	3, 32, 54
Juvenile G_{M1} gangliosidosis (G_{M1} gangliosidosis type II)	β-Galactosidase (activity 1% of normal or less)	G_{M1}	Neurons (G_{M1} is deposited exclusively in the CNS); spleen, liver, kidneys (epithelial cells of the glomeruli), bone marrow, etc.: less keratan-sulfate-like-glycosaminoglycan than in type I	Ataxia, progressive mental and motor deterioration; no cherry-red spot in the macular region; only slight bone deformities; no hepatomegaly and no clouding of the cornea; spasticity, quadriplegia, hyperacusis; convulsions from the 16th month of life on, decerebrate rigidity after the 2nd year of life; death in most cases at the age of 3–10 years	6–20 months (mostly more than 12 months)	3, 32
Adult G_{M1} gangliosidosis (G_{M1} gangliosidosis type III)	β-Galactosidase (activity circa 5% of normal)	G_{M1} (?)	Neurons of cerebellum (?)	Progressive cerebellar ataxia, dysarthria and spasticity; little intellectual impairment	Childhood	3, 37, 54
G_{M1} gangliosidosis with sialidosis (type I: infantile form; type II: juvenile form)	Unstable β-galactosidase and sialidase in lysosomes (lack of a protective glycoprotein)	G_{M1} and sialyloligosaccharides	Neurons, spleen, liver, bone marrow, kidneys	Type I: as generalized gangliosidosis Type II: progressive neurologic deficits with ataxia, myoclonus, mild to moderate mental retardation, macular cherry-red spots, coarse facies, bony deformities; no visceromegaly; normal life expectancy (?)	Type I: early infancy Type II: 3–20 years	17, 38
Tay-Sachs disease (infantile amaurotic familial idiocy; G_{M2} gangliosidosis type I)	β-N-Acetylhexosaminidase A absent in type B, present (but activator protein absent) in type AB; an altered enzyme is present in type AMB	G_{M2}	Intraneuronal (white and gray matter of the brain); small quantities in spleen and liver	Very early hyperacusis; cherry-red spot in the macular region; progressive cerebral degeneration; in 90% death at the age of 1–5 years	Mostly between 4 and 6 months (storage of the ganglioside begins in utero)	32, 34, 39
Sandhoff's disease (G_{M2} gangliosidosis type II; G_{M2} gangliosidosis type 0) (a) Infantile form (b) Juvenile (late infantile) form	β-N-Acetylhexosaminidases A and B	G_{M2} and G_{A2}; globoside in kidneys and spleen; N-acetylglucosaminyl-oligosaccharides in tissues and urine	As in Tay-Sachs disease; somewhat larger quantities in spleen and liver	(a) As in Tay-Sachs disease (b) Slow progression; no cherry-red spot	(a) As in Tay-Sachs disease (b) 1st year of life	3, 32
Juvenile G_{M2} gangliosidosis (G_{M2} gangliosidosis type III) (a) Late infantile form (b) Juvenile form	β-N-Acetylhexosaminidase A (variable loss of activity)	G_{M2}	As in Tay-Sachs disease	As in Tay-Sachs disease, but in most cases no cherry-red spot in the macular region, as well as slower progression; death during childhood	(a) 2nd year of life (b) From 4th year of life on	32

Disease	Stored substance	Enzyme	Site	Clinical features	Age	Ref
Adult G_{M2} gangliosidosis	G_{M2}	β-N-Acetylhexosaminidase A (or its activator protein in some cases)	As in Tay-Sachs disease	Normal at first, then behavioral and neurological abnormalities progressing rapidly; death in a few years; sometimes spinocerebellar degeneration, ataxia or motor abnormalities; some are unaffected	18–40 years (occasionally first signs at the age of 2–4 years with slow progression); some survive without symptoms	40
G_{M3} sphingolipodystrophy (G_{M3} gangliosidosis)	G_{M3}	(N-Acetylneuraminyl)-galactosylglucosylceramide N-acetylgalactosaminyltransferase (deficient synthesis of G_{M2} and G_{M1})	Brain, liver	Largely like generalized gangliosidosis; death in the 1st year of life	Birth (1 case)	41
Metachromatic leukodystrophy (late infantile form)	Sulfatides (galactosylsulfate ceramide and lactosylsulfate ceramide)	Cerebroside-sulfatase (arylsulfatase A); activity 3–5% of normal	White matter of the brain and peripheral nerve sheaths (exclusively galactosylsulfate ceramide); kidneys (both sulfatides), gall bladder	Progressive: motor disturbances, later speech regression, ataxia and convulsions (~50% of the cases); cherry-red spot in the macular region (in about one-third of the cases); cerebral degeneration; posture of decerebrate rigidity; death before the 12th year of life (mostly at the age of 3–7 years)	1–4 years (in most cases between 12 and 18 months)	30
Metachromatic leukodystrophy of adults (a) Juvenile form (b) Adult form	The same sulfatides as in the late infantile form	Cerebroside-sulfatase (arylsulfatase A); activity lowered, but higher than in the late infantile form (an unstable enzyme may be formed); in a few cases, cerebroside-sulfatase normal, but activator protein absent	As in the late infantile form, but the gray matter of the brain is more affected than the white matter	Schizophrenia-like psychosis with sudden onset and progressing over a few years; later dementia; still later progressive motor disturbances; death usually 5–10 years after onset	(a) 3–16 years (b) 16–62 years	30,42
Metachromatic leukodystrophy due to multiple sulfatase deficiency (mucosulfatidosis)	Gangliosides, sulfatides, cholesterylsulfate, dehydroepiandrosterone sulfate; sulfated glycosaminoglycans	9 distinct sulfatases acting on sulfatides, steroids and glycosaminoglycans; also β-galactosidase (probably secondary)	Neurons, liver; excretion of glycosaminoglycans in the urine; Alder-Reilly bodies in the leukocytes	As in the late infantile form of metachromatic leukodystrophy; moderate hepatosplenomegaly	1–4 years	30,43
Gaucher's disease (a) Chronic ('adult') form (at least 2 subtypes) (b) Infantile neuronopathic form (c) Juvenile neuronopathic form (Norbottnian) (d) Prenatal neuronopathic form	Glucosylceramide	Glucosylceramidase; total lack in (b) and (d); activity in (a) ~15% of normal, in (c) ~2.5% of normal	Spleen, liver, bone marrow, lymph nodes, leukocytes; brain in (b), (c) and (d); lungs in some cases of (b)	Splenomegaly, often very severe; hepatomegaly; anemia, pancytopenia; ostealgia and osteoporosis; purpura; cerebral degeneration in (b) and (c); slow progression in (a) with death at any age (depending on subtype), due to infections or liver dysfunction; in (b) death in the 1st or 2nd year of life; in (c) death in adolescence or early adult life; in (d) stillbirth or neonatal death (ascites and hydrops fetalis)	(a) 1–60 years (b) 1st year of life (c) 6–20 years (d) in utero	28,44
Krabbe's disease (galactosylceramide lipidosis; globoid cell leukodystrophy)	Excess of galactosylceramide in the axons, but not in the myelin sheaths	Galactosylceramidase	Almost total disappearance of myelin; as a rule considerable infiltration by globoid cells; less involvement of peripheral nerves	Hypersensitivity, hyperacusis; severe, rapidly progressing mental and motor deficiencies; decerebration and blindness within months; death in most cases within the first 2 years of life, a few with a milder form survive for several years or even to adult life	3–6 months	29

Table 4   Sphingolipidoses (continued) (for structure of some of the stored lipids see Table 5)

Condition	Defective enzyme	Stored lipid	Site	Clinical features	Age at first manifestation	Reference
Fabry's disease (α-galactosidase A deficiency: angiokeratoma corporis diffusum)	Galactosylgalactosylglucosylceramidase (α-galactosidase A)	Ceramide trihexoside (galactosylgalactosylglucosylceramide); also digalactosylceramide in kidneys and urine	Plasma, vessel walls, kidneys, urine and bone marrow: neurons of the central autonomic nervous system (brain stem, amygdaloid supraoptic nucleus, thalamus, etc.), as well as the peripheral autonomic nervous system	Only males are severely affected; severe, intermittent pains in hands and feet; telangiectases and/or angiokeratomas on the lower abdomen; mild superficial clouding of the cornea; hypertension; frequently cerebrovascular episodes after the second decade of life; progressive kidney dysfunction; death in most cases before the 50th year of life; neuropsychiatric symptoms in some older patients	Late childhood or adolescence	31
Farber's disease (disseminated lipogranulomatosis)	Acylsphingosine deacylase (ceramidase)	Ceramide, glycolipids; in a few cases, dermatan sulfate	Subcutaneous tissue and tendons, especially at the joints; neurons	Hoarseness, then later markedly noisy respiration; joint swellings and subcutaneous nodules; progressive growth retardation and arthropathy; death as a rule between 7 and 22 months (some survive)	Mostly early infancy	26, 45
Niemann-Pick disease type A	Sphingomyelin phosphodiesterase (activity in the liver less than 10% of normal)	Sphingomyelin and cholesterol (markedly increased)	Neurons, liver, spleen, bone marrow, lymphatic tissue, lungs	Progressive, pronounced hepatosplenomegaly; at the age of about 1 year retardation of mental, physical and motor development; lung involvement, in a few cases anemia; continued deterioration during the 2nd year of life; cherry-red spot in the macular region in ~ 50% of the cases; death mostly at the age of 2–3 years	First half year of life (deposition of sphingomyelin begins in utero)	27, 45
Niemann-Pick disease type B (non-neurological variant)	Sphingomyelin phosphodiesterase (activity in the liver ~ 10% of normal)	Sphingomyelin and cholesterol (moderately to markedly increased)	Spleen, liver, bone marrow, lungs	Hepatosplenomegaly; recurring lung infection in only a few cases; otherwise no findings (no CNS involvement)	6 months to 4 years	27, 45
Niemann-Pick disease type C (subacute or juvenile form)	Deficiency of activator protein for sphingomyelin phosphodiesterase (?)	Sphingomyelin and cholesterol (normal to moderately increased, mainly in the spleen); lysobisphosphatidic acid	Neurons of the CNS; spleen, lymph nodes, bone marrow, lungs, but not liver	Pronounced splenomegaly, but only slight hepatomegaly; onset of slowly progressing neurological deficiencies mostly between 5 and 10 years; death in most cases between 5 and 15 years	First half year of life	27, 36, 45
Niemann-Pick disease type D (Nova Scotia variant)	Not known (normal total activity of sphingomyelin phosphodiesterase)	As in type C	Neurons, spleen, lymph nodes, lungs, less in the liver	Neonatal jaundice, recurrent jaundice, fibrosis of the liver; otherwise like type C	From birth	27, 45, 46
Niemann-Pick disease type E	Not known (normal or lowered activity of sphingomyelin phosphodiesterase)	Sphingomyelin and cholesterol	Spleen, bone marrow, liver	Benign	Data lacking (few cases)	27, 45
Neuronal ceroid lipofuscinosis; familial amaurotic idiocy (Santavuori type [infantile]; Jansky-Bielschowsky type [late infantile]; Batten-Spielmeyer-Vogt type [juvenile]; Kufs type [adult])	Unknown (metabolism of dolichol-linked oligosaccharides?)	Dolichol and dolichyl phosphate; ceroid and lipofuscin; arachidonic acid (in the form of phosphoglycerides in the brain and serum) moderately increased	Neurons (cytoplasmic osmiophilic fluorescent globules with positive PAS reaction) with fingerprint-like arrangement	Progressive cerebral degeneration with optic atrophy; onset of mental and motor deficiencies as well as blindness at different times; late form: ataxia, dysarthria, dementia, but no blindness; death from 5 years to the 6th decade of life, depending on the time of the first manifestation	12 months to adulthood, depending on type	47, 48, 51

Table 5 *Trivial name and structure of stored glycosphingolipids*

Trivial name	Structure
Glucosylceramide	Cer—Glc
Galactosylceramide.	Cer—Gal
Lactosylceramide.	Cer—Glc—Gal
Digalactosylceramide	Cer—Gal—Gal
Sulfogalactosylceramide . . .	Cer—Gal3SO₄
Myelin ganglioside	Cer—Gal—NeuAc
Psychosine . . . . (galactosylsphingosine)	Sphingosine—Gal
Ceramide trihexoside . . . . . (trihexosylceramide)	Cer—Glc—Gal—Gal
Globoside.	Cer—Glc—Gal—Gal—GalNAc
Hematoside (G$_{M3}$).	Cer—Glc—Gal $\mid$ NeuAc
Tay-Sachs ganglioside. . . . . (G$_{M2}$)	Cer—Glc—Gal—GalNAc $\mid$ NeuAc
Asialo-G$_{M2}$ (G$_{A2}$)	Cer—Glc—Gal—GalNAc
Monosialoganglioside. . . . . (G$_{M1}$)	Cer—Glc—Gal—GalNAc—Gal $\mid$ NeuAc
Asialo-G$_{M1}$ (G$_{A1}$) . . . . (gangliotetraosylceramide)	Cer—Glc—Gal—GalNAc—Gal

ferred to as 'lactosylceramidosis' seems to be another variant of Niemann-Pick disease[33].

A clinically indistinguishable variant of Tay-Sachs disease, designated 'G$_{M2}$ gangliosidosis type AB', has normal β-N-acetylhexosaminidases A and B, but lacks an activator protein necessary for the action of β-N-acetylhexosaminidase A on its membrane-bound substrate[34]. Similarly, there is a variant of metachromatic leukodystrophy in which the cerebroside-sulfatase (arylsulfatase A) is normal but its specific activator protein is lacking[35]. Deficiency of a somewhat different activator protein for sphingomyelin phosphodiesterase has been reported to cause Niemann-Pick disease type C[36], though this has been disputed.

G$_{M3}$ sphingolipodystrophy is not caused by a catabolic defect like the other diseases, but rather by an impairment of synthesis, and is not a lysosomal disease.

Inheritance of Fabry's disease is X-linked recessive, whereas the other diseases are inherited as autosomal recessive characters. Gaucher's disease is the most common inherited metabolic disorder of glycolipid metabolism; there are more than 4000 patients with type I in the United States. The chronic ('adult') form of Gaucher's disease and Tay-Sachs disease are more prevalent among Jews of Ashkenazic ancestry than in any other population[28].

The treatment of sphingolipidoses is frustrating. Approaches are enzyme replacement by direct enzyme substitution[3] (placental galactosylgalactosylceramidase in Fabry's disease, placental glucosylceramidase in Gaucher's disease for example), as well as bone-marrow transplantation to repopulate tissues with enzymatically competent cells[13] (Gaucher's disease[49], metachromatic leukodystrophy[50]).

References

[1] HERS and VAN HOOF (Eds.), *Lysosomes and Storage Diseases*, Academic Press, London, 1973.

[2] STANBURY et al., *The Metabolic Basis of Inherited Disease*, 5th ed., Part 5: Disorders of lysosomal enzymes, McGraw-Hill, New York, 1983, page 749.

[3] DURAND and O'BRIEN (Eds.), *Genetic Errors of Glycoprotein Metabolism*, Springer, New York, 1983; WARNER and O'BRIEN, *Ann. Rev. Genet.*, 17, 395 (1983); KORNFELD, S., *J. clin. Invest.*, 77, 1 (1986).

[4] WILLIAMS et al., *New Engl. J. Med.*, 311, 152 (1984).

[5] O'BRIEN, J. F., *Mayo Clin. Proc.*, 57, 192 (1982).

[6] SEWELL et al., *Klin. Wschr.*, 57, 581 (1979); SEWELL, A. C., *Europ. J. Pediat.*, 134, 183 (1980).

[7] McKUSICK and NEUFELD, in STANBURY et al., *The Metabolic Basis of Inherited Disease*, 5th ed., McGraw-Hill, New York, 1983, page 751.

[8] HOPWOOD and MULLER, *Clin. Sci.*, 57, 265 (1979).

[9] LEE et al., *Amer. J. Dis. Child.*, 139, 57 (1985).

[10] COPPA et al., *Europ. J. Pediat.*, 140, 130 (1983).

[11] BECK et al., *Clin. chim. Acta*, 141, 7 (1984); SCHLAEPFER et al., *Helv. paediat. Acta*, 36, 543 (1981).

[12] CRAWFURD et al. (Eds.), *Advances in the Treatment of Inborn Errors of Metabolism*, Wiley, Chichester, 1982; HIRSCHHORN and WEISSMANN, *Progr. med. Genet.*, NS 1, 49 (1976).

[13] BARRANGER, J. A., *New Engl. J. Med.*, 311, 1629 (1984).

[14] BEAUDET, A. L., in STANBURY et al., *The Metabolic Basis of Inherited Disease*, 5th ed., McGraw-Hill, New York, 1983, page 788.

[15] NEUFELD and McKUSICK, in STANBURY et al., *The Metabolic Basis of Inherited Disease*, 5th ed., McGraw-Hill, New York, 1983, page 778.

[16] NÄNTÖ-SALONEN et al., *Clin. chim. Acta*, 146, 111 (1985).

[17] LOWDEN and O'BRIEN, *Amer. J. hum. Genet.*, 31, 1 (1979).

[18] RENLUND, M., *J. Pediat.*, 104, 232 (1984); RENLUND et al., *Neurology (Minneap.)*, 33, 57 (1983).

[19] GEHLER et al., in *Third International Symposium on Inborn Errors of Metabolism in Humans*, Munich 1984, Abstracts, Karger, Basle, 1984, page 88.

[20] STEVENSON et al., *Pediatrics*, 72, 441 (1983); THOMAS et al., *Pediat. Res.*, 17, 307 (1983); TONDEUR et al., *Europ. J. Pediat.*, 139, 142 (1982); HANCOCK et al., *J. Neurochem.*, 38, 803 (1982).

[21] KAMERLING et al., *Biochim. biophys. Acta (Amst.)*, 583, 403 (1979); FONTAINE et al., *Helv. paediat. Acta*, 23, Suppl. 17, 1 (1968).

[22] PALO et al., *Clin. chim. Acta*, 145, 237 (1985).

[23] SLY and SUNDARAM, in LLOYD and SCRIVER (Eds.), *Genetic and Metabolic Disease in Pediatrics*, Butterworth, London, 1985, page 91; MUELLER et al., *Clin. chim. Acta*, 150, 175 (1985); MUELLER et al., *J. clin. Invest.*, 72, 1016 (1983).

[24] CAIMI et al., *J. inherited metab. Dis.*, 5, 218 (1982); LIVNI and MERIN, *Arch. Path. Lab. Med.*, 102, 600 (1978).

[25] VOLK and SCHNECK (Eds.), *The Gangliosidoses*, Plenum, New York, 1975.

[26] MOSER and CHEN, in STANBURY et al., *The Metabolic Basis of Inherited Disease*, 5th ed., McGraw-Hill, New York, 1983, page 820.

[27] BRADY, R. O., in STANBURY et al., *The Metabolic Basis of Inherited Disease*, 5th ed., McGraw-Hill, New York, 1983, page 831.

[28] BRADY and BARRANGER, in STANBURY et al., *The Metabolic Basis of Inherited Disease*, 5th ed., McGraw-Hill, New York, 1983, page 842.

[29] SUZUKI and SUZUKI, in STANBURY et al., *The Metabolic Basis of Inherited Disease*, 5th ed., McGraw-Hill, New York, 1983, page 857.

[30] KOLODNY and MOSER, in STANBURY et al., *The Metabolic Basis of Inherited Disease*, 5th ed., McGraw-Hill, New York, 1983, page 881.

[31] DESNICK and SWEELEY, in STANBURY et al., *The Metabolic Basis of Inherited Disease*, 5th ed., McGraw-Hill, New York, 1983, page 906.

[32] O'BRIEN, J. S., in STANBURY et al., *The Metabolic Basis of Inherited Disease*, 5th ed., McGraw-Hill, New York, 1983, page 945.

[33] WENGER et al., *Science*, 188, 1310 (1975).

[34] LI et al., *Amer. J. hum. Genet.*, 35, 520 (1983); HECHTMAN et al., *Pediat. Res.*, 16, 217 (1982); CONZELMANN and SANDHOFF, *Proc. nat. Acad. Sci. (Wash.)*, 75, 3979 (1978).

[35] FUJIBAYASHI et al., *J. Pediat.*, 104, 739 (1984); STEVENS et al., *Amer. J. hum. Genet.*, 33, 900 (1981).

[36] CHRISTOMANOU, H., *Hoppe-Seylers Z. physiol. Chem.*, 361, 1489 (1980).

[37] WENGER et al., *Clin. Genet.*, 17, 323 (1980).

[38] D'AZZO et al., *Proc. nat. Acad. Sci. (Wash.)*, 79, 4535 (1982); GRAVEL et al., *Amer. J. hum. Genet.*, 31, 669 (1979); WENGER et al., *Biochem. biophys. Res. Commun.*, 82, 589 (1978); PALMERI et al., *Amer. J. hum. Genet.*, 38, 137 (1986).

[39] INUI et al., *Amer. J. hum. Genet.*, 35, 551 (1983).

[40] CONZELMANN et al., *Amer. J. hum. Genet.*, 35, 900 (1983).

[41] MAX et al., *New Engl. J. Med.*, 291, 929 (1974).

[42] VON FIGURA et al., *Proc. nat. Acad. Sci. (Wash.)*, 80, 6066 (1983).

[43] ETO et al., *Arch. Neurol. (Chic.)*, 30, 153 (1974); MURPHY et al., in BERNSOHN and GROSSMAN (Eds.), *Lipid Storage Diseases*, Academic Press, London, 1971, page 67.

[44] PENTCHEV et al., *Amer. J. hum. Genet.*, 35, 621 (1983); WENGER et al., *Pediat. Res.*, 17, 344 (1983).

[45] ELLEDER and JIRÁSEK, *Acta Univ. Carol. Med. (Praha)*, 29, 259 (1983); CROCKER, A. C., in BERNSOHN and GROSSMAN (Eds.), *Lipid Storage Diseases*, Academic Press, London, 1971, page 27.

[46] WINSOR and WELCH, *Amer. J. hum. Genet.*, 30, 530 (1978).

[47] ZEMAN and SIAKOTOS, in HERS and VAN HOOF (Eds.), *Lysosomes and Storage Diseases*, Academic Press, London, 1973, page 519; ZEMAN et al., in VINKEN and BRUYN (Eds.), *Handbook of Clinical Neurology*, Volume 10, North-Holland, Amsterdam, 1970, page 588.

[48] EGESKOV JENSEN et al., *Scand. J. clin. Lab. Invest.*, 38, 309 (1978); NEIMANN et al., *Méd. et Hyg. (Genève)*, 33, 1464 (1975); HAGBERG et al., *Acta paediat. scand.*, 63, 753 (1974); DEKABAN and HERMAN, *Arch. Path.*, 97, 65 (1974).

[49] RAPPEPORT and GINNS, *New Engl. J. Med.*, 311, 84 (1984).

[50] BAYEVER et al., *Lancet*, 2, 471 (1985).

[51] HALL and PATRICK, *J. inherited metab. Dis.*, 8, 178 (1985).

[52] NÄNTÖ-SALONEN et al., *J. inherited metab. Dis.*, 8, 212 (1985).

[53] VAN DER HORST et al., *Amer. J. med. Genet.*, 16, 261 (1983).

[54] HOOGEVEEN et al., *J. biol. Chem.*, 259, 1974 (1984).

Table 1   *Classification of lipoprotein particles*

Lipoprotein class	Density range	Electro-phoretic mobility	Diameter	Mean composition				Apolipoproteins
				Total choles-terol	Triacyl-glycerols	Phospho-lipids	Protein	
	g/mL		nm	Mass fraction (relative to dry mass of total lipoprotein) as percent				
Chylomicrons	0.9–0.95	Origin	75–1000	2–9	80–95	4–18	1–2	AI, AII, AIV, B48, CI, CII, CIII, E, H
VLDL..........	0.97–1.006	Pre-β	28–75	12	60	18	10	B 100, CI, CII, CIII, E, H (trace)
IDL............	1.006–1.019	Between β and pre-β	21–35	36	19	24	20	B 100 (traces of E, CI, CII, CIII)
LDL	1.006–1.05	β	20–24	50	10	15	25	B 100 (~95%)
Lp(a)...........	1.05–1.08	Pre-β₁	22–26	39	3	20	38	B 100, apo-Lp(a)
HDL₂	1.08–1.125	α	7–12	22	4.5	30	41	AI, AII, CI, CII, CIII, D, E (in some
HDL₃	1.125–1.21	α	4–7.5	15	4.1	22.5	55	subfractions, traces of F and G)
VHDL	> 1.21	α	–	3.5	4.6	28	62	–

Table 2   *Classification of apolipoproteins*

Apolipoprotein	M_r	Lipoprotein density class	Function
AI.......	28 300	HDL......................	Activates phosphatidylcholine–sterol acyltransferase
AII	17 400	HDL......................	Enhances phosphatidylcholine–sterol acyltransferase (?), activates hepatic lipase (?)
AIII or D .	32 000	HDL........................	Cholesterol ester exchange between lipoproteins
AIV......	46 000	Chylomicrons	Unknown
Apo-Lp(a)	900 000	LDL, HDL..................	Unknown
B 100.....	549 000	LDL, VLDL, IDL.............	Binds to LDL receptor in peripheral tissues
B 48......	264 000	Chylomicrons	Stabilizes chylomicrons (?)
CI	6 000	Chylomicrons, VLDL, IDL, HDL	Activates phosphatidylcholine–sterol acyltransferase
CII	8 800	VLDL, HDL	Activates lipoprotein lipase
CIII-0	~9 000	HDL......................	Unknown
CIII-1	~9 000	VLDL.....................	Unknown
CIII-2	~9 000	VLDL.....................	Inhibits lipoprotein lipase (?)
E	35 000	VLDL.....................	Binds to receptor on liver cells
F	30 000	HDL......................	Unknown
G........	75 000	HDL......................	Unknown
H........	43 000	Chylomicrons, VLDL..........	Activates lipoprotein lipase

Myocardial infarction related to hypercholesterolemia is a major cause of mortality and morbidity; for example, 1 person in ~ 500 is a heterozygote for a mutant gene at the low-density lipoprotein (LDL) receptor locus and suffers a myocardial infarction before 45 years of age[1]. Homozygotes (frequency ~ 1:10⁶) suffer myocardial infarction at 5–15 years of age.

The normal gene codes for a protein of M_r ~ 110 000, which is glycosylated in the Golgi apparatus to give the receptor protein (M_r ~ 164 000); this protein then enters the cell membrane in 'coated pits'[1,2]. The receptor binds LDL, which thereby enters the cell in 'coated vesicles' that fuse with lysosomes. The cholesterol in the LDL inhibits hydroxymethylglutaryl-CoA reductase (NADPH), the rate-limiting enzyme in the synthesis of cholesterol (feedback inhibition)[1]. One kind of mutant gene fails to form the receptor apoprotein; a second group of mutations results in failure of normal glycosylation of the receptor apoprotein; a third mutation produces a variant glycoprotein of M_r ~ 210 000 which, though it enters 'coated pits' at the cell surface, has a markedly reduced ability to bind LDL. In yet a fourth type, the receptor binds LDL normally at the cell surface, but the LDL is not internalized[1]. The resultant failure to control cholesterol biosynthesis leads to hyperlipidemia with plasma LDL concentrations ~ 2.5 times the normal for heterozygotes and ~ 6 times the normal for homozygotes. Cholesterol and other lipids are, in consequence, deposited in various tissues, above all in the intima of the coronary arteries, by mechanisms not involving the LDL receptor.

The B 100 apolipoprotein of LDL binds to the glycoprotein receptor, which has a high affinity for apo-B 100 and also for apo-E, present in some high-density lipoproteins (HDL)[3]. The receptor also binds Lp(a) lipoprotein, which contains apo-B 100. However, the cholesterol in Lp(a) appears to be relatively ineffective in inhibiting hydroxymethylglutaryl-CoA reductase (NADPH), and the presence of Lp(a) is associated with three times the frequency of coronary heart disease found in Lp(a)-negative individuals[4].

An abnormality of an apolipoprotein may prevent binding or metabolism of plasma lipids, resulting in hyperlipidemia. Until recently the hyperlipidemias were classified on the basis of the lipids or lipoproteins found in the plasma (Fredrickson's types I to V). Today the synthesis of LDL receptor glycoprotein in cultured fibroblasts or leukocytes and the various apolipoproteins in the plasma can be investigated; studying both propositi and close relatives permits a classification by genotype[5].

Triacylglycerols and cholesterol are transported in the plasma as lipoproteins and chylomicrons[6] (Table 1). Very-low-density lipoproteins (VLDL) are synthesized in the liver; chylomicrons are formed in the intestine. Lipoprotein lipase in vascular endothelium hydrolyzes triacylglycerols both in chylomicrons and in VLDL. VLDL is thereby converted, via intermediate-density lipoprotein (IDL), to LDL with the loss not only of triacylglycerol and some phospholipid, but also of apolipoproteins C and E, which are transferred to HDL. There are several HDL subclasses. Whereas VLDL and LDL transport cholesterol or triacylglycerol from the liver to peripheral tissues, HDL transports cholesterol from the peripheral tissues to the liver; hypercholesterolemia tends to cause atherosclerosis if the cholesterol is mainly in LDL, but deficiency of HDL-bound cholesterol is also associated with premature coronary artery disease[4,7]. The apolipoproteins (Table 2) function by binding the lipoproteins, of which they form part, to specific receptors on cells in the liver, muscle, endothelium and fibroblasts, and/or by activating or inhibiting enzymes involved in lipoprotein metabolism, as well as by stabilizing the lipoprotein particles[6].

Inherited abnormalities in the synthesis or structure of some apolipoproteins are associated with specific diseases (Table 3); while some are rare inborn errors of metabolism, others of these variant apolipo-

(Continued on page 283)

Table 3 *Inborn errors of the metabolism of lipoproteins, cholesterol and triacylglycerols*

Condition	Defective enzyme, impaired mechanism	Plasma lipids, Fredrickson phenotype	Storage of lipids	Clinical features	Incidence, Age at first manifestation, Inheritance	Reference
Familial hypercholesterolemia	Deficient number or functioning of LDL receptors	Cholesterol level 8–16 mmol/L in heterozygotes, often over 20 mmol/L in homozygotes; β-lipoprotein increased Type IIa, rarely IIb	Cholesterol (mainly esterified) in tendon sheaths and arterial walls	Xanthomata, coronary artery diseases, arcus corneae. Treatment by means of a diet high in polyunsaturated fatty acids and low in saturated fatty acids and cholesterol, as well as with drugs such as cholestyramine or nicotinic acid	~0.2% of the population, ~3–6% of myocardial infarction patients Hypercholesterolemia from birth; xanthomata in homozygotes in early childhood, in adulthood in heterozygotes; arteriosclerosis in childhood in homozygotes, from 30 years on in heterozygotes Autosomal dominant	1
Familial combined hyperlipidemia	Unknown (overproduction of VLDL [?]; excess of apolipoprotein B [?])	Cholesterol (heterozygotes 5 to 10 mmol/L) and/or triacylglycerols increased Type IIa, IIb, IV, rarely V	—	Xanthomata only rarely. Dietetic treatment as in familial hypercholesterolemia	~1.5% of the population and ~11–20% of myocardial infarction patients Increased lipid concentration only in adulthood Autosomal dominant	5, 15
Polygenic hypercholesterolemia	Not consistent	Cholesterol increased, extent of increase varying from individual to individual	—	No (?) xanthomata. Dietetic treatment as in familial hypercholesterolemia	~5% of the population Risk of arteriosclerosis in adulthood increased Polygenic inheritance	5
Type III hyperlipoproteinemia ('broad β-disease'; dys-β-lipoproteinemia)	Abnormal apo-E (almost exclusively phenotype E2/2), a defect resulting in accumulation of VLDL and chylomicron remnants	Cholesterol level ~12 mmol/L, triacylglycerol level ~8 mmol/L; massive accumulation of β-VLDL ('β-floating') Type III	Cholesterol (mainly esterified) in tendon sheaths and arterial walls	Xanthomata in skin over elbows, knees and buttocks; coronary artery and systemic disease. Dietetic treatment as in familial hypercholesterolemia, in addition restriction of carbohydrate and ethanol consumption, as well as administration of nicotinic acid or clofibrate	~1 in 5000 of the population has complete syndrome (~1% of myocardial infarction patients) 16–95 years Most patients are homozygous for apo-E2 (autosomal recessive), a few have liver receptor defect (autosomal dominant); ~1% of the population is homozygous for apo-E2, but normolipidemic	7, 16
Familial hypertriglyceridemia	Synthesis or catabolism of VLDL (?); possible excess of apo-CIII-2; mutant apo-AI in some cases	Triacylglycerol level 6 mmol/L; pre-β-lipoproteins increased Type IV, rarely V	Cholesterol (mainly esterified) in arterial walls	Hepatosplenomegaly, arteriosclerosis. Restriction of carbohydrate and ethanol consumption, possibly administration of nicotinic acid	~1% of the population and ~5% among myocardial infarction patients Adulthood, possibly childhood Autosomal dominant	5
Familial hyperlipoproteinemic type V (probably several subtypes)	Synthesis of VLDL triacylglycerols; clearance of triacylglycerol-rich lipoproteins; prevalence of apo-E4 (?)	Cholesterol slightly increased; triacylglycerols 10–30 mmol/L; chylomicrons, pre-β-lipoprotein increased Type V	—	Xanthomata, episodic abdominal pain (with or without pancreatitis), hepatosplenomegaly, lipaemia retinalis, hyperuratemia, abnormal glucose tolerance, ischemic heart disease in ~20%. Protein-rich, low-energy diet poor in long-chain fatty acids; if necessary, administration of nicotinic acid, oxandrolone, norethindrone (in women) or clofibrate	Rare Usually 20–45 years; rarely in childhood Autosomal dominant with variable penetrance	17, 18

Table 3   *Inborn errors of the metabolism of lipoproteins, cholesterol and triacylglycerols (continued)*

Condition	Defective enzyme, impaired mechanism	Plasma lipids Fredrickson phenotype	Storage of lipids	Clinical features	Incidence Age at first manifestation Inheritance	Reference
Familial lipoprotein lipase deficiency (hyperchylomicronemia)	Lipoprotein lipase (diacylglycerol lipase) of tissue	Triacylglycerol level up to 170 mmol/L, mostly 20–60 mmol/L; massive increase of chylomicrons Type I	—	Repeated abdominal pain; recurrent acute pancreatitis; in about 50% eruptive xanthomata on skin and mucous membranes; moderate hepatosplenomegaly from about 6 months on. Fat-free diet beneficial	Very rare 3 weeks or later Autosomal recessive	19, 20
Familial apolipoprotein CII deficiency	Apo-CII (the plasma activator for lipoprotein lipase)	As for familial lipoprotein lipase deficiency Type I	—	Recurrent acute pancreatitis, often mild; anemia; some cases asymptomatic; life expectancy usually normal	23 cases known up to 1984 10–60 years Autosomal recessive	19, 21
Wolman's disease	Acid lipase <4% of normal	Mainly normal	Cholesterol esters and triacylglycerols in adrenal glands, liver, spleen, bone marrow, capillaries, endothelium, ganglion cells of mesenteric plexus and mucosa of the small intestine	Vomiting; distended abdomen; progressive anemia; hepatosplenomegaly (sometimes very pronounced); adrenal calcification and enlargement; rapid deterioration; death usually between 3 and 6 months	40 cases known up to 1983 First weeks of life Autosomal recessive	8, 22
Cholesterol-ester storage disease	Hepatic acid lipase ~ 25% of normal	Cholesterol (sometimes also triacylglycerols) elevated Type IIa or IIb	Cholesterol-ester storage in liver, spleen, intestinal mucosa, lymph nodes, aorta, cultured fibroblasts (concentrations 120 to 350 times the normal)	Hepatomegaly; eventually hepatic fibrosis; sometimes a bleeding tendency and/or jaundice; splenomegaly in one third of the cases; relatively benign	25 cases known up to 1985 Autosomal recessive	8, 23
Abetalipoproteinemia (Bassen-Kornzweig syndrome)	Absence of apolipoproteins B48, B100 and CIII-1	Cholesterol and triacylglycerols reduced; no chylomicrons and no VLDL, LDL and Lp(a)	—	Acanthocytosis (50–100% of the erythrocytes); retinitis pigmentosa; steatorrhea (very early); areflexia, proprioreceptive breakdowns, ataxia, muscle weakness, Babinski's sign, spinocerebellar demyelination; skeletal deformities	Rare Childhood Autosomal recessive	24
Hypobetalipoproteinemia	Resembles abetalipoproteinemia (some cases may be heterozygotes for abetalipoproteinemia)	Resembles abetalipoproteinemia; some LDL present	—	Resembles abetalipoproteinemia; heterozygotes may be asymptomatic	Rare Autosomal recessive	24
Anderson's disease	Assembly of chylomicrons; absence of apo-B48; very little apo-B100	Resembles abetalipoproteinemia	Intestinal lining cells packed with triacylglycerols and apolipoprotein B	Diarrhea; steatorrhea; failure to thrive	Very rare Birth Probably autosomal recessive	25
Normotriglyceridemic abetalipoproteinemia	Absence of apo-B100	Cholesterol and triacylglycerols reduced, but the latter increases after oral fat load; no LDL	—	Acanthocytosis (possibly similar to abetalipoproteinemia)	2 cases known Birth (?)	26

Disease	Basic defect	Plasma lipids / laboratory	Tissue accumulation	Clinical features	Frequency / inheritance	Ref.
Hypoalphalipoproteinemia	Apo-AII (?), apo-AI and/or apo-CIII (?)	Low HDL cholesterol; total cholesterol normal; triacylglycerols normal	—	Premature coronary artery disease and stroke	Rare; Adults; Autosomal dominant	47
Analphalipoproteinemia ('Tangier disease' [from Tangier Island off the coast of Virginia])	Structural defect of apo-AI	Cholesterol reduced, triacylglycerides normal to increased; abnormal HDL; absence of normal HDL	Cholesterol esters in liver, spleen, lymph nodes, cornea, skin, etc.	Tonsils hypertrophied and orange-yellow; splenomegaly; foam cells in bone marrow; lymphadenopathy and hepatomegaly in a few cases; peripheral neuropathy only later and only rarely; premature atherosclerosis, but about normal life expectancy	Rare; From 5 years on; Autosomal recessive	24,34
Fish eye disease	Low apo-AI and apo-AII	Triacylglycerols increased, but cholesterol normal; very low HDL; raised cholesterol and triacylglycerols in VLDL and LDL	—	Severe corneal opacities develop gradually; seriously impaired vision by 7th or 8th decade; otherwise normal. Some family members with very low plasma concentration of HDL have normal eyes	2 families known; Probably dominant (autosomal or X-linked)	27
Familial lecithin–cholesterol acyltransferase deficiency	Phosphatidylcholine–sterol acyltransferase (lecithin–cholesterol acyltransferase)	Cholesterol and triacylglycerols increased; lysophosphatidylcholine and cholesterol esters lowered; multiple lipoprotein abnormalities	—	Proteinuria; clouding of the cornea; anemia with target cells; in a few cases, foam cells in bone marrow and kidneys. Therapy by enzyme replacement	More than 30 cases known up to 1985; Adulthood; Autosomal recessive	28,29
Triglyceride storage disease Type I	Adenylate cyclase (?); catecholamine receptor (?)	—	Triacylglycerols in some adipose tissues	Low body mass at birth; extreme emaciation; mental and physical retardation; microcephaly; optic atrophy; death in childhood	2 cases known; From birth	30
Type II	Protein kinase (?)	—	Triacylglycerols in adipose tissues	Obesity	3 cases known	
Type III	Unknown; extralysosomal lipase (?)	—	Triacylglycerol-laden vacuoles in leukocytes and many tissues	Asymptomatic	1 case known (adult)	
Pancreatic lipase deficiency ('butter stool')	Lipase of the pancreatic juice	—	Triacylglycerols in the feces	Fat absorption about 70%; normal growth. Enzyme substitution effective	Very rare; Birth up to 3 years; Probably autosomal recessive	31
Cerebrotendinous xanthomatosis	Mitochondrial steroid 26-hydroxylase; a defect resulting in impaired bile acid synthesis and accumulation of cholesterol	Cholesterol normal in most cases; various bile alcohols in bile and urine	Cholestanol (free and esterified) plus smaller amounts of cholesterol (both free and esterified) in the white matter of the cerebrum and cerebellum; demyelinization in the cerebellum, brain stem and forebrain	Slowly progressing cerebellar ataxia and dementia; cataracts; xanthomata of the Achilles tendon and other tendons, as well as on the lungs; increasing spasticity; in a few cases, tremors, Babinsky's sign, distal muscular atrophy, loss of the ability to perceive vibrations; death in most cases in the 4th or 5th decade, sometimes later. Treatment with cholic acid	46 cases known up to 1983; Late childhood; Autosomal recessive	32,33

Table 4   Inborn errors of the metabolism of fatty acids and related substances

Condition	Defective enzyme, impaired mechanism	Plasma lipids and other compounds in body fluids	Storage of lipids	Clinical features	Incidence, Age at first manifestation, Inheritance	Reference
Adrenoleukodystrophy (a) juvenile (b) connatal/neonatal (c) adrenomyeloneuropathy	(a) Lignocerate-CoA ligase (b) Deficiency of peroxisomes (similar to Zellweger's syndrome (c) Milder form of (a) (?)	Very-long-chain fatty acids ($>C_{22}$); long-chain dicarboxylic acids in the urine	Very-long-chain fatty acids (C_{24} to C_{30}, mainly C_{25} and C_{26}) accumulate as cholesterol esters in CNS myelin, adrenals and testes	(a) Adrenal insufficiency with progressive dementia, behavioral abnormalities, visual impairment and spasticity; sudanophil demyelination; death 2–4 years after onset (b) Seizures; profound hypotonia and mental retardation; death before 3 years (c) Peripheral neuropathy; hormonal insufficiencies; sphincter disturbance; slowly progressive spastic paraparesis	(a) ~ 1:30000 First decade X-linked recessive (b) 12 cases known up to 1983 Fetal or from birth Autosomal recessive (?) (c) Rare Young adult X-linked incompletely recessive (?)	35–37, 49.52
Pseudo-Zellweger syndrome	Several peroxisomal enzymes (multiple defect)	Similar to Zellweger's syndrome	Similar to adrenoleukodystrophy and Zellweger's syndrome	Similar to Zellweger's syndrome	1 case Neonatal	51
Zellweger's syndrome (cerebrohepatorenal syndrome)	Peroxisomes (absent from liver and kidneys); a defect resulting in various metabolic disturbances (see text)	Very-long-chain fatty acids ($>C_{22}$); cholic acid absent from plasma and bile; pipecolic acidemia; pipecolic acid and long-chain dicarboxylic acids in the urine	Very-long-chain fatty acids ($>C_{22}$, mainly C_{25} and C_{26}, especially $C_{26:1}$) accumulate as cholesterol esters in myelin; plasmalogens absent or deficient in tissues	Multiple craniofacial dysmorphisms; congenital cataracts; profound hypotonia; 'ragged-red' muscle fibers in some cases; failure to thrive; hepatomegaly; micronodular cirrhosis (variable); renal cortical cysts; dysmyelination; cerebral dysgenesis; death within 2 years (usually in first 8 months)	At least 1:100000 Neonatal Autosomal recessive	13,14, 38.49
Infantile phytanic-acid storage disease	Phytanic-acid α-hydroxylase and other peroxisomal enzymes	Phytanic acid 3–125 mg/L; hypocholesterolemia; sometimes hypoalphalipoproteinemia; pipecolic acidemia; very-long-chain fatty acids; low HDL level	Very-long-chain fatty acids ($>C_{22}$) in hepatocytes, etc.	Mild facial dysmorphism; hepatomegaly; retinitis pigmentosa and deafness in infancy; mental retardation (nonprogressive); expressionless facies; progressive storage of lipid in Kupffer cells and hepatocytes, resembling adrenoleukodystrophy by electron microscopy	Rare First 2 years of life Autosomal recessive (?)	39
Phytanic-acid storage disease (Refsum's disease)	Phytanic-acid α-hydroxylase (isolated defect)	Phytanic acid 5–37% of total fatty acids (200–3100 mg/L; normal: <2 mg/L)	Phytanic acid in liver (over 50% of total fatty acids), kidneys and other organs; adipose tissue (phytanic acid 5% of total fatty acids) is the main storage site	Gradually progressive, chronic polyneuropathy; atypical retinitis pigmentosa with night blindness; cerebellar ataxia; high protein concentration in the CSF. Diet low in phytol and phytanic acid (avoidance of milk fat, meat from ruminants, nuts, coffee, green vegetables); plasma exchange	Rare From early childhood to 5th decade Autosomal recessive	40
'Nonketotic' dicarboxylic aciduria	Medium-chain acyl-CoA dehydrogenase	Saturated, unsaturated and hydroxylated C_6 to C_{12} straight-chain dicarboxylic acids; high excretion of these acids and their conjugates with glycine, carnitine and glucuronic acid in the urine	—	Life-threatening attacks of hypoketotic hypoglucosemia resembling Reye's syndrome or sudden infant death syndrome; irreversible brain damage in some cases. Treatment with carnitine	Rare Early childhood Autosomal recessive	41–43

proteins occur at a frequency high enough to constitute polymorphism. Apolipoprotein E, for instance, is often found as E2 with cysteine residues at positions 112 and 158, E3 with cysteine at position 112 and arginine at position 158, or E4 with arginine at both positions; each of these primary peptides is sialylated to varying degrees to give several subtypes[6,7]. Homozygotes for the apo-E2 variant, if they also overproduce VLDL, develop type III hyperlipidemia (broad β-disease) with its attendant xanthomata in 68 to 100% of affected subjects and coronary artery atherosclerosis in 19–37%. Recent reports link xanthomatosis and atherosclerosis to abnormalities of apolipoproteins E or B even in the absence of hypercholesterolemia or hypertriglyceridemia[6]. Apolipoprotein C III is normally present in 3 forms (C III-0, C III-1, C III-2) varying in the number of sialic-acid residues per molecule.

Phytosterolemia closely resembles homozygous familial hypercholesterolemia, but requires different treatment, plant sterols being stored[48].

Wolman's disease and cholesterol-ester storage disease are caused by a lysosomal enzyme defect; the two disorders are probably the expression of different mutant alleles at the same locus, and other alleles producing intermediate phenotypes probably exist as well[8].

Metabolism of long-chain fatty acids (β-oxidation) involves esterification of the fatty acids with carnitine, catalyzed by carnitine palmitoyltransferase I, transport of these esters across the inner mitochondrial membrane and their hydrolysis by carnitine palmitoyltransferase II. Inborn errors of metabolism involving each or both of these enzymes, as well as two forms of congenital carnitine deficiency, are known[9]. All four lead to skeletal muscle disorders resembling McArdle's syndrome (page 247), but with lipid rather than glycogen deposited in the muscles and with cardiomyopathy in some cases. Of the two forms of carnitine deficiency, one involving a defect in carnitine biosynthesis, the other a defect in carnitine transport into skeletal muscle, the former is associated with multiple episodes of acute encephalopathy resembling Reye's syndrome[10]. Both can be treated with large doses of carnitine. Carnitine deficiency is also a sign of medium-chain acyl-CoA dehydrogenase deficiency, since the medium-chain dicarboxylic acids produced in high amounts become partly conjugated with carnitine[41].

β-Oxidation – particularly that of very-long-chain fatty acids – takes place not only in mitochondria but also in peroxisomes[11]. The peroxisomal β-oxidation system does not require carnitine and is not linked to the mitochondrial electron transfer system. Peroxisomes have a variety of physiological functions; more than 40 enzymes have been localized to this organelle[12]. It can be assumed that a defect of peroxisomes leads to a series of biochemical derangements; in Zellweger's syndrome, for example, there is a disturbance not only in the β-oxidation of fatty acids, but also in the metabolism of bile acids and lysine (giving rise to pipecolic acid) and in the synthesis of plasmalogens[13,14]. A classification scheme of peroxisomal disorders has been suggested[50].

Glycerol kinase deficiency has been described in about 20 individuals[44,45]. It causes a 50-fold rise in plasma glycerol concentration and glyceroluria. Two principal groups have been identified: children presenting with adrenal hypoplasia or insufficiency as well as variable neuromuscular and skeletal abnormalities, and adults diagnosed incidentally and showing no symptoms. The deficiency is inherited as an X-linked character; the glycerol kinase locus seems to be in the X,p21 band (close to the Duchenne muscular dystrophy locus)[46].

References

[1] GOLDSTEIN and BROWN, in STANBURY et al., *The Metabolic Basis of Inherited Disease*, 5th ed., McGraw-Hill, New York, 1983, page 672; MYANT, N. B., *Klin. Wschr.*, **61**, 383 (1983); ANDERSON, R. G., *Amer. J. Physiol.*, **243**, E5 (1982); BROWN and GOLDSTEIN, *Science*, **232**, 34 (1986).

[2] SCHNEIDER et al., *Molec. Biol. Med.*, **1**, 353 (1983); TOLLESHAUG et al., *Cell*, **32**, 941 (1983).

[3] MAHLEY, R. W., *Med. Clin. N. Amer.*, **66**, 375 (1982).

[4] BERG, K., *Progr. med. Genet.*, NS **5**, 35 (1984).

[5] BRUNZELL and MOTULSKY, *Progr. clin. biol. Res.*, **147**, 403 (1984); SCHONFELD, G., *Progr. clin. biol. Res.*, **147**, 375 (1984); MOTULSKY, A. G., *New Engl. J. Med.*, **294**, 823 (1976); CUTHBERT et al., *New Engl. J. Med.*, **314**, 879 (1986).

[6] SCHAEFER and LEVY, *New Engl. J. Med.*, **312**, 1300 (1985); KREISBERG, R. A., *Ann. intern. Med.*, **99**, 713 (1983); GALTON et al., *Clin. Sci.*, **64**, 559 (1983); BRESLOW, J. L., *Ann. Rev. Biochem.*, **54**, 699 (1985).

[7] MAHLEY and ANGELIN, *Advanc. intern. Med.*, **29**, 385 (1984); BREWER et al., *Ann. intern. Med.*, **98**, 623 (1983); HAVEL, R. J., *Med. Clin. N. Amer.*, **66**, 441 (1982).

[8] HOEG et al., *Amer. J. hum. Genet.*, **36**, 1190 (1984); ASSMAN and FREDRICKSON, in STANBURY et al., *The Metabolic Basis of Inherited Disease*, 5th ed., McGraw-Hill, New York, 1983, page 803.

[9] REBOUCHE and ENGEL, *Mayo Clin. Proc.*, **58**, 533 (1983).

[10] DiDONATO et al., *J. neurol. Sci.*, **50**, 207 (1981).

[11] OSMUNDSEN, H., *Ann. N. Y. Acad. Sci.*, **386**, 13 (1982).

[12] TOLBERT, N. E., *Ann. Rev. Biochem.*, **50**, 133 (1981).

[13] SINGH et al., *Proc. nat. Acad. Sci. (Wash.)*, **81**, 4203 (1984); MOSER et al., *New Engl. J. Med.*, **310**, 1141 (1984).

[14] BJÖRKHEM et al., *Scand. J. clin. Lab. Invest.*, **45**, Suppl. 177, 23 (1985); KASE et al., *J. clin. Invest.*, **75**, 427 (1985); BAKKEREN et al., *Clin. chim. Acta*, **138**, 325 (1984); DATTA et al., *New Engl. J. Med.*, **311**, 1080 (1984).

[15] GOLDSTEIN et al., *J. clin. Invest.*, **52**, 1544 (1973).

[16] BROWN et al., in STANBURY et al., *The Metabolic Basis of Inherited Disease*, 5th ed., McGraw-Hill, New York, 1983, page 655.

[17] GREENBERG et al., *Ann. intern. Med.*, **87**, 526 (1977); YESHURUN et al., *J. Amer. med. Ass.*, **238**, 2518 (1977); FALLAT and GLUECK, *Atherosclerosis*, **23**, 41 (1976).

[18] KESANIEMI and GRUNDY, *J. Amer. med. Ass.*, **251**, 2542 (1984); GHISELLI et al., *J. clin. Invest.*, **70**, 474 (1982).

[19] NIKKILÄ, E. A., in STANBURY et al., *The Metabolic Basis of Inherited Disease*, 5th ed., McGraw-Hill, New York, 1983, page 622.

[20] MANZATO et al., *J. Lab. clin. Med.*, **104**, 778 (1984); FELLIN et al., *Atherosclerosis*, **49**, 55 (1983).

[21] GOTTO, A. M., *New Engl. J. Med.*, **310**, 1664 (1984); SAKU et al., *Amer. J. Med.*, **77**, 457 (1984).

[22] MAEHIRA et al., *Biochem. Med.*, **32**, 322 (1984).

[23] KELLY et al., *Biochem. Med.*, **33**, 29 (1985).

[24] HERBERT et al., in STANBURY et al., *The Metabolic Basis of Inherited Disease*, 5th ed., McGraw-Hill, New York, 1983, page 589.

[25] INFANTE et al., in *Third International Symposium on Inborn Errors of Metabolism in Humans*, Munich 1984, Abstracts, Karger, Basle, 1984, page 107.

[26] TAKASHIMA et al., *Pediatrics*, **75**, 541 (1985); MALLOY et al., *J. clin. Invest.*, **67**, 1441 (1981).

[27] CARLSON, L. A., *Europ. J. clin. Invest.*, **12**, 41 (1982).

[28] GLOMSET et al., in STANBURY et al., *The Metabolic Basis of Inherited Disease*, 5th ed., McGraw-Hill, New York, 1983, page 643.

[29] OWEN et al., *Biochem. Soc. Trans.*, **13**, 20 (1985); MURAMAYA et al., *Europ. J. clin. Invest.*, **14**, 122 (1984); ALBERS et al., *Acta med. scand.*, **210**, 455 (1981).

[30] RECKLESS et al., in COLLIPP, P. J. (Ed.), *Childhood Obesity*, 2nd ed., PSG Publishing, Littleton, Mass., 1980, page 79.

[31] FIGARELLA et al., *J. Pediat.*, **96**, 412 (1980); FRÉZAL and REY, *Advanc. hum. Genet.*, **1**, 275 (1970); SHELDON, W., *Arch. Dis. Childh.*, **39**, 268 (1964); GARROD, A. E., *Inborn Errors of Metabolism*, 2nd ed., Frowde, Hodder & Stoughton, London, 1923.

[32] SALEN et al., in STANBURY et al., *The Metabolic Basis of Inherited Disease*, 5th ed., McGraw-Hill, New York, 1983, page 713.

[33] KOOPMAN et al., *Clin. chim. Acta*, **152**, 115 (1985); KOOPMAN et al., *Clin. chim. Acta*, **142**, 103 (1984); BJÖRKHEM et al., *J. clin. Invest.*, **71**, 142 (1983).

[34] SCHMITZ et al., *Proc. nat. Acad. Sci. (Wash.)*, **80**, 6081 (1983), KAY et al., *Proc. nat. Acad. Sci. (Wash.)*, **79**, 2485 (1982).

[35] DAVIS et al., *Amer. J. Med.*, **66**, 342 (1979); GRIFFIN et al., *Neurology (Minneap.)*, **27**, 1107 (1977); SCHAUMBURG et al., *Arch. Neurol. (Chic.)*, **32**, 577 (1975).

[36] JAFFE et al., *Amer. J. Path.*, **108**, 100 (1982); ULRICH et al., *Acta neuropath. (Berl.)*, **43**, 77 (1978).

[37] GOLDFISCHER et al., *Science*, **227**, 67 (1985); O'NEILL and MOSER, *Canad. J. neurol. Sci.*, **9**, 449 (1982); MOSER et al., *Johns Hopk. med. J.*, **147**, 217 (1980).

[38] TRIJBELS et al., *Pediat. Res.*, **17**, 514 (1984); KELLEY, R. I., *Amer. J. med. Genet.*, **16**, 503 (1983); GOVAERTS et al., *Europ. J. Pediat.*, **139**, 125 (1982); KELLEY, R. I., *Amer. J. med. Genet.*, **16**, 503 (1983).

[39] BUDDEN et al., *J. Pediat.*, **108**, 33 (1986); POULOS et al., *Clin. Genet.*, **26**, 579 (1984); SCOTTO et al., *J. inherited metab. Dis.*, **5**, 83 (1982).

[40] STEINBERG, D., in STANBURY et al., *The Metabolic Basis of Inherited Disease*, 5th ed., McGraw-Hill, New York, 1983, page 731.

[41] DURAN et al., *J. Pediat.*, **107**, 397 (1985); DURAN et al., *Clin. chim. Acta*, **152**, 253 (1985).

[42] GREGERSEN, N., *Scand. J. clin. Lab. Invest.*, **45**, Suppl. 174, 11 (1985).

[43] BOUGNÈRES et al., *J. Pediat.*, **106**, 918 (1985); AMENDT and RHEAD, *J. clin. Invest.*, **76**, 963 (1985); ROE et al., *J. Pediat.*, **108**, 13 (1986).

[44] POMETTA et al., *Europ. J. clin. Invest.*, **14**, 103 (1984); McCABE, E. R., *Biochem. Med.*, **30**, 215 (1983); McCABE et al., *J. inherited metab. Dis.*, **5**, 177 (1982).

[45] WIRTH et al., *Dtsch. med. Wschr.*, **110**, 843 (1985); GINNS et al., *J. Pediat.*, **104**, 736 (1984).

[46] BARTLEY et al., *J. Pediat.*, **108**, 189 (1986); DUNGER et al., *Lancet*, **1**, 585 (1986).

[47] ORDOVAS et al., *New Engl. J. Med.*, **314**, 671 (1986); THIRD et al., *Metabolism*, **33**, 136 (1984); VERGANI and BETTALE, *Clin. chim. Acta*, **114**, 45 (1981).

[48] McARTHUR et al., *J. Pediat.*, **108**, 254 (1986).

[49] ROCCHICCIOLI et al., *Pediat. Res.*, **20**, 62 (1986).

[50] MOSER, H. W., *J. Pediat.*, **108**, 89 (1986).

[51] GOLDFISCHER et al., *J. Pediat.*, **108**, 25 (1986).

[52] HASHMI et al., *FEBS Lett.*, **196**, 247 (1986).

The defects of steroid synthesis[1-5], which are probably all inherited as autosomal recessive traits, involve the adrenal cortex alone, the gonads alone, or both organs together. The clinical picture is always characterized by either an isolated or a combined disorder in the synthesis of mineralocorticoids, glucocorticoids and androgens, depending on the site of the defect.

If *mineralocorticoid synthesis* (with the end-product aldosterone) is impaired, a potentially life-threatening salt-wasting disorder (SW) results.

A disturbance of *glucocorticoid synthesis* (with the end-product cortisol) is a cause of the adrenogenital syndrome, which is most often accompanied by salt wasting and ambiguous differentiation of the external genitalia in girls (FPH).

Impaired *androgen synthesis* will result in male pseudohermaphroditism.

Disorders of mineralocorticoid synthesis

21-Hydroxylation and subsequently 11-hydroxylation, as well as 18-oxidation, are necessary for the synthesis of aldosterone from progesterone. Disturbances of the first two steps are described under 'Disorders of glucocorticoid synthesis' (see below).

18-Hydroxylase or 18-hydroxysteroid dehydrogenase deficiency (enzymes E6 or E7 in facing Figure). When the conversion of corticosterone to 18-hydroxycorticosterone is affected, plasma levels of both 18-hydroxycorticosterone and aldosterone are subnormal; reduced conversion of 18-hydroxycorticosterone to aldosterone results in a high plasma 18-hydroxycorticosterone/aldosterone ratio. In both conditions, cortisol production is normal, so that no stimulus exists for the development of hyperplasia of the adrenal cortex, and there is thus no increase in the formation of adrenocortical androgens. Aldosterone deficiency is expressed as a salt-wasting disorder (hyponatremia, hyperkalemia) with anorexia, vomiting, loss of body mass, dehydration, fever with thirst and circulatory collapse. A deficiency of 18-hydroxysteroid dehydrogenase appears to account for virtually all the cases of congenital isolated aldosterone deficiency described[12].

Disorders of glucocorticoid synthesis

A defect in cortisol synthesis leads to compensatory hyperplasia of the adrenal cortex. Cortisol deficiency brings about an increased release of ACTH via the negative feedback mechanism. This in turn brings about an accumulation of cortisol precursors, depending on the enzyme defect under consideration; many of these precursors exert a clinically significant androgenic effect.

21-Hydroxylase deficiency. The deficiency of steroid 21-hydroxylase is genetically linked to the human leukocyte antigen (HLA) complex; several variants may be differentiated. The classical form, present at birth, may occur with or without salt wasting; the 'late-onset' form presents either in late childhood, peripubertally or post-pubertally. In Europe and the United States the incidence of classical 21-hydroxylase deficiency ranges from 1:5000 to 1:15000; the salt-wasting variety occurs in approximately 50–80% of patients, with a particularly high incidence among Yupik Eskimos in Alaska (~ 1:700)[6]. The nonclassical form seems to have an amazingly high incidence (~ 1:111 [sum of several ethnic groups])[6]. The molecular basis of 21-hydroxylase deficiency has been traced to a defect in a gene coding for P-450$_{C21}$ – a protein which is part of the catalytic complex involved in the 21-hydroxylation of steroids[7].

21-Hydroxylase deficiency without salt wasting (enzyme E4 in reaction b of facing Figure): most frequently a 21-hydroxylase deficiency exclusively in the glucocorticoid synthesis pathway is the basis for the adrenogenital syndrome. The resulting cortisol deficiency causes an increase in the release of ACTH, and this in turn produces an excessive and premature production of adrenal androgens, which leads to the characteristic signs of somatic and sexual precocity in males and virilization in females.

21-Hydroxylase deficiency with salt wasting (enzyme E4 in reactions a and b of facing Figure): in these cases 21-hydroxylase deficiency extends not only to the synthesis of cortisol (conversion of 17-hydroxyprogesterone), but also to the synthesis of aldosterone (conversion of progesterone). The fact that this enzyme defect proceeds both with and without salt wasting may be explained, according to one theory, by the occurrence of 2 substrate-specific forms of steroid 21-hydroxylase.

Nonclassical (late-onset) 21-hydroxylase deficiency: the main clinical features are hirsutism and menstrual disorders.

11β-Hydroxylase deficiency (enzyme E5 in facing Figure). It has been thought that only about 5% of cases of adrenogenital syn-

drome are attributable to this defect, but depending on specific techniques of biochemical diagnosis a higher prevalence must be assumed[13]. The synthesis not only of cortisol, but also of aldosterone is impaired. However, the salt-retaining 11-deoxycorticosterone accumulates in increasing amounts as the precursor of corticosterone, which prevents the occurrence of salt wasting and usually leads to hypertension. Since this symptom is not found on a regular basis, steroid 11β-hydroxylase may possibly be substrate-specific, as steroid 21-hydroxylase is also assumed to be.

3β-Hydroxy-Δ⁵-steroid dehydrogenase deficiency (enzyme E2 in facing Figure). In this rare defect, biosynthesis of all corticosteroids and of the major androgens is impaired, resulting in a high production of 17-hydroxypregnenolone and dehydroepiandrosterone. The glucocorticoid and mineralocorticoid deficiency leads to salt wasting. Due to the lack of highly active androgens, differentiation of the external genitalia is impaired in boys. In girls the external genitalia are either unchanged or at most slightly virilized by the action of dehydroepiandrosterone, which has only a weak androgenic action. The enzyme in the testes, adrenal cortex and liver may be under different genetic control.

C-20,22 Lyase deficiency (enzyme E1 in facing Figure). In this very rare defect any synthesis of steroid hormones from cholesterol fails to occur. The clinical consequences are the same as in 3β-hydroxy-Δ⁵-steroid dehydrogenase deficiency. The defect is also named 'congenital lipoid hyperplasia', since the cortical cells of the enlarged adrenals are filled with lipid material (cholesterol and cholesterol esters).

17α-Hydroxylase deficiency (enzyme E3 in facing Figure). The rare deficiency of 17α-hydroxylase results in diminished secretion of glucocorticoids and sex steroids and in increased secretion of mineralocorticoids. Females show primary amenorrhea (Biglieri's syndrome); in genetic males, pseudohermaphroditism (New's syndrome) is observed. Hypertension in this deficiency has been attributed to excessive 11-deoxycorticosterone.

Disorders of androgen synthesis

In the female organism, stimulation of the Müllerian duct and inhibition of the Wolffian duct take place even when the gonads are absent. Male sex differentiation, however, requires the secretion of 2 testicular factors. Testosterone is the first factor; locally, it stimulates differentiation of the Wolffian duct during embryogenesis and, systemically, it induces masculinization of the undifferentiated external genitalia. The second factor, a glycoprotein, composed of 2 protein subunits covalently linked by disulfide bonds, induces the regression of the Müllerian duct ('Müllerian inhibiting substance' [MIS]). Two androgens are probably involved in male sex differentiation: testosterone leads to the development of the Wolffian duct and to differentiation in the epididymis, vas deferens and seminal vesicles, whereas differentiation of the external genitalia requires the conversion of testosterone to 5α-dihydrotestosterone.

Defects located at the beginning of the steroid synthesis pathway lead not only to an adrenogenital syndrome – possibly accompanied by salt wasting –, but also to male pseudohermaphroditism, owing to the likewise impaired synthesis of androgens. If androgen synthesis is exclusively involved, male pseudohermaphroditism appears as the only symptom.

C-17,20 Lyase deficiency (enzyme E8 in facing Figure). Up to 1982, this defect had been observed in 12 genetic males from 6 families[8]. In C-17,20 lyase deficiency, 17-hydroxypregnenolone cannot be converted to dehydroepiandrosterone, and 17-hydroxyprogesterone cannot be converted to androstenedione. Mineralocorticoid synthesis and glucocorticoid synthesis are not involved. The most obvious symptom is intersexual external genitalia, due to the testosterone deficiency.

17β-Hydroxysteroid dehydrogenase deficiency (enzyme E9 in facing Figure). Up to 1985, this defect has been observed in at least 50 genetic males[11]. Since androstenedione cannot be converted to testosterone in the testicles, differentiation of the male external genitalia does not occur in the XY karyotype. Mineralocorticoid synthesis and glucocorticoid synthesis are not involved.

5α-Reductase deficiency (enzyme E10 in facing Figure). A specific form of male pseudohermaphroditism, also named 'pseudovaginal perineoscrotal hypospadias', is due to dihydrotestosterone deficiency – the consequence of a defect in testosterone reduction. The affected persons are 46,XY males. At puberty there is a rapid growth of the penis and assumption of male gender role, while prostate de-

Inborn enzyme deficiencies of steroid synthesis

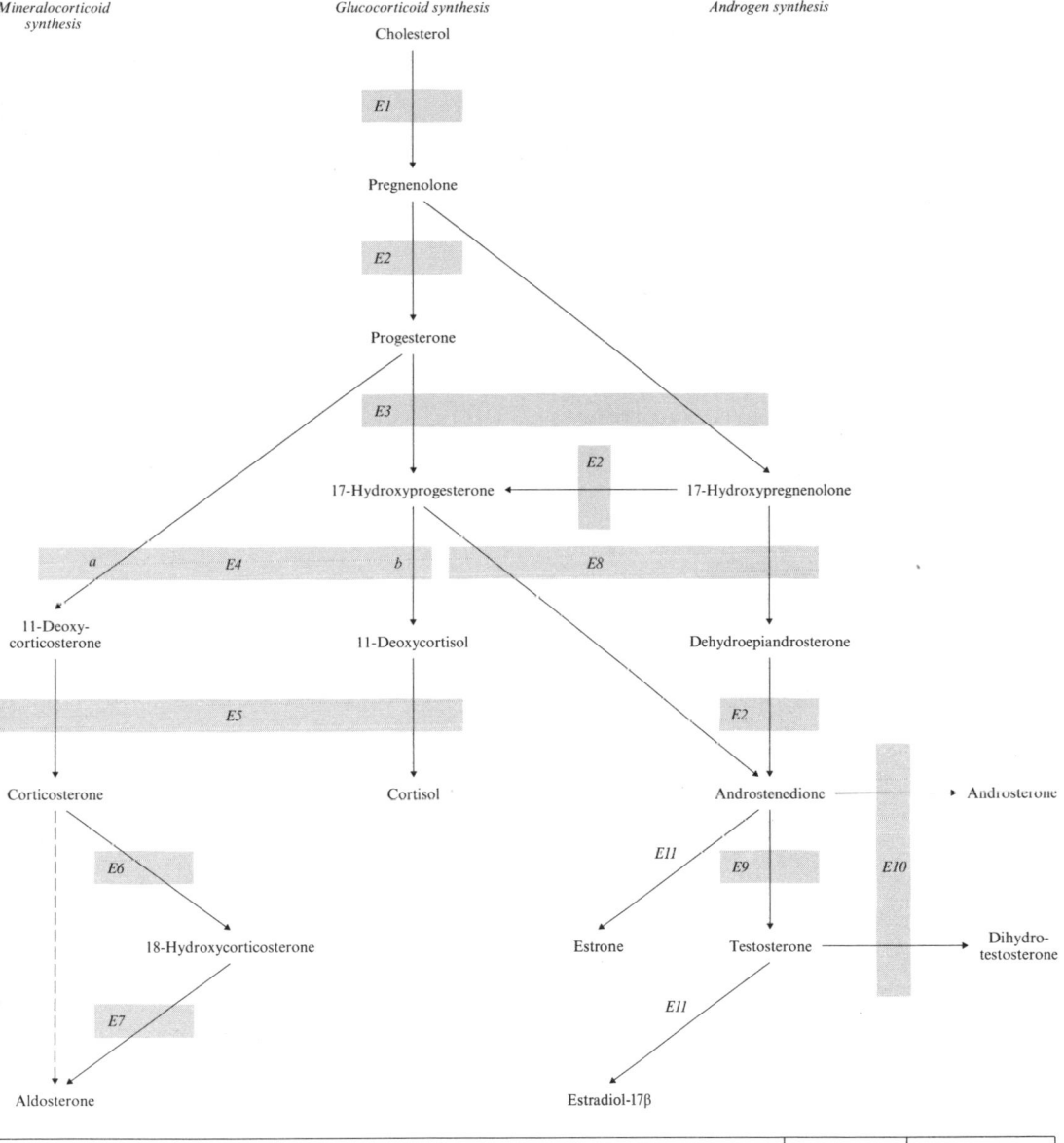

Enzymes	Inheritance*	Leading symptoms of deficiency*
E1	C-20,22 Lyase (20,22-desmolase, cholesterol monooxygenase [side-chain-cleaving])	AR	SW, MPH
E2	3β-Hydroxy-Δ⁵-steroid dehydrogenase.	AR	SW, MPH
E3	Steroid 17α-monooxygenase (steroid 17α-hydroxylase)	AR (?)	MPH, (HT)
E4	Steroid 21-monooxygenase (steroid 21-hydroxylase)	AR	(SW), SSP, FPH
E5	Steroid 11β-monooxygenase (steroid 11β-hydroxylase)	AR	(HT), SSP, FPH
E6	Corticosterone 18-monooxygenase (corticosterone 18-hydroxylase, methyloxidase I)	AR	SW
E7	18-Hydroxysteroid dehydrogenase (methyloxidase II)	AR	SW
E8	C-17,20 Lyase (17,20-desmolase, 17α-hydroxyprogesterone aldolase)	AR (?), X (?)	MPH
E9	3(or 17)β-Hydroxysteroid dehydrogenase (17-oxosteroid reductase)	AR (?), X (?)	MPH
E10	Cholestenone 5α-reductase (5α-reductase)	AR	MPH
E11	'Aromatase'	–	–

*AR: autosomal recessive; X: X-linked recessive; SW: salt wasting; MPH: male pseudohermaphroditism; HT: hypertension; SSP: somatic precocity, sexual precocity in males; FPH: female pseudohermaphroditism. (Parentheses indicate that not all patients exhibit this sign.)

velopment and beard growth lag behind as a consequence of the di-hydrotestosterone deficiency. The disorder is due to the homozygous state of a rare autosomal gene, and heterogeneity has been reported.

Disorders of the cytosolic androgen receptor, a protein necessary for the action of both testosterone and dihydrotestosterone, result in 4 distinct phenotypes: complete testicular feminization, incomplete testicular feminization, Reifenstein syndrome and infertile male syndrome – each of which is inherited as an X-linked trait. Complete testicular feminization (complete androgen resistance), in which individuals of karyotype XY have unambiguously female external genitalia and are raised as girls, is not rare, accounting for ~ 10% of all cases of primary amenorrhea. Patients retain their female gender role after puberty. 'Aromatase' converts the high levels of testosterone to estrogens, giving rise to female breast development at puberty.

Male development defects may also be caused by receptor-positive androgen resistance: the 5α-reductase levels are normal, as is the level of androgen receptors. The defect is presumed to be at the intranuclear site(s) of action of the hormone–receptor complex.

Placental steroid sulfatase deficiency[9,10]

This inborn error of metabolism is inherited as an X-linked recessive trait. In affected males, the steroid sulfatase activity in placenta, leukocytes, epidermal cells and other tissues is reduced. The deficiency is associated with decreased estriol production during fetal life; women carrying affected fetuses occasionally show failure of parturition mechanisms. Postnatally, steroid sulfatase deficient males develop ichthyosis. X-linked ichthyosis may not be rare; an incidence of 1:6000 males has been suggested.

References

[1] ZURBRÜGG, R.P., in GARDNER, L.I. (Ed.), *Endocrine and Genetic Diseases of Childhood and Adolescence*, 2nd ed., Saunders, Philadelphia, 1975, page 476; VISSER, H.K., in GARDNER, L.I. (Ed.), *Endocrine and Genetic Diseases of Childhood and Adolescence*, 2nd ed., Saunders, Philadelphia, 1975, page 513.

[2] FINKELSTEIN and SHAEFER, *Physiol. Rev.*, **59**, 353 (1979).

[3] NEW et al., in STANBURY et al., *The Metabolic Basis of Inherited Disease*, 5th ed., McGraw-Hill, New York, 1983, page 973.

[4] WILSON et al., in STANBURY et al., *The Metabolic Basis of Inherited Disease*, 5th ed., McGraw-Hill, New York, 1983, page 1001; GRIFFIN and WILSON, *New Engl. J. Med.*, **302**, 198 (1980).

[5] NEW and LEVINE, in MAKIN, H.L. (Ed.), *Biochemistry of Steroid Hormones*, 2nd ed., Blackwell, Oxford, 1984, page 595.

[6] NEW, M.I., *Ann. N.Y. Acad. Sci.*, **458**, 1 (1985); NEW and LEVINE, *Ann. Rev. Med.*, **35**, 649 (1984).

[7] PHILLIPS and SHEPHARD, *Nature*, **314**, 130 (1985).

[8] ZACHMANN et al., *J. clin. Endocr.*, **55**, 487 (1982).

[9] SHAPIRO, L.J., in STANBURY et al., *The Metabolic Basis of Inherited Disease*, 5th ed., McGraw-Hill, New York, 1983, page 1027.

[10] HARKNESS et al., *Brit. med. J.*, **287**, 2 (1983).

[11] BALDUCCI et al., *Clin. Endocr.*, **23**, 439 (1985).

[12] LEE et al., *J. clin. Endocr.*, **62**, 225 (1986).

[13] ZACHMANN, M., *Schweiz. med. Wschr.*, **116**, 408 (1986).

Inherited defects in the metabolism of copper, iron, zinc and molybdenum are known[1]. They can lead either to deficiency symptoms or, in the case of excessive accumulation in the organs, to toxic symptoms.

Copper. The basic defect in Wilson's disease[2,19] is still not known. The defects in copper metabolism are (a) a reduction in biliary copper excretion, and (b) a marked reduction in the rate of copper incorporation into apoceruloplasmin. The immediate effect is accumulation of copper in the liver. The increased level of nonceruloplasmin copper in plasma leads not only to an increased renal excretion of copper, but also to the deposition of copper in various extrahepatic tissues, resulting eventually in cell necrosis. Anemia – due to a disorder of iron metabolism following the reduced ceruloplasmin concentration – is not a usual symptom of Wilson's disease, though hemolytic anemia is not uncommon. The disease is found worldwide with an incidence in Switzerland[3], for example, of at least 1:45000, and of at least 1:35000 in Britain[4]; the incidence may be considerably higher in some geographic areas and/or ethnic groups.

The basic defect of Menkes' disease is not fully defined[2]. A cellular defect seems to be responsible for abnormal levels of copper accumulating in a form or location which renders it inaccessible for the synthesis of copper enzymes. It is not known for certain whether or not this defect involves an alteration of metallothionein – a cysteine-rich protein of low molecular mass that binds heavy metal ions. The clinical manifestations of Menkes' disease are mostly explicable in terms of failure of copper enzymes. In Melbourne, the incidence of the disease is probably in the range of 1:50000 to 1:100000[2].

Iron. Hereditary hemochromatosis[5,6] is characterized by an increased iron uptake by mucosal cells of the duodenum and by deposits of hemosiderin in many organs, especially in liver, pancreas, heart and adrenal glands. Skin pigmentation is virtually always present. The bronze color is due to melanin in the deeper layer of the epidermis. When in addition hemosiderin deposits are present, the color is slate gray.

The inheritance of the disease is autosomal recessive, with partial expression in approximately one-third of male heterozygotes and in

Table 1 *Some copper enzymes in man*

Enzyme	Functional role	Known or expected consequence of deficiency
Cytochrome-*c* oxidase...............	Electron transfer system	Encephalomyopathy (see page 256)
Superoxide dismutase	Free radical detoxification	Uncertain
Monophenol monooxygenase (tyrosinase)	Melanin production	Failure of pigmentation
Dopamine β-monooxygenase..........	Norepinephrine production	Familial dysautonomia (Riley-Day syndrome)
Protein-lysine 6-oxidase (lysyl oxidase)...	Cross-linking of collagen and elastin	Vascular rupture
Ceruloplasmin	Ferroxidase; other roles (?)	Anemia
Factor V..........................	Blood coagulation	Parahemophilia
Enzyme not known	Cross-linking of keratin (disulfide bonds)	'Steel-wool' hair (pili torti)

Table 2 *Inborn errors of metal metabolism*

Condition	Defect	Biochemical findings	Clinical features	Treatment	Inheritance
Wilson's disease (hepatocerebral degeneration)	Copper transport defect in the hepatocytes; failure of ceruloplasmin formation	Excessive accumulation of copper in liver, brain, kidneys, cornea (Kayser-Fleischer rings); ceruloplasmin level in plasma lowered, but concentration of albumin-bound copper elevated; increased excretion of copper in the urine	Cirrhosis of the liver; neurological symptoms (tremor, dysarthria, states of confusion); skeletal changes; hemolytic crises and/or anemia; renal tubular dysfunction; presenting symptoms mainly hepaticohemolytic in childhood, neurologic in adolescence and early adulthood, psychiatric in older adults	Diet low in copper; D-penicillamine, triethylenetetramine	Autosomal recessive
Menkes' disease (steely-hair disease; trichopoliodystrophy)	Copper transport defect in many tissues	Low copper and ceruloplasmin concentrations in plasma	Cerebral degeneration; convulsions; disorders of mental and physical development; depigmented 'steel-wool' hair; arterial rupture; hypothermia; death in early childhood	No guaranteed therapy known (intravenous copper substitution?)	X-linked recessive
Hereditary hemochromatosis (primary hemochromatosis)	Increased enteral absorption of iron	Total body iron 20–60 g (normally about 4 g); hemosiderin deposits primarily in the liver; hyperferremia; transferrin saturation 90% or more; high serum ferritin level (up to 10^4 µg/L or more, normally about 10^2 µg/L)	Skin pigmentation; hepatomegaly, splenomegaly; diabetes; cardiac insufficiency; arrhythmia; hypogonadism; arthropathy	Phlebotomy; desferrioxamine	Autosomal recessive
Atransferrinemia	Failure of transferrin synthesis	Serum iron and transferrin levels considerably lowered	Growth disorders; hypochromic anemia	Transferrin substitution	Not known
Acrodermatitis enteropathica	Zinc transport defect in the intestinal wall (?)	Low serum zinc level; decreased zinc excretion in the urine; decreased zinc content in the hair	Vesicular-pustular eruptions in the acral and periorificial regions; paronychia, alopecia; severe diarrhea; apathy; retarded growth	Zinc sulfate orally	Autosomal recessive

one-sixth of female heterozygotes[7]. Even in homozygotes, environmental factors – e.g. dietary iron content and ethanol consumption – modify the expression of the disease.

The predominant occurrence of hereditary hemochromatosis in males may be explained by the menstrual and pregnancy iron losses in women, which protect against iron accumulation. While the disease is uncommon, it is not altogether rare, even though approximately 10% of the population may be heterozygous for the hemochromatosis gene, and 2.5 to 3 in 1000 may be homozygous[7]. The hemochromatosis gene is located on the short arm of chromosome 6 and is closely linked to the *HLA-A* locus. Hereditary diseases in which iron accumulation is prominent include hereditary sideroachrestic anemia[8] and β-thalassemia major[6].

Congenital atransferrinemia[9] up to now has been described in only 5 families. As a result of restricted iron transport in the plasma the symptoms correspond to those of iron deficiency. Iron deficiency in 3 siblings has been explained by impaired intestinal iron absorption and utilization similar to that observed in the *mk/mk* mouse[10].

Zinc. Acrodermatitis enteropathica[11] is a hereditary defect of zinc metabolism which may be localized in the intestinal wall[12]. An abnormality of tryptophan metabolism has also been suggested as a cause following the observation of high kynurenine and low picolinate levels in the plasma of some patients[13]. The disease seems to be heterogeneous since cases without hypozincemia are known[13].

The hyperzincemia discovered in one family does not seem to be accompanied by any specific symptoms[14]; possibly the transfer of albumin-bound zinc to tissue is impaired[15].

Molybdenum. A few children with mental retardation and dislocation of the ocular lenses had severe deficiency of xanthine oxidase and sulfite oxidase (page 257)[16]. Both enzymes need a molybdenum cofactor – a complex of molybdenum and molybdopterin[20] – for their activity. Plasma levels of molybdenum were normal in these patients, but the molybdenum content of the liver was reduced to very low values.

Treatment for disorders of metal metabolism consists either in a substitution of the deficient metal or in a removal of the accumulated metal. In Wilson's disease it is critical to begin treatment before functional disorders occur[17]; D-penicillamine is the chelating agent of first choice, but if it cannot be tolerated triethylenetetramine dihydrochloride may be used[18]. Homozygotes of hereditary hemochromatosis with excess body iron require phlebotomy, whereas heterozygotes do not need treatment[21].

References

[1] HARKNESS and POLLITT (Eds.), *J. inherited metab. Dis.*, **6**, Suppl. 1 and 2 (1983).

[2] DANKS, D. M., in STANBURY et al., *The Metabolic Basis of Inherited Disease*, 5th ed., McGraw-Hill, New York, 1983, page 1251; SASS-KORTSAK and BEARN, in STANBURY et al. (Eds.), *The Metabolic Basis of Inherited Disease*, 4th ed., McGraw-Hill, New York, 1978, page 1098.

[3] TSCHUMI et al., *Schweiz. med. Wschr.*, **103**, 89 and 140 (1973).

[4] PARKES, D., *Brit. med. J.*, **288**, 1180 (1984).

[5] MILDER et al., *Medicine (Baltimore)*, **59**, 34 (1980).

[6] BOTHWELL et al., in STANBURY et al., *The Metabolic Basis of Inherited Disease*, 5th ed., McGraw-Hill, New York, 1983, page 1269.

[7] EDWARDS et al., *Progr. Hemat.*, **12**, 43 (1981).

[8] HOFFBRAND and KONOPKA, *Ciba Found. Symp.*, NS 51, 269 (1977); BOTTOMLEY, S. S., *Semin. Hemat.*, **14**, 169 (1977).

[9] HERSHKO, C., *Progr. Hemat.*, **10**, 105 (1977).

[10] BUCHANAN and SHEEHAN, *J. Pediat.*, **98**, 723 (1981).

[11] MOYNAHAN, E. J., *Lancet*, **2**, 399 (1974); NELDNER and HAMBIDGE, *New Engl. J. Med.*, **292**, 879 (1975); LEUPOLD et al., *Helv. paediat. Acta*, **31**, 109 (1976); LUNGAROTTI et al., *Helv. paediat. Acta*, **31**, 117 (1976).

[12] LOMBECK et al., *Z. Kinderheilk.*, **120**, 181 (1975).

[13] KRIEGER et al., *Pediatrics*, **69**, 773 (1982).

[14] SMITH et al., *Science*, **193**, 496 (1976).

[15] FAILLA et al., *J. Lab. clin. Med.*, **100**, 943 (1982).

[16] DANKS and CAMAKARIS, *Advanc. hum. Genet.*, **13**, 149 (1983).

[17] STERNLIEB and SCHEINBERG, *New Engl. J. Med.*, **278**, 352 (1968); CARTWRIGHT, G. E., *New Engl. J. Med.*, **298**, 1347 (1978).

[18] WALSHE, J. M., *Lancet*, **1**, 643 (1982).

[19] WALSHE, J. M., *J. inherited metab. Dis.*, **6**, Suppl. 1, 51 (1983); NAZER et al., *Clin. Pediat. (Phila.)*, **22**, 755 (1983).

[20] RAJAGOPALAN, K. V., *Biochem. Soc. Trans.*, **13**, 401 (1985).

[21] VALBERG and GHENT, *Ann. Rev. Med.*, **36**, 27 (1985).

Table 1 *Pharmacogenetic and ecogenetic phenomena[17]*

Predisposing factor	Drugs	Disorders Disease	Defective protein Determinant	Incidence	Inheritance
Slow N-acetylation phenotype	Isoniazid, phenelzine, hydralazine, sulfadimidine, dapsone, aromatic amines	Polyneuritis (isoniazid), vertigo (phenelzine), bladder cancer	Arylamine acetyltransferase	Caucasians, Negroes: ~60% Orientals: ~10–20%	Autosomal recessive
Cholinesterase polymorphism	Succinyldicholine	Succinyldicholine sensitivity, prolonged apnea	Cholinesterase	Caucasians: 0.004% Orientals, Negroes: very rare	Autosomal recessive
Aldehyde dehydrogenase I deficiency	Ethanol	Ethanol intolerance, facial flush, cardiovascular symptoms	Aldehyde dehydrogenase isoenzyme I	Orientals: 30–50%	Autosomal codominant
Catalase deficiency	Hydrogen peroxide	Acatalasia, oral gangrene, gingivitis, ulceration	Catalase (erythrocytes)	Very rare	Autosomal recessive
Debrisoquin hydroxylation deficiency	Debrisoquin, sparteine, nortriptyline, metoprolol, etc.	Overdose effects	A distinct P-450 deficiency	Poor metabolizers (Caucasians: 6–9%; Orientals: 30% [?])	Autosomal recessive
Phenacetin toxicity	Phenacetin	Methemoglobinemia, cyanosis	A distinct P-450 deficiency	Unknown	Autosomal recessive
Mephenytoin hydroxylation deficiency	Mephenytoin, mephobarbital	Overdose toxicity	A distinct P-450 deficiency	Caucasians: 5% Japanese: 23%	Autosomal recessive
Phenytoin hydroxylation deficiency	Phenytoin	Overdose toxicity, ataxia, nystagmus	A distinct P 450 deficiency	Very rare	Autosomal recessive
Glucose-6-phosphate dehydrogenase deficiency	Primaquine, dapsone, phenylhydrazine, sulfapyridine	Hemolysis, drug-induced hemolytic anemia	Glucose-6-phosphate dehydrogenase (erythrocytes)	Very high in tropical and subtropical countries; common among American Blacks	X-linked incomplete codominant
NADH dehydrogenase deficiency	Dapsone, primaquine, chloroquine	Cyanosis	NADH dehydrogenase	Heterozygous carriers: ~1%; very common among American Indians and Eskimos	Autosomal recessive; heterozygous carriers affected
Unstable hemoglobins	Sulfonamides, environmental oxidants, lead	Hemolysis, hemoglobinopathies	Hemoglobins HbH, HbZurich	Very rare	Autosomal dominant
Porphobilinogen synthase inducibility	Barbiturates	Porphyria	Porphobilinogen synthase (aminolevulinate dehydratase)	Rare	Autosomal dominant
N-Glucosidation deficiency	Amobarbital	Unknown	N-β-Glucosyltransferase	Caucasians: 2%	Autosomal recessive
Warfarin resistance	Warfarin and similar coumarin derivatives	Reduced anticoagulant effect: 25 times the normal dose required	Receptor defect; increased affinity to vitamin K	Very rare	Autosomal dominant
Low catechol O-methyltransferase activity	Isoproterenol, L-dopa, methyldopa	Unknown	Catechol O-methyltransferase	Rare	Autosomal recessive
Malignant hyperthermia with muscular rigidity	Halothane, succinyldicholine, methoxyflurane	Hyperthermia, hyperrigidity (high fatality)	Ca^{2+} binding to membrane of sarcoplasmic reticulum	Caucasians: 0.005%	Autosomal dominant
Glaucoma	Glucocorticoids	Ocular hypertension	Unknown	Caucasians: 5% with high response	Autosomal recessive
Taste sensitivity	Phenylthiocarbamide and other thiourea derivatives, anethole trithione	Bitter taste	Unknown	Non-tasters (Caucasians: ~30%; Chinese: 10%; Negroes: 3%)	Autosomal dominant

*This chapter on 'Pharmacogenetics and Ecogenetics' (pages 289–300) has been compiled in collaboration with H. W. GOEDDE, Institute of Human Genetics, University of Hamburg, Hamburg (FRG).

Fig. 1 *Health as an equilibrium between the organism and the environment; disease as disturbed equilibrium, caused by a mutated gene product, e.g. an enzyme variant[15]*

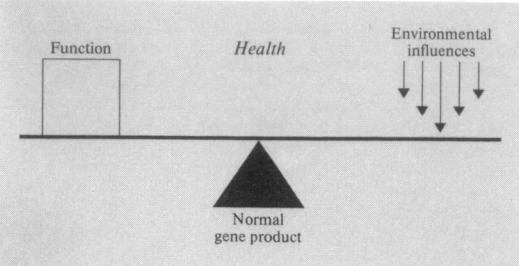

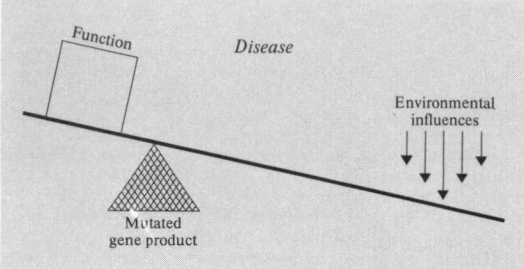

The marked phenotypic diversity among individuals of a given species is partly caused by alterations of the genetic information for protein synthesis. Genetically controlled enzymatic reactions are often the reason both for inborn errors of metabolism and for hereditary incompatibility to xenobiotics. Different mean values for quantitative traits and also different frequencies of certain protein variants in various populations – so-called 'genetic polymorphisms' – are of interest in this respect.

Pharmacogenetics and ecogenetics deal with genetically determined phenomena in connection with substances in the environment which are to a varying degree transformed in the body[1,2], for example synthetic chemicals (xenobiotics◊) such as drugs, food additives, pesticides, weed-controlling agents, industrial allergens, as well as pollutants in the air, and naturally occurring substances such as ethanol, lactose, aflatoxins, heavy metals, etc. Ecogenetics[2], therefore, is an extension of the well-known discipline of pharmacogenetics[2-11].

Genetically determined phenomena of metabolism can often be traced to polymorphism of proteins, especially enzymes catalyzing these metabolic reactions. The investigation of 104 gene loci responsible for the synthesis of proteins has led to the detection of polymorphism for 33 enzymes in at least one of the major ethnic groups[12]. A similar frequency of polymorphism must be assumed for enzymes that participate in the metabolism of drugs, or of xenobiotics in general[13]. Because of this diversity of protein variants it is very unlikely that any two individuals will behave the same way in all metabolic reactions – with the exception, of course, of monozygotic twins. The notion of 'biochemical individuality' thus includes 'pharmacological and ecological individuality'[14]. Such considerations are of special importance for preventive and industrial medicine, since intoxications and occupational diseases only afflict some individuals – depending on a genetically determined predisposition in their reaction to environmental influences –, but not others (Fig. 1).

A polygenic mode of inheritance must be considered for several pharmacogenetic and ecogenetic reactions[16]. For many other such phenomena, however, a monogenic trait has been demonstrated (Table 1).

Of particular practical importance is glucose-6-phosphate dehydrogenase deficiency causing harmful side effects with quite a number of drugs. Other well-known pharmacogenetic phenomena are succinyldicholine sensitivity due to serum cholinesterase variants and differences in certain hydroxylation reactions, as well as deficiency of an aldehyde dehydrogenase isoenzyme (genetically determined ethanol sensitivity).

◊ See the chapter on 'Metabolism of Xenobiotics' (pages 207–216).

Investigations with so-called 'probe drugs' have made the detection of pharmacogenetic traits easier. Some examples of such drugs include isoniazid or sulfamethazine (for investigating N-acetylation), debrisoquin (for investigating a specific aspect of the P-450 monooxygenase system) and antipyrine (for investigating several aspects of the P-450 monooxygenase system).

Studies of ecological genetic traits are often of great importance not only for preventive medicine, with respect to intoxication reactions in a given population, but also for therapy with certain drugs in different populations.

The mutagenic and teratogenic effects of different substances can be studied nowadays not only in microorganisms and experimental animals, but also in human cell lines by observing sister chromatid exchanges as well as chromosome breaks and gaps.

Pharmacogenetic phenomena

Cholinesterase polymorphism[18-21]

At accepted clinical dosages the short-acting muscle relaxant succinyldicholine is degraded to succinylmonocholine within about 10 minutes by human cholinesterase, a normal plasma constituent. Suc-

$$CH_2 \cdot COO \cdot CH_2 \cdot CH_2 \cdot \overset{+}{N}(CH_3)_3$$
$$CH_2 \cdot COO \cdot CH_2 \cdot CH_2 \cdot \overset{+}{N}(CH_3)_3$$

Succinyldicholine (suxamethonium)

cinylmonocholine is inactive as regards muscle relaxation at the resulting concentration. Many other drugs are hydrolyzed by cholinesterase, e.g. heroin, cocaine, procaine, etc.

Certain enzyme variants of cholinesterase – as a result of a mutation – also hydrolyze succinyldicholine, but at a lower rate. These variants can lead to severe prolonged apnea in certain individuals. The formal genetics of cholinesterase polymorphism are well known (Table 2). The genetic model includes 3 variants of the usual enzyme: 10 phenotypes are considered for locus 1. The most frequent variant which can be distinguished from the usual enzyme is the so-called 'atypical' or 'dibucaine-resistant' variant, characterized by a reduced affinity to various substrates and inhibitors. The so-called 'dibucaine number' expresses the extent to which the reaction rate with the substrate benzoylcholine is reduced by the anesthetic dibucaine (cinchocaine). This atypical variant can hydrolyze succinyldicholine only at a much higher concentration than the pharmacologically accepted one[22]. It has been suggested that this enzyme variant results from the substitution of a neutral amino acid by a dibasic one[23].

Another variant is distinguished by its sensitivity to the inhibitor sodium fluoride. A third variant, the expression of a silent gene, is characterized by an almost complete absence of immunologically detectable protein and hence of enzyme activity[24]. Homozygotes for the silent gene are very rare (Table 2); a higher frequency is found in a certain Alaskan population. There appear to be other variants in addition to these three, but their inheritance has not yet been definitely ascertained. One variant[25], designated C_5^+, has been found in about 10% of Europeans. A gene locus E_2, not linked to gene locus E_1, is probably responsible for its synthesis[19]. By using benzoylcholine as substrate, in only 80% of patients with prolonged apnea after administration of succinyldicholine[26] a corresponding cholin-

Table 2 *Cholinesterase variants: properties and sensitivity to succinyldicholine[11]*

Genotypes of cholinesterase variants	Enzyme activity	Dibucaine number	Fluoride number	Incidence of phenotypes in Caucasians	Succinyldicholine sensitivity
E_1^u/E_1^u	Moderately reduced	22	27	1:3200	+++
E_1^s/E_1^s	Absent	0	0	1:170000	++++
E_1^f/E_1^f	Slightly reduced	66	35	1:28000	++
E_1^u/E_1^s	Reduced	22	27	1:11000	+++
E_1^u/E_1^f	Slightly reduced	49	33	1:2500	+++
E_1^f/E_1^s	Slightly reduced	67	43	1:33000	++
E_1^u/E_1^u	Normal	80	59	95%	Normal
E_1^u/E_1^u	Slightly reduced	62	48	3%	(+)
E_1^u/E_1^f	Slightly reduced	74	50	1%	(+)
E_1^u/E_1^s	Slightly reduced	80	59	1:200	Not known

Table 3   *Incidence of the atypical cholinesterase allele E_1^a in various populations[24]*

Low incidence (0–0.002)		Medium incidence (0.005–0.1)		High incidence (> 0.014)	
Thais........................	0	Australians..................	0.0051	North Africans	0.0142
Koreans	0	Negroes (Seattle).............	0.0053	Czechoslovakians	0.0144
Japanese.....................	0	Lapps	0.0076	Brazilians	0.0149
Eskimos	0	Mexican Indian tribes.........	0.0093	Greeks	0.0162
South American Indian popula-		Moroccan Jews	0.0098	Germans.....................	0.0162
tions	0			White Americans..............	0.0163
Negroes (Congo)..............	0.0009			Portuguese	0.0168
Chinese (Taiwan)..............	0.0015			Berbers	0.0182
Filipinos	0.0024			Finns........................	0.0188
				British......................	0.0192
				Israelis	0.0312

esterase variant could be assigned. Other variants detected in the meantime may be involved[27].

The symptoms of prolonged apnea can be avoided in the carriers of this enzyme defect by injection of purified normal cholinesterase before or shortly after administration of succinyldicholine[28].

A cholinesterase variant (cynthiana) discovered in one family is characterized by intensified hydrolysis of succinyldicholine due to increased enzyme activity[29].

Table 3 shows genetic differences among various populations with regard to the atypical cholinesterase allele E_1^a. This variant is generally rare in Oriental populations and particularly rare in Eskimos. The silent variant, on the other hand, is found in approximately 1.5% of Alaskan Eskimos[30] and in about 2% of the Vysyas in India[31], but it is very rare in almost all other populations investigated. In Caucasians the frequency of this gene is about 1:100000.

Paraoxonase polymorphism[32-34]

Paraoxon (E 600), a metabolite of the widely used insecticide parathion (E 605), shows an anticholinesterase effect and is also used in

$$C_2H_5O \diagdown \quad \diagup O$$
$$\qquad P$$
$$C_2H_5O \diagup \quad O - \!\!\!\!\bigcirc\!\!\!\! - NO_2$$

Paraoxon (O,O-diethyl-O-[4-nitrophenyl] phosphate)

the treatment of glaucoma. Paraoxon is hydrolyzed to 4-nitrophenol and diethyl phosphate by the enzyme paraoxonase, a specific arylesterase, the activity of which seems to be associated with the high-density lipoprotein complex[35]. The enzyme also splits methyl-

Table 4   *Incidence of the homozygous phenotype for low-activity serum paraoxonase in various populations[40]*

Ethnic group	Percentage of the general population	Ethnic group	Percentage of the general population
Europeans	53%	Palestinians	35%
Eskimos (Greenland) .	9%	Turks	40%
Eskimos (North Amer-		Iranians	50%
ica)	6%	Afghans	41%
Negroes (USA)	15%	Indians (India)......	37%
Central American In-		Singhalese (Sri Lanka)	33%
dians	0–10%	Indonesians	10%
Jamaicans..........	14%	Malaysians.........	14%
Atacameños (Chile)...	64%	Vietnamese.........	10%
Zulus..............	12%	Filipinos...........	20%
Zimbabweans........	0%	Chinese............	33%
Zambians..........	0%	Japanese..........	9%
Nigerians	6%	Aborigines (Australia)	0%
Senegalese	7%	Maori	0%
Berbers	22%	Tongans	0%
Ethiopians	17%		

paraoxon and other organic phosphoric-acid esters, but not parathion. The physiological substrate of the enzyme, however, is not known.

The paraoxonase locus (*PON*) is closely linked to the locus for cystic fibrosis[36]; these loci seem to be on chromosome 7[37].

There are 2 common alleles at this locus – designated by the symbols *ESA*A* and *ESA*B –*, resulting in the 3 phenotypes A, AB and B[34]. The gene frequency in Caucasians is about 0.70 for the variant with low enzyme activity (*ESA*A*) and 0.30 for the variant with high enzyme activity (*ESA*B*). Low enzyme activity is inherited as an autosomal recessive trait. Qualitative differences in the enzymatic properties of the variants have been detected by stimulation of the enzyme activity with NaCl[38] in the presence of $CaCl_2$[39], thus facilitating the differentiation of the phenotypes. Data from several such studies in various populations are summarized in Table 4[40].

Individuals with the highly active paraoxonase variant are possibly better protected against intoxications by organophosphorus insecticides, whereas individuals with the low-activity variant presumably are more susceptible than others to toxic reactions to parathion and structurally related organophosphorus substrates. This may be important for individuals working in agriculture and in industries producing organophosphorus compounds.

N-Acetylation polymorphism[2-4, 19, 41]

The rates of acetylation of a series of drugs or their metabolites (see Fig. 2) are individually different and genetically determined. The polymorphism shows a bimodal distribution of various pharmacokinetic parameters[24, 42-46], e.g. the isoniazid concentration in the plasma after the administration of the drug (Fig. 3). Individuals may be categorized as 'rapid (fast) acetylators' or 'slow acetylators'. The heterogeneity is controlled by 2 autosomal alleles at a single locus, the trait for rapid acetylation (*AcR*) being dominant and that for slow acetylation (*AcS*) recessive. Although 3 genotypes exist for acetylation (Table 5), usual phenotyping techniques differentiate only 2 phenotypes: rapid acetylators with the genotypes *AcR/AcR* or *AcR/AcS* and slow acetylators with the genotype *AcS/AcS* (Fig. 4). It has been claimed, however, that the heterozygous type *AcR/AcS* can be distinguished[47]. Several screening methods for phenotyping – mostly using sulfamethazine as the probe drug[48-50] – have been described. According to such studies, Caucasians and Negroes are predominantly slow acetylators, while Lapps, Eskimos, Japanese and Chinese are predominantly rapid acetylators (Table 6).

The basis of the polymorphism seems to be due to qualitative differences in the structure of arylamine acetyltransferase (2.3.1.5) (N-acetyltransferase) in the liver and possibly also in the duodenal mucosa (mainly studied in the rabbit)[41, 51].

The 2 phenotypes differ with regard to the clinical efficacy and side effects of many drugs[2, 52, 53]. For instance, slow acetylators are more

Table 5   *Polymorphism of arylamine acetyltransferase (N-acetyltransferase) (2 alleles, Ac^R and Ac^S, on one autosomal gene locus*)*

Genotype	Pheno-type	Acetylation rate
Ac^S/Ac^S	Ac(SS)	Slow
Ac^R/Ac^S	Ac(RS)	Rapid
Ac^R/Ac^R	Ac(RR)	Rapid

* S: slow; R: rapid.

Fig. 2   *Drugs subject to N-acetylation*

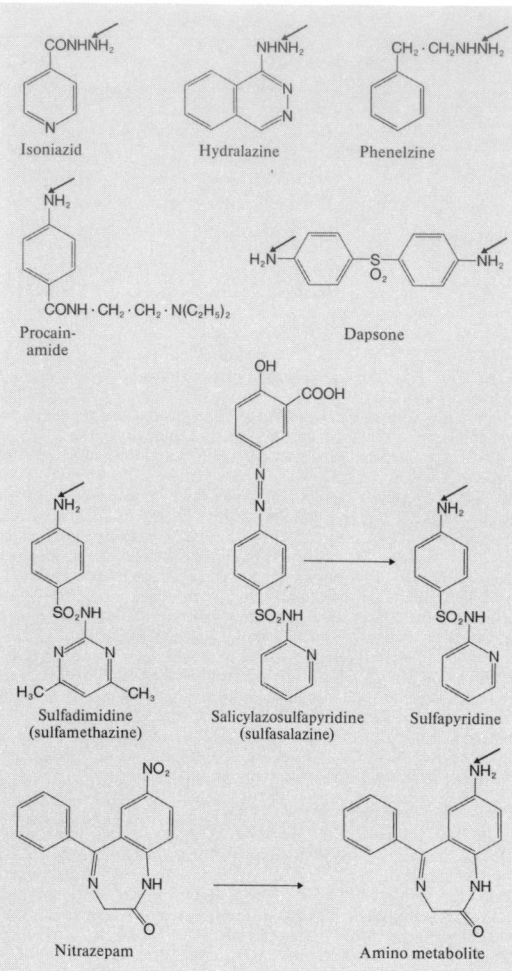

Isoniazid   Hydralazine   Phenelzine

Procain-amide   Dapsone

Sulfadimidine (sulfamethazine)   Salicylazosulfapyridine (sulfasalazine)   Sulfapyridine

Nitrazepam   Amino metabolite

Fig. 3   *Bimodal distribution of plasma isoniazid concentration in 267 Caucasians*[42]

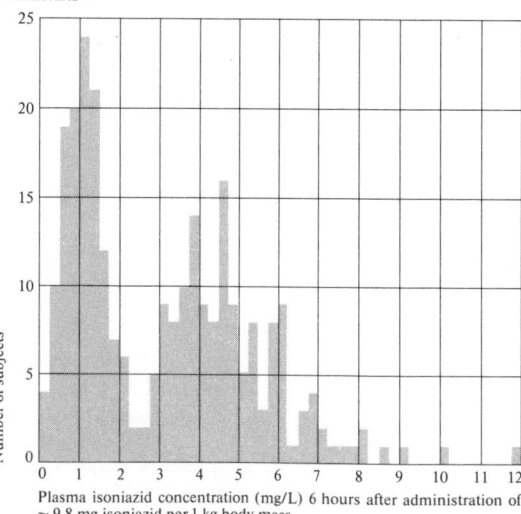

Plasma isoniazid concentration (mg/L) 6 hours after administration of ~ 9.8 mg isoniazid per 1 kg body mass

Fig. 4   *Inheritance of isoniazid N-acetyltransferase variants*

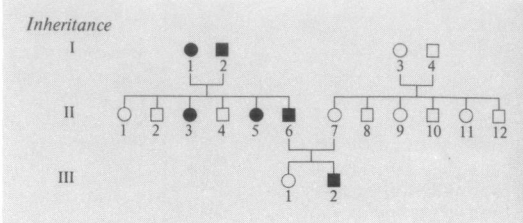

Inheritance

I/1 and 2: Ac(RS); I/3 and 4: Ac(SS); II/1, 2, 4, 7–12: Ac(SS); II/6: Ac(RS); II/3 and 5: Ac(RS) or Ac(SS); III/1: Ac(SS); III/2: Ac(RS). O: female; □: male; filled-in symbols: rapid inactivation or acetylation; blank symbols: slow inactivation or acetylation.

Table 6
Incidence of the gene for slow acetylation in various populations

Ethnic group	Gene frequency
Eskimos	0.22–0.52
Japanese	0.34
Chinese	0.39
Thais	0.53–0.76
Europeans	0.70
Negroes	0.74
Jews	0.84

Fig. 5   *Serotonin metabolism*

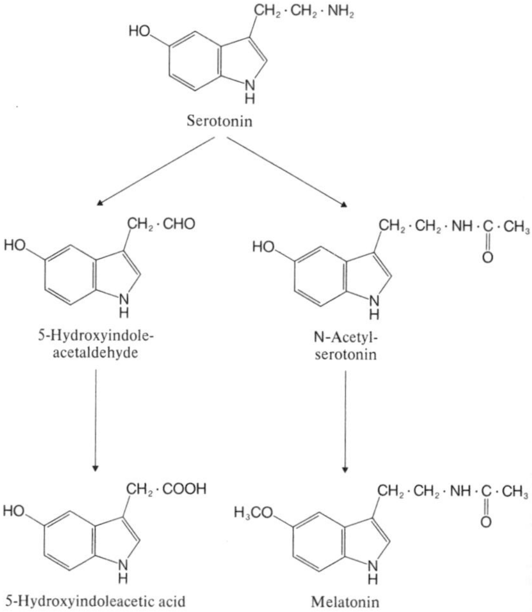

Serotonin

5-Hydroxyindole-acetaldehyde   N-Acetyl-serotonin

5-Hydroxyindoleacetic acid   Melatonin

inclined to develop antinuclear antibodies after prolonged procain-amide therapy[54], giving rise in some cases to a syndrome resembling lupus erythematosus. Side effects from phenelzine, such as vertigo, are also more frequent in slow acetylators, who are likewise more often affected by side effects from isoniazid (polyneuritis, for example). The latter can be prevented in some cases by administration of vitamin B_6 since these symptoms are probably related to the increased elimination of this vitamin caused by isoniazid. Individual differences in the interference of diphenylhydantoin with isoniazid are also related to N-acetyltransferase polymorphism[55]: the higher plasma isoniazid level in slow acetylators inhibits the hydroxylation of diphenylhydantoin to such an extent that its toxicity threshold is exceeded (ataxia and nystagmus have been observed in various cases).

It has been postulated that rapid acetylators have a higher susceptibility to isoniazid-induced liver damage[56], but because of conflicting and complex biochemical and epidemiological data, this hypothesis is still disputed[53, 57].

Several studies suggest that slow acetylators may be slightly more susceptible to bladder cancer than rapid acetylators[53, 58]. Furthermore, in patients with idiopathic lupus erythematosus the slow acetylator phenotype seems to be more prevalent, although this remains somewhat controversial[53].

The polymorphism is also of importance for the acetylation of the natural substrate serotonin to N-acetylserotonin[24] (Fig. 5), a reaction which is inhibited by various psychotropic drugs[4]. The acetylation reaction competes with the serotonin breakdown by amine oxidase (flavin-containing) (1.4.3.4) (monoamine oxidase), so that the acetylator phenotype may be expected to have an influence on the metabolism of some psychotropic drugs[2].

Polymorphic oxidation of debrisoquin, sparteine and other drugs[59–63, 69]

In population studies it has been observed that 4-hydroxylation of debrisoquin and formation of 2- and 5-dehydrosparteine from sparteine were grossly impaired or nearly absent in some individuals. In view of the close relation between the metabolic ratios of sparteine and debrisoquin it seems quite certain that these genetic polymorphisms are related entities, probably involving the same enzyme or enzyme regulator. The 2 phenotypes were designated EM and PM ('extensive metabolizer' and 'poor metabolizer').

The oxidation of these drugs is determined by 2 alleles at a single gene locus, and the poor metabolizers are homozygous for an autosomal recessive gene. Poor metabolizers are at a higher risk of developing drug-related side effects when standard doses of these drugs are administered[64]. Studies among different ethnic groups have shown pronounced interethnic variations in the frequency of the PM phenotype (some figures for the incidence of poor debrisoquin metabolizers are given in Table 7). The incidence of poor sparteine metabolizers in Germany is about 5%[65].

It has been suggested that homozygous poor metabolizers have a 'silent' or 'defective' gene for regulating the synthesis of microsomal P-450 isoenzyme, which catalyzes the formation of 4-hydroxydebrisoquin. Because of the close linkage between polymorphic sparteine oxidation and the P_1 blood group it can be assumed that the gene for this polymorphism is located on chromosome 22[62].

The debrisoquin and sparteine polymorphism seems to control also the oxidation of several other drugs: phenformin[66], perhexiline[67], bufuralol[63, 68], guanoxan[69], encainide[70], metoprolol[63, 71], timolol[63, 72], nortriptyline[73], N-propylajmaline[74] and dextromethorphan[75]. Polymorphisms of distinct P-450 systems seem to be involved in the oxidation of phenacetin[17, 61], phenytoin[17, 61], the (S) isomer of mephenytoin[76], S-carboxymethylcysteine[77] and tolbutamide[78] (the metabolism of antipyrine is discussed below).

Several consequences of administering these drugs to poor metabolizers have been described (e.g. a greater tendency to develop postural hypotension following low doses of debrisoquin[79]; in the case of phenformin, an induction of lactacidosis[81]; and with phenacetin, an increased formation of the toxic 2-hydroxylated metabolite by an alternative pathway and higher production of methemoglobin[80]).

Table 7
Incidence of poor debrisoquin metabolizers in various populations[7]

Ethnic group	N	Percentage of the general population
Caucasians:		
– UK	258	8.9
– Canada	48	6.3
Nigerians	123	8.1
Ghanaians	80	5.0
Egyptians	72	1.4
Saudi Arabians	102	1.0
Orientals*	19	31.6

*Mostly Chinese immigrants into Canada from Hong Kong.

Polymorphism of amobarbital metabolism

Amobarbital (amylobarbitone) is converted to 2 major metabolites: 3′-hydroxyamylobarbitone and 1-(β-D-glucopyranosyl)amylobarbitone[82]. A deficiency of N-glucosidation in about 2% of the Canadian population has been reported. N-Glucosidation of amylobarbitone seems to be a recessive autosomal trait. The overall pharmacological action of the drug is not altered since 3′-hydroxylation compensates for the loss of N-glucosidation. Ethnic variations have been found in amylobarbitone metabolism[83]: Oriental subjects excrete equal amounts of the 3′-hydroxy and the N-glucosyl metabolite in the urine; the ratio of these 2 metabolites in Caucasians, however, is 2:1.

Polymorphism of antipyrine metabolism[84]

Antipyrine is used as a probe drug for the investigation of an individual's capacity to metabolize drugs. Main metabolites are 4-hydroxyantipyrine, 3-hydroxymethylantipyrine and N-demethylantipyrine. Each metabolite seems to be formed by a separate combination of hepatic P-450 monooxygenases, but the metabolism of antipyrine is not dependent on that of debrisoquin and sparteine. A polymorphism of antipyrine oxidation has been reported[84].

Glucose-6-phosphate dehydrogenase deficiency[85–88]

A number of glucose-6-phosphate dehydrogenase (G-6-PD) variants cause hemolysis after consumption of fava beans (*Vicia faba*) or especially after intake of certain drugs (sulfonamides, primaquine and similar compounds, as well as furazolidone and related substances). The most frequent variant is type A, occurring among individuals in Greece, southern Italy, etc. In the A⁻ variant, juvenile cells still have normal enzyme activity, and cells less than 50 days old still have enough activity to provide protection against the hemolytic effect of the drug. The risk therefore in such cases is less than for other deficiency variants; consumption of fava beans, for example, is harmless. In the Mediterranean variant there is a severe enzyme defect in juvenile cells as well, with a residual activity of only 0–4%. Hence the number of potentially dangerous drugs is higher; hemolysis is not self-limiting, but by contrast often life-threatening.

World prevalence of G-6-PD deficiency is to be seen from the epidemiological point of view. This genetic abnormality affects probably about 400 million people or roughly 10% of the world population. Figure 6 shows that it is extremely common. It is not limited to Mediterranean and African countries, but widely distributed in tropical, subtropical and also temperate climates throughout Africa, Europe, Asia and Oceania. It seems that it has never been encountered in populations indigenous to the new continent, although the frequency is now quite considerable in North and South America due to migrations which have taken place in relatively recent history. G-6-PD deficiency is therefore a global problem.

The mechanism responsible for the drug intolerance is not completely understood. G-6-PD is necessary to provide reduced glutathione, which is required for erythrocyte membrane stability. In the presence of the above-mentioned drugs, the glutathione concentration needed for this reaction is probably not high enough in cells with G-6-PD deficiency.

Unstable hemoglobins[89–91]

For many of the unstable hemoglobins (page 224) it must be assumed that certain drugs, especially sulfonamides, primaquine and some others, will cause the formation of Heinz bodies and hemolytic episodes in their carriers. However, the effect of those drugs is often difficult to distinguish from the influence of the underlying defect itself. In carriers of Hb Zurich, Hb Shepherd's Bush, Hb M$_{Saskatoon}$, Hb Torino, Hb Hasharon, Hb Leiden, Hb Bushwick and Hb Petersborough, sulfonamides can cause or aggravate hemolysis. Carriers of Hb H are likewise sensitive to those drugs which also cause side effects in glucose-6-phosphate dehydrogenase deficiency. Hb H disease, a form of α-thalassemia (page 225), is very frequent in Thailand (about 1:300).

Glaucoma[92]

After repeated application of glucocorticoids a rise in intraocular pressure occurs which is roughly inversely proportional to the facility of outflow of the aqueous humor. This rise in pressure was observed to be trimodally distributed in a nonselected sample, with a relative frequency of 66%, 29% and 5% for groups with low, intermediate and high intraocular pressure, respectively. A gene with 2 alleles – one responsible for the low rise in intraocular pressure, the other for high pressure – probably determines the 3 phenotypes. In homozygotes and heterozygotes for the allele causing high pressure, this phenomenon can be further enhanced by continued treatment

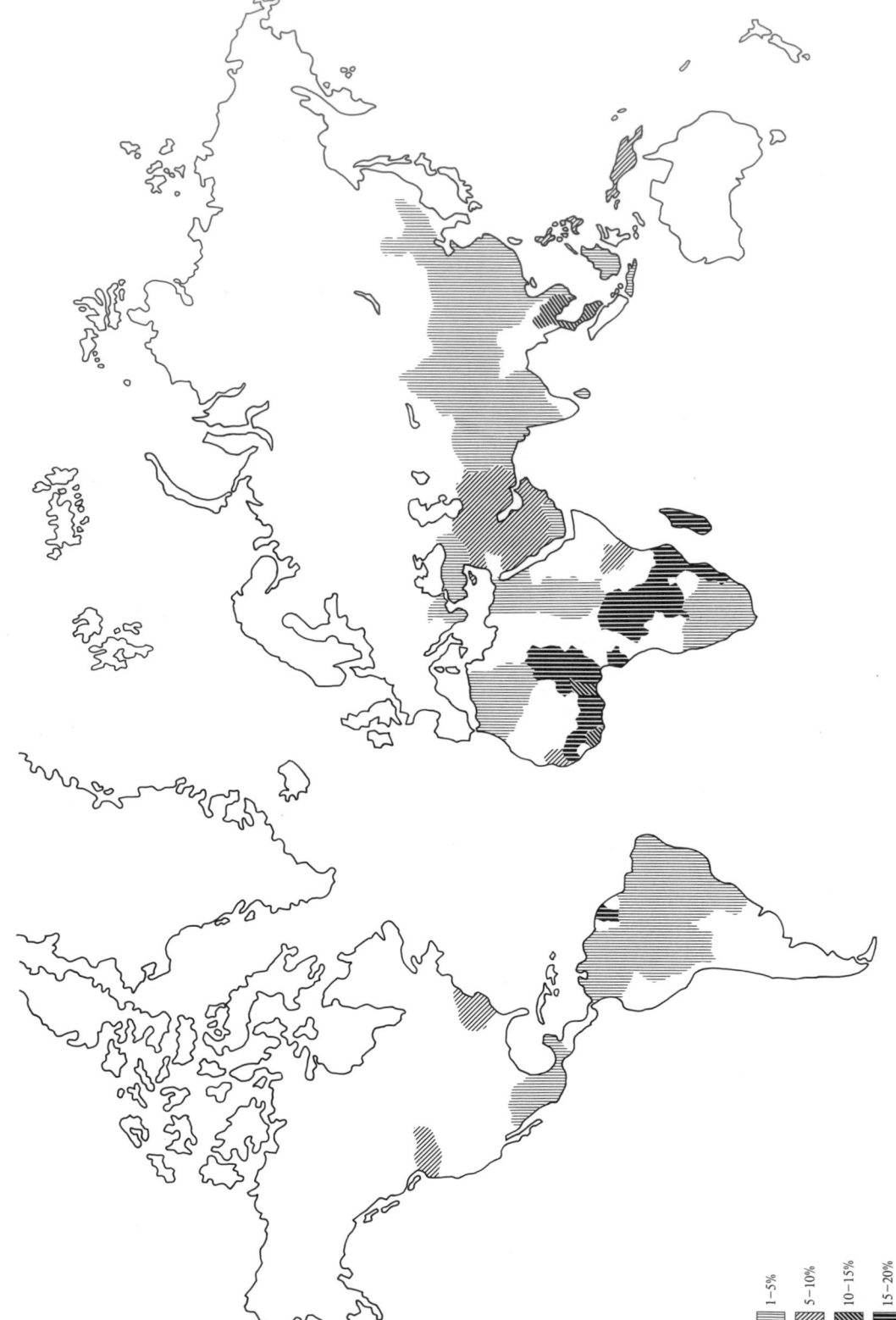

Fig. 6   *Incidence of glucose-6-phosphate dehydrogenase deficiency in various populations*

1–5%
5–10%
10–15%
15–20%

with glucocorticoids, probably causing glaucoma lesions. The rise in intraocular pressure is reversible when the drug is discontinued.

Genetically determined warfarin resistance[93, 94]

In a few individuals, 10 times the normal dose of this 4-hydroxy-coumarol derivative is required to achieve a reduction in the plasma prothrombin level, although there are no discernible differences in the pharmacokinetic parameters. However, these individuals also respond more strongly to the effect of vitamin K, so that an alteration in the receptors for vitamin K and warfarin may be suspected.

Table 8   *Mutagenic effect of drugs and chemicals*

Category of substances and drugs	Chromosome aberrations (breaks, gaps)		
	Human cell material		Other assay systems
	In vitro	In vivo	
Alkylating substances			
Cyclophosphamide	(+)	+	+
Busulfan	+	+	+
Triaziquone, tetramine	+	+	+
Nitrogen derivatives	+	+	+
Psychotropic drugs			
Psilocybin	+	+	?
Phenothiazines (e.g. promazine)	(±)	(±)	(±)
Lysergide	±	±	+
Anticonvulsants	+	+	?
Nucleic-acid antimetabolites			
Cytarabine	+	+	+
Propylthiouracil	+	+	?
Methotrexate	−	+	+
Azathioprine	+	+	?
Pyrimethamine	+	+	?
Mercaptopurine	+	+	+
Antibiotics			
Mitomycin C	+	+	+
Daunorubicin	+	+	?
Pesticides (organic phosphoric-acid esters)	+	+	+

Malignant hyperthermia with muscular rigidity[95, 96]

Hyperthermia – the temperature may reach 44°C or more – and hyper-rigidity occurs in about 1 in 40000 adult and 1 in 15000 pediatric surgery cases after the administration of certain inhalation agents or muscle relaxants (Table 1). The defect is probably inherited as an autosomal dominant trait. In some carriers serum creatine kinase activity is elevated, but this observation cannot be used for screening[97]. In most cases, the carriers can be identified by assay of muscle biopsy samples which show abnormal contraction in response to halothane or caffeine[98]. The defect is probably related to impaired binding of Ca^{2+} to the membrane of the sarcoplasmic reticulum[99].

Genetic variation in taste sensitivity of thiourea derivatives[100, 101]

Phenylthiocarbamide and other thiourea derivatives, as well as a substance of quite different structure, anethole trithione[101], are perceived by the majority of individuals as having a bitter taste. This trait shows quite different frequencies in different populations. However, in a small number of individuals in which an increased frequency of goiter was also observed these compounds are tasteless.

Pharmacogenetic phenomena in animals

Pharmacogenetic phenomena also occur in various species of animals. For example, some mouse strains are distinguished by their rate of oxidation of hexobarbital[102]. In a certain rat strain, a particularly rapid breakdown of methoxyflurane has been demonstrated, the consequence of which is a high concentration of fluoride ions in the blood; kidney damage has been observed as well[103]. The toxic side effects of this anesthetic in humans may also have a genetic basis.

While rats usually exhibit an anaphylactic reaction after dextran injection, some rats of certain Wistar strains do not. A recessive inheritance seems to be present for the characteristic 'nonresponse to dextran'[104].

Polymorphism for a nonspecific B-esterase has been found in rabbits: this esterase breaks down atropine, scopolamine and various morphine esters[105]. Two alleles, A^B and a^B, seem to be responsible for different activity; $a^B a^B$ homozygotes have no activity at all.

In rabbits, polymorphism for arylamine acetyltransferase (N-acetyltransferase) has been demonstrated not only in the liver, where this enzyme acetylates isoniazid and sulfadiazine, but also in blood cells, where it is responsible for the acetylation of 4-aminobenzoic acid[41, 106]. In monkeys, *M. mulatta rhesus* and *Cercopitheus aethiops sabaeus*, liver N-acetyltransferase polymorphism has been described similar to that in man[107].

Mutagenic effect of xenobiotics

Mutation can be caused not only by natural substances, such as aflatoxins, but also by synthetic substances, such as drugs, pesticides, etc. (Table 8). Structural chromosomal defects have, for example, been found in the peripheral blood lymphocytes of patients under cyclophosphamide therapy[108]. However, it is not known how the genetic constitution influences a mutation. (For mutagenicity assay systems, see Table 9.)

Table 9   *Systems of mutagenicity assays*

Assay systems	Type of mutation detected	Mammalian metabolism	Comments
Microorganisms (phages, bacteria, low fungi)	Point mutation	No	Used routinely
Higher plants (maize, *Vicia faba*, arabidopsis)	Point mutation Chromosome mutation Mutation of genome	No	Used routinely
Drosophila	Point mutation Chromosome mutation Mutation of genome	No	Used routinely
Mammals (e.g. mouse, hamster, rat)	Chromosome mutation Mutation of genome	Yes	Used routinely
Host-mediated assay (microorganisms in mammal organism)	Point mutation Chromosome mutation	Yes	Used routinely
Human cells in vitro	Chromosome mutation Mutation of genome Point mutation	No (1%)	Used routinely
Cell culture from patients after exposure to mutagenic substances	Chromosome mutation Mutation of genome	Yes	Limited use

Ecogenetic phenomena

Various potentially toxic substances exist in our environment and may cause damage to certain individuals, but not to others; the study of genetic aspects of ecology is referred to as 'ecogenetics'[1,2]. (A few ecogenetic phenomena are included in Table 1.) In the light of the increasing number and rising concentrations of new synthetic compounds in the environment it can be assumed that ultimately there will no longer be any individual who does not show some sort of abnormal reaction to one or more foreign substances.

Problems related to ecogenetics are extremely important for industrial health services, as well as for the transport of chemicals, drugs and food from one population to a genetically different one.

Aldehyde dehydrogenase deficiency and racial differences in ethanol sensitivity

Various social, environmental and genetic factors have been found to play a part in individual variations in the metabolism of ethanol and its toxic effects[109-114]. Subjective symptoms of ethanol sensitivity were observed 10 times more frequently in Orientals compared to Caucasians (Table 10). Flushing of the face has been noted in 50 to 80% of Oriental subjects as against only about 10% in Caucasians (Table 11). For the high steady-state blood acetaldehyde levels found in Japanese and Chinese after ethanol consumption, various explanations have been suggested: differential rates of ethanol metabolism among different racial groups; faster rates of ethanol absorption observed in Chinese and American Indians; ethnic differences in acetaldehyde clearance; genetic polymorphism of alcohol dehydrogenase (ALD) and/or aldehyde dehydrogenase (ALDH). The metabolism of ethanol in normal, non-ethanol-dependent subjects is shown in Figure 7: more than 80% of ethanol is oxidized by the action of alcohol dehydrogenase ⓐ, and about 10% by the action of microsomal ethanol-oxidizing system (MEOS) ⓑ; oxidation with the aid of catalase ⓒ is of very minor importance.

The biochemistry and genetics of alcohol dehydrogenase have been studied extensively; however, it has been shown that the so-called 'atypical form'[117] is not the main factor responsible for ethanol sensitivity. No significant difference in the rate of ethanol metabolism has been found between normal and atypical alcohol dehydro-

Table 10   Frequency of subjective symptoms after ethanol consumption in Caucasian and Oriental adults[115]

Symptom	34 Caucasians	78 Orientals
	Percentage of subjects	
Burning sensation in stomach	5.8	52.5
Palpitations	0	25.7
Tachycardia	2.9	43.5
Muscle weakness	2.9	25.7
Dizziness	8.6	37.2
Sleepiness	5.8	33.4
Falling asleep	0	18.0

Table 11
Incidence of adverse response to ethanol in various populations[116]

Ethnic group	Percentage of the general population
Caucasians	
Europeans	4–10
North Americans	12
Native Americans	80
Orientals	
Japanese	58–85
Chinese	57
Hawaiians	60
Vietnamese	60
Koreans	60
Taiwanese	67

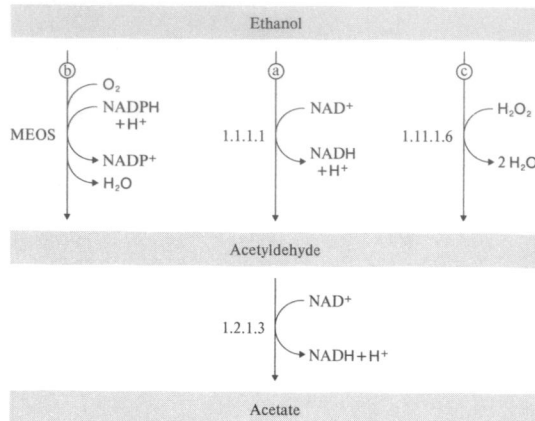

Fig. 7   *Ethanol metabolism*

Enzymes involved:
1.1.1.1   Alcohol dehydrogenase
1.2.1.3   Aldehyde dehydrogenase (NAD+)
1.11.1.6 Catalase
MEOS   Microsomal ethanol-oxidizing system

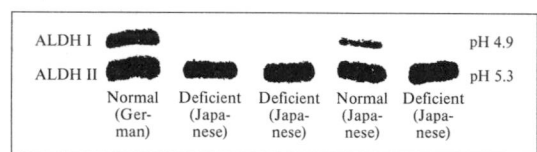

Fig. 8   *Normal and deficient ALDH isoenzymes in postmortem liver samples*[130]

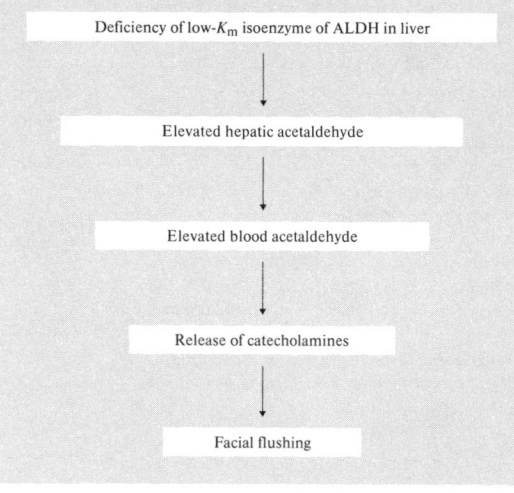

Fig. 9   *Mechanism of sensitivity to ethanol in mongoloids*[122]

Table 12   *Peak blood acetaldehyde and ethanol levels in normal and deficient Japanese subjects after an acute dose of ethanol*[124]

Aldehyde dehydrogenase isoenzymes	N	Acetaldehyde	Ethanol
		µmol/L	mmol/L
Normal pattern	25	2.1	10.3
Deficiency	19	35.4	10.9

Fig. 10 *Phenotypes of ALDH isoenzymes in liver, fibroblasts and hair roots, respectively[126]*

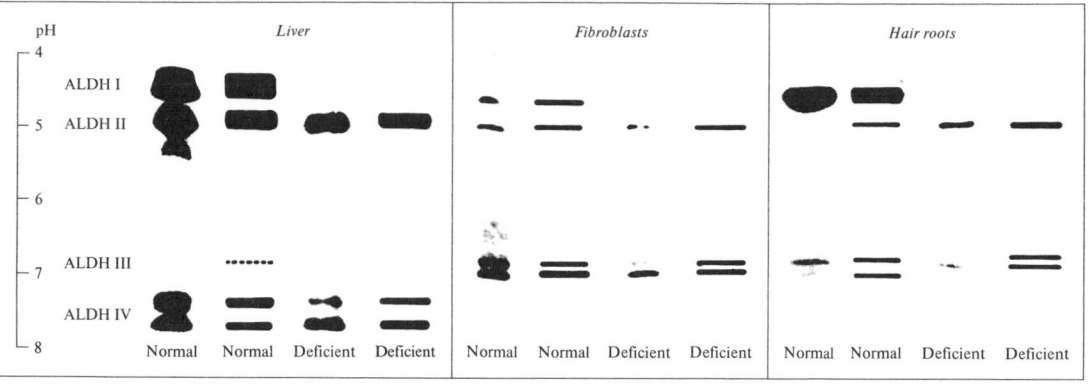

Table 13 *Frequency of ALDH I deficiency in various populations[130]*

Ethnic group	N	Percentage of subjects
Orientals		
Japanese	184	44
Chinese:		
– Mongolian	198	30
– Zhuang	106	25
– Han	120	45
– Korean (Manchu)	209	25
South Koreans	75	27
Vietnamese	138	53
Indonesians	30	39
Thais (North)	110	8
Filipinos	110	13
Ainu	80	20
South American Indians		
Shuaras (Ecuador)	99	42
Atacameños (Chile)	133	43
Mapuches (Chile)	64	41
North American Indians		
Sioux (North Dakota)	90	5
Navajos (New Mexico)	56	2
Mexican Indians		
Mestizos (Mexico City)	43	4
Other populations		
Germans	300	0
Egyptians	260	0
Sudanese	40	0
Kenyans	23	0
Fangs	37	0
Liberians	184	0
Turks	65	0
Israelis	77	0
Hungarians	177	0
Matyó	106	0
Roma	84	0
Indians (India)	50	0

Table 14 *Frequency of ALDH I phenotypes in Japanese patient groups compared with healthy subjects[132]*

Subjects	N	ALDH I isoenzyme deficient	normal
		Percentage of subjects	
Healthy persons	105	41.0	59.0
Alcoholics	175	2.3	97.6
Drug-dependents	47	48.9	51.1
Schizophrenics (nonalcoholics)	86	41.9	58.1

grating ALDH I isoenzyme was missing (Fig. 8). This so-called 'ALDII-deficient type' (or 'unusual type') has lower affinity for the substrate acetaldehyde[121].

In view of the polymorphic nature of aldehyde dehydrogenase in Japanese, it has been postulated[119, 122, 123] that the ethanol sensitivity frequently observed in Japanese subjects could be due to the inability of these individuals to metabolize acetaldehyde quickly in the absence of ALDII I (Fig. 9). This has been proved by administering an acute dose of ethanol to ALDH I-deficient individuals and determining the blood acetaldehyde level (Table 12).

Aldehyde dehydrogenase deficiency could also be demonstrated in human scalp, fibroblasts and hair roots[125, 126]. As shown in Figure 10, the characteristics of ALDH I and ALDH II from various sources are quite similar – in both normal and deficient subjects.

Family and population genetic studies have demonstrated ALDH I deficiency only in Oriental populations, and not in Caucasians, Egyptians, Sudanese, Liberians or Kenyans[127-129] (Table 13). Studies in several families from China, Japan and Korea suggest an autosomal codominant mode of inheritance[131].

The polymorphism of aldehyde dehydrogenase indicates a genetic basis of biological sensitivity to ethanol. Comparative studies in Japanese subjects (control subjects, alcoholics, drug-dependents and nonalcoholic patients with schizophrenia) clearly showed that the deficient aldehyde dehydrogenase type occurred in only about 2% of alcoholics; in the other groups the frequency of aldehyde dehydrogenase deficiency was found to be between 40% and 50% (Table 14)[122, 132]. These data point to a protective role for aldehyde dehydrogenase in many Oriental subjects because of their physiological aversion to ethanol. It is known that the incidence of alcoholism in Japan is considerably lower than in so-called 'Western societies'.

Aldehyde dehydrogenase has been characterized at the molecular level[133]. Specific DNA probes for human ALDH I and ALDH II have been isolated from different liver cDNA libraries using different strategies[130, 134, 135]. Adult liver shows about 5 times more transcription of this gene as compared to the fetal liver[134]. This observation may have some implication in the fetal alcohol syndrome.

Induction of unspecific monooxygenase (1.14.14.1) (aryl hydrocarbon hydroxylase)

The discovery that the inducibility of aryl hydrocarbon hydroxylase is genetically controlled not only in mice[136], but also in man[137], may be of importance for industrial medicine. This enzyme oxidizes

genase[109]; also, no difference in the elimination rate of ethanol was observed between individuals with and those without flushing symptoms[118]. However, a polymorphism of the second enzyme involved in ethanol metabolism – aldehyde dehydrogenase – has been detected[119, 120]. In European postmortem liver specimens, 2 major (ALDH I, ALDH II) and 2 minor (ALDH III, ALDH IV) isoenzymes have been observed. In only about 40–50% of Japanese specimens, however, could the same pattern of isoenzymes be demonstrated as in Europeans; in the other Japanese samples the fast-mi-

Table 15 *Inducibility of aryl hydrocarbon hydroxylase (AHH) in normal individuals and in subjects with lung cancer[137]*

Subjects	N	AHH inducibility			Gene	
		AA	AB	BB	AHH^a	AHH^b
		Percentage of subjects			Frequency	
Normal.............	85	44.7	45.9	9.4	0.676	0.324
Lung cancer patients....	50	4.0	66.0	30.0	0.370	0.630

AA   Phenotype for low inducibility
AB   Phenotype for intermediate inducibility
BB   Phenotype for high inducibility
AHH^a Gene for low inducibility
AHH^b Gene for high inducibility

polycyclic hydrocarbons to epoxides (page 208), which may be carcinogenic. Enzyme activity in leukocytes or fibroblast cultures using benzpyrene as substrate[137] can be induced by barbiturates, methylcholanthrene and benzanthracene, and a trimodal distribution of the degree of inducibility, corresponding to the phenotypes AA, AB and BB, has been reported. In a study the incidence of these phenotypes in normal persons and in patients with lung cancer differed (Table 15). To accord with these findings, the risk for lung cancer would be 16 times higher for individuals with phenotype AB and 36 times higher for those with phenotype BB than for those with phenotype AA. Several later studies have confirmed the association between the degree of aryl hydrocarbon hydroxylase inducibility, smoking habits and carcinogenesis[138-140].

α1-Antitrypsin deficiency (proteinase-inhibitor deficiency)

The inheritance of the α_1-antitrypsin system is autosomal codominant, and the gene is located on chromosome 14. More than 50 electrophoretic variants, including a *null* allele, have been recognized at the *Pi* locus[141]. (For the incidence of the more frequent alleles, see Tables 16 and 17.) A predisposition to pulmonary insufficiency and emphysema is found among carriers of certain defect variants of

Table 16 *α1-Antitrypsin: gene frequencies and incidence of phenotypes in Caucasians*

Allele	Gene frequency*	Phenotype	Incidence of phenotypes (%)	Relative α1-antitrypsin concentration in serum (%)	Predisposition for pulmonary insufficiency and emphysema
Pi^M	0.969	PiMM	93.01	100	–
Pi^S..........	0.019	PiSS	0.25	60	(++)
		PiMS	5.30	80	(+)
Pi^Z..........	0.008	PiZZ	0.05	10	++++
		PiMZ	1.07	50–60	++

*The values do not sum up to 1 since other very rare alleles occur.

Table 17 *α1-Antitrypsin: gene frequencies in various populations*

Population	N	Allele	Range
Europeans	24317	Pi^M	0.8488–0.9963
		Pi^S	0–0.1473
		Pi^Z	0–0.0240
Lapps	770	Pi^M	0.9819–1.0000
		Pi^S	0–0.0180
		Pi^Z	0
Middle East Orientals	428	Pi^M	0.8838–0.9824
		Pi^S	0–0.0221
		Pi^Z	0.0176–0.0353
African Negroes	830	Pi^M	0.9818–1.0000
		Pi^S	0–0.0018
		Pi^Z	0–0.0059

α_1-antitrypsin[141-143]. Emphysema has been found in 85% of homozygotes for the alleles Pi^Z and Pi^S; conversely, in patients with emphysema, the frequency of carriers of these variants is 15 times as high as in normal persons[144]. Examples of pathogenic factors are cigarette smoke and exhaust fumes. Neonatal hepatitis and juvenile liver cirrhosis are also correlated with α_1-antitrypsin deficiency (alleles Pi^Z, Pi^S)[145].

Studies at the gene and protein level have shown that the Pi^S and Pi^Z genes each code for proteins which differ from the M protein by a single amino acid[146,147]: in the S variant Glu^{264} is replaced by Val, and in the Z variant Glu^{342} is replaced by Lys.

Variations in poisoning by heavy metals

In cases of heavy metal contamination of the organism, a number of effects indicate that genetic factors are involved. Thus, certain individuals show an adaptation to exposure to lead, while others do not. The Minamata and itai-itai diseases in Japan, in which neurological symptoms occurred after intoxication with organic mercury compounds and cadmium, show a high degree of variability among individuals subjected to identical exposure. A genetic factor is probably also involved in certain renal disorders resembling Fanconi's syndrome. Such symptoms are observed after contact with heavy metals such as uranium, lead, mercury and cadmium.

Foods producing variable abnormal reactions

Foods which can produce abnormal reactions on account of a genetically determined predisposition include fava beans (*Vicia faba*), lactose and gluten-containing cereals. The consumption of fava beans, as already discussed (page 293), or the inhalation of *V.faba* pollen gives rise to hemolysis in carriers of the Mediterranean variant of glucose-6-phosphate dehydrogenase.

Lactose intolerance. This is the result of genetically determined lactose deficiency in the intestinal mucosa[148-152]. During infancy the lactase activity necessary to metabolize lactose is present in almost all mammals. In most populations, however, the lactase activity decreases markedly with age, and when lactose is consumed, e.g. by drinking milk, lactose malabsorption may result in abdominal pain and severe diarrhea. With regard to the breakdown of lactose in adult intestinal mucosa, 2 phenotypes can be distinguished – a selectively low activity of intestinal lactase resulting in lactose intolerance, and a hereditary persistence of high intestinal lactase activity. The latter phenotype prevails in North European and a few other populations (Fig. 11) and seems to be related to heavy consumption of milk for many generations. On the other hand, lactose intolerance is prevalent in most other populations; it is transmitted as an autosomal recessive trait.

For the export of foodstuffs to famine areas in the Third World this intolerance has considerable implications. Powdered milk, for instance, cannot always be considered as a nutritional substitute.

Gluten-sensitive enteropathy (celiac disease). This condition is characterized by intolerance to gluten or its alcoholic extract gliadin, causing damage to the villi in the proximal small intestine, and ultimately malabsorption. Gluten is present in all grains other than rice and maize. Genetic studies show a familial pattern of the disease with reported incidences of 1:1500 in England, 1:6500 in Sweden and 1:300 in Western Ireland[153]. There is a predominance of the histocompatibility antigen *HLA-DR3*[154].

The primary defect is unknown. Proline and glutamine-rich polypeptides derived from intraluminal digestion of gliadin may be involved in the damage of the small intestinal mucosa[155]. The toxicity of gliadin has also been attributed to a specific oligosaccharide chain structure attached to the polypeptide chain[156].

Conclusions

The human organism metabolizes a whole range of drugs and agents of most heterogeneous structure, although it is certain that in the course of evolution no specific enzymes or other biological catalysts were formed or acquired for this task.

Individual responses to xenobiotics may have genetic *or* environmental causes. However, when individuals' reactions to drugs and environmental agents are being studied, the possibility of a genetic predisposition should always be borne in mind. Some of the results of tests with probe drugs and similar substances mentioned in this review may help to predict whether a genetic predisposition is present in certain individuals (or populations) or not. Some screening tests are now available to ascertain whether it is safe for a certain individual to be treated with a specific drug, to work in a specific environment, or to be given a certain food without his being endangered. Such considerations are of great importance in ecogenetics[157].

Fig. 11   *Incidence of lactose malabsorption in indigenous populations*[152]

	< 25%
	25–50%
	50–80%
	> 80%

References

[1] BREWER, G. J., *Amer. J. hum. Genet.*, **23**, 92 (1971).

[2] GOEDDE, H. W., *Ann. Biol. clin.*, **36**, 181 (1978).

[3] GOEDDE et al. (Eds.), *Hum. Genet.*, **9**, No. 3 (1970).

[4] GOEDDE, H. W., *Pharm. Weekbl.*, **107**, 437 (1972).

[5] KALOW, W., in WOLSTENHOLME and PORTER (Eds.), *Drug Responses in Man*, Churchill, London, 1967, page 220; KALOW, W., *Pharmacogenetics, Heredity and the Response to Drugs*, Saunders, Philadelphia, 1962.

[6] KALOW, W., *Canad. J. Physiol. Pharmacol.*, **60**, 1 (1982).

[7] KALOW, W., *Clin. Pharmacokinet.*, **7**, 373 (1982).

[8] VESELL, E. S., *Fed. Proc.*, **31**, 1253 (1972).

[9] VESELL, E. S., *Amer. J. Med.*, **66**, 183 (1979); VESELL, E. S., *Progr. med. Genet.*, **9**, 291 (1973).

[10] VESELL, E. S., *Fed. Proc.*, **43**, 2319 (1984); VESELL, E. S., *Hepatology*, **4**, 959 (1984).

[11] WHO Scientific Group on Pharmacogenetics, *Wld Hlth Org. techn. Rep. Ser.*, No. **524**, 5 (1973).

[12] HARRIS et al., *Proc. nat. Acad. Sci. (Wash.)*, **74**, 698 (1977).

[13] EVANS, D. A., in WOLSTENHOLME and PORTER (Eds.), *Drug Responses in Man*, Churchill, London, 1967, page 233.

[14] LA DU, B. N., *Ann. Rev. Med.*, **23**, 453 (1972).

[15] SCRIVER et al., *Science*, **200**, 946 (1978).

[16] VESELL, E. S., *Clin. Pharmacol. Ther.*, **22**, 659 (1977).

[17] GOEDDE, H. W., in KALOW et al. (Eds.), *Ethnic Differences in Reactions to Drugs and Xenobiotics*, Liss, New York, 1986, page 9.

[18] GOEDDE et al., *Nature*, **196**, 1296 (1962); GOEDDE et al., *Pseudocholinesterasen – Pharmakogenetik, Biochemie, Klinik*, Springer, Berlin, 1967.

[19] LA DU, B. N., *Fed. Proc.*, **31**, 1276 (1972).

[20] ALTLAND, K., in BECKER, P. E. (Ed.), *Humangenetik*, Volume I/3, Thieme, Stuttgart, 1975, page 327.

[21] BROWN et al., *Advanc. clin. Chem.*, **22**, 1 (1981).

[22] KALOW, W., *Anesthesiology*, **20**, 505 (1959); GOEDDE et al., *Molec. Pharmacol.*, **4**, 274 (1968).

[23] MUENSCH et al., *Europ. J. Biochem.*, **70**, 217 (1976); MUENSCH et al., *Amer. J. hum. Genet.*, **30**, 302 (1978); YAMATO et al., *Biochem. Genet.*, **21**, 135 (1983).

[24] GOEDDE and ALTLAND, *Ann. N. Y. Acad. Sci.*, **151**, 540 (1968); GOEDDE, H. W., *Ann. N. Y. Acad. Sci.*, **151**, 708 (1968); GOEDDE et al., *Ann. N. Y. Acad. Sci.*, **151**, 742 (1968).

[25] HARRIS et al., *Ann. hum. Genet.*, **26**, 359 (1963); ALTLAND et al., *Hum. Genet.*, **8**, 158 (1969).

[26] KALOW, W., *Anaesthesist*, **15**, 13 (1966); THOMPSON and WHITTAKER, *Acta genet. (Basel)*, **16**, 209 (1966); GOEDDE et al., *Prakt. Anästhesie*, **11**, 339 (1976).

[27] GOEDDE and AGARWAL, *Hum. Genet.*, Suppl. 1, 45 (1978).

[28] GOEDDE et al., *Med. Klin.*, **62**, 1631 (1967); GOEDDE and ALTLAND, *Ann. N. Y. Acad. Sci.*, **179**, 695 (1971).

[29] YOSHIDA and MOTULSKY, *Amer. J. hum. Genet.*, **21**, 486 (1969).

[30] SCOTT and WRIGHT, *Amer. J. hum. Genet.*, **28**, 253 (1976).

[31] RAO and GOPALAM, *Hum. Genet.*, **52**, 139 (1979).

[32] GELDMACHER-v. MALLINCKRODT et al., *Hum. Genet.*, **17**, 331 (1972/3).

[33] PLAYFER et al., *J. med. Genet.*, **13**, 337 (1976).

[34] ECKERSON et al., *Amer. J. hum. Genet.*, **35**, 1126 (1983); LA DU and ECKERSON, *Fed. Proc.*, **43**, 2338 (1984).

[35] DON et al., *Biochem. J.*, **151**, 625 (1975).

[36] EIBERG et al., *Clin. Genet.*, **28**, 265 (1985).

[37] WAINWRIGHT et al., *Nature*, **318**, 384 (1985); TSUI et al., *Science*, **230**, 1054 (1985).

[38] ECKERSON et al., *Amer. J. hum. Genet.*, **31**, 46A (1979).

[39] CARRO-CIAMPI et al., *Canad. J. Physiol. Pharmacol.*, **59**, 904 (1981).

[40] Symposium on Population Biology – Methodological Problems and Research Results, Xanthi, Greece, September 1984.

[41] WEBER and HEIN, *Pharmacol. Rev.*, **37**, 25 (1985).

[42] EVANS et al., *Brit. med. J.*, **2**, 485 (1960).

[43] ELLARD, G. A., *Clin. Pharmacol. Ther.*, **19**, 610 (1976).

[44] LUNDE et al., *Clin. Pharmacokinet.*, **2**, 182 (1977).

[45] ELLARD and GAMMON, *Brit. J. clin. Pharmacol.*, **4**, 5 (1977).

[46] OLSEN and MØRLAND, *Acta med. scand.*, **210**, 119 (1981).

[47] CHAPRON et al., *Clin. Pharmacol. Ther.*, **27**, 104 (1980).

[48] HOO et al., *J. clin. Chem.*, **15**, 329 (1977).

[49] DU SOUICH et al., *Clin. Pharmacol. Ther.*, **26**, 757 (1979).

[50] WHELPTON et al., *Clin. Chem.*, **27**, 1911 (1981).

[51] WEBER, W. W., *Fed. Proc.*, **43**, 2332 (1984).

[52] DRAYER and REIDENBERG, *Clin. Pharmacol. Ther.*, **22**, 251 (1977).

[53] WEBER et al., *Fed. Proc.*, **42**, 3086 (1983).

[54] WOOSLEY et al., *New Engl. J. Med.*, **298**, 1157 (1978).

[55] KUTT, H., *Ann. N. Y. Acad. Sci.*, **179**, 704 (1971).

[56] MITCHELL et al., *Ann. intern. Med.*, **84**, 181 (1976).

[57] TIMBRELL et al., *J. Pharmacol. exp. Ther.*, **213**, 364 (1980); BERNSTEIN, R. E., *Amer. Rev. resp. Dis.*, **121**, 429 (1980).

[58] HANSSEN et al., *Europ. Urol.*, **11**, 263 (1985).

[59] SLOAN et al., *Brit. med. J.*, **2**, 655 (1978).

[60] EICHELBAUM, M., *Clin. Pharmacokinet.*, **7**, 1 (1982).

[61] EICHELBAUM, M., *Fed. Proc.*, **43**, 2298 (1984).

[62] EICHELBAUM, M., in KALOW et al. (Eds.), *Ethnic Differences in Reactions to Drugs and Xenobiotics*, Liss, New York, 1986, page 157.

[63] LENNARD et al., *Clin. Pharmacokinet.*, **11**, 1 (1986).
[64] RITCHIE et al., *Ciba Found. Symp.*, NS 76, 219 (1980).
[65] EICHELBAUM et al., *Europ. J. clin. Pharmacol.*, **16**, 183 (1979).
[66] OATES et al., *Clin. Pharmacol. Ther.*, **32**, 81 (1982).
[67] IDLE et al., *Brit. J. clin. Pharmacol.*, **11**, 418 P (1981); SHAH et al., *Brit. med. J.*, **284**, 295 (1982).
[68] DAYER et al., *Brit. J. clin. Pharmacol.*, **13**, 750 (1982).
[69] IDLE and SMITH, *Drug Metab. Rev.*, **9**, 301 (1979).
[70] WANG et al., *J. Pharmacol. exp. Ther.*, **228**, 605 (1984); WOOSLEY et al., *Clin. Pharmacol. Ther.*, **39**, 282 (1986).
[71] LENNARD et al., *New Engl. J. Med.*, **307**, 1558 (1982).
[72] MCGOURTY et al., *Clin. Pharmacol. Ther.*, **38**, 409 (1985).
[73] DAVIES et al., *Brit. J. clin. Pharmacol.*, **11**, 89 (1981); MELLSTRÖM et al., *Clin. Pharmacol. Ther.*, **30**, 189 (1981).
[74] ZEKORN et al., *Klin. Wschr.*, **63**, 1180 (1985).
[75] SCHMID et al., *Clin. Pharmacol. Ther.*, **38**, 618 (1985).
[76] KÜPFER and PREISIG, *Europ. J. clin. Pharmacol.*, **26**, 753 (1984).
[77] WARING et al., *Biochem. Pharmacol.*, **31**, 3151 (1982); MITCHELL et al., *Brit. J. clin. Pharmacol.*, **18**, 507 (1984).
[78] SCOTT and POFFENBARGER, *Diabetes*, **28**, 41 (1979).
[79] IDLE et al., *Life Sci.*, **22**, 979 (1978).
[80] SHAHIDI, N. T., *Ann. N. Y. Acad. Sci.*, **151**, 822 (1968).
[81] OATES et al., *Lancet*, **1**, 837 (1981).
[82] TANG et al., *Res. Commun. chem. Path. Pharmacol.*, **21**, 45 (1978).
[83] KALOW et al., *Clin. Pharmacol. Ther.*, **26**, 766 (1979).
[84] PENNO and VESELL, *J. clin. Invest.*, **71**, 1698 (1983); VESELL and PENNO, *Fed. Proc.*, **43**, 2342 (1984).
[85] MOTULSKY, A. G., *Fed. Proc.*, **31**, 1286 (1972).
[86] LUZZATTO and TESTA, *Curr. Top. Hemat.*, **1**, 1–70 (1978).
[87] WINTROBE et al., *Clinical Hematology*, 8th ed., Lea & Febiger, Philadelphia, 1981, page 786.
[88] BEUTLER, E., in STANBURY et al., *The Metabolic Basis of Inherited Disease*, 5th ed., McGraw-Hill, 1983, page 1629.
[89] NAGEL and RANNEY, *Semin. Hemat.*, **10**, 269 (1973).
[90] ZINKHAM, W. H., *Arch. intern. Med.*, **137**, 1365 (1977).
[91] WINTROBE et al., *Clinical Hematology*, 8th ed., Lea & Febiger, Philadelphia, page 828.
[92] ARMALY, M. F., *Ann. N. Y. Acad. Sci.*, **151**, 861 (1968).
[93] O'REILLY et al., *Ann. N. Y. Acad. Sci.*, **151**, 913 (1968); O'REILLY, R. A., *New Engl. J. Med.*, **282**, 1448 (1970).
[94] ALVING et al., *Arch. intern. Med.*, **145**, 499 (1985).
[95] BRITT and KALOW, *Ann. N. Y. Acad. Sci.*, **151**, 947 (1968); KALOW, W., *Fed. Proc.*, **31**, 1270 (1972).
[96] Leading article, *Brit. med. J.*, **1**, 249 (1973); MERZ, B., *J. Amer. med. Ass.*, **255**, 709 (1986).
[97] PAASUKE and BROWNELL, *J. Amer. med. Ass.*, **255**, 769 (1986).
[98] MOULDS and DENBOROUGH, *Brit. med. J.*, **2**, 245 (1974).
[99] MOULDS and DENBOROUGH, *Brit. med. J.*, **2**, 241 (1974).
[100] HARRIS and KALMUS, *Ann. Eugen. (Lond.)*, **15**, 24 and 32 (1949).
[101] GOEDDE and OHLIGMACHER, *Hum. Genet.*, **1**, 423 (1964/5); GOEDDE and OHLIGMACHER, *Acta genet. (Basel)*, **16**, 350 (1966).
[102] JAY, G. E., *Proc. Soc. exp. Biol. (N. Y.)*, **90**, 378 (1955).
[103] MAZZE et al., *J. Pharmacol. exp. Ther.*, **184**, 481 (1973).
[104] WEST and HARRIS, *Ann. N. Y. Acad. Sci.*, **118**, 441 (1964).
[105] MARGOLIS and FEIGELSON, *Biochim. biophys. Acta (Amst.)*, **90**, 117 (1964).
[106] WEBER et al., *Drug Metab. Dispos.*, **4**, 94 (1976).
[107] GOEDDE et al., *Biochem. Pharmacol.*, **13**, 1671 (1964); GOEDDE et al., *Hum. Genet.*, **1**, 141 (1964/5); GOEDDE et al., *Biochem. Pharmacol.*, **16**, 1793 (1967).
[108] SCHMID and BAUCHINGER, *Dtsch. med. Wschr.*, **93**, 1149 (1968).
[109] EDWARDS and EVANS, *Clin. Pharmacol. Ther.*, **8**, 824 (1967).
[110] VESELL, E. S., *Ann. N. Y. Acad. Sci.*, **197**, 79 (1972).
[111] FENNA et al., *Canad. med. Ass. J.*, **105**, 472 (1971).

[112] HANNA, J. M., *Alcoholism (N. Y.)*, **2**, 89 (1978); REED, T. E., *Alcoholism (N. Y.)*, **2**, 83 (1978); FARRIS and JONES, *Alcoholism (N. Y.)*, **2**, 77 (1978); ZEINER and PAREDES, *Alcoholism (N. Y.)*, **2**, 71 (1978).
[113] GOODWIN et al., *Arch. gen. Psychiat.*, **31**, 164 (1974).
[114] EWING et al., *Amer. J. Psychiat.*, **131**, 206 (1974).
[115] WOLFF, P. H., *Science*, **175**, 449 (1972).
[116] AGARWAL and GOEDDE, in KALOW et al. (Eds.), *Ethnic Differences in Reactions to Drugs and Xenobiotics*, Liss, New York, 1986, page 99.
[117] VON WARTBURG and SCHÜRCH, *Ann. N. Y. Acad. Sci.*, **151**, 936 (1968).
[118] MIZOI et al., *Pharmacol. Biochem. Behav.*, **10**, 303 (1979).
[119] GOEDDE et al., *Hum. Genet.*, **51**, 331 (1979).
[120] HARADA et al., *Hum. Genet.*, **44**, 181 (1978).
[121] HARADA et al., *Life Sci.*, **26**, 1773 (1980).
[122] GOEDDE et al., *Isozymes Curr. Top. Biol. Med. Res.*, **8**, 175 (1983).
[123] AGARWAL et al., *Alcoholism (N. Y.)*, **5**, 12 (1981).
[124] HARADA et al., *Lancet*, **2**, 982 (1981).
[125] GOEDDE et al., *Clin. Genet.*, **16**, 29 (1979).
[126] GOEDDE et al., *Enzyme*, **25**, 281 (1980).
[127] GOEDDE et al., *Amer. J. hum. Genet.*, **35**, 769 (1983).
[128] GOEDDE et al., *Pharmacol. Biochem. Behav.*, **18**, Suppl. 1, 161 (1983).
[129] GOEDDE et al., *Amer. J. hum. Genet.* (1986) (in press).
[130] GOEDDE and AGARWAL, in KALOW et al. (Eds.), *Ethnic Differences in Reactions to Drugs and Xenobiotics*, Liss, New York, 1986, page 113.
[131] GOEDDE et al., *Alcohol*, **2**, 383 (1985).
[132] HARADA et al., *Lancet*, **2**, 827 (1982).
[133] HEMPEL et al., *Europ. J. Biochem.*, **141**, 21 (1984).
[134] BRAUN and GOEDDE, *Europ. J. Biochem.* (1986) (in press).
[135] YOSHIDA et al., *Alcohol*, **2**, 103 (1985).
[136] NEBERT and GIELEN, *Fed. Proc.*, **31**, 1315 (1972).
[137] KELLERMANN et al., *Amer. J. hum. Genet.*, **25**, 327 (1973); KELLERMANN et al., *New Engl. J. Med.*, **289**, 934 (1973).
[138] TRELL et al., *Lancet*, **2**, 140 (1976); TRELL et al., *Lancet*, **1**, 109 (1978).
[139] ANDRÉASSON et al., *Postgrad. med. J.*, **58**, 138 (1982).
[140] EMERY et al., *Lancet*, **1**, 470 (1978); PAIGEN et al., *Amer. J. hum. Genet.*, **30**, 561 (1978).
[141] KAMBOH, M. I., *Dis. Marker*, **3**, 135 (1985).
[142] FAGERHOL, M. K., *Postgrad. med. J.*, **52**, Suppl. 2, 73 (1976); FAGERHOL and COX, *Advanc. hum. Genet.*, **11**, 1 (1981).
[143] GARVER et al., *New Engl. J. Med.*, **314**, 762 (1986).
[144] KUEPPERS, F., *Hum. Genet.*, **11**, 177 (1971); LIEBERMAN, J., *Chest*, **70**, 62 (1976); MITTMAN, C., *Amer. Rev. resp. Dis.*, **118**, 649 (1978).
[145] SHARP et al., *J. Lab. clin. Med.*, **73**, 934 (1969); SVEGER, T., *Pediatrics*, **62**, 22 (1978).
[146] YOSHIDA et al., *Amer. J. hum. Genet.*, **29**, 233 (1977); YOSHIDA et al., *Proc. nat. Acad. Sci. (Wash.)*, **73**, 1324 (1976).
[147] LONG et al., *Biochemistry*, **23**, 4828 (1984).
[148] FLATZ and ROTTHAUWE, *Progr. med. Genet.*, NS 2, 205 (1977).
[149] DAHLQVIST, A., *Postgrad. med. J.*, **53**, Suppl. 2, 57 (1977).
[150] BAYOUMI et al., *Amer. J. phys. Anthropol.*, **58**, 173 (1982); HUSSEIN et al., *Hum. Hered.*, **32**, 94 (1982).
[151] FLATZ et al., *Hum. Genet.*, **62**, 152 (1982); ROSENKRANZ et al., *Hum. Genet.*, **62**, 158 (1982).
[152] FLATZ, G., in KALOW et al. (Eds.), *Ethnic Differences in Reactions to Drugs and Xenobiotics*, Liss, New York, 1986, page 55.
[153] CICLITIRA and THOMPSON, in McLEOD and SIKORA (Eds.), *Molecular Biology and Human Disease*, Blackwell, 1984, page 198; Editorial, *Nutr. Rev.*, **39**, 365 (1981).
[154] McKENNA et al., *Tissue Antigens*, **22**, 175 (1983).
[155] CALDWELL, K. A., *Amer. J. clin. Nutr.*, **33**, 293 (1980); JOS et al., *Clin. chim. Acta*, **134**, 189 (1983).
[156] FOTTRELL, P. F., *Ciba Found. Symp.*, NS 50, 299 (1977).
[157] GOEDDE, H. W., *Fortschr. Med.*, **97**, 127 and 165 (1979).

Notizen

Notizen

Notizen

Notizen

Notizen

Notizen

14615/2 e USA